The
Voucher
Worth
£1

MAY BE REDEEMED IN ACCORDANCE WITH THE
CONDITIONS OVERLEAF AT ANY OF THE ESTABLISHMENTS
WHOSE GAZETTEER ENTRY SHOWS THE SYMBOL £.

Worth
£1

MAY BE REDEEMED IN ACCORDANCE WITH THE
CONDITIONS OVERLEAF AT ANY OF THE ESTABLISHMENTS
WHOSE GAZETTEER ENTRY SHOWS THE SYMBOL £.

The
Voucher
Worth
£1

MAY BE REDEEMED IN ACCORDANCE WITH THE
CONDITIONS OVERLEAF AT ANY OF THE ESTABLISHMENTS
WHOSE GAZETTEER ENTRY SHOWS THE SYMBOL £.

The
Voucher
Worth
£1

MAY BE REDEEMED IN ACCORDANCE WITH THE
CONDITIONS OVERLEAF AT ANY OF THE ESTABLISHMENTS
WHOSE GAZETTEER ENTRY SHOWS THE SYMBOL £.

The
Voucher
Worth
£1

MAY BE REDEEMED IN ACCORDANCE WITH THE
CONDITIONS OVERLEAF AT ANY OF THE ESTABLISHMENTS
WHOSE GAZETTEER ENTRY SHOWS THE SYMBOL £.

The
Voucher
Worth
£1

MAY BE REDEEMED IN ACCORDANCE WITH THE
CONDITIONS OVERLEAF AT ANY OF THE ESTABLISHMENTS
WHOSE GAZETTEER ENTRY SHOWS THE SYMBOL £.

Conditions

A COPY OF AA INSPECTED BED AND BREAKFAST IN BRITAIN 1991 MUST BE PRODUCED WITH THIS VOUCHER. ONLY ONE VOUCHER PER PERSON OR PARTY ACCEPTED. NOT REDEEMABLE FOR CASH. NO CHANGE GIVEN. THE VOUCHER WILL NOT BE VALID AFTER 31ST DECEMBER, 1991. USE OF THE VOUCHER IS RESTRICTED TO WHEN PAYMENT IS MADE BEFORE LEAVING THE PREMISES. THE VOUCHER WILL ONLY BE ACCEPTED AGAINST ACCOMMODATION AT FULL TARIFF RATES.

Conditions

A COPY OF AA INSPECTED BED AND BREAKFAST IN BRITAIN 1991 MUST BE PRODUCED WITH THIS VOUCHER. ONLY ONE VOUCHER PER PERSON OR PARTY ACCEPTED. NOT REDEEMABLE FOR CASH. NO CHANGE GIVEN. THE VOUCHER WILL NOT BE VALID AFTER 31ST DECEMBER, 1991. USE OF THE VOUCHER IS RESTRICTED TO WHEN PAYMENT IS MADE BEFORE LEAVING THE PREMISES. THE VOUCHER WILL ONLY BE ACCEPTED AGAINST ACCOMMODATION AT FULL TARIFF RATES.

Conditions

A COPY OF AA INSPECTED BED AND BREAKFAST IN BRITAIN 1991 MUST BE PRODUCED WITH THIS VOUCHER. ONLY ONE VOUCHER PER PERSON OR PARTY ACCEPTED. NOT REDEEMABLE FOR CASH. NO CHANGE GIVEN. THE VOUCHER WILL NOT BE VALID AFTER 31ST DECEMBER, 1991. USE OF THE VOUCHER IS RESTRICTED TO WHEN PAYMENT IS MADE BEFORE LEAVING THE PREMISES. THE VOUCHER WILL ONLY BE ACCEPTED AGAINST ACCOMMODATION AT FULL TARIFF RATES.

Conditions

A COPY OF AA INSPECTED BED AND BREAKFAST IN BRITAIN 1991 MUST BE PRODUCED WITH THIS VOUCHER. ONLY ONE VOUCHER PER PERSON OR PARTY ACCEPTED. NOT REDEEMABLE FOR CASH. NO CHANGE GIVEN. THE VOUCHER WILL NOT BE VALID AFTER 31ST DECEMBER, 1991. USE OF THE VOUCHER IS RESTRICTED TO WHEN PAYMENT IS MADE BEFORE LEAVING THE PREMISES. THE VOUCHER WILL ONLY BE ACCEPTED AGAINST ACCOMMODATION AT FULL TARIFF RATES.

Conditions

A COPY OF AA INSPECTED BED AND BREAKFAST IN BRITAIN 1991 MUST BE PRODUCED WITH THIS VOUCHER. ONLY ONE VOUCHER PER PERSON OR PARTY ACCEPTED. NOT REDEEMABLE FOR CASH. NO CHANGE GIVEN. THE VOUCHER WILL NOT BE VALID AFTER 31ST DECEMBER, 1991. USE OF THE VOUCHER IS RESTRICTED TO WHEN PAYMENT IS MADE BEFORE LEAVING THE PREMISES. THE VOUCHER WILL ONLY BE ACCEPTED AGAINST ACCOMMODATION AT FULL TARIFF RATES.

Conditions

A COPY OF AA INSPECTED BED AND BREAKFAST IN BRITAIN 1991 MUST BE PRODUCED WITH THIS VOUCHER. ONLY ONE VOUCHER PER PERSON OR PARTY ACCEPTED. NOT REDEEMABLE FOR CASH. NO CHANGE GIVEN. THE VOUCHER WILL NOT BE VALID AFTER 31ST DECEMBER, 1991. USE OF THE VOUCHER IS RESTRICTED TO WHEN PAYMENT IS MADE BEFORE LEAVING THE PREMISES. THE VOUCHER WILL ONLY BE ACCEPTED AGAINST ACCOMMODATION AT FULL TARIFF RATES.

AA

INSPECTED
*B*ED AND
BREAKFAST
IN BRITAIN
1991

AA

PRODUCED BY THE PUBLISHING DIVISION OF THE AUTOMOBILE ASSOCIATION

GAZETTEER: Compiled by the AA's Research Unit, Information Control, in co-operation with AA Hotels Services, and generated by the AA's Establishment Database.

MAPS: prepared by the Cartographic Department of The Automobile Association © The Automobile Association 1990

COVER ILLUSTRATIONS: The Paul Hampson Partnership

HEAD OF ADVERTISEMENT SALES: Christopher Heard Tel (0256) 20123

ADVERTISEMENT PRODUCTION: Karen Weeks Tel (0256) 20123

Typeset and printed by William Clowes Ltd, Beccles, Suffolk

Colour supplement printed by J.B. Shears & Sons Ltd, Basingstoke, Hampshire

Cover photography by Gordon Hammond ABIPP, Southampton

PUBLISHED BY THE AUTOMOBILE ASSOCIATION, FANUM HOUSE, BASINGSTOKE, HAMPSHIRE RG21 2EA

ISBN 0 7495 0202 9

Contents

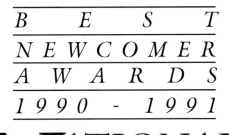

BEST NEWCOMER AWARDS

1990 - 1991

NATIONAL AWARD WINNER

Cockle Warren Cottage Hotel,
Hayling Island

Bed and Breakfast can mean different things to different people – from the point of view of owners as well as guests – but at Cockle Warren we found a place that simply could not fail to please. Owners David and Diane Skelton are very friendly and helpful without being intrusive, and service is correct and efficient without being too formal – all in all, the perfect balance.

Built twelve years ago as a family home, the attractive traditional-style house gradually developed into a private hotel. Originally one room was let for bed and breakfast; now there are four rooms available in the house, one in an annexe, and plans in hand for another.

Diane, formerly a draughtswoman for Portsmouth City Council Highways Department, has always loved cooking and soft furnishing and her talents in both fields are much in evidence. The bedrooms are pretty and furnished with some attractive pieces of stripped pine, comfortable seating and more little extras than you would find in most hotels – mineral water, sugared almonds, sewing kit, magazines, cards, Woods of Windsor toiletries and even an iron and ironing board in the wardrobe. Each room has direct dial telephone and radio alarm and each has a private bath or shower room. One has a four-poster bed.

Downstairs is a cosy lounge, with a wrought iron screen separating it from the small bar and the lovely conservatory dining room. Pre-dinner drinks are served here, with delicious canapés, before you are escorted to your table. Dinner is a set meal, but you have the opportunity when booking of stating any particular dislikes. Guests can enjoy a wonderful homemade port pâté with cognac, served with green salad, homemade bread and toasted homemade brioche (for which Diane obtains French flour at considerable effort). The main course might be chicken cooked with vegetables in cider and cream, with new potatoes and green beans, followed by

chocolate and apricot gâteau and a cheeseboard with a good choice of French and English cheeses. The house wine is a pleasant white Bordeaux. Rather than hover around the tables, they have installed a brass push-button bell beside each table so

business in wholesale hosiery to help run the hotel, it is he who has most contact with guests and, from the welcoming (and complimentary) pot of tea to the friendly farewell, he leaves nothing to chance to ensure that you enjoy your stay and are never left wondering about anything.

The hotel is set back from the seafront road, away from the bustle of the resort's main streets, and there is nothing but a parking area between it and the beach. If sea-bathing is not for you, there is an inviting heated swimming pool in the paved and walled garden at the rear, overlooked by the conservatory dining room and attractively lit after dark.

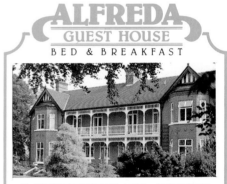
that you can summon your next course when you are ready. Coffee is served in the lounge after dinner, with a small plateful of selected mint chocolates. At the same time, David makes enquiries about your requirements for the following morning, early morning call, tea, newspaper and the time you would like to have breakfast.

David Skelton is, in fact, a splendid host. Having given up his

B	E	S	T
N E W C O M E R			
A	W A R	D	S
1 9 9 0	-	1 9	9 1

NORTH OF ENGLAND

Cobwebs Country House
Kirkby Lonsdale

Kirkby Lonsdale lies in the romantically named Valley of the Lune, admired by writer John Ruskin as 'one of the loveliest scenes in England'. Just outside this market town is Cowan Bridge, where Charlotte and Emily Bronte went to the school which Charlotte later described as Lowood in *Jane Eyre,* and near to which Cobwebs Country House can be found.

Cobwebs is a square Victorian house with cobbled courtyard and set amid four acres of farmland. One of its triumphs is that it is so peaceful yet so close, not only to Kirkby Lonsdale, but also to the major beauty spots of Cumbria. Kendal is about 15 miles north west, and the Yorkshire Dales are just two miles away. Near by are Ingleton Falls, White Scar Caves and Whernside National Pot-Holing Centre.

The name 'Cobwebs' has been with the house for years, way before 1986 when Paul Kelly and his fiancée Yvonne took it over and completely renovated and redecorated the five bedroomed building in keeping with its Victorian origins. Fireplaces were opened up, bathrooms installed, windows replaced and everywhere painted. The result is far from what the name conjures up, not a cobweb in sight and a bright and comfortable house for people to enjoy.

Yvonne and Paul take great pleasure in having people to their house, which they do with spontaneity but without intrusiveness. Bedrooms all have views over the Pennines and the Lune Valley fields, and are well-proportioned, comfortable and private with attractive fabrics and some antiques. They also have TVs, direct dial telephones and tea-making facilities.

Cobwebs has been described as 'a restaurant with rooms' which emphasizes the thought and dedication that Yvonne and Paul put into the food and drink they provide for guests. A novel touch to the evening meal is that, as guests gather in the sitting room before dinner to have a drink and read the menu, Paul arrives to give a résumé of the forthcoming meal which Yvonne has devised and prepared using imaginative combinations of herbs and textures. She keeps the menu

short – two choices of starter and a main course followed by pudding and a cheeseboard which includes many local varieties – and enjoys experimenting. The physics of a 'split soup' are explained – the simultaneous ladling of two separate yet complementary soups of similar texture ensures that they do not merge – resulting in a visually attractive combination of colours: thus carrot and onion soup and sage soup combine. Details are given of sauces and courses – excellent ingredients with unusual and delicious sauces, such as lobster and cucumber sauce with fish and orange and green peppercorn sauce with the meat ensuring that you know exactly what to expect of your meal.

While the cooking is Yvonne's province, Paul is responsible for the very adventurous wine list – over 300 labels including a large number of Australian wines. Paul was regional finalist for the Sunday Express Wine Taster of the Year competition and his enthusiasm for his work can be seen in his visit to many Australian vineyards during his holiday last year and the resulting extensive Australian list. In a similar way to his explanation of the menu to guests, he features in his wine list a selection of 30 wines, describing them and giving details of the vineyards. Each month the list is changed.

For the dedicated diner, one night a month Cobwebs has a gourmet night of seven courses and five wines. If you need to walk this off the next day, they can arrange either a guided walk or for walkers to be collected from a particular point.

Cobwebs is a welcome newcomer to the guidebook, offering enthusiastic service with good meals and wine, in peaceful surroundings that are comfortable and informal. It gives the visitor an excellent base for enjoying a slightly less well-known area of the country and one that has wonderful fells, rivers and waterfalls as well as tasty local produce such as the local cheeses, fish and game which you are sure to find on the Cobwebs' dinner menu.

B	E	S	T
N E W	C O	M	E R
A	W A	R	D S
1 9 9 0	-	1 9	9 1

Scotland

Fresh Fields
Twynholm

Fresh Fields is an apt name for this newcomer to our bed and breakfast guidebook. The house is fresh and bright, with pretty, country-style fabrics and gleaming paintwork, and the fields on either side of the house have the luxuriant green that comes from the warmth of the Gulf Stream.

Twynholm is in the Stewartry division of Dumfries and Galloway in the south-west corner of Scotland. It is a village with a strong sense of community, with its church, school, post office, smithy, couple of pubs and the village store. The harbour town of Kirkcudbright, which appeals to painters and fishermen alike, is three miles to the south, whilst

Dumfries is a thirty-minute car ride away.

In this relatively unspoilt region, the visitor can go hill walking, river or loch fishing, walking by the sea, or visiting the many castles, gardens with their sub-tropical cabbage palms and tree ferns, or the museums and craft centres. Between the towns are evergreen forests, tree-lined valleys and lush pastures that are notable for their absence of people.

Ivy and Len Stanley moved to this relaxing setting in 1988. For ten years previously they had opened the doors of their house to guests in the Lake District but latterly felt that the soul was to some extent going from the region. They found Fresh Fields – then an ordinary 1930s four-up and four-down house, bought it and set about renovating it and making an additional wing. They opened for business in 1989 and continued to provide an atmosphere of relaxing informality combined with exceptionally high standards of housekeeping and excellent cooking and service.

Bedrooms are very inviting with their attractive and good quality curtains and matching quilts, and from either side of the house the views are of hilly green fields with, at the back, the possibility of eye-to- eye contact with a cow or two.

Ivy's cooking – all done on her new Aga – is mouth-watering wholesome English/Scottish fare with her own individual touches. Dinner is a four-course meal at which you might be tempted by Lentil Brö (a Shetland recipe) or Squiffy Salmon (a steak of locally caught salmon served in a whisky, cream and tomato sauce) or Fred Barber's Country Hot Pot (named after one of their guests) which is a casserole of beef cooked with carrots, dried fruit and topped with herby dumplings. Scallops from nearby Kirkcudbright also feature on the menu. Desserts are difficult to resist; Edwardian Chocolate Trifle, Treacle Tart or Crunchy Crumble. Anyone with special needs is equally well catered for, as Ivy will provide tasty vegetarian dishes or low fat dishes if you let her know your requirements. Her enthusiasm for cooking is further revealed by her homemade bread and ice creams. However long your stay with them is, you can be sure that you will not get the same meal twice. There is a small and comprehensive wine list plus the usual range of spirits, beers and soft drinks.

The Stanleys give a sense of working extremely happily as a team and it is probably this, as well as the quality of the accommodation and cooking, that draws people to return to them again and again. Over their years at Windermere, and now in Twynholm, they have photographs and memories of their customers which are kept in albums in the sitting room for their guests to browse through. Amazing coincidences of people recognising friends from the past or of knowing someone who knew someone else have come to light, and this sense of sharing their lives and home with so many people has created a sort of extended family or club-like feeling to their business. This would explain why in 1989 they received 400 Christmas cards and why they get calls advising of a birth or marriage.

Ivy's and Len's genuine interest in their customers, combined with a love of home-making and high quality of service, make their guesthouse a welcoming place in which to stay.

B	E	S	T
N	E W C O	M	E R
A	W A	R	D S
1 9 9 0	-	1 9 9 1	

WALES

Park Hall, *New Quay*

Park Hall Hotel can be approached either through a fine wooded valley or more spectacularly via a very steep winding road that leads to the quiet hamlet of Cwmtydu, some four miles south of New Quay.

Park Hall itself is set on a hillside overlooking the picturesque Cwmtydu Bay, where seals are often more in evidence than people.

A warm welcome is assured from your hosts Peter and Chris McConnell who will greet you with the offer of afternoon tea which is

served in the comfortable lounge. As you relax you cannot fail to notice the fascinating array of antique furniture and Victoriana.

A small bar, set in the corner of the room, will later provide you with after-dinner drinks as a finishing touch to round off an excellent meal served in the Victorian-style conservatory. This delightful new addition to Park Hall gives you an excellent view of the beautiful Cwmtydu Bay whilst you enjoy your evening meal.

All the bedrooms have been coordinated in keeping with Victorian style whilst offering modern-day levels of comfort, including en-suite facilities and TVs.

A large selection of touring guides and local information is displayed in the lobby.

SOUTH WEST ENGLAND

Thomas Luny House
Teignmouth

Alison and John Allen gave up a busy and thriving hotel and restaurant in Whimple in order to find a business which would be more compatible with raising a young family. In Thomas Luny House they have found the perfect place to do that and it is, first and foremost, their home.

The beautifully proportioned Georgian house was built in the late 18th century for the well-known marine artist, Thomas Luny, and although it is not far from the fish quay, it is surprisingly peaceful, with a walled courtyard in front of the house and a small garden at the rear. It had been a hotel before the Allens bought it in the autumn of 1988, but had been allowed to go into something of a decline. After a year of concentrated effort and extensive renovation the Grade II listed building, restored to its former glory, was again ready to accept guests.

There are no formalities on arrival, just a warm welcome and the offer of a pot of tea – eventually you will be asked to sign the visitors' book, but initially all you have to do is settle in and relax. The bedrooms are beautiful, with magnificent beds, lovely old furniture and the best

The Allens are a charming couple and people who stay here are sure to become acquainted with their children and the family pets. Thomas Luny House is truly a family home which takes guests.

B	E	S	T
N E W	C O	M E	R
A	W A	R D	S
1990	-	1991	

CENTRAL ENGLAND

quality fabrics – each is different in size and style, but they all have private bath or shower room, remote control colour television, direct dial telephone and such homely touches as mineral water, fresh flowers, books and nice toiletries.

Downstairs, the drawing room is large and comfortable, with an open fire, lots of books and pictures and interesting ornaments and china. The dining room has one large polished table, and here a set meal of excellent quality and taste is presented. Visitors can enjoy a baked avocado starter, followed by slices of lamb, roasted pink, with a delicious watercress sauce and lightly cooked vegetables. For dessert a surprising combination of marinated strawberries and coffee ice–cream actually goes together quite nicely. Cheese is then offered, followed by coffee which is taken in the lounge and where the owners sometimes ask if they might join you for coffee. During this time you can arrange for early morning tea to be brought up to your room next morning and decide the time you would like to have breakfast.

Shrewley House, *Shrewley*

Set in peaceful countryside only six miles from Warwick, Shrewley House is a gabled 16th- to 17th-century former farmhouse, surrounded by gardens and fields. The building itself has immense charm, and the rooms, including the very attractive residents' lounge and dining room, are well proportioned, light and airy. The house is beautifully decorated and well maintained. Bedrooms (four in all including one family room which is actually two connecting rooms with private bathroom) are spacious, comfortable

15

and very pretty. Wallpaper, curtains, bed hangings and bedcovers all match, and the fabrics are of good quality. All are provided with tea and coffee-making facilities, fruit, biscuits and a selection of drinks; fresh flowers and ornaments make them home-like. Bathrooms include a full range of toiletries and hairdriers. TV and radio complete the amenities.

Mr and Mrs Green are very welcoming in a completely natural way. Guests are met at the door with genuine enthusiasm, shown up to their room and brought a tray of tea. They are then asked if they have all they need, and left to settle in. Dinner is by arrangement as most of their guests prefer to eat out, but there is a choice of three or four items for each course, and it is good home cooking – for example,

homemade soup or pâté for starters, followed by salmon with hollandaise sauce, or lamb cutlets, steak or lasagne, and a choice of puddings. Mrs Green is also happy to cater for vegetarians if she has some warning.

The Greens have owned the house for seven years, gradually restoring and redecorating it. They did not originally intend to run a guesthouse, but decided to convert the stables as holiday cottages first, and then, as their children grew up and moved away, realised that there was a demand for good bed and breakfast accommodation in the area, so began that side of the business in September 1989. They have no plans to increase the number of letting bedrooms, but a new conservatory dining room is to be built, overlooking the gardens

Quality Assessment

Quality assessment is now made for all the establishments listed in the gazetteer. It is made on a subjective basis, following each inspection, to indicate the overall quality of the facilities and services provided by each establishment.

The quality assessment is shown as follows:

FALMOUTH Cornwall Map **2** SX25

⊢⊷⊣ **GH** Q Q **Ram Hotel** High Road XY21 1AB
☎(05036) 4321 Plan 9 C2

FH Q Q Q Mr & Mrs J Smith **Homestead** DX8 1WY (SX261567)
☎(05036) 3421

Each establishment receives from one to four symbols in ascending order of merit, denoting:

Q

A simple establishment with clean, modest accommodation and adequate bathroom facilities.

Q Q

A sound establishment offering a higher standard of accommodation in terms of furnishing, decor and comfort; likely to have some en suite facilities.

Q Q Q

A well-appointed establishment offering superior accommodation with comfortable public areas. En suite facilities may be provided.

Q Q Q Q
SELECTED

The very best of AA-listed establishments, offering excellent standards of accommodation, a high degree of comfort, good food and hospitable, caring hosts. Many provide a high proportion of en suite facilities.

This year 196 have been awarded the 'Selected' distinction this year, and their gazetteer entries are highlighted by means of a tinted panel. A full list of the 'Selected' estabishments will be found on pages 18–22.

'Selected' Guesthouses, Farmhouses and Inns

The county index which follows is a list of all the guesthouses, farmhouses and inns — 196 in all — which have been awarded the AA's highest quality rating of four **Q** symbols and the designation **'S E L E C T E D'**. You will find full details of each in the gazetteer and the entries are highlighted by means of a tinted panel.

'S E L E C T E D' means that these establishments offer higher standards of comfort, hospitality and cooking than are normally to be found in this type of accommodation. See p 17 for a full explanation of the **Q** awards.

ENGLAND

AVON

Bath	GH	Laura Place Hotel
Bath	GH	Orchard House Hotel
Bath	GH	Paradise House
Bath	GH	Somerset House Hotel & Restaurant
Bath	GH	Old School House

CHESHIRE

Broxton	GH	Frogg Manor
Chester	GH	Redland Private Hotel

CORNWALL & ISLES OF SCILLY

Boscastle	GH	St Christophers Country House Hotel
Crackington Haven	FH	Manor Farm
Crackington Haven	FH	Trevigue
Fowey	GH	Carnethic House
Looe	GH	Harescombe Lodge
Newquay	GH	Priory Lodge Hotel
Penryn	GH	Prospect House
St Just in Roseland	GH	Rose-da-Mar Hotel
Trevone	GH	Green Waves Private Hotel

St Marys	GH	Carnwethers Country House
St Marys	GH	Brantwood Hotel

CUMBRIA

Ambleside	GH	Grey Friar Lodge Country House Hotel
Ambleside	GH	Rothay Garth Hotel
Ambleside	GH	Rydal Lodge
Caldbeck	GH	High Greenrigg House
Catlowdy	FH	Bessiestown Farm
Cockermouth	GH	Low Hall Country Guest House
Coniston	GH	Coniston Lodge Hotel
Kendal	GH	Lane Head Country House Hotel
Keswick	GH	The Gales Country House Hotel
Kirkcambeck	FH	Cracop Farm
Kirkby Lonsdale	GH	Cobwebs Country House
Kirkby Lonsdale	GH	Hipping Hall
Kirkoswald	GH	Prospect Hill Hotel
Kirkby Stephen	GH	The Town Head House
Penruddock	FH	Highgate Farm
Near Sawrey	GH	Eees Wyke Country House
Near Sawrey	GH	The Garth

Windermere	GH	The Hawksmoor Guest House

DERBYSHIRE

Bakewell	GH	Merlin House Country Hotel
Shottle	FH	Dannah Farm

DEVON

Bickington	FH	East Burne Farm
Bovey Tracey	FH	Willmead Farm
Brixham	GH	Greenbrier Hotel
Colyford	GH	Swallows Eaves Hotel
Colyton	GH	Old Bakehouse
Croyde	GH	Whiteleaf at Croyde
Dartmouth	GH	Captains House
Feniton	GH	Colestocks House Guest House
Holne	FH	Wellpritton Farm
Kingston	GH	Trebles Cottage Hotel
Lynmouth	GH	Countisbury Lodge Hotel
Lynton	GH	Waterloo House Hotel
Morchard Bishop	FH	Wigham
Mortehoe	GH	Sunnycliffe Hotel
Teignmouth	GH	Thomas Luny House
Tiverton	FH	Lower Collipriest Farm
Torquay	GH	Glenorleigh Hotel
Totnes	GH	Old Forge at Totnes
West Down	GH	The Long House

DORSET

Beaminster	GH	Hams Plot
Bournemouth	GH	Cliff House Hotel
Chideock	GH	Betchworth House Hotel
Horton	GH	Northill House
Wareham	FH	Redcliffe Farm
Wimborne Minster	GH	Beechleas

ESSEX

Chelmsford	GH	Boswell House Hotel
Southend-On-Sea	GH	Ilfracombe House

GLOUCESTERSHIRE

Cheltenham	GH	Lypiatt House
Laverton	GH	Leasow House
Willersey	GH	Old Rectory

HAMPSHIRE

Hayling Island	GH	Cockle Warren Cottage Hotel
Milford On Sea	GH	Seaspray Guest House
Ringwood	GH	Little Forest Lodge Hotel
Winchester	INN	The Wykeham Arms

HEREFORD & WORCESTER

Bishampton	FH	Nightingale Farm
Bredwardine	GH	Bredwardine Hall
Hanley Castle	GH	Old Parsonage Farm
Hereford	GH	Hermitage Manor
Leominster	GH	Withenfield
Redditch	GH	The Old Rectory
Ruckhall	INN	The Ancient Camp Inn
Ullingswick	GH	The Steppes
Vowchurch	GH	The Croft Country House
Whitney-on-Wye	INN	The Rhydspence Inn

HUMBERSIDE

Barmby Moor	GH	Barmby Moor Country Hotel

KENT

Canterbury	GH	Thanington Hotel

LANCASHIRE

Blackpool	GH	Sunray Private Hotel
Harrop Fold	FH	Harrop Fold Country Farmhouse Hotel
Lancaster	GH	Edenbreck House
Slaidburn	GH	Parrock Head Farm House Hotel
Thornton	GH	The Victorian House

'SELECTED' GUESTHOUSES, FARMHOUSES AND INNS

LINCOLNSHIRE

Lincoln	GH	D'Isney Place Hotel
Sturton by Stow	FH	The Village Farm

LONDON (GREATER)

(Postal Districts)

W14	GH	Aston Court Hotel
W2	GH	Byron Hotel

NORFOLK

Barney	GH	The Old Brick Kilns
Kings Lynn	GH	Russet House Hotel

NORTHUMBERLAND

Alnmouth	GH	Marine House Private Hotel
Haltwhistle	FH	Broomshaw Hill Farm
Haydon Bridge	GH	Langley Castle
Housesteads	FH	Beggar Bog Farm
Kirkwhelpington	FH	Shieldhall

NOTTINGHAM

Southwell	GH	Upton Fields

OXFORDSHIRE

Chislehampton	INN	The Coach & Horses
Woolstone	INN	The White Horse
Kidlington	GH	Bowood House
Kingston Bagpuize	FH	Fallowfields
Lew	FH	The Farmhouse Hotel & Restaurant
Milton-under-Wychwood	GH	Hillborough Hotel
Oxford	GH	Cotswold House
Oxford	GH	Tilbury Lodge Private Hotel
Thame	FH	Upper Green Farm

SHROPSHIRE

Church Stretton	FH	Rectory Farm

Diddlebury	GH	The Glebe

SOMERSET

Beercrocombe	FH	Frog Street Farm
Beercrocombe	FH	Whittles Farm
Bruton	GH	Fryerning
Glastonbury	FH	Berewell Farm Country Guest House
Kilve	INN	The Hood Arms
Langport	GH	Hillards Farm
Taunton	GH	Meryan House Hotel
Wells	GH	Coach House

STAFFORDSHIRE

Cheddleton	GH	Choir Cottage & Choir House

SUFFOLK

Gislingham	GH	The Old Guildhall
Higham	GH	The Old Vicarage
Needham Market	GH	Pipp's Ford Farm

SUSSEX (EAST)

Brighton	GH	Adelaide Hotel
Hastings & St Leonards	GH	Parkside House
Rye	GH	Jeakes House
	GH	The Old Vicarage Hotel & Restaurant
Uckfield	GH	Hooke Hall
Winchelsea	GH	The Country House at Winchelsea

SUSSEX (WEST)

Bepton	GH	The Park House Hotel
Billingshurst	FH	Old Wharf
Rogate	FH	Mizzards Farm

WARWICKSHIRE

Atherstone	GH	Chapel House
Hatton	GH	Northleigh House
Shrewley	GH	Shrewley House

WIGHT, ISLE OF

Sandown	GH	St Catherine's Hotel
Shanklin	GH	Chine Lodge
Shanklin	GH	Osbourne House

YORKSHIRE (NORTH)

Harrogate	GH	Alexa House & Stable Cottages
Hubberholme	GH	Kirkgill Manor
Kirkbymoorside	GH	Appletree Court
Patrick Brompton	GH	Elmfield House
Raskelf	GH	Old Farmhouse Country Hotel
Richmond	FH	Whashton Springs Farm
Scotch Corner	INN	Vintage Hotel
Starbotton	GH	Hilltop Country Guest House
Whitby	GH	Dunsley Hall
York	GH	Grasmead House Hotel

WALES

CLWYD

| Llanfair Dyffryn Clwyd | GH | Eyarth Station |
| St Asaph | FH | Bach-y-Craig |

DYFED

Gwaun Valley	FH	Tregynon Country Farmhouse Hotel
Llanfair Clydogau	FH	Pentre Farm
New Quay	GH	Park Hall

GWENT

| Abergavenny | GH | Llanwenarth House |

GWYNEDD

Aberdovey	GH	Morlan Guesthouse
Harlech	GH	Castle Cottage Hotel
Llanddeiniolen	FH	Ty'n Rhos Farm
Llandudno	GH	Craiglands Private Hotel

Llanfachreth	GH	Ty Isaf Guest House
Betws-y-Coed	GH	Tan-Y-Foel
Rhoscolyn	GH	The Old Rectory

POWYS

| Penybont | GH | Ffaldau Country House & Restaurant |
| Sennybridge | FH | Brynfedwen Farm |

CHANNEL ISLANDS

GUERNSEY

| St Peter Port | GH | Midhurst House |

JERSEY

| St Aubin | GH | The Panorama |

SCOTLAND

BORDERS

Jedburgh	GH	The Spinney
Tweedsmuir	GH	Menzion Farmhouse
West Linton	GH	Medwyn House

CENTRAL

| Bo'ness | FH | Kinglass Farm |

DUMFRIES & GALLOWAY

Clarencefield	GH	Comlongon Castle
Kirkbean	GH	Cavens House
Moffat	GH	Gilbert House
Twynholm	GH	Fresh Fields

GRAMPIAN

Aberdeen	GH	Cedars Private Hotel
Ballater	GH	Moorside Guesthouse
Bridge of Marnoch	GH	The Old Manse of Marnoch
Keith	FH	The Haughs
Forres	GH	Parkmount House Hotel

HIGHLAND

Carrbridge	GH	Fairwinds Hotel
Gairloch	GH	Horisdale House
Grantown-On-Spey	GH	Culdearn House
Grantown-On-Spey	GH	Dunstaffnage House
Grantown-On-Spey	GH	Garden Park
Kirkhill	GH	Moniack View
Rogart	FH	Rovie Farm

LOTHIAN

Edinburgh	GH	Dorstan Private Hotel
Edinburgh	GH	The Lodge Hotel

STRATHCLYDE

Abington	FH	Netherton Farm
Arrochar	GH	Mansefield Country House
Connel	GH	Loch Etive Hotel
Machrihanish	GH	Ardell House

TAYSIDE

Aberfeldy	GH	Guinach House
Blairgowrie	GH	Rosebank House
Brechin	FH	Blibberhill Farm
Pitlochry	GH	Dundarave House

Using the Guide

This guidebook is for those travellers who are looking for the personal attention, comfortable accommodation and warm reception often to be found in a good guesthouse, small hotel, farmhouse or inn. We list approximately 2650 such establishments all over Britain, at each of which you can be assured of good value for money, and that standards will be acceptable, because AA Inspectors visit regularly and we update our information every year. We also rate every establishment for quality, on a scale of one to four. Please see page 17 for a full explanation of the quality assessment.

In addition to the 'Quality' assessment, establishments where the standards are exceptionally good are also highlighted in the gazetteer under the heading 'S E L E C T E D' and the entries are enclosed in a tinted panel. A full list of these places is given on pages 18–22. They have been chosen by our Inspectors as offering standards of cooking, accommodation and hospitality that are well above the normal requirements for an AA listing. In all, only 196 establishments have been awarded the distinction this year.

WHAT IS A GUESTHOUSE

The term 'guesthouse' can lead to some confusion, particularly when many include the word 'hotel' in their name. For our purposes, we include small and private hotels in this category when they cannot offer all the services required for our star classification system.

This is not to say that they are inferior to hotels — just that they are different — and many offer a very high standard of accommodation. It is not unusual to be offered en suite bathrooms, for instance, or to find a colour television in your room. It is true that some guesthouses will only offer a set meal in the evening, but many provide a varied and interesting menu, and a standard of service which one would expect of a good restaurant. At the other end of the scale, some guesthouses offer bed and breakfast only, and it would also be wise to check if there are any restrictions to your access to the house, particularly late in the morning and during the afternoon.

We do have certain basic requirements which establishments must meet if they are to be listed in this Guide, although, as we have said, many will exceed these. They must offer at least two bedrooms. There should be a general bathroom and toilet for every six bedrooms which do not have private facilities. Fully licensed premises are now considered for inclusion, although many have a residential or restaurant licence only. We also stipulate that parking facilities, if not on the premises, should be within a reasonable distance. Guesthouses in the London section of the book are treated differently. They are actually all small hotels. Of course, London prices tend to be higher than those in the provinces, but those that we list offer cost-conscious accommodation, although normally only bed and breakfast is provided. To allow for all eventualities, we have also included a few which provide a full meal service and the charges for these will naturally be higher.

STAYING AT A FARMHOUSE

Farmhouse accommodation has a special quality, and is particularly noted for being inexpensive and cosy, with a high standard of good home-cooking. Those listed in our book are generally working farms, and some farmers are happy to allow visitors to look around, or even to help feed the animals. However, we must stress that the modern farm is a potentially dangerous place, especially where machinery and chemicals are concerned and visitors must be prepared to exercise care, particularly if they bring children. Never leave children unsupervised around the farm. Sometimes, guest accommodation is run as a separate concern from the farm on which it stands, and visitors are discouraged from venturing beyond the house and garden. In other cases, the land has been sold off, and although the gazetteer entry states the acreage and the type of farming carried out, it is advisable to check when booking to make sure that your requirements are met. To qualify for inclusion in the book, farms must have a minimum of two letting bedrooms, preferably fitted with washbasins, together with a bathroom with hot and cold running water and an inside toilet. As with the guesthouses, standards will vary considerably, and are often far above what one would expect. Some of our farmhouses are grand ex-manor houses furnished with antiques and offering a stylish way of life, and again some will have a residential or restaurant licence. All of the farmhouses are listed under town or village names, but obviously many will be some distance from other habitation. Proprietors will, of course, give directions when you book, and we publish a six-figure map reference against the gazetteer entry which can be used in conjunction with Ordnance Survey maps.

INNS

We all know what we can expect to find in a traditional inn — a cosy bar, a convivial atmosphere, good beer and pub food. Nevertheless, we have a few criteria which must be met here, too. There must be a minimum of two, and ideally a maximum of fifteen, letting bedrooms, each having a washbasin with hot and cold running water. Most bedrooms should be served by a bathroom and toilet on the same floor, and although a residents' lounge is not essential, there must be a suitable breakfast room.

Breakfast is a must, of course, but the inn should also serve at least light meals during licensing hours. Our inn category may also include a number of small, fully licensed hotels, and the character of the properties will vary according to whether they are pretty country inns or larger establishments in towns.

COMMON TO ALL

Whatever the type of establishment, there are certain requirements common to all, including a well-maintained exterior, clean and hygienic kitchens; good standards of furnishing; friendly and courteous service; access to the premises at reasonable times; the use of a telephone; full English breakfast; bedrooms equipped with comfortable beds, a wardrobe, a bedside cabinet, a washbasin with soap, towel, mirror and shaver socket and at least a carpet beside the bed; there should not be an extra charge for the use of baths or lavatories, and heating should be unmetered.

NB Where an establishment shows the central heating symbol, it does not necessarily mean that central heating will be available all year round. Some places only use it in winter, and then at their own discretion.

BOOKING

Book as early as possible, particularly if accommodation is required during the peak holiday period (from the beginning of June to the end of September, plus public holidays and, in some parts of Scotland, during the skiing season).

Although it is possible for chance callers to find a night's accommodation, it is by no means a certainty, especially at peak holiday times and in the popular areas, so to be certain of obtaining the accommodation you require, it is always advisable to book as far in advance as possible. Some establishments will also require a deposit on booking.

We have tried to provide as much information as possible about the establishments in our gazetteer, but if you should require further information before deciding to book, you should write to the establishment concerned. Do remember to enclose a stamped addressed envelope, or an international reply-paid coupon if writing from overseas, and please quote this publication in any enquiry.

CANCELLATION

If you later find that you must cancel your visit, let the proprietor know at once, because if the room you booked cannot be re-let, you may be held legally responsible for partial payment. Whether it is a matter of losing your deposit, or of being liable for compensation, you should seriously consider taking out cancellation insurance, such as *AA Travelsure*.

It is regretted that the AA cannot at the present time undertake to make any reservations.

COMPLAINTS

AA members who have any cause to complain are urged to do so *on the spot*. This should provide an opportunity for the proprietor to correct matters. If a personal approach fails, AA members should inform the AA head office at Basingstoke.

FIRE PRECAUTIONS

Many of the establishments listed in the Guide are subject to the requirements of the Fire Precautions Act of 1971. As far as we can discover, every establishment in this book has applied for, and not been refused, a fire certificate.

The Fire Precautions Act does not apply to the Channel Islands, or the Isle of Man, which exercise their own rules regarding fire precautions for hotels.

FOOD AND DRINK

In some parts of Britain, particularly in Scotland, high tea (i.e. a savoury dish followed by bread and butter, scones, cakes, etc) is sometimes served instead of dinner. Dinner may, however, be available on request. The last time at which high tea or dinner may be ordered on weekdays is shown, but this may be varied at weekends.

On Sundays, many establishments serve the main meal at midday, and provide only a cold supper in the evening.

If you intend to take dinner at the establishment, note that sometimes the meal must be ordered in advance of the actual meal time. In some cases,

this may be at breakfast time, or even on the previous evening. If you have booked on bed, breakfast and evening meal terms, you may find that the tariff includes a set menu, but you can usually order from the à la carte menu, if there is one, and pay a supplement.

LICENCES

The gazetteer entry will show whether or not the establishment is licensed to serve alcoholic drinks. Most places in the guesthouse category do not hold a full licence, but all inns do. Licensed premises are not obliged to remain open throughout the permitted hours, and they may do so only when they expect reasonable trade.

Note that in establishments which have registered clubs, club membership does not come into effect, nor can a drink be bought, until 48 hours after joining.

THE MONEY-OFF VOUCHER SCHEME

In the front of this book you will find six £1 vouchers which can be redeemed against your bill for accommodation at any of the establishments which show the £ symbol in the gazetteer.

Only one voucher may be presented for one room bill irrespective of the number of nights stayed. You must show your copy of the 1991 Guide in order to claim the discount and it is advisable to do this when you check in at reception. The vouchers are not valid if you are already benefitting from a discount under some other scheme, or from special off-peak rates.

PAYMENT

Most proprietors will only accept cheques in payment of accounts if notice is given and some form of identification (preferably a cheque card) is produced. If a hotel accepts credit or charge cards, this is shown in its gazetteer entry (see page 28 for details).

PRICES

It should be noted that *daily* terms quoted throughout this publication show minimum and maximum prices for both *one* and *two* persons and include a full breakfast. If dinner is also included this will be indicated in the gazetteer entry. *Weekly* terms, where available, show minimum and maximum prices *per person*, which take into account minimum double occupancy and maximum single occupancy, where appropriate, and may include the price of an evening meal — where this is the case it will be indicated in the text as such.

The Hotel Industry Voluntary Code of Booking Practice was revised in 1986, and the AA encourages its use in appropriate establishments. Its prime object is to ensure that the customer is clear about the precise services and facilities he/ she is buying, and what price will have to be paid, before entering into a contractually binding agreement. If the price has not been previously confirmed in writing, the guest should be handed a card at the time of registration, stipulating the total obligatory charge. The Tourism (Sleeping Accommodation Price Display) Order 1977 compels hotels, motels, guesthouses, farmhouses, inns and self-catering accommodation with four or more letting bedrooms to display in entrance halls the minimum and maximum prices charged for each category of room. This order complements the Voluntary Code of Booking Practice.

The tariffs quoted in the gazetteer of this book may be affected in the coming year by inflation, variations in the rate of VAT and many other factors.

You should always ascertain the current prices before making a booking. Those given in this book have been provided by proprietors in good faith, and must be accepted as indications rather than firm quotations.

In some cases, proprietors have been unable to provide us with their 1990 charges, but to give you a rough guide we publish the 1990 price, prefixed with an asterisk(*). It is also a good idea to ascertain exactly what is included in the price. Weekly terms can vary according to what meals are included. The text indicates whether weekly price includes bed and breakfast or bed, breakfast and evening meal. It is possible, that at the height of the season, some establishments will offer accommodation only on a weekly basis — often Saturday to Saturday — and this, too, is indicated in the gazetteer. We cannot indicate whether or not you are able to book mid-week, so if this is your intention, do check when making your reservation. Where information about 1991 prices is not given, you are requested to make enquiries direct.

VAT is payable, in the United Kingdom and in the Isle of Man, on both basic prices and any service. VAT does not apply in the Channel Islands. With this exception, prices quoted in this Guide are inclusive of VAT (and service where applicable).

Introducing
The Gazetteer

The gazetteer lists place-names alphabetically throughout England, Scotland and Wales, the Isle of Man and the Channel Islands.
Establishments on islands are listed under the appropriate island heading. The example of a gazetteer entry (see below) is to help you find your way through the entries. All the abbreviations and symbols are explained on pages 29 and 30. *Using the Guide* on pages 23–26 gives further information.

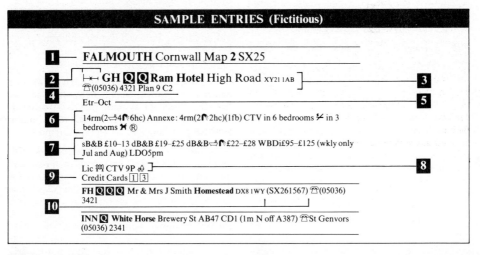

SAMPLE ENTRIES (Fictitious)

1 **FALMOUTH** Cornwall Map **2** SX25

2 **3** GH Q Q **Ram Hotel** High Road XY21 1AB
4 ☎(05036) 4321 Plan 9 C2

5 Etr–Oct

6 14rm(2⇆4🅵6hc) Annexe: 4rm(2🅵2hc)(1fb) CTV in 6 bedrooms ✂ in 3 bedrooms ✕ ®

7 sB&B £10–13 dB&B £19–£25 dB&B⇆🅵£22–£28 WBDi£95–£125 (wkly only Jul and Aug) LDO5pm

Lic ♿ CTV 9P ♨ **8**
9 Credit Cards ① ③

10 FH Q Q Q Mr & Mrs J Smith **Homestead** DX8 1WY (SX261567) ☎(05036) 3421

INN Q **White Horse** Brewery St AB47 CD1 (1m N off A387) ☎St Genvors (05036) 2341

---

1 **Towns** (including London) are listed in strict alphabetical order followed by the county or region. This is the administrative county, or region, and not necessarily part of the correct postal address. Towns on islands (not connected to the mainland by a bridge) are listed under the island name. With Scottish regions or islands, the old county name follows in italics. The map reference denotes first the map number, then the grid reference. To find the location on the atlas, first find the appropriate square (indicated by two letters), then read the 1st figure across and the 2nd figure vertically.

2 ⊨⊷ This symbol indicates that the establishment expects to provide bed and breakfast for under £13 per person, per night during 1991, but remember that circumstances can change during the currency of the Guide.

3 **Establishment Name**, address, postal code and telephone number. When establishments' names are shown in italics the particulars have not been confirmed by the proprietor. Guesthouses are identified by the letters **GH**, Farmhouses by **FH** and Inns by **INN** — this is also the order in which they are listed beneath the town headings.
All establishments are now rated for quality on a scale of one to four. This is denoted by the letter **Q**. See page 17 for a full explanation.
The **telephone exchange** (STD code) is usually that of the town heading. Where it differs from the town heading the exchange is given after the ☎ symbol, and before the dialling code and number. In some areas, numbers are likely to be changed during the currency of this book. In case of difficulty, check with the operator.

4 **Town Plans** There are street plans of some major towns and resorts at the end of the gazetteer. If there is a town plan, each establishment is given a key number and located on the plan. The London street plans, however, appear next to the London entries in the gazetteer.

5 **Opening details** Unless otherwise stated, the establishments are open all year, but where dates are shown they are inclusive: *eg* 'Apr–Oct' indicates that the establishment is open from the beginning of April to the end of October. Although some places are open all year, they may offer a restricted service during the less busy months, and we indicate this in the gazetteer by using the **rs** abbreviation. This may mean that there is a reduction in meals served and/or accommodation available, and where not indicated in the text, you should telephone in advance to find out the nature of the restriction.

6 **Accommodation details** The first figure shows the number of letting bedrooms. Where rooms have en suite bath or shower and wc or hot and cold water (hc), the number precedes the appropriate symbol.

Annexe – bedrooms available in an annexe are shown. Their standard is acceptable, but facilities may not be the same as in the main building, and it is advisable to check the nature of the accommodation and the tariff before making a reservation.

⊁ – number of bedrooms for non-smokers.

fb – family bedrooms.

CTV/TV – colour or black and white television available in lounge. This may also mean televisions permanently in bedrooms or available on request from the management. Check when making reservations.

✕ – no dogs allowed in bedrooms. Some establishments may restrict the size of dogs permitted and the rooms into which they may be taken. Establishments which do not normally accept dogs may accept guide dogs. Generally, dogs are not allowed in the dining room. Check when booking, the conditions under which pets are accepted.

7 **Prices** Bed and breakfast per person/two persons, per night and per person, per week (inclusive of dinner at times). For full explanation see page 25. Prices given have been provided by the proprietor in good faith, and are indications rather than firm quotations. Some establishments offer free accommodation to children provided they share the parents' room. Check current prices before booking. See also page 25.

8 **Facilities** For key to symbols see pages 29 and 30.

🚍 – no coaches. This information is published in good faith from details supplied by the establishments concerned. Inns, however, have well-defined legal obligations towards travellers, and any member with cause for complaint should take this up with the proprietor or the local licensing authority.

nc – establishments listed accommodate children of all ages unless a minimum age is given (*eg* nc4yrs), but they may not necessarily be able to provide special facilities. **nc** by itself indicates 'no children'. For very young children, check before booking about such provisions as cots and high chairs, and any reductions made.

🛝 – establishments with special facilities for children, which will include babysitting service or baby intercom system, playroom or playground, laundry facilities, drying and ironing facilities, cots, high chairs and special meals.

Note – disabled people may be accommodated, and where this is the case reference to this may be made in the description. Further details for disabled people will be found in the AA's *Guide for the Disabled Traveller* available from AA shops, free to members, £3.50 to non-members. Intending guests with any form of disability should notify proprietors, so that arrangements can be made to minimise difficulties, particularly in the event of an emergency.

9 **Payment details** (the following cards or discount vouchers may be accepted, but check current details when booking)

1	– Access/Eurocard/Mastercard
2	– American Express
3	– Barclaycard/Visa
5	– Diners
£	– Establishment accepts AA Money-Off Vouchers as detailed on page 25.

10 **Ordnance Survey Map Reference** This is shown for farmhouse entries only. As they are often in remote areas, we provide a six-figure map reference which can be used with Ordnance Survey maps.

Symbols and Abbreviations

	ENGLISH		FRANÇAIS		DEUTSCH
⊢←⊣	Bed and breakfast for £13 or under	⊢←⊣	Chambre et petit déjeuner pour moins de £13	⊢←⊣	Bett mit Frühstück für unter £13
Q	Quality assessment (see p. 17)	Q	Symbole AA d'évaluation qualitative (voir p. 17)	Q	AA Katagorisierung der Qualität (siehe S. 17)
☎	Telephone number	☎	Numéro de téléphone	☎	Telefonnummer
⇴	Private bath and WC	⇴	Salle de bain privée avec WC	⇴	Privatbadezimmer mit WC
℟	Private shower and WC	℟	Douche privée et WC	℟	Privatdusche mit WC
⚥	Bedrooms set aside for non-smokers	⚥	Chambres réservées aux non-fumeurs	⚥	Zimmer für Nichtraucher
✗	No dogs	✗	Chiens interdits	✗	Hundeverbot
ℝ	Tea/coffee-making facilities in bedrooms	ℝ	Possibilité de faire le thé/le café dans les chambres	ℝ	Tee/Kaffeemöglichkeiten im Zimmer
✳	1990 prices	✳	Prix 1990	✳	1990 Preise
▥	Full central heating	▥	Chauffage central intégral	▥	Vollfernheizung
P	Parking for cars	P	Stationnement pour voitures	P	Parkplatz
P̸	No parking on premises	P̸	Pas de stationnement sur place	P̸	Kein Parkplatz
⛟	Garage accommodation for . . . cars	⛟	Garage pour . . . voitures	⛟	Garagen für . . . Autos
🚌	Coach parties not accepted	🚌	Groups en autocar pas reçus	🚌	Reisebusgesellschaften nicht aufgenommen
⚗	Special facilities for children (see p. 28)	⚗	Facilités spéciales pour enfants – (voir p. 28)	⚗	Sonderdienstleistungen für Kinder – (siehe S. 28)
▣	Indoor swimming pool	▣	Piscine à l'intérieur	▣	Hallenbad
◠	Outdoor swimming pool	◠	Piscine à l'extérieur	◠	Freibad
▶9▶18	9-hole or 18-hole golf course	▶9▶18	Terrain de golf à 9 trous ou 18 trous	▶9▶18	Golfplatz mit 9 oder 18 holes
♟	Tennis court(s)	♟	Court(s) de tennis	♟	Tennisplatz (Platze)
⨍	Fishing	⨍	Pêche	⨍	Angeln
℧	Riding stables on premises	℧	Ecuries d'équitation sur les lieux	℧	Reitstall an Ort und Stelle
sB&B	Single room including breakfast per person per night	sB&B	Chambre à un lit et petit déjeuner par personne et par nuit	sB&B	Übernachtung in einem Einzelzimmer mit Frühstück pro Person
dB&B	Double room (2 persons sharing a room) including breakfast per night	dB&B	Chambre à deux lits (2 personnes à une chambre) avec petit déjeuner par nuit	dB&B	Doppelzimmer (2 Personer in einem Zimmer) mit Frühstück pro Nacht
WB&B	Weekly terms, bed and breakfast, per person	WB&B	Prix par semaine et par personne, chambre et petit déjeuner inclus	WB&B	Wochenpreis pro Person, Übernachtung mit Frühstück
WBDi	Weekly terms bed, breakfast and evening meal, per person	WBDi	Prix par semaine et par personne, chambre, petit déjeuner et diner inclus	WBDi	Wochenpreis pro Person, Übernachtung mit Frühstück und Abendessen
alc	A la carte	alc	A la carte	alc	A la carte
CTV	Colour television	CTV	TV en couleurs	CTV	Farbfernsehen
Etr	Easter	Etr	Pâques	Etr	Ostern
fb	Family bedroom	fb	Chambre de famille	fb	Familienzimmer
fr	From	fr	A partir de	fr	Von
hc	Number of bedrooms with hot and cold water	hc	Nombre de chambres avec eau chaude et froide	hc	Zimmer mit Warm- und Kaltwasser
LDO	Time last dinner can be ordered	LDO	Le dîner est à commander avant cette heure	LDO	Letzte Bestellzeit für Abendessen
Lic	Licensed	Lic	Licence de boissons	Lic	Ausschank alkoolischer Getränke
mdnt	Midnight	mdnt	Minuit	mdnt	Mitternacht
nc	No children. nc . . . yrs, no children under . . . years of age	nc	Enfants pas admis. nc . . . ans, enfants au-dessous de . . . ans pas admis	nc	Kinder nicht willkommen. nc . . Jahren, Kinder unter . . Jahren nicht willkommen
rm	Letting bedrooms in main building	rm	Nombre de chambres dans le bâtiment principal	rm	Zimmeranzahl im Hauptgebäude
rs	Restricted service	rs	Service réduit	rs	Beschränkte Dienstleistungen
TV	Black and white television	TV	TV en noir et blanc	TV	Schwarzweissfernsehen
⊡	Credit cards (p. 28)	⊡	Cartes de crédit (p. 28)	⊡	Kreditkarten (p. 28)
£	Voucher scheme (p. 25)	£	Bons (p. 25)	£	Gutschein (p. 25)
→	Entry continued overleaf	→	Suite au verso	→	Fortsetzung umseitig

29

Symbols and Abbreviations

ITALIANO

⊢⊣ Camera e prima colazione a meno di 13 sterline
Ⓠ Simbolo di valutrazione qualitativa della AA (vedi p. 17)
☎ Numero telefonica
🛁 Bagno e servizi privati
🚿 Doccia e servizi privati
🚭 Camere per non fumatori
✖ Proibito ai cani
Ⓡ Attrezzatura per fare il té o il caffé nelle camere
✻ Prezzi del 1990
♨ Riscaldemento centrale in tutte le camere
P Parcheggio macchine
P̸ Senza parcheggio sul posto
🚗 Garage per . . . macchine
🚌 Non si accettano comitive in gita turistica
👶 Attrezzature speciali per í bambini – (vedi p. 28)
🏊 Piscina coperta
🏊 Piscina scoperta
▶9▶18 Campo da golf a 9 o 18 buche
♟ Campo(i) da tennis
🎣 Pesca
Ⴓ Scuola d'equitazione sul posto

sB&B Prezzo di una camera singola con la colazione compresa (per notte)
dB&B Prezzo di una camera doppia (2 persone per camera) con la colazione compresa (per notte)
WB&B Tariffe settimanali per persona, camera e prima colazione
WBDi Tariffe settimanali per persona, sono compresi la camera, la prima colazione e il pranzo
alc Alla carta
CTV Televisione a colori
Etr Pasqua
fb Camera familiare
fr Da
hc Numero di camera con acqua calda e fredda
LDO Ora in cui si accettano le ultime ordinazioni
Lic Autorizzato alla vendita alcolici
mdnt Mezzanotte
nc Proibito ai bambini. nc . . . anni, proibito ai bambini sottoi . . . anni
rm Numero di camere nell' edificio principale
rs Servizio limitato
TV Televisione in bianco e nero

▯ Carte di credito (p. 28)
£ Documento di riduzione (p. 25)
→ La lista delle voci continua a tergo

ESPANOL

⊢⊣ Cama y desaguno a menos de 13 libras esterlinas
Ⓠ Simbolo de evaluación calitativa de la AA (Véase p. 17)
☎ Numero de teléfono
🛁 Baño y servicios en cada habitación
🚿 Ducha y servicios en cada habitación
🚭 Habitaciones reservados para los no fumadores
✖ Se prohibe a los porros
Ⓡ Facilidades para hacer el té o el café en los habitaciones
✻ Precios de 1990
♨ Calafacción central
P Aparcamiento para automóviles
P̸ No poder estacionarse junto al establecimiento
🚗 Garaje o espacio cubierto para . . . automóviles
🚌 No se aceptan los grupos de viajeros en coches de linea
👶 Facilidades especialies para los niños (p. 28)
🏊 Piscina cubierta
🏊 Piscina descubierta
▶9▶18 Campo de golf de 9 o 18 hoyos
♟ Cancha(s) de tenis
🎣 Pesca
Ⴓ Escuela hípica

sB&B Precio por noche de una habitación individual con desayuno incluido
dB&B Precio por noche de una habitación para dos personas (2 personas compartiendo una habitación) con desayuno incluido
WB&B Tarifas semanales cama y desayuno
WBDi Tarifas semanales, el precio incluye a la cama, al desayuna y a la comida
alc A la carta
CTV Televisión en colores
Etr Pascua de Resurrección
fb Habitación familiar
fr De
hc Número de habitaciones con agua fría y caliente
LDO Últimas ordenes
Lic Con licencia para vender bebidas alcóholicas
mdnt Medianoche
nc Se prohibe le entrada a los niños. nc . . . años, se prohibe la entrada a los niños de menos de . . . años
rm Número de habitaciones del edifico principal
rs Servicio limitado
TV Televisión en blanco y negro

▯ Tarjetas de crédito (p. 28)
£ Documento de rehaja (p. 25)
→ La lista continúa a la vuelta

ABBOTS BICKINGTON Devon Map **02** SS31

⊢⊣**FH** [Q][Q] Mrs E Bellew **Court Barton** *(SS384133)* EX22 7LQ
☎Milton Damerel(040926) 214
May-Oct
This elegant stone-built farmhouse offers spacious bedrooms and comfortable public rooms. Guests will enjoy home cooking and a warm welcome on this 650-acre mixed farm.
4rm(3hc)(1fb) [R] 🚫 sB&B£11-£12
dB&B£22-£24 WB&B£67-£74 WBDi£85-£90 LDO 5pm
♨ CTV 10P nc3yrs 🎣 rough shooting 640 acres arable beef sheep
[£]

ABBOTS BROMLEY Staffordshire Map **07** SK02

FH [Q][Q] Mrs M K Hollins ***Marsh*** *(SK069261)* WS15 3EJ
☎Burton-on-Trent(0283) 840323
Closed Xmas
Surrounded by farmland, this deceptively large house specialises in catering. Coach parties are welcome for lunches or teas, but Mrs Hollins never forgets her resident guests.
2hc (1fb) CTV in 1 bedroom [R] LDO 5pm
♨ CTV 6P 87 acres mixed

ABERDEEN Grampian *Aberdeenshire* Map **15** NJ90

GH [Q][Q][Q] **Bimini** 69 Constitution St AB2 1ET
☎(0224) 646912
This small, family-run guesthouse is situated in the east end, and is convenient for the beach and recreation facilities. It has a friendly atmosphere and offers good value bed and breakfast accommodation.
7hc (1fb) CTV in all bedrooms [R] 🚫 (ex guide dogs) *
sB&B£14-£16 dB&B£24-£28
♨ CTV 7P
Credit Cards [1] [3] [£]

GH [Q][Q] **Broomfield Private Hotel** 15 Balmoral Place AB1 6HR
☎(0224) 588758
Closed Jan
This is a family-run guesthouse situated in a residential area of the town's west end. It caters for those on business as well as tourists, having a friendly atmosphere and providing comfortable accommodation.
8hc [R] * sB&B£15-£20 dB&B£26-£28 LDO 3pm
♨ CTV 10P
[£]

SELECTED

GH [Q][Q][Q][Q] **Cedars Private Hotel** 339 Great Western Rd AB1 6NW ☎(0224) 583225
Conveniently situated in the town's west end, this friendly establishment is efficiently run and offers high standards of comfort. The bedrooms are well equipped and breakfast is served in the smart dining room, which features a beautiful ornate ceiling.
13rm(2🛁2🚿9hc)(2fb) CTV in all bedrooms [R] *
sB&B£25-£35 sB&B🛁🚿£35 dB&B£38
dB&B🛁🚿£40 WBDi£175-£245
♨ CTV 13P training/keep fit area
Credit Cards [2] [£]

GH [Q][Q][Q] **Corner House Hotel** 385 Great Western Rd AB1 6NY ☎(0224) 313063
Conveniently situated in the West End, this hotel provides a relaxing atmosphere for business people and tourists. Bedrooms are individually furnished and well equipped, and there is a comfortable lounge and restaurant. Service is good and personally supervised by the proprietors.
17🛁🚿 (3fb) CTV in 15 bedrooms [R] sB&B🛁🚿£26-£34
dB&B🛁🚿£36-£46 WB&B£140-£190 WBDi£200-£250 LDO 8.30pm
Lic ♨ CTV 12P
Credit Cards [1] [3] [£]

GH [Q][Q][Q] **Craiglynn Hotel** 36 Fonthill Rd AB1 2UJ
☎(0224) 584050
An attractive Victorian house, this hotel is situated in a residential area south of the city centre. It offers a choice of tastefully appointed lounges and the bedrooms are comfortable and well equipped.
9rm(6🛁🚿3hc)(2fb) CTV in all bedrooms 🚫 sB&B£27
sB&B🛁🚿£35 dB&B£38
dB&B🛁🚿£46 WB&B£133-£245 WBDi£217-£329 LDO 7.30pm
Lic ♨ CTV 7P
Credit Cards [1] [2] [3] [5] [£]

GH [Q][Q][Q] **Fourways** 435 Great Western Rd AB1 6NJ
☎(0224) 310218
This guesthouse, situated in the town's west end, offers convenient access to the ring road and Deeside. It has a friendly atmosphere, and provides comfortable, well-equipped accommodation.
7rm(6🛁🚿1hc)(2fb) CTV in all bedrooms [R] 🚫 (ex guide dogs)
* sB&B£15-£18 sB&B🛁🚿fr£18 dB&B🛁🚿£30 LDO 4pm
♨ CTV 7P
[£]

GH [Q][Q] **Klibreck** 410 Great Western Rd AB1 6NR
☎(0224) 316115
Closed Xmas & New Year
This is a small, family-run guesthouse, located on the main Deeside road, and is close to the ring road. The accommodation offered is practical and it has a friendly atmosphere.
6hc (1fb)🚭in all bedrooms [R] 🚫 * sB&Bfr£15
dB&Bfr£25 LDO 3pm
♨ CTV 3P
[£]

GH [Q][Q][Q] **Open Hearth** 349 Holburn St AB1 6DQ
☎(0224) 596888
This efficiently run guesthouse is situated in a residential area and offers convenient access to both the ring road and the city centre. It has a friendly atmosphere and provides comfortable, modern accommodation.
11hc (2fb) CTV in all bedrooms [R] sB&Bfr£16.10
dB&Bfr£25.30
♨ CTV 5P

⊢⊣**GH** [Q] **Strathboyne** 26 Abergeldie Ter AB1 6EE
☎(0224) 593400
A pleasant atmosphere prevails at this small, personally run guesthouse, which is in a residential area south of the city centre. It offers traditional comforts and good value, practical accommodation.
6hc (2fb) CTV in all bedrooms [R] sB&B£12.50-£13
dB&B£23-£24 LDO 3.30pm
♨ CTV P̸
[£]

ABERDOVEY Gwynedd Map **06** SN69

During the currency of this publication Aberdovey telephone numbers are liable to change.

GH [Q][Q] ***Brodawel*** Tywyn Rd, Brodawel LL35 0RT
☎(065472) 347
Closed Jan-Feb
This small, well-maintained family-run hotel is situated on the outskirts of the town, opposite to the golf course. The bedrooms are well-equipped and many have en suite facilities, the house is fronted by pleasant gardens and has the advantage of its own car park.

▶

7rm(3🛏4hc)(1fb) CTV in 6 bedrooms ® LDO noon
Lic ⚑ 8P

GH |Q||Q| **Cartref** LL35 0NR ☎(065472) 273 due to change to (0654) 767273
The resident owners of this attractive detached house provide a warm welcome and all-round home comforts.
7rm(1⇨3🛏3hc)(2fb) CTV in 4 bedrooms ® ✻ sB&Bfr£13
dB&Bfr£25 dB&B⇨🛏fr£30 LDO 5pm
⚑ CTV 8P

SELECTED

GH |Q||Q||Q||Q| **Morlan** LL35 0SE ☎(065472) 7706
This small, single-storeyed, family-run guesthouse is set in very attractive gardens and situated on the outskirts of the town, in an elevated position overlooking the golf course and Cardigan Bay. The good quality bedrooms are very well equipped, including many thoughtful extra touches. All have good en suite facilities, and French windows have recently been installed to provide each room with its own access to the garden. The lounge and attractive dining room are furnished to a high standard. The guesthouse benefits from having its own car park and an extra facility is the availability of golf concessions at the nearby championship course.
4rm(1⇨3🛏)⚥in all bedrooms CTV in all bedrooms ®
✖ (ex guide dogs) ✻ dB&B⇨🛏£32-£36 LDO 2pm
Lic ⚑ CTV 6P nc16yrs

ABERFELDY Tayside *Perthshire* Map **14** NN84

GH |Q||Q| **Balnearn House Hotel** Crieff Rd PH15 2BJ ☎(0887) 20431
This holiday guesthouse stands on the town's fringe, close to the famous Breks of Aberfeldy. It has a friendly atmosphere and provides traditional comforts.
13rm(1⇨2🛏10hc)(2fb) ® LDO 6.30pm
CTV 15P

GH |Q||Q||Q| **Caber-Feidh** 56 Dunkeld St PH15 2AF ☎(0887) 20342
This modernised stone house is situated on the main road above town-centre shops and offers pleasant and comfortable accommodation. Both high tea and dinner are available.
6hc (2fb) ® ✻ sB&Bfr£13
dB&Bfr£26 WB&Bfr£89 WBDifr£139 LDO 8.45pm
Lic ⚑ CTV 5P
£

SELECTED

GH |Q||Q||Q||Q| *Guinach House* By The Birks PH15 2BT ☎(0887) 20251
15 Mar-Oct
Under the caring ownership of Bert and Marianne Mackay, this lovely Edwardian house, set in 2 acres of secluded grounds, offers a high standard of modern-day comfort while retaining much of its original charm and character. The individually decorated and furnished bedrooms have been thoughtfully equipped, while the public rooms invite peaceful relaxation. Mr Mackay is a member of the World Master Chefs Society.
7rm(3⇨3🛏1hc) CTV in all bedrooms ® LDO 8.30pm
Lic ⚑ 8P 1🚗 nc8yrs croquet

ABERGAVENNY Gwent Map **03** SO21

GH |Q||Q| **Belchamps** 1 Holywell Rd NP7 5LP ☎(0873) 3204
Just off the A40, close to the Gaveny River 1 mile south of the town, this guesthouse has simple, comfortable accommodation suitable for tourists and commercial visitors alike.

5hc (2fb) CTV in all bedrooms ® ✖ (ex guide dogs)
sB&B£16-£18
dB&B£28-£32 WB&B£78-£90 WBDi£108-£132 LDO 7pm
⚑ CTV 5P
£

SELECTED

GH |Q||Q||Q||Q| **Llanwenarth House** Govilon NP7 9SF ☎Gilwern(0873) 830289
rs Jan-Feb
This 16th-century mansion with historical connections stands in beautiful, peaceful countryside in the Brecon Beacons National Park. It has been carefully restored and renovated and rooms have been tastefully decorated and are equipped with period furniture. The bedrooms with superb views look over the Vale of Usk are spacious with good en suite facilities and are well equipped with modern comforts. Complemented by a well-chosen wine list, the food is of excellent quality and is served by candlelight.
5rm(3⇨2🛏)(1fb) CTV in all bedrooms ®
sB&B⇨🛏£43-£49 dB&B⇨🛏£53-£59 LDO 6.30pm
Lic ⚑ 6P nc10yrs

FH |Q||Q| Mrs D Miles *Great Lwynfranc* (*SO327193*)
Llanvihangel Crucorney NP7 8EN (off A465 3m N) ☎Crucorney(0873) 890418
Mar-Nov
Enjoying an elevated position well back from the A465 north of the town, with excellent views of the countryside, this pleasant farmhouse has comfortable, traditional accommodation and the Miles family offer warm hospitality.
3hc (1fb) ®
⚑ CTV 10P 154 acres mixed

FH |Q||Q| Mrs M E Smith *Lower House* (*SO314159*) Old Hereford Rd NP7 7HR ☎(0873) 3432
Etr-Oct
Isolated stone-built farmhouse with mountain views, 3 miles from Abergavenny.
3hc ®
⚑ CTV 6P 200 acres arable beef sheep

FH |Q||Q| Mrs J Nicholls **Newcourt** (*SO317165*) Mardy NP7 8AU ☎(0873) 2300
Closed Xmas wk
17th-century, stone-built farmhouse, with fine views of the Sugar Loaf mountain.
3rm(1🛏2hc)⚥in all bedrooms CTV in all bedrooms ®
✖ (ex guide dogs) ✻ sB&Bfr£15 dB&B£28-£32
dB&B🛏£30-£36 WB&B£90-£125
⚑ CTV 10P nc6yrs 160 acres arable beef dairy
£

INN |Q| **The Great George** Cross St NP7 5ER ☎(0873) 4230
This 16th-century inn stands in the town centre and has simple but pleasant bar and restaurant facilities. The spacious and comfortable accommodation is suitable for tourists and commercial visitors alike.
3hc (1fb) CTV in all bedrooms ® ✖ sB&Bfr£25
dB&B£40 Lunch £1.75-£9alc Dinner £1.75-£9alc LDO 9pm
⚑ 50P 4🚗
Credit Cards 1

Every effort is made to provide accurate information, but details can change after we go to print. It is advisable to check prices etc. before you make a firm booking.

ABERHOSAN Powys Map **06** SN89

FH [Q][Q][Q] Mrs A Lewis **Bacheiddon** *(SN825980)* SY20 8SG ☎Machynlleth(0654) 702229

May-Oct

Set in magnificent rugged countryside between Machywlleth and Llanidloes, this pleasant farmhouse has bright, well-maintained bedrooms and guests can relax in front of the log fire in the comfortable lounge.

3🚿 [R] 🚫 * sB&B🚿fr£16 dB&B🚿fr£32 WB&Bfr£112

CTV 3P 830 acres mixed sheep

ABERPORTH Dyfed Map **02** SN25

GH [Q][Q] ***Ffynonwen Country*** SA43 2HT ☎(0239) 810312

Run by the friendly Duckworth family, this converted farmhouse lies between Aberporth and the A487. It has neat bedrooms, a spacious lounge and a bar where local functions are popular.

6rm(3🛁3hc)(2fb)

Lic ♨ 30P games room

ABERSOCH Gwynedd Map **06** SH32

GH [Q][Q] ***Llysfor*** LL53 7AL ☎(075881) 2248

Etr-Oct

Detached Victorian house near beach and shops.

8rm(1🛁7hc)(2fb) [R] LDO Breakfast

Lic CTV 12P

ABERYSTWYTH Dyfed Map **06** SN58

GH [Q][Q][Q] **Glyn-Garth** South Rd SY23 1JS ☎(0970) 615050

Closed 1 wk Xmas rs Oct-Etr

Victorian, double-fronted, mid-terrace property adjacent to beach, harbour and castle, quarter of a mile from the shops.

10rm(4🛁2🚿4hc)(3fb)🚭in 3 bedrooms CTV in all bedrooms [R] 🚫 * sB&B£14-£15 dB&B£28-£30 dB&B🛁🚿£32-£38 LDO 4.30pm

Lic ♨ CTV 4🚗 (£1.50 per night) nc7yrs

[£]

GH [Q][Q] ***Llety Gwyn Hotel*** Llanbadarn Fawr SY23 3SX (1m E A44) ☎(0970) 623965

Closed 25-26 Dec

Situated in a residential area on the eastern outskirts of the town, this family-run hotel has the benefit of a fully equipped gymnasium, sauna and solarium as well as extensive public areas.

8rm(4🚿4hc)Annexe 6rm(1🛁3🚿2hc)(3fb) CTV in all bedrooms [R] LDO 5pm

Lic ♨ CTV 50P snooker sauna solarium gymnasium

Credit Cards [1] [3]

GH [Q][Q] **Plas Antaron** Penparcau SY23 1SF ☎(0970) 611550

Set in its own grounds, just 1.5 miles from the city centre on the A487 Aberaeron road, this large family-run guesthouse provides spacious, well-equipped bedrooms and comfortable public rooms.

8🚿 (1fb) CTV in all bedrooms [R] *

dB&B🚿£25-£30 WB&B£87.50-£105 WBDi£129.50-£147 LDO noon

Lic ♨ CTV 40P

Credit Cards [1] [3] [£]

GH [Q] **Shangri-La** 36 Portland St SY23 2DX ☎(0970) 617659

Closed 25 & 26 Dec

Single-fronted, mid-terrace Victorian building adjacent to shops and quarter of a mile from beach.

6hc (3fb) TV in all bedrooms [R] * sB&B£12 dB&B£22-£24

♨ CTV P̸

This guide is updated annually – make sure you use an up-to-date edition.

ABINGDON Oxfordshire Map **04** SU49

INN [Q][Q][Q] **Barley Mow Hotel** Clifton Hampden OX14 3EH (through village on road to Didcot) (Berni/Chef & Brewer) ☎Clifton Hampden(086730) 7847

Full of old-world character, this thatched inn is situated in Cufton Hampden (on the Didcot Road) just outside Abingdon. The bedrooms are of a high standard, attractively furnished and have modern facilities. These are complemented by popular bars and an attractive restaurant.

4rm(1🚿3hc) CTV in all bedrooms [R] 🚫 (ex guide dogs) * sB&B£34.50 sB&B🚿£41

dB&B🚿£54 Lunch £8-£15 Dinner £8-£15 LDO 9.30pm

♨ 250P

Credit Cards [1] [2] [3] [5]

ABINGTON Strathclyde *Lanarkshire* Map **11** NS92

⊢⊣**FH** [Q][Q][Q] Mrs M L Hodge **Craighead** *(NS914236)* ML12 6SQ ☎Crawford(08642) 356

May-Oct

This large farm building in courtyard design is set amid rolling hills on the banks of the River Duneaton. The main buildings date from 1780. The farm is set off the unclassified Crawfordjohn Road, 1 mile north of the A74/A73 junction.

3rm(2hc) 🚫 (ex guide dogs) sB&B£11.50-£12.50 dB&B£23-£24 WB&Bfr£80 WBDi£120-£122 LDO 5pm

♨ CTV 6P 4🚗 🎣 600 acres mixed

[£]

Street plans of certain towns and cities will be found in a separate section at the back of the book.

SELECTED

FH [Q][Q][Q][Q] Mrs J Hyslop **Netherton** *(NS908254)*
ML12 6RU (on unclass road joining A74 & A73)
☏Crawford(08642) 321
Situated just north of Abington, this former shooting lodge is in a peaceful location and yet has easy access to the A47. Guests will appreciate the airy, spacious bedrooms, all beautifully maintained and thoughtfully equipped. Public rooms, too, are comfortable, and in the splendid, traditional dining room, Mrs Hyslop serves her fine cuisine in houseparty style.
3rm(2hc)⚲in all bedrooms ® ✖ ✱ sB&B£12-£13
dB&B£24-£38 LDO 4pm
🛏 CTV 3P ⏀ 3000 acres beef sheep
ⓔ

ACASTER MALBIS North Yorkshire Map **08** SE54

INN [Q][Q][Q] **Ship** YO2 1XB ☏York(0904) 705609 & 703888
This 17th-century coaching house is in a lovely setting on the River Ouse, 3.5 miles from the city centre. The quaint bedrooms are furnished in pine, and the cosy bars and restaurant provide delightful surroundings for substantial meals.
8rm(2⇋6ᶇ)⚲in all bedrooms CTV in all bedrooms ®
✖ (ex guide dogs) sB&B⇋ᶇ£25-£30
dB&B⇋ᶇ£38-£60 WB&B£114-£180 WBDi£180-£285 Lunch
£6.95-£8.95&alc High tea £4.95-£6.95 Dinner £7.75-£15alc
LDO 9.30pm
🛏 60P ⏀ river cruises private moorings
Credit Cards [1][3]ⓔ
See advertisement under YORK on page 412

ACHARACLE Highland *Argyllshire* Map **13** NM66

FH [Q][Q] Mrs M Macaulay **Dalilea House** *(NM735693)*
PH36 4JX ☏Salen(096785) 253
Etr-Oct
Delightfully situated on the shore of Loch Shiel, this fine turreted 15th-century farmhouse is an ideal base for the touring holidaymaker. It offers genuine Highland hospitality with traditional comforts and provides enjoyable farmhouse (including vegetarian) fare.
6rm(4ᶇ2hc)(1fb) ✱ sB&Bfr£13 dB&Bfr£24
dB&Bᶇfr£32 LDO 7pm
Lic 🛏 8P ⏀ canoes 1300 acres beef fish sheep

ADFORTON Hereford & Worcester Map **07** SO47

GH [Q][Q][Q] **Lower House** SY7 0NF ☏Wigmore(056886) 223
Etr-Nov
4rm(2ᶇ2hc)(2fb) ® ✖ ✱ sB&B£23-£25 sB&Bᶇ£28-£30
dB&B£46-£50
dB&Bᶇ£55-£60 (incl dinner) WB&B£105-£150
WBDi£150-£190 LDO 7pm
🛏 CTV 8P nc10yrs

AIRDRIE Strathclyde *Lanarkshire* Map **11** NS76

FH [Q][Q] Mrs E C Hunter **Easter Glentore** *(NS813717)*
Greengairs ML6 7TJ (on B803) ☏Greengairs(023683) 243
2hc (1fb) ✖ ✱ sB&B£13.50-£16.50 dB&B£25-£28 LDO 4pm
🛏 CTV 6P nc3yrs 245 acres beef sheep
ⓔ

ALDEBURGH Suffolk Map **05** TM45

GH [Q][Q][Q] **Cotmandene** 6 Park Ln IP15 5HL ☏(0728) 453775
This double-fronted red-brick house is set in a residential area of the town. The accommodation offered is comfortable and thoughtfully furnished, with some en suite facilities, and some

rooms having colour televisions. Mrs Tibbenham is a cheerful hostess.
7rm(2⇋2ᶇ3hc)(2fb) TV in all bedrooms ® ✖ (ex guide dogs)
LDO 7.30pm
🛏 CTV ⏀
Credit Cards [1][3]

ALDERTON Wiltshire Map **03** ST88

FH [Q][Q][Q] Mrs V Lippiatt **Manor** *(ST840831)* SN14 6NL
☏Malmesbury(0666) 840271
Apr-Oct
Midway between Acton Turville and Luckington, this large Cotswold farmhouse has attractive, well-equipped bedrooms and a tastefully furnished drawing room with no television so guests can relax, talk or read. A hearty breakfast is taken around a large table.
3rm(2⇋3ᶇ1hc) CTV in all bedrooms ® ✖ sB&B⇋ᶇ£18.50
dB&B⇋ᶇ£37-£40
10P nc12yrs 600 acres arable beef
See advertisement under MALMESBURY

ALDWARK Derbyshire Map **08** SK25

FH [Q][Q][Q] J N Lomas **Lydgate** *(SK228577)* DE4 4HW
☏Carsington(062985) 250
Set in the centre of this rural village within the Peak National Park, this inviting 17th-century farmhouse has friendly proprietors and combines modern facilities and comfort. The heavily beamed bedrooms are light and spacious and have individual character.
3rm (1fb)⚲in 2 bedrooms ® ✖ ✱ sB&B£15.50-£17.50
dB&B£25-£31 WB&B£87
🛏 CTV 5P 300 acres mixed
ⓔ

ALFRISTON East Sussex Map **05** TQ50

FH [Q][Q][Q] Mrs D Y Savage *Pleasant Rise* *(TQ516027)*
☏(0323) 870545
Closed Xmas wk
Set in beautiful surroundings close to the South Downs Way, this modern farmhouse has extensive indoor and outdoor leisure facilities including tennis, badminton, cricket and horseriding. Self-contained accommodation adjoins the main house and breakfast room.
Annexe 4rm(1ᶇ3hc) ®
🛏 CTV 8P nc9yrs ⏀(hard)100 acres mixed working

ALKMONTON Derbyshire Map **07** SK13

FH [Q][Q][Q] Mr A Harris **Dairy House** *(SK198367)* DE6 3DG
☏Great Cubley(0335) 330359
Closed Xmas
Mr and Mrs Harris provide a friendly welcome and stay at their comfortably modernised 16th-century farmhouse, which is found three miles up Woodyard Lane after turning off the A50 at Foston.
7rm(1⇋2ᶇ4hc)(1fb)⚲in all bedrooms ® ✖ (ex guide dogs)
sB&B£14 sB&B⇋ᶇ£20 dB&B£28
dB&B⇋ᶇ£34 WB&B£98-£119 WBDi£154-£175 LDO 8pm
Lic 🛏 CTV 8P nc5yrs ⏀ bowls croquet 82 acres dairy

ALNMOUTH Northumberland Map **12** NU21

GH [Q][Q][Q] **Blue Dolphin** 11 Riverside Rd NE66 2SO
☏Alnwick(0665) 830893
Set in an attractive, peaceful location, this guesthouse offers very comfortable bedrooms, all of which are well-appointed. The cheerful proprietors provide a friendly service.
5rm(2⇋3ᶇ) CTV in all bedrooms ® ✱ dB&B⇋ᶇ£35-£40
5P
ⓔ

SELECTED

GH QQQQ **Marine House Private Hotel** 1 Marine Dr NE66 2RW ☎Alnwick(0665) 830349
Feb-Nov
Managed by the friendly resident proprietors, this comfortable seafront hotel has the advantage of delightful views over the golf links to the attractive bay beyond. This is the ideal hotel for families, being close to all the amenities and having its own games room. The accommodation throughout is inviting and comfortable, while the dinner menu is changed daily and all dishes are freshly prepared from good quality local produce.
10rm(4⇱6🏠)(4fb)
dB&B⇱🏠£58-£66 (incl dinner) WBDif£200-£228 LDO 4pm
Lic ㎰ CTV 12P nc5yrs
£

ALNWICK Northumberland Map **12** NU11

GH QQ *Aln House* South Rd NE66 2NZ ☎(0665) 602265
Set back from the main road to the south of the town centre, this well-maintained guesthouse offers comfortable accommodation with smart en suite facilities. There is also a pleasantly furnished and relaxing lounge.
8rm(2⇱1🏠5hc)(3fb) ®
Lic ㎰ CTV 8P nc4yrs

⊷GH QQ **Aydon House** South Rd NE66 2NT
☎(0665) 602218
Standing back from the main road to the south of the town, this Victorian house has well-maintained accommodation.
10hc (4fb) CTV in all bedrooms sB&B£11-£14
dB&B£22-£28 WB&Bfr£75 WBDifr£120 LDO 5pm
Lic ㎰ 12P

GH QQQ **Bondgate House Hotel** Bondgate Without
NE66 1PN ☎(0665) 602025
Friendly, town-centre house with quaint, comfortable rooms.
8rm(3🏠5hc)(3fb) CTV in all bedrooms ® 🗶 (ex guide dogs)
dB&B£26-£28
dB&B🏠£28-£31 WB&B£98-£112 WBDif£150.50-£164.50 LDO 4.30pm
Lic ㎰ 8P
£

ALSTON Cumbria Map **12** NY74

FH Q Mrs P M Dent **Middle Bayles** *(NY706451)* CA9 3BS
☎(0434) 381383
May-Oct rs Tue
Situated about 1 mile west of Alston, just off the A686, this non-smoking cosy farmhouse has 2 good size bedrooms and a comfortable lounge where meals are taken around a communal table, adding to the informal atmosphere.
2hc (1fb)⅊in all bedrooms ® 🗶 (ex guide dogs)
dB&B£22-£24 WB&B£70-£77 WBDif£106-£112 LDO 4pm
㎰ CTV 2P 300 acres cattle sheep
£

ALTON Hampshire Map **04** SU73

INN QQ **White Hart** London Rd, Holybourne GU34 6EX
☎(0420) 87654
This hotel has attractive, comfortable bedrooms with colour televisions. Tea and coffee are always available on the landing. Barbecues are enjoyed in the pleasant garden, and freshly prepared meals are available in the bar and restaurant.
4hc CTV in all bedrooms ® 🗶 (ex guide dogs) ✳
sB&B£23-£25
dB&B£34-£40 Lunch £1.25-£10.50alc Dinner £1.25-£10.50alc
LDO 10pm

▶

Marine House Private Hotel

ALNMOUTH, NORTHUMBERLAND NE66 2RW
Telephone: Alnmouth (0665) 830349

RUNNERS UP FOR AA Best Family Holiday in Britain 1984 and Northumbria Tourist Board, Holiday Hosts Award 1985. Relax in the friendly atmosphere of this 200-year-old recently modernised Granary of considerable charm, overlooking the golf links and beautiful beaches. 10 comfortable bedrooms, all with ensuite facilities. Traditional home cooking. Cocktail Bar and Games Room. Spacious lounge with colour TV. Children and pets welcome. Two adjacent self-catering cottages. Sheila and Gordon Inkster.
SPECIAL GOLFING BREAKS AND FAMILY HOLIDAY PRICES PLUS SPECIAL INTEREST WEEK-ENDS.

Cotmandene Guest House

6 Park Lane, Aldeburgh, Suffolk IP15 5HL
Tel: (0728) 453775

Situated in a very quiet residential road, but only a minute's walk from town and beach.
The large, comfortable bedrooms have en suite bathroom, shaver point, full central heating, radio alarm, colour television and tea/coffee making facilities. Hair dryer available.
Dining room. Video and stereo are available in residents' lounge.
Laundry facilities available at extra cost.
Residential licence.   Visa and Access accepted.

♨ 40P
Credit Cards [1] [3] [£]

ALTRINCHAM Greater Manchester Map **07** SJ78

GH [Q] ***Bollin Hotel*** 58 Manchester Rd WA14 4PJ
☎061-928 2390
Situated on the A56 and close to the town centre, this is a small commercial guesthouse. The accommodation provided is comfortable and is in surroundings which have been freshly decorated.
10rm (2fb) [R]
♨ CTV 10P

ALYTH Tayside *Perthshire* Map **15** NO25

INN [Q][Q] ***Losset*** Losset Rd PH11 8BT ☎(08283) 2393
Dating back to 1730, this small friendly inn is family run and offers compact bedrooms which have been refurbished in modern style. The public areas retain the original character.
3🚿 CTV in all bedrooms [R] LDO 9pm
♨ 10P

AMBLESIDE Cumbria Map **07** NY30

GH [Q][Q][Q] Compston House Hotel Compston Rd LA22 9DJ
☎(05394) 32305
This comfortable guesthouse, under the personal supervision of the proprietors, Ann and Graham Smith, occupies a corner site in the centre of Ambleside. Every bedroom now has en suite facilities, a colour television and tea-making facilities.
8🚿 (1fb)🚭in 2 bedrooms CTV in all bedrooms [R]
🐕 (ex guide dogs) ✱ dB&B£25-£39
dB&B🚿£25-£39 WB&B£87.50-£136.50 WBDi£180.50 LDO 5pm
Lic ♨ Ᵽ nc5yrs
[£]

GH [Q][Q][Q] Gables Private Hotel Church Walk, Compston Rd LA22 9DJ ☎(05394) 33272
Closed Dec rs Jan & Feb
Close to the church in a central position, this long-established family-run hotel has been upgraded to provide all rooms with en suite facilities, colour TV and tea-making facilities. There is also a private car park.
13🛁🚿 (4fb) CTV in all bedrooms [R] sB&B🛁🚿£17-£20
dB&B🛁🚿£35-£40 WBDifr£189 LDO 5pm
Lic ♨ CTV 10P

SELECTED

GH [Q][Q][Q][Q] Grey Friar Lodge Country House Hotel
Brathay LA22 9NE (1m W off A593) ☎(05394) 33158
Mar-Oct
This charming Victorian vicarage is situated on the A593, 1 mile west of Ambleside, with lovely views of Brathay River and Valley. Surrounded by well-tended gardens and woodland, it is furnished with antiques, books and bric-a-brac. One of the en suite bedrooms boasts a four-poster bed, and all have a colour TV. Sheila and Tony Sutton serve a 5-course set menu in the dining room and provide first-class service.
8🛁🚿 🚭in all bedrooms CTV in all bedrooms [R] 🐕
dB&B🛁🚿£59-£79 (incl dinner) WBDi£185-£255 LDO 7.30pm
Lic ♨ 12P nc12yrs
[£]

GH [Q][Q] ***Hillsdale Hotel*** Church St LA22 0BT
☎(05394) 33174
This attractive terraced house of Lakeland stone is situated in the centre of Ambleside. The bedrooms each have a television and tea-making facilities, and there is a comfortable lounge for guests' use.
8rm(1🛁7hc) CTV in all bedrooms [R] 🐕
♨ Ᵽ

GH [Q][Q][Q] Lyndhurst Hotel Wansfell Rd LA22 0EG
☎(05394) 32421
This compact, modern guesthouse has well-equipped bedrooms, 2 of which are in an adjacent building just 10 yards away.
6🚿 Annexe 2🚿 (3fb)🚭in 1 bedroom CTV in all bedrooms [R]
🐕 sB&B🚿£17.50-£19.50
dB&B🚿£35-£44 WBDi£175-£205 LDO 8pm
Lic ♨ 8P
[£]

GH [Q][Q][Q] Riverside Lodge Country House Rothay Bridge LA22 0EH ☎(05394) 34208
This charming early-Georgian house is reached by a footbridge over the River Rothay. Three acres of grounds create a peaceful atmosphere although the house is a short walk from the town centre, and a high standard of accommodation is provided.
4rm(3🛁1🚿)(1fb) CTV in all bedrooms [R] 🐕
dB&B🛁🚿£40-£53 WB&B£140-£168
Lic ♨ 20P nc10yrs ⛳
Credit Cards [1] [3] [£]

SELECTED

GH [Q][Q][Q][Q] Rothay Garth Hotel Rothay Rd LA22 0EE
☎(05394) 32217 FAX (05394) 34400
The elegant restaurant, which is open to non-residents, is a feature of this attractive and well-maintained private hotel which is set in neat gardens. The bedrooms are individually furnished and decorated to a very good standard and are particularly well-equipped. The hotel offers a comfortable lounge, cocktail bar and extremely well-appointed restaurant which offers table d'hôte menus including 5 separate courses and coffee.
16rm(14🛁🚿2hc)(3fb)🚭in 8 bedrooms CTV in all bedrooms [R] sB&B£26-£46 sB&B🛁🚿£32-£52
dB&B£52-£92
dB&B🛁🚿£64-£104 (incl dinner) WB&B£170-£245
WBDi£223-£317 LDO 8pm
Lic ♨ CTV 17P
Credit Cards [1] [2] [3] [5] [£]

GH [Q][Q][Q] Rydal Holme Rydal LA22 9LR ☎(05394) 33110
FAX (05394) 33251
mid Mar-Oct
This well-furnished Lakeland house is close to Ambleside and overlooks Rydal Water. It stands in delightful gardens and offers pretty bedrooms and comfortable public rooms.
6rm(3🚿3hc)(1fb)🚭in all bedrooms [R] dB&B£32-£38
dB&B🚿£36-£44 WB&B£112-£154
♨ CTV 8P

SELECTED

GH [Q][Q][Q][Q] ***Rydal Lodge Hotel*** LA22 9LR (2m NW A590) ☎(05394) 33208
Closed 7 Jan-4 Feb
Just north of Ambleside on the A591, this charming country house stands beside the River Rothay and offers immaculate accommodation in congenial surroundings. The upstairs drawing room overlooks the pleasant gardens and there is also a small lounge downstairs. Dinner, cooked by proprietor Steven Owen, is served in the well-appointed dining room. The best fresh ingredients are always used. Friendly and well-situated, this hotel also has ample parking space.
8rm(1🚿7hc)(1fb) LDO 7pm
Lic CTV 12P ⌂ ⛳
Credit Cards [1] [3] [5]

See advertisement on page 39

RYDAL HOLME

In a unique position overlooking Rydal Water and surrounded by gardens and lawns, this spacious Victorian country house warmly welcomes Lakeland visitors.
Bed & breakfast in a comfortable and relaxing atmosphere. Many local restaurants close by. Some rooms en-suite; all with tea/coffee making facilities.
Non-smoking. Private parking. Central heating. Lake views. Marvellous centre for walking and touring.
Peter & Susan Jackson, Rydal Holme, Rydal, Ambleside LA22 9LR. Telephone: (05394) 33110.

Lyndhurst Hotel
Wansfell Road, Ambleside, Cumbria LA22 0EG

Attractive Victorian, Lakeland stone family run hotel with private car park quietly situated in its own garden. Good food, friendly service, lovely rooms all with private facilities. Beautiful Special Occasions Room with 4 poster bed. All with colour TV and tea and coffee trays. Full central heating for all year comfort. Cosy bar. Winter & spring breaks. A delightful base from which to explore the Lakes either by car or as a walker. Evening dinner, bed & breakfast or bed & breakfast.

Phone or write for brochure
Helen & Chris Green
Ambleside (05394) 32421

Riverside Lodge Country House

Near Rothay Bridge, Ambleside, Cumbria LA22 0EH
Telephone: Ambleside (05394) 34208

Proprietors: Gillian & Alan Rhone

A superbly situated Country House in idyllic riverside setting offering superior "Bed & Breakfast" and luxury "Self-Catering" accommodation just a short walk from the centre of Ambleside.

GREY FRIAR LODGE
COUNTRY HOUSE HOTEL
Brathay, Ambleside, Cumbria LA22 9NE
Tel: 05394-33158

Beautiful country house, ideally set in its own grounds in the heart of the Lake District, between Ambleside and Skelwith Bridge. Magnificent views, tasteful well appointed rooms. Highest standards of hospitality, friendly service and imaginative home cooking.

GH **Q** **Q** **Rysdale Hotel** Rothay Rd LA22 0EE ☎(05394) 32140
Closed 1 Dec-9 Jan
The Rysdale hotel is an attractive late-Victorian house situated
close to the town centre overlooking a bowling green and sports
ground. The front of the hotel commands fine views of the
surrounding fells.
9rm(1⇔3♠5hc)(4fb)⚇in 3 bedrooms CTV in all bedrooms ®
✠ (ex guide dogs) LDO 5pm
Lic ⛺2P
Credit Cards ① ③ ⓔ

GH **Q** **Q** **Smallwood Hotel** Compston Rd LA22 9DJ
☎(05394) 32330
Spacious detached house close to town centre, offering pleasant,
comfortable accommodation with an attractive lounge and pretty
dining room where home-cooked meals are served.
13rm(1⇔1♠11hc)Annexe 1⇔ (4fb) ® ✻ sB&B£14 dB&B£28
dB&B⇔♠£33 WB&B£98 WBDi£142-£157 LDO 6pm
Lic ⛺CTV 13P
ⓔ

GH **Q** **Thrang House** Compston Rd LA22 9DJ ☎(05394) 32112
Mar-Dec
A slate-built house serving good, hearty breakfasts.
6rm(2♠4hc) CTV in all bedrooms ® ✠ sB&B£14-£16
dB&B£28-£32
dB&B♠£32-£40 WB&Bfr£95 WBDifr£160 LDO 6pm
⛺5P nc9yrs

INN **Q** **Q** **Q** **Drunken Duck** Barngates LA22 0NG
☎Hawkshead(09666) 347
Skilfully renovated to retain its delightful character, this country
inn serves a fine collection of real ales and hearty home-cooked
meals. The 'cottage' bedrooms are thoughtfully equipped. 'The
Duck' is 3 miles south of Ambleside on the B5286.
8⇔ Annexe 2♠ CTV in all bedrooms ® sB&B⇔♠£30-£40
dB&B⇔♠£56.50-£69.50 LDO 8.45pm
⛺40P ♪
Credit Cards ① ③

ANCASTER Lincolnshire Map **08** SK94

├─┤FH **Q** Mrs F Mival **Woodlands** *(SK966437)* West
Willoughby NG32 3SH (off the A153 between Sleaford and
Grantham, 1m W of Ancaster) ☎Loveden(0400) 30340
Etr-Oct
This delightful 19th-century stone-built farmhouse situated in the
rolling Lincolnshire countryside offers comfortable accommodation
as well as wholesome home-cooked food.
3rm (1fb) CTV in 1 bedroom ® sB&B£10-£12
dB&B£20-£24 WB&Bfr£70 WBDifr£105
CTV 3P 12 acres mixed
ⓔ

L'ANCRESSE VALE

See **GUERNSEY under CHANNEL ISLANDS**

ANNAN Dumfries & Galloway *Dumfriesshire* Map **11** NY16

GH **Q** **Q** **Ravenswood Private Hotel** St Johns Rd DG12 6AW
☎(04612) 2158
This neat establishment is well cared for and is managed by the
friendly proprietress. The bedrooms are spacious and comfortable,
and the home-cooked dinner offers a choice of dishes.
8hc (2fb) ® ✠ (ex guide dogs) sB&B£15 dB&B£26 LDO 8pm
Lic ⛺CTV ℙ

ANSTRUTHER Fife Map **12** NO50

├─┤INN **Q** **The Royal Hotel** 20 Rodger St KY10 3DU
☎(0333) 310581
Cosy bedrooms are offered in this quaint village inn, that is family
owned and run. A courteous, friendly service is provided, and lunch
and dinner offer very good value for money, with freshly cooked
dishes.
12rm(1⇔2♠8hc) ® ✠ (ex guide dogs) sB&B£11-£16
sB&B⇔♠£14-£19 dB&B£22
dB&B⇔♠£28 WB&B£101.50-£152 WBDi£139-£189.50
Lunch fr£7.50alc Dinner fr£7.50&alc LDO 8.45pm
⛺CTV 6P
Credit Cards ③

APPLEBY-IN-WESTMORLAND Cumbria Map **12** NY62

GH **Q** **Q** **Bongate House** Bongate CA16 6UE
☎Appleby(07683) 51245
Closed Xmas and New Year
This comfortable Georgian house stands in an acre of gardens on
the approach to the town from Brough and Scotch Corner. It
features well-appointed bedrooms, a comfortable lounge and a cosy
residents' bar.
8rm(1⇔4♠3hc)(4fb) ® ✠ (ex guide dogs) sB&B£13.50
dB&B£27
dB&B⇔♠£32 WB&B£85-£100 WBDi£125-£140 LDO 6pm
Lic ⛺CTV 8P 2☂ nc7yrs croquet & putting lawn
ⓔ

ARBROATH Tayside *Angus* Map **12** NO64

├─┤GH **Q** **Kingsley** 29 Market Gate DD11 1AU ☎(0241) 73933
This is a family-run guesthouse situated close to the bustling
fishing harbour. It has a friendly atmosphere, and offers
accommodation that is simply appointed but practical.
14hc (8fb) sB&B£12-£13
dB&B£24-£26 WB&Bfr£80 WBDifr£105 LDO 7.30pm
Lic ⛺CTV 4P snooker solarium childrens play ground
ⓔ

ARDBRECKNISH Strathclyde *Argyllshire* Map **10** NN02

FH **Q** **Q** **Q** Mrs Hodge **Rockhill** *(NN072219)* PA33 1BH
☎Kilchrenan(08663) 218
May-Sep
A 17th-century, stone-built, lochside farmhouse, offering simple,
cottage-style accommodation. Warm and personal attention
combined with lovely gardens and splendid views make this
secluded farm well worth a visit.
5rm(1⇔5♠4hc)(3fb) CTV in all bedrooms ® ✠
✻ dB&B⇔♠fr£52 (incl dinner) WBDifr£144 LDO 7pm
Lic 8P nc8yrs ♪ 200 acres horses sheep
See advertisement on page 41

ARDERSIER Highland *Inverness-Shire* Map **14** NH85

├─┤FH **Q** **Q** **Q** Mrs L E MacBean **Milton-of-Gollanfield**
(NH809534) Gollanfield IV1 2QT ☎(0667) 62207
May-Nov
A warm welcome awaits guests at Mrs MacBean's Victorian
farmhouse which stands in its garden just off the A96 about 5 miles
west of Nairn. It is an ideal base for the tourist, offering traditional
comforts and enjoyable home cooking.
3hc (1fb) ® ✠ (ex guide dogs) sB&B£13-£16 dB&B£24-£30
CTV 0P 360 acres mixed arable beef sheep
ⓔ

Q is for quality. For a full explanation of this AA quality
award, consult the Contents page.

See the regional maps of popular holiday
areas at the back of the book.

ARDGAY Highland *Sutherland* Map **14** NH58

GH QQ Croit Mairi Kincardine Hill IV24 3DJ ☎(08632) 504
Fine views over Dornoch Firth can be obtained from this detached house, set in an elevated position above the A9 just south of the village.
5hc (2fb)⊬in all bedrooms ® ✕ (ex guide dogs) ✱ sB&Bfr£12 dB&Bfr£24 WB&Bfr£84 WBDifr£133 LDO 6pm
CTV 10P nc3yrs
Credit Cards [1] [3]

ARDROSSAN Strathclyde *Ayrshire* Map **10** NS24

GH Q Ellwood House 6 Arran Place KA22 8DR ☎(0294) 61130
Simple, pleasantly appointed, small seafront guesthouse set in a terrace of listed buildings overlooking the beach.
9hc (2fb) ® ✱ sB&B£11 dB&B£22 WB&B£77
CTV P̸
£

ARRAN, ISLE OF Strathclyde *Buteshire* Map **10**

BRODICK Map **10** NS03

GH QQQ Allandale KD27 8BJ ☎(0770) 2278
Closed Nov-Dec
Enjoying an elevated position to the south of Brodick, this friendly house is surrounded by gardens and offers a good standard of accommodation in well-equipped bedrooms. There is a most comfortable lounge in which to relax.
4rm(2⇌2↑)Annexe 2⇌ (1fb) CTV in all bedrooms ® ✱
sB&B⇌↑£15-£17.50
dB&B⇌↑£30-£35 WBDi£150 LDO 6pm
Lic 12P

GH QQQ Tuathair House Shore Rd KA27 8AJ ☎(0770) 2214
Apr-Sep
Non-smokers are especially welcome at Chris and Howard Wood's lovely seafront home. Tastefully appointed throughout, it offers comfortable, well-equipped bedrooms and an attractive relaxing lounge.
4↑ ⊬in all bedrooms CTV in all bedrooms ®
✕ (ex guide dogs) sB&B↑fr£16
dB&B↑fr£32 WB&Bfr£100 WBDifr£140
4P nc

LOCHRANZA Map **10** NR95

GH Q *Kincardine Lodge* KA27 8HL ☎(077083) 267
Apr-Oct
Conveniently placed for the Claonaig ferry, this guesthouse has pleasant views of the bay and castle. The bedrooms are fairly spacious and modestly furnished and there are 2 traditional lounges, 1 with TV. The house features an attractive wooden staircase.
7hc (4fb) ®
CTV 6P

ARROCHAR Strathclyde *Dunbartonshire* Map **10** NN20

SELECTED

GH QQQQ Mansefield Country House G83 7AG ☎(03012) 282
This fine Victorian house sits in gardens well back from the road, overlooking Loch Long. Paintings by the owner are displayed in the dining room which is most attractive. The bedrooms, 2 of which are particularly spacious, are thoughtfully equipped, and dinner is served every night except Sunday.
5hc (1fb)⊬in all bedrooms CTV in 3 bedrooms TV in 2 bedrooms ® ✱
dB&Bfr£27 WB&Bfr£90 WBDifr£135 LDO 6pm
CTV 8P
£

ARUNDEL West Sussex Map **04** TQ00

GH QQ Arden 4 Queens Ln BN18 9JN ☎(0903) 882544
Closed 10 Dec-1 Feb
This friendly hotel is quietly situated off the main road but is within easy walking distance of the castle and town centre. The bedrooms are freshly decorated, neat and well equipped, and the attractive breakfast room has pine furniture.
8rm(2↑6hc)(1fb) CTV in all bedrooms ® ✕ (ex guide dogs)
dB&B£24-£28 dB&B↑£30-£34
4P nc2yrs

GH QQ Bridge House 18 Queen St BN18 9JG ☎(0903) 882142 & 882779
Closed Xmas wk
With views of the castle, the river and the South Downs, this 18th-century house has a friendly atmosphere. The choice of rooms includes family accommodation, and annexe rooms in the 16th-century cottage. The dining area is non-smoking.
11rm(4↑7hc)Annexe 3rm(1⇌2↑)(6fb) CTV in all bedrooms ® sB&B£16-£18 sB&B⇌↑£23-£26 dB&B£28-£30
dB&B⇌↑£34-£38 LDO 8.30pm
Lic CTV 9P 4
Credit Cards [1] [3]

INN QQ Swan Hotel High St BN18 9AG ☎(0903) 882314
This is a popular and lively free house with real ale and a good selection of homemade dishes, served in the bar and restaurant, sometimes with live entertainment. The bedrooms are modern and well equipped, all having private facilities.
13rm(11⇌2↑) CTV in all bedrooms ® ✕ (ex guide dogs)
sB&B⇌↑£47
dB&B⇌↑£60 Bar Lunch £1.50-£8.50 Dinner £10&alc LDO 9.30pm
Credit Cards [1] [2] [3] [5] £

ASCOT Berkshire Map **04** SU96

GH QQ Highclere Hotel Kings Road, Sunninghill SL5 9AD ☎(0990) 25220 FAX (0990) 872528
rs 24 Dec-2 Jan
Well-maintained accommodation is offered at this attractive Victorian house, which has been sympathetically modernised and extended. There is a small television lounge, and a welcoming bar lounge which adjoins the dining room overlooking the garden.
12rm(1⇌11↑)(2fb) CTV in all bedrooms ®
sB&B⇌↑£35-£65
dB&B⇌↑£46-£72 WB&B£295 WBDi£345 LDO 9pm
Lic CTV 10P 2 putting green
Credit Cards [1] [3] £

ASHBOURNE Derbyshire

See **Waterhouses**

ASHBURTON Devon Map **03** SX76

See also **Bickington**

GH QQQ Gages Mill Buckfastleigh Rd TQ13 7JW ☎(0364) 52391
mid Mar-mid Nov
Mr and Mrs Cox are the owners of this hospitable guesthouse, which was formerly a 16th-century wool mill. Within an acre of gardens, Gages Mill stands on the edge of Dartmoor National Park. The accommodation has been carefully converted to retain its character, and is comfortable and bright. Mrs Cox provides freshly cooked food.

8rm(7⇨🛉1hc)(1fb)® 🗶
dB&B⇨🛉£35-£39.50 WB&Bf110-£120 WBDif170-£180
LDO 3pm
Lic ᵐᵐ CTV 10P nc5yrs

FH Ⓠ Mrs H Young **Bremridge** *(SX785701)* Woodland
TQ13 7JX (2m E unclass towards Denbury) ☎(0364) 52426
Closed Dec
5rm(1⇨4hc)(3fb) sB&B£13.50-£15.50 sB&B⇨£13.50-£15.50
dB&B£27-£30
dB&B⇨£27-£30 WB&B£85-£95 WBDif95-£110 LDO 6pm
ᵐᵐ CTV 6P ☶ 8 acres mixed
£

'Selected' establishments, which have the highest
quality award, are highlighted by a tinted panel.
For a full list of these establishments, consult the
Contents page.

allandale house

Brodick, Isle of Arran KA27 8BJ
Telephone (0770) 2278

Proprietors V & M Young

Beautiful privately-owned Guest House with
lovely views over the hills. Five minutes' walk
from ferry terminal and village centre.

All rooms are well appointed with private
facilities, colour TVs, tea/coffee makers, electric blankets and heating. South facing guest
lounge and cosy dining room where breakfast
and evening meals are served, all prepared by
resident proprietor with Scottish fare a speciality.
Vegetarians catered for. Packed lunches on
request.

A warm welcome assured. Write or telephone
for brochure and details.

Ye Olde
Crown Hotel

**Waterhouses, Stoke on Trent,
Staffordshire ST10 3HL
Telephone: Waterhouses (0538) 308204**

**Welcome to this small family owned and run 17th
century Coaching Inn. Situated in a picturesque
village on the edge of the Peak District Park and
the Staffordshire Moorlands. An ideal base for the
many local places of interest. Good home cooked
meals in the full and varied menu also snacks
available. Open all year.**

Rockhill Farm
Country House

Ardbrecknish, By Dalmally, Argyll PA33 1BH
Tel: 086 63 218

Rockhill is situated on the south-east shore of
Lochawe and commands panoramic views of Cruachan
Mountain. Breeding Hanoverian horses and sheep.
Attractively modernised farmhouse. En-suite or pri-
vate facilities. Peaceful holidays, beautiful surround-
ings, first class home cooking. Guests keep returning.
Facilities include Loch fishing, and guests may bring
their own boat, hill walking and pony trekking in the
area. Residential licence. Fire certificate granted.
SAE please for comprehensive brochure from Helena
Hodge and Helen & Brian Whalley.

ASHFORD Kent Map **05** TR04

GH [Q][Q][Q] Croft Hotel Canterbury Rd Kennington TN25 4DU ☎(0233) 622140
Comfortable, simple accommodation with a more modern annexe.
15🛁🚿 Annexe 13🛁🚿 (3fb) CTV in all bedrooms Ⓡ ✱
sB&B🛁🚿£31-£40 dB&B🛁🚿£42-£50 LDO 8pm
Lic ♨ CTV 30P croquet
Credit Cards [1] [3]

GH [Q][Q] Downsview Willesborough Rd, Kennington TN24 9QP ☎(0233) 621953
A large country house on the fringe of town, Downsview has compact, well-equipped en suite bedrooms. The public rooms are comfortable, with a bright, nicely appointed dining room.
21rm(4🛁17🚿)(6fb) CTV in all bedrooms Ⓡ ✱
sB&B🛁🚿£32-£34 dB&B🛁🚿£49-£56 LDO 8.30pm
Lic ♨ CTV 25P pool table putting green
Credit Cards [1] [2] [3] [5] [£]

INN [Q][Q] *The George* 68 High St TN24 8TB ☎(0233) 625512
Closed Xmas Day
Small, olde worlde inn with cosy well-decorated bedrooms.
16rm(2🛁2🚿12hc)(2fb) CTV in all bedrooms Ⓡ
🐕 (ex guide dogs) LDO 10pm
♨ CTV 5P 8🚗
Credit Cards [1] [2] [3] [5]

ASHOVER Derbyshire Map **08** SK36

FH [Q][Q] Mr J A Wootton **Old School** *(SK323654)* Uppertown S45 0JF ☎Chesterfield(0246) 590813
Mar-Oct
With all rooms on the ground floor, this modern stone-built farmhouse is ideal for young children and elderly guests. Surrounded by farmland it stands on the opposite side of the A632 from the village of Ashover.
4hc (2fb)🚭in all bedrooms 🐕 ✱ sB&Bfr£12
dB&Bfr£24 WB&B£70-£84 WBDi£98-£126 LDO 9.30am
♨ CTV 10P 45 acres poultry & sheep

ASHTON-UNDER-LYNE Greater Manchester Map **07** SJ99

GH [Q][Q][Q] Welbeck House Hotel 324 Katherine St OL6 7BD ☎061-344 0751
This privately owned small hotel, situated in a residential area close to the town centre, offers well-maintained accommodation and good off-street parking. The modern bedrooms, although generally compact, are comfortably furnished and well equipped.
8🛁🚿 (2fb) CTV in all bedrooms Ⓡ ✱ sB&B🛁🚿£38-£48
dB&B🛁🚿£52 LDO 8pm
Lic ♨ CTV 12P games room
Credit Cards [1] [2] [3] [5]

ASHWELL Hertfordshire Map **04** TL23

INN [Q][Q][Q] *Three Tuns Hotel* 6 High St SG7 5NL ☎(046274) 2387
Country inn with pleasant individually furnished bedrooms.
4hc Annexe 6rm(1🛁1🚿4hc)(1fb) CTV in all bedrooms Ⓡ
LDO 10.30pm
♨ 25P
Credit Cards [1] [2] [3] [5]

See the regional maps of popular holiday areas at the back of the book.

ASTBURY Cheshire Map **07** SJ86

INN [Q] *Egerton Arms Hotel* CW12 4RQ ☎Congleton(02602) 73946
This village inn lies south of Congleton on the A34. A choice of meals is available, including a children's and a vegetarian menu, and to the rear are a small garden area and a large car park.
7hc CTV in all bedrooms Ⓡ LDO 9.30pm
♨ CTV 100P
Credit Cards [3] [5]

ASTHALL Oxfordshire Map **04** SP21

INN [Q][Q][Q] Maytime OX8 4HW (0.25m N off A40) ☎(0993) 822068
An ideal Cotswold retreat standing in the picturesque Windrush Valley, this 16th-century inn provides high standards of accommodation and has a popular bar. Excellent food is to be had in both the bar and restaurant, which are equally well-appointed.
Annexe 6🛁 CTV in all bedrooms Ⓡ ✱ sB&B🛁fr£42.50
dB&B🛁fr£55 LDO 11pm
100P 🏊(heated) ⛳ 18 🎾(hard)
Credit Cards [1] [2] [3]

ASTON Staffordshire Map **07** SJ74

FH [Q][Q] Mrs N Y Bourne **Larksfield Country Accommodation** *(SJ747415)* Larksfield, Stoniford Ln TF9 4JB (off A525 0.75m E of Woore) ☎Pipegate(063081) 7069
A modern farmhouse in a peaceful rural setting conveniently positioned for the main Shropshire, Staffordshire and Cheshire tourist areas. Expert shotgun tuition is available.
7rm(5🚿2hc)(4fb) CTV in all bedrooms Ⓡ sB&B£16
sB&B🚿£18 dB&B£30 dB&B🚿fr£32
♨ CTV 8P 🎣 clay pigeon shooting 30 acres arable
[£]

ASTON MUNSLOW Shropshire Map **07** SO58

GH [Q][Q][Q] Chadstone SY7 9ER ☎Munslow(058476) 675
Mar-Oct
Set in a quiet village, this modern dormer-style bungalow offers quality, uncluttered rooms. The elegant dining room has panoramic views of the countryside and a stay here is enhanced by the attentive service of the resident proprietors.
5rm(2🛁🚿3hc)🚭in all bedrooms CTV in 1 bedroom Ⓡ 🐕
sB&B£19 dB&B£35 dB&B🛁🚿£38
♨ CTV 6P nc12yrs
[£]

ATHERSTONE Warwickshire Map **04** SP39

SELECTED

GH [Q][Q][Q][Q] Chapel House Friar's Gate CV9 1EY ☎(0827) 718949
Closed Xmas
Mainly Georgian in origin this former Dover house has been tastefully extended and improved by owners David and Pat Roberts to provide a private hotel with a good combination of charm and modern facilities. The bedrooms are furnished with Victorian and Edwardian furniture with en suite facilities and thoughtful extras. The 2 dining rooms offer imaginative food and there is a comfortable lounge with an attractive conservatory extension. The hotel offers well-tended gardens and an attractive patio.
13rm(11🛁🚿2hc) CTV in all bedrooms 🐕 sB&B£35-£42
sB&B🛁🚿£35-£42 dB&B£48-£55
dB&B🛁🚿£48-£55 LDO 7pm
Lic ♨ 10P
Credit Cards [1] [3] [5]

ATTLEBOROUGH Norfolk Map **05** TM09

INN QQ **Griffin Hotel** Church St NR17 2AH ☎(0953) 452149
Located in the town centre on the main thoroughfare, this hotel has
car parking to the rear. Many of its 16th-century characteristics
have been retained, the rooms being modest but well equipped. The
convivial atmosphere complements the popular bar meals.
8hc CTV in 4 bedrooms TV in 3 bedrooms ® ✳
sB&B£16-£18.50
dB&B£25-£30 Sunday Lunch fr£7 Dinner £9.50-£16.05alc
LDO 10pm
20P
£

AUCHTERMUCHTY Fife Map **11** NO21

FH QQQ Mr I Steven *Ardchoille* (*NO248096*) Dunshalt
KY14 7EY ☎(0337) 28414
Closed Xmas & New Year
Just 1 mile from Auchtermuchty on the B936, this modern
farmhouse has thoughtfully equipped bedrooms. Meals are served
around a communal dining table, and the good food is
complemented by genuine hospitality.
3rm(2↑1hc)(1fb) CTV in all bedrooms ® ✗ (ex guide dogs)
LDO 6pm
♈ CTV 8P ↻ 2 acres horses

AUDLEY Staffordshire Map **07** SJ75

FH QQQ Mrs E E Oulton **Domvilles** *(SJ776516)*
Barthomley Rd ST7 8HT ☎Stoke-on-Trent(0782) 720378
Closed 25 Dec
This large farmhouse is beautifully furnished and has a welcoming
atmosphere. Guests are offered friendly service and real comfort.
The gardens are well tended, and even the farmyard is clean and
tidy
5rm(4↑1hc)(2fb)⚗in 3 bedrooms CTV in all bedrooms ®
✗ (ex guide dogs) ✳ sB&B£16-£18 sB&B↑£18 dB&Bfr£24
dB&B↑£28 LDO 6pm
CTV 8P table tennis 120 acres dairy mixed

AULDGIRTH Dumfries & Galloway *Dumfriesshire*
Map **11** NX98

⊷⊷FH QQQ Mr P A Burford **Allanton House** *(NX915840)*
DG2 0RY ☎(038774) 509
Enjoying direct access off the A76, this impressive mansion house
has lofty, spacious rooms. The friendly proprietors invite guests to
explore the farm with its dogs, ducks and peacocks, as well as the
normal livestock.
3hc (1fb)⚗in 1 bedroom ® sB&B£13
dB&B£24 WBDi£115.50 LDO 6pm
♈ CTV 0P 20 acres beef sheep
See advertisement under DUMFRIES on page 139

AUSTWICK North Yorkshire Map **07** SD76

FH QQ Mrs M Hird **Rawlinshaw** *(SD781673)* LA2 8DD
☎Settle(07292) 3214
Etr-Sep
200-year-old farmhouse, set in attractive countryside.
2hc (1fb) ® ✗ (ex guide dogs) dB&B£20-£24
♈ CTV 10P ↻ 206 acres beef dairy horses sheep

AVIEMORE Highland *Inverness-Shire* Map **14** NH81

GH QQQ *Corrour House* Inverdruie PH22 1QH
☎(0479) 810220
Closed Nov-26 Dec
Stone-built house standing in tree-studded grounds half a mile east
of Aviemore on B970.
8rm(3⚗4↑1hc)(2fb) CTV in all bedrooms ® LDO 8pm
Lic ♈ CTV 15P nc1yr
Credit Cards ①③

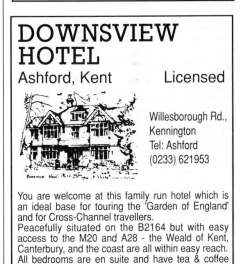

GH QQ Craiglea Grampian Rd PH22 1RH ☎(0479) 810210
This long-established town-centre guesthouse has modern family bedrooms, some on the ground floor, equipped in the modern style. Mr and Mrs Nunn and their family make children particularly welcome.
11rm(1⑥10hc)(4fb) ® ✱ sB&B£12.50-£13.50 dB&B£25-£27 dB&B⑥£26-£28 WB&B£84-£90
CTV 12P sauna
£

GH QQ Ravenscraig Grampian Rd PH22 1RP ☎(0479) 810278
Standing on the main road north of the town centre, this guesthouse has compact modern annexe bedrooms, well furnished in traditional style. The comfortable lounge has coffee-making facilities and there is a well-appointed breakfast room.
5rm(3⑥2hc)Annexe 6⑥ (3fb) ® dB&B⑥£29-£32
CTV 12P

AXBRIDGE Somerset Map **03** ST45

FH QQQ Mr L F Dimmock **Manor** *(ST420549)* Cross BS26 2ED ☎(0934) 732577
Closed Xmas
This guesthouse is situated at the junction of the A38 and the A371 roads. It offers simple but well-maintained accommodation, and is personally supervised by the proprietors, who offer good hospitality.
7rm(2hc)(2fb) ® sB&Bfr£12.50
dB&Bfr£25 WB&Bfr£85 WBDifr£125 LDO 5pm
CTV 10P 250 acres beef horses sheep
£

AYR Strathclyde *Ayrshire* Map **10** NS32

GH QQ *Arrandale Hotel* 2-4 Cassillis St KA7 1DW ☎(0292) 289959
rs Winter
Used by both tourists and commercial travellers, this is a friendly, family-run hotel. There are nice bedrooms and en suite facilities, and a comfortable lounge. The dining room has a residents' bar.
13rm(1⇌1⑥11hc)(6fb) CTV in 8 bedrooms ✕ (ex guide dogs) LDO 3pm
Lic CTV P
Credit Cards 1 3

GH QQ The Parkhouse Hotel 1A Ballantine Dr KA7 2RG ☎(0292) 264151
This period house is set in a residential area on the south side of the town. There are public shower rooms for guests' use.
7hc (2fb) CTV in all bedrooms ® ✕ ✱ sB&Bfr£18 dB&Bfr£26
Lic CTV P
£

GH QQ Windsor Hotel 6 Alloway Place KA7 2AA ☎(0292) 264689
This attractive terraced guesthouse is situated just a short distance from the centre of town. The bedrooms are bright and comfortable, and most have en suite facilities.
10rm(7⇌⑥2hc)(4fb) CTV in all bedrooms ® ✱ sB&B£18-£30 sB&B⇌⑥£20-£30 dB&B£32-£36 dB&B⇌⑥£32-£36 WBDi£150-£164 LDO 6pm
CTV P
£

FH QQ Mr & Mrs A Stevenson **Trees** *(NS386186)* KA6 6EW ☎(0292) 570270
Closed Xmas & New Year
White farmhouse offering good quality accommodation at modest prices.
3hc (1fb) ✕ sB&B£13-£15
dB&B£23-£24 WB&Bfr£70 LDO 3pm
CTV 6P 75 acres grazing
£

AYTON, GREAT North Yorkshire Map **08** NZ51

INN Q *Royal Oak Hotel* High Green TS9 6BJ ☎(0642) 722361
A cosy village inn offering good value bar and restaurant meals.
5rm(1⇌4hc) CTV in all bedrooms ® LDO 9.15pm
Credit Cards 1 3

BABELL Clwyd Map **07** SJ17

FH QQ Mrs M L Williams **Bryn Glas** *(SJ155737)* CH8 7PZ ☎Caerwys(0352) 720493
Feb-Nov
This dormer-style bungalow, which stands opposite The Black Lion Inn, is surrounded by farmland. It offers bright rooms and a relaxed atmosphere.
2hc (1fb)⊁in all bedrooms TV in all bedrooms ® ✱ sB&Bfr£15 dB&Bfr£25
CTV 2P pony trekking 40 acres beef mixed sheep
£

BADACHRO Highland *Ross And Cromarty* Map **13** NG77

GH QQ Harbour View IV21 2AA ☎(044583) 316
Feb-Oct
Set in a garden overlooking the bay, this former fisherman's cottage has been refurbished to provide comfortable, compact accommodation. There is also a small twin-bedded chalet in the garden.
4⇌⑥ Annexe 1⑥ (1fb)⊁in 4 bedrooms CTV in 2 bedrooms TV in 3 bedrooms ®
dB&B⇌⑥£27-£29 WB&B£91-£98 WBDi£143.50-£150.50 LDO 5pm
5P

BAKEWELL Derbyshire Map **08** SK26

GH QQ Cliffe House Hotel Monsal Head DE4 1NL ☎Great Longstone(062987) 376
Pleasant house at the head of Monsal Dale.
10rm(5⇌5⑥)(3fb) CTV in all bedrooms ® ✕ (ex guide dogs) sB&B⇌⑥£24-£28
dB&B⇌⑥£34-£38 WB&B£110-£125 WBDi£162-£170 LDO 10am
Lic CTV 14P
Credit Cards 1 3 £

SELECTED

GH QQQQ Merlin House Country Hotel Ashford Ln, Monsal Head DE4 1NL ☎Great Longstone(062987) 475
Mar-Oct
Well-tended lawns, shrubs and trees provide attractive surroundings for this quiet retreat in the Peak District. The immaculately kept and well-proportioned rooms include an attractive dining room with adjoining coffee lounge, a pretty sun lounge and a small bar. Mr and Mrs Berisford are tireless in their efforts to ensure that their guests have an enjoyable stay.
6rm(1⇌3⑥2hc) ® ✕ sB&B⇌⑥£19-£22
dB&B⇌⑥£38-£44 WB&B£133
Lic CTV 6P nc

BALA Gwynedd Map **06** SH93

GH QQ Frondderw LL23 7YD ☎(0678) 520301
Mar-Nov
Set on a hillside overlooking the town, this charming period mansion provides accommodation, food and service of a good standard.

8rm(1⇌1↑6hc)(3fb) ® ✖ (ex guide dogs) sB&B£10-£11
dB&B£20-£22
dB&B⇌↑£24-£26 WB&B£63.50-£81.50
WBDi£112.50-£130.50 LDO 5pm
Lic ♨ CTV 10P
£

See advertisement on page 47

GH Ⓠ **Plas Teg** Tegid St LL23 7EN ☎(0678) 520268
*Semidetached late 19th-century house, set back from the road with
garden in front.*
6hc (5fb) ® ✱ sB&B£14
dB&B£28 WB&B£84 WBDi£132 LDO 5pm
Lic CTV 12P
£

FH ⓆⓆ Mrs E Jones **Eirianfa** *(SH967394)* Sarnau LL23 7LH
(4m N on A494) ☎Llandderfel(06783) 389
Mar-Nov
*This modern farmhouse is in an isolated position overlooking the
Berwyn Mountains. The bedrooms are neat and well furnished and
a friendly family atmosphere prevails.*
3hc (1fb) ® ✖ ✱ sB&B£14-£16 dB&B£22-£26 LDO 6pm
♨ CTV 4P ◢ 150 acres mixed
£

BALLACHULISH Highland *Argyllshire* Map **14** NN05

GH ⓆⓆⓆ **Ballachulish House** Ballachulish House PA39 4JX
☎(08552) 266
*Set in 2 acres of grounds, this delightful house has strong
connections with the Glencoe Massacre and the Appin Murder,
and is famous for its ghost. The accommodation is comfortable and
relaxing, and the dinner menu regularly features game and local
shellfish.*
▶

4🛁 (2fb)🚭in all bedrooms [R] sB&B🛁£18.50-£30
dB&B🛁£35-£60 LDO 6pm
10P

GH [Q][Q][Q] *Lyn-Leven* White St PA39 4JW ☎(08552) 392
Closed Xmas
Comfortable and well-appointed modern bungalow, situated close to A82 overlooking Loch Leven.
8rm(7🚿1hc)(1fb) CTV in all bedrooms [R] LDO 8pm
Lic ♨ 12P

BALLATER Grampian *Aberdeenshire* Map **15** NO39

SELECTED

GH [Q][Q][Q][Q] Moorside Braemar Rd AB3 5RL
☎(03397) 55492
Mar-Nov
Situated on the main road, not far from the village centre, this former church manse has been sympathetically restored and is an ideal base for the touring holidaymaker. It has a welcoming atmosphere and offers comfortable and well-equipped bedrooms together with enjoyable home cooking.
9rm(3🛁6🚿)(3fb) CTV in all bedrooms [R]
🐕 (ex guide dogs) ✱ sB&B🛁🚿fr£21
dB&B🛁🚿fr£28 WB&Bfr£91 WBDifr£176 LDO 7pm
Lic ♨ 10P
Credit Cards [1] [3] [£]

GH [Q][Q][Q] Morvada Braemar Rd AB3 5RL ☎(03397) 55501
27 Apr-7 Oct
On the main road, not far from the village centre, this comfortable house is a popular base for golfers and holidaymakers. John and Freda Nimmo run Morvada with efficiency, and provide well-equipped bed and breakfast accommodation.
7rm(6🚿1hc) CTV in all bedrooms [R] LDO 6pm
Lic ♨ 7P

GH [Q][Q] Netherley 2 Netherley Place AB3 5QE
☎(03397) 55792
Closed Feb rs Nov-Jan
Beside the village green, just off the main street, this family- run guesthouse proves popular with tourists and golfers. The accommodation offered is good value and there is a friendly atmosphere.
9rm(1🛁3🚿5hc)(2fb) CTV in 4 bedrooms [R] sB&B£14-£16
dB&B£24-£28 dB&B🛁🚿£29-£32 WBDi£130-£160 LDO 5pm
CTV nc4yrs
[£]

BAMPTON Devon Map **03** SS92

GH [Q] Bridge House Hotel Luke St EX16 9NF ☎(0398) 31298
This attractive, family-run hotel and restaurant is set in the centre of Bampton. It offers comfortable accommodation and an imaginative menu.
7rm(3🛁1🚿3hc)(2fb) 🐕 (ex guide dogs) sB&B£18-£21
sB&B🛁🚿fr£21 dB&Bfr£32 dB&B🛁🚿fr£35 LDO 10pm
Lic ♨ CTV 🎾 🎣 game & clay pigeon shooting
Credit Cards [1] [3] [£]

GH [Q][Q][Q] *Courtyard Hotel & Restaurant* 19 Fore St EX16 9ND
☎(0398) 31536
Closed Xmas & New Year
Standing in the town centre, this attractive stone building has well-equipped bedrooms and old-world public rooms. The busy restaurant is open to non-residents and offers an à la carte menu. The proprietors and friendly staff provide personal service.
6rm(2🛁1🚿3hc)(1fb) CTV in all bedrooms [R] 🐕 LDO 9pm
Lic ♨ CTV 35P
Credit Cards [1] [2] [3] [5]

INN [Q][Q][Q] Exeter Tiverton Rd EX16 9DY ☎(0398) 31345
This ancient country inn has 8 bedrooms with en suite facilities and all modern conveniences. Food is available in the bar and more formal restaurant. Salmon and trout fishing and clay pigeon shooting are available as well as stabling for guests' horses.
8rm(4🛁3🚿1hc) CTV in all bedrooms [R] 🐕 (ex guide dogs)
sB&B🛁🚿£21.50
dB&B🛁🚿£39.50 WB&Bfr£125 WBDifr£188 Lunch fr£6.95alc Dinner fr£8.95&alc LDO 10pm
♨ 50P 🎣 🐎 clay pigeon & game shooting
Credit Cards [1] [3] [£]

BAMPTON Oxfordshire Map **04** SP30

FH [Q][Q][Q] Mrs J Rouse ***Morar*** *(SP312026)* Weald St
OX8 2HL (0.5m SW off A4095) ☎Bampton Castle(0993) 850162
Telex no 83343
Closed 21-28 Dec
Small, modern farmhouse with bright, spotlessly clean bedrooms, and comfortable lounge. There are extensive farm views, and sheep graze next to the house.
3hc 🚭in all bedrooms [R] 🐕 LDO noon
Lic ♨ CTV 4P nc6yrs 500 acres arable beef dairy

BANAVIE Highland *Inverness-Shire* Map **14** NN17

FH [Q][Q][Q] Mrs A C MacDonald ***Burnside*** *(NN138805)*
Muirshearlich PH33 7PB ☎Corpach(03977) 275
Apr-Sep
Small, stone-built farmhouse, situated 3 miles north east of the town, off the B8004, with open views over the Caledonian Canal and towards the north face of Ben Nevis.
3hc LDO 4.30pm
CTV 3P 69 acres mixed

BANBURY Oxfordshire Map **04** SP44

See also Charlton (Northants)

GH [Q][Q] Belmont 34 Crouch St OX16 9PR ☎(0295) 262308
This well-maintained and attractive guesthouse has a warm, informal atmosphere. The accommodation is comfortable and the pleasant bedrooms are adequately equipped. Good home-cooked meals are served in the bright dining room.
8rm(5🚿3hc)(3fb)🚭in 2 bedrooms CTV in all bedrooms [R]
sB&B£16-£20 sB&B🚿£20-£25 dB&B£25-£30 dB&B🚿£30-£35
Lic ♨ 6P
Credit Cards [1] [3]

GH [Q][Q][Q] La Madonette Country North Newington
OX15 6AA (3m W off B4035) ☎(0295) 730212
Closed Xmas & New Year
This converted 17th-century former miller's house is set in traditional Cotswold surroundings bordered by the mill stream. Patti Ritter offers a warm welcome and the bedrooms are well equipped and comfortably furnished. There is a charming dining room and small reception/lounge in addition to the garden and outdoor swimming pool.
6rm(3🛁3🚿) CTV in all bedrooms [R] 🐕 (ex guide dogs) ✱
sB&B🛁🚿fr£35 dB&B🛁🚿£45-£55
Lic ♨ 20P 🏊(heated)
Credit Cards [1] [3]

GH [Q][Q] Tredis 15 Broughton Rd OX16 9QB ☎(0295) 264632
Standing close to the town centre and run by friendly owners this guesthouse has bright accommodation with an attractive dining room. The adjacent lounge has patio doors leading to small gardens.
11rm(1🛁2🚿8hc)(1fb) CTV in all bedrooms [R]
🐕 (ex guide dogs) ✱ sB&Bfr£17.25 sB&B🛁🚿fr£23
dB&Bfr£32.20 dB&B🛁🚿fr£40.25 LDO noon
♨ 5P

BANFF Grampian *Banffshire* Map **15** NJ66

GH [Q] Carmelite House Hotel Low St AB4 1AY ☎(02612) 2152
This charming period house stands in the town centre and has a spacious, comfortable lounge and a pleasant dining room. The functional bedrooms are well equipped.
10rm(3🚿7hc)(4fb) CTV in 3 bedrooms [R] 🐕 (ex guide dogs)
LDO 7.45pm
Lic CTV 10P
Credit Cards [1] [3] [£]

BANTHAM Devon Map **03** SX64

INN [Q][Q] Sloop TQ7 3AJ ☎Kingsbridge(0548) 560489 & 560215
Situated in the village centre close to the beach, this inn retains its character along with many original features. The comfortable bedrooms all have colour TV and most have en suite facilities. Meals are served in the popular bars.
5rm(4🛁1hc)(2fb) CTV in all bedrooms [R] * sB&B£19-£22
sB&B🛁£20-£24 dB&B£38-£42
dB&B🛁£40-£44 WBDi£199-£220 Lunch £5.50-£7alc Dinner £5.50-£12alc LDO 10pm
♨ 35P

BARMBY MOOR Humberside Map **08** SE74

SELECTED

GH [Q][Q][Q][Q] Barmby Moor Country Hotel Hull Rd YO4 5EZ (2m W off A1079) ☎Pocklington(0759) 302700
This ivy-clad coaching inn was built in the 18th century, and its former stable block now contains 6 bedrooms to complement the 4 in the main building. The pleasant Honeysuckle Restaurant serves a good table d'hôte dinner and overlooks a courtyard containing a solar heated swimming pool. Interesting antiques furnish the stone-flagged reception foyer. The hotel is conveniently located on the York/Hull A1079, just 20 minutes from the city wall.
10rm(6🛁4🚿) CTV in all bedrooms [R] 🐕 *
sB&B🛁🚿£40-£42
dB&B🛁🚿£50-£52 WB&Bfr£160 WBDifr£238 LDO 8pm
Lic ♨ 30P 🏊(heated)
Credit Cards [1] [2] [3] [£]

BARMOUTH Gwynedd Map **06** SH61

GH [Q][Q] Cranbourne Hotel 9 Marine Pde LL42 1NA ☎(0341) 280202
This small family-run hotel is situated on the promenade, overlooking Cardigan Bay and the beach. The accommodation is modest but well maintained and many of the bedrooms have en suite facilities.
10rm(8🛁🚿2hc)(6fb) CTV in all bedrooms [R]
🐕 (ex guide dogs) * sB&Bfr£17.50 sB&B🛁🚿fr£17.50
dB&Bfr£37
dB&B🛁🚿fr£40 WB&Bfr£129.50 WBDifr£166 LDO 5pm
Lic ♨ CTV 4P (85p per day)
Credit Cards [1] [3] [£]

GH [Q][Q] *Morwendon* LLanaber LL42 1RR ☎(0341) 280566
Closed Jan-Mar rs Oct-Dec
This large detached house, 1.5 miles north of Barmouth on the A496 coast road, enjoys good sea views. There is a private car park and every bedroom has an en suite shower and toilet.
6🚿 (3fb) CTV in all bedrooms [R] 🐕 (ex guide dogs) (wkly only Jul & Aug) LDO 5pm
Lic ♨ CTV 7P

INN [Q] Tal-y-Don St Anne's Square LL42 1DL ☎(0341) 280508
Situated in the town centre, this is a small public house providing simple accommodation. It also offers a choice of 3 bars and a beer garden to the rear.
7hc (3fb) CTV in all bedrooms [R] 🐕
♨ CTV 🚫P

BARNARD CASTLE Co Durham Map **12** NZ01

FH [Q] Mrs D M Lowson **West Roods** *(NZ022141)* Boldron DL12 9SW ☎Teesdale(0833) 690116
Mar-Dec
Surrounded by meadows and stone walls, this farm is 2.5 miles East from Bowes and West off the A66 dual carriageway. It is signposted 'Lamb Hill', 'West Roods' and 'Roods House'. Two of the traditional bedrooms have en suite facilities and there are plenty of books, games and information.
3rm(2🚿1hc)(1fb)🚭in all bedrooms CTV in all bedrooms [R] *
sB&B£12-£15
dB&B🚿£24-£30 WB&Bfr£80 WBDi£122-£149 LDO 6pm
♨ 6P 58 acres dairy

INN [Q][Q][Q] The Fox and Hounds Country Inn & Restaurant Cotherstone DL12 9PF ☎Teesdale(0833) 50241 & 50811
3🛁🚿 CTV in all bedrooms [R] 🐕 (ex guide dogs)
sB&B🛁🚿£30
dB&B🛁🚿£40 Lunch £9-£15alc Dinner £9-£15alc LDO 9pm
♨ CTV 30P nc9yrs
Credit Cards [1] [3] [£]

Street plans of certain towns and cities will be found in a separate section at the back of the book.

Fronddерw

Bala, Gwynedd LL23 7YD. N. Wales
Tel: Bala (0678) 520301

FRONDDERW is a charming period mansion set on the hillside overlooking the town of Bala, with magnificent views of the Berwyn Mountains and Llyn Tegid (Bala Lake).

Guest accommodation includes one downstairs suite suitable for partially disabled visitors. All rooms have modern amenities and tea/coffee making facilities. Cots are available on request with linen.

The front lounge is spacious and comfortable. There is a separate television lounge with colour TV and a large dining room.

An excellent evening meal is available on request. Ample parking space is available free of charge. No garage accommodation. Sorry, no guests' pets allowed in the house.

Closed December, January & February.

BARNEY Norfolk Map 09 TF93

SELECTED

GH QQQQ **The Old Brick Kilns** Little Barney
NR21 0NL ☎Thursford(0328) 878305
*To find this guesthouse guests should follow caravan site signs
from Little Barney and continue along the narrow lane. As its
name implies, the building has been converted to afford
attractive en suite accommodation together with an elegant
lounge and dining room. Tessa Gent is an excellent hostess
offering high-quality meals and warm hospsitality.*
3⇌♠ CTV in all bedrooms ® ✕ (ex guide dogs)
sB&B⇌♠£17-£20
dB&B⇌♠£34-£40 WB&B£107-£126 WBDi£184-£203
LDO 10am
Lic ♀♀♀ CTV 10P ♨
£

BARNSTAPLE Devon Map 02 SS53

↤GH QQ **Cresta** 26 Sticklepath Hill EX31 2BU
☎(0271) 74022
Closed Xmas
*This small guesthouse is next to the main Barnstaple to Bideford
road, 1 mile from the centre of Barnstaple. The accommodation is
simple in style, with a bright, cosy lounge, and the benefit of on-site
parking.*
5rm(1♠4hc)Annexe 1⇌ (1fb) CTV in all bedrooms ® ✕
sB&B£13-£16 sB&B⇌♠£17-£19 dB&B£24-£28
dB&B⇌♠£28-£32 WB&B£77-£98
♀♀♀ CTV 6P nc
£

GH QQ **Yeo Dale Hotel** Pilton Bridge EX31 1PG
☎(0271) 42954
*Family-run hotel dating back to the 16th century, overlooking
Pilton Park and river.*
10rm(1⇌4♠)(3fb) CTV in all bedrooms ®
sB&B£14.50-£16 sB&B⇌♠£20.50-£22 dB&B£28-£30
dB&B⇌♠£34-£38 WB&B£101.50-£154 WBDi£147-£245
LDO 5pm
Lic ♀♀♀ CTV ✗
Credit Cards 1 3 £

FH QQ Mr & Mrs J Dallyn **Rowden Barton** *(SS538306)*
Roundswell EX31 3NP (2m SW B3232) ☎(0271) 44365
*Mr and Mrs Dallyn provide true farmhouse hospitality at their
small modern home, which enjoys views across rolling countryside.
With a choice of lounges, bright cosy bedrooms and wholesome
home cooking, this is a convenient retreat for tourists.*
2rm ⅍in all bedrooms ® ✕ (ex guide dogs) ✳ sB&B£12
dB&B£24 WB&B£80 WBDi£130
♀♀♀ P 90 acres beef sheep
£

BASINGSTOKE Hampshire Map 04 SU65

GH QQ **May's Bounty Hotel** 12 Fairfields Rd RG21 3DR
☎(0256) 471300
Friendly, well-run accommodation, close to all amenities.
11♠ (2fb) CTV in all bedrooms ® ✕ (ex guide dogs)
sB&B£28-£55.50 dB&B♠£38-£65.50 WB&B£266 LDO 8pm
Lic ♀♀♀ CTV 16P
Credit Cards 1 3

BASSENTHWAITE Cumbria Map 11 NY23

GH QQQ **Ravenstone Hotel** CA12 4QG
☎Bassenthwaite Lake(059681) 240
Mar-Oct
*Situated 2.5 miles south of the village, and enjoying views across
the lake, this fine period house has comfortable public rooms, a
cosy bar and attractive bedrooms.*
14⇌♠ (3fb) CTV in all bedrooms ® sB&B⇌♠£28-£30
dB&B⇌♠£56-£60 (incl dinner) WB&B£147-£161
WBDi£189-£203 LDO 6pm
Lic ♀♀♀ 25P snooker

FH QQ Mrs P Trafford **Bassenthwaite Hall (East)**
(NY231322) CA12 4QP ☎Bassenthwaite Lake(059681) 393
Apr-Oct rs Jan & Dec
*Fully modernised 17th-century farmhouse in picturesque village
close to quiet stream.*
2hc (1fb) sB&B£15-£20 dB&B£25-£30 WB&B£80-£90
♀♀♀ CTV 6P nc2yrs 250 acres beef poultry sheep
£

BATH Avon Map 03 ST76

See Town Plan Section
See also Keynsham and **Timsbury**
GH Q **Arden Hotel** 73 Great Pulteney St BA2 4DL
☎(0225) 466601 & 330039 FAX (0225) 465548
Closed mid Dec-2 Jan
*Hotel will be undergoing extensive alterations and refurbishment
at the beginning of 1989.*
10⇌♠2fb) CTV in all bedrooms ® ✕ (ex guide dogs)Lic ♀♀♀
CTV 10P
Credit Cards 1 3 £

GH Q **Arney** 99 Wells Rd BA2 3AN ☎(0225) 310020
7rm(1♠6hc)(3fb) ✳ sB&B£18-£20 dB&B£28-£30
♀♀♀ CTV ✗
£

GH QQ **Ashley Villa Hotel** 26 Newbridge Rd BA1 3JZ
☎(0225) 421683
Closed 2 wks Xmas
*Situated on the A4 west of the town, this large Victorian villa has
been refurbished by the hosts, Mr and Mrs Kitcher, to offer good
bed and breakfast accommodation. A patio garden and outdoor
heated swimming pool are also provided.*
14rm(4⇌10♠)(3fb) CTV in all bedrooms ®
sB&B⇌♠£35-£40 dB&B⇌♠£45-£60 WB&B£140-£240
Lic ♀♀♀ CTV 10P ⚊(heated)
Credit Cards 1 3 £

See advertisement on page 51

GH Q **Astor House** 14 Oldfield Rd BA2 3ND ☎(0225) 429134
Apr-Oct
*Particularly popular with foreign visitors, this establishment is set
in a pleasant residential area convenient for the city centre. The
accommodation here is simple and functional.*
7hc ® ✕ (ex guide dogs) ✳ dB&B£28-£32
♀♀♀ CTV 4P nc7yrs
£

GH QQ **Avon Hotel** 9 Bathwick St BA2 6NX
☎(0225) 446176 & 422226 FAX (0225) 447452
Closed 25 & 26 Dec
*Georgian end-of-terrace house with well-furnished bedrooms.
Ample parking and close to shops and tourist sites.*
12♠ (5fb)⅍in 2 bedrooms CTV in all bedrooms ®
sB&B♠£35-£39 dB&B♠£49.50-£58
Lic ♀♀♀ CTV 20P
Credit Cards 1 3 £

See advertisement on page 53

GH Ⓠ Ⓠ Ⓠ **Brompton House Hotel** St John's Rd BA2 6PT
☎(0225) 420972 & 448423
Closed Xmas
Delightful Regency residence which was once the rectory to St Mary's Church, adjacent.
12rm(1⇄11♠)(1fb) CTV in all bedrooms ® ✕ ✱
sB&B⇄♠£30-£35 dB&B⇄♠£50-£55
Lic ⁇ 12P
Credit Cards ①③
See advertisement on page 51

GH Ⓠ Ⓠ Ⓠ **Carfax Hotel** Great Pulteney St BA2 4BS
☎(0225) 462089 FAX (0225) 443257
Formally three Regency houses on the famous Great Pulteney Street, close to the town centre, this unlicensed hotel offers modern bedrooms, many with good en suite facilities, and bright public rooms.
39rm(34⇄♠5hc)(3fb)✕in 5 bedrooms CTV in all bedrooms ® ✕ (ex guide dogs) sB&B£20-£24 sB&B⇄♠£27.50-£42 dB&B£40-£45
dB&B⇄♠£48-£60 WB&B£154-£189 WBDi£173.50-£236.25
LDO 7.50pm
lift ⁇ 13P 4🚗 (£2 per day) ♨
Credit Cards ①②③ⓔ

GH Ⓠ Ⓠ Ⓠ **Cedar Lodge** 13 Lambridge, London Rd BA1 6BJ
☎(0225) 423468
Closed 24-27 Dec
3rm(1♠2hc)(1fb)✕in all bedrooms CTV in all bedrooms
✕ (ex guide dogs) sB&B£25-£30
dB&B£33-£45 WB&B£100-£130
⁇ CTV 6P ♨ ∪

Book as early as possible for busy holiday periods.

Ⓐ

ARDEN HOTEL
· BATH ·

The Arden Hotel is situated in Great Pulteney Street, Europe's Grandest Classical Parade . . . the epitome of eighteenth century elegance and just a few minutes walk from many historical sites in and around the city centre. The Grade I listed building designed by Thomas Baldwin has recently been restored and refurbished and offers the comfort of a luxurious Georgian Town House.
We have 10 beautifully decorated and well appointed bedrooms, each with its own bathroom or shower room. For the comfort of our guests there is an elegant ground floor drawing room facing Great Pulteney Street.
Restaurant opening 1990. Function and Conference facilities also available.
Please do not hesitate to contact us for further information.

73 Great Pulteney Street, Bath,
Avon BA2 4DL.
Tel: 0225 466601. Fax: 0225 465548.

GH [Q][Q][Q] Cheriton House 9 Upper Oldfield Park BA2 3JX ☎(0225) 429862
Closed Xmas and New Year
This is a charming guesthouse on the outskirts of Bath and has some fine views over the city. Excellent standards are maintained here and the rooms are beautifully decorated and have good facilities.
9rm(2🛁7🚿) CTV in all bedrooms Ⓡ 🚫 (ex guide dogs) sB&B🛁🚿£32-£35 dB&B🛁🚿£44-£50
♨ 9P nc
Credit Cards [1][3] [£]

GH [Q][Q][Q] Dorian House 1 Upper Oldfield Park BA2 3JX ☎(0225) 426336
7rm(3🛁4🚿)(2fb) CTV in all bedrooms Ⓡ 🚫 (ex guide dogs) ✱ sB&B🛁🚿£29-£35 dB&B🛁🚿£44-£54
Lic ♨ 8P 3🚗
Credit Cards [1][2][3][5] [£]

GH [Q][Q][Q] Dorset Villa 14 Newbridge Rd BA1 3JZ ☎(0225) 425975
West of the city on the main A4 road, this small hotel has been refurbished recently and provides well-furnished accommodation with good facilities.
7rm(5🚿2hc)(1fb) CTV in all bedrooms sB&B£25-£27 sB&B🚿£30-£32 dB&B£35-£37 dB&B🚿£40-£42 WB&B£105-£192 WBDi£161-£248 LDO 9pm
Lic ♨ CTV 6P
Credit Cards [1][3] [£]

See advertisement on page 55

GH [Q][Q][Q] Eagle House Church St, Bathford BA1 7RS (3m NE A363) ☎(0225) 859946
Closed 23-30 Dec
Set in delightful Bathford, this lovely Georgian house stands in spacious, attractive gardens. Owners John and Rosamund Napier provide a warm and friendly welcome and well-equipped accommodation.
6🛁🚿 Annexe 2🛁🚿 (2fb) CTV in all bedrooms Ⓡ sB&B🛁🚿£26-£35 dB&B🛁🚿£38-£49.50
Lic ♨ 10P croquet lawn
[£]

GH [Q][Q][Q] Edgar Hotel 64 Gt Pulteney St BA2 4DN ☎(0225) 420619
Original Georgian town house in historic city centre.
14🚿 (1fb) CTV in all bedrooms Ⓡ 🚫
Lic ♨ CTV P̸
[£]

GH [Q][Q] Grove Lodge 11 Lambridge, London Rd BA1 6BJ ☎(0225) 310860
Situated on London Road, the A4, 1 mile from the city centre, this strictly non-smoking, fine detached Regency house offers spacious bedrooms on a room and breakfast basis only. There are some good pictures and pieces of furniture.
8hc (2fb)🚭in all bedrooms CTV in all bedrooms 🚫 (ex guide dogs) sB&B£22-£25 dB&B£36-£40 WB&B£110-£120
Lic P̸
[£]

GH [Q][Q][Q] Highways House 143 Wells Rd BA2 3AL ☎(0225) 421238
Closed 24-27 Dec
Enthusiastically run, this small hotel is in a residential area and offers a warm welcome to guests. High standards are maintained throughout, and a particularly comfortable lounge is provided.
7rm(6🛁🚿1hc) CTV in all bedrooms Ⓡ 🚫 (ex guide dogs) sB&B£30-£36 dB&B£42-£50 dB&B🛁🚿£46-£52
♨ 8P nc5yrs
[£]

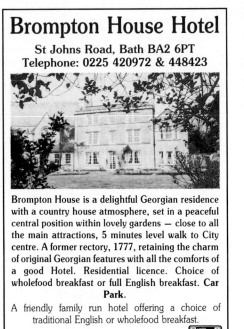

GH Q Q Q **Kennard Hotel** 11 Henrietta St BA2 6LL
☎(0225) 310472
Situated close to Pulteney Bridge, this period terrace house offers modern, well-equipped bedrooms, many with good en suite shower facilities. The bright and attractive breakfast room has a garden theme.
12rm(9♪3hc)(2fb) CTV in all bedrooms ® ✱ sB&Bfr£25
sB&B♪fr£30 dB&Bfr£35 dB&B♪£45-£55
🎮 ✗
Credit Cards 1 2 3 £

SELECTED

GH Q Q Q Q **Laura Place Hotel** 3 Laura Place, Great
Pulteney St BA2 4BH ☎(0225) 463815
Mar-21 Dec
Situated in the fountain-centred square at the city end of the renowned Great Pulteney Street, this fine former Georgian town house has been very carefully restored to provide a private hotel of quality with good modern amenities. The bedrooms are of a good size and the majority have good en suite facilities. Extras include remote control colour television sets and direct dial telephones. Excellent taste has been introduced in décor and co-ordinating soft furnishings.
10rm(6⇨♪4hc) CTV in all bedrooms ®
🐾 (ex guide dogs) ✱ sB&Bfr£20 sB&B⇨♪£45 dB&B£50
dB&B⇨♪£60-£70
🎮 10P
Credit Cards 1 2 3 £

GH Q Q Q **Leighton House** 139 Wells Rd BA2 3AL
☎(0225) 314769
rs May-Oct
This large Victorian house offers quality bed and breakfast facilities close to the city centre. The bedrooms are well equipped with modern en suite facilities and lots of extras. in addition to the spacious dining room, there is a cosy and comfortable lounge. David and Kathleen Slape are charming and attentive hosts who create the impression that one is an honoured personal guest.
7⇨♪ (2fb) CTV in all bedrooms ®
dB&B⇨♪£50-£56 WB&B£161-£294 LDO 2pm
Lic 🎮 7P
Credit Cards 1 3

GH Q Q **Millers Hotel** 69 Great Pulteney St BA2 4DL
☎(0225) 465798
Closed Xmas wk
Bright, agreeable Georgian terraced house in historic part of city centre.
14rm(5⇨♪8hc)(3fb) CTV in 8 bedrooms 🐾 (ex guide dogs)
sB&B£23-£25 sB&B⇨♪£34-£38 dB&B£34-£38
dB&B⇨♪£45-£52
Lic 🎮 CTV ✗
£

GH Q Q Q **Oldfields** 102 Wells Rd BA2 3AL ☎(0225) 317984
This detached Victorian house has a well-kept garden and is tastefully furnished and decorated throughout. High standards are maintained and a relaxed, friendly atmosphere prevails.
14rm(1⇨7♪6hc) CTV in all bedrooms ® 🐾 (ex guide dogs) ✱
sB&B£33 sB&B⇨♪£42 dB&B£43 dB&B⇨♪£52
🎮 10P
Credit Cards 1 3

'Selected' establishments, which have the highest
quality award, are highlighted by a tinted panel.
For a full list of these establishments, consult the
Contents page.

SELECTED

GH Q Q Q Q **Old School House** Church St, Bathford
BA1 7RR (3m NE on A363) ☎(0225) 859593
*This former Victorian school has been tastefully converted
into a non-smoking, private hotel, offering very comfortable
bedrooms with en suite bathrooms and many extras. A warm
and relaxing atmosphere is provided in the very well-furnished
public areas.*
4⇨🛏 ⚹in all bedrooms CTV in all bedrooms ® ✗
sB&B⇨🛏£35
dB&B⇨🛏£48-£52 WB&B£200-£292 WBDif£316-£404
LDO am
Lic 🏧 CTV 6P
Credit Cards 1 3 £

SELECTED

GH Q Q Q Q **Orchard House Hotel** Warminster Rd
(A36), Bathampton BA2 6XG ☎(0225) 466115
*Situated 2 miles from the city centre, this purpose-built,
modern stone-faced hotel offers bright and attractive open
plan-public areas. The bedrooms have been decorated with
pretty colour schemes and have very well-equipped en suite
bathrooms. Additional facilities include a health area with
sauna and solarium.*
14⇨🛏 (3fb) CTV in all bedrooms ® ✳
sB&B⇨🛏£43-£46 dB&B⇨🛏£57-£60 LDO 7.45pm
Lic 🏧 16P sauna solarium
Credit Cards 1 2 3 5 £

GH Q **Oxford Private Hotel** 5 Oxford Row Lansdown Rd
BA1 2QN ☎(0225) 314039
*Situated close to the centre of the town, in a Regency terrace on
Lansdowne Road, this establishment offers convenient bed and
breakfast accommodation.*
11rm(4🛏7hc)(3fb) CTV in 7 bedrooms ® ✗ ✳ sB&B£17-£20
dB&B£32-£36 dB&B🛏£32-£36 LDO 10pm
Lic 🏧 ✗ nc5yrs

SELECTED

GH Q Q Q Q **Paradise House Hotel** Holloway BA2 4PX
☎(0225) 317723
Closed 20-28 Dec
*Situated in a quiet cul-de-sac in an elevated position with fine
views over the city, this spacious Georgian house has been
tastefully modernised by the Cutting family whilst retaining
many original features including fine staircases, moulded
windows and decorative cornices. The bedrooms are spacious
and comfortably furnished, with excellent colour co-ordination
in décor and soft furnishings. All but 2 have good en suite
facilities. Paradise House has the added benefit of a very well-
tended and spacious walled garden.*
9rm(6⇨1🛏2hc)(1fb) CTV in all bedrooms ® ✗
sB&B£33-£41 sB&B⇨🛏£41-£53 dB&B£40-£48
dB&B⇨🛏£48-£60 WB&B£126-£190
🏧 2P 3🚗 (£2 per night) croquet lawn
Credit Cards 1 3 £

GH Q Q **Parkside** 11 Marlborough Ln BA1 2NQ
☎(0225) 429444
Closed Xmas wk
*Standing on the edge of Victoria Park, this Edwardian property
offers easy access to the city centre. The rooms are spacious and
comfortable, and the resident proprietors provide a pleasant
atmosphere and a warm welcome.*

5hc (1fb) CTV in all bedrooms ® sB&B£22-£29
dB&B£32-£36 WB&B£138.60-£182.70 WBDif£201.60-£245.70
LDO 5pm
🏧 CTV 2P nc4yrs

GH Q Q Q **Hotel St Clair** 1 Crescent Gdns, Upper Bristol Rd
BA1 2NA ☎(0225) 425543
*This spacious, semi-detached Victorian villa is on the Bristol Road,
near Royal Crescent. The hosts, Mr and Mrs Codd, provide
friendly services, in addition to the modern, well-equipped
bedrooms, and the cosy dining room.*
10rm(2🛏8hc)(1fb) CTV in all bedrooms ® ✗ sB&B£20-£26
sB&B🛏£26-£35 dB&B£30-£38
dB&B🛏£36-£45 WB&B£120-£150
Lic 🏧 ✗ nc3yrs
Credit Cards 1 3

SELECTED

GH Q Q Q Q **Somerset House Hotel & Restaurant** 35
Bathwick Hill BA2 6LD ☎(0225) 466451
*Situated on Bathwick Hill at Cleveland this fine period house
is operated by the Seymor family who have introduced modern
facilities whilst retaining many original features such as fine
moulded cornices and open fireplaces. There is a choice of
sitting rooms in either the first floor drawing room or the
ground floor library cum music room. The basement dining
room has an attractive kitchen theme complete with original
hearth ovens, and imaginative well-cooked food is offered. The
bedrooms have either en suite or private facilities together with
comfortable furnishings. This is a strictly non-smoking
establishment.*
9⇨🛏 (4fb)⚹in all bedrooms ® sB&B⇨🛏£36.55-£44
dB&B⇨🛏£73.10-£88 (incl dinner) WBDif£248.50-£287
LDO 6.30pm
Lic 🏧 CTV 12P nc10yrs
Credit Cards 1 2 3 £

GH Q Q Q **The Tasburgh Bath** Warminster Rd, Bathampton
BA2 6SH ☎(0225) 425096
*Sympathetically restored, this Victorian house is surrounded by
1.5 acres of garden and has some fine views. The high standard of
accommodation is maintained by owners who offer warm
hospitality to their guests.*
13rm(12⇨🛏1hc)(4fb)⚹in 2 bedrooms CTV in all bedrooms
® ✗ sB&B£28-£30 sB&B⇨🛏£32-£40 dB&B£42
dB&B⇨🛏£52-£46
Lic 🏧 CTV 15P
Credit Cards 1 2 3 5

See advertisement on page 57

GH Q Q Q **Underhill Lodge** Warminster Rd, Bathampton
BA2 6XQ ☎(0225) 464992
rs Xmas wk
*Two miles from the city centre, on the Warminster Road at
Bathampton, this Victorian villa has been tastefully restored by
June and Don Mather to provide quality accommodation with en
suite bedrooms. There is a fine display of oriental artefacts.*
4⇨🛏 ⚹in all bedrooms CTV in all bedrooms ® ✗ ✳
sB&B⇨🛏£42 dB&B⇨🛏£50-£55 LDO noon
Lic 🏧 10P nc10yrs
Credit Cards 1 3 £

See advertisement on page 57

GH Q Q Q **Villa Magdala Private Hotel** Henrietta Rd
BA2 6LX ☎(0225) 466329
Feb-Dec
*Built in 1868, and named after a famous battle, this beautifully
maintained house stands in attractive grounds. A few minutes'
walk from the city centre, the accommodation is well equipped, and
the hotel's parking facilities are an asset in this city.*

▶

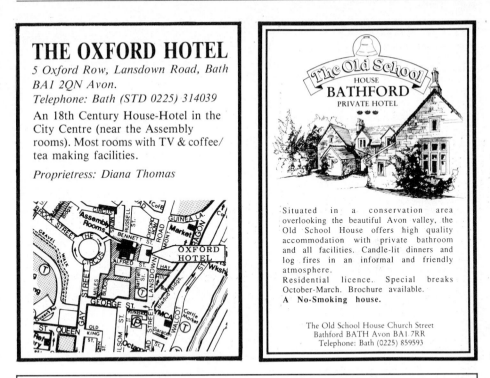

17rm(13➪4♠)(3fb) CTV in all bedrooms ® ✖ ✳
sB&B➪♠£40-£42 dB&B➪♠£52-£67
♨ 13P 2☎ (£3 per night) nc6yrs
Credit Cards 1 3

GH QQ Waltons 17 Crescent Gardens, Upper Bristol Rd
BA1 2NA ☎(0225) 426528
*This is an uncomplicated guesthouse, popular with commercial
guests and tourists alike. It is situated close to the Victoria Park,
and is only a few minutes from the city centre. The rooms are
simply furnished, providing a relaxing atmosphere.*
15hc (3fb) ✳ sB&B£20-£25 dB&B£30-£40
♨ CTV ₽

GH QQQ Wentworth House Hotel 106 Bloomfield Rd
BA2 2AP ☎(0225) 339193
Closed mid Dec-mid Jan
*Under the personal supervision of owners, Mr and Mrs Kitching,
this large guesthouse offers thoughtfully equipped rooms, well
maintained and comfortable throughout. There is a lounge bar and
the dining room has a conservatory which overlooks the outdoor
swimming pool.*
20rm(7➪7♠6hc)(2fb) CTV in all bedrooms ® sB&B£20-£21
sB&B➪♠£28-£30 dB&B£33-£35
dB&B➪♠£42-£48 LDO 6.30pm
Lic ♨ CTV 20P ⌑
Credit Cards 1 3

INN QQ Chequers 50 Rivers St BA1 2QA ☎(0225) 424246
*Situated in a residential area close to the Royal Crescent, this
Georgian house provides attractive open-plan bars and
comfortable, well-equipped bedrooms.*
4hc (1fb) CTV in 2 bedrooms ® ✖ (ex guide dogs)
sB&Bfr£17.50
dB&Bfr£35 Bar Lunch £1.75-£5.95 LDO 9.45pm
♨ ₽
Credit Cards 1 2 3 5

INN QQ County Hotel 18-19 Pulteney Rd BA2 4DN
☎(0225) 425003 & 466493
Closed 25 & 26 Dec
*Situated close to the town centre, this spacious, detached stone
hotel offers modern, well-equipped bedrooms and bright, attractive
public areas. Bar snacks are available at lunchtime, and more
substantial meals are offered during the evenings in the restaurant.*
22rm(1➪11♠10hc)(5fb) CTV in all bedrooms ® ✳
sB&B£30-£32.50 sB&B➪♠£47.50-£50 dB&B£50-£55
dB&B➪♠£60-£65 LDO 10pm
♨ CTV 60P
Credit Cards 1 3

BATTLE East Sussex Map **05** TQ71

GH QQQ Netherfield Hall Netherfield TN33 9PQ (3 m NW
of B2096) ☎(04246) 4450
*This attractive coach house has been adapted to offer pleasant,
comfortable accommodation, and is situated in a pleasant village
surrounded by woodlands. As Mr Blake deals in giftwear, there is
a large selection of pictures and china to choose from as a souvenir.
The house has a family atmosphere and pleasant, informal style.*
4rm(2♠2hc)Annexe 1♠ TV in 2 bedrooms ®
♨ CTV 6P
£

See advertisement on page 59

FH QQQ Paul & Alison Slater **Little Hemingfold Farmhouse
Hotel** *(TQ774149)* Telham TN33 0TT (2.5m SE on N side of
A2100) ☎(04246) 4338
*Peacefully situated beside a small lake, with 40 acres of woodland
and walks, guests at this farmhouse hotel will find many things to
do. Bedrooms are individually furnished, and there are good
lounge facilities and high standards of cooking.*

▶

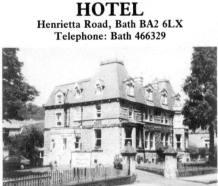

4rm(3⇩1hc)Annexe 9rm(7⇩) CTV in all bedrooms ®
sB&B⇩£25-£30
dB&B⇩£45-£60 WB&B£157.50-£210 WBDi£244-£296 LDO
7pm
Lic ♛ 30P nc8yrs ► 18 ♪(grass)✓ boules swimming in lake 40
acres mixed
Credit Cards 1 3 £

BEAMINSTER Dorset Map **03** ST40

SELECTED

GH QQQQ Hams Plot Bridport Rd DT8 3LU
☎(0308) 862979
Apr-Oct
*This charming country house has been carefully furnished
with fine antiques and Victorian water-colours. Bedrooms are
spacious and comfortable, and there are fine public rooms.
The proprietors ensure a tranquil and relaxing atmosphere
and a comfortable stay.*
5rm(3⇩2↑) ® ✗ ✻ dB&B⇩↑£40-£46
Lic ♛ CTV 7P nc10yrs ⊿ ♪(hard)croquet

BEAMISH Co Durham Map **12** NZ25

GH QQ *Coppy Lodge* Coppy Farm, Beamish Lodge DH6 0RQ
☎Stanley(0207) 231479
*This one-time cow byre and dairy is now an attractive guesthouse
with particularly well-appointed bedrooms. It is situated in
Beamish Park and is close to the golf club and the Beamish Open
Air Museum.*
6rm(2⇩4↑) TV available ® LDO 9pm
Lic ♛ 40P ∪ snooker

BEATTOCK Dumfries & Galloway *Dumfriesshire*
Map **11** NT00

FH QQ Mr & Mrs Bell *Cogrie's* (*NY106974*) DG10 9PP (3m S
off A74) ☎Johnstone Bridge(05764) 320
Mar-Nov
*Although this farm has direct access from the A47, visitors will be
impressed by the peaceful location of this house. Attractive,
comfortable accommodation is complemented by a very hospitable
proprietress.*
4hc (3fb)✗in all bedrooms ® ✗ LDO 6pm
♛ CTV 6P 275 acres dairy mixed

BEAULY Highland *Inverness-Shire* Map **14** NH54

⊢⊶**GH QQ** Arkton Hotel Westend IY4 7BT ☎(0463) 782388
*Close to the village square, this small guesthouse caters mostly for
the touring holidaymaker. It has a friendly atmosphere and offers
good value, practical accommodation.*
8hc (1fb) CTV in 1 bedroom ® sB&B£12.50-£25
dB&B£25-£32 WB&B£84-£105 WBDi£140-£175
Lic ♛ CTV 8P
£

GH QQQ Chrialdon Hotel Station Rd IV4 7EH
☎Inverness(0463) 782336
*This substantial, sandstone house has bedrooms furnished in a
pleasing blend of traditional and modern styles and two lounges in
which to relax.*
7rm(1⇩2↑4hc)(2fb) CTV in all bedrooms ®
✗ (ex guide dogs) sB&B£14.30-£17.60 dB&B£28.60-£35.20
dB&B⇩↑£32.60-£39.20 WB&B£100.10-£123.20
WBDi£163.10-£186.20 LDO 7.30pm
Lic ♛ CTV 15P

⊢⊶**GH QQQ** Heathmount Station Rd IV4 7EQ
☎(0463) 782411
Closed Xmas & New Year

---

*Comfortable accommodation and a friendly atmosphere are to be
found in this neatly appointed Victorian villa.*
5hc (2fb) CTV in all bedrooms ® sB&B£12-£12.50
dB&B£24-£25 WB&B£84-£87.50
♛ CTV 5P

FH QQQ Mrs M R Munro **Thornhill** (*NH531475*) IV4 7AS
☎(0463) 782338
May-Sep
*A modernised, bungalow-style farmhouse in a secluded setting
offering compact, tastefully decorated and furnished bedrooms and
public rooms.*
3hc ✗ sB&B£12-£15 dB&B£22-£24 WB&B£70-£75
♛ CTV 3P 3🏠 nc9yrs 100 acres arable mixed
£

BEAUMARIS Gwynedd Map **06** SH67

GH QQ Sea View 10 West End LL58 8BG ☎(0248) 810384
Closed Xmas
*This small and friendly hotel has a welcoming atmosphere and
enjoys excellent views across the Menai Straits to Snowdonia. The
accommodation is well maintained and comfortable, and smoking
is now prohibited in all areas.*
6hc ✗in all bedrooms ✗ ✻ sB&B£15-£16
dB&B£26-£28 LDO 2pm
CTV 5P nc10yrs

BEDALE North Yorkshire Map **08** SE28

See also **Hunton** and **Patrick Brompton**

FH QQQ Mrs D I Knox **Blairgowrie Country House**
(*SE241921*) Crakehall DL8 1JZ ☎Richmond(0748) 811377
Closed New Year
*Surrounded by fields and meadows and its own neat garden, this
charming country house provides traditional warmth and
hospitality. It stands north of Crakehall village – follow signs for
Hackford at the bridge; after a mile, turn right for Langthorne,
and Blairgowrie is a few hundred yards along on the right.*
2rm(1↑1hc)✗in all bedrooms ® ✗ ✻
dB&B↑£28-£30 WB&Bfr£90
♛ CTV 6P nc16yrs ✓ 3 acres small holding

BEDFORD Bedfordshire Map **04** TL04

GH QQ Clarendon House Hotel 25/27 Ampthill Rd MK42 9JP
☎(0234) 266054
Closed 24 Dec-2 Jan
*The accommodation at this small private hotel is basic and nicely
equipped. A short dinner menu offers mainly English cuisine.*
17rm(13↑4hc) CTV in all bedrooms ® ✗ (ex guide dogs)
sB&B£21.50 sB&B↑£29.50-£33.50
dB&B↑£35.50-£43 LDO 7.45pm
Lic ♛ CTV 15P
Credit Cards 1 2 3 5 £

GH QQ Hertford House Hotel 57 De Parys Av MK40 2TR
☎(0234) 50007 & 54470
Closed 24 Dec-2 Jan
*A friendly, informal atmosphere prevails at this privately owned
establishment. The bedrooms are adequately appointed and the
small first floor breakfast room serves a good, freshly cooked
breakfast.*
16rm(5⇩2↑9hc)(2fb) CTV in all bedrooms ® ✻
sB&B£30-£32.50 sB&B⇩↑£37.50-£42.50 dB&B£40-£45
dB&B⇩↑£50-£60
♛ CTV 4P
Credit Cards 1 2 3 5 £

GH QQQ Kimbolton Hotel 78 Clapham Rd MK41 7PN
☎(0234) 54854
Closed 25-31 Dec

This small private commercial hotel is personally supervised by the proprietors and has a friendly, informal atmosphere. It provides pleasant, basic accommodation.
14rm(3⇨11♠) CTV in all bedrooms ® ✠
sB&B⇨♠£36.80-£39.10
dB&B⇨♠£46-£50.60 WB&Bfr£246 LDO 8.30pm
Lic ㎐ CTV 15P nc3yrs
Credit Cards ① ② ③

BEER Devon Map **03** SY28

⊢⊶**GH ◨ Bay View** Fore St EX12 3EE ☎Seaton(0297) 20489
Etr-mid Nov
Property at the end of the village overlooking the beach and sea.
6hc (1fb) ® sB&B£10.50-£15 dB&B£21-£30 WB&B£73-£76
㎐ CTV ⋆ nc5yrs
ⓕ

BEERCROCOMBE Somerset Map **03** ST32

SELECTED

FH ◨◨◨◨ Mrs V A Cole **Frog Street Farm**
(ST317197) Frog St TA3 6AF
☎Hatch Beauchamp(0823) 480430
Mar-Nov
This ancient Somerset longhouse has an outdoor pool in the sheltered garden, and is convenient for Taunton and the M5. The 3 tastefully decorated bedrooms all offer en suite facilities, whilst 3 comfortable lounges have character, with beams and inglenook fireplaces. Veronica Cole serves excellent home-cooked fare at one large dinner table. The house won the Farmhouse of the Year award in 1988.
3rm(2⇨1♠) ® ⋆ sB&B⇨♠£20-£22
dB&B⇨♠£40-£44 WB&B£126-£140 WBDif£196-£210
LDO 2pm
㎐ CTV 0P nc11yrs ⌒(heated) 160 acres dairy mixed stud
ⓕ
See advertisement under TAUNTON on page 355

SELECTED

FH ◨◨◨◨ Mr & Mrs Mitchem **Whittles** *(ST324194)*
TA3 6AH ☎Hatch Beauchamp(0823) 480301
The Mitcham family give a warm welcome in their ivy-clad farmhouse, which has easy access to the country town and motorway interchange. Their emphasis on quality and good taste is reflected in the very high standard of accommodation offered. The 3 centrally heated bedrooms have en suite bathrooms and colour televisions, and are complemented by a snug lounge. Dinner is served on 3 nights of each week.
3⇨ CTV in all bedrooms ® ✠ ✳ sB&B⇨♠£25-£27.50
dB&B⇨♠£38-£41 WB&B£130-£182 LDO 6.30pm(previous day)
Lic ㎐ 4P nc12yrs 200 acres beef dairy

BEESTON Nottinghamshire Map **08** SK53

GH ◨ Brackley House Hotel 31 Elm Av NG9 1BU
☎Nottingham(0602) 251787
Closed Xmas & New Year
A continental atmosphere prevails at this well-furnished guesthouse set in a quiet side road. Good, all-round facilities are provided.
15rm(12⇨3hc)(1fb) CTV in all bedrooms ® ✠ ✳
sB&Bfr£25 sB&B⇨♠fr£30 dB&Bfr£55
dB&B⇨♠fr£60 LDO 8.15pm
Lic ㎐ CTV 15P nc9yrs ⌒(heated) sauna
Credit Cards ① ② ③ ⓕ

See advertisement on page 61

GH Q Fairhaven Private Hotel 19 Meadow Rd NG9 1JP
☎Nottingham(0602) 227509
Closed 25-26 Dec
Large house 3.5 miles south west of Nottingham and close to
Beeston Station. Simple but comfortable accommodation.
10hc (1fb) ✱ sB&B£16.50-£20
dB&B£25-£30 WB&B£87.50-£133 WBDi£115.50-£161 LDO
2pm
Lic ♒ CTV 12P

BELL BUSK North Yorkshire Map **07** SD95

GH QQ Tudor BD23 4DT ☎Airton(07293) 301
mid Feb-mid Nov
This friendly, hospitable little guesthouse by the Settle-Carlisle
line was once Bell Busk Station.
4rm(1♠3hc)(1fb) ® ✱ (ex guide dogs) ✱ sB&B£12
dB&B£24-£26 dB&B♠£29 WB&B£75-£90 WBDi£131-£146
Lic ♒ CTV 6P games room
£

BELTON Leicestershire Map **04** SK80

FH QQQ Mrs S L Renner *Old Rectory (SK814008)*
LE15 9LE ☎Belton In Rutland(057286) 279
Lovely old house incorporating a rural museum, craft shop, a
miniature farm and a children's play area.
1♠ Annexe 6♠ CTV in 4 bedrooms ® LDO 9.30pm
Lic lift ♒ CTV 6P 6🐾 30 acres pastural

BEPTON (nr Midhurst) West Sussex Map **04** SU81

SELECTED

GH QQQQ The Park House Hotel GU29 0JB
☎Midhurst(073081) 2880 FAX (073081) 5643
The main section of this delightful country hotel dates back to
the 1600s, and the charm and tranquility of the hotel is
enhanced by extensive, beautiful rural views and well-kept
gardens which include grass tennis courts, croquet and an
outdoor swimming pool. The bedrooms are tastefully
decorated and, in many cases, furnished with antiques.
Modern facilities are provided to add to the guests' comfort
and relaxation. There is a spacious and elegant drawing room,
charming dining room and separate hospitality lounge. Service
is willing and friendly.
10rm(8⇌2♠)Annexe 2⇌ CTV in 10 bedrooms ®
sB&B⇌♠fr£46
dB&B⇌♠fr£82 WB&Bfr£362 WBDifr£476 LDO noon
Lic ♒ CTV 25P ⚐(heated) ♬(grass)
Credit Cards [1][3]
See advertisement under MIDHURST on page 261

BERKELEY Gloucestershire Map **03** ST69

FH QQ Mrs B A Evans **Green Acres** *(ST713008)*
Breadstone GL13 9HF (2m W off A38) ☎Dursley(0453) 810348
Closed 4 Dec-2 Jan
New Cotswold stone-built farmhouse in rural surroundings.
3rm(1⇌2♠)⊁in all bedrooms ® ✱ ✱
sB&B⇌♠£14.50-£18.50
dB&B⇌♠£30-£33 WB&B£99.50-£110.50
♒ CTV 10P nc10yrs snooker 47 acres horse breeding

BERRYNARBOR Devon Map **02** SS54

GH QQ The Lodge Country House Hotel EX34 9SG
(Berrynarbor 1.5m W of A399) ☎Combe Martin(0271) 883246
Closed Xmas
8rm(1⇌3♠4hc)(2fb) CTV in all bedrooms ®
sB&B£13.50-£16.50 dB&B£27-£33
dB&B⇌♠£32-£38 WB&B£81-£99 WBDi£120-£140 LDO 6pm
Lic ♒ 8P nc2yrs 9 hole putting

£
See advertisement under COMBE MARTIN

BETHESDA Gwynedd Map **06** SH66

⊢⊶**FH Q** Mrs D Williams **Maes Caradog** *(SH635626)* Nant
Ffrancon LL57 3DQ ☎(0248) 600266
This small, stone-built traditional farmhouse is over 100 years old,
and is situated amidst rugged and spectacular mountain scenery,
only 3 miles south of Bethesda. It provides simple, comfortable
accommodation and is ideal for the climbers and walkers which
this area attracts.
2hc (1fb) ® sB&B£10-£11
dB&B£20-£22 WB&B£70-£72 LDO 6pm
♒ CTV 12P 636 acres sheep

BETLEY Staffordshire Map **07** SJ74

FH QQQ Mrs S Berrisford *Adderley Green (SJ775474)*
Heighley Castle Ln CW3 98A ☎Crewe(0270) 820203
Closed 24-26 Dec
An elegant and very comfortable Georgian farmhouse surrounded
by 250 acres of pastureland, the home of the Beresford family, is
reached by a narrow, winding lane off the A531 (signposted Cook
Gate and Shraley Brook) though it is only 10 minutes' drive from
junction 16 of the M6.
3rm(1♠2hc)(1fb) CTV in all bedrooms ® LDO previous day
♒ CTV 6P 3🐎 (50p per night) ♨ ♩ snooker/pool table 250
acres dairy, mixed

BETTISCOMBE Dorset Map **03** ST30

GH QQQ Marshwood Manor DT6 5NS
☎Bridport(0308) 68442
Mar-Nov
A 19th-century country manor house set in 10 acres of well-kept
grounds. The rooms are all elegantly decorated and home-cooked
food, using local produce, is served in the dining room.
8rm(5⇌♠3hc)(5fb) CTV in all bedrooms ® ✱
sB&B⇌♠£50 dB&B⇌♠fr£60 (incl dinner) WBDifr£170
Lic ♒ 15P ⚐croquet putting
See advertisement under BRIDPORT

BETWS-Y-COED Gwynedd Map **06** SH75

⊢⊶**GH QQQ The Ferns** LL24 0AN ☎(06902) 587
On the A5 close to the village centre, this well-maintained house
provides modern accommodation, some bedrooms having en suite
facilities. The Ferns has the advantage of its own car park.
5rm(3♠2hc)(2fb) CTV in 3 bedrooms ® sB&B£12-£15
dB&B£22-£26
dB&B♠£26-£32 WB&B£77-£105 WBDi£168-£196 LDO
breakfast
♒ CTV 6P nc3yrs

GH QQQ Glenwood LL24 0BN ☎(06902) 508
Etr-Nov
Set back from the main road in its own gardens, this delightful
house enjoys beautiful forest views to the rear. Furnishings are of a
high standard and the resident owners are delightful hosts.
6hc (3fb) ✱
♒ CTV 18P nc4yrs

SELECTED

GH QQQQ Tan-y-Foel LL26 0RE 3m SE ☎(06902) 507
16 Feb-14 Jan
Tan-y-Foel is a 16th-century manor house perched high on a
hillside, and is being lovingly restored by Hazel and Barrie
Michael. The views are outstanding, and there are spectacular
views of Snowdonia from the grounds. Peace, tranquility and
hospitality are made perfect by the good dinners – there is a
set menu – which are served at a huge refectory table in what

was the original dairy. Tan-y-Foel was the winner for Wales of the AA's Best Newcomer Award for 1989/90.

6➪🛏 ⨂in 3 bedrooms ® ✠ (ex guide dogs)
sB&B➪🛏£40-£50
dB&B➪🛏£55-£60 WB&B£192.50-£210 WBDi£280-£295
LDO 6.30pm
Lic ♨ 10P 6🚗 nc14yrs ▣(heated) ♪ ∪ snooker croquet

See advertisement on page 63

GH|Q|Q|Q| *Tyn-Y-Celyn* Llanrwst Rd LL24 0HD
☎(06902) 202
30 Mar-2 Jan
Situated just north of Betws-y-Coed, on the A470, this is a small but well-maintained, family-run hotel. The bedrooms are well equipped and all have en suite facilities.
8rm(2➪6🛏)(2fb) CTV in all bedrooms ®
Lic ♨ CTV 10P

FH|Q| Mrs E Jones *Maes-y-Garnedd (SH816584)* LL26 0RR
(3m E unclass off A470) ☎(06902) 428
Apr-Sep
A 19th-century house in a working farm situated close to the town.
2rm(1➪1hc)(1fb) ✠
CTV 2P 153 acres beef mixed sheep

BEXHILL East Sussex Map 05 TQ70

▷━GH|Q|Q| **The Arosa** 6 Albert Rd TN40 1DG
☎(0424) 212574
A warm welcome is offered by the proprietors of this hotel, which is conveniently situated for the shops, the seafront and the centre of town. Pleasant accommodation is provided, as well as home-style cooking and personal service.
▶

Green Acres Farm
Breadstone, Berkeley, Glos
Tel: Dursley (0453) 810348

New Cotswold stone built house set in beautiful Berkeley Vale twixt Cotswolds & River Severn. Beautiful views. Tastefully furnished. Every convenience, warm welcome. Ideal for touring Cotswolds, Forest of Dean and Bath. Visit Berkeley Castle, Severnvale Wild Fowl, Gloucester Waterways Museum. Horse riding can be arranged. Many good eating places in the area. Cottage also available.

TY'N-Y-CELYN HOUSE

Betws-Y-Coed
Llanrwst Road (A470), Gwynedd, LL24 0HD
Tel: 06902 202

This spacious Victorian Guest House overlooks picturesque village of Betws-y-Coed and has beautiful scenic views of the Llugwy Valley. There are eight bedrooms completely and tastefully re-furnished. Each one has CTV, beverage makers, central heating, en-suite facilities, etc.

You are assured of warm welcome by Maureen and Clive Muskus, comfortable accommodation and robust breakfast.

Brackley House Hotel

New Cotswold stone...

Hildegard's German Restaurant & Bar
31 Elm Avenue, Beeston, Nottingham NG9 1BU
Telephone: 0602 251787 Fax: 0602 256739

First class accommodation at reasonable prices. Colour TV, video system, satellite TV in all rooms. Sauna, outdoor heated swimming pool, large gardens and private car park. Conferences, wedding receptions catered for.
BTB, AVD of Germany listed.

9rm(2⇆🏠7hc)(1fb) CTV in all bedrooms ® ✠ (ex guide dogs)
sB&B£13-£15 sB&B⇆🏠£18-£20 dB&B£22-£26
dB&B⇆🏠£34-£38 WB&B£70-£85 WBDi£112-£120 (wkly only
Oct-Feb) LDO noon ⊞ CTV ⚓ ⓔ

BEYTON Suffolk Map 05 TL96

FH ⓠⓠ Mrs E Nicholson **The Grange** *(TL940632)* IP30 9AG
☎(0359) 70184
*Centrally located towards the village green, this farmhouse stands
in its own well-maintained grounds. It offers a peaceful retreat with
spacious, comfortable rooms, one, with en suite facilities, enjoying
ground floor access.*
3rm(1⇆1🏠1hc)(1fb)⚲in all bedrooms CTV in 1 bedroom ®
✠ (ex guide dogs) sB&B£14 sB&B⇆🏠£16 dB&B£28
dB&B⇆🏠£32 LDO By arrangement
⊞ CTV 3P 6 acres hens horses pigs ⓔ

BICKINGTON (nr Ashburton) Devon Map 03 SX77

SELECTED

FH ⓠⓠⓠⓠ Mrs E A Ross **East Burne** *(SX799711)*
TQ12 6PA ☎Bickington(0626) 821496
Closed Xmas & New Year
*Mr and Mrs Ross provide a friendly and relaxed atmosphere
in their south Devon farmhouse home which has medieval
origins. The bedrooms are well-decorated and comfortable
with good quality attractive furnishings. The sitting room and
dining room are full of character – ideal for sitting down to
discuss the day's events or plan the next. The set 4-course
dinner is served at 7pm . The food is simple, honestly prepared
home cooking and is attractively presented. Several of the
barns outside have been sympathetically converted to self-
catering accommodation and a well-fenced outdoor heated
swimming pool is an added attraction. East Burne Farm is an
ideal centre from which to tour Dartmoor and south Devon so
it is essential to book.*
3rm(2🏠1hc) ® ✠ (ex guide dogs) ✳ sB&Bfr£15
sB&B🏠fr£15 dB&Bfr£25
dB&B🏠fr£25 WB&Bfr£85 LDO 24hrs notice
CTV 8P ⌂(heated) 40 acres beef mixed sheep ⓔ

FH ⓠⓠ Mrs J Birkenhead **Gale Farm** *(SX795716)* TQ12 6PG
☎Bickington(0626) 821273
3rm(1hc) CTV in 1 bedroom TV in 1 bedroom ® ✳
sB&Bfr£12.50 dB&Bfr£23 LDO 5pm CTV 4P sauna 5 acres ⓔ

BIDEFORD Devon Map 02 SS42

See also Westward Ho
⟻GH ⓠ **Kumba** Chudleigh Road, East-the-Water EX39 4AR
☎(0237) 471526
*Set in an elevated position overlooking the River Torridge, this
family-run guesthouse has comfortable bedrooms and provides set
meals.*
9rm(1⇆3🏠5hc)(5fb)⚲in 2 bedrooms CTV in 4 bedrooms ®
sB&B£13-£15 sB&B⇆🏠£14-£17 dB&B£24-£26
dB&B⇆🏠£28-£32 WB&B£80-£100 WBDi£130-£150
Lic CTV 14P 2🏠 oᴐ putting green ⓔ

GH ⓠⓠ **Mount Private Hotel** Northdown Rd EX39 3LP
☎(0237) 473748
*Standing in its semi-walled garden this Georgian building of
character is close to the town centre and quay. Comfortable
accommodation is provided here together with a warm welcome
and a relaxing atmosphere.*
8rm(1⇆4🏠3hc)(2fb)⚲in all bedrooms ® ✠ (ex guide dogs)
sB&B£18.50-£23 sB&B⇆🏠£20-£23 dB&B£32-£39
dB&B⇆🏠£36-£39 WB&B£100-£160 WBDi£154-£210 LDO
5pm Lic ⊞ CTV 4P nc5yrs Credit Cards ①③ ⓔ

Best
Newcomer Award
1989-1990

Tan-y-Foel,
Capel Garmon, Betws-y-Coed.
Telephone: 06902 507
0690 710507

EXTRACT FROM LAST YEARS INSPECTORS REPORT

"Tan-y-Foel - "the house under the hillside" - stands in a remote and tranquil setting amidst steep wooded valleys in North Wales, where you can exchange noise and traffic for clear air, sparkling rivers and spectacular views towards the sea or Snowdonia.

Barrie and Hazel Michael have opened their 16th-century home to guests who wish to spend a peaceful break in comfortable surroundings - whether they simply want to relax or whether their interests lie in walking, bird-watching or, like Barrie, before he turned his full attention to the guesthouse, photography.

The real hallmark of Tan-y-Foel. however, is its informality. The Michael's are perfect hosts, as is apparent from the welcome pot of tea with which they greet their guests, and the generous measures of pre-dinner drinks they serve; their sense of humour is infectious.

The comfortable bedrooms all have en-suite bathrooms and are thoughtfully furnished with extras such as a hairdryer, disposable razors, a sewing kit and even spare toothbrushes for the forgetful!

Dinner is served in the former dairy, now transformed and featuring a dark polished refectory table, purchased from a monastery.

Whenever possible, vegetables for the evening's menu come from the well-stocked gardens of Tan-y-Foel and a typical menu might include home-grown asparagus, boeuf en croûte with fresh vegetables and strawberry gâteau.

Breakfast is equally plentiful to set you up for the day ahead, whether it is spent exploring the surrounding mountains of Snowdonia, or less strenuously, relaxing within the 88 acres at Tan-y-Foel, at the antique billiard table, in the heated indoor pool or reading by a roaring log fire in the library."

GH |Q||Q||Q| **Pines at Eastleigh** Old Barnstaple Rd, Eastleigh
EX39 4PA (3m E off A39 at East-the-Water)
☎Instow(0271) 860561
*Surrounded by gardens on the edge of the village approximately 4
miles from Bideford, this 200-year-old house has comfortable and
elegant accommodation. A choice of home-cooked meals is
available in the restaurant. The resident proprietors assure good
service.*
6rm(1⇨2♠3hc)Annexe 2♠ (3fb) ⓡ sB&B£18-£20
sB&B⇨♠£22-£26 dB&B£32-£36
dB&B⇨♠£40-£44 WB&B£96-£126 WBDi£165-£198 LDO
5pm Lic ⊠ CTV 12P Art courses Credit Cards |1||3| ⓔ

BILLINGSHURST West Sussex Map **04** TQ02

GH |Q| **Newstead Hall** Adversane RH14 9JH ☎(0403) 783196 &
784734
*Situated in a pleasant district with good access, this older style
house has a new wing with bedrooms offering modern
accommodation. It also has a lounge, small bar and restaurant.*
17⇨♠ CTV in all bedrooms ⓡ ✟ (ex guide dogs) ✷
sB&B⇨♠£25-£45 dB&B⇨♠£35-£65
WB&B£167-£283 WBDi£232-£346 LDO 9pm Lic ⊠ 26P
Credit Cards |1||2||3||5| ⓔ

SELECTED

FH |Q||Q||Q||Q| Mrs M Mitchell **Old Wharf** *(TQ070256)*
Wharf Farm, Newbridge RH14 0JG ☎(0403) 784096
*Peacefully set amid wooded farmland, this converted
warehouse was built in 1839 and has been elegantly
modernised yet retains its original features and charm. The
individually designed bedrooms are all well equipped, and the
superb sitting room is complemented by a separate breakfast
room. Guests here receive enthusiastic and friendly service.*
4⇨♠ ✟in all bedrooms CTV in all bedrooms ⓡ ✟ ✷
sB&B⇨♠£40 dB&B⇨♠£50-£70
⊠ CTV 6P nc12yrs ✦ 200 acres beef sheep
Credit Cards |1||2||3|

BINGLEY West Yorkshire Map **07** SE13

GH |Q||Q||Q| **Hall Bank Private Hotel** Beck Ln BD16 4DD
☎Bradford(0274) 565296
Closed Xmas
*Set in its own grounds, this hotel is in an elevated situation on the
side of the Aire Valley. It is well furnished throughout, with good
facilities in the bedrooms, a comfortable lounge, a games room and
a sun lounge.*
10rm(9⇨♠1hc)(2fb) CTV in all bedrooms ⓡ ✟
sB&B⇨♠£30-£35 dB&B⇨♠£40-£46 WB&B£200-£230 LDO
7.30pm Lic ⊠ CTV 20P nc4yrs games room ⓔ

BIRKENHEAD Merseyside Map **07** SJ38

GH |Q| **Gronwen** 11 Willowbank Rd, Devonshire Park L42 7JU
☎051-652 8306
Pleasantly furnished small guesthouse set in quiet residential area.
6hc (1fb) CTV in all bedrooms ⓡ sB&B£15
dB&B£26 WB&B£84 WBDi£110 LDO 7.30pm ⊠ CTV ✗

BIRMINGHAM West Midlands Map **07** SP08

See Town Plan Section
See also Rowley Regis & Warley
GH |Q| **Awentsbury Hotel** 21 Serpentine Rd, Selly Park
B29 7HU ☎021-472 1258 FAX 021-428 1527
*Standing in a quiet residential area close to the university,
Awentsbury has bedrooms which are simply furnished with good
facilities.*
16rm(5♠11hc)(2fb) CTV in all bedrooms ⓡ sB&B£22
sB&B♠£32 dB&B£36 dB&B♠£44 WBDi£183-£273 LDO 6pm
⊠ 13P Credit Cards |1||3| ⓔ

GH |Q||Q| **Beech House Hotel** 21 Gravelly Hill North,
Erdington B23 6BT ☎021-373 0620
Closed Xmas & New Year 2 wks
*A few minutes' drive from 'Spaghetti Junction' on the M6, this
hotel has comfortable bedrooms and 2 lounges. The resident
proprietor pays personal attention to all guests.*
10rm(3⇨♠7hc)(2fb) CTV in all bedrooms ⓡ ✷
sB&B£25.30-£27.50 sB&B⇨♠£32.20-£34.20
dB&B£39.10-£41.20
dB&B⇨♠£46-£48 WB&B£177.10-£192.50
WBDi£256.20-£271.60 LDO noon
⊠ CTV 10P nc5yrs Credit Cards |1||3|

GH |Q||Q||Q| **Bridge House Hotel** 49 Sherbourne Rd, Acocks
Green B27 6DX ☎021-706 5900
Closed Xmas & New Year
*With easy access to the airport and National Exhibition Centre,
this hotel has rooms with modern facilities. The Hopwood family
have this year added a 'Movie Bar' as part of their improvements.*
30rm(2⇨28♠) CTV in all bedrooms ⓡ ✷
sB&B⇨♠£22-£25.40 dB&B⇨♠£35-£40.25 LDO 8.30pm
Lic ⊠ CTV 48P Credit Cards |1||2||3|

GH |Q| **Cape Race Hotel** 929 Chester Rd, Erdington B24 0HJ
☎021-373 3085
*Conveniently placed for access to the M5, M6, NEC and the city
centre, this hotel has its own outdoor swimming pool and tennis
court. The rooms, although limited for space, are well equipped
and the proprietors' personal service is assured.*
9rm(6♠3hc) CTV in all bedrooms ⓡ ✟ (ex guide dogs)
sB&B£25-£30 sB&B♠£30 dB&B£35-£38
dB&B♠£38-£42 LDO 8.30pm
Lic ⊠ CTV 15P ◢(heated) ℘(hard)
Credit Cards |1||3| ⓔ

GH |Q||Q| **Heath Lodge Hotel** Coleshill Road, Marston Green
B37 7HT ☎021-779 2218
*This hotel, located 1.5 miles from the NEC and airport, has easy
access to the Midlands motorway network. Some of the rooms and
shower rooms are compact, but there is a comfortable television
lounge and a small bar.*
12rm(6♠6hc)(2fb) CTV in all bedrooms ⓡ ✷ sB&Bfr£26
sB&B♠fr£32 dB&Bfr£37 dB&B♠fr£45 LDO 8.30pm
Lic ⊠ CTV 15P
Credit Cards |1||2||3| ⓔ

GH |Q| *Hurstwood Hotel* 775-777 Chester Rd, Erdington
B24 0BY ☎021-382 8212
*This small hotel has a regular clientele, so it is important to book
well in advance.*
10♠ (2fb) CTV in all bedrooms ⓡ ✟ (ex guide dogs) LDO
8.30pm
Lic ⊠ CTV 15P pool table
Credit Cards |1||2||3||5|

GH |Q| **The Linden Lodge Hotel** 79 Sutton Road, Erdington
B23 5XA ☎021-382 5992
*With separate lounges for smokers and non-smokers, this friendly
household provides simple accommodation.*
6hc (1fb) CTV in 1 bedroom ✟ ✷ sB&Bfr£13 ⊠ CTV 8P

GH |Q||Q| **Lyndhurst Hotel** 135 Kingsbury Road, Erdington
B24 8QT ☎021-373 5695
*Popular with commercial guests, this centrally situated guesthouse
is within easy reach of 'Spaghetti Junction'. Accommodation is
modest and well kept, several of the rooms having en suite showers.*
14rm(1⇨9♠4hc)(3fb) CTV in all bedrooms ⓡ
✟ (ex guide dogs) sB&B£27.50-£32.50
sB&B⇨♠£32.50-£35.75 dB&B£39.50-£43.50
dB&B⇨♠£43.50-£47.50 WB&B£170-£200 WBDi£240-£270
LDO 8.15pm
Lic ⊠ CTV 15P
Credit Cards |1||2||3||5| ⓔ

GH 🅀🅀 **Robin Hood Lodge Hotel** 142 Robin Hood Ln, Hall Green B28 0JX ☎️021-778 5307

Standing on the A4040, 5 miles from the city centre, this establishment has well-equipped bedrooms, most of which have shower units. Annexe accommodation is provided in a nearby house.

7rm(1⇋2🅵4hc)(1fb) CTV in all bedrooms ® ✱ sB&B£21 sB&B⇋🅵£25 dB&B£38-£42 dB&B⇋🅵£45-£50 LDO 7.30pm
Lic ▦ CTV 11P
Credit Cards 1 3 5 £

GH 🅀🅀 **Rollason Wood Hotel** 130 Wood End Road, Erdington B24 8BJ ☎️021-373 1230

35rm(1⇋10🅵24hc)(4fb) CTV in all bedrooms ®
sB&B£15.70-£22 sB&B⇋🅵£27-£32 dB&B£26.40-£38.50 dB&B⇋🅵£37-£46 WB&B£108-£187 LDO 9pm
Lic ▦ CTV 35P games room
Credit Cards 1 2 3 5

GH 🅀 **Tri-Star Hotel** Coventry Road, Elmdon B26 3QR ☎️021-782 1010 & 021-782 6131

Conveniently situated on the A45, midway between the National Exhibition Centre and airport, this privately owned guesthouse has simple and well-maintained accommodation.

15rm(2🅵13hc)(3fb) CTV in all bedrooms ® ✈ ✱
sB&B£27.60-£41.40 sB&B🅵£41.40 dB&B£39.10-£46 dB&B🅵£46 LDO 8pm
Lic ▦ CTV 25P pool table
Credit Cards 3

GH 🅀🅀 *Willow Tree Hotel* 759 Chester Rd, Erdington B24 0BY ☎️021-373 6388

rs Xmas

This is a pleasant guesthouse enjoying easy access to the town centre. The accommodation is well kept, with a good array of modern facilities. The house has a friendly atmosphere created by the hospitable proprietor.

7rm(5🅵2hc)(2fb) CTV in all bedrooms ® ✈ LDO 8pm
Lic ▦ CTV 7P
Credit Cards 1 3

BISHAMPTON Hereford & Worcester Map 03 SO95

SELECTED

FH 🅀🅀🅀🅀 Mrs H K Robertson *Nightingale* *(SO988512)* WR10 2NN ☎️Evesham(0386) 82384

The Midlands winner of the AA's 'Best Newcomer' award for 1988/89 continues to maintain its high standards, with comfortable, attractively furnished accommodation with good facilities. There are 2 delightful lounge areas, with excellent seating, fresh flowers, magazines and books, and the restaurant has earned a good local reputation. Equally suited to tourists and business travellers (small meetings can be accommodated), Nightingale Farm is welcoming and comfortable, and Mr and Mrs Robertson are excellent hosts.

3⇋(1fb) CTV in all bedrooms ® ✈ (wkly only Oct-Mar) LDO 9pm
Lic ▦ 20P nc6yrs snooker 200 acres arable beef
Credit Cards 1 3

BISHOP'S CLEEVE Gloucestershire Map 03 SO92

GH 🅀 **The Old Manor House** 43 Station Rd GL52 4HH ☎️(024267) 4127

6hc (3fb) ® ✈ ✱ sB&Bfr£18.50 dB&Bfr£29
CTV 8P ↻

This guide is updated annually – make sure you use an up-to-date edition.

BISHOP'S STORTFORD Hertfordshire Map 05 TL42

GH 🅀🅀 **Cottage** 71 Birchanger Ln, Birchanger CM23 5QF ☎️(0279) 812349

Carefully modernised to retain its character, this late 17th-century cottage stands in attractive gardens and provides warm, comfortable accommodation including a pretty dining room and panelled lounge.

10rm(8🅵1hc)⊁in all bedrooms CTV in all bedrooms ®
✈ (ex guide dogs) ✱ sB&B🅵£28
dB&B🅵£40 WB&B£133-£186.20 WBDi£185.20-£238.70 LDO 9.30am
Lic ▦ 10P croquet
Credit Cards 1 £

BISHOPSTON West Glamorgan Map 02 SS58

See also Langland Bay and **Mumbles**

GH 🅀🅀🅀 *Winston Hotel* 11 Church Ln, Bishopston Valley SA3 3JC ☎️(044128) 2074

Closed 24-29 Dec

An indoor swimming pool and a snooker table are available to guests at this hotel which is run by the friendly Clarke family. Set in a lovely wooded valley, it offers pretty bedrooms which are well equipped, and comfortable lounges.

14rm(3🅵3hc)Annexe 5rm(4⇋1🅵)(2fb) CTV in 5 bedrooms ® LDO 10.30am
Lic ▦ CTV 20P ◳(heated) snooker sauna solarium
Credit Cards 1 3

BLACKPOOL Lancashire Map 07 SD33

See Town Plan Section

GH 🅀🅀 *Arosa Hotel* 18-20 Empress Dr FY2 9SA ☎️(0253) 52555

Apr-Nov & Xmas

In a residential area close to the seafront, this friendly hotel offers pleasant, well-maintained accommodation.

21rm(4⇋17🅵)(7fb) CTV in all bedrooms ® LDO 4pm
Lic ▦ CTV 7P

GH 🅀🅀 **Ashcroft Private Hotel** 42 King Edward Av FY2 9TA ☎️(0253) 51538

Close to the promenade, this privately managed guesthouse offers neat accommodation and personal service.

10hc (3fb) ® ✈ (ex guide dogs) ✱ sB&B£14-£15.50 dB&B£28-£31 WB&B£95-£105 WBDi£114-£125 LDO 2pm
Lic ▦ CTV 3P 1🐾
£

GH 🅀🅀🅀 **Berwick Private Hotel** 23 King Edward Av FY2 9TA ☎️(0253) 51496

Closed 29 Dec-11 Jan

Set in a quiet side road, this is a modern, well-furnished hotel with friendly atmosphere.

8rm(4🅵4hc)(1fb) ® ✈ dB&B£26-£30
dB&B🅵£28-£32 (incl dinner) WB&B£77-£85 WBDi£91-£99 LDO 3pm
Lic ▦ CTV 4P nc3yrs

GH 🅀🅀 **Brooklands Hotel** 28-30 King Edward Av FY2 9TA ☎️(0253) 51479

Situated close to Queen's Promenade, this friendly, family-run small hotel offers well-maintained accommodation which includes a neat dining room and a comfortable lounge with a small bar.

18rm(9🅵9hc)(3fb) CTV in all bedrooms ® ✈ (ex guide dogs) sB&B£14-£15 dB&B£28-£30
dB&B🅵£34-£36 WB&B£98-£105 WBDi£112-£133 LDO 3.30pm
Lic ▦ CTV 5P
£

GH QQ **Burlees Hotel** 40 Knowle Av FY2 9TQ
☎(0253) 54535
Feb-Nov
Situated in a quiet, pleasant residential road, this guesthouse,
which is well cared for, is only a short walk from the promenade.
Smart modern shower rooms have been added to the bedrooms.
10rm(7🟊3hc)(2fb) CTV in 7 bedrooms ® ✖ sB&B£14-£16.50
sB&B🟊£16.75-£19.50 dB&B£28-£33
dB&B🟊£33.50-£39 WB&B£93.10-£128 WBDi£133-£170 LDO
4pm
Lic ⁗ CTV 5P 1🐾
Credit Cards [1][3] £

⊢⊶GH QQ **Cliff Head Hotel** 174 Queens Promenade,
Bispham FY2 9JN ☎(0253) 591086
This neat and well-maintained property enjoys sea views, is
situated at the northern end of Queen's Parade, and is convenient
for the Cavendish Road tram stop. The bedrooms are fairly
compact, but are comfortable and well equipped.
7rm(3🟊4🟊)(1fb) CTV in all bedrooms ® sB&B🟊🟊fr£12.65
dB&B🟊🟊fr£25.30 WB&B£88.50-£120 WBDi£97.75-£160
LDO 8.30pm
Lic ⁗ CTV 3P nc2yrs
£

GH QQ **Cliftonville Hotel** 14 Empress Dr, Northshore
FY2 9SE ☎(0253) 51052
Etr-Nov
A lift, and bedrooms with private facilities, are features of this
private hotel near the seafront.
19🟊 (8fb) ® ✖
sB&B🟊£14.50-£17.50 WB&B£90-£117 WBDi£105-£130
Lic lift ⁗ CTV 2P
Credit Cards [1][3]

Blackpool

GH QQ **Denely Private Hotel** 15 King Edward Av FY2 9TA
☎(0253) 52757
A delightful, small, privately run hotel in a quiet side road on the north shore.
9rm(2♠7hc)(2fb) ⊁ ✳ sB&B£12-£15 dB&B£24-£30
dB&B♠£29.50-£38 WB&B£84-£105 WBDi£108.50-£126
卿 CTV 6P
£

GH QQ **Derwent Private Hotel** 8 Gynn Av FY1 2LD
☎(0253) 55194
Mar-3 Nov
Situated in a quiet street, close to the seafront, this friendly small hotel offers compact, well-maintained accommodation at very reasonable prices.
12rm(4♠8hc) ® ⊁ (ex guide dogs) dB&B£25-£36
dB&B♠£29-£40 (incl dinner) WB&B£87.50-£100
WBDi£100-£114 LDO 2pm
Lic 卿 CTV 4P

GH QQ **The Garville Hotel** 3 Beaufort Av, Bispham FY2 9HQ
(2m N) ☎(0253) 51004
Pleasant, family-run guesthouse close to the seafront.
7rm(2♠5hc)(2fb)⊬in all bedrooms CTV in 5 bedrooms ® ✳
sB&B£8.50-£11 dB&B£17-£22
dB&B♠£21-£26 WB&B£60-£75 WBDi£82-£98 LDO 1pm
Lic 卿 CTV 5P
£

GH QQ **Hartshead Hotel** 17 King Edward Av FY2 9TA
☎(0253) 53133 & 57111
Closed end Nov-2 wk Dec
Friendly proprietors, home-cooked dinners and comfortable rooms ensure an enjoyable visit to this small hotel.
10rm(1⇨2♠7hc)(2fb) CTV in all bedrooms ®
⊁ (ex guide dogs) sB&B£15-£18 sB&B⇨♠£17.50-£21
dB&B£25-£32
dB&B⇨♠£31-£38 WB&B£88-£100 WBDi£105-£116 LDO
2pm
Lic 卿 CTV 7P nc3yrs
£

GH QQQ **Lynstead Private Hotel** 40 King Edward Av
FY2 9TA ☎(0253) 51050
Closed 1st 2 wks Jan
Good value and good food have earned this hotel an outstanding reputation. The friendly proprietors maintain a high standard of accommodation.
10♠ (4fb) ® ⊁ (ex guide dogs) ✳ sB&B♠£14.50-£17.50
dB&B♠£29-£35 WB&B£101-£110 WBDi£115-£125 LDO 3pm
Lic lift 卿 CTV ⊬ nc3yrs
£

↞GH QQQ **Lynwood** 38 Osborne Rd FY4 1HQ
☎(0253) 44628
Closed Xmas & New Year
This comfortable and friendly hotel offers very good accommodation, the bedrooms having many extras not generally found in this category or establishment. Home-cooked meals are always served.
8rm(1⇨5♠2hc)(1fb) CTV in all bedrooms ® ⊁ sB&B£10-£12
sB&B⇨♠£13-£17 dB&B£20-£24
dB&B⇨♠£26-£32 WB&B£70-£105 WBDi£91-£119 LDO
breakfast
卿 ⊬
Credit Cards 1 2 3 £

GH QQ **Motel Mimosa** 24A Lonsdale Rd FY1 6EE
☎(0253) 41906
Closed Xmas
This is a modern establishment situated close to the promenade and the central pier. It offers comfortable bedrooms to which breakfast is delivered.

15⇨♠ (3fb) CTV in all bedrooms ® ✳ sB&B⇨♠£15-£30
dB&B⇨♠£30-£40 WB&B£105-£210 LDO 8.30pm
Lic 卿 13P 2🚗
Credit Cards 1 3 £

GH QQ **New Austin** 164-166 North Promenade FY1 1RE
☎(0253) 295371
This small hotel is close to the town centre. It is well furnished and there is a licensed restaurant serving a wide range of meals.
9♠ (3fb) CTV in all bedrooms ® ⊁ LDO 9.30pm
CTV ⊬ 🐕
Credit Cards 1 2 3 5

GH QQ **North Mount Private Hotel** 22 King Edward Av
FY2 9TD ☎(0253) 55937
A charming, guesthouse standing in peaceful surroundings on Blackpool's North Shore.
8hc (1fb) ® sB&B£14-£17
dB&B£28-£34 (incl dinner) WBDi£92-£110 LDO 3.30pm
Lic 卿 CTV 1P
£

GH QQ **Rewa Private Hotel** 561 New South Prom FY2 9TB
☎(0253) 42463
Apr-Oct
19rm(1⇨7♠11hc)(3fb) CTV in 9 bedrooms ® ⊁
Lic 卿 CTV 12P
Credit Cards 3

↞GH QQQ **Sunny Cliff** 98 Queens Promenade, Northshore
FY2 9NS ☎(0253) 51155
Etr-9 Nov & 4 days Xmas
Sunny Cliff enjoys a quiet seafront location with easy access to all amenities, and offers unpretentious, well-maintained accommodation.

▶

12hc (4fb) ℝ sB&Bfl2.50-£14
dB&B£25-£28 WB&Bfr£87.50 WBDifr£110 LDO 5pm
Lic CTV 8P
£

SELECTED

GH ℚℚℚℚ **Sunray Private Hotel** 42 Knowle Av,
Queens Promenade FY2 9TQ ☎(0253) 51937
Closed 15 Dec-5 Jan
*Set in a quiet residential area yet only a short walk from the
town centre and seafront, this hotel has a high standard of
accommodation. The inviting and comfortable lounge is
complemented by an attractive dining room. The amenities in
the bedrooms include colour television, radio/alarms and
direct dial telephones.*
9rm(1⇌8ℕ)(2fb) CTV in all bedrooms ℝ
sB&B⇌ℕ£20-£27
dB&B⇌ℕ£40-£50 WB&B£135-£173 WBDi£200-£243
LDO 3pm
🏧 CTV 6P
£

←GH ℚℚ **Surrey House Hotel** 9 Northumberland Av
FY2 9SB ☎(0253) 51743
Apr-Oct rs Mar & early Nov
*Standing in a quiet side road just off Queen's Promenade to the
north of the town, this long-established small hotel offers pleasant,
well-maintained accommodation with a friendly atmosphere.*
11rm(2⇌7ℕ2hc)(2fb)⊁in 1 bedroom ℝ sB&B£12-£17.50
sB&B⇌ℕ£13-£17.50 dB&B£22-£35
dB&B⇌ℕ£25-£35 WB&B£77-£119 WBDi£100-£140 LDO
4.30pm
🏧 CTV 6P 1🛋 (£0.75) nc3mths table tennis pool table
£

GH ℚℚℚ **Westmorland Hotel** 256 Queens Promenade
FY2 9HB ☎(0253) 54974
17rm(11ℕ6hc)(6fb) CTV in all bedrooms ℝ ✳ sB&B£14-£20
sB&Bℕ£18-£26 dB&B£30-£40
dB&Bℕ£36-£44 WB&B£126 WBDi£140-£168 LDO 7pm
Lic lift 🏧 CTV 6P
Credit Cards 1 3

GH ℚℚℚ **Windsor Hotel** 21 King Edward Av, Queens
Promenade FY2 9TA ☎(0253) 53735
*Close to the Queen's Promenade in a residential area, this
establishment is well cared for, and offers particularly pleasant and
comfortable public rooms including a stylish dining room. The
bedrooms, too, are comfortable and well equipped.*
8rm(1⇌4ℕ3hc)⊁in 1 bedroom CTV in all bedrooms ℝ ✳
sB&B£14-£16 sB&B⇌ℕ£16-£18 dB&B£28-£32
dB&B⇌ℕ£32-£35 (incl dinner) WB&B£90-£100
WBDi£98-£105 LDO 5pm
Lic 🏧 CTV 4P nc
£

GH ℚℚ **Woodleigh Private Hotel** 32 King Edward Av, North
Shore FY2 9TA ☎(0253) 593624
Mar-Oct
*This well-maintained, friendly guesthouse is close to the Queen's
Promenade and offers comfortable, pleasant accommodation.
Some bedrooms are fairly compact, and guests may need to share
tables in the dining room.*
10rm(6ℕ4hc)(3fb) CTV in all bedrooms ℝ ✖ ✳
sB&B£10-£15.50 dB&B£24-£31
dB&Bℕ£27-£35 WB&B£65-£77 WBDi£76-£99.50 LDO 2pm
🏧 CTV

BLACKWOOD Gwent Map **03** ST19

INN ℚℚ *Plas* Gordon Rd NP2 1D ☎(0495) 224674
*This friendly, family-run inn is in an elevated position with good
views of the valley. It provides attractive, well-equipped bedrooms,
a lounge bar and a restaurant offering a good range of food.*
6rm(4ℕ2hc)(1fb) CTV in 6 bedrooms ℝ LDO 9.45pm
🏧 50P
Credit Cards 1 3 5

BLAGDON Avon Map **03** ST55

INN ℚℚℚ **Seymour Arms** Bath Rd BS18 6TH ☎(0761) 62279
*Situated in the heart of the village, on the main Bath road, this
Victorian inn has been completely refurbished to provide attractive
open-plan public areas and pretty bedrooms, many with good en
suite facilities.*
4rm(3ℕ1hc)(1fb) CTV in all bedrooms ℝ ✖ (ex guide dogs) ✳
sB&B£17 dB&B£30
dB&Bℕ£30 Lunch £5-£10alc Dinner £5-£10alc LDO 9.30pm
🏧 30P nc5yrs
£

BLAIRGOWRIE Tayside *Perthshire* Map **11** NO14

GH ℚℚ **Ivybank House** Boat Brae, Rattray PH10 7BH
☎(0250) 3056
*A well-furnished, large Victorian house standing in own grounds,
with floodlit tennis court.*
6hc (2fb) CTV in all bedrooms ℝ ✳ sB&B£15.50
dB&B£27 LDO 6pm
🏧 CTV 6P ♪(hard)
£

SELECTED

GH ℚℚℚℚ **Rosebank House** Balmoral Rd PH10 7AF
☎(0250) 2912
last wk Jan-Oct
*This handsome Georgian establishment stands in its own
garden beside the Braemar road. It has a tranquil country
house atmosphere, comfortable individual bedrooms, and Jean
and Roy Miller spare no effort to ensure that their guests are
well looked after.*
6rm(5ℕ1hc)(2fb) CTV in 2 bedrooms ℝ
✖ (ex guide dogs) sB&B£30.25-£31.95
sB&Bℕ£32.25-£33.95 dB&B£56.50-£59.90
dB&Bℕ£59.50-£62.90 (incl dinner) WB&B£133-£143.50
WBDi£178-£188 LDO 6pm
Lic 🏧 CTV 12P nc9yrs
£

BLAKENEY Gloucestershire

See **Lydney**   see advertisement on page 73

BLEDINGTON Gloucestershire Map **04** SP22

INN ℚℚℚ **Kings Head Inn & Restaurant** The Green
OX7 6HD ☎Kingham(060871) 365
*This delightful 15th-century inn looks out over the quiet village
green, complete with brooks and ducks. Comfortable, well-
appointed bedrooms (all en suite) are popular, as is the restaurant.
Imaginatively prepared food is offered in a wide choice of daily
dishes, all reasonably priced and very tasty.*
6⇌ (2fb)⊁in 3 bedrooms CTV in all bedrooms ℝ
✖ (ex guide dogs) ✳ sB&B⇌£30
dB&B⇌£49 Bar Lunch £3.95-£8alc Dinner £6.50-£14alc LDO
10pm
🏧 CTV 70P

BOAT OF GARTEN Highland *Inverness-Shire* Map **14** NH91

GH Q Q Q **Moorfield House Hotel** Deshar Rd PH24 3BN
☎(047983) 646
Closed Nov
Standing in its own grounds in the centre of the village, this pink granite house makes a good base for those exploring the Spey Valley. The bedrooms are comfortably furnished, and the public rooms include an inviting lounge and separate cocktail bar.
6rm(3♠3hc)(3fb) ® ✳ sB&B£15-£18 dB&B£30-£36
dB&B♠£35-£41 WB&B£105-£126 WBDi£182-£203 LDO 6pm
Lic ⅏ CTV 12P

BODEDERN Gwynedd Map **06** SH38

INN Q *Crown Hotel* LL65 3TU ☎Valley(0407) 740734
A warm friendly village inn, The Crown is well furnished and has a pleasant 'local' atmosphere. A good selection of meals is available and it is conveniently placed for the car ferry and beaches.
5hc (2fb) CTV in 3 bedrooms TV in 2 bedrooms LDO 9.45pm
⅏ 50P

BODENHAM Hereford & Worcester Map **03** SO55

FH Q Q Q Mr & Mrs P J Edwards **Maund Court** *(SO561505)*
HR1 3JA ☎(056884) 282
Closed mid Dec-mid Jan
Situated on the A417 east of Leominster, Maud Court Farm is an ideal base from which to explore this lovely countryside. The proprietors thoughtfully provide guests with maps and tourist information. Rooms are comfortable and well equipped, each different in style and furnishings. There is an outdoor swimming pool for the more energetic, or guests can enjoy a game of croquet on the lawn.
3rm(1⇨1♠1hc)(1fb) CTV in all bedrooms ® ✳ sB&B£15.50
sB&B♠£15.50 dB&B£30 dB&B⇨£30 WB&B£100
⅏ CTV 6P ⌁(heated) croquet 130 acres mixed

BODLE STREET GREEN East Sussex Map **05** TQ61

FH Q Q Mr & Mrs P Gentry **Stud** *(TQ652144)* BN27 4RJ
☎Herstmonceux(0323) 833201
Closed Xmas
This busy farm is full of character and is situated in peaceful rural surroundings, offering an ideal base for family holidays. The functional accommodation is complemented by a sitting room, 2 dining rooms and cheerful service from the proprietors.
3rm(1♠2hc)⊁in all bedrooms ® ✖ sB&B£18-£20
sB&B♠£18-£20 dB&B£28-£32
dB&B♠£28-£32 WB&B£98-£126
⅏ CTV 3P 70 acres cattle sheep

BODMIN Cornwall & Isles of Scilly Map **02** SX06

See also Mount
FH Q Q Q Mrs P A Smith **Treffry** *(SW073637)* PL30 5AF
☎(0208) 74405
Closed Xmas rs 20 Oct-18 Mar
Standing in mature gardens, this welcoming stone-built farmhouse is part of a working dairy farm. The bedrooms are attractively decorated and furnished and fresh home-cooked food is served. Self-catering units are also available.
3rm(1♠2hc)⊁in all bedrooms CTV in 2 bedrooms ®
✖ (ex guide dogs) ✳ sB&Bfr£15 dB&Bfr£28
dB&B♠fr£30 WB&Bfr£90 WBDifr£140 (wkly only Jul & Aug)
LDO noon
⅏ CTV 4P nc3yrs pony for young children play area 200 acres
dairy
£

Book as early as possible for busy holiday periods.

BOLLINGTON Cheshire Map **07** SJ97

INN Q *Turners Arms Hotel* 1 Ingersley Rd SK10 5RE
☎(0625) 73864
Standing on the edge of the town, this inn offers meals every day of the week, including a competitively-priced, traditional Sunday lunch. Value for money is certainly one of the proprietor's priorities.
8rm(1⇨1♠6hc)(2fb) CTV in all bedrooms ® LDO 9.30pm
⅏ 2P pool darts

BONDLEIGH (nr North Tawton) Devon Map **03** SS60

FH Q Q Q Mrs M C H Partridge **Caddition** *(SS644050)*
EX20 2AW ☎North Tawton(0837) 82450
Mar-Nov
Attractive, friendly farmhouse with old beams and fireplaces.
2hc (1fb)⊬in all bedrooms TV available ® ✖ LDO noon
⅏ CTV 114 acres beef dairy

BO'NESS Central *West Lothian* Map **11** NS98

SELECTED

FH Q Q Q Q Mrs A Kirk **Kinglass** *(NT006803)*
Borrowstoun Rd EH51 9RW ☎(0506) 822861 & 824185
The sincere and enthusiastic manner of the hostess, plus many little personal touches, make Kinglass a true home-from-home. The well-equipped bedrooms appeal to the regular business guests, whilst a real farming environment, which Mrs Kirk will be pleased to show guests, attracts the tourist. Within the house, which is only a few minutes' drive from the leisure centre, are an attractive dining room and a comfortable lounge.
6rm(1♠5hc)(1fb) CTV in 7 bedrooms ® ✳ sB&Bfr£13.50
sB&B♠fr£24.50 dB&Bfr£27
dB&B♠fr£42 WB&Bfr£94.50 WBDifr£143.50 LDO
5.30pm
Lic ⅏ CTV 20P 120 acres arable

BONSALL Derbyshire Map **08** SK25

GH Q Q **Sycamore** 76 High St, Town Head DE4 2AA
☎Wirksworth(0629) 823903
Guests can relax on the front lawn of this 18th-century house which enjoys an elevated position overlooking the village. There is a choice of meals in the evening and prepared lunches are available.
7rm(1♠6hc)(1fb) CTV in all bedrooms ® sB&B£16.50-£17.50
dB&B£29-£32
dB&B♠£33-£35 WB&B£100-£110 WBDi£140-£150 LDO 5pm
Lic ⅏ CTV 7P
£
See advertisement under MATLOCK on page 259

GH Q Q **Town Head Farmhouse** 70 High St DE4 2AR
☎Wirksworth(0629) 823762
Tastefully converted and modernised in keeping with its 18th-century character, this house and its outbuildings are built around a small cottage garden and sited at the top of the town.
6♠ CTV in all bedrooms ® sB&B♠£22.50
dB&B♠£40 WB&B£140 WBDi£210 LDO noon
Lic ⅏ CTV 8P nc10 yrs
£
See advertisement under MATLOCK on page 259

BOROUGHBRIDGE North Yorkshire Map **08** SE36

INN Q Q Q **The Crown** Roecliffe YO5 9LY ☎(0423) 322578
FAX (0423) 324060
This welcoming country inn stands in the quiet village of Roacliffe, close to the A1. The bedrooms are extremely comfortable. Table d'hôte and à la carte menus are available in the restaurant, and freshly prepared meals are also served in the bar.

6🛁🚿 CTV in all bedrooms Ⓡ ✱ sB&B🛁🚿fr£28 dB&B🛁🚿fr£38 WB&Bfr£150 WBDifr£200 Bar Lunch £2.95-£5.80 Dinner £8.25-£10.75 LDO 9.30pm
🛗 70P ⛳
Credit Cards [1] [3] [£]

BORROWDALE Cumbria Map **11** NY21

GH [Q][Q] ***The Grange*** CA12 5UQ ☎(059684) 251
19 Mar-Oct Closed 31 Oct-18 Mar
Attractive house of lakeland slate set in its own gardens.
7rm(1🛁6hc)(1fb) Ⓡ 🐕 (ex guide dogs)
🛗 8P

GH [Q][Q][Q] Greenbank CA12 5UY ☎(059684) 215
Closed Dec
Set in its own grounds in the beautiful Borrowdale Valley about 3.5 miles from Keswick, this charming house has tastefully furnished accommodation with spacious en suite bedrooms and delightful public rooms. An excellent 4-course dinner is served daily.
10rm(9🛁1🚿)(1fb)🚭in all bedrooms Ⓡ 🐕 sB&B🛁🚿£20.50 dB&B🛁🚿£37-£41 WB&B£108.50-£122.50 WBDi£171.50-£185.50 LDO 5pm
Lic 🛗 CTV 15P
[£]

GH [Q][Q] ***Mary Mount Hotel*** CA12 5UX (Stakis) ☎(059684) 223
Telex no 64305
Mar-Oct
Under the same management as the nearby Lodore Swiss Hotel, this small hotel stands near the peaceful lake. The en suite bedrooms are well equipped and there is a cosy bar, a comfortable lounge and spacious dining room.
7🚿 Annexe 5🛁 CTV in all bedrooms Ⓡ 🐕
Lic 🛗 40P
Credit Cards [1] [2] [3] [5]
See advertisement under KESWICK on page 201

BORTH Dyfed Map **06** SN68

GH [Q][Q] Glanmor Hotel Princess St SY24 5JP ☎(0970) 871689
A seafront hotel with comfortable accommodation, good food and warm hospitality. Opposite safe, sandy beach.
7rm(2🚿5hc)(3fb) CTV in 4 bedrooms Ⓡ sB&B£14.50 dB&B£29
dB&B🚿£29 WB&B£101.50 WBDi£150.15 LDO 6pm
Lic CTV 10P 2🚗
[£]

BOSCASTLE Cornwall & Isles of Scilly Map **02** SX09

⟷**GH [Q][Q][Q] Melbourne House** New Rd PL35 0DH ☎(08405) 650
Enjoying a commanding position overlooking the Jordan Valley and village, this fine house has been tastefully restored yet retains its charm and character. The en suite bedrooms are well furnished and contain many thoughtful extras.
6rm(1🛁2🚿3hc) CTV in all bedrooms Ⓡ sB&B£12-£14 sB&B🛁🚿£14-£16 dB&B£24-£28 dB&B🛁🚿£28-£32 WB&B£84-£112 WBDi£119-£145 LDO 6pm
Lic 🛗 8P nc
Credit Cards [1] [3] [£]

See advertisement on page 75

GH [Q][Q][Q] Old Coach House Tintagel Rd PL35 0AS
☎(08405) 398
Closed 23 Dec-2 Jan rs Nov-Mar
Conveniently located on the B3263, this 300-year-old coaching house has been skilfully converted to provide modern facilities whilst retaining some original features. Bedrooms are well equipped, have quality furnishing and well-kept bath or shower rooms. There is a cosy lounge and a spacious conservatory dining room with views across a wooded valley.
6rm(1🛁5🚿)(1fb) CTV in all bedrooms [R] 🐕 (ex guide dogs) * sB&B🛁🚿£13-£20
dB&B🛁🚿£26-£40 WB&B£90-£133 WBDi£140-£183 LDO 11am
Lic ♨ 7P nc6yrs
Credit Cards [1] [2] [3]

SELECTED

GH [Q][Q][Q][Q] St Christophers Country House Hotel High St PL35 0BD ☎(08405) 412 due to change to (0840) 250412
Mar-Oct & Xmas
Set on a steep hill in a residential area, this family-run hotel has warm, comfortable bedrooms and a dining room where home-cooked meals, in generous portions, are served. After dinner, guests can relax in the lounge.
9rm(7🚿2hc) [R] sB&B🚿£16-£17 dB&B£28-£30
dB&B🚿£32-£34 WB&B£112-£119 WBDi£155-£160 LDO 8pm
Lic ♨ CTV 8P nc12yrs
Credit Cards [1] [3] [£]

BOSTON SPA West Yorkshire Map **08** SE44

INN [Q][Q][Q] The Royal Hotel 182 High St LS23 7AY (Berni/Chef & Brewer) ☎(0937) 842142

13🛁🚿 CTV in all bedrooms [R] 🐕 (ex guide dogs) *
sB&B🛁🚿£38-£42
dB&B🛁🚿£50 Lunch £8-£15 Dinner £8-£15 LDO 10pm
♨ 60P
Credit Cards [1] [2] [3] [5]

BOURNEMOUTH Dorset Map **04** SZ09

See Town Plan Section
See also Christchurch and **Poole**

GH [Q] *Albemarle Private Hotel* BH2 5PH ☎(0202) 551351
Close to the International Centre, shops and sea, this terraced Victorian house offers simply furnished, compact bedrooms, a comfortable lounge and neat dining room.
12rm(4🚿8hc)(3fb) CTV in all bedrooms [R] 🐕 (ex guide dogs) LDO 11am
Lic ♨ CTV P̸
Credit Cards [1] [3]

GH [Q][Q] Alum Bay Hotel 19 Burnaby Rd BH4 8JF
☎(0202) 761034
A few minutes' walk from Alum Chine and the beach, this Victorian house with its resident proprietors, offers well-equipped, comfortable bedrooms.
12rm(2🛁5🚿5hc)(4fb) CTV in all bedrooms [R]
sB&B£19-£22.50 sB&B🛁🚿£21.50-£25 dB&B£34-£41
dB&B🛁🚿£39-£46 WB&B£102-£149 WBDi£147-£192 LDO noon
Lic ♨ CTV 10P
Credit Cards [1] [3] [£]

GH [Q][Q][Q] *Alum Grange Hotel* 1 Burnaby Rd BH4 8JF
☎(0202) 761195
Spacious, freshly decorated bedrooms, equipped to a high standard, are provided here together with a sun lounge and bar/dining room. A riot of colour with summer flowers, Alum Grange offers books to read.
14rm(4🛁6🚿4hc)(5fb) CTV in all bedrooms [R] LDO noon
Lic ♨ CTV 10P
Credit Cards [3]

GH [Q][Q] Amitie 1247 Christchurch Rd BH7 6BP
☎(0202) 427255
Well placed for the shops and sea, this small, friendly guesthouse has been redecorated and refurnished to a high standard. The neat bedrooms are very well equipped.
8hc (2fb) CTV in all bedrooms [R] 🐕 (ex guide dogs) *
sB&B£11-£15 dB&B£22-£26 WB&B£73-£77
♨ 8P nc3yrs

GH [Q][Q] Braemar Private Hotel 30 Glen Rd BH5 1HS
☎(0202) 396054
Mar-Oct
Simple accommodation is offered at this gabled hotel near Boscombe Pier.
10rm(1🛁5🚿4hc)(4fb) CTV in all bedrooms [R] 🐕
dB&B£28-£44
dB&B🛁🚿£32-£48 (incl dinner) WB&B£75-£95
WBDi£95-£125 (wkly only Jul & Aug) LDO 6pm
Lic ♨ CTV 6P
[£]

GH [Q][Q] Carisbrooke Hotel BH2 5NT ☎(0202) 290432
Feb-Dec
Modern, family-run hotel near the Winter Gardens.
22rm(19🛁🚿3hc)(6fb) CTV in all bedrooms [R]
🐕 (ex guide dogs) * sB&B£18.50-£26 sB&B🛁🚿£20-£39
dB&B🛁🚿£36-£49 WB&B£120-£150 WBDi£135-£180 LDO 7pm
Lic ♨ CTV 18P
Credit Cards [1] [2] [3] [£]

GH [Q] *Cintra Hotel* 10-12 Florence Rd BH5 1HF
☎(0202) 396103
Close to the shops and the sea, this establishment has an indoor bowling green. The modest bedrooms provide some modern facilities, and there is a bar with a dance floor.
40rm(5🛁4🚿31hc)(6fb) CTV in all bedrooms [R] LDO 6.30pm
Lic lift CTV 10P indoor bowling green

SELECTED

GH [Q][Q][Q][Q] Cliff House Hotel 113 Alumhurst Rd BH4 8HS ☎(0202) 763003
Mar-Nov & Xmas
The generally spacious bedrooms at Cliff House provide all the modern facilities expected at a hotel, and are all very well kept, most enjoying good sea views. There is a comfortable lounge, in which to relax, that opens into a well-appointed dining room. Many guests return year after year to the warm hospitality provided by the proprietors, Mr and Mrs Clark.
12rm(2🛁9🚿1hc)(4fb) CTV in all bedrooms [R] 🐕 *
sB&B£24-£27 dB&B£48
dB&B🛁🚿£52 WB&B£168 WBDi£185-£200 LDO 6.30pm
Lic lift ♨ 12P nc7yrs snooker

GH [Q][Q] Cransley Private Hotel 11 Knyveton Rd BH1 3QG
☎(0202) 290067
Apr-Oct
This detached house is in a quiet location and has a neat garden and parking space. Well-equipped bedrooms are complemented by a comfortable lounge and dining room.
12rm(5🛁5🚿2hc)(2fb) CTV in all bedrooms [R] *
sB&B£12-£20 sB&B🛁🚿£14-£22 dB&B£24-£40
dB&B🛁🚿£28-£44 WB&B£70-£109 WBDi£90-£139
Lic CTV 10P
Credit Cards [1] [3] [£]

GH Q Q Q **Croham Hurst Hotel** 9 Durley Rd South BH2 5JH
☎(0202) 552353
Closed Jan
This hotel now has more delightful bedrooms of a good size, all with en suite bathrooms. There are good lounges and a bar, together with a dance floor and regular entertainment. A new air-conditioned dining room has attractive Spanish furnishings. The propritors pay much attention to detail and maintain a friendly, family atmosphere.
40⇌↑ (7fb) CTV in all bedrooms ® ✗ sB&B⇌↑£24-£30 dB&B⇌↑£48-£60 WB&B£136.50-£188.50 WBDi£154-£206 LDO 7.15pm
Lic lift ⁴⁴⁴ 20P
Credit Cards ① ③
See advertisement on page 77

⊢⊶**GH** Q Q **Derwent House** 36 Hamilton Rd BH1 4EH
☎(0202) 309102
Detatched property with Mansard roof, close to Boscombe shops.
9rm(4↑5hc)(3fb) CTV in all bedrooms ® sB&B£11-£15 dB&B£22-£30
dB&B↑£26-£34 WB&B£70-£100 WBDi£90-£125 LDO 5pm
Lic ⁴⁴⁴ CTV 10P
Credit Cards ① ③ ⓔ

GH Q Q *Egerton House Private Hotel* 385 Holdenhurst Rd
BH8 7AN ☎(0202) 394024
This friendly family-run hotel offers freshly decorated accommodation, with most of the bedrooms of good size.
8hc (4fb) CTV in 6 bedrooms TV in 2 bedrooms ® ✗ LDO 6.45pm
Lic ⁴⁴⁴ CTV 7P

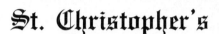

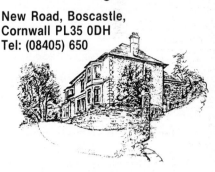

GH ❑❑❑ **Golden Sands Hotel** BH4 8HR ☎(0202) 763832
Mar-Oct & Xmas
Attractive guesthouse close to Alum Chine. Good standard of furnishings and very comfortable bedrooms.
11⇌🏠 (2fb) CTV in all bedrooms ® ✖ (ex guide dogs)
sB&B⇌🏠£22-£26.50
dB&B⇌🏠£37-£48 WB&B£110-£143 WBDif£140-£175 LDO 4pm
Lic 10P nc3yrs
£

GH ❑❑ **Highclere Hotel** 15 Burnaby Rd BH4 8JF
☎(0202) 761350
Apr-Sep
Neat, well-maintained hotel with sea views. Easy walk to Alum Chine and beach.
8rm(4⇌4🏠)(5fb) CTV in all bedrooms ®
sB&B⇌🏠£15.50-£17.50
dB&B⇌🏠£31-£35 WB&B£108.50-£132.50 WBDif£130-£150 LDO 4pm
Lic ⅏ CTV 7P nc3yrs solarium
£

GH ❑❑❑ **Holmcroft Hotel** 5 Earle Rd BH4 8JQ
☎(0202) 761289
The well-equipped bedrooms of this neat hotel have modern furnishings. Downstairs there is a small bar with a grand piano, a comfortable foyer lounge and a spacious dining room.
19⇌🏠 (3fb) CTV in all bedrooms ® sB&B⇌🏠£27-£32
dB&B⇌🏠£54-£64 (incl dinner) WB&B£130-£165
WBDif£154-£175 LDO 5pm
Lic ⅏ CTV 13P
Credit Cards 1 3 £

GH ❑❑ **Kelmor Lodge** 30 Stourcliffe Av, Southbourne
BH6 3PT ☎(0202) 424061
In a pleasant residential area close to the sea, this small family hotel has cosy bedrooms, a lounge and a nicely appointed dining room.
8rm(2⇌6hc)(1fb) CTV in all bedrooms ® ✖ ✳
sB&B£15-£16.75 dB&B£28-£31.50
dB&B⇌🏠£30.50-£34 (incl dinner) WB&B£70-£84
WBDif£93-£106 (wkly only Aug) LDO 9am
Lic ⅏ CTV 6P nc8yrs
Credit Cards 3

GH ❑❑❑ *Linwood House Hotel* BH5 1ND ☎(0202) 397818
Mar-Oct
Attractively decorated guesthouse in quiet road near beach and Boscombe town centre.
10rm(5🏠5hc)(2fb) CTV in 3 bedrooms TV in 1 bedroom ® ✖
(wkly only mid Jun-mid Sep)
Lic ⅏ CTV 7P nc6yrs

⊷⊶**GH** ❑❑❑ **Lynthwaite Hotel** 10 Owls Rd BH5 1AF
☎(0202) 398015
This Victorian villa, with a first floor lounge and balcony, is situated close to the shops and the sea. The newly decorated and furnished bedrooms are of a high standard, offering both comfort and modern facilities.
14rm(10⇌1🏠3hc)(3fb) CTV in all bedrooms ® ✖
sB&B£13-£17 sB&B⇌🏠£16-£21 dB&B£26-£34
dB&B⇌🏠£32-£39 WB&B£79-£122 WBDif£119-£162 LDO 5pm
Lic ⅏ CTV 17P nc3yrs
Credit Cards 1 3 £

GH ❑ **Mae-Mar Private Hotel** 91/95 West Hill Rd BH2 5PQ
☎(0202) 553167
In the heart of West Cliff hotel area.
43rm(2⇌24🏠17hc)(12fb) CTV in all bedrooms ®
sB&B£15-£19.50 sB&B⇌🏠£17.50-£22 dB&B£30-£39
dB&B🏠£35-£44 WBDif£112.50-£168 LDO 5.30pm

Lic lift ⅏ CTV
Credit Cards 1 3 £

GH ❑❑ **Mayfield Private Hotel** 46 Frances Rd BH1 3SA
☎(0202) 551839
Closed Dec
Situated in quiet area within easy walk to beach.
8rm(3🏠5hc)(1fb) ® sB&B£15-£18 dB&B£30-£36
dB&B🏠£35-£41 (incl dinner) WB&B£63-£85 WBDif£85-£110
(wkly only 2wks-Jul/Aug) LDO 9am
Lic ⅏ CTV 5P nc7yrs
£

GH ❑❑❑ *Naseby-Nye Hotel* Byron Rd BH5 1JD
☎(0202) 394079
This large, detached, brick-built house stands in well-tended, colourful gardens, close to the cliff-top and Boscombe promenade. The lounges are comfortable and the hotel has well-appointed bedrooms.
13rm(3⇌10hc)(1fb) LDO 7pm
Lic ⅏ CTV 12P nc5yrs

GH ❑❑ *Newfield Private Hotel* 29 Burnaby Rd BH4 8JF
☎(0202) 762724
This happy and relaxed guesthouse is a short distance from Alum Chine and its attractive beach. Good home cooking is provided.
12rm(1⇌5🏠6hc)(3fb) CTV in all bedrooms ®
Lic ⅏ CTV 4P

GH ❑ *Norland Private Hotel* 6 Westby Rd BH5 1HD
☎(0202) 396729
Inexpensive, comfortable accommodation can be found in this Victorian semidetached house, situated close to Boscombe's shopping centre. The well-maintained bedrooms are freshly decorated, and are suitable for both commercial and holiday use.
9rm(1⇌2🏠6hc)(2fb) CTV in all bedrooms ® LDO 4.30pm
Lic ⅏ CTV 8P

GH ❑❑ **Northover Private Hotel** 10 Earle Rd BH4 8JQ
☎(0202) 767349
Apr-Oct & Xmas
Not far from Alum Chine, this small, family-run hotel has simply furnished bedrooms, some with en suite facilities. The public lounge is comfortable and drinks may be ordered from reception.
10rm(6🏠4hc)(6fb) ® sB&B£15-£20 sB&B🏠£17-£23
dB&B£30-£40
dB&B🏠£34-£46 WB&B£95-£120 WBDif£120-£150 LDO 5pm
Lic ⅏ CTV 11P
£

GH ❑❑ **Oak Hall Private Hotel** 9 Wilfred Rd BH5 1ND
☎(0202) 395062
Nov-1 Oct
This detached house is in a pleasant area of the resort, between the shops and the popular sandy beaches. Its modern facilities are combined with a traditional style of comfort offered by the hospitable proprietors.
13rm(1⇌8🏠4hc)(2fb) CTV in all bedrooms ® ✳
sB&B£16-£18.50 dB&B£37.50-£42.50
dB&B⇌🏠£37.50-£42.50 (incl dinner) WB&B£108-£120.75
WBDif£128.50-£158 (wkly only mid Jun-end Aug) LDO 3pm
Lic ⅏ CTV 9P
Credit Cards 1 3 £

GH ❑❑ **St John's Lodge Hotel** 10 St Swithun's Rd South
BH1 3RQ ☎(0202) 290677
This centrally located family-run hotel is close to the railway and bus stations and within walking distance of the Chine and pier. The bedrooms and public rooms are pleasant and smoking is not permitted in the dining room.
15rm(5🏠10hc)(2fb) CTV in all bedrooms ® ✖
sB&B£15-£16.50 sB&B🏠£18-£19.50 dB&B£30-£33
dB&B🏠£36-£39 WB&B£105-£115.50 WBDif£122-£139 LDO 4pm

Lic ⚥ CTV 14P sauna jacuzzi
Credit Cards [1] [3] (£)

GH [Q][Q] **Sea-Dene Hotel** 10 Burnaby Rd BH4 8JF
☎(0202) 761372
Pleasant, detached house with forecourt parking, close to the beach at Alum Chine.
7rm(5↿2hc)(3fb) CTV in all bedrooms ® ✠ (ex guide dogs) ✱
sB&B£11–£13 sB&B↿£13–£16 dB&B£22–£26
dB&B↿£26–£32 WB&B£69–£98 WBDi£110–£145 (wkly only mid Jul–mid Sep) LDO 7pm
Lic ⚥ CTV 4P nc3yrs
Credit Cards [1] [3]

GH [Q][Q] *Sea View Court Hotel* BH5 1AZ ☎(0202) 397197
Two minutes' walk from Boscombe Pier, an attractive gabled house with good bedrooms.
17⇆↿ (7fb) CTV in all bedrooms ® ✠ LDO 3pm
Lic CTV 20P
Credit Cards [1] [3]

GH [Q][Q][Q] **Silver Trees Hotel** BH3 7AL ☎(0202) 556040
A modernised, late-Victorian house standing in its own grounds and offering comfortable accommodation.
8rm(5↿3hc)(2fb)✗in 4 bedrooms CTV in all bedrooms ✠
sB&B£24–£28 sB&B↿£27–£30 dB&B£33–£37 dB&B↿£37–£40
⚥ 10P nc3yrs
Credit Cards [1] [3]

⊢⊷**GH** [Q][Q] **Hotel Sorrento** 16 Owls Rd BH5 1AG
☎(0202) 394019
rs Xmas
Situated half way between the Boscombe shopping area and the pier, this holiday hotel has an informal, relaxed atmosphere. A smart bar, TV lounge and attractive restaurant complement the bedrooms, which vary in size.
▶

17rm(12🛁🚿5hc)(5fb) CTV in all bedrooms Ⓡ sB&B£13-£17 dB&B£26-£34
dB&B🛁🚿£31-£39 WBDi£113-£163.50 LDO 6pm
Lic ♨ CTV 19P solarium gymnasium

GH [Q][Q][Q] Tudor Grange Hotel BH1 3EE ☎(0202) 291472
Mar-Dec
Mr and Mrs Heeley's mock-Tudor house, set in pleasant gardens, has panelled public rooms and ornate moulded ceilings. There is a lounge, bar and dining room. The comfortable bedrooms have well-maintained modern facilities.
12🛁🚿 (4fb) CTV in all bedrooms Ⓡ sB&B£20-£23
sB&B🛁🚿£22-£27
dB&B🛁🚿£44-£54 WB&B£120-£165 WBDi£160-£210 LDO 7pm
Lic ♨ CTV 11P
Credit Cards [3] [£]

GH [Q][Q][Q] *Valberg Hotel* 1a Wollstonecraft Rd BH5 1JQ
☎(0202) 394644
Quietly situated a short walk from the sea and shops, this hotel has light airy bedrooms with en suite showers, colour TV and tea facilities. The attractive, colourful garden is overlooked by the lounge and dining room, with a small bar.
10🚿 (2fb) CTV in all bedrooms Ⓡ 🐕 LDO 12pm
♨ CTV 9P nc4yrs

GH [Q][Q][Q] Weavers Hotel 14 Wilfred Rd BH5 1ND
☎(0202) 397871
Apr-Oct
In quiet residential area close to sea. A small, friendly hotel offering good cooking.
7rm(6🚿1hc)(1fb) CTV in all bedrooms Ⓡ 🐕 sB&B£17-£18
dB&B£34-£36
dB&B🚿£36-£38 (incl dinner) WB&B£105-£122.50
WBDi£119-£129 (wkly only mid May-mid Sep) LDO 5pm
Lic ♨ 7P nc7yrs
[£]

GH [Q][Q][Q] West Dene Private Hotel 117 Alumhurst Rd
BH4 8HS ☎(0202) 764843
Mar-Oct
Set at the foot of Alum Chine, this well-presented private hotel overlooks the sea and has nicely equipped, modern bedrooms.
17rm(5🛁7🚿5hc)(4fb) CTV in 15 bedrooms Ⓡ 🐕 ✱
sB&B£20.50 dB&B£41
dB&B🛁🚿£48 WB&B£123-£144 WBDi£150-£204 LDO 3.30pm
Lic ♨ CTV 17P nc4yrs
Credit Cards [1] [2] [3] [5]

GH [Q][Q] Woodford Court Hotel 19-21 Studland Rd BH4 8HZ
☎(0202) 764907 FAX (0202) 761214
Mar-15 Nov
This family-managed establishment is in a residential area near Alum Chine. With the recent purchase of the adjacent property the hotel now has 36 en suite bedrooms and busy public lounges and bars.
35rm(8🛁18🚿9hc)(11fb) CTV in all bedrooms Ⓡ
sB&B£16.50-£23 sB&B🛁🚿£16.50-£23 dB&B£33-£46
dB&B🛁🚿£33-£46 WB&B£120-£160 WBDi£147-£175 LDO 6.15pm
Lic ♨ CTV 18P nc2yrs
Credit Cards [1] [2] [3]

GH [Q][Q] Woodlands Hotel 28 Percy Rd, Boscombe BH5 1JG
☎(0202) 396499
In a quiet residential area quite close to the sea, this pretty house offers good food and comfortable accommodation.
11rm(5🚿6hc)(3fb) CTV in 9 bedrooms Ⓡ ✱ sB&B£14-£16.50
sB&B🚿£16.50-£19 dB&B£27-£32
dB&B🚿£32-£37 WB&B£86-£105 WBDi£125-£150 LDO 6.15pm
Lic ♨ CTV 7P
Credit Cards [1] [3] [£]

GH [Q][Q][Q] Wood Lodge Hotel 10 Manor Rd BH1 3EY
☎(0202) 290891
Etr-Oct
Peaceful and elegant house opposite East Cliff with attentive service and good accommodation.
15rm(7🛁7🚿1hc)(5fb) CTV in all bedrooms Ⓡ ✱
sB&B£14-£16 sB&B🛁🚿£16-£18
dB&B🛁🚿£32-£36 WB&B£110-£156 WBDi£146-£191 LDO 6pm
Lic ♨ CTV 12P 9 hole putting green
Credit Cards [1] [3]

GH [Q][Q] Woodside Private Hotel 29 Southern Rd BH6 3SR
☎(0202) 427213
This comfortable house is quietly located, yet only a short walk to Southbourne Overcliffe Drive.
10rm(2🚿8hc)(3fb) Ⓡ 🐕 ✱ sB&B£12-£14 dB&B£24-£28
dB&B🚿£27-£32 WB&B£85-£110 WBDi£120-£145 LDO 10am
Lic ♨ CTV 5P
Credit Cards [1] [3] [5] [£]

BOVEY TRACEY Devon Map **03** SX87

GH [Q] Blenheim Hotel Brimley Rd TQ13 9DH ☎(0626) 832422
rs 25 & 26 Dec
This fine detached Victorian house is situated within its own secluded grounds and gardens on the outskirts of the village. There is a choice of comfortable lounges and the bedrooms are simply appointed and bright.
6🚿 (1fb) Ⓡ sB&B£19.50-£22
dB&B£39-£43 WB&B£120-£125 WBDi£195-£212 LDO 7.30pm
Lic ♨ CTV 8P
[£]

SELECTED

FH [Q][Q][Q][Q] Mrs H Roberts **Willmead** *(SX795812)*
TQ13 9NP ☎Lustleigh(06477) 214
Closed Xmas & New Year
This thatched and beamed farmhouse has been tastefully modernised to form a cosy, personal, family-run property. The bedrooms, comfortably furnished and decorated, are bright and airy, with modern en suite facilities. Stylish lounges, centred around the hall with its impressive minstrels' gallery, are richly furnished and offer colour television and a library. Commendable home cooking here features a good grill breakfast and Mrs Robert's homemade preserves.
3rm(1🚿2hc)🚭in all bedrooms 🐕 dB&Bfr£38
dB&B🚿fr£42 WB&Bfr£133
♨ CTV 0P nc10yrs 32 acres beef

BOWNESS-ON-WINDERMERE Cumbria

See **Windermere**

BOX Wiltshire Map **03** ST86

INN [Q][Q] *Baylys Ale House* High St SN14 9NA
☎Bath(0225) 743622
Closed Xmas
3🚿 CTV in all bedrooms Ⓡ LDO 10pm
♨ 15P snooker
Credit Cards [1] [3]

[Q] is for quality. For a full explanation of this AA quality award, consult the Contents page.

BRADFORD West Yorkshire Map **07** SE13

GH Q Q **Maple Hill** 3 Park Dr, Heaton BD9 4DP
☎(0274) 544061 FAX (0274) 481154
Large, comfortable Victorian house with many original features.
13rm(3♠10hc)(1fb)✕in 1 bedroom CTV in all bedrooms ®
sB&B£35.88 sB&B♠£42.78 dB&B£49.68
dB&B♠£56.58 WB&B£r£251 WBDif£321
Lic 🍽 20P 2🎱 half size snooker table
Credit Cards ①③ £

GH Q Q Q **Park Drive Hotel** 12 Park Dr BD9 4DR
☎(0274) 480194
*This attractive stone-built house stands within its gardens in a
pleasant residential area. A good standard of accommodation is
offered here, together with friendly personal service.*
11rm(3⇨8♠)(1fb) CTV in all bedrooms ® 🏃 (ex guide dogs)
sB&B⇨♠£35-£43
dB&B⇨♠£45-£53 WB&B£173 WBDif£222 LDO 6pm
Lic 🍽 7P
Credit Cards ①②③ £

GH Q Q Q **P L S Hotel** Sherbridge Mill, Great Horton Rd
BD7 1PX ☎(0274) 306775 FAX (0274) 724296
*A converted woollen mill is now a well-furnished and comfortable
hotel, and is close to the town centre.*
19rm(1⇨18♠) CTV in all bedrooms ® 🏃 (ex guide dogs)
sB&B⇨♠£35-£40 dB&B⇨♠£45-£50
Lic lift 🍽 CTV 19P 4🎱
Credit Cards ①③

FH Q Q Q Mr & Mrs Priestley **Brow Top** *(SD112310)*
Baldwin Lanem, Clayton BD14 6PS ☎(0274) 882178
Closed Xmas

*Situated in lovely countryside, yet only 15 minutes from Bradford
town centre, this cottage and barn conversion, of a very high
standard and much character, provides well-furnished bedrooms.*
3⇨ (1fb) CTV in all bedrooms ® 🏃 (ex guide dogs) ✱
sB&B⇨£17 dB&B⇨£27
🍽 CTV 4P 300 acres beef dairy

BRADFORD ON AVON Wiltshire Map **03** ST86

GH Q Q Q **Widbrook Grange** Trowbridge Rd BA15 1UH
☎(02216) 3173 & 4750 Telex no 444337
Closed Xmas & New Year
*One mile from the town yet nestling in rolling countryside, this
impressive house has attractively furnished bedrooms with
thoughtful extras. Both drawing rooms are very comfortable and
the dining room, where homemade meals are served, is elegantly
furnished.*
4rm(3⇨♠1hc)Annexe 8⇨♠ (2fb)✕in 4 bedrooms CTV in all
bedrooms ® 🏃 ✱ sB&B⇨♠£21.50 sB&B⇨♠£39.50-£43
dB&B⇨♠£49.50-£64
Lic 🍽 50P 10🎱
Credit Cards ①②③ £

BRAEMAR Grampian *Aberdeenshire* Map **15** NO19

GH Q **Callater Lodge Hotel** 9 Glenshee Rd AB3 5YQ
☎(03397) 41275
Closed mid Oct-26 Dec
*This family-run hotel offers the holidaymaker good value and
practical accommodation. It is set in its own grounds on the edge of
the village, overlooking the surrounding hills.*
9rm(2♠7hc)(1fb) ® ✱ sB&B£15 dB&B£30
dB&B♠£34 WB&B£105-£119 WBDif£166-£184 LDO 7pm
▶

Lic ᵐ CTV 14P
Credit Cards 1 3

BRAMBER West Sussex Map **04** TQ11

INN Q *The Castle Hotel* The Street BN4 3WE
☎Steyning(0903) 812102 & 815993
Closed Xmas & Boxing Day
*This is a popular and lively village inn which offers a good
standard of bar food and also has an à la carte restaurant. The
accommodation is functional and in keeping with the style.*
8rm(3🟊5hc)(2fb) CTV in 5 bedrooms ® ✱ (ex guide dogs)
LDO 9.45pm
ᵐ 30P 2🐾 🔽
Credit Cards 3
See advertisement under STEYNING on page 339

BRAMLEY South Yorkshire Map **08** SK49

GH QQQ *Stonecroft* Main St, Bramley S66 0SF (4m E of
Rotherham) ☎Rotherham(0709) 540922
*Standing in walled gardens, this ivy-clad house is comfortable and
well furnished with antiques. The tasteful accommodation includes
well-appointed bedrooms.*
4rm(1⇨3hc)Annexe 3🟊 (2fb) CTV in all bedrooms ®
Lic ᵐ CTV 10P

BRAMPTON Cumbria Map **12** NY56

See also Castle Carrock and **Kirkcambeck**
INN QQQ *Abbey Bridge Inn & Mill* Lanercost CA8 2HG (2.5
m NE of Brampton) ☎(06977) 2224
Closed Xmas & New Year
*On the banks of the River Irving, close to Hadrian's Wall, this inn
offers accommodation of a high standard. A good range of bar
meals is available, and the Abbey Mill across the road contains a
buttery and craft shop.*
7rm(3⇨1🟊3hc)⤚in all bedrooms CTV in 1 bedroom LDO
9pm
ᵐ CTV 30P

INN QQQ **The Blacksmiths Arms** Talkin Village CA8 1LE
☎(06977) 3452
*Situated 2 miles south east of Brampton, this charming inn, under
the supervision of proprietors Pat and Tom Bagshaw, has well-
appointed and attractively decorated bedrooms, all with full en
suite facilities. Good home-cooked meals are served.*
5rm(3⇨2🟊) CTV in all bedrooms ® ✱ (ex guide dogs)
sB&B⇨🟊fr£20
dB&B⇨🟊fr£35 WB&B£105-£120 Lunch £4.70-£12.80alc
Dinner £4.70-£12.80alc LDO 9pm
12P games room
Credit Cards 1 3 £

BRANDON Co Durham Map **12** NZ23

INN QQ **Bay Horse** DH7 8ST ☎091-378 0498
*Off the A690 3 miles from Durham, this traditional stone-built inn
has modern bedrooms in an annexe to the rear. Each has en suite
facilities, TV, telephone and beverage facilities. Bar meals are
served, including Yorkshire pudding with a variety of fillings.*
Annexe 4🟊 ⤚in all bedrooms CTV in all bedrooms ® ✳
sB&B🟊£24
dB&B🟊£32 Lunch £2-£5.50 Dinner £2-£5.50 LDO 9.30pm
ᵐ 15P
Credit Cards 1 £
See advertisement under DURHAM on page 141

See the regional maps of popular holiday
areas at the back of the book.

BRANSCOMBE Devon Map **03** SY18

GH QQQ **The Bulstone** Higher Bulstone EX12 3BL
☎(029780) 446
Feb-Nov rs Dec-Jan
*Children are especially catered for here, with play areas indoors
and outside, and special children's menu. The comfortable
accommodation includes prettily furnished bedrooms, and guests
may smoke in the lounge only. A warm welcome and personal
service is assured.*
12rm(6⇨🟊6hc)(10fb)⤚in all bedrooms ® ✱ dB&B£32-£38
dB&B⇨🟊£40-£49 LDO 7.30pm
Lic ᵐ CTV 30P ♿

BRAUNTON Devon Map **02** SS43

GH QQQ **Brookdale Hotel** 62 South St EX33 2AN
☎(0271) 812075
*This family-run guesthouse offers excellent value for money, with
prettily decorated bedrooms and cosy public rooms. Mr and Mrs
Sargeant are congenial hosts who upgrade the hotel every season.*
8hc (2fb)⤚in all bedrooms CTV in all bedrooms
✱ (ex guide dogs) ✳ sB&B£14.50-£17
dB&B£29-£34 WB&B£91.35-£107.10 WBDi£158.20-£166.95
LDO 11am
Lic ᵐ CTV 9P 2🐾 nc10yrs
£

FH QQQ Mr & Mrs Barnes **Denham Farm & Country House**
(SS480404) North Buckland EX33 1HY
☎Croyde(0271) 890297
*Recently refurbished bedrooms in this quiet village farmhouse have
en suite shower rooms, colour TV and beverage facilities. Jean and
Tony Barnes offer a warm welcome and home cooked meals in the
informal restaurant. A championship golf course is not far away.*
10⇨🟊 (2fb) CTV in all bedrooms ® ✱ (ex guide dogs)
dB&B⇨🟊fr£38 WB&Bfr£120 (wkly only 18 Jul-30 Aug) LDO
6pm
Lic CTV 8P 3🐾 160 acres beef

BRECHIN Tayside *Angus* Map **15** NO56

SELECTED

⤙FH QQQQ Mrs M Stewart **Blibberhill** *(NO553568)*
DD9 6TH (5m WSW off B9134) ☎Aberlemno(030783) 225
*Secluded in the lovely Vale of Strathmore, this 18th-century
farmhouse is an ideal touring base. Two of the comfortably
furnished bedrooms have en suite facilities. Mrs Stewary
extends a warm welcome and provides home cooking and
homemade preserves.*
3rm(2⇨🟊1hc)⤚in all bedrooms ® ✱ (ex guide dogs)
sB&Bfr£12 dB&Bfr£22 dB&B⇨🟊fr£25
ᵐ CTV 4P 300 acres arable beef mixed
£

FH QQQ Mrs J Stewart **Wood of Auldbar** *(NO554556)*
Aberlemno DD9 6SZ ☎Aberlemno(030783) 218
*A friendly atmosphere, comfortable accommodation and good
home cooking are all part of the appeal at this tastefully appointed
Victorian farmhouse, which is peacefully set in the vale of
Strathmore a few miles south west of the town.*
3rm (1fb)⤚in all bedrooms ✱ (ex guide dogs) ✳ sB&Bfr£12
dB&Bfr£22 LDO 8pm
ᵐ CTV 4P 187 acres arable mixed
£

This guide is updated annually – make sure you
use an up-to-date edition.

BRECON Powys Map **03** SO02

GH Q Beacons 16 Bridge St LD3 8AH ☎(0874) 3339

This Georgian house is situated near the River Usk and is a short walk from the centre of the town. The accommodation is continually being improved, and modern en suite facilities have now been added.

11rm(8⇌↟3hc)(2fb) CTV in 8 bedrooms ® ✱ sB&B£13-£15 sB&B⇌↟£15 dB&B£26 dB&B⇌↟£30 WB&B£78-£90 WBDi£123.50-£135.50 LDO 7pm
Lic 𝍖 CTV 12P
Credit Cards 1 3 £

GH QQQ The Coach Orchard St, Llanfaes LD3 8AN ☎(0874) 3803

Closed 22 Dec-7 Jan

Standing opposite the town's Christ College, this very comfortable hotel is run by the friendly Ashton family. Originally an early 19th-century inn, it has been carefully modernised, providing well-equipped bedrooms and public rooms.

6⇌↟ (2fb) CTV in all bedrooms ® ✗ (ex guide dogs) dB&B⇌↟£30-£32
Lic 𝍖 5P

GH QQ *The Grange* The Watton LD3 7ED ☎(0874) 4038

A short walk from the town centre, this small, family-run guesthouse has been recently modernised and provides bright accommodation.

7rm(2↟5hc)Annexe 1↟ (4fb) CTV in 1 bedroom ® LDO 6pm
Lic 𝍖 CTV 8P

BREDWARDINE Hereford & Worcester Map **03** SO34

SELECTED

GH QQQQ Bredwardine Hall HR3 6DB
☎Moccas(09817) 596

Mar-Nov

Set in the tranquil village amid its own wooded grounds, Bredwardine Hall is an imposing manor house. With the Golden Valley and River Wye close by, this is the perfect place to unwind, and Wendy and Maurice Jancey ensure guests of an enjoyable stay. The accommodation is generally spacious, very well maintained, with very good modern facilities, and guests may help themselves to drinks from the courtesy bar in the comfortable lounge.

5rm(3⇌1↟1hc)(1fb) CTV in all bedrooms ®
✗ (ex guide dogs) sB&B£26-£28 sB&B⇌↟£26-£28 dB&B£40-£44 dB&B⇌↟£40-£44 WB&B£135-£149 WBDi£198-£212 LDO 4.30pm
Lic 𝍖 7P nc10yrs

See advertisement on page 83

INN QQQ *Red Lion* HR3 6BU ☎Moccas(09817) 303 & 215

rs Nov-Mar

This large 17th-century former coaching inn is on the B4352, in a small, pleasant rural village, 12 miles west of Hereford. The accommodation is simple but well equipped, and is equally suitable for tourists and travelling business people.

7rm(4⇌3hc)Annexe 2⇌ (3fb) CTV in all bedrooms ® LDO 9pm
𝍖 35P 3🚗 ♪
Credit Cards 1 2 3 5

Q is for quality. For a full explanation of this AA quality award, consult the Contents page.

The Blacksmiths Arms

TALKIN VILLAGE, BRAMPTON, CUMBRIA
Telephone: BRAMPTON 3452

The Blacksmith's Arms *offers all the hospitality and comforts of a traditional Country Inn. Enjoy tasty meals served in our bar lounges or linger over dinner in our well-appointed restaurant. We also have five lovely bedrooms all en suite and offering every comfort. We guarantee the hospitality you would expect from a family concern and we can assure you of a pleasant and comfortable stay. Peacefully situated in the beautiful village of Talkin, the Inn is convenient for the Borders, Hadrian's Wall and the Lake District. Good Golf course, pony trekking, walking and other country pursuits nearby. Personally managed by proprietors Pat and Tom Bagshaw.*

CALLATER LODGE

Braemar, Aberdeenshire AB3 5YQ
Telephone: Braemar (03397) 41275

A small comfortable hotel situated in grounds of over one acre on the south side of Braemar, with accommodation for 18 persons. All rooms have pleasant views of surrounding hills, hot & cold water, electric fires, razor sockets, tea & coffee making facilities and comfortable beds. Some rooms with private facilities. An ideal centre for climbing, fishing, touring ski-ing, hang-gliding and an 18-hole golf course nearby. Glenshee Ski Centre — nine miles and Balmoral — eight miles. Ample car parking.

Under the personal supervision of the proprietors - Mr & Mrs W J O Rose.

BRENDON Devon Map **03** SS74

GH [Q] Brendon House EX35 6PS ☎(05987) 206
Closed Xmas wk rs 7 Jan-Mar
Set in Exmoor's beautiful Lyn Valley, this house offers simple accommodation which is ideal for guests touring the North Devon coast. Cream teas are served in the season.
5rm(1🛁1🚿3hc)(1fb) ® ✱ sB&Bfr£15 dB&Bfr£30 dB&B🛁🚿fr£35 WB&Bfr£95 WBDifr£147 LDO 5pm
Lic ♨ CTV 5P
Credit Cards [1] [£]

GH [Q][Q][Q] *Millslade Country House Hotel* EX35 6PS ☎(05987) 322
Situated in the heart of an attractive Exmoor village, this delightful Georgian house, recently renovated, stands in its own very pretty grounds next to the river, and affords commanding views of the valley and woodlands. Accommodation consists of cosy bedrooms, richly furnished with pleasing décor and soft, comfortable fabrics. The well-appointed restaurant, together with the tea garden, is open to the public and offers commendable standards of fresh food.
6rm(1🛁4🚿1hc)(1fb) CTV in all bedrooms ® LDO 9pm
Lic ♨ CTV 50P 🎣
Credit Cards [1] [2] [3] [5]

FH [Q] Mrs C A South ***Farley Water*** *(SS744464)* EX35 6LQ ☎(05987) 272
May-Sep
Peacefully situated on the edge of Exmoor, this farmhouse offers comfortable accommodation and a friendly atmosphere.
4rm(3hc)(2fb) CTV in 1 bedroom
nc 223 acres beef sheep

BRENT ELEIGH Suffolk Map **05** TL94

FH [Q][Q][Q] Mrs J P Gage **Street** *(TL945476)* CO10 9NU ☎Lavenham(0787) 247271
Closed mid Dec-mid Jan
Set at the heart of the village, with access from the A114 Lavenham/Hadleigh road, this 16th-century timbered farmhouse and its well-maintained walled garden are surrounded by 140 acres of arable land. Rooms are furnished individually and exceptionally well with period antique pieces, the lounge featuring an inglenook fireplace. A particularly hospitable proprietor offers a warm welcome to guests.
4rm(1🛁1🚿1hc) ® 🐕 ✱ sB&B🛁🚿£16 dB&B🛁🚿£32
♨ CTV 4P nc9yrs 143 acres arable
[£]

BRICKHILL, GREAT Buckinghamshire Map **04** SP93

INN [Q][Q] *Duncombe Arms* 32 Lower Way MK17 9AS ☎Great Brickhill(052526) 226
This is a small country inn, noted for its excellent views and hospitality. The accommodation provided is modest but comfortable. There is a small but popular restaurant which offers some well-prepared dishes, with the emphasis on English cuisine.
3🚿 CTV in all bedrooms ® 🐕 (ex guide dogs) LDO 10.30pm
♨ 12P 2🚗 🚌 petanque putting green garden skittles
Credit Cards [1] [3]

BRIDESTOWE Devon Map **02** SX58

⊢⊣**FH [Q][Q]** Mrs J E Down **Little Bidlake** *(SX494887)* EX20 4NS ☎(083786) 233
Whit-Oct
Neat, clean and efficient farmhouse adjacent to A30 between Bridestowe and Launceston.
2hc 🚭in all bedrooms 🐕 sB&B£11 dB&B£22 WB&B£70 WBDi£105
♨ CTV 0P 🎣 putting 150 acres beef dairy mixed
[£]

FH [Q][Q] Mrs J Northcott ***Town*** *(SX504905)* ☎(083786) 226
May-end Sep
Attractive Devonshire farmhouse situated in the centre of a typical Dartmoor village. Offers comfortable accommodation and friendly service.
3hc (1fb) ® LDO 6pm
♨ CTV 4P 160 acres dairy

FH [Q][Q] Mrs M Hockridge ***Week*** *(SX519913)* EX20 4HZ ☎(083786) 221
Large friendly 17th-century stone-built farmhouse set in peaceful Devon countryside.
6rm(2🚿4hc)(4fb) CTV in 3 bedrooms ® LDO 5pm
♨ CTV 10P 200 acres dairy sheep
See advertisement under OKEHAMPTON on page 279

BRIDGE OF EARN Tayside *Perthshire* Map **11** NO11

GH [Q][Q][Q] *Rockdale* Dunning St PH2 9AA ☎(0738) 812281
Set just off the main street, this small and comfortable house provides well-maintained accommodation. The bedrooms are bright, cheery and compact, and guests can enjoy a 'taste of Scotland' at dinner.
7rm(1🚿6hc)(1fb) ® LDO 7pm
Lic ♨ CTV 🚫P

BRIDGE OF MARNOCH Grampian *Aberdeenshire* Map **15** NJ55

SELECTED

GH [Q][Q][Q][Q] Old Manse of Marnoch AB5 5RS (off B9117 10m N of Huntly) ☎Aberchirder(04665) 873 due to change to (0466) 780873
Patrick and Karen Carter's lovely Georgian home is peacefully set in 3 acres of grounds amid the gentle rolling hills of the Devon Valley. The house is tastefully appointed throughout and offers comfortable bedrooms which have been individually decorated and furnished and an attractive, relaxing lounge. Imaginative food, featuring herbs and vegetables from the kitchen garden, is served at the communal table in the dining room. The Old Manse won the AA's Best Newcomer Award in 1988/89.
4rm(1🛁1🚿2hc) ® sB&B£25 sB&B🛁🚿£35 dB&B£35 dB&B🛁🚿£45 LDO 7pm
♨ CTV 6P cookery courses
[£]

BRIDGNORTH Shropshire Map **07** SO79

GH [Q][Q] Severn Arms Hotel Underhill St, Low Town WV16 4BB ☎(0746) 764616
Closed 23 Dec-2 Jan
A comfortable family hotel, this tall, terraced house is close to the bridge at Lowtown. Popular with anglers and their families, it is equally suitable for commercial visitors.
9rm(2🛁3🚿4hc)(5fb) CTV in 5 bedrooms TV in 2 bedrooms ® sB&B£21-£26 sB&B🛁🚿£32 dB&B£34 dB&B🛁🚿£41 WB&B£115-£140 WBDi£145-£170 LDO 7pm
Lic ♨ CTV 🎣
Credit Cards [1] [3] [£]

INN [Q] *Kings Head Hotel* Whitburn St WV16 4QN ☎(0746) 762141
Retaining many of its original 17th-century features, this town centre inn has well-equipped bedrooms. Bar meals are served here and there is a small dining room available for guests who prefer a little more privacy.
5hc (3fb) CTV in all bedrooms ® 🐕 (ex guide dogs) LDO 8pm
♨ 8P

BRIDLINGTON Humberside Map **08** TA16

GH **Q Q** **Bay Ridge Hotel** Summerfield Rd YO15 3LF
☎(0262) 673425
Spacious, well-designed conversion of two semidetached houses, close to South Bay.
14rm(6⇆6♠2hc)(5fb) CTV in all bedrooms ®
sB&B£17.50-£18.50 sB&B⇆♠£17.50-£18.50 dB&B£35-£37
dB&B⇆♠£35-£37 (incl dinner) WB&B£89-£95
WBDi£112-£120 LDO 5.45pm
Lic � CTV 6P bar billiards, library
£

GH **Q Q Q** **Langdon Hotel** Pembroke Ter YO15 3BX
☎(0262) 673065
This hotel is centrally placed in a quiet position on the south side of the town, and enjoys views of the sea. It has spacious lounges, a small, snug bar and well-equipped comfortable accommodation. Guests are cared for by friendly staff.
20rm(11♠9hc)(8fb) CTV in all bedrooms ® ✖ (ex guide dogs)
✳ sB&B£18-£19 sB&B♠£21-£22 LDO 5pm
Lic lift ♫

GH **Q Q Q** **Southdowne Hotel** South Marine Dr YO15 3NS
☎(0262) 673270
Bright and cheerful house facing the sea.
12rm(8♠4hc)(2fb) TV in 1 bedroom ® ✖ LDO 5.30pm
Lic ♫ CTV 10P
£

BRIDPORT Dorset Map **03** SY49

See also Bettiscombe, Chideock & Nettlecombe
GH **Q Q Q** *Bridge House* 115 East St DT6 3LB ☎(0308) 23371
This early 18th-century house with its low beamed ceilings is full of character. The comfortable, well-appointed accommodation features an intimate basement dining room which offers a short but interesting menu. The food is freshly prepared by Mrs Badger the proprietress.
10rm(7⇆1♠2hc)(4fb) ® LDO 9pm
Lic ♫ CTV 15P
Credit Cards [1] [3]

GH **Q Q Q** **Britmead House** 154 West Bay Rd DT6 4EG
☎(0308) 22941
The bedrooms here provide many extras such as hairdryers and electric blankets. Mr and Mrs Walker offer warm hospitality and fresh food.
7rm(5⇆2hc)(1fb) CTV in all bedrooms ® sB&B£18.50-£23
sB&B⇆£21.50-£26 dB&B£28-£34
dB&B⇆£37-£40 WB&B£91-£126 WBDi£155.75-£196 LDO
6pm
Lic ♫ 8P nc5yrs
Credit Cards [1][2][3][5] £
See advertisement on page 84

BRIGHTON & HOVE East Sussex Map **04** TQ30

See Town Plan Section
See also Rottingdean

SELECTED

GH **Q Q Q Q** **Adelaide Hotel** 51 Regency Square BN1 2FF
☎Brighton(0273) 205286 FAX (0273) 220904
mid Jan-23 Dec
This charming hotel is conveniently located in the prestigious square. Friendly and comfortable, it offers a choice of well-equipped and tastefully furnished accommodation. Meals may be taken in the attractive dining room but room service is also available. The hotel also has a comfortable and well-appointed lounge.
▶

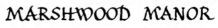

MARSHWOOD MANOR
Bettiscombe, Nr. Bridport, Dorset DT6 5NS
Telephone: (0308) 68442 or 68825

Marshwood Manor, Dorset

Set in the lovely Marshwood Vale within easy reach of the local beaches. Licensed. Really good food from our own kitchen garden. Home baked bread and jams a speciality. Swimming pool, putting, and croquet in large gardens. Nine spacious bedrooms, all with colour TV and most en-suite. Children and dogs welcome.

The resident proprietors Terry and Tricia Shakeshaft invite you to spend a comfortable and relaxing holiday in beautiful surroundings.

BREDWARDINE HALL

Mr & Mrs Jancey,
Bredwardine Hall Guest House, Bredwardine,
Nr Hereford HR3 6DB Moccas (09817) 596

The Hall is a charming 19th-century Manor House with immense character and literary interest standing in secluded wooded gardens, providing elegant well appointed accommodation; five delightful bedrooms; spacious en-suite bathrooms; full central heating; tea/coffee facilities; colour TV's; ample parking. Excellent food and wine; relaxed friendly atmosphere; personal service. Situated in the tranquil unspoiled Wye Valley; 7 miles Hay-on-Wye; 12 miles Hereford. Sorry no pets or children under 10.

12🛁🚿 (1fb) CTV in all bedrooms [R] 🐕
sB&B🛁🚿£33-£35
dB&B🛁🚿£55-£70 WB&B£173-£220 WBDi£250-£297
LDO 5pm
Lic ♨ 🅿
Credit Cards [1] [2] [3] [5] [£]

GH [Q][Q][Q] Allendale Hotel 3 New Steine BN2 1PB
☎Brighton(0273) 672994 & 675436
Set on a pleasant garden square, close to the seafront and local amenities, this charming Regency house offers well-equipped, modern accommodation. Completely refurbished to offer thoughtfully appointed rooms, a ground floor dining room and an adjoining, cosy lounge.
13rm(5🚿8hc)(5fb) CTV in all bedrooms [R] 🐕 (ex guide dogs) ✱ sB&B£22-£24 dB&B£34-£40
dB&B🚿£48-£52 wkly only (Dec-Etr) ♨ 🅿 nc8yrs
Credit Cards [1] [2] [3]

GH [Q][Q][Q] Ambassador Hotel 22 New Steine BN2 1PD
☎Brighton(0273) 676869
Conveniently situated close to the seafront, Palace Pier and within walking distance of the town, this hotel has bedrooms with modern facilities, all of which are en suite. There is also a TV lounge.
9rm(2🛁7🚿)(4fb) CTV in all bedrooms [R] 🐕
sB&B🛁🚿£22-£25 dB&B🛁🚿£40-£50
Lic ♨ CTV 🅿
Credit Cards [1] [2] [3] [5]

GH [Q][Q] Amblecliff Hotel 35 Upper Rock Gardens BN2 1QF
☎Brighton(0273) 681161 & 676945
The friendly proprietors here offer a hospitable atmosphere which complements the well-maintained and modern accommodation. There is also a snug television lounge, and the dining room offers a good selection of meals.
11rm(7🛁🚿4hc)🚭in 3 bedrooms CTV in all bedrooms [R] 🐕 (ex guide dogs) ✱ sB&B£17.50-£19.50 dB&B£35-£39
dB&B🛁🚿£42-£48
Lic ♨ CTV 3P (£1-£1.50) nc4yrs
Credit Cards [1] [2] [3] [5] [£]

GH [Q][Q][Q] Arlanda Hotel 20 New Steine BN2 1PD
☎Brighton(0273) 699300
This family-run, charming Regency-style hotel stands on a garden square and is close to the local amenities. Well-equipped modern accommodation is offered, together with a pleasant, well-appointed dining room and adjoining lounge with a piano.
12rm(2🛁10🚿)(4fb) CTV in all bedrooms [R] 🐕 (ex guide dogs)
sB&B🛁🚿£30-£35
dB&B🛁🚿£50-£60 WB&B£168-£240 LDO 4pm
Lic ♨ 🅿
Credit Cards [1] [2] [3] [5] [£]

GH [Q][Q][Q] Ascott House Hotel 21 New Steine, Marine Pde BN2 1PD ☎Brighton(0273) 688085
This appealing hotel is close to the seafront and town. Every effort has been made to ensure guests' comfort and the bedrooms are well equipped with modern conveniences. There is also a comfortable lounge and small bar.
12rm(9🚿)(7fb) CTV in all bedrooms [R] 🐕 ✱ sB&B£24-£28
sB&B🚿£26-£30 dB&B£40-£46 dB&B🚿£40-£58
Lic ♨ 🅿 nc3yrs
Credit Cards [1] [2] [3] [5]

GH [Q][Q] Cavalaire House 34 Upper Rock Gardens, Kemptown BN2 1QF ☎Brighton(0273) 696899
Closed Xmas-Feb
Within walking distance of the beach and local amenities, this pleasant Victorian hotel offers neat, well-kept accommodation with modern facilities. There is a small cosy lounge and a pleasant breakfast room.
9rm(2🚿7hc)(2fb) CTV in all bedrooms [R] sB&B£16-£18
dB&B£24-£29 dB&B🚿£32-£39
♨ 🅿 nc9yrs
[£]

GH [Q][Q][Q] Claremont House Second Av BN3 2LL
☎Brighton(0273) 735161
Gracious Victorian house retaining many original features. The bedrooms are comfortable and well appointed.
12🛁🚿 (2fb) CTV in all bedrooms [R] sB&B🛁🚿£33-£48
dB&B🛁🚿£58-£75 WB&B£260 WBDi£295 LDO 10pm
Lic ♨ CTV 🅿 ⌂
Credit Cards [1] [2] [3] [5]

GH [Q][Q] Cornerways Private Hotel 18-20 Caburn Rd BN3 6EF
☎Brighton(0273) 731882
A large Victorian corner house, Cornerways offers a variety of accommodation, mostly furnished in traditional style. There is a small bar, cosy TV lounge and a traditional dining room.
10rm(1🚿9hc)(2fb) CTV in 2 bedrooms [R] sB&Bfr£15
dB&Bfr£30 LDO 2pm
Lic ♨ CTV 🅿

GH [Q][Q] Croft Hotel 24 Palmeira Av BN3 3GB
☎Brighton(0273) 732860
Well-established guesthouse, pleasantly situated within easy walking distance of the beach.
10hc (2fb) CTV in all bedrooms [R] ✱ sB&B£20 dB&B£35
Lic ♨ CTV 🅿
[£]

GH [Q][Q] Le Flemings 12a Regency Square BN1 2FG
☎Brighton(0273) 27539 & 821928
Closed 24 Dec-1 Jan
Overlooking a grassy area which hides an underground car park, this hotel has well-equipped rooms on 3 floors. There is also a comfortable bar/lounge and an attractive breakfast room.
▶

9rm(1🛁8🚿)(3fb) CTV in all bedrooms [R] ✱
sB&B🛁🚿£25-£35 dB&B🛁🚿£40-£50
Lic ♨ CTV
Credit Cards [1] [2] [3] [5]

GH [Q][Q][Q] **Gullivers** 10 New Steine BN2 1PB
☎Brighton(0273) 695415
Just off the seafront this hotel is part of a listed Regency terrace and has been tastefully furnished. Comfortable, well-equipped bedrooms are complemented by friendly and helpful service.
9rm(5🚿4hc)(3fb) CTV in all bedrooms [R] sB&Bfr£20
sB&B🚿fr£36 dB&Bfr£38 dB&B🚿£48-£54
♨
Credit Cards [1] [3] [£]

GH [Q][Q] **Kempton House Hotel** 33/34 Marine Pde BN2 1TR
☎Brighton(0273) 570248
Two seafront Regency houses have been combined to provide bedrooms with modern facilities, and a pleasant bar and dining room. Kempton House is close to the Palace Pier and other amenities.
13rm(12🚿1hc)(4fb) CTV in all bedrooms [R] sB&B🚿fr£30
dB&B🚿£40-£50 WB&B£126-£157.50 WBDi£196-£227.50
LDO 9am
Lic ♨
Credit Cards [1] [2] [3] [5] [£]

GH [Q][Q] **Malvern Hotel** 33 Regency Square BN1 2GG
☎Brighton(0273) 24302
Standing in the square, overlooking the sea, this pleasant Regency-style hotel has well-equipped pleasant accommodation. In addition to the bar there is a small lounge.
12🚿 CTV in all bedrooms [R] 🐕 sB&B🚿£30-£38
dB&B🚿£44-£60 WB&Bfr£150
Lic ♨
Credit Cards [1] [2] [3] [5] [£]

GH [Q][Q][Q] **New Steine Hotel** 12a New Steine, Marine Pde
BN2 1PB ☎Brighton(0273) 681546
rs Xmas & New Year
This attractive Regency-style house has been refurbished to offer a good standard of accommodation. The caring proprietors offer genuine hospitality and the hotel is conveniently located for the beach and amenities.
11rm(4🚿7hc)(2fb) CTV in all bedrooms [R] ✱ sB&B£13-£15
sB&B🚿£25-£27 dB&B🚿£36-£39
♨ CTV P̸ nc8yrs

GH [Q][Q][Q] **Prince Regent Hotel** 29 Regency Square BN1 2FH
☎Brighton(0273) 29962
rs closed Xmas Eve & New Years Eve
Charming and elegant, this Regency hotel captures the grace of the bygone era. The bedrooms have modern facilities, and the public areas are tastefully appointed. The hotel enjoys a fine position overlooking lawns and the sea.
20rm(2🛁18🚿)🚭in 1 bedroom CTV in all bedrooms [R]
🐕 (ex guide dogs) sB&B🛁🚿fr£28 dB&B🛁🚿fr£48
Lic ♨ CTV P̸ nc12yrs
Credit Cards [1] [3] [5] [£]

GH [Q][Q] **Regency Hotel** 28 Regency Square BN1 2FH
☎Brighton(0273) 202690 FAX (0273) 220438
This elegant Regency-style house offers well-equipped accommodation, with bedrooms decorated in a variety of styles. The hotel offers a nicely appointed dining room, a comfortable lounge and a small bar.
14rm(1🛁10🚿3hc)(1fb) CTV in all bedrooms [R]
🐕 (ex guide dogs) ✱ LDO noon
Lic ♨ CTV P̸
Credit Cards [1] [2] [3] [5] [£]

GH [Q][Q][Q] **Sutherland Hotel** 9-10 Regency Square BN1 2FG
☎Brighton(0273) 27055
The accommodation here is well equipped and furnished to the highest standard. The lounge is quiet and comfortable; dinner can be served by request.
26rm(20🛁🚿6hc)(2fb) CTV in all bedrooms [R]
🐕 (ex guide dogs) ✱ sB&B£18-£20 sB&B🛁🚿£25-£30
dB&B£30 dB&B🛁🚿£35-£80 WB&Bfr£110 LDO 9pm
Lic lift ♨ P̸
Credit Cards [1] [2] [3] [5] [£]

GH [Q][Q][Q] **Trouville Hotel** 11 New Steine, Marine Pde
BN2 1PB ☎Brighton(0273) 697384
Closed Jan
Located close to the seafront, and within walking distance of the centre of the town, this is a well-maintained hotel offering attractive accommodation, including a cosy lounge and a nicely appointed dining room.
9rm(2🚿7hc)(2fb) CTV in all bedrooms [R] 🐕 sB&Bfr£15
dB&Bfr£26 dB&B🚿fr£42 WB&B£85-£140
Lic ♨ CTV
Credit Cards [1] [2] [3] [£]

GH [Q][Q][Q] **Twenty One** 21 Charlotte St, Marine Pde BN2 1AG
☎Brighton(0273) 686450
The bedrooms of this establishment, which is close to the beach, include a pleasant room with a separate sitting room on the lower ground floor which overlooks the ivy-clad courtyard, and a charming room with a four-poster bed on a higher floor. Meals other than breakfast must be ordered in advance.
7rm(5🚿2hc) CTV in all bedrooms [R] 🐕 (ex guide dogs) ✱
sB&B£32 sB&B🚿£37-£50 dB&B£45
dB&B🚿£48-£68 LDO 9am
Lic ♨ nc12yrs
Credit Cards [1] [2] [3] [£]

BRIGSTEER (nr Kendal) Cumbria Map 07 SD48

FH [Q][Q] Mrs B Gardner **Barrowfield** *(SD484908)* LA8 8BJ
☎Crosthwaite(04488) 336
Apr-Oct
This Elizabethan farmhouse, situated on a dairy farm just north of the village, is surrounded by fields and woods. It is found by taking the Kendal road from the village, and then a Forestry Commission road at the hill's top.
3rm(2hc)(1fb) 🐕 dB&Bfr£22
♨ CTV 6P 180 acres dairy sheep
[£]

BRISTOL Avon Map 03 ST57

See Town Plan Section
See also Redhill (Avon)

GH [Q][Q] **Alandale Hotel** Tyndall's Park Rd, Clifton BS8 1PG
☎(0272) 735407
Closed 2wks Xmas
Centrally situated in Clifton, close to the university, this guesthouse offers functional accommodation, popular with commercial travellers. A comfortable lounge and a small bar are available for residents' use.
17rm(5🛁12🚿)(1fb) CTV in all bedrooms [R] sB&B🛁🚿fr£35
dB&B🛁🚿fr£48
Lic ♨ 10P
Credit Cards [1] [3] [£]

GH [Q][Q] **Alcove** 508-510 Fishponds Rd, Fishponds BS16 3DT
☎(0272) 653886
Situated north east of the city, close to the M32 yet offering easy access to the centre, a friendly, pleasant guesthouse provides well-kept and comfortable accommodation with some modern facilities.

9rm(2🔥7hc)(2fb) CTV in all bedrooms ® ✖ (ex guide dogs) ✱
sB&B£17-£25 sB&B🔥£25 dB&B£30-£36
dB&B🔥£36 LDO 4pm
Lic ♨ CTV 8P 1🐾

GH Q Birkdale Hotel 11 Ashgrove Road, Redland BS6 6LY
☎(0272) 733635 & 736332 FAX (0272) 739964
Closed Xmas wk
*Situated north west of the city centre, off Whiteladies Road, this
large Victorian house caters mainly for commercial guests. Many
of the bedrooms are located in 2 separate annexes close to the main
building.*
42rm(34🔥8🔥) CTV in all bedrooms ® sB&Bfr£34.50
sB&B🔥🔥fr£40.25 dB&Bfr£57.50
dB&B🔥🔥fr£66.70 WB&Bfr£241.50 LDO 8pm
Lic ♨ 16P snooker
Credit Cards [1][3]

See advertisement on page 89

GH Q Chesterfield Hotel 3 Westbourne Place, Clifton BS8 1LX
☎(0272) 734606 Telex no 449075
Closed Xmas
*Situated on the edge of Clifton, this nice terraced house provides
low-cost, comfortable accommodation, ideal for the businessman.
Evening meals are available at a nearby sister hotel.*
13hc (2fb) CTV in all bedrooms ® ✱ sB&B£21 dB&B£35
♨ ⅌
Credit Cards [1][2][3][5]

GH QQQ Downlands 33 Henleaze Gardens, Henleaze
BS9 4HH ☎(0272) 621639
*A short drive from the city centre, Downlands is situated in a
pleasant residential area. Rooms are well decorated and
furnished; the house is comfortable and friendly.* ▶

10rm(1🛁9hc)(1fb) CTV in all bedrooms [R] sB&Bfr£20 dB&Bfr£35 dB&B🛁fr£38 WB&Bfr£120
♨ ⊘

GH [Q][Q][Q] Glenroy Hotel Victoria Square, Clifton BS8 4EW
☎(0272) 739058
Closed Xmas wk
Privately owned and run, this pleasant hotel stands in a leafy area of Clifton, and has some rooms in the adjacent property. Accommodation varies in size and standards but all rooms are comfortable with good facilities.
26rm(9🛁17🚿)Annexe 24rm(4🛁20🚿)(5fb) CTV in all bedrooms [R] * sB&B🛁🚿£40
dB&B🛁🚿£52-£60 WB&B£177-£270
Lic ♨ 16P
Credit Cards [1] [3] [£]

GH [Q] Oakfield Hotel 52-54 Oakfield Rd, Clifton BS8 2BG
☎(0272) 735556
Closed 23 Dec-1-Jan
This simple guesthouse offers well-kept, functional accommodation, and is particularly popular with commercial clients. Early morning tea, and hot drinks and biscuits in the evening are thoughtfully provided.
27hc (4fb) CTV in all bedrooms [R] sB&B£23-£25
dB&B£34-£36 LDO 7pm
♨ CTV 4P 2🚗

GH [Q][Q][Q] *Seeleys Hotel* 17-27 St Pauls Rd, Clifton BS8 1LX
☎(0272) 738544
Closed Xmas wk
This large hotel offers accommodation with excellent modern facilities, many rooms having spa or air baths. Jacuzzi, sauna and steam baths are available in the small health centre, and the lively basement restaurant features live entertainment 3 times a week.
53rm(14🛁29🚿10hc)Annexe 10🛁🚿 (20fb) CTV in all bedrooms [R] 🚫 (ex guide dogs) LDO 10.30pm
Lic ♨ 13P 22🚗 🏊 sauna solarium gymnasium
Credit Cards [1] [2] [3]

GH [Q][Q] Washington Hotel 11-15 St Pauls Rd, Clifton BS8 1LX
☎(0272) 733980 Telex no 449075
Closed 23 Dec-3 Jan
The car park belonging to this large, unlicensed private hotel is a particular bonus in this area. The rooms are modern and well equipped but public areas are limited.
43rm(21🛁8🚿14hc)(5fb) CTV in all bedrooms [R] * sB&B£26
sB&B🛁🚿£42 dB&B£42 dB&B🛁🚿£56
Lic ♨ 20P
Credit Cards [1] [2] [3] [5]

GH [Q][Q] The Willow 209 Gloucester Rd, Patchway BS12 5AD
☎Almondsbury(0454) 612276
One mile south of junction 16 of the M5, on the A38, this double-fronted house has a Tudor-style dining room where a good range of dishes is offered. Many of the well-equipped bedrooms have good en suite facilities.
16rm(13🚿3hc)(3fb) CTV in all bedrooms [R] sB&B🚿fr£35
dB&B🚿fr£42 LDO 10pm
Lic ♨ CTV 14P
Credit Cards [1] [3]

BRIXHAM Devon Map **03** SX95

See Town Section

GH [Q][Q] Cottage Hotel Mount Pleasant Rd TQ5 9SD
☎(0803) 882123
7hc [R] 🚫 (ex guide dogs) * sB&Bfr£12
dB&Bfr£26 WBDi£146 LDO 8pm
Lic ♨ CTV 6P

SELECTED

GH [Q][Q][Q][Q] Greenbrier Hotel Victoria Rd TQ5 9AR
☎(0803) 882113
Etr-Oct
Standing in attractive gardens with beautiful views across the bay, this comfortable hotel has en suite bedrooms with colour TV/video. Those on the first floor have a little extra space and commanding views. The pleasant public rooms have a cosy atmosphere. The Lunn family provide bed and breakfast accommodation only, with friendly service, and the hotel has the benefit of its own car park.
10rm(2🛁8🚿)(2fb) CTV in all bedrooms [R]
🚫 (ex guide dogs) * sB&B🛁🚿£21-£23
dB&B🛁🚿£33-£46 WB&B£122.50-£147
Lic ♨ CTV 17P
Credit Cards [1] [3] [£]

GH [Q][Q][Q] Harbour Side 65 Berry Head Rd TQ5 9AA
☎(08045) 58899 due to change to (0803) 858899
Friendly guesthouse overlooking harbour and coastline.
6rm(1🚿5hc)(2fb) CTV in all bedrooms [R] 🚫 (ex guide dogs)
sB&B£14-£18 dB&B£24-£28
dB&B🚿£28-£32 WB&B£76-£100 WBDi£123-£138 LDO 10am
CTV ⊘
[£]

GH [Q][Q] Raddicombe Lodge 105 Kingswear Rd TQ5 0EX
☎(0803) 882125
14 Apr-14 Oct
8rm(3🚿5hc)(2fb) CTV in all bedrooms [R] 🚫
sB&B£14.30-£21.60 dB&B£28.60-£35.60
dB&B🚿£35.60-£40.60 WB&B£100.10-£130.90
CTV 9P
Credit Cards [1] [3] [£]

GH [Q][Q] *Ranscombe House Hotel* Ranscombe Rd TQ5 9UP
☎(0803) 882337
This detached property dates back to 1743 and is within walking distance of the harbour. The well-equipped bedrooms have en suite facilities and the restaurant offers an interesting à la carte menu. Guests receive a warm welcome and good service here.
9rm(6🛁3🚿)(2fb) CTV in all bedrooms [R] 🚫 (ex guide dogs)
LDO 7pm
Lic ♨ 16P
Credit Cards [1] [2] [3]

GH [Q][Q] Sampford House 59 King St TQ5 9TH ☎(08045) 7761
Mar-Oct
This family-run terraced property enjoys an elevated position providing views of the inner harbour. The cosy bedrooms are furnished to make good use of the available space. Sampford House provides bed and breakfast and has no private parking.
6hc (2fb) CTV in 3 bedrooms TV in 3 bedrooms [R] *
sB&B£12-£14 dB&B£24-£32 WB&B£80-£105 LDO 10am
CTV ⊘
[£]

GH [Q][Q][Q] Woodlands Parkham Rd TQ5 9BU
☎(0803) 852040
Apr-Oct
Overlooking the town and harbour, this attractive Victorian house provides quality bed and breakfast accommodation for non-smokers. Mr and Mrs Doling offer modern facilities and, after living in Holland, make this hotel especially popular with Dutch tourists. The guesthouse is 'no smoking' throughout.
5🚿 (1fb)🚭in all bedrooms CTV in all bedrooms [R] 🚫
sB&B🚿£16-£17 dB&B🚿£32-£34 WB&B£100-£107
♨ 4P
Credit Cards [1] [3]

BROAD HAVEN (nr Haverfordwest) Dyfed Map **02** SM81

GH QQ ***Broad Haven Hotel*** SA62 3JN
☎Haverfordwest(0437) 781366
This is a large family holiday hotel, standing opposite the beach. The bedrooms, nearly all of which are en suite, are well equipped with modern facilities. There are good leisure facilities, and the bars are popular with tourists and locals.
39rm(31⇨4↱4hc)(7fb) CTV in all bedrooms ® LDO 8pm
Lic 100P ⩯(heated) snooker solarium table tennis
Credit Cards [1] [2] [3]

BROAD MARSTON Hereford & Worcester Map **04** SP14

GH QQQ Broad Marston Manor CV37 8XY
☎Stratford-on-Avon(0789) 720252
Closed 24-27 Dec
This 12th-century Cotswold stone manor house is set in 5 acres of grounds and gardens. It has a wealth of charm and character, with an abundance of exposed beams and antique furniture.
7rm(4⇨↱3hc)(2fb)⊬in all bedrooms CTV in 3 bedrooms TV in 4 bedrooms ® ✗ (ex guide dogs) ✱ sB&B£20-£25 sB&B⇨↱£25-£28 dB&B£39-£45 dB&B⇨↱£45-£55
20P nc12yrs
See advertisement under STRATFORD-UPON-AVON on page 343

BROADSTAIRS Kent Map **05** TR36

GH QQQ Bay Tree Hotel 12 Eastern Esplanade CT10 1DR
☎Thanet(0843) 62502
This attractive, modernised Victorian house has magnificent sea views. The bedrooms are comfortable and well kept and some have en suite facilities. The bar lounge and dining room are comfortable and attractive and a warm and friendly atmosphere prevails.
11rm(2⇨7↱2hc) CTV in all bedrooms ® ✗ (ex guide dogs) LDO 2pm
▶

Lic 🍽 12P nc10yrs
Credit Cards 1 3

GH Q Q **Devonhurst Hotel** Eastern Esplanade CT10 1DR
☎Thanet(0843) 63010
*A pleasant welcome is extended to guests at this family-run hotel,
which offers nicely appointed bedrooms and a friendly atmosphere.
The comfortable first floor lounge has a balcony affording
magnificent views of the sea and coastline.*
8rm(7♠1hc)(1fb) CTV in all bedrooms ® ✖ (ex guide dogs) ✱
dB&B£33-£35
dB&B♠£35-£41 WB&B£112-£133 WBDi£147-£168 LDO 6pm
Lic 🍽 ⚡ nc5yrs
£

GH Q Q *East Horndon Private Hotel* 4 Eastern Esplanade
CT10 1DP ☎Thanet(0843) 68306
*Large 3-storeyed detached house enjoying an elevated position
overlooking the sea. Bedrooms are well equipped and the hotel has
a small lounge bar and television room.*
11rm(1⇨1♠9hc)(4fb) CTV in 9 bedrooms TV in 1 bedroom
®
Lic 🍽 ⚡
Credit Cards 1 3

BROADWAY Hereford & Worcester Map **04** SP03

SELECTED

GH Q Q Q Q **Leasow House** WR12 7NA
☎Stanton(038673) 526
(For full entry see Laverton)

SELECTED

GH Q Q Q Q **Old Rectory** WR12 7PN ☎(0386) 853729
(For full entry see Willersey)

GH Q Q **Olive Branch Guest House** 78 High St WR12 7AJ
☎(0386) 853440
Closed 24-31 Dec
*The rooms in this fine 16th-century house are situated above both a
grocery shop and an antique shop. To the rear is a secluded garden
and a large car park.*
9rm(7♠2hc)(2fb) CTV in all bedrooms ® ✖ (ex guide dogs) ✱
sB&B£16.75 dB&B£32
dB&B♠£35 WB&B£117.50 LDO 9.30pm
Lic CTV 9P ♨
£

BRODICK

See **ARRAN, ISLE OF**

BROMLEY Greater London

London plan **4** F2 (pages 230-231)
GH Q Q **Glendevon House** 80 Southborough Rd, Bickley
BR1 2EN (2m E off A22) ☎081-467 2183
*Mrs Dignam runs this small commercial hotel in a warm and
friendly manner. Situated in a residential area within easy reach of
Bickley station and Bromley shopping centre, it has modern
bedrooms and generous public areas.*
10rm(1♠9hc)(1fb) CTV in 6 bedrooms ® ✱ sB&B£18-£24
dB&B£30-£34 LDO 9pm
🍽 CTV 7P
Credit Cards 1 3 £

BROMPTON REGIS Somerset Map **03** SS93

FH Q Mrs G Payne **Lower Holworthy** *(SS978308)* TA22 9NY
☎(03987) 244
Closed Xmas
*Small 18th-century hill farm overlooking and bordering
Wimbleball Lake in Exmoor National Park.*
3rm(2hc) ® ✖ (ex guide dogs)
🍽 CTV 6P 200 acres beef sheep

BROMSGROVE Hereford & Worcester Map **07** SO97

INN Q **The Forest** 290 Birmingham Rd B61 0XO
☎(0527) 72063
Closed Xmas
*A large house at the junction of the A38 and M42 north of the
town, The Forest offers simple and comfortable accommodation
and a good selection of wholesome food. It caters mainly for
commercial guests.*
9hc CTV in all bedrooms ® ✱ sB&B£30-£35
dB&B£40-£50 LDO 9.15pm
🍽 70P
Credit Cards 1 2 3

BRONLLYS Powys Map **03** SO13

GH Q Q **Beacons Edge Country Hotel** Pontithel LD3 0RY
☎Brecon(0874) 711182
*Situated alongside the A438, Brecon to Hereford road, this is a
cosy, family-run inn offering good, friendly hospitality. The
bedrooms are compact but well equipped and the restaurant has
earned a good local reputation.*
7rm(1⇨6♠)(1fb) CTV in all bedrooms ® ✱
sB&B⇨♠£22-£26
dB&B⇨♠£40-£48 WB&B£125-£145 WBDi£170-£190 LDO
9.30pm
Lic 🍽 24P
Credit Cards 1 3 £

BROUGH Cumbria Map **12** NY71

FH Q Q Q Mrs J M Atkinson **Augill House** *(NY814148)*
CA17 4DX ☎(09304) 305
Closed Xmas & New Year
*Situated just off the southern end of the bypass, this attractive
Georgian house is run by a friendly proprietress and offers
comfortable accommodation.*
3hc TV in all bedrooms ® ✱ sB&Bfr£12.50
dB&B£25 LDO 4pm
🍽 CTV 6P nc7yrs ✔ 40 acres mixed
£

BROXTON Cheshire Map **07** SJ45

SELECTED

GH Q Q Q Q *Frogg Manor* Barnhill, Nantwich Rd
CH3 9JH ☎(0829) 782629 & 782280
*Nine acres of landscaped gardens lie to the rear of this
Georgian manor house on the A534. Individually furnished
and artistically decorated, the bedrooms have many extras
and an air of comfort and elegance prevails throughout.
English cuisine is served in the intimate restaurant, chosen
from à la carte and set menus. A private dining room is
available for small parties. Frogg Manor is a thoroughly
English hotel, run by a caring host.*
7rm(4⇨3♠)(1fb) CTV in all bedrooms ® LDO 10pm
Lic 🍽 24P nc5yrs ⌧(heated) ♪(hard)sauna gymnasium
mature gardens
Credit Cards 1 2 3 5

BRUAR Tayside *Perthshire* Map **14** NN86

⊢⊣INN Ⓠ Ⓠ **Bruar Falls Hotel** PH18 5TW
☎Calvine(0796) 83243
This small and friendly family-run hotel in a picturesque setting just off the A9 offers simple sleeping accommodation. Meals are available throughout the day in the neat public rooms.
7hc (2fb) CTV in all bedrooms Ⓡ sB&B£12.50-£15.50
dB&B£25-£31 WB&B£87.50-£108.50 Bar Lunch
£4.30-£14.75alc LDO 10pm
🍴 80P 👌 pool table
Credit Cards 1️⃣ 2️⃣ 3️⃣ 5️⃣ Ⓔ

BRUTON Somerset Map **03** ST63

SELECTED

GH Ⓠ Ⓠ Ⓠ Ⓠ *Fryerning* Frome Road, Burrowfield
BA10 0HH ☎(0749) 812343
This charming house stands on the fringe of the town and has well-furnished, spacious bedrooms and a relaxing lounge with plenty of books. Mr and Mrs King offer hospitality of the highest standard.
4rm(3⇆1♠) CTV in 2 bedrooms TV in 2 bedrooms Ⓡ
LDO 7pm
Lic 🍴 CTV 6P nc9yrs

BRYNGWYN Powys Map **03** SO14

FH Ⓠ Mrs H E A Nicholls **Newhouse** *(SO191497)* LD2 3JT
☎Painscastle(04975) 671
200-year-old, 2-storeyed, stone-built farmhouse in rolling countryside.
2hc ⅟ᴸin all bedrooms Ⓡ ✠ (ex guide dogs) sB&B£15
dB&B£26 WB&Bfr£84
🍴 CTV 3P ⤜ pony treking 150 acres beef sheep

BRYNSIENCYN Gwynedd Map **06** SH46

FH Ⓠ Ⓠ Ⓠ Mrs M Roberts *Plas Trefarthen (SH483661)* Plas
Trefarthen LL61 6SZ ☎Bangor(0248) 73379
Closed Xmas
This large Georgian house is beautifully preserved and maintained. Quietly situated, it enjoys excellent views of Snowdonia across the Menai Straits. The bedrooms are spacious and well equipped.
7rm(4⇆1♠)(6fb) CTV in all bedrooms Ⓡ ✠ (ex guide dogs)
LDO 2pm
🍴 20P snooker 200 acres arable, beef, sheep

BUCKFAST Devon Map **03** SX76

GH Ⓠ Ⓠ Ⓠ *Black Rock Hotel* Buckfast Road, TQ11 0EA (at
Buckfast 1m N) ☎Buckfastleigh(0364) 42343
Standing in its own gardens beside the River Dart, on the edge of the village, this property has great character. The rooms are attractive with their own colour television and private facilities and there is a spacious bar and restaurant serving home-cooked fare. The hotel benefits from its own fishing and car park.
10rm(8♠2hc)(3fb) CTV in all bedrooms Ⓡ ✠ (ex guide dogs)
LDO 8.30pm
Lic 🍴 CTV 43P ⤜
Credit Cards 1️⃣ 3️⃣

See advertisement on page 93

GH Ⓠ Ⓠ **Furzeleigh Mill Country Hotel** Dart Bridge TQ11 0JP
☎Buckfastleigh(0364) 43476
This 16th-century mill house has been converted into a pleasant, relaxed hotel. The compact bedrooms have colour TV and some have en suite facilities. The comfy lounge has a well-stocked bar and in the restaurant a table d'hôte menu offers interesting home-cooked dishes.

▶

15rm(13⇨3♠2hc)(2fb) CTV in all bedrooms ®
sB&B£19.25-£21.95 sB&B⇨3♠£21.85-£23.95 dB&B£32-£36.50
dB&B⇨3♠£36-£40.50 WBD£136.25-£183.50 LDO 8pm
Lic ⚏ CTV 32P ⚙
Credit Cards [1][2][3] £

BUCKNELL Shropshire Map **07** SO37

FH[Q] Mrs C Price *The Hall (SO356737)* SY7 0AA
☎(05474) 249
Mar-Nov
*A large Georgian farmhouse providing comfortable
accommodation in peaceful rural surroundings close to the village
centre.*
3hc (1fb) ✖ LDO noon
CTV 4P nc7yrs 225 acres arable sheep

BUDE Cornwall & Isles of Scilly Map **02** SS20

⊷⊶**GH**[Q] **Atlantic Beach** 25 Downs View EX23 2RG
☎(0288) 353431
*This terraced house, set close to the sea, and overlooking the golf
course and Downs, offers fresh, modern accommodation suitable
for family holidays. There is a small bar and lounge, as well as a
pretty dining room.*
9rm(4♠5hc)(3fb) CTV in all bedrooms ® ✖ (ex guide dogs)
sB&B£12.50-£14 dB&B£25-£28
dB&B♠£29-£32 WB&B£87.50-£108.50 WBD£129.50-£150.50
LDO 6.30pm
Lic ⚏ CTV 4P
Credit Cards [1][2][3] £

GH[Q][Q][Q] **Cliff Hotel** Maer Down, Crooklets EX23 8NG
☎(0288) 353110
Apr-Oct
*The purpose-built hotel stands in an elevated position, surrounded
by grounds which include a putting green, tennis court and
children's play area; an indoor heated pool, spa bath and solarium
are also available for guests' use. All bedrooms have en suite
bathrooms and the restaurant features imaginative, home-cooked
meals.*
15⇨ (12fb) CTV in all bedrooms sB&B⇨£21-£25
dB&B⇨£40-£48 WB&B£90-£125 WBD£130-£175 LDO 6pm
Lic CTV 15P ⬛(heated) ♪(hard)solarium indoor spa pool
£

⊷⊶**GH**[Q][Q][Q] **Corisande Hotel** 24 Downs View EX23 8RG
☎(0288) 353474
Closed Xmas
*Close to the beach and overlooking the golf course, this family-run
hotel has comfortable bedrooms with good facilities. A variety of
home-cooked food is served in the dining room by friendly
proprietors.*
9rm(5♠4hc)(2fb) CTV in all bedrooms ® sB&B£12-£14
dB&B£24-£28
dB&B♠£28-£32 WB&B£80-£95 WBD£105-£130 LDO
5.30pm
Lic ⚏ 3P nc3yrs
Credit Cards [1][3] £

GH[Q][Q][Q] **Dorset House Hotel** 47 Killerton Rd EX23 8EN
☎(0288) 352665
*This attractive licensed hotel with its wood-panelled walls, retains
much of its original charm. The bedrooms are of ample size, and
have good bath and shower facilities, and the public rooms are
complemented by a bar and pool room.*
6rm(1⇨5hc)(2fb)✖in all bedrooms ® ✖ ✱ sB&Bfr£15
dB&Bfr£30
dB&B⇨frf36 WB&B£84-£91 WBD£98-£117 LDO 6.30pm
Lic ⚏ CTV 6P games room
Credit Cards [1][3] £

GH[Q][Q] **Kisauni** 4 Downs View EX23 8RF ☎(0288) 352653
*Occupying a convenient position overlooking the golf course, this
guesthouse has bright bedrooms and a very comfortable lounge.
There is a licensed bar and guests can enjoy interesting home-
cooked food and friendly service in the separate dining room.*
6hc (4fb) CTV in all bedrooms ® ✱ sB&B£10.50-£12.50
dB&B£21-£25 WB£66-£80 WBD£104-£125.50 LDO
4.30pm
Lic ⚏ CTV 5P

GH[Q] **Links View** 13 Morwenna Ter EX23 8BU
☎(0288) 352561
Closed Dec
*Enjoying an elevated position overlooking the Downs, this hotel
offers compact accommodation with cosy public rooms and well-
furnished and equipped bedrooms.*
7hc (2fb) CTV in all bedrooms ® ✖ (ex guide dogs) ✱
sB&B£11.50-£13 dB&B£23-£26 WB&B£72-£82
Lic ⚏ CTV 2P 1🚗
£

⊷⊶**GH**[Q][Q] **Pencarrol** 21 Downs View EX23 8RF
☎(0288) 352478
Closed Dec
*This friendly guesthouse offers cheerful accommodation and has 2
bedrooms on the ground floor. There is a first floor lounge and
separate dining room where home-cooked food is served, using
home-grown produce whenever possible.*
8rm(1♠7hc)(2fb) CTV in 2 bedrooms ® ✖ (ex guide dogs)
sB&B£11-£13 dB&B£22-£26
dB&B♠£26-£30 WB&B£69-£82 WBD£114.50-£127.50 LDO
5pm
CTV 1🚗
£

GH[Q][Q] *Wayfarer Hotel* 23 Downs View EX23 8RG
☎(0288) 352253
31 Mar-21 Apr & 14 Jul-2 Sep
9rm(2⇨2♠5hc)(5fb) CTV in all bedrooms ® LDO 6.30pm
Lic ⚏ CTV 4P

FH[Q][Q] Mrs S Trewin **Lower Northcott** *(SS215087)* Poughill
EX23 7EL ☎(0288) 352350
Closed Dec
*Standing in 470 acres with views over countryside and coastline,
this Georgian farmhouse has a secure garden with swings and
young animals, and guests can take tours around the farm.
Families are well catered for with spacious bedrooms.*
5rm(1⇨2♠2hc)(3fb) ✖ ✱ sB&Bfr£14 dB&Bfr£28
dB&B⇨♠frf28 WB&Bfr£90 WBDfr£110 (wkly only Jul-
Aug) LDO 6.30pm
⚏ CTV 4P 470 acres arable beef dairy sheep

BUDLEIGH SALTERTON Devon Map **03** SY08

GH[Q][Q][Q] **Copperfields** 7 Upper Stoneborough Ln EX9 6SZ
☎(03954) 3430
Etr-Sep
*This delightful Victorian house is set in a quiet location just 5
minutes' walk from the sea and town centre. Whilst retaining its
original charm, Copperfields offers modern-day comfort, including
bright bedrooms with en suite showers, lavatory and television.*
6rm(3♠3hc)(1fb) CTV in all bedrooms ® sB&B£16-£17.50
dB&B£30-£33
dB&B♠£35-£39 WB&B£1214-£122.50 WBD£160-£176 LDO
5pm
Lic ⚏ 8P nc9yrs

GH[Q][Q][Q] **Long Range Hotel** Vale's Rd EX9 6HS
☎(03954) 3321
Apr-Oct
*This modern detached building within attractive gardens, is 15
minutes' walk from the town centre and seafront. After major
refurbishment, 6 of the 7 bedrooms have en suite facilities and all*

are well equipped. All areas are tastefully decorated, and the sun lounge offers access to the lounge garden. A choice of evening meal is provided, and owners Mr and Mrs Griffin are always available to give guests their personal attention.
7rm(2⇔4↑1hc)(2fb) CTV in all bedrooms ® ✈ ✳
sB&B£19.50 sB&B⇔↑£19.50
dB&B⇔↑£39 WB&B£136.50 WBDi£175 LDO 7pm
🍴CTV 8P 2🚗 (£1 per night) nc4yrs

GH Q *Tidwell House Country Hotel* EX9 7AG ☎(03954) 2444
Closed 24 Dec-1 Jan
Beautiful Georgian manor in extensive gardens.
9rm(3⇔4↑2hc)(5fb) ® LDO 9.15pm
Lic 🍴CTV 24P 4🚗 ∪

GH QQ *Willowmead* 12 Little Knowle EX9 6QS
☎(03954) 3115
6rm(2↑4hc) ® ✳ sB&B↑fr£13 dB&Bfr£26
dB&B↑fr£31 WB&B£65-£70 WBDi£115-£130
🍴CTV 6P nc5yrs
£

BUNESSAN

See **MULL, ISLE OF**

BURFORD Oxfordshire Map **04** SP21

GH QQQ Andrews Hotel High St OX8 4RJ ☎(099382) 3151
Set in the centre of this charming Cotswold town, this hotel has character and provides well-appointed, spacious bedrooms and comfortable public rooms. There is a popular tea room which provides homemade cakes. A warm welcome is assured.
10⇔↑ (1fb)✂in all bedrooms CTV in all bedrooms ®
✈ (ex guide dogs) ✳ sB&B⇔↑£24.75-£42.75
dB&B⇔↑£48.75-£62.75 WB&Bfr£140

▶

Lic ♿ CTV ⚲
Credit Cards [1] [2] [3] [5]

BURGH ST PETER Norfolk Map **05** TM49

FH Q Q Mrs R M Clarke **Shrublands** *(TM473926)* NR34 0BB
☎Aldeby(050277) 241

*Mr and Mrs Clark provide comfortable accommodation at their
farmhouse which is surrounded by arable land, and is close to the
village. Well-tended lawns and shrubberies contrast with the busy
farmyard to the other side of the house. The Waveney River
Centre is just 1 mile away.*

3hc (1fb) ® ✹ dB&B£26-£30 WB&B£182-£210
♿ CTV 6P nc5yrs ♟(hard)480 acres arable beef pigs
£

BURNHAM-ON-CROUCH Essex Map **05** TQ99

GH Q Q **Cromwell House** 42 High St CM0 8AA
☎Maldon(0621) 783654

*A tastefully modernised Victorian house offering well-appointed
and spacious accommodation. Some rooms have retained their
original Victorian fireplaces and there is also a small sun terrace to
the rear.*

5⇨♣ (2fb) CTV in all bedrooms ® ✳ sB&B⇨♣£23
dB&B⇨♣£34.50 WB&Bfr£241.50
♿ ⚲
Credit Cards [1] [3]

BURNSALL North Yorkshire Map **07** SE06

GH Q **Manor House** BD23 6BW ☎(075672) 231
Closed Jan

Small, private hotel whose gardens run down to River Wharfe.

7hc (2fb) ✹ LDO 5pm
Lic ♿ CTV 7P ✔ ☋ solarium

BURROWBRIDGE Somerset Map **03** ST32

GH Q **The Old Bakery** TA7 0RB ☎(082369) 234
Mar-24 Dec

*A warm and friendly welcome is to be had at this family-run
guesthouse. Standing on the A361, halfway between Street and
Taunton, it offers comfortable, simply appointed accommodation
and an extensive menu.*

6rm(1⇨5hc)(2fb)✟in all bedrooms ✹ (ex guide dogs) ✳
sB&B£12.50-£14.50 dB&B£25-£29
dB&B⇨£29-£33 LDO 9.30pm
Lic ♿ CTV 8P
Credit Cards [1] [3]

BURTON BRADSTOCK Dorset Map **03** SY48

GH Q Q Q **Common Knapp House** Coast Rd DT6 4RJ
☎(0308) 897428
Closed Dec-Jan

*This modern house is on the coast road and has spacious, well-
equipped bedrooms with en suite showers. There is a cosy bar
lounge with books and games and a spacious dining room. This is a
'no smoking' house.*

12rm(9♣3hc)(1fb)✟in all bedrooms CTV in 9 bedrooms ®
✹ (ex guide dogs) ✳ sB&B£18-£20 dB&B£36-£40
dB&B♣£40-£44 WB&B£140-£154 WBDif£192.85-£206.25
LDO 4pm
Lic ♿ 12P nc4yrs

See advertisement under DORCHESTER

BURTON UPON TRENT Staffordshire Map **08** SK22

GH Q Q Q **Delter Hotel** 5 Derby Rd DE14 1RU
☎(0283) 35115

*This bright and cheerful hotel is situated on the edge of the town,
on the Derby road. The bedrooms are well equipped, and in the
evening, snacks are served in the small basement bar.*

5rm(1⇨4♣)(1fb) CTV in all bedrooms ® ✹ (ex guide dogs)
sB&B⇨♣£28 dB&B⇨♣£38 LDO noon
Lic ♿ CTV 5P
Credit Cards [1] [3] £

GH Q **Edgecote Hotel** 179 Ashby Rd DE15 0LB
☎Burton on Trent(0283) 68966

*This family-run hotel is a large, detached house situated on the
edge of the town on the A50, Ashby road. It has a well-maintained
rear garden and an oak-panelled dining room.*

12rm(1♣11hc)(3fb)✟in all bedrooms CTV in all bedrooms ®
✹ (ex guide dogs) sB&B£17 sB&B♣fr£28 dB&B£28
dB&B♣fr£38 LDO 8.15pm
Lic ♿ CTV 6P 2🚗
Credit Cards [1] [3] £

BURWASH East Sussex Map **05** TQ62

FH Q Q Mrs E Sirrell **Woodlands** *(TQ656242)* TN19 7LA
☎(0435) 882794
Etr-Oct

*Remotely situated and surrounded by woodland, this 16th-century
cottage-style farmhouse has functional modern bedrooms (2 with
en suite bathrooms) and a breakfast room. There is a private track
access from the main road. This farmhouse offers very good value
for money.*

4rm(1♣1hc) ✹✹ sB&Bfr£14.50 dB&Bfr£24
dB&B♣£28-£32 LDO am
♿ CTV 4P 55 acres mixed

INN Q **Admiral Vernon** Etchingham Rd TN19 7BJ
☎(0435) 882230

*This cosy old fasioned 'free house' offers home cooking, and good
views over the Rother Valley. The rear garden is delightful.*

5hc (2fb) CTV in 1 bedroom TV in 4 bedrooms ® LDO
8.15pm
♿ CTV 30P 2🚗 nc9yrs

BURY ST EDMUNDS Suffolk Map **05** TL86

See also Beyton

GH Q Q Q **The Chantry Hotel** 8 Sparhawk St IP33 1RY
☎(0284) 767427 FAX (0284) 760946
rs wknds

*South of the town centre, within walking distance of the Abbey,
this 16th-century listed terrace building with its Tudor annexe
offers good quality, well-equipped accommodation. The hotel
benefits from a residents' bar, restaurant and a good car park.*

14rm(5⇨9♣)Annexe 3⇨♣ (1fb) CTV in all bedrooms ®
sB&B⇨♣£36.50-£39.50
dB&B⇨♣£48.50-£58.50 LDO 6.45pm
Lic ♿ 16P
Credit Cards [1] [3] £

GH Q Q Q **Dunston House Hotel** 8 Springfield Rd IP33 3AN
☎(0284) 767981

Well-extended, Victorian house with bright, well-equipped rooms.

12rm(6♣6hc)Annexe 5hc (5fb) CTV in all bedrooms ® ✹ ✳
sB&B£16-£20 sB&B♣£22-£25 dB&B£28-£30
dB&B♣£32-£36 WB&B£112-£140 WBDif£182-£245 LDO
10pm previous day
Lic ♿ CTV 12P
£

GH Q Q Q **The Olde White Hart** 35 Southgate St IP33 2AZ
☎(0284) 755547

*Easily found if approached from the most easterly exit of the A45,
this inn near the town centre was originally an 11th-century chapel
beside the river Linnet before being converted into a Tudor public
house and then an 18th-century maltings. Most of the original
buildings still remain and have been converted into a small luxury
hotel. The accommodation is in good order with every modern
facility, including en suite rooms.*

10⇨📺 (2fb) CTV in all bedrooms ® ✖ (ex guide dogs) ✻
sB&B⇨📺£38-£42 dB&B⇨📺£48-£54
Lic ㎜ 7P
Credit Cards ①②③ ⓔ

BUTLEIGH Somerset Map 03 ST53

FH ⓠⓠ Mrs Atkinson **Court Lodge** *(ST517339)* BA6 8SA
☎Baltonsborough(0458) 50575
*This pretty house nestles in secluded gardens in the village of
Butleigh and has commanding views of the surrounding
countryside. The rooms have traditional style and charm, and
substantial breakfasts are served in the bright dining room.*
2rm TV available ✻ sB&Bfr£10.50 dB&Bfr£21
㎜ CTV 4P 110 acres beef
ⓔ

FH ⓠⓠⓠ Mrs J M Gillam **Dower House** *(ST517333)*
BA6 8TG ☎Baltonsborough(0458) 50354
Feb-Nov
Attractive 18th-century farmhouse with friendly atmosphere.
3rm(1⇨2hc)(1fb) ® ✖ (ex guide dogs) ✻ sB&B£13.50
dB&B£24 dB&B⇨£30 LDO 4.30pm
㎜ CTV 6P 80 acres non-working
ⓔ

BUXTON Derbyshire Map 07 SK07

GH ⓠⓠ **Buxton Lodge Private Hotel** 28 London Rd SK17 9NX
☎(0298) 23522
*This modern hotel is close to the town centre, on the main road out
of Buxton towards Ashbourne. Families are encouraged and a
children's room is provided. On summer evenings barbecues are
held in the rear gardens.*
7rm(3📺4hc)(1fb) CTV in all bedrooms ® sB&B£17-£21
sB&B📺£19.50-£24.50 dB&B£30-£31
dB&B📺£34-£33 WB&B£119-£175 WBDi£175-£203 LDO 4pm
Lic ㎜ CTV 5P ⚬
Credit Cards ③ ⓔ

GH ⓠⓠ **Buxton View** 74 Corbar Rd SK17 6RJ ☎(0298) 79222
Mar-Nov
*Standing on the north side of the town, this well-equipped, stone-
built house is in a quiet residential area with commanding views
over the town.*
5⇨📺 (1fb)✂in all bedrooms CTV in all bedrooms ® ✻
sB&B⇨📺£18-£20
dB&B⇨📺£27-£30 WB&B£95-£125 WBDi£150-£180 LDO
9am
Lic ㎜ CTV 5P 2🛏

GH ⓠ **Griff** 2 Compton Rd SK17 9DN ☎(0298) 23628
*A busy house set in a residential area of the town, Griff offers fully
equipped bedrooms and has parking facilities.*
6hc (1fb) CTV in all bedrooms ® ✻ sB&B£10.50-£12
dB&B£21-£24 WB&B£70-£80 WBDi£100-£115 LDO noon
㎜ CTV 5P

GH ⓠ **Hawthorn Farm** Fairfield Rd SK17 7ED ☎(0298) 23230
Apr-Oct
*This charming, fully converted farmhouse and its outbuildings are
fronted by well-kept gardens and lawns, and stand on the outskirts
of Buxton.*
5hc Annexe 7hc (1fb) ® ✻ sB&B£14-£15 dB&B£28-£30
㎜ CTV 12P 2🛏

GH ⓠ *Kingscroft* 10 Green Ln SK17 9DP ☎(0298) 22757
Mar-Dec
Large, stone-built town house in a suburban area.
7hc (2fb)✂in 2 bedrooms CTV in all bedrooms ® LDO 5pm
Lic ㎜ CTV 9P 2🛏 nc5yrs

↦GH Ⓠ **The Old Manse** 6 Clifton Rd, Silverlands SK17 6QL
☎(0298) 25638
*Close to the town centre this stone-built semi detached house
provides simple accommodation with a comfortable atmosphere
and the advantage of having its own small car park.*
8rm(4♠4hc)(2fb) Ⓡ sB&B£13 sB&B♠£15 dB&B£26
dB&B♠£30 WB&B£87.50-£91.50 WBDi£136.50-£150.50 LDO
5pm
Lic ⁗ CTV 3P nc2yrs

GH Ⓠ **Roseleigh Private Hotel** 19 Broad Walk SK17 6JR
☎(0298) 24904
Closed Xmas-Jan rs Feb & Dec
*Roseleigh has an enviable position overlooking the Pavilion
Gardens and lake. Small and comfortable, the hotel has vehicular
access via Hartington Road as Broadwalk is for pedestrians only.*
13rm(7♠6hc)(1fb) CTV in all bedrooms Ⓡ sB&B£15-£16
dB&B£30-£32
dB&B♠£35-£38 WB&Bfr£105 WBDi£155-£162 LDO 5pm
Lic CTV 12P

GH ⒬⒬ **Swanleigh** 7 Grange Rd SK17 6NH ☎(0298) 24588
*Centrally situated in a quiet residential area, this semi detached
house offers attractive, well-equipped rooms and bright,
comfortable public rooms. The friendly proprietors give personal
and professional service.*
7hc (1fb) TV in all bedrooms Ⓡ ✕ (ex guide dogs) ✷
sB&B£13-£15 dB&B£26-£30 WB&B£84-£98
⁗ CTV 6P

GH ⒬⒬ **Templeton** 13 Compton Rd SK17 9DN ☎(0298) 25275
*A semi detached house in a quiet residential area, Templeton
provides bright, warm and well-equipped accommodation close to
the town centre. Good home-cooked meals are provided and there
is ample parking space.*
6rm(2♠4hc)(2fb) CTV in 4 bedrooms Ⓡ ✕ dB&B£25-£29
dB&B♠£30-£34 WB&B£80-£98 WBDi£125-£144 LDO noon
Lic ⁗ CTV 6P
⒡

GH ⒬⒬⒬ **Thorn Heyes Private Hotel** 137 London Rd
SK17 9NW ☎(0298) 23539
Closed last 2 wks Nov & Jan
*Set in large attractive gardens, this Victorian house provides guests
with almost every convenience they require on holiday. Mrs Green
prepares the meals, and her husband has a store of local
knowledge, having lived in Buxton all his life.*
8♠ Annexe 3♠ (2fb) CTV in all bedrooms Ⓡ ✷
sB&B♠£17.50-£28
dB&B♠fr£35 WB&Bfr£120 WBDifr£170 LDO 6pm
Lic ⁗ 12P nc14yrs

GH ⒬⒬⒬ **Westminster Hotel** 21 Broadwalk SK17 6JT
☎(0298) 23929
Feb-Nov & Xmas
*Set in a quiet residential area with views of the lake in the Pavillion
Gardens, this friendly hotel provides well-equipped
accommodation. Because Broad Walk is closed to traffic the hotel
is approached via Hartington Road.*
12rm(5⇨7♠) CTV in all bedrooms Ⓡ ✕ (ex guide dogs)
sB&B⇨♠fr£22
dB&B⇨♠£36-£38 WBDi£165-£179 LDO 3pm
Lic ⁗ 14P
Credit Cards ①②③⒡

FH ⒬⒬⒬ Mrs M A Mackenzie **Staden Grange** *(SK075717)*
Staden Ln SK17 9RZ (1.5m SE off A515) ☎(0298) 24965
FAX (0298) 72067
*Don't be put off by the approach to this spacious farm, as once
through the industrial estate, you will be in a very rural district.
Superior accommodation is offered here, as well as a caravan site
and self-catering accommodation.*

3rm(1⇨1♠1hc)(1fb) CTV in all bedrooms Ⓡ sB&Bfr£18.50
sB&B⇨♠fr£18.50 dB&Bfr£37
dB&B⇨♠fr£37 WB&Bfr£129.50 WBDifr£185.50
Lic ⁗ CTV 20P ☽ snooker spa pool 250 acres mixed

BYFORD Hereford & Worcester Map **03** SO34

GH ⒬⒬ **Old Rectory** HR4 7LD ☎Bridge Sollars(098122) 218
Etr-Nov
3rm(1♠2hc)(1fb)⊁in all bedrooms CTV in 2 bedrooms
✕ (ex guide dogs) ✷ sB&B£15-£20 sB&B♠£20-£30
dB&B£22-£25 dB&B♠£28-£32 WB&B£70-£87.50
⁗ 6P
⒡

BYRNESS Northumberland Map **12** NT70

FH ⒬⒬ Mrs A Anderson *Blakehope Burnhaugh* (*NT783002*)
NE19 1SW (1.5m along A68 towards Rochester) ☎(0830) 20267
Mar-Oct
*Set in the seclusion of Redesdale Forest, this attractive, stone-built
farm offers pleasant, roomy bedrooms with modern furnishings.
The public rooms have a blend of natural stone walls and pine
furniture.*
3hc (1fb) Ⓡ LDO 4pm
⁗ CTV 5P 3🐾 150 acres beef

CADNAM Hampshire Map **04** SU21

FH ⒬⒬⒬ Mrs A M Dawe **Budds** *(SU310139)* Winsor Rd,
Winsor SO4 2HN ☎Southampton(0703) 812381
Apr-Oct
*This thatched farmhouse dates from 1700 and has 2 lovely
bedrooms which are spacious and well furnished. The lounge
features beams and wood-burning stoves and the breakfast room is
furnished with antiques. Service is personally provided by Mrs
Dawe.*
2hc (1fb)⊁in all bedrooms ✕ (ex guide dogs) ✷ sB&B£13-£14
dB&B£26-£28 WB&Bfr£85
⁗ CTV 3P 200 acres beef dairy

FH ⒬⒬⒬ Mrs A Dawe **Kents** *(SU315139)* Winsor Rd,
Winsor SO4 2HN ☎Southampton(0703) 813497
Apr-Oct
*This recently renovated 16th-century thatched farmhouse has
comfortable cottage décor with oak beams, an inglenook fireplace
and a secluded garden.*
2rm(1⇨1♠)(1fb)⊁in all bedrooms ✕
dB&B⇨♠fr£27 WB&Bfr£90
⁗ CTV 4P nc2yrs 200 acres beef dairy

CAERNARFON Gwynedd Map **06** SH46

See also **Llanddeiniolen**
GH ⒬⒬⒬ **Caer Menai** 15 Church St LL55 1SW ☎(0286) 2612
Mar-Dec
*This small family-run hotel is situated in a quiet road, close to the
town walls and within a short walk of both the castle and the
harbour. It is impeccably maintained and provides good quality,
well-equipped accommodation.*
7rm(3♠4hc)(3fb)⊁in 3 bedrooms CTV in all bedrooms Ⓡ
✕ (ex guide dogs) sB&B£15-£20 sB&B♠£20-£22
dB&B£26-£28 dB&B♠£36-£38 WB&B£105-£147
CTV ⎘ solarium
⒡

GH Ⓠ **Menai View Hotel** North Rd LL55 1BD ☎(0286) 4602
*This small family-run hotel is situated on the A487, just north of
the town, and overlooks the Menai Straits. The accommodation is
simple, but all bedrooms are equipped with colour televisions and
central heating.*
6hc (3fb) CTV in all bedrooms Ⓡ ✷ sB&B£14-£16
dB&B£26-£28 WB&B£91-£98 WBDi£140-£147 LDO 8pm

Lic ▥ CTV ⊁
£

FH Q Q Q Mr & Mrs D Mackinnon **Plas Tirion** *(SH524628)*
Llanrug LL55 4PY (Llanrug 3m E A4086) ☎(0286) 673190
May-Sep
This delightfully furnished farmhouse offers home comforts and
accommodation of a high standard, with a very pleasant lounge.
Good service is provided and a stay here is excellent value for
money.
3♠ (1fb) CTV in 2 bedrooms ® ✹ ✳
dB&B♠£32-£36 LDO midday
Lic ▥ CTV 6P ⚓ rough shooting 450 acres mixed
£

CALDBECK Cumbria Map **11** NY33

SELECTED

GH Q Q Q Q **High Greenrigg House** CA7 8HD
☎(06998) 430
Mar-Oct
This carefully restored, isolated 17th-century farmhouse with
splendid views, is 3 miles west of Caldbeck, just off the B5299.
Fran and Robin Jacobs have created an engaging and
hospitable atmosphere, and have also provided facilities to
meet guests' everyday needs without detracting from the
house's charm and character. A games room, bar lounge, two
general lounges – one with a television, and an imaginative 3-
course evening meal are provided.
8rm(6⇆♠2hc)(1fb)⊱in all bedrooms sB&B£19.50-£24.50
dB&B⇆♠fr£39 WB&Bfr£117 WBDifr£192 LDO 5pm
Lic ▥ CTV 8P
£

FH Q Q Q Mrs D H Coulthard *Friar Hall* *(NY324399)*
CA7 8DS ☎(06998) 633
Mar-Oct
Spacious bedrooms and a comfortable lounge are features of this
warm, friendly farmhouse, parts of which date back to the 12th
century. It is part of a dairy and sheep farm in the village centre
and overlooks the river.
3hc (2fb) ✹ (ex guide dogs)
CTV 3P 140 acres dairy mixed sheep

FH Q Q Q Mr & Mrs A Savage *Swaledale Watch*
(NY308398) Whelpo CA7 8HQ ☎(06998) 409
Closed Xmas
This modern bungalow is on a working farm alongside the B5299,
three quarters of a mile west of Caldbeck. With a hospitable
atmosphere and comfortable, well-appointed accommodation,
Swaledale Watch also has a spacious lounge.
3hc (1fb)⊱in all bedrooms ® ✹ (ex guide dogs) LDO 2pm
▥ CTV 10P 300 acres dairy sheep

CALLANDER Central *Perthshire* Map **11** NN60

GH Q Q **Abbotsford Lodge** Stirling Rd FK17 8DA
☎(0877) 30066
A popular base for a touring holiday, this friendly guesthouse is
conveniently situated on the edge of the town. The bedrooms
provide traditional comforts.
19rm(4⇆3♠12hc)(7fb) ® ✳ sB&Bfr£15.50
sB&B⇆♠fr£19.50 dB&Bfr£25
dB&B⇆♠fr£31 WBDi£139-£159.50 LDO 7pm
Lic ▥ CTV 20P

⊱→**GH** Q Q **Annfield** 18 North Church St FK17 8EG
☎(0877) 30204
Attractive stone-built house on a quiet street in the town centre.
8rm(2♠6hc)(2fb) ® sB&B£11 dB&B£22
dB&B♠£24 WB&B£77

▥ CTV 9P
£

GH Q Q Q **Arden House** Bracklinn Rd FK17 8EQ
☎(0877) 30235
Feb-Nov
Attractive stone house standing on hillside close to golf course,
formerly used in the making of Dr Finlay's Casebook.
8rm(6♠2hc)(3fb) ® dB&B£40-£44
dB&B♠£44-£48 (incl dinner) WBDi£135-£150 LDO 7pm
▥ CTV 12P ⚓ putting green
£

GH Q Q Q **Brook Linn Country House** Leny Feus FK17 8AU
☎(0877) 30103
Etr-Oct
Set in its own grounds overlooking the town, this attractive
Victorian house is comfortably appointed and has a country-house
atmosphere.
7rm(5♠2hc)(2fb)⊱in all bedrooms CTV in all bedrooms ®
sB&Bfr£15 dB&Bfr£16
dB&B♠fr£18 WBDi£160-£168 LDO 5pm
Lic ▥ 10P

GH Q **Greenbank** 143 Main St FK17 8BH ☎(0877) 30296
Pleasant house standing in the main street.
6hc (2fb) CTV in 1 bedroom TV in 1 bedroom ✳ sB&B£12
dB&B£24 WB&Bfr£75 WBDifr£120 LDO 6pm
Lic ▥ CTV 5P
£

GH Q Q Q *Highland House Hotel* South Church St FK17 8BN
☎(0877) 30269
mid Mar-mid Nov
This attractive terraced Georgian house is situated just off the
main street and is conveniently placed for the town's facilities. The
compact bedrooms are bright and airy and there is an attractive
lounge as well as a bar, which features a railway theme and serves
a fine range of malt whiskies.
10rm(3♠6hc)(1fb)⊱in all bedrooms ® LDO 7pm
Lic ▥ CTV ⊁

GH Q Q *Riverview House Private Hotel* Leny Rd FK19 8AL
☎(0877) 30635
Etr-Oct
Standing in its own grounds at the west end of town, this friendly,
family-run private hotel offers neat and comfortable
accommodation and home cooking.
6rm(3♠3hc) CTV in all bedrooms ® LDO 7.15pm
Lic ▥ 8P

GH Q Q *Rock Villa* 1 Bracklinn Rd FK17 8EH ☎(0877) 30331
This guesthouse stands in its own gardens close to the town centre,
the bedrooms here are simple and comfortable. There is a
traditional-style lounge and home-cooked meals are provided in
the bright, airy dining room.
6rm(2♠4hc)(1fb) CTV in 2 bedrooms ® LDO 4.30pm
▥ CTV 7P

CAMBRIDGE Cambridgeshire Map **05** TL45

GH Q **Antwerp** 36 Brookfields CB1 3NW ☎(0223) 247690
Off-street car parking is provided at this hotel, situated on a main
intersection on the outskirts of the town. The rooms are modest but
neat, and the friendly, caring atmosphere meets the demands of
those seeking simple accommodation.
8rm(2♠6hc)(1fb) CTV in all bedrooms ® ✹ (ex guide dogs) ✳
sB&B£22-£27 sB&B♠fr£27 dB&B£28-£35
dB&B♠fr£35 LDO 5pm
Lic ▥ CTV 8P
£

Cambridge

GH **QQ** **Assisi** 193 Cherry Hinton Rd CB1 4BX
☎(0223) 211466 & 246648
Closed 15 Dec-5 Jan
Close to the city centre, with off-street parking, this newly converted guesthouse has good quality en suite facilities, an open-plan breakfast/dining room and lounge and an attractive reception/lobby.
8rm(7⇨🟊1hc)(1fb) CTV in all bedrooms 🐾 sB&Bfr£18
sB&B⇨🟊frf£25 dB&B⇨🟊frf£35
💷 CTV 12P
Credit Cards 1 2 3

GH **QQ** **Bon Accord House** 20 St Margarets Square CB1 4AP
☎(0223) 411188 & 246568
Closed Xmas & New Year
Situated in a quiet residential cul-de-sac off Cherry Hinton Road. Mr and Mrs Northrop provide comfortable accommodation which is well maintained and equipped. There is a large dining room and a small, comfortable lounge. The guesthouse is 'no smoking' throughout.
12rm(1🟊11hc)(1fb)✗in all bedrooms CTV in all bedrooms ®
🐾 sB&B£18-£20 sB&B🟊£24-£28 dB&B£30-£34
dB&B🟊£36-£38
💷 12P 2🛥
Credit Cards 1 3 £

GH **QQ** **Fairways** 141-143 Cherry Hinton Rd CB1 4BX
☎(0223) 246063 FAX (0223) 212093
Closed 24-26 Dec
This friendly, family-run guesthouse is popular with commercial guests and tourists. The accommodation is well equipped with some en suite facilities. Fairways is situated on a main road, close to the city centre, and has off-street parking.
14rm(8🟊6hc)(2fb)✗in 2 bedrooms CTV in all bedrooms ®
🐾 (ex guide dogs) ✳ sB&B£18 sB&B🟊£23 dB&B£30
dB&B🟊£34-£35 WB&B£119-£154
Lic 💷 20P pool table

GH **QQ** **Hamilton Hotel** 156 Chesterton Rd CB4 1DA
☎(0223) 65664
Detached house in busy city road with car parking at rear.
10rm(5🟊5hc)(3fb) CTV in all bedrooms ® 🐾 ✳ sB&B£18-£25
sB&B🟊£21-£25 dB&B£25-£30 dB&B🟊£30-£40 LDO noon
Lic 💷 10P nc4yrs
Credit Cards 3 £

GH **QQQ** **Helen Hotel** 167-169 Hills Rd CB2 2RJ
☎(0223) 246465 FAX (0223) 214406
Closed 15 Dec-5 Jan
Situated in a residential area south of the city (B1307), this friendly, caring establishment is run by Gino Agodino and his wife. Homemade dishes are served in the dining room which overlooks the garden, and off-street parking is available.
23rm(20⇨🟊3hc)Annexe 6rm(5🟊1hc)(4fb) CTV in all
bedrooms ✳ sB&B£29-£43 sB&B⇨🟊£40-£43 dB&B£45-£50
dB&B⇨🟊£50-£55 WB&B£196-£280 WBDi£275-£360 LDO
7.30pm
Lic 💷 CTV 20P
Credit Cards 1 3

GH **QQQ** **Lensfield Hotel** 53 Lensfield Rd CB2 1EN
☎(0223) 355017 Telex no 818183 FAX (0223) 312022
Closed 2wks Xmas
The Paschalis family run this friendly hotel which stands on the ring road, a few minutes' walk from the city centre, with a large public car park to the rear. The accommodation is very well equipped and comfortable.
36rm(2⇨18🟊16hc)(4fb) CTV in all bedrooms ® 🐾 LDO
8.45pm
Lic 💷 CTV 5P 2🛥
Credit Cards 1 2 3 5

See advertisement on page 101

Helen Hotel

167/169 Hills Road, Cambridge CB2 2RJ
Tel. Cambridge (0223) 246465 Telex: 81365

Proprietors: Helen and Gino Agodino
This fine middle-sized hotel, situated about one mile from the city centre, offers personal and friendly service.

★ *29 Bedrooms – most with private shower, toilet, telephone and colour TV*
★ *A charming Italian-style garden*
★ *Bar and TV lounge*

HAMILTON HOTEL

A family run hotel approx one mile from the City Centre and within ½ mile of the river and parks.

All rooms have H/C, tea and coffee making facilities, colour TV, central heating, most rooms have en-suite shower and toilet. Our licensed bar offers a variety of meals and snacks.

We offer a choice menu full English breakfast. Ample car parking.

Reservations: (0223) 65664
156 Chesterton Road, Cambridge

98

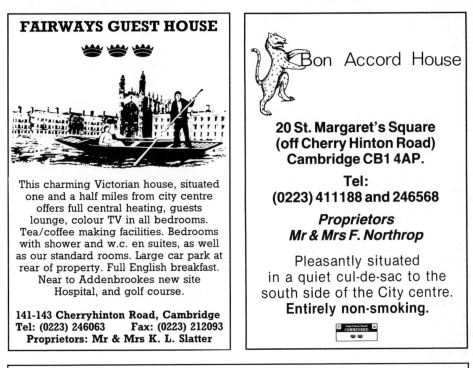

GH Q Q Q **Number Eleven** 11 Glisson Rd CB1 2HA
☎(0223) 461142
Off Hills Road (but more easily found via Tennison Road), this establishment is close to the city centre and offers a quiet and elegant retreat, with comfortable and well-furnished and decorated rooms. Breakfast is taken in the drawing room around a large oval table.
5rm(1⇨2♠2hc)(1fb) CTV in all bedrooms ®
✹ (ex guide dogs) ✳ dB&B£32-£35 dB&B⇨♠£36-£40
Ⓟ

GH Q Q *Sorrento Hotel* 196 Cherry Hinton Rd CB1 4AN
☎(0223) 243533
A family-run hotel in a residential area with ample private parking.
24rm(5⇨19♠)(5fb) CTV in all bedrooms ® LDO 8.30pm
Lic ⴹ CTV 25P petanque terraine
Credit Cards 1 3

GH Q Q Q **Suffolk House Private Hotel** 69 Milton Rd
CB4 1XA ☎(0223) 352016
Standing on the A1134 in a residential area north of the city centre, Suffolk House offers refurbished en suite accommodation, which is most attractive. Mrs Cuthbert is a friendly host, and provides a buffet-style breakfast.
8♠ (3fb) CTV in all bedrooms ® ✹ ✳ dB&B♠£50-£60
Lic ⴹ CTV 11P nc4yrs
Credit Cards 1 3

CAMELFORD Cornwall & Isles of Scilly Map **02** SX18

GH Q Q *Countryman Hotel* Victoria Rd PL32 9XA
☎(0840) 212250
An impressive stone-built hotel standing on the outskirts of the small market town.
12rm(2⇨10hc)(4fb) CTV in 3 bedrooms ® LDO 7pm
Lic ⴹ CTV 12P

CANTERBURY Kent Map **05** TR15

GH Q **Castle Court** 8 Castle St CT1 2QF ☎(0227) 463441
12hc ✳ sB&B£14-£18 dB&B£26-£33
ⴹ CTV 2P
Credit Cards 1 3 £

GH Q Q Q **Ebury Hotel** New Dover Rd CT1 3DX
☎(0227) 768433 FAX (0227) 459187
Closed 25 Dec-14 Jan
This charming Victorian hotel offers well-equipped accommodation of a high standard. The delightful, spacious lounge houses a display of clocks, and the elegant restaurant serves English food. Guests have the use of the recently opened indoor pool and spa.
17⇨♠ (6fb) CTV in all bedrooms ® sB&B⇨♠£35-£48
dB&B⇨♠£50-£56 WBDi£200-£220 LDO 8.3Opm
Lic ⴹ CTV 20P 1🚗 (£2) ⌷(heated)
Credit Cards 1 2 3 £

GH Q Q Q **Ersham Lodge** 12 New Dover Rd CT1 3AP
☎(0227) 463174 FAX (0227) 455482
Apr-Dec
Comfortable modern accommodation with well-equipped bedrooms.
14rm(2⇨11♠1hc)(2fb) CTV in all bedrooms
✹ (ex guide dogs) ✳ sB&B⇨♠£39-£47.50
dB&B⇨♠£47.50-£54
Lic ⴹ 11P 1🚗 (£3)
Credit Cards 1 2 3 £

GH Q Q **Highfield Hotel** Summer Hill, Harbledown CT2 8NH
☎(0227) 462772
Feb-Nov
Georgian-style country house, family-run and providing value for money.

8rm(3♠5hc) ® ✹ sB&B£21-£24 dB&B£31-£37
dB&B♠£41-£47
Lic ⴹ 12P nc5yrs
Credit Cards 1 3

GH Q Q Q **Magnolia House** 36 St Dunstan's Ter CT2 8AX
☎(0227) 765121
This small, cosy guesthouse is in a quiet and pleasant residential area close to the Westgate Towers. Family run, the accommodation is comfortable and well maintained.
6rm(3⇨♠3hc)✂in all bedrooms ® ✹ sB&B£20-£26
sB&B⇨♠£22-£28 dB&B£36-£40 dB&B⇨♠£42-£48
ⴹ CTV 4P

GH Q Q Q **Pointers Hotel** 1 London Rd CT2 8LR
☎(0227) 456846
Closed Xmas & New Year
Charming Regency-style hotel, comfortably furnished. Bedrooms are well equipped, food is good, and the hospitality is warm.
14rm(12⇨♠)(2fb) CTV in all bedrooms ® ✳ sB&B£28
sB&B⇨♠£32 dB&B£40
dB&B⇨♠£45-£50 WB&B£140-£224 WBDifr£175 LDO 8.15pm
Lic ⴹ 10P
Credit Cards 1 2 3 5 £

See advertisement on page 103

SELECTED

GH Q Q Q Q **Thanington Hotel** 140 Wincheap CT1 3RY
☎(0227) 453227
Built around 1800, this house has lots of distinctive architectural features. The accommodation has been tastefully furnished and particularly well equipped, with every modern convenience. Breakfast is served in the elegant dining ▶

room and guests can relax in the lounge or garden room. Mr and Mrs Jenkins provide personal service and pay close attention to detail, making this a perfect venue for relaxation and comfort.
10⇄ (2fb) CTV in all bedrooms ® sB&B⇄£42-£47 dB&B⇄£50-£55
卿 CTV 8P 2🌤
Credit Cards 1 3 £

CAPERNWRAY Lancashire Map **07** SD57

GH Q Q Q New Capernwray Farm LA6 1AD
☎Carnforth(0524) 734284
Three miles from junction 35 of the M6, this house dates from 1697 and now offers comfortable accommodation of character. The dairy is now the dining room where diners eat around a communal table. Guests may bring their own drinks.
3rm(1⇄)⚥in all bedrooms CTV in all bedrooms ®
sB&B⇄£34.50-£36.50 dB&B⇄£49-£53 LDO 2pm
卿 4P nc10yrs clay pigeon shooting arranged
See advertisement under LANCASTER on page 211

CAPUTH Tayside *Perthshire* Map **11** NO04

FH Q Q Mrs R Smith *Stralochy (NO086413)* PH1 4LQ
☎(073871) 250
May-Oct
Approached by a rough track, this small farmhouse has lovely views of the surrounding countryside. Providing a welcoming atmosphere and traditional comforts, Stralochy offers good value for money.
2rm ® ✘ LDO 4pm
CTV 2P 239 acres arable beef sheep

CARDIFF South Glamorgan Map **03** ST17

GH Q Q Balkan Hotel 144 Newport Rd CF2 1DJ
☎(0222) 463673
This hotel has been run by the same friendly family for many years. Close to the city centre and Broadway shopping complex, it provides comfortable accommodation.
14rm(5♠9hc)(3fb) CTV in 13 bedrooms ® ✘ ✱ sB&B£15-£20
sB&B♠£28-£34 dB&B£28-£34
dB&B♠£34-£39 WB&B£72-£98 WBDi£114-£140 LDO 7pm
卿 CTV 18P
Credit Cards 1 2

GH Q Q Q Clare Court Hotel 46/48 Clare Rd, Grangetown
CF1 7QP ☎(0222) 344839
Closed Xmas Day & Boxing Day
A short walk from the city centre, this family-run hotel offers very well-equipped large bedrooms, each with comfortable armchairs. The public rooms and small bar are pleasant and cosy.
9⇄♠ (2fb) CTV in all bedrooms ® ✘ (ex guide dogs) ✱
sB&B⇄♠£20-£25 dB&B⇄♠£32-£38 LDO 7.45pm
Lic 卿 CTV ⚘
Credit Cards 1 2 3

GH Q Domus 201 Newport Rd CF2 1AJ ☎(0222) 495785
20 Jan-20 Dec
This Victorian house has a comfortable lounge and small bar.
10rm(2♠8hc)(2fb) CTV in all bedrooms ® ✘ (ex guide dogs)
✱ sB&Bfr£16 sB&B♠fr£20 dB&Bfr£32 LDO noon
Lic 卿 CTV 10P nc2yrs

GH Q Q Q Ferrier's (Alva) Hotel 130/132 Cathedral Rd
CF1 9LQ ☎(0222) 383413
Closed 2wks Xmas & New Year
Close to the Sophia Gardens and convenient for the National Sports Centre, this friendly, family-run hotel offers pretty, well-equipped bedrooms and comfortable public rooms.
26rm(1⇄4♠21hc)(4fb) CTV in all bedrooms ® sB&B£23
sB&B⇄♠£33 dB&B£40 dB&B⇄♠£46 LDO 7.45pm

Lic 卿 CTV 10P
Credit Cards 1 2 3 5

GH Q Q Princes 10 Princes St, Roath CF2 3PR
☎(0222) 491732
Standing in a residential part of the city, this small, family-run guesthouse has pretty, well-furnished bedrooms and a cosy and comfortable lounge.
6hc (1fb) CTV in all bedrooms ® ✘ (ex guide dogs) LDO noon
卿 CTV 3🌤

GH Q Q Tane's Hotel 148 Newport Rd CF2 1DJ
☎(0222) 491755 & 493898
Convenient for the Broadway shopping area and within walking distance of the city centre, this bright hotel has good bedrooms and an attractive, comfortable lounge.
9hc (1fb) CTV in all bedrooms ® ✘ ✱ sB&B£16-£20
dB&B£28-£32 WB&B£112-£140 WBDi£154-£182 LDO 7pm
Lic 卿 CTV 10P nc6yrs
Credit Cards 2 3 £

CARDIGAN Dyfed Map **02** SN14

⊢⊶**GH Q Q Q Brynhyfryd** Gwbert Rd SA43 1AE
☎(0239) 612861
Small guesthouse run by enthusiastic family on pleasant outskirts of town.
6rm(2♠4hc)(2fb) CTV in all bedrooms ® ✘ (ex guide dogs)
sB&B£13 dB&B£26
dB&B♠£30 WB&B£91 WBDi£125 LDO 7.30pm
卿 CTV
£

Visit your local AA Centre.

GH QQQ *Highbury* Pendre SA43 1JU ☎(0239) 613403
Just 2 minutes from the centre of town, this recently modernised town house provides comfortable and well-equipped bedrooms. A variety of watersports can be arranged for guests.
6rm(3♠3hc) CTV in all bedrooms ®
Lic ∰ ⏚
Credit Cards ①③

GH QQ *Maes-A-Mor* Gwbert Rd SA43 1AE ☎(0239) 614929
Situated only a short walk from the town centre, this friendly, family-run guesthouse has pretty and well-furnished bedrooms, a comfortable and cosy lounge and an attractive dining room.
3rm(2♠1hc)(3fb)⌀in all bedrooms CTV in all bedrooms ®
∰ CTV 4P ⚓

CARDROSS Strathclyde *Dunbartonshire* Map **10** NS37

GH QQQ *Kirkton House* Darleith Rd G82 5EZ (0.5m N of village) ☎(0389) 841951
Tastefully converted, this farmhouse stands in a quiet rural setting above the village with lovely views of the Clyde and Argyll hills. All bedrooms have direct dial telephones.
6rm(4⇨♠2hc)(3fb) CTV in all bedrooms ® sB&B£20
sB&B⇨♠£25-£29.50 dB&B£35
dB&B⇨♠£45 WB&B£115.50-£206.50 WBDi£196-£287 LDO 6pm
Lic ∰ CTV 12P ⚓ ⟳
Credit Cards ①③ £
See advertisement under HELENSBURGH on page 181

CARLISLE Cumbria Map **11** NY45

See also Catlowdy

GH QQ *Angus Hotel* 14 Scotland Rd CA3 9DG ☎(0228) 23546
rs 24-31Dec
Situated on the A7, approximately three quarters of a mile north of the city centre, this small guesthouse provides simple, well-maintained accommodation suitable for tourists and commercial guests alike. A free public car park is within a few yards.
9rm(4♠5hc)(4fb)⌀in 4 bedrooms CTV in 1 bedroom ®
sB&Bfr£17 sB&B♠£25 dB&Bfr£27 dB&B♠£37 LDO 7.45pm
Lic ∰ CTV 8⚓
Credit Cards ①③

GH QQ *Crossroads House* Brisco CA4 0QZ ☎(0228) 28994
Closed Xmas & New Year
Standing at a crossroads three quarters of a mile from junction 42 of the M6, this detached house is nicely decorated throughout and has a comfortable lounge and a sun lounge. A striking feature is the 100 foot Roman well (safely covered).
5hc (1fb)⌀in all bedrooms TV in 2 bedrooms sB&Bfr£15
dB&B£26-£30
Lic ∰ CTV 6P
£

GH QQ *East View* 110 Warwick Rd CA1 1JU ☎(0228) 22112
Family-run, friendly guesthouse offering good value.
7♠ (2fb) CTV in all bedrooms ® ✳ sB&B♠£15-£18
dB&B♠£25-£30 WB&B£105
∰ 4P

⤞GH QQ *Kenilworth Hotel* 34 Lazonby Ter CA1 2PZ
☎(0228) 26179
Standing on the A6, three quarters of a mile south of the city centre, this guesthouse has nearby street parking. The simple, well-maintained accommodation is equally suitable for tourists and business people.
6hc (2fb) ® sB&B£11-£13 dB&B£20-£22 WB&B£70-£77
∰ CTV 5P

CARMARTHEN Dyfed

See Llanfynydd

CARRADALE Strathclyde *Argyllshire* Map **10** NR83

GH QQ *Ashbank Hotel* PA28 6RY ☎(05833) 650
Apr-Oct
Adjacent to golf course offering comfortable but compact accommodation.
5rm(3♠2hc) ® ✕ (ex guide dogs) LDO 7pm
Lic ∰ 6P

GH QQ *Dunvalanree* Portrigh PA28 6SE ☎(05833) 226
Etr-Oct
Large house with attractive rockery garden beside small sandy bay to the south of Carradale Harbour.
12hc (3fb) LDO 4pm
Lic ∰ CTV 9P ponytrekking, windsurfing, fishing

CARRBRIDGE Highland *Inverness-Shire* Map **14** NH92

GH QQQ *Carrmoor* Carr Rd PH23 3AD ☎(047984) 244
A charming little house where you will get a warm welcome from the owners, with bright airy cottage-style bedrooms and comfortable lounge in which to relax. Good home cooking.
5rm(1♠4hc)(1fb) ® dB&B£23-£27
dB&B♠£25-£29 WB&B£84-£91 WBDi£144-£147 LDO 5.30pm
Lic ∰ CTV 4P
£

SELECTED

GH QQQQ *Fairwinds Hotel* PH23 3AA ☎(047984) 240
Closed 3 Nov-15 Dec
Attractively modernised, this stone-built manse stands back from the road in 6 acres of grounds, with a small loch and a backdrop of mature pine woods. The well-appointed bedrooms offer comfort with charm, and the public rooms are well furnished and feature flower arrangements. The meals are interesting and the service is friendly and attentive.
5⇨♠ (1fb) CTV in all bedrooms ® ✕ sB&B⇨♠£20-£21
dB&B⇨♠£36-£38 WB&B£120-£125 WBDi£180-£187
LDO 4pm
Lic ∰ 8P
Credit Cards ①③ £

CARRONBRIDGE Central *Stirlingshire*

See Denny

CASTLE CARROCK Cumbria Map **12** NY55

FH Q B W Robinson *Gelt Hall (NY542554)* CA4 9LT
☎Hayton(0228) 70260
Simple, neat accommodation is provided by this friendly little village centre farmhouse. Guests can enjoy a true farm atmosphere at this sheep and dairy farm.
3rm(1⇨)(1fb) ✕ ✳ sB&B£12-£13 dB&B£22-£26
dB&B⇨£22-£26 LDO 5pm
∰ CTV 6P 1⚓ 250 acres beef dairy sheep
£

CASTLE DONINGTON Leicestershire Map **08** SK 42

GH |Q||Q| **The Four Poster** 73 Clapgun St DE7 2LF
☎Derby(0332) 810335 & 812418
Tastefully restored and modernised old ivy-clad house in quiet street.
7rm(3⇨3♠4hc)Annexe 4hc ✗in 7 bedrooms CTV in all bedrooms ® ✱ sB&B£12.50-£15 dB&B£30-£40
dB&B⇨♠£30-£50
₩ CTV 18P 4☜
£

GH |Q||Q| **Park Farmhouse Hotel** Melbourne Rd, Isley Walton
DE7 2RN ☎Derby(0332) 862409
Closed Xmas & New Year
8rm(3⇨3♠2hc)(2fb) CTV in all bedrooms ® sB&B£27-£29
sB&B⇨♠£39-£42 dB&B£37-£39
dB&B⇨♠£46-£49 LDO 8pm
Lic ₩ 20P
Credit Cards |1||2||3||5| £

INN |Q||Q| **Le Chevalier Bistro Restaurant** 2 Borough St
DE7 2LA ☎Derby(0332) 812005 & 812106
Locals and businessmen find the food and friendly atmosphere at this popular little Bistro worth the visit. The bedrooms have their own entrance via a courtyard where guests can enjoy a pre-dinner drink or after dinner coffee.
4⇨♠ (1fb) CTV in all bedrooms ® ✗ (ex guide dogs) ✱
sB&B⇨♠fr£30
dB&B⇨♠fr£38 Lunch fr£9.50alc High tea fr£2.50alc Dinner fr£9.50alc LDO 10.30pm
₩ CTV 100P 2☜ ⚬ pool table
Credit Cards |1||2||3||5|

CASTLE DOUGLAS Dumfries & Galloway
Kirkcudbrightshire Map **11** NX76

GH |Q||Q||Q| **Rose Cottage** Gelston DG7 1SH ☎(0556) 2513
Feb-Oct
In a rural setting, 2 miles from the town centre on the B736, this delightful whitewashed cottage is as quaint inside as it appears outside. The accommodation is all on the ground floor, and is neat, cosy and most inviting.
3hc Annexe 2hc (1fb) TV in 3 bedrooms ® ✱ sB&B£12-£14
dB&B£24-£26 WB&B£82-£84 WBDi£125-£143.50
₩ CTV 15P

See advertisement on page 107

CATLOWDY Cumbria Map **12** NY47

SELECTED

FH |Q||Q||Q||Q| Mr & Mrs J Sisson *Bessiestown*
(NY457768) CA6 5QP ☎Nicholforest(022877) 219
This small beef and sheep rearing farm is situated close to the Scottish border in pleasant open countryside. The house has much charm and character, and the bedrooms are individually decorated and furnished in a most attractive style with lots of extra touches. Margaret Sisson's traditional home cooking is served in the very pretty, beamed dining room. There is a cosy television lounge and a very comfortable, period-styled lounge bar. Across the courtyard, guests can take advantage of a large indoor swimming pool. This very hospitable farm has received many awards in recent years – and justifiably so.
7rm(3⇨4♠)✗in 2 bedrooms ® ✗ (wkly only mid Jul-end Aug) LDO 4pm
Lic ₩ CTV 10P ☒(heated) ∪ 55 acres beef mixed sheep

See advertisement on page 109

FH |Q||Q| Mr & Mrs Lawson **Craigburn** *(NY474761)* CA6 5QP
☎Nicholforest(022877) 214
Closed Dec ▶

Signposted from Catlowdy village, this large farmhouse enjoys a lovely rural location. All bedrooms have en suite facilities and there is a large dining room, a comfy lounge with TV and a residents' bar.

7rm(4⇨3♠)(3fb) ® sB&B⇨♠£18-£20
dB&B⇨♠£36-£40 WB&B£113.40-£126 WBDi£163.80-£189
LDO 5.30pm
Lic ℙ CTV 20P ♨ snooker 250 acres beef mixed sheep
£

See advertisement on page 109

CENARTH Dyfed Map 02 SN24

⊢⊶**FH** Q Q Q Mr & Mrs J D Cuthbertson **Penwernfach** *(SN267437)* Pont-Hirwaun SA43 2RL
☎Newcastle Emlyn(0239) 710694
Conveniently situated for touring the area, this modernised farmhouse provides good, comfortable accommodation. It also has a complex of holiday cottages.
2hc CTV in all bedrooms ® sB&B£11 dB&B£22 WB&B£70
ℙ CTV 2P ✔ games room 6 acres non-working
£

CHAGFORD Devon Map 03 SX78

GH Q Q Q **Bly House** Nattadon Hill TQ13 8BW
☎(0647) 432404
Closed 8 Nov-Dec
Situated in a quiet position, Bly House makes an excellent base for exploring the national park. Every room is furnished with beautiful pictures and objets d'art, bedrooms being spacious, with en suite facilities, colour television and tea and coffee-making equipment.
7⇨ CTV in all bedrooms ®
dB&B⇨£38-£40 WB&B£259-£273
ℙ CTV 10P nc9yrs croquet
£

GH Q Q **Glendarah** TQ13 8BZ ☎(0647) 433270
Mar-Dec
A stable has been converted to provide 1 of the 7 bedrooms of this attractive guesthouse. It is tastefully decorated with a lounge and dining room, and Mr and Mrs Willett extend a warm welcome to the guests.
7hc Annexe 1⇨ (2fb) CTV in 1 bedroom ® ✖ (ex guide dogs)
sB&B£14.50-£15.50 dB&B£29
dB&B⇨£37 WB&B£98-£126 WBDi£154-£182 LDO 6.30pm
Lic ℙ CTV 9P ♨
£

CHANNEL ISLANDS Map 16

GUERNSEY

L'ANCRESSE VALE

GH Q Q Q **Lynton Park Hotel** Hacse Ln
☎Guernsey(0481) 45418
Set in 3 acres of rural grounds, this small family-run hotel offers bright, comfortable bedrooms, limited but comfortable public rooms and an attractive dining room. The cooking is a main feature of the hotel, offering table d'hôte and comprehensive à la carte menus.
15⇨♠ (1fb) CTV in all bedrooms ® ✖ (ex guide dogs)
sB&B⇨♠£32.50-£40
dB&B⇨♠£53-£68 (incl dinner) WB&B£154-£206.50
WBDi£185.50-£238 LDO 9pm
Lic ℙ 20P nc5yrs croquet
Credit Cards ① ③ £

£ Remember to use the money-off vouchers.

GRANDES ROCQUES

GH Q Q Q **La Galaad Hotel** Rue des Francais
☎Guernsey(0481) 57233
27 Mar-Oct
Situated in a quiet rural setting, this well-maintained, privately owned hotel offers nicely appointed bedrooms, comfortable public rooms and an attractive dining room. The hotel has a warm and friendly atmosphere.
12rm(2⇨10♠)(4fb) CTV in all bedrooms ® ✖
sB&B⇨♠£17-£27
dB&B⇨♠£34-£54 (incl dinner) LDO 9.30am
Lic ℙ 14P

PERELLE

GH Q Q **La Girouette Country Hotel**
☎Guernsey(0481) 63269 FAX (0481) 63023
mid Mar-Oct
This small country house with an informal and friendly atmosphere is just a short distance from Perelle Bay in a particularly attractive setting. The accommodation offers comfortable public rooms and bedrooms which vary in size and style.
14rm(6⇨6♠2hc)(2fb) CTV in all bedrooms ®
✖ (ex guide dogs) ✳ sB&B£22 dB&B⇨♠£44 LDO 7.30pm
Lic ℙ 15P nc5yrs
Credit Cards ① ② ③

ST PETER PORT

⊢⊶**GH** Q Q Q **Marine Hotel** Well Rd
☎Guernsey(0481) 24978 due to change to 724978
A warm, relaxing atmosphere prevails at this comfortable, family-run private hotel.
11⇨♠ (3fb) ® ✖ (ex guide dogs) sB&B⇨♠£12.75-£21.50
dB&B⇨♠£25.50-£43
Lic ℙ CTV ✗
£

SELECTED

GH Q Q Q Q **Midhurst House** Candie Rd
☎Guernsey(0481) 24391 due to change to 724391
mid Apr-mid Oct
Brian and Jan Goodenough and their staff provide warmth and hospitality at this house. Lovingly restored, the hotel combines elegance and comfort in the bedrooms – 5 in the main house and 3 in a cottage-style extension overlooking the garden with its unusual, exotic plants. The lounge has a domed conservatory skylight which creates an indoor garden atmosphere. Brian's excellent cooking uses local produce, and includes homemade soups, rolls, mousses and featherlight pastries.
5rm(2⇨3♠)Annexe 3♠ (1fb) CTV in all bedrooms ® ✖
✳ sB&B⇨♠£25-£30 dB&B⇨♠£39-£46 LDO 6.45pm
Lic ℙ 1🚗 nc8yrs

GH Q Q Q *Les Ozouets Lodge* Ozouets Rd
☎Guernsey(0481) 21288
Mar-Oct
Run by the chef-patron, this well-kept private hotel offers excellent cooking complemented by a well-chosen wine list. Its outstanding gardens have putting and bowling greens and a tennis court. The simply appointed bedrooms all have private facilities.
11rm(5⇨6♠) CTV in all bedrooms ✖ LDO 7.45pm
Lic ℙ CTV 15P nc5yrs ♪(grass)
Credit Cards ③

Book as early as possible for busy holiday periods.

ST SAMPSON

GH Q Q **Ann-Dawn Private Hotel** Route des Capelles
☎Guernsey(0481) 725606
Etr-Oct
Traditional Guernsey house with informal atmosphere, large lawned and landscaped gardens.
14rm(3⇨9🟨2hc) CTV in all bedrooms ® ✲
sB&B£19.25-£24.75 sB&B⇨🟨£21.25-£26.75
dB&B⇨🟨£28.50-£53.50 (incl dinner) WB&B£120.75-£173.25
WBDi£134.75-£187.25 LDO 5pm
Lic 🍽 12P nc12yrs
Credit Cards 1 3

JERSEY

GOREY

GH Q Q **Royal Bay Hotel** ☎Jersey(0534) 53318
May-Oct
Family-run hotel near the beach in a picturesque village.
16⇨🟨 (2fb) sB&B⇨🟨fr£17
dB&B⇨🟨fr£34 (incl dinner) LDO 9.30am
Lic 🍽 CTV 11P nc6yrs

GREVE DE LECQ BAY

GH Q Q Q **Des Pierres** (on B65 near beach)
☎Jersey(0534) 81858 FAX (0534) 85273
Closed Xmas & New Year
14rm(7⇨7🟨)(3fb) CTV in all bedrooms ® ✲ ✳
WB&B£145-£196 WBDi£175-£231
Lic 🍽 CTV 13P
Credit Cards 1 3 ⓔ

GROUVILLE

GH Q Q Q **Lavender Villa Hotel** Rue A Don
☎Jersey(0534) 54937
Mar-Nov
21rm(10⇨11🟨)(3fb) CTV in all bedrooms ® ✲
sB&B⇨🟨£20-£30
dB&B⇨🟨£40-£70 (incl dinner) WB&B£119-£224
WBDi£140-£245 LDO 7.15pm
Lic 🍽 CTV 20P nc3yrs ⌂

ST AUBIN

GH Q Q **Bryn-y-Mor** Route de la Haule
☎Jersey(0534) 20295 Telex no 4192638
Overlooking St Aubin Bay, this small hotel is being upgraded. Simple, comfortable accommodation is provided, with well-equipped bedrooms and a wood-panelled dining room which serves predominantly English cuisine.
14rm(11⇨🟨3hc)(4fb) CTV in all bedrooms ✳ sB&B£17-£27
dB&B£34-£54 dB&B⇨🟨£40-£60 (incl dinner) LDO 7pm
Lic 6P ⌂
Credit Cards 1 2 3

SELECTED

GH Q Q Q Q **The Panorama** JE3 8BR
☎Jersey(0534) 42429 FAX (0534) 45940
Etr-Xmas
Set high above the town, this hotel has views across the bay and terraced garden. The bedrooms have every modern facility, and the basement breakfast room is complemented by the lounge with its 200-year-old fire place. Afternoon teas are served in the conservatory 'Terrace Tea Pot' garden – in a silver pot on a silver tray. John and Jill Squinks provide attentive and enthusiastic service.
17⇨🟨 (2fb) CTV in all bedrooms ® ✲
sB&B⇨🟨£20-£32 dB&B⇨🟨£34-£54 (wkly only Jun-Sep)

🍽 🎋 nc10yrs Tea garden
Credit Cards 1 2 3 5 ⓔ

ST HELIER

GH Q Q Q **Almorah Hotel** Lower Kings Cliff
☎Jersey(0534) 21648 FAX (0534) 68600
Enjoying an elevated position above the town centre, this listed terrace building has tastefully furnished, well-equipped bedrooms. The other accommodation includes an old-world Breton-style dining room where guests receive friendly service.
16rm(13⇨3🟨)(4fb) CTV in all bedrooms ® ✲ (ex guide dogs)
✱ dB&B⇨🟨£50-£70 (incl dinner) WB&B£140-£175
WBDi£175-£245 LDO 6.30pm
Lic 🍽 CTV 10P
Credit Cards 1 2 3 5 ⓔ

GH Q Q Q **Cliff Court Hotel** St Andrews Rd, First Tower
☎(0534) 34919
14 Apr-29 Oct
Enjoying a quiet situation overlooking St Aubins Bay, this hotel has extensive accommodation with bright modern bedrooms, a large lounge with separate bar and a large dining room. Service is friendly and under the personal supervision of resident proprietors.
16rm(15⇨1hc)(4fb) ® ✲ (ex guide dogs) LDO 7.30pm
Lic 🍽 CTV 14P ⌂(heated)
Credit Cards 3

GH Q Q Q **Cornucopia Hotel & Restaurant** Mont Pinel
☎Jersey(0534) 32646 FAX (0534) 66199
15rm(4⇨11🟨)(2fb) CTV in all bedrooms ® ✱
sB&B⇨🟨£21.38-£30.50
dB&B⇨🟨£34.66-£57 WB&B£120.60-£213
WBDi£164.70-£262 LDO 2.30pm

▶

Lic 🏱 21P ♨ ⌒(heated) solarium gymnasium games room jacuzzi turkish bath
Credit Cards 1 2 3 £

GH Q Q Millbrook House Rue De Trachy JE2 3JN
☎Jersey(0534) 33036
27 Apr-7 Oct
Set in 2 acres of wooded grounds, this Georgian and Colonial-style house stands on the bay, 500 yards from the beach, and has a country-house atmosphere.
24⇨♪ (2fb) CTV in all bedrooms ® ✠ sB&B⇨♪£21-£32.50
dB&B⇨♪£42-£65 (incl dinner) LDO 7pm
Lic lift CTV 20P
£

GH Q Q Q Runnymede Court Hotel 46/52 Roseville St
JE2 4PN ☎Jersey(0534) 20044 FAX (0534) 27880
mid Feb-mid Dec
Extensively refurbished, this establishment offers a choice of comfortable, bright bedrooms equipped with every modern facility – some situated around the rear garden. The public rooms are tastefully furnished and include a bar, spacious dining room and lounge. The beach and shopping centre are within easy reach. The comfort of the guests is Mr Bruno Carpenter's prime concern as proprietor.
57⇨♪ (6fb) CTV in all bedrooms ® ✠ (ex guide dogs)
sB&B⇨♪£22-£30
dB&B⇨♪£44-£60 (incl dinner) WB&B£119-£196
WBDi£154-£210 (wkly only 27 Apr-5 Oct) LDO 7.15pm
Lic lift 🏱 CTV ♪ nc3yrs
Credit Cards 1 2 3 £

TRINITY

GH Q Q Q Highfield Country Hotel Route Du Ebenezer
JF3 5DS ☎Jersey(0534) 62194 FAX (0534) 65342
30 Mar-30 Oct
Standing in an acre of grounds, this hotel has bright, pretty bedrooms, a comfortable bar and lounge and a small dining room. Good car parking is available. Mr David Lord also provides a laundry room and swimming pool. Ground floor self-catering apartments are available.
25rm(14⇨11♪)(4fb) CTV in all bedrooms ® ✠
sB&B⇨♪£23-£33 (incl dinner) LDO 7.45pm
Lic 🏱 25P ⌒
Credit Cards 1 2 3 5 £

CHARD Somerset Map 03 ST30

⊢⊣GH Q Q Q **Watermead** 83 High St TA20 1QT
☎(0460) 62834
This is a small and friendly guesthouse with good-sized, comfortable bedrooms that are nicely equipped. The simple and honest cooking is served in the spacious dining room.
9rm(6♪3hc)⚡in 3 bedrooms CTV in all bedrooms ®
sB&B£12.50-£13 sB&B♪£15-£16 dB&B£25-£27
dB&B♪£30-£32 WB&B£80-£100 WBDi£120-£140 LDO noon
Lic 🏱 CTV 9P 2🐾 ♨
£

CHARFIELD Gloucestershire Map 03 ST79

INN Q Q Huntingford Mill Hotel GL12 8EX
☎Dursley(0453) 843431
Standing outside the village, astride the river, Huntingford Mill was the last working grain mill in Gloucestershire. Now it provides cosy accommodation with simple, soundly equipped rooms together with a good steak restaurant.
5hc (1fb) CTV in all bedrooms ® ✠ (ex guide dogs) sB&B£25
dB&B£35 WB&B£175-£245 Lunch £14.95&alc Dinner
£14.95&alc LDO 10pm
🏱 25P ♨ ♪
Credit Cards 1 2 3 5

Bessiestown Farm

Catlowdy, Penton, Carlisle. CA6 5QP
Telephone: Nicholforest (0228 77) 219
Your hosts: Jack and Margaret Sisson

AA | AWARD WINNER ETB ♛♛♛
Commended

- ★ Warm relaxed atmosphere
- ★ Delicious home cooking
- ★ Full central heating
- ★ Tea making facilities
- ★ Residential licence
- ★ Restricted smoking

- ★ Pretty bedrooms all en suite
- ★ Three adjoining luxury suites
- ★ **Indoor heated swimming pool** (pool open mid May-mid Sept)
- ★ **Winter breaks**

Ideal base for touring Lake District, Roman Wall, Solway and Galloway coasts. Stop over enroute to & from Scotland and Northern Ireland.

Craigburn Farm

Craigburn Farm, Catlowdy, Penton, Carlisle CA6 5QP
Telephone: (0228 77) 214

A friendly atmosphere and personal attention awaits visitors, at this 18th Century, 250 acre working farm. Situated in a quiet setting, delicious home cooking with fresh produce, *Winner of a Certificate of Merit in the Great British Breakfast 1989*, also finalist in Food and Farming Year National Cookery Competition 1989. Excellent for touring and stop overs, to and from Scotland.

* 7 bedrooms all ensuite, four poster bed
* Central heating
* Tea making facilities
* Residential licence
* Games room
* Oct to March – bargain breaks

CHARING Kent Map 05 TQ94

FH Q Q Q Mrs P Pym **Barnfield** *(TQ924477)* TN27 0BN
☎(023371) 2421

Built around 1415 and furnished throughout with antiques, this ancient farmhouse has a comfortable sitting room with plenty of books. Good leisure facilities are available along with a barn for functions. Ordnance Survey map 189 is recommended for location details.

5rm(4hc)(1fb)⊁in all bedrooms ® ✖ sB&B£16 dB&B£32-£36 CTV 0P 1🐎 ♗(hard)500 acres arable sheep

CHARLTON Northamptonshire Map 04 SP53

GH Q Q **Home Farm** Main St OX17 3DR
☎Banbury(0295) 811683

Set in half an acre of walled garden, Colonel and Mrs Grove-White's cottage-style farmhouse offers 2 country bedrooms, each with private bathrooms and one with a small lounge. The accommodation is reached by a winding staircase. A third bedroom is in a building across the courtyard, which can also be let as a self-catering unit.

2⇔🏠 Annexe 1⇔🏠 ⊁in 2 bedrooms CTV in all bedrooms ®
sB&B⇔🏠£24-£26 dB&B⇔🏠£40-£44
CTV 3P nc12yrs

CHARLWOOD Surrey

For accommodation details see under **Gatwick Airport**

CHARMOUTH Dorset Map 03 SY39

GH Q Q **Newlands House** Stonebarrow Ln DT6 6RA
☎(0297) 60212
Mar-Oct

Well-appointed and comfortable, this converted 16th-century farmhouse stands on the fringe of the village, close to the beach.

12rm(7⇔4🏠1hc)(2fb)⊁in all bedrooms CTV in all bedrooms
® sB&B£17.50-£20.50 sB&B⇔🏠£17.50-£20.50 dB&B£35-£41
dB&B⇔🏠£35-£41 WB&B£112.50-£130 WBDi£171.60-£188
LDO noon
Lic 网 CTV 12P nc6yrs

CHEDDAR Somerset Map 03 ST45

FH Q Mrs C A Ladd **Tor** *(ST473513)* Nyland BS27 3UP
☎(0934) 743710 & 742549

Three miles south of Cheddar, a 1.5-mile single-track unclassified road leads to this recently built farmhouse overlooking the Somerset Levels. Simple family accommodation is offered.

8rm(3⇔2hc)(1fb)⊁in all bedrooms ✖ sB&B£15
dB&B£20-£28
dB&B⇔🏠£32 WB&B£63-£101 WBDi£112-£150 LDO 9.30am
网 CTV 10P ✔ 33 acres mixed
£

CHEDDLETON Staffordshire Map 07 SJ95

SELECTED

GH Q Q Q Q Q **Choir Cottage and Choir House** Ostlers Ln ST13 7HS ☎Churnet Side(0538) 360561

Bedrooms here are delightfully furnished ; each is fully self-contained, and one has its own small patio. The setting is on the edge of the village, with delightful gardens overlooking lovely countryside, and the service is very friendly. Evening meals are by arrangement.

2rm(1⇔1🏠)Annexe 2🏠 ⊁in 2 bedrooms CTV in all bedrooms ® sB&B⇔🏠£20-£28
dB&B⇔🏠£32-£38 WB&B£106-£119 WBDi£206-£219
LDO 24hrs notice
网 CTV 5P
£

CHELMSFORD Essex Map 05 TL70

GH Q Q Q **Beechcroft Private Hotel** 211 New London Rd
CM2 0AJ ☎(0245) 352462
Closed Xmas & New Year

Under the personal supervision of the proprietor, Beechcroft is a friendly, traditional guesthouse.

20rm(8🏠12hc)(2fb) CTV in 13 bedrooms ®
sB&B£24.95-£26.60 sB&B🏠fr£32.20 dB&Bfr£39
dB&B🏠fr£51.50
网 CTV 15P
Credit Cards 1 3

SELECTED

GH Q Q Q Q **Boswell House Hotel** 118-120 Springfield Rd CM2 6LF ☎(0245) 287587
Closed 10 days Xmas

The friendly and enthusiastic proprietors offer efficient service at this well well-managed hotel, which is a tastefully renovated Victorian building. A cosy bar complements the bedrooms which are freshly decorated and well equipped, with pine furnishings enhancing the warm atmosphere.

13rm(9⇔4🏠)(2fb)⊁in 4 bedrooms CTV in all bedrooms
® sB&B⇔🏠£33-£38
dB&B⇔🏠£45-£51 WB&B£231-£266 WBDi£287-£322
LDO 8.30pm
Lic 网 CTV 15P
Credit Cards 1 2 3 5 £

GH Q Q *Tanunda Hotel* 219 New London Rd CM2 0AJ
☎(0245) 354295
Closed 2wks Xmas

This commercial guesthouse is fairly large and offers a choice of accommodation to meet guests' requirements, and interesting restaurant facilities.

20rm(2⇔9🏠9hc) CTV in 12 bedrooms ® LDO 7.25pm
Lic 网 CTV 20P

CHELTENHAM Gloucestershire Map 03 SO92

See also Bishop's Cleeve

GH Q Q **Abbey Hotel** 16 Bath Pde GL53 7HN ☎(0242) 516053
Telex no 227188 FAX (0242) 227765

Situated behind Stanford Park and close to the town centre, this former early Victorian terraced house has been carefully modernised to provide attractive well-equipped bedrooms and cosy public areas.

14rm(7🏠7hc)(2fb) CTV in all bedrooms ® ✖ ✱ sB&B£15-£18
sB&B🏠£22 dB&B£36
dB&B🏠£40 WB&B£90-£130 WBDi£130-£170 (wkly only 11-14 Mar) LDO 7.30pm
Lic 网 ♗ ♨
Credit Cards 1 3 £

GH Q Q Q **Allards** Shurdington Rd GL51 5XA
☎(0242) 862498

Guests are assured of a warm welcome at this elegant, period villa, personally run by Mr and Mrs Castle. Accommodation is spacious and attractive, and the house is situated about two miles from the town centre.

11🏠 (2fb) CTV in all bedrooms ® ✖ sB&B🏠£19-£26
dB&B🏠£40-£42 LDO 8pm
网 15P 1🐎
Credit Cards 1 3 £

GH Q Q **Askham Court Hotel** Pittville Circus Rd GL52 2PZ
☎(0242) 525547
rs Xmas

This hotel is an early Victorian house, located within walking distance of the town centre. The bedrooms are spacious, many with en suite facilities. The large public areas retain many original features, such as moulded cornices and fireplaces.
18rm(4⇌7🛏7hc)(3fb) CTV in 11 bedrooms Ⓡ LDO 6.30pm
Lic ⴹ CTV 20P

GH ⒬⒬ **Beaumont House Hotel** 56 Shurdington Rd GL53 0JE
☎(0242) 245986
A listed Victorian house with picturesque garden, and spacious attractive bedrooms, close to town centre.
18rm(6⇌11🛏1hc)(3fb) CTV in all bedrooms Ⓡ sB&B£16-£17
sB&B⇌🛏£22-£30
dB&B⇌🛏£40-£50 WB&B£108.50-£203 WBDi£175-£276
LDO 4pm
Lic ⴹ CTV 20P 2🛆
Credit Cards ①③£

GH ⒬⒬⒬ **Beechworth Lawn Hotel** 133 Hales Rd GL52 6ST
☎(0242) 522583
This spacious Victorian house, located half a mile from the town centre on Broadway Road, has been modernised by the hosts, Mr and Mrs Brian Toombs. It provides comfortable and well-equipped accommodation whilst retaining much of its character.
7rm(3🛏4hc)(2fb) CTV in all bedrooms Ⓡ ✳ sB&B£17-£24
sB&B🛏£22-£26 dB&B£32-£35 dB&B🛏£36-£40 LDO 4pm
ⴹ CTV 10P
£

See advertisement on page 113

GH ⒬ **Cleevelands House** 38 Evesham Rd GL52 2AH
☎(0242) 518898
12rm(9🛏3hc)(3fb) CTV in all bedrooms Ⓡ ✳ sB&B£20-£25
sB&B🛏£30-£35 dB&B£40-£45
dB&B🛏£45-£50 WB&B£140-£160 WBDi£175-£230 LDO
8.30pm
▶

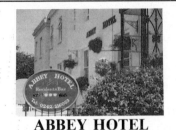

ABBEY HOTEL

Adjacent to Sanford Park and only 3 minutes' walk from town centre. Fully refurbished, decorated and furnished in 1990. All facilities offered by 3 crown hotels and more. Charming family owned and run hotel. Delicious home cooking. Direct dial phones, fax, telex, 24 hr access. 8 en suites to choose from.

14/16 Bath Parade, Cheltenham GL53 7HN.
Tel: (0242) 516053 Fax: (0242) 227765
Telex: 336080 MALTEXG

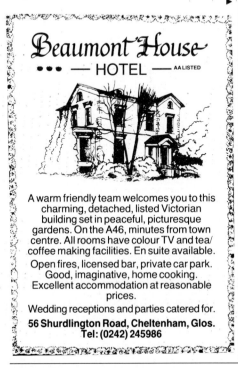

Lic ♛ CTV 10P ♨
Credit Cards ⑴ ⑶ £

GH QQ Hallery House 48 Shurdington Rd GL53 0JE
☎(0242) 578450
*Situated on the main Stroud road out of Cheltenham, this Grade II
listed Victorian house has a friendly atmosphere.*
16rm(10⇨6hc)(1fb)⊁in 2 bedrooms CTV in all bedrooms
® ✱ sB&B£16-£20 sB&B⇨£22-£35 dB&B£30-£40
dB&B⇨£37-£50 WB&B£110-£230 WBDi£170-£300 LDO
6.30pm
Lic ♛ 20P 3⊜ (£1.50 per night) ♨
Credit Cards ⑴ ⑶ £

GH QQQ Hannaford's 20 Evesham Rd GL52 2AB
☎(0242) 515181
*Attractive, comfortable, terrace house, near centre and public car
park.*
10rm(9⇨1hc)(1fb) CTV in all bedrooms ® ✱
sB&B⇨£27-£32 dB&B⇨£42-£44 LDO 5pm
Lic ♛ CTV nc7yrs
Credit Cards ⑴ ⑶ £

GH QQQ Hollington House Hotel 115 Hales Rd GL52 6ST
☎(0242) 519718 FAX (0242) 570280
*Situated half a mile from the town centre, this large Cotswold
stone Victorian house has 9 spacious bedrooms with en suite
facilities, beverages and colour television, as well as a comfortable
lounge and bar. Juergen and Annette Berg provide friendly service
in a pleasant and relaxed atmosphere. Good food is offered at
breakfast and dinner with a choice of menu.*
9rm(8hc)(2fb) CTV in all bedrooms ® ✱ sB&B£28-£32
dB&B£38-£47 WB&B£133-£147 WBDi£193-£207 LDO 7pm
Lic ♛ 12P nc3yrs
Credit Cards ⑴ ⑵ ⑶ £

GH QQ Ivy Dene 145 Hewlett Rd GL52 6TS
☎(0242) 521726 & 521776
*Situated close to the town centre on the way to Prestbury, this
Victorian house has been greatly modernised. It offers well-
equipped, well-managed bedrooms and comfortable public areas.
The accommodation is on a room and breakfast basis only.*
10hc (2fb) CTV in all bedrooms ® ✱ sB&B£12.50-£13.50
dB&B£25-£27
♛ CTV 8P
£

⊷GH QQ Knowle House 89 Leckhampton Rd GL53 0BS
☎(0242) 516091
Closed 24-27 Dec
*This is a spacious Edwardian house situated approximately one
mile from the town centre. It offers bed and breakfast in modern
rooms, and has the additional benefit of a lounge for residents.*
5hc (1fb) ® sB&B£12-£15 dB&B£24-£30 WB&B£80-£100
♛ CTV 6P
£

GH QQ Lawn Hotel 5 Pittville Lawn GL52 2BE
☎(0242) 526638
9hc (2fb) CTV in all bedrooms ® ✱ LDO noon
Lic ♛ CTV 8P

GH QQ Leeswood Hotel 14 Montpelier Dr GL50 1TX
☎(0242) 524813
7hc CTV in all bedrooms ®
CTV 6P

Every effort is made to provide accurate
information, but details can change after we go to
print. It is advisable to check prices etc. before
you make a firm booking.

SELECTED

GH QQQQ Lypiatt House Lypiatt Rd GL50 2QW
☎(0242) 224994 FAX (0242) 224996
Closed 23 Dec-2 Jan
*This lovely Victorian house has been sympathetically restored
to its former splendour, and is set in the privacy of its own
small grounds. The drawing room is large, impressive and
comfortable, and good meals are available in the small,
intimate restaurant. Bedrooms offer quality and comfort with
all modern facilities. All aspects of the hotel are
complemented by the friendly service from the enthusiastic
young proprietors, Michael and Susan Malloy. Lypiatt House
was the winner for Central England of the AA's Best
Newcomer Award for 1989/90.*
10rm(9⇨1) CTV in all bedrooms ® ✱
sB&B⇨£37-£55 dB&B⇨£48-£65 LDO 2pm
Lic ♛ 14P nc12yrs
Credit Cards ⑴ ⑶ £

GH QQQ Milton House 12 Royal Pde, Bayshill Rd
GL50 3AY ☎(0242) 582601 FAX (0242) 222326
*Elegant, Regency terraced house, recently converted with
comfortable bedrooms.*
9rm(1⇨8)(4fb)⊁in 2 bedrooms CTV in all bedrooms ® ✱
✱ sB&B⇨£28.75-£38 dB&B⇨£40-£48 LDO 9am
Lic ♛ CTV 5P
Credit Cards ⑴ ⑵ ⑶ £

GH QQQ North Hall Hotel Pittville Circus Rd GL52 2PZ
☎(0242) 520589
Closed Xmas
*This hotel, situated in the Pitville district close to the town centre,
is an elegant early-Victorian detached house. It offers comfortable
and well-equipped bedrooms, and attractive public rooms, many of
which still retain the original features.*
20rm(6⇨6 8hc)(1fb) CTV in all bedrooms ® sB&Bfr£18
sB&B⇨£27.50-£30 dB&Bfr£31
dB&B⇨fr£43 WBDi£165-£222 LDO 7.15pm
Lic ♛ CTV 20P
Credit Cards ⑴ ⑶ £

GH QQQ Regency House Hotel 50 Clarence Square
GL50 4JR ☎(0242) 582718
Closed Xmas & New Year
*Refurbished and redecorated throughout, Regency House has
comfortable, well-equipped bedrooms, most of which are en suite.
Guests may enjoy a drink in the elegant drawing room or with their
evening meal.*
8 CTV in all bedrooms ® ✱ (ex guide dogs) sB&B£25-£28
dB&B£40-£45 LDO am
Lic ♛ ℙ
Credit Cards ⑴ ⑶

GH QQQ Stretton Lodge Western Rd GL50 3RN
☎(0242) 528724 & 570771
*Elegant 19th-century house in a residential area. There is a
friendly atmosphere and accommodation is comfortable with well-
equipped bedrooms and a spacious lounge.*
9⇨ (3fb)⊁in 5 bedrooms CTV in all bedrooms ®
✱ (ex guide dogs) sB&B⇨£28.50-£45
dB&B⇨£47.50-£55 WB&B£150-£170 WBDi£218-£240
LDO noon
Lic ♛ CTV 6P
Credit Cards ⑴ ⑵ ⑶ £

GH QQ Willoughby 1 Suffolk Square GL50 2DR
☎(0242) 522798
Closed Xmas & New Year

▶

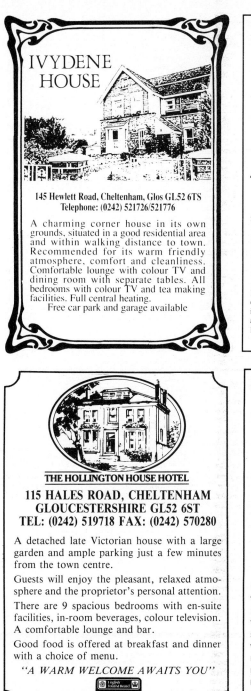
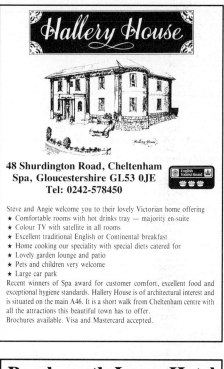

Located within the Montpellier District and occupying a prominent position on the Square, this fine late Georgian Cotswold stone house offers spacious and well-equipped bedrooms, while retaining many of its original features.
10rm(5🚿5hc)(1fb) CTV in all bedrooms [R] ✱ sB&Bfr£23 sB&B🚿fr£27.50 dB&Bfr£42 dB&B🚿fr£46 LDO 4pm
♨ CTV 10P
[£]

GH [Q][Q] Wishmoor 147 Hales Rd GL52 6TD ☎(0242) 238504
This is a small and friendly establishment, situated in a residential area on the eastern side of Cheltenham. The sound accommodation is complemented by a comfortable ground floor lounge which incorporates an open fireplace.
9rm(4🚿5hc)(1fb) CTV in all bedrooms [R] 🐕 (ex guide dogs) sB&B£15-£20 sB&B🚿£20-£25 dB&B£30-£35 dB&B🚿£40-£45 WB&B£105-£140 WBDi£168-£203 LDO noon
♨ 10P
[£]

CHERITON FITZPAINE Devon Map 03 SS80

FH [Q][Q] Mrs D M Lock **Brindiwell** *(SS896079)* EX17 4HR ☎(03636) 357
Period farmhouse with oak beams and panelling; on the side of a valley with views of the Exe Valley and Dartmoor.
4rm(1hc)(1fb)🚭in 1 bedroom CTV in 1 bedroom [R] 🐕 ✱ sB&B£12-£14
dB&B£24-£28 WB&Bfr£84 WBDifr£100 LDO 5pm
CTV 4P 1🚗 120 acres sheep
[£]

CHESTER Cheshire Map 07 SJ46

GH [Q][Q] Bawnpark Hotel 10 Hoole Rd, Hoole CH2 3NH ☎(0244) 324971
This large, semi detached Victorian residence has a rear car park, and stands on the outskirts of Chester. The cheerfully decorated bedrooms have many amenities expected at a hotel.
5🛁 (2fb) CTV in all bedrooms [R] ✱ sB&B🛁£30-£36 dB&B🛁£36-£38
♨ CTV 12P
Credit Cards [1] [3] [£]

GH [Q][Q][Q] Brookside Hotel 12 Brook Ln CH2 2AN ☎(0244) 381943 FAX (0244) 379701
Closed Xmas wk
Large, well-furnished hotel with attractive restaurant and Victorian-style lounges.
24rm(16🛁8🚿)(6fb) CTV in all bedrooms [R] sB&B🛁🚿£27-£30 dB&B🛁🚿£42-£47 LDO 8.30pm
Lic ♨ CTV 14P sauna solarium gymnasium pool table
Credit Cards [1] [3] [£]

GH [Q][Q][Q] *Cavendish Hotel* 44 Hough Green CH4 8JQ ☎(0244) 675100 FAX (0244) 679942
Standing on the A549, one mile from the city centre with gardens to the front and rear, this restored Victorian house has an elegant lounge with a grand piano. The bedrooms are comfortable and well appointed.
20rm(5🛁11🚿4hc)(5fb) CTV in all bedrooms LDO 8pm
Lic ♨ CTV 37P
Credit Cards [1] [2] [3] [5]

GH [Q][Q][Q] *Chester Court Hotel* 48 Hoole Rd (A56) CH2 3NL ☎(0244) 320779 & 311098
Closed 24 Dec-5 Jan
This charming, creeper-clad building has particularly well-equipped bedrooms, some of whch are tastefully designed chalets set in the grounds. An attractive lounge adjoins the bar and there is an equally appealing dining room.
8rm(1🛁4🚿)Annexe 12rm(6🛁6🚿)(2fb) CTV in all bedrooms [R] LDO 8pm
Lic ♨ 25P
Credit Cards [1] [2] [3] [5]

GH [Q] Devonia 33-35 Hoole Rd CH2 3NP ☎(0244) 322236
Catering for tourists and business people, this family-run hotel offers good value for money. It is roughly one mile from the city centre on the A56.
10hc (6fb) CTV in all bedrooms [R] ✱ sB&B£17.50-£20 dB&B£25-£27.50 LDO 4pm
Lic ♨ CTV 15P
[£]

GH [Q] Eaton Hotel 29 City Rd CH1 3AE ☎(0244) 320840
Situated alongside the Shropshire Union Canal and close to the main railway station, most bedrooms at this hotel have en suite facilities and are well equipped. There is a small bar and an attractive dining-room.
22rm(6🛁7🚿9hc)(3fb) CTV in all bedrooms [R] ✱ sB&Bfr£24.50 sB&B🛁🚿fr£29.50 dB&Bfr£37 dB&B🛁🚿fr£42 WB&B£129.50-£206.50 WBDi£171.50-£248.50 LDO 8pm
Lic ♨ CTV 8P 1🚗
Credit Cards [1] [2] [3] [5] [£]

GH [Q][Q] Egerton Lodge Hotel 57 Hoole Rd, Hoole CH2 3NJ ☎(0244) 320712
Closed 19 Dec-3 Jan
Situated about three quarters of a mile from the city centre on the A56, this attractive mid-terrace Victorian house offers accommodation in compact, attractvie and well-equipped rooms.
4rm(3🚿1hc)(3fb) CTV in all bedrooms [R] 🐕 ✱ sB&B🚿£17.50-£21 dB&B🚿£27-£32
5P nc3yrs
Credit Cards [1] [2] [3] [£]

GH [Q][Q] *Elizabethan Park Hotel* 78 Hoole Rd CH2 3NT ☎(0244) 310213
Comfortable and spacious bedrooms are a feature of this large house, which stands on the A56 on its eastern approach to the city. There is also an attractive dining room.
7rm(2🛁5🚿)(3fb) CTV in all bedrooms [R] LDO noon
♨ 20P 1🚗
Credit Cards [1] [3]

GH [Q][Q] Eversley Hotel 9 Eversley Park CH2 2AJ ☎(0244) 373744
Closed 24 Dec-2 Jan
This Victorian property is situated in a residential area just off the A5116, about one mile from the city centre, and has well-equipped accommodation.
11rm(4🛁5🚿2hc)(3fb) CTV in all bedrooms [R] 🐕 sB&B£22 dB&B£39 dB&B🛁🚿£42 LDO 8pm
Lic ♨ CTV 17P 🏠
Credit Cards [1] [3] [£]

GH [Q] *Gables* 5 Vicarage Rd, Hoole CH2 3HZ ☎(0244) 323969
This end-terrace Victorian house is in a quiet residential area just off the Hoole road leading to the town. Limited parking space is available but street parking is permitted.
7hc (4fb) CTV in all bedrooms [R]
CTV 7P
Credit Cards [1]

GH [Q][Q][Q] Green Gables 11 Eversley Park CH2 2AJ ☎(0244) 372243
A semi detached, Victorian gabled house, Green Gables is beautifully furnished and decorated, with neat lawns and gardens, about a mile from the centre of Chester. All bedrooms have an en suite bathroom, telephone, television and tea-making facilities. There is a very comfortable lounge and a light and modern little breakfast room.
4rm(3🚿1hc)(1fb) CTV in all bedrooms [R] 🐕 (ex guide dogs) sB&B🚿£20-£25 dB&B🚿£30-£33 WB&B£85-£90 LDO 9.30pm
▶

📺 CTV 8P 3🚗
[£]

GH [Q][Q] **Hamilton Court** 5-7 Hamilton St CH2 3JG
☎(0244) 345387
Closed Xmas wk
Just off the A56, 1 mile from the city centre, 2 gabled houses make up this well-appointed, hospitable hotel which has an attractive restaurant.
12rm(6🚿6hc)(5fb) CTV in all bedrooms Ⓡ LDO 6.30pm
Lic 📺 CTV 8P 10🚗
Credit Cards [1] [3]

SELECTED

GH [Q][Q][Q][Q] ***Redland Private Hotel*** 64 Hough Green CH4 9JY ☎(0244) 671024
This gem of a hotel stands on the edge of town on the busy A549. Theresa and Bill White have painstakingly restored the house to its former glory, with large and thoughtfully furnished bedrooms with modern facilities. The interior has been likened to a baronial hall, and Redlands, with its friendly, welcoming atmosphere, has a quality found at the best hotels.
11🛁 (3fb) CTV in all bedrooms
Lic 📺 CTV 10P 3🚗 snooker
Credit Cards [1] [3]

GH [Q][Q] ***Riverside Recorder Hotel*** 19 City Walls CH1 1SB
☎(0244) 311498
Situated on the Roman city wall at the top of the Recorder Steps, this comfortable guesthouse, with views over the River Dee, provides many facilities in its well-appointed bedrooms, some of which have four-poster beds.
10🛁🚿 (2fb) CTV in all bedrooms Ⓡ LDO 8.30pm
Lic 📺 CTV 15P

GH [Q] ***The Riverside Hotel*** 22 City Walls, Off Lower Bridge St CH1 1SB ☎(0244) 326580 & 325278
Well-furnished modern hotel on city walls next to the River Dee.
13rm(11🛁2hc)(2fb) CTV in all bedrooms Ⓡ LDO 9pm
Lic 📺 CTV 25P
Credit Cards [1] [3]

CHIDEOCK Dorset Map 03 SY49

SELECTED

GH [Q][Q][Q][Q] **Betchworth House Hotel** DT6 6JW
☎(0297) 89478
Cosy cottage-style guesthouse located in a most beautiful part of Dorset. Bedrooms are comfortable, public areas attractive, food home cooked and the atmosphere is friendly.
6rm(3🚿3hc)(1fb) Ⓡ 🚫 (ex guide dogs) sB&B£18-£20 dB&B£16-£18 dB&B🚿£18-£20 WB&B£108.50-£136.50
Lic 📺 CTV 15P nc7yrs
[£]

CHINNOR Oxfordshire Map 04 SP70

FH [Q][Q][Q] Mr & Mrs Steel **Chinnor Hill Manor** *(SU762994)* OX9 4BG ☎Kingston Blount(0844) 51469
Guests have open access to the 15 acres of grounds in which this charming house is set. The comfortably appointed bedrooms are spacious, and complement the good public rooms and attractive dining room, the heated pool and grass tennis court.
3rm ✱ sB&B£20 dB&B£40
📺 CTV 0P 2🚗 🏊(heated) 🎾(grass)15 acres horses

CHIPPENHAM Wiltshire Map 03 ST97

GH [Q][Q][Q] **Oxford Hotel** 32/36 Langley Rd SN15 1BX
☎(0249) 652542
Tidy, detached guesthouse on edge of town on Swindon Road.
13rm(7🚿6hc)(1fb) CTV in all bedrooms Ⓡ ✱ sB&B£22 sB&B🚿£32 dB&B£34
dB&B🚿£42 WB&B£132-£192 WBDi£190-£250 LDO 5.30pm
Lic 📺 9P
Credit Cards [1] [2] [3] [£]

CHIPPING CAMPDEN Gloucestershire Map 04 SP13

GH [Q][Q][Q] **The Malt House** Broad Campden GL55 6UU
☎Evesham(0386) 840295
Closed 23 Dec-1 Jan rs Sun
Mrs Robinson provides a personal welcome to this 17th-century country house, which has been lovingly converted from Cotswold stone cottages. Public rooms are tastefully furnished with antiques, comfortable armchairs and sofa, open log fires and beams. Bedrooms all have views overlooking the 4.5 acres of well-kept grounds and gardens. Dinner can be arranged (please ask on booking). A combination of English and French dishes are usually offered, and complemented by a choice of wines.
3rm(2🛁1hc) CTV in all bedrooms Ⓡ 🚫 (ex guide dogs) ✱ dB&B🛁£58.50-£70 LDO noon
Lic 📺 8P nc12yrs

CHISELBOROUGH Somerset Map 03 ST41

FH [Q][Q] Mrs E Holloway **Manor** *(ST468151)* TA14 6TQ
☎(093588) 203
Apr-Oct
This Ham stone house with leaded windows has comfortable bedrooms, some with antique furniture and easy chairs. The large lounge has a log fire, and freshly prepared meals are taken around the large dining table.
4hc (1fb) CTV in all bedrooms Ⓡ 🚫 ✱ sB&B£15-£16 dB&B£30-£32
📺 CTV 4P 🎣 450 acres mixed
[£]

CHISELDON Wiltshire Map 04 SU17

FH [Q][Q] M Hughes **Parsonage** *(SU185799)* SN4 0NJ
☎Swindon(0793) 740204
This 16th-century building with spacious rooms is set in pleasant, lawned gardens backing on to the church.
4rm(2🛁🚿) Ⓡ ✱ sB&B£20-£25 dB&B🛁🚿£30-£40
Lic 📺 CTV 8P 2🚗 🐎 400 acres arable
[£]

CHISLEHAMPTON Oxfordshire Map 04 SU59

SELECTED

INN [Q][Q][Q][Q] **Coach & Horses** Stadhampton Rd OX9 7UX ☎Stadhampton(0865) 890255 Telex no 83602
Standing beside the B480, just 7 miles from Oxford, this 16th-century, stone-built inn has log fires which blaze in the heavily beamed bars. There are 9 very well equipped en suite bedrooms, which are situated around a central courtyard, offering warm, tastefully decorated and comfortably furnished accommodation. Extensive à la carte and table d'hôte menus are offered in the busy restaurant.
9🛁🚿 CTV in all bedrooms Ⓡ 🚫 (ex guide dogs)
sB&B🛁🚿£34.50-£51.50
dB&B🛁🚿£48.50-£67.50 WB&B£177.50-£283
WBDi£260-£367 Lunch fr£11.50&alc Dinner fr£11.50&alc LDO 10pm
42P
Credit Cards [1] [2] [3] [5] [£]

CHOLDERTON Wiltshire Map **04** SU24

GH [Q][Q][Q] Cholderton Country Hotel Parkhouse Corner SP4 0EG ☎(098064) 484 & 487
Closed Xmas & New Year
14🛁🚿 (2fb) CTV in all bedrooms ® 🐕 (ex guide dogs)
sB&B🛁🚿£32-£38 dB&B🛁🚿£42-£48 (Oct-Mar) LDO 8.30pm
Lic 🍴 CTV 25P
Credit Cards [1] [2] [3] [5] [£]

CHOLMONDELEY Cheshire Map **07** SJ55

GH [Q][Q][Q] The Cholmondeley Arms SY14 8HN ☎(082922) 300
An excellent range of bar meals is served at this one-time village school. The modern en suite bedrooms in the adjacent schoolhouse contrast with the old wooden benches and ink-stained school desks which lend a touch of nostalgia to the bar/dining area.
4🚿 (1fb) CTV in all bedrooms ® sB&B🚿fr£30
dB&B🚿fr£40 LDO 10pm
Lic 🍴 0P
Credit Cards [1] [3] [£]

CHRISTCHURCH Dorset Map **04** SZ19

See also Bournemouth
GH [Q] Belvedere Hotel 59 Barrack Rd BH23 1PD
☎(0202) 485978
Large Victorian hotel on main Christchurch to Bournemouth road.
7hc (3fb) CTV in all bedrooms ® sB&Bfr£16
dB&Bfr£32 WB&Bfr£105 LDO 4pm
Lic 🍴 CTV 12P

See the regional maps of popular holiday areas at the back of the book.

CHURCH STOKE Powys Map 07 SO29

FH QQ Mrs C Richards *The Drewin (SO261905)* SY15 6TW
☎(05885) 325
Apr-Oct
A Border farmhouse with beams and inglenook fireplace. Fine
views of surroundin g countryside. Offa's Dyke footpath runs
through the farm.
2hc (1fb) CTV in 1 bedroom TV in 1 bedroom ®
✗ (ex guide dogs) LDO 7pm
♨ CTV 6P ♨ games room 102 acres mixed

CHURCH STRETTON Shropshire Map 07 SO49

GH QQ *Belvedere* Burway Rd SY6 6DP ☎(0694) 722232
The recent improvements to this large detached house include a
large, split-level lounge and 2 en suite rooms. All the bedrooms
have fine countryside views.
12rm(6🔥6hc)(2fb) ® sB&B£15.50 sB&B🔥£17 dB&B£31
dB&B🔥£34 WB&B£97.65-£107.10 WBDi£144.90-£154.35
LDO 6pm
Lic ♨ CTV 9P 1🛥
£

GH QQ *Dudgeley Mill* All Stretton SY6 7JL (2m N B4370)
☎(0694) 723461
A courtyard full of ducks, horses and dogs gives guests the feeling
of a farm holiday at this country guesthouse. The quiet garden and
relaxing Shropshire countryside add to the appeal. Smoking is
discouraged in the house.
8rm(3🔥5hc)(1fb)✗in all bedrooms CTV in all bedrooms ® ✗
LDO 6pm
Lic CTV 8P

GH QQQ *Willowfield Country House* Lower Wood, All
Stretton SY6 6LF ☎Leebotwood(06945) 471
Etr-Oct
Beautifully preserved, this Edwardian house provides spacious,
comfortable, well-maintained acommodation with a pleasant
atmosphere. It stands in peaceful rural surroundings 3.5 miles
north of Church Stretton.
5rm(2🔥3🔥)(2fb)✗in all bedrooms CTV in 4 bedrooms ®
✗ (ex guide dogs) LDO 10am
♨ 5P

↦⚬FH QQ Mrs J C Inglis *Hope Bowdler Hall (SO478925)*
Hope Bowdler SY6 7DD (1m E B4371) ☎(0694) 722041
Apr-Oct rs Mar-2 Nov
Set on the edge of the tiny village of Hope Bowdler and surrounded
by hills, this 17th-century manor house has been modernised to a
very high standard. It is 'no smoking' throughout.
3hc ✗in all bedrooms ✗ sB&B£12.50-£15 dB&B£25-£28
♨ 6P nc12yrs ♫(hard)22 acres sheep woodland

FH QQQ Mrs C J Hotchkiss *Olde Hall (SO509926)* Wall-
under-Heywood SY6 7DU ☎Longville(06943) 253
Feb-Nov
Beautifully preserved Elizabethan farmhouse with cruck timbers
and a fine Jacobean staircase.
3hc (1fb) CTV in all bedrooms ® ✗ ✳
dB&B£27-£30 WB&Bfr£90
♨ CTV 6P 275 acres dairy
£

FH QQQQ Mrs J A Davies *Rectory (SO452985)*
Woolstaston SY6 6NN (3.5m off B4370 at All Stretton)
☎Leebotwood(06945) 306
Mar-Nov
Jeanette and John Davies have maintained the historic
attributes of this Elizabethan house while incorporating
modern luxuries. Standing on a hill, the house has panoramic

views across countryside to the Wrekin. All the bedrooms are
extremely comfortable and have rural views. The ground
lounge is relaxing with a central fireplace, and barns have
been converted to a gallery-style TV lounge. The friendly
atmosphere and a hearty breakfast give guests a feeling of
wellbeing and satisfaction.
3🔥 TV available ✗ ✳ sB&B🔥£20 dB&B🔥£30
♨ CTV 10P nc12yrs 170 acres beef

CINDERFORD Gloucestershire Map 03 SO61

INN QQ *White Hart Hotel* St Whites Road, Ruspidge GL14
(B4227) ☎Dean(0594) 23139
Satisfactory inn with good-value restaurant.
4rm(2🔥2hc)(2fb) CTV in all bedrooms ® ✗ (ex guide dogs)
LDO 9.45pm
CTV 0P
Credit Cards ①③ £

CIRENCESTER Gloucestershire Map 04 SP00

GH QQ *La Ronde Hotel* 52-54 Ashcroft Rd GL7 1QX
☎(0285) 654611 & 652216
Situated in the centre of the town, this hotel offers well-equipped en
suite bedrooms and cosy public areas that include a good dining
room where a range of imaginative and well cooked dishes are
served.
10rm(2🔥8🔥)(2fb) CTV in all bedrooms ®
sB&B🔥£39.50-£44.50
dB&B🔥fr£44.50 WB&Bfr£236.25 WBDifr£299.25 LDO
9pm
Lic ♨ 9P
Credit Cards ①③ £

GH QQQ *Wimborne House* 91 Victoria Rd GL7 1ES
☎(0285) 653890
This friendly guesthouse caters for non-smokers only. Just 5
minutes' walk from the town centre, it offers well-equipped rooms,
together with private parking and gardens to the front and rear.
5🔥 (1fb)✗in all bedrooms CTV in all bedrooms ® ✗
sB&B🔥£20-£25 dB&B🔥£28-£32 LDO 4pm
♨ 8P nc5yrs
£

INN QQQ *Eliot Arms* Clark's Hay, South Cerney GL7 5UA
☎(0285) 860215
Set in the charming hamlet of South Cerney, this stone-built inn
has attractive open plan public rooms, a cosy dining area and very
attractive and well-equipped en suite bedrooms.
6🔥 (1fb) CTV in all bedrooms ® ✳ sB&B🔥£28.50-£30
dB&B🔥£40-£45 LDO 9.45pm
♨ 28P
Credit Cards ①③ £

CLACTON-ON-SEA Essex Map 05 TM11

GH QQQ *Chudleigh Hotel* Agate Rd CO15 1RA
☎(0255) 425407
Closed 15 Dec-6 Jan
Conveniently situated a short distance from the seafront, pier and
shopping centre, this comfortable hotel has a pleasant, informal
atmosphere. The chef/proprietor is keen to produce good food for
the guests.
12rm(10🔥2hc)(3fb) CTV in all bedrooms ® ✳
sB&B£20-£22 sB&B🔥£25 dB&B£40-£44
dB&B🔥£44-£45 WB&B£140-£150 WBDi£180-£185 LDO
7pm
Lic ♨ 7P nc2yrs
Credit Cards ①②③ £

GH [Q][Q][Q] Le Vere House 15 Agate Rd CO15 1RA
☎(0255) 423044 FAX (0255) 822160
The town centre, pier and beaches are within walking distance of this attractive house. The tastefully decorated bedrooms are equipped with tea and coffee, colour TV and en suite facilities.
6🛁🚿 (3fb)🚭in all bedrooms CTV in all bedrooms Ⓡ
sB&B🛁🚿£19.50-£22.50
dB&B🛁🚿£36-£39 WB&B£126.50-£128 WBDi£150-£155
LDO 6.30pm
Lic 🍴 CTV 2P
Credit Cards [1] [2] [3] [5] [£]

See advertisement on page 121

GH [Q][Q][Q] Sandrock Hotel 1 Penfold Rd CO15 1JN
☎(0255) 428215
Some 500 yards from the seafront, this two-storeyed Edwardian house has well well-equipped bedrooms, some with sea views. This immaculate hotel is family run.
7🚿 (3fb) CTV in all bedrooms Ⓡ sB&B🚿fr£30
dB&B🚿fr£47 WB&Bfr£127 WBDifr£170.50 LDO 6pm
Lic 🍴 6P
Credit Cards [1] [3]

CLAPHAM North Yorkshire Map **07** SD76

INN [Q][Q] The Flying Horseshoe LA2 8ES ☎(04685) 229
Set in some beautiful countryside, this stone-built inn is located next to the railway station. The comfortable bedrooms are complemented by the friendly service and extensive menu that are provided.
5rm(1🛁4🚿) CTV in all bedrooms Ⓡ 🐕 (ex guide dogs) ✱
sB&B£15 sB&B🛁🚿£20 dB&B£30
dB&B🛁🚿£30 WB&B£90 WBDi£130 LDO 10.30pm
🍴 50P 2🚗 🎣
[£]

WIMBORNE HOUSE

91 Victoria Road
Cirencester, Glos GL7 1ES
Telephone: (0285) 653890

Dianne and Marshall Clarke invite you to enjoy the comfort of their house with good home cooking.

ALL ROOMS
En suite bathroom & shower. Colour TV. Tea/Coffee making facilities. Clock radio alarm. Full central heating. Private car park.

BED & BREAKFAST
Double or Twin room £25.00 to £30.00
Evening Meal £7.50 per person
ALL PRICES INCLUDE V.A.T.

SAE please for brochure   A NON-SMOKING HOUSE

CHUDLEIGH HOTEL
Agate Road, Clacton-on-Sea
CO15 1RA
Tel: (0255) 425407

The Hotel is central, near the Pier and Seafront gardens and within easy reach of Theatres, Cinemas, Shops and Coach and Bus Station. Expert attention is given to the planning of the Menus and preparation of all meals.

- 12 well appointed bedrooms, most with private bath/shower/toilet
- All bedrooms with colour TV, radio/alarm/intercom and tea/coffee making facilities
- Residential licensed bar
- Full English breakfast menu
- Pleasant and relaxing lounge
- Parking on premises
- French & Italian spoken

Further details from resident proprietors: Carol & Peter Oleggini

Access BARCLAYCARD VISA AMERICAN EXPRESS English Tourist Board

La Ronde Hotel 52/54 ASHCROFT ROAD
CIRENCESTER
GLOS. GL7 1QX
Telephone: (0285) 654611

A detached Victorian Cotswold stone house well situated just off the town centre. Within minutes of Cirencester Park, Abbey grounds, Corinium museum, and the Cirencester leisure centre. The ideal base for touring the Cotswolds.

★ Renowned for the warmth of welcome and excellent freshly prepared food.
★ Attractive candlelit dining room. Lunches and dinner except Sunday. Bar snacks. Chilled beer.
★ Varied menu with extensive wine list.
★ Cosy beamed cocktail bar. ★ Lounge area.
★ Full central heating.
★ Fully fire protected & certificated.
★ All rooms with en-suite facilities.
★ Private parking at rear of hotel.
★ All rooms with colour TV and tea/coffee making facilities.
★ Fully licensed.
★ Special Weekend Breaks available.

Owned and managed by The Shales Family
Travellers Britain (Arthur Eperon)
Member of the Heart of England Tourist Board
Listed by Arthur Frommer in U.S.A.

CLARENCEFIELD Dumfries & Galloway *Dumfriesshire*
Map **11** NY16

SELECTED

GH [Q][Q][Q][Q] **Comlongon Castle** DG1 4NA ☎(038787) 283
Mar-Nov rs Dec-1 Jan

Comlongon is a genuine castle, sympathetically converted to feature the original character and atmosphere. The impressive old wood-panelled bedrooms are very spacious and lofty public areas contribute to the ambience. The highlight of a visit is in the evening when guests are taken on a conducted tour of the castle before enjoying their chosen dishes in the impressive wood-panelled dining room.

9rm(4🛁1🚿4hc)(1fb) CTV in all bedrooms
🚫 (ex guide dogs) sB&B£28-£40 sB&B🛁🚿£28-£40
dB&Bfr£60 dB&B🛁🚿fr£60 LDO 8.15pm
Lic ♨ 50P 🎣 wildfowl reserve
Credit Cards [1] [3] [£]
See advertisement under DUMFRIES on page 139

CLAVERDON Warwickshire Map **04** SP16

FH [Q][Q] Mrs F E Bromilow **Woodside** *(SP186644)* Langley Rd CV35 8PJ (0.75m S of B4095) ☎(092684) 2446
Closed Xmas wk

Woodside Farm is a quiet, comfortable house set in attractive gardens and adjacent to a 17-acre woodland nature conservancy. Close to Stratford and the tourist routes, it is well off the beaten track.

3hc (1fb) CTV in 1 bedroom TV in 1 bedroom ® sB&B£14-£19 dB&B£28-£32 WB&B£95-£108 WBDi£182.50-£195.50 LDO 2pm
♨ CTV 12P 1🚗 ⌂ 🎾(hard)croquet 22 acres small holding nature reserve
[£]

CLAYTON-LE-WOODS Lancashire Map **07** SD52

GH [Q][Q][Q] **Brook House Hotel** 662 Preston Rd PR6 7EH
☎Preston(0772) 36403

Beside the A6 at Clayton-le-Woods, a mile from the M6 and M61, this 19th-century house has been carefully modernised to provide comfortable, well-equipped accommodation, with a high standard of housekeeping.

12rm(7🚿5hc)(3fb) CTV in all bedrooms ® 🚫 (ex guide dogs)
* sB&B£20 sB&B🚿£28 dB&B£32 dB&B🚿£40 LDO 8.30pm
Lic ♨ CTV 15P
Credit Cards [1] [3] [£]

CLEARWELL Gloucestershire Map **03** SO50

GH [Q][Q][Q] **Tudor Farmhouse Hotel** GL16 8JS
☎Dean(0594) 33046 FAX (0594) 37093

Lovingly restored by Sheila and James Reid, this old house has retained all its charm and character, with a fine spiral staircase. The bedrooms are very individual with good en suite facilities and the food is imaginative and wholesome.

6🛁🚿 Annexe 3🛁🚿 CTV in all bedrooms ® *
sB&B🛁🚿£30-£39.50 dB&B🛁🚿£38-£50 LDO 9pm
Lic ♨ 15P 2🚗 nc8yrs
Credit Cards [1] [2] [3] [£]

CLEETHORPES Humberside Map **08** TA30

GH [Q][Q] ***Mallow View*** 9-11 Albert Rd DN35 8LX
☎(0472) 691297

Three terraced houses, close to the seafront and town centre, are combined to form this guesthouse. There is a small reception lounge, a separate bar lounge and a cosy dining room. The bedrooms are compact and nicely equipped.

15rm(1🚿14hc)(1fb) CTV in all bedrooms ® LDO 7pm
Lic CTV 🚫P

CLIFTON UPON TEME Hereford & Worcester
Map **03** SO76

INN [Q][Q][Q] ***The Lion*** WR6 6DH
☎Shelsley Beauchamp(08865) 617 & 238

Dating from the 12th century, The Lion is one of Worcestershire's oldest coaching inns. The attractive accommodation, with its old beams and natural stone is comfortable and well appointed. An intimate restaurant serves good home-cooked meals.

3🛁 (1fb) CTV in all bedrooms ® 🚫 (ex guide dogs) LDO 9.30pm
♨ 20P nc5yrs
Credit Cards [1] [2] [3] [5]

CLIFTONVILLE Kent

See **Margate**

CLITHEROE Lancashire Map **07** SD74

GH [Q][Q][Q] **Brooklyn** 32 Pimlico Rd BB7 2AH ☎(0200) 28268

Close to the town centre in a quiet residential street, this house is particularly well maintained. Most of the comfortable bedrooms have en suite facilities and an annex across the road offers more accommodation with its own lounge. Umbrellas are thoughtfully provided

4rm(2🚿2hc)Annexe 4🚿 CTV in all bedrooms ®
🚫 (ex guide dogs) sB&B£13.50 sB&B🚿£15
dB&B🚿£30 WB&B£89.50-£100 WBDi£138.50-£149 LDO 10am
♨ CTV 1🚗
[£]

CLOUGHTON North Yorkshire Map **08** TA09

⊢⊣**GH** [Q] **Cober Hill** Newlands Rd YO13 0AR
☎Scarborough(0723) 870310

Set in 6.5 acres, this large guesthouse offers very good value for money. It is 6 miles north of Scarborough and specialises in group activity holidays, with comfortable accommodation in simple style, and ample lounges.

48hc Annexe 31rm(17🛁14🚿)(13fb) ® sB&B£11.50-£16.50
sB&B🛁🚿£16.50-£21.50 dB&B£23-£33
dB&B🛁🚿£33-£43 WB&B£69-£129 WBDi£102-£162 LDO 7pm
♨ 60P 🎾(hard)bowling green croquet table-tennis
See advertisement under SCARBOROUGH on page 327

CLOVELLY Devon Map **02** SS32

FH [Q][Q][Q] Mrs E Symons ***Burnstone*** *(SS325233)* Higher Clovelly EX39 5RX ☎(02373) 219

This attractive 17th-century Devon longhouse retains many original features and is tastefully decorated and furnished. Guests will find bed and breakfast accommodation here, together with warm welcome.

2hc (2fb) ®
♨ CTV 3P 500 acres dairy sheep mixed
Credit Cards [3]

FH [Q][Q] Celia Goaman ***Stitworthy*** *(SS298220)* EX39 5SG
☎(02373) 265 due to change to (0237) 431265
mid Jan-mid Dec Closed 15 Dec-15 Jan
3hc (2fb) ® 🚫 (ex guide dogs) LDO 5pm
♨ CTV 3P 🎣 500 acres arable dairy

CLUNTON Shropshire Map **07** SO38

⊢⊣**FH** [Q][Q] Mrs J Williams **Hurst Mill** *(SO318811)* SY7 0JA
☎Clun(05884) 224

Surrounded by woods and almost encircled by the river Clun, this hospitable farm offers warm accommodation and home-cooked meals. Children and dogs are also made welcome.

3rm(2hc)(1fb)⚛in 1 bedroom CTV in 1 bedroom TV in 1
bedroom ® sB&B£12-£14
dB&B£24-£28 WB&B£80-£90 WBDi£115-£130 LDO 6.30pm
CTV 4P 2🐾 ✦ 2 ponies 100 acres mixed
Ⓔ

COCKERMOUTH Cumbria Map **11** NY13

SELECTED

GH Ⓠ Ⓠ Ⓠ Ⓠ **Low Hall Country** Brandlingill CA13 0RE
(3m S on unclass off A5086) ☎(0900) 826654
Etr-Nov rs New Year
*David and Dani Edwards have successfully blended old and
new at their 17th-century farmhouse, to retain throughout an
atmosphere of warmth and relaxation. Mrs Edwards serves
delicious dinners, with the menu changing daily, to include
many traditional Lakeland dishes, seasonal items, dishes from
other countries and even other centuries Low Hall is ideally
located for touring anywhere in the Lake District or even
further afield.*
6rm(1⇨2↑3hc)⚛in all bedrooms ® ✗ (ex guide dogs)
dB&Bfr£38
dB&B⇨↑fr£44 WB&B£133-£161 WBDi£217-£245 LDO
3pm
Lic ₥ CTV 12P nc10yrs
Credit Cards ① ③

CODSALL Staffordshire Map **07** SJ80

FH Ⓠ Ⓠ Mrs D E Moreton **Moors Farm & Country
Restaurant** *(SJ859048)* Chillington Ln WV8 1QH
☎(09074) 2330
*Guests at Moors Farm can enjoy the rural life with friendly service
and comfortable accommodation. Home-produced meat,
vegetables and eggs are used here, and as the restaurant is open to
non-residents, booking is essential.*
6rm(2↑4hc)(3fb) CTV in all bedrooms ® ✗ ✳ sB&B£20-£21
sB&B↑£24-£25 dB&B£32-£34
dB&B↑£40-£42 WB&B£105-£170 WBDi£160-£225 LDO 9pm
Lic ₥ CTV 20P nc4yrs 100 acres mixed

COLCHESTER Essex Map **05** TL92

GH Ⓠ Ⓠ **Four Sevens** 28 Inglis Rd CO3 3HU ☎(0206) 46093
*Half a mile from the town centre in a quiet residential area, this
establishment has simple, attractive accommodation with good
facilities and some en suite bedrooms. Calyso Demitri is the
friendly proprietor.*
6rm(2↑4hc)(1fb) CTV in all bedrooms ® ✗ ✳ sB&B£20-£26
sB&B↑£20-£26 dB&B£28-£30 dB&B↑£30-£35
₥
Ⓔ

COLEFORD Gloucestershire Map **03** SO51

FH Ⓠ Mrs Sylvia Davis **Lower Tump** *(SO588160)* Eastbach,
English Bicknor GL16 7EU ☎Dean(0594) 60253
*Set in a lovely position close to the beautiful Forest of Dean, this
farmhouse provides simply appointed accommodation.*
2rm(1⇨1↑)(1fb) CTV in all bedrooms ® sB&B⇨↑fr£15
dB&B⇨↑£23-£24 WB&B£70-£72
₥ 10P 150 acres mixed
Ⓔ

COLESBOURNE Gloucestershire Map **03** SO91

INN Ⓠ Ⓠ Ⓠ **Colesbourne** GL53 9NP ☎Coberley(024287) 376 &
396 FAX (024287) 397
*The young, friendly staff contribute largely to the atmosphere and
character of this traditional Cotswolds coaching inn. Good food
and ale from the wood feature in the bars, and the converted stable*
▶

block provides comfortable annexe bedrooms, all with private bath/shower rooms.
Annexe 10rm(6🛁4🚿) CTV in all bedrooms ®
sB&B🛁🚿fr£28
dB&B🛁🚿fr£48 WB&Bfr£150 WBDifr£250 Bar Lunch £5.80-£9.25alc Dinner £8.25-£19.55alc LDO 10pm
70P
Credit Cards [1] [2] [3] [5] [£]
See advertisement under CHELTENHAM on page 115

COLMONELL Strathclyde *Aryshire* Map **10** NX18

⊢⊣**FH** [Q][Q] Mrs G B Shankland **Burnfoot** *(NX162862)* KA26 0SQ ☎(046588) 220 & 265
Apr-Oct
Welcoming farmhouse in peaceful country setting beside River Stinchar.
2hc (1fb) CTV in all bedrooms ® sB&B£11
dB&B£22 WB&B£66-£77 WBDi£102-£119 LDO 4.30pm
♨ 2P 157 acres beef sheep
[£]

COLNE Lancashire Map **07** SD84

FH [Q][Q][Q] Mrs C Mitson **Higher Wanless** *(SD873413)* Red Ln BB8 7JP ☎(0282) 865301
Overlooking the Leeds/Liverpool canal, close to Barrowford, this farm is within easy reach of 'Pendle Witch' and 'Brontë' country. Mrs Mitson gives a warm welcome and provides a relaxed atmosphere in which guests can unwind. One of the two bedrooms is en suite; both are spacious, comfortable and very well equipped. A wholesome home-cooked meal is available on request.
2rm(1🚿1hc)(2fb) CTV in 1 bedroom ® 🐕 * sB&B£16-£22
sB&B🚿£18-£25 dB&B£30-£32 dB&B🚿£36-£42 LDO 9am
♨ CTV 4P nc3yrs 25 acres Shire horses, sheep
[£]

COLWYN BAY Clwyd Map **06** SH87

GH [Q] **Alwyn House Hotel** 4 Upper Promenade LL28 4BS ☎(0492) 532004
This terraced property is located close to the seafront. The simple but pleasant, well-maintained accommodation is equally suitable for holidaymakers and commercial travellers, and is popular with local actors.
8rm(1🛁🚿7hc)(5fb) CTV in all bedrooms ® *
sB&B£11 WB&B£72 WBDi£102 LDO 6pm
Lic ♨ CTV
[£]

GH [Q][Q][Q] ***Broxholme*** 112 Conwy Rd LL29 7LL ☎(0492) 530244
Standing on the main road through the town, and with parking space in front, this well-furnished house has a charming lounge bar.
6rm(2🛁1🚿3hc)(2fb)🚭in all bedrooms CTV in all bedrooms ® 🐕
Lic 6P

GH [Q][Q][Q] **Cabin Hill Private Hotel** College Avenue, Rhos-on-Sea LL28 4NT ☎(0492) 44568 & 874642
Mar-Nov
Fully modernised, this Edwardian house stands in a quiet residential area and offers comfortable, well-equipped accommodation. There is a car park to the rear.
10rm(7🚿3hc)(2fb) CTV in all bedrooms ® 🐕 sB&Bfr£15
dB&B£27.50-£33 dB&B🚿fr£33 WBDi£115.50-£131 LDO 5pm
Lic ♨ CTV 6P nc3yrs
[£]

GH [Q] **Grosvenor Hotel** 106-108 Abergele Rd LL29 7PS ☎(0492) 530798 & 531586
A cellar bar and games room are available to guests at this large double-fronted house which stands on the town's main road, and has a front car park.
18rm(2🛁16hc)(8fb) CTV in 7 bedrooms ® *
sB&B£14.50-£15.50 dB&B£29-£31
dB&B🛁£33.50-£35.50 LDO 7pm
Lic CTV 16P pool table darts
Credit Cards [3]

GH [Q][Q][Q] **Northwood Hotel** 47 Rhos Rd, Rhos-on-Sea LL28 4RS ☎(0492) 49931
Detached Edwardian hotel, a short walk from village and promenade.
13rm(1🛁9🚿3hc)(2fb) CTV in all bedrooms ® sB&B£14
sB&B🛁🚿£16 dB&B£28
dB&B🛁🚿£32 WB&B£91-£105 WBDi£109-£135 LDO 6.15pm
Lic ♨ CTV 11P
Credit Cards [1] [3] [£]

COLYFORD Devon Map **03** SY29

SELECTED

GH [Q][Q][Q][Q] **Swallows Eaves Hotel** Swan Hill Rd EX13 6QJ ☎Colyton(0297) 53184
This comfortable little hotel is ideally located for touring Dorset, Devon and Somerset, and Mr and Mrs Beck are always on hand to ensure a warm welcome and a comfortable stay. The 6 bedrooms have en suite facilities and are furnished and equipped to a high standard. Pre-dinner drinks are served in the cosy lounge and excellent home cooked dinners are taken in the elegant dining room.
8rm(6🛁2🚿)🚭in 4 bedrooms CTV in all bedrooms ® 🐕 (ex guide dogs) sB&B🛁🚿£31-£35
dB&B🛁🚿£45-£53 WB&B£155-£160 WBDi£224-£249 LDO 8pm
Lic ♨ 10P nc14yrs
Credit Cards [2] [£]

COLYTON Devon Map **03** SY29

SELECTED

GH [Q][Q][Q][Q] ***Old Bakehouse*** Lower Church St EX13 6ND ☎(0297) 52518
Dating back to the 17th century, this former bakery stands in the centre of Colyton and has been carefully converted to offer accommodation of character with stone walls, beams and open fireplaces. All rooms have en suite facilities and a colour television. The varied menu offers freshly cooked food, painstakingly prepared, and personal service is provided by the resident proprietors and their staff who make guests feel at home.
6rm(5🛁1🚿)(1fb) CTV in all bedrooms ® LDO 9.30pm
Lic ♨ 8P
Credit Cards [3]

COMBE MARTIN Devon Map **02** SS54

See also Berrynarbor

GH [Q][Q][Q] **Channel Vista** EX34 0AT ☎(0271) 883514
Etr-Oct & Xmas
This charming Edwardian house is only 150 yards from the picturesque cove. The resident proprietors provide home cooking and friendly service in comfortable accommodation with good facilities.
7rm(2🛁5🚿)(3fb) CTV in 3 bedrooms ® 🐕 (ex guide dogs)
dB&B🛁🚿£34-£40 WB&B£99-£123 WBDi£119-£143 LDO 3pm
Lic ♨ CTV 9P nc3yrs
Credit Cards [1] [3]

GH Q *The Woodlands* 2 The Woodlands EX34 0AT
☎(0271) 882769
Mar-Oct
Close to the sheltered cove and village centre, this small, friendly guesthouse is on the edge of Exmoor National Park.
8hc (2fb) ✗ (wkly only last 2wks Jul & Aug) LDO 5pm
Lic CTV 8P nc2yrs
Credit Cards ③

COMRIE Tayside *Perthshire* Map **11** NN72

⊢⊷**GH Q** *Mossgiel* Burrell St PH6 2JP ☎(0764) 70567
Etr-Oct
This small friendly guesthouse is situated on the main road at the west end of the town. Offering good value, it is a popular base for the touring holidaymaker.
6hc TV in 1 bedroom sB&Bfr£10
dB&Bfr£20 WB&Bfr£70 WBDifr£91 LDO 5.30pm
卿 CTV 6P nc5yrs

FH QQ Mrs J H Rimmer *West Ballindalloch* (*NN744262*)
Glenlednock PH6 2LY ☎(0764) 70282
Mar-Oct
Cosy, small farmhouse with neat garden set amid hills in secluded glen, 4 miles from Comrie.
2rm ® ✗ (ex guide dogs)
CTV 3P 1500 acres sheep hill farm

CONISHOLME Lincolnshire Map **09** TF39

GH QQQ *Wickham House* Church Ln LN11 7LX
☎North Somercotes(050785) 465 due to change to
(0507) 358465
Closed Xmas & New Year
Formerly 3 cottages, Wickham House has been tastefully modernised to provide comfortable en suite accommodation. A library and cosy lounge makes this an ideal base, with views across farmland and the sea a few miles' away.
4rm(2⊸2♪) CTV in all bedrooms ® ✗ (ex guide dogs)
sB&B⊸♪£16-£17.50 dB&B⊸♪£30-£33 LDO noon
卿 4P nc8yrs
£

CONISTON Cumbria Map **07** SD39

SELECTED

GH QQQQ *Coniston Lodge Hotel* Sunny Brow
LA21 8HH ☎(05394) 41201
rs Sun & Mon pm
Anthony and Elizabeth Robinson have built a magnificent extension to their home and decorated and furnished it to the highest standard, creating a cottage style effect. A strictly non-smoking house, the accommodation offered here includes 6 superior bedrooms which are thoughtfully equipped, and a delightful first floor lounge leading to an attractive, cosy dining room. Dinners are not served on Sundays or Mondays.
6⊸♪ ⊁in all bedrooms CTV in all bedrooms ®
✗ (ex guide dogs) sB&B⊸♪£24-£31.50
dB&B⊸♪£48-£62 WB&B£168-£192.50 LDO 7.30pm
Lic 卿 3P 6⊷ nc10yrs
Credit Cards ① ③ £

This is one of many guidebooks pubished by
the AA. The full range is available at any
AA Centre or good bookshop.

CONNEL Strathclyde *Argyllshire* Map **10** NM93

SELECTED

GH QQQQ *Loch Etive Hotel* Main St PA37 1PH
☎(063171) 400
mid Apr-mid Oct
Françoise Weber and Bill Mossman run their small private hotel with enthusiasm. The bedrooms are nicely decorated and well equipped and there is a small lounge and open plan dining room, where a choice of dishes is served at both dinner and breakfast. Loch Etive nestles by the side of a small river in a quiet part of the village well off the A85.
6rm(4⊸♪2hc)(2fb) CTV in all bedrooms ® sB&B£19.75
sB&B⊸♪£22.25 dB&B£32.50
dB&B⊸♪£37.50 WB&B£113.75-£131.25
WBDi£159.08-£174.83 LDO 7pm
Lic 卿 8P
£
See advertisement under OBAN on page 279

CONSTANTINE Cornwall & Isles of Scilly Map **02** SW72

INN Q *Trengilly Wartha* Nancenoy TR11 5RP
☎Falmouth(0326) 40332
Enjoying a peaceful rural setting, this traditional-style country inn has simple, comfortable accommodation and a friendly atmosphere. Traditional English cooking is prepared by the chef/ proprietor.
6rm(5⊸♪1hc) CTV in all bedrooms ® sB&B£34-£40
sB&B⊸♪£38-£44
dB&B⊸♪£45-£50 WB&B£115-£130 WBDi£200-£220 Bar
Lunch £6-£15 Dinner fr£15 LDO 9.30pm
卿 55P

▶

Credit Cards ① ② ③ ⓔ
See advertisement under FALMOUTH on page 155

CONWY Gwynedd Map **06** SH77

See also Roewen
GH ⓠⓠ **The Old Ship** Lancaster Square LL32 8DE
☎Aberconwy(0492) 596445
This small cosy guesthouse dates back some four hundred years, and retains a lot of it's original character. Situated in the town centre it is conveniently close to the railway station and has parking facilities nearby.
6rm(2🔥4hc)(3fb)⅄in 2 bedrooms CTV in all bedrooms ⓡ ✳
sB&B£12-£14 dB&B£26-£28 dB&B🔥£34-£36 WB&B£77-£91
Lic ⁗ CTV 𝄃

GH ⓠ *Sunnybanks* Llanrwst Rd, Woodlands LL32 8LT
☎(0492) 593845
A small, family-run hotel situated in an elevated position close to the Castle walls.
7hc (2fb) CTV in all bedrooms ⓡ LDO 8pm
Lic ⁗ CTV 8P

COOKLEY Suffolk Map **05** TM37

FH ⓠⓠⓠ Mr & Mrs A T Veasy **Green** *(TM337772)* IP19 0LH
☎Linstead(098685) 209
Apr-Nov
This old farmhouse is best approached from Linstead Parva, and is just past the church. In 12 acres of land with outbuildings and duck ponds, Green Farm is comfortable and full of character, and Mrs Veasy is a charming hostess.
3hc ⓡ ✖ (ex guide dogs) ✳ dB&B£28-£32 LDO 3pm
CTV 3P nc8yrs 12 acres non-working

COOMBE BISSETT Wiltshire Map **04** SU12

FH ⓠⓠ A Shering **Swaynes Firs** *(SU068221)* Grimsdyke
SP5 5RF ☎Martin Cross(072589) 240
4rm(3🔥1hc)(1fb) CTV in all bedrooms ⓡ ✳ sB&B£13-£14
dB&B🔥£30-£32 WB&B£100
⁗ CTV 6P 11 acres beef, horses, poultry
ⓔ

COPMANTHORPE North Yorkshire Map **08** SE54

GH ⓠⓠ **Duke of Connaught Hotel** Copmanthorpe Grange
YO2 3TN ☎Appleton Roebuck(090484) 318
Closed Xmas wk
Nicely converted former stables in open rural surroundings.
14rm(2↪12🔥)(2fb)⅄in 4 bedrooms CTV in all bedrooms ⓡ
✖ (ex guide dogs) LDO 6pm
Lic ⁗ 40P

CORBRIDGE Northumberland Map **12** NY96

FH ⓠⓠⓠ Mr & Mrs T Jones **Low Barns** *(NY009641)*
Thornbrough NE45 5LX ☎(043463) 2408
5rm(3↪🔥2hc)(2fb) CTV in all bedrooms ⓡ ✖ (ex guide dogs)
dB&B£30
dB&B↪🔥£35 WB&B£105-£122.50 WBDi£189-£206.50 LDO
6pm
⁗ 5P ♨ 2 acres cattle hens sheep smallholding
ⓔ

'Selected' establishments, which have the highest
quality award, are highlighted by a tinted panel.
For a full list of these establishments, consult the
Contents page.

CORFE CASTLE Dorset Map **03** SY98

GH ⓠⓠⓠ **The Old Rectory** Church Knowle BH20 5NG
☎(0929) 480695
Mar-Nov
In the small village of Church Knowle, on an unclassified road, this large Victorian house stands in 3 acres and offers 3 beautiful bedrooms with modern facilities, and a cosy lounge. Breakfast is served around a large Cuban mahogany table.
3hc (1fb)⅄in all bedrooms CTV in all bedrooms ⓡ ✖
sB&B£25-£30 dB&B£32-£40
⁗ 5P

CORSTON Wiltshire Map **03** ST98

↦⊶**FH** ⓠⓠ Mrs R Favis **Manor** *(ST922837)* SN16 0HF
☎Malmesbury(0666) 822148
This comfortable Cotswold stone farmhouse has spacious bedrooms, 1 with en suite facilities. The proprietors create a very warm atmosphere.
5rm(1↪🔥4hc)(2fb)⅄in 2 bedrooms ⓡ ✖ sB&B£12-£15
dB&B£24-£30 dB&B↪🔥£30-£36
⁗ CTV 8P 436 acres arable dairy
ⓔ

CORTACHY Tayside *Angus* Map **15** NO35

↦⊶**FH** ⓠⓠ Mrs Joan Grant **Cullew** *(NO387609)* DD8 4QP
☎(05754) 242
Apr-Oct
Set in a secluded position at the south end of a picturesque Glen Clova. This substantial stone-built farmhouse offers traditional hospitality and comfortable accommodation.
2rm (1fb)⅄in all bedrooms CTV in 1 bedroom
✖ (ex guide dogs) sB&B£10-£10.50 dB&B£19-£20 WB&Bfr£70
⁗ CTV 3P fishing permits 850 acres arable mixed
ⓔ

CORWEN Clwyd Map **06** SJ04

↦⊶**GH** ⓠ **Coleg-y-Groes** LL21 0AU ☎(0490) 2169
This Christian guesthouse, formerly a row of 18th-century alms-houses, provides simple accommodation. It is quietly located behind the church, yet is convenient for the town centre and the A5.
6hc (2fb)⅄in all bedrooms ⓡ sB&B£11-£13
dB&B£22-£26 WB&B£73-£80 WBDi£111.50-£120 LDO
previous evening
⁗ CTV 6P

GH ⓠⓠ **Corwen Court Private Hotel** London Rd LL21 0DP
☎(0490) 2854
Mar-Nov rs Dec-Feb
This small, friendly hotel, once a police station and courthouse will provide guests with certificates for spending a night in the 'cells'
10rm(4↪🔥6hc)(3fb) ✳ sB&B£11-£12
dB&B↪🔥£22-£24 WB&B£73.10-£79.80 WBDi£113-£119.70
LDO 6pm
⁗ CTV 𝄃
ⓔ

COTHERIDGE Hereford & Worcester Map **03** SO75

FH ⓠⓠ Mr & Mrs V A Rogers *Little Lightwood* *(SP798554)*
WR6 5LT (3m W of Worcester on A44) ☎(090566) 236
Feb-Nov
The farm is situated on the A44, just 3 miles west of Worcester. The accommodation is attractive and well kept, and a comfortable lounge is provided for the use of guests. The house is non-smoking throughout.
3hc (1fb)⅄in all bedrooms ⓡ ✖ LDO 10am
⁗ CTV 6P 60 acres dairy

COUNTISBURY (nr Lynton) Devon Map **03** SS74

FH ◯◯◯ Mrs R Pile **Coombe** *(SS766489)* EX35 6NF
☎Brendon(05987) 236
Apr-Oct rs Nov & Dec
Dating back to the 17th century, this stone-built farmhouse is part of a sheep farm lying within the Exmoor National Park. The comfortable accommodation and true farmhouse hospitality make it an ideal centre for touring the North Devon coastline.
5rm(2🛏3hc)(2fb) ® ✗ ✱ dB&B£28-£30
dB&B🛏£31-£36 WB&B£80-£115 WBDi£143-£185 LDO 5pm
Lic ᠁ CTV 6P 365 acres beef sheep

COVENTRY West Midlands Map **04** SP37

GH ◯ **Ashleigh House** 17 Park Rd CV1 2LH ☎(0203) 23804
Closed Xmas
Set in a quiet cul-de-sac close to the railway station, this house provides modest accommodation. There is an attractive dining room with its own small bar, and car parking is available to the rear of the house.
10hc (5fb) CTV in all bedrooms ® ✗ ✱ sB&B£18-£20
dB&B£26-£28 LDO 8.45pm
Lic ᠁ CTV 12P
£

GH ◯ *Croft Hotel* 23 Stoke Green, Off Binley Rd CV3 1FP
☎(0203) 457846
This hotel is situated just off the Rugby road, one and a half miles from the town centre. The atmosphere is friendly and welcoming and this year will see a complete refurbishment of the establishment.
12rm(1🛏11hc)(1fb) CTV in 5 bedrooms ® LDO 9.30pm
Lic ᠁ CTV 20P solarium pool table

GH ◯ *Fairlight* 14 Regent St CV1 3EP ☎(0203) 224215
Closed 24 Dec-2 Jan
This terraced property stands within easy reach of the town centre and provides simple but well-kept accommodation. The resident proprietors provide a friendly, relaxed atmosphere, and guests are assured of a warm welcome.
12rm(1🛏11hc)(1fb) CTV in 11 bedrooms ®
᠁ CTV 6P

GH ◯◯ *Hearsall Lodge Hotel* 1 Broad Ln CV5 7AA
☎(0203) 674543
A friendly hotel close to the common and town centre. Hearsall Lodge has been recently extended and offers good accommodation with excellent facilities.
13hc (2fb) CTV in all bedrooms ® LDO 7.30pm
Lic ᠁ CTV 13P solarium

GH ◯ **Spire View** 36 Park Rd CV1 2LD ☎(0203) 251602
rs Xmas Day
Set in a quiet location in a residential area close to the railway station, this guesthouse has simple accommodation in rooms of varying sizes.
7rm(4🛏3hc)(3fb) CTV in all bedrooms ® ✗ (ex guide dogs) ✱
sB&B£14-£18 sB&B🛏£15-£20 dB&B£26-£30
dB&B🛏£32-£36 LDO 10am
᠁ 3P
£

COWDENBEATH Fife Map **11** NT19

GH ◯◯ *Struan Bank Hotel* 74 Perth Rd KY4 9BG
☎(0383) 511057
This is a small, family-run hotel on the north side of the town used by tourists and commercial travellers alike. There is a small bar in the lounge, but this is used mainly by residents and diners.
8hc ® ✗ LDO 6pm
Lic ᠁ CTV 8P

CRACKINGTON HAVEN Cornwall & Isles of Scilly
Map **02** SX19

FH ◯◯◯◯ Mrs M Knight **Manor** *(SX159962)*
EX23 0JW ☎St Gennys(08403) 304
This delightful, 12th-century manor house is found by taking the more southerly road from Crackington Haven beach, turning left after one mile into Church Park Road, then after 200 yards, take the turning right. The comfortable bedrooms are furnished with quiet, good taste, while a series of lounges provides comfortable elegance, Mrs Knight's Cordon Bleu-style cookery being served on one long table. The house has a no-smoking policy.
4rm(2🛏2hc)Annexe 2🛏 ✄in all bedrooms ✗
sB&B🛏£20-£25
dB&B🛏£40-£50 WB&B£140-£175 WBDi£210-£259
LDO 5pm
Lic ᠁ CTV 6P nc18yrs snooker table tennis 40 acres beef

See advertisement on page 127

FH ◯◯◯◯ Mrs J Crocker *Trevigue* *(SX136951)*
EX23 0LQ ☎St Gennys(08403) 418
Mar-Sep
This 16th-century stone farmhouse offers breath-taking views of coastal scenery. The comfortable bedrooms have antique furnishings as well as more modern facilities, including colour televisions. The cosy lounge has a log-burner and many books to borrow, and the bright, cheerful dining room serves Mrs Crocker's good home cooking. There is a small shop and tea ▶

room, while a no-smoking policy operates in the dining room and bedrooms.
4⇨ CTV in 2 bedrooms ® ✖ LDO 8.30pm
Lic CTV 20P nc12yrs 500 acres dairy mixed

INN QQ *Coombe Barton* EX23 0JG ☎St Gennys(08403) 345
Mar-Oct
7rm(3⇨4hc)(1fb) CTV in 3 bedrooms ® LDO 9.30pm
뼹 40P

CRAIL Fife Map **12** NO60

GH QQQ *Caiplie* 51-53 High St KY10 3RA ☎(0333) 50564
Mar-Sep Closed Dec-Jan rs Oct-Nov & Feb-1 Mar
Neatly maintained guesthouse in main street, with well-furnished bedrooms, shower rooms and bistro-style dining room.
7hc (1fb) ® LDO 4pm
Lic 뼹 CTV ⊁

CRASTER Northumberland Map **12** NU22

INN QQQ **Cottage** Dunstan Village NE66 3SZ
☎Embleton(066576) 658
Nestling in a copse in the tiny hamlet of Dunston, this friendly inn has comfortable accommodation and a cheerful conservatory lounge. The menus in the bar and elegant restaurant, which is open to non-residents, offer an interesting selection of good value dishes.
17rm(10⇨7hc)(2fb) CTV in 10 bedrooms ® ✖ (ex guide dogs) ✳ sB&B£16 sB&B⇨£25.50-£35 dB&B£32
dB&B⇨£51 WB&B£112-£153 WBDi£199.50-£228 Lunch £7.50 Dinner £12.50&alc LDO 9.30pm
뼹 32P
Credit Cards ①③

CRAVEN ARMS Shropshire Map **07** SO48

⊷**FH** QQ Mrs C Morgan **Strefford Hall** *(SO444856)*
Strefford SY7 8DE ☎(0588) 672383
Closed Xmas & New Year
This spacious Victorian farmhouse stands in a 360-acre mixed farm. The comfortable bedrooms and cosy lounge all have interesting views of the countryside.
3hc (1fb)⊁in all bedrooms ® sB&Bfr£12.50
dB&Bfr£25 WB&Bfr£79 WBDifr£131 LDO 6pm
CTV 3P 350 acres arable beef sheep
£

CRAWLEY West Sussex

For accommodation details see **Gatwick Airport**

CREDITON Devon Map **03** SS80

FH QQ Mr & Mrs M Pennington **Woolsgrove** *(SS793028)*
Sandford EX17 4PJ ☎Copplestone(0363) 84246
Feb-Nov
17th-century farmhouse overlooking grassland. Three miles north west on unclassified road and 1 mile north of A377.
3hc (2fb) ® ✖ (ex guide dogs) ✳ sB&Bfr£12.50
dB&Bfr£25 WB&Bfr£87.50 WBDifr£115.50 LDO 6pm
CTV 4P ♨ 150 acres mixed
£

INN QQQ **Thelbridge Cross** Thelbridge EX17 4SQ On the
B3042 ☎Tiverton(0884) 860316
Tucked away just north of Crediton, this inn has cosy, pleasant bars and restaurant, together with a new complex of bright bedrooms equipped with colour TV, direct dial telephones and tea facilities. Home-cooked meals are available with prompt, friendly service.

8⇨➊ (1fb) CTV in all bedrooms ® ✖ (ex guide dogs) sB&B⇨➊£23-£33
dB&B⇨➊£46-£66 WB&Bfr£127.50 WBDifr£197.50 Lunch £8-£12.50&alc Dinner £8-£12.50&alc LDO 9pm
뼹 CTV 50P
Credit Cards ①③£

See advertisement on page 129

CREWE Cheshire Map **07** SJ75

GH QQ **The Folly** Middlewich Rd, Minshull Vernon
CW1 4RD ☎Church Minshull(027071) 244
Happy and cheerful hosts ensure you have an enjoyable stay at the old vicarage house at the rear of St. Peter's church. The gardens are typically English even to croquet lawns and a 'tinkers' caravan.
3rm(1⇨2hc) CTV in all bedrooms ® ✳ (ex guide dogs)
sB&B⇨fr£12.50 dB&Bfr£25 WB&Bfr£87.50
6P nc14yrs Croquet lawns putting

CREWKERNE Somerset Map **03** ST40

GH QQQ **Broadview** 43 East St TA18 7AG ☎(0460) 73424
The colonial bungalow home of Gillian and Robert Swann stands in landscaped gardens and has views over the town. Three bedrooms offer private facilities and superior furnishings with modern amenities. A sun lounge adjoins the dining room where home-cooked meals are taken around a large table.
3⇨➊ CTV in all bedrooms ® sB&B⇨➊£22.50
dB&B⇨➊£29 WB&B£101.50 WBDi£161 LDO 9am
뼹 3P 2🚗
£

Visit your local AA Centre.

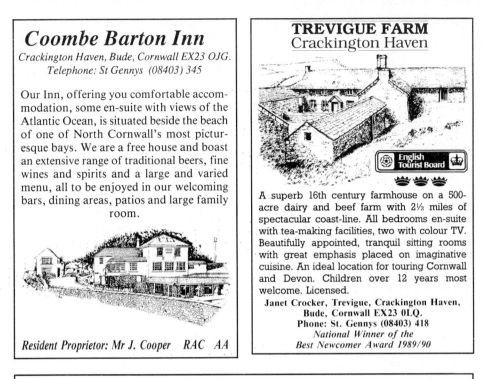

CRIANLARICH Central *Perthshire* Map **10** NN32

GH QQQ **Glenardran Guest House** FK20 8QS ☎(08383) 236
Standing on the eastern fringe of the village, overlooking Ben More, this friendly, family-run guesthouse offers pleasant, comfortable accommodation.
6hc (1fb) CTV in all bedrooms ® sB&B£16.50
dB&B£30 WB&B£105-£115.50 WBDi£182-£1196 LDO 6pm
Lic ♔ 6P ♪
Credit Cards ① ③

CRICCIETH Gwynedd Map **06** SH43

GH QQ *Glyn-Y-Coed Private Hotel* Portmadoc Rd LL52 0HL
☎(0766) 522870
Closed Xmas & New Year
This well-furnished, family-run hotel faces south and overlooks the sea. It offers home comforts and friendly service.
10rm(1➪6↑3hc)(5fb) CTV in all bedrooms ®
✱ (ex guide dogs) LDO 4pm
Lic ♔ CTV 14P

GH QQ **Min-y-Gaer Private Hotel** Porthmadog Rd LL52 0HP
☎(0766) 522151
Mar-Oct
Close to the beach and castle this semi detatched house is situated on the A497 East of the town centre. All but one of the bedrooms is equipped with en suite shower and toilet.
10rm(9↑1hc)(3fb) CTV in all bedrooms ® sB&B£13.50-£15
sB&B↑£15.50-£17 dB&B£27-£30
dB&B↑£31-£34 WB&B£89-£109 WBDi£136-£156 LDO 4pm
Lic ♔ CTV 12P
Credit Cards ① ③ £

GH QQ **Mor Heli Hotel** Marine Ter LL52 0EF
☎(0766) 522878
Apr-Sep rs Mar & Oct
Family run, this very friendly hotel overlooks the sea, is well furnished and offers good value for money.
10rm(2➪8hc)(2fb) CTV in 4 bedrooms ✱ sB&B£12.50
dB&B£25 dB&B➪£30 LDO 5pm
Lic CTV ♪

GH QQ **Neptune Hotel** Marine Ter LL52 0EF ☎(0766) 522794
Apr-Sep
This pleasantly furnished seafront hotel is next to the castle and offers accommodation of a good standard with friendly service.
10rm(1➪3↑6hc)(2fb) CTV in 4 bedrooms ✱ sB&B£12.50
sB&B➪£15 dB&B£25 dB&B➪↑£30 LDO 5pm
Lic CTV ♪

CRICKHOWELL Powys Map **03** SO21

GH QQQ **Dragon House Hotel** High St NP8 1BE
☎(0873) 810362
This town centre hotel has been carefully converted and extended to provide very attractive and well-equipped bedrooms. The bar and lounge are both cosy and comfortable and good food, including vegetarian meals, are available.
14rm(6➪↑8hc)Annexe 3➪↑ (3fb)⊁in 5 bedrooms CTV in 9 bedrooms ® ✱ (ex guide dogs) ✱ sB&B£15-£21
sB&B➪↑£30-£45 dB&B£30-£32
dB&B➪↑£45-£50 WB&B£90-£140 WBDi£140-£175 LDO 8.30pm
Lic ♔ CTV 15P
Credit Cards ① ③ £

Street plans of certain towns and cities
will be found in a separate section
at the back of the book.

CRICKLADE Wiltshire Map **04** SU09

GH QQQ **Chelworth Hotel** Upper Chelworth SN6 6HD
☎Swindon(0793) 750440
Closed mid Dec-mid Jan
Thoughtfully extended to retain its 16th-century character, this farmhouse has been refurbished to provide compact, well-appointed bedrooms. A small à la carte menu offers well-prepared English food. Mr and Mrs Hopkins create a warm, friendly atmosphere.
7rm(6↑1hc)(1fb) CTV in 6 bedrooms ® ✱ (ex guide dogs) ✱
sB&B£25-£28 sB&B↑£30-£35 dB&B£34-£36
dB&B↑£45-£50 WB&B£175-£210 WBDi£231-£315 LDO 7pm
Lic ♔ CTV 10P

CRIEFF Tayside *Perthshire* Map **11** NN82

GH QQQ **Heatherville** 29-31 Burrell St PH7 4DT
☎(0764) 2825
Feb-Nov
An ideal base for touring Tayside, this small family-run guesthouse provides comfortable accommodation with a friendly atmosphere.
5rm(1↑4hc)(2fb) ® ✱ sB&B£11.50-£12 dB&B£23-£24
dB&B↑£28-£29 WB&B£75.50-£79 WBDi£117.50-£124.50
LDO noon
Lic ♔ CTV 5P
£

CROESGOCH Dyfed Map **02** SM83

FH QQ **Mrs A Charles Torbant** *(SM845307)* SA62 5JN
☎(0348) 831276
rs Oct-Etr
This busy working farm provides spacious public rooms and a function suite. The farmhouse dates back to the 17th century and stands just off the A487.
6rm(2➪1↑3hc)(2fb) ® ✱ (ex guide dogs) ✱ sB&B£12-£16
dB&B£24-£32
dB&B➪↑£28-£36 WB&B£80-£100 WBDi£115-£140 LDO 6pm
Lic ♔ CTV 40P 110 acres dairy
£
See advertisement under ST DAVID'S on page 319

FH QQ **Mrs M B Jenkins Trearched** *(SM831306)* SA62 5JP
☎(0348) 831310
Etr-Sep
Just off the A487, this 18th-century farm, with its roadside lodge cottage, provides cosy accommodation with a choice of 2 lounges. Outside it has well-tended lawns and a duck pond.
6hc ® ✱ ✱ sB&B£14-£16
dB&B£28-£32 WB&B£90-£105 LDO noon
♔ CTV 12P 67 acres arable

CROMER Norfolk Map **09** TG24

GH Q **Chellow Dene** 23 MacDonald Rd NR27 9AP
☎(0263) 513251
This pleasant guesthouse in a street leading down to the seafront is only a short walk from the town centre. Mr and Mrs Leach offer traditional hospitality and the bedrooms are airy and comfortable.
7hc (2fb) CTV in all bedrooms ® sB&Bfr£14
dB&Bfr£28 LDO 5pm
Lic ♔ CTV 6P

GH QQQ *Morden House* 20 Cliff Av NR27 0AN
☎(0263) 513396
Closed 3-4wks Spring/Autumn
Within walking distance of the shops and seafront, this detached house has generally spacious bedrooms, which are light and airy. Mr and Mrs Votier are jovial, caring hosts, and offer an evening menu of homemade dishes. This is an excellent place to stay.
7rm(3↑4hc)(2fb) ® ✱ (ex guide dogs) LDO 5pm
Lic ♔ CTV 3P

GH QQ **Sandcliff Private Hotel** Runton Rd NR27 9AS
☎(0263) 512888
Feb-10 Dec
Catering for both tourists and commercial users, this hotel is only a few minutes' walk from the town centre. Many rooms offer sea views, as well as some en suite facilities. The nicely furnished lounge and dining room complement the bar.
24rm(9⇨10🟔5hc)(10fb) CTV in 15 bedrooms ®
sB&Bfr£18.20 sB&B⇨🟔fr£20.20 dB&Bfr£36.40
dB&B⇨🟔£40.40-£38.40 WBDifr£140 LDO 6pm
Lic CTV 10P

GH QQQ **Westgate Lodge Private Hotel** 10 MacDonald Rd
NR27 9AP ☎(0263) 512840
Mar-29 Nov
Close to the cliff top road and promenade, this exceptionally well-maintained house has an attractive restaurant, small, cosy bar and well-equipped accommodation, many rooms having en suite facilities. Mr and Mrs Robson ensure guests of a relaxing stay.
11🟔 (4fb) CTV in all bedrooms ® ✖ ✱ WB&Bfr£152.95
WBDifr£170.78 LDO 7pm
Lic ∰ 14P nc3yrs

INN QQ **Red Lion Hotel** Brook St NR27 9HD
☎(0263) 514964
This large Victorian building stands on the seafront close to the town centre. Rooms are attractive, and all have good en suite facilities. A solarium, sauna and snooker room are available.
12⇨🟔 (4fb) CTV in all bedrooms ® ✖ LDO 9.30pm
∰ 10P 3🚗 snooker sauna solarium gymnasium
Credit Cards ① ③

See advertisement on page 131

CROMHALL Avon Map 03 ST69

FH QQ Mrs S Scolding **Varley** *(ST699905)* Talbots End
GL12 8AJ ☎Chipping Sodbury(0454) 294292
Etr-Sep
Tucked away just outside the small village of Cromhall, this stone-clad farmhouse provides a good standard of accommodation in attractively decorated rooms.
4hc (3fb)✂in all bedrooms ® ✖ ✱ sB&B£13.50-£14.50
dB&B£24-£26 WB&Bfr£84
∰ CTV 5P 75 acres dairy
£

CROSTHWAITE Cumbria Map 07 SD49

GH QQQ **Crosthwaite House** LA8 8BP ☎(04488) 264
mid Mar-mid Nov
Enjoying an elevated position overlooking the Lythe Valley, this charming Georgian house has well-appointed rooms with their own facilities.
6🟔 CTV in 3 bedrooms ® sB&B🟔£19-£22
dB&B🟔£38-£44 WB&B£130-£150 WBDi£200-£220 LDO 5pm
Lic ∰ CTV 10P 2🚗
See advertisement under KENDAL on page 195

CROYDE Devon Map 02 SS43

GH QQQ **Moorsands House Hotel** Moor Ln EX33 1NP
☎(0271) 890781
Mar-Oct
Within walking distance of the beaches and village centre, this Victorian house provides 2 comfortable lounges, one with a bar and the other with TV. Most of the bedrooms have en suite facilities and simple, home-cooked meals are offered.
8🟔 (3fb) CTV in all bedrooms ® sB&B🟔£18-£20
dB&B🟔£32-£36 WB&B£98-£126 WBDi£150.50-£178.50 LDO 6pm
Lic ∰ CTV 8P nc3yrs
Credit Cards ① ③ £

SELECTED

GH QQQQ **Whiteleaf At Croyde** EX33 1PN
☎(0271) 890266
Built in the 1930s, this detached house standing in its own attractive gardens retains its character. The en suite bedrooms are individually styled and offer modern facilities. The public areas are well furnished and have a friendly atmosphere. Mr Wallington uses local produce in the imaginative menu while Mrs Wallington receives her guests with a warm welcome to make them feel at home.
5⇨🟔 (1fb) CTV in all bedrooms ® sB&B⇨🟔£27-£29
dB&B⇨🟔£44-£48 WB&B£154-£168 WBDi£235-£255
LDO 8.15pm
Lic ∰ 10P
Credit Cards ① ③

CROYDON Greater London

London plan **4** D1 (pages 000-000)
GH QQ **Kirkdale Hotel** 22 St Peter's Rd CR0 1HD
☎081-688 5898
Closed 2 wks Xmas
Set in a residential area, this attractive Victorian house, run by friendly proprietors, offers a good standard of well-maintained accommodation which will include a new extension providing bedrooms with en suite facilities.
18rm(7🟔11hc) CTV in all bedrooms ® ✖ (ex guide dogs) ✱
sB&Bfr£23 sB&B🟔fr£28 dB&Bfr£35 dB&B🟔fr£40
∰ CTV 12P
Credit Cards ① ③

𝒯helbridge 𝒞ross 𝒯nn

Between Exmoor and Dartmoor

An attractive country Inn set in peaceful country-side with views of Dartmoor to the front and Exmoor from the rear. Noted for excellent food, ales and wines. The eight en suite bedrooms are all comfortable and well equipped. Perfectly located for a peaceful break yet within a short drive of all that mid Devon offers.

**Thelbridge Cross Inn, Thelbridge,
Nr. Crediton, Devon EX17 4SQ
Telephone & Fax No: (0884) 860316**

GH |Q||Q| **Lonsdale Hotel** 158 Lower Addiscombe Rd CR0 6AG
℡081-654 2276
*Functional accommodation is offered at this hotel, with modern
bedrooms, a bright breakfast room and a combined bar/lounge
with a pool table. The friendly proprietors provide friendly service.*
12rm(3↑9hc)(2fb) CTV in all bedrooms ® ⊁ ✻ sB&B£32-£37
sB&B↑£42-£47 dB&B£46-£50
dB&B↑£58-£62 WB&B£200-£250 WBDi£277-£327 LDO 2pm
Lic ⊞ CTV 12P pool table
Credit Cards |1| |2| |3| ⓔ

GH |Q||Q||Q| **Markington Hotel** 9 Haling Park Rd CR2 6NG
℡081-681 6494 FAX 081-688 6530
4 Jan-16 Dec rs Xmas
*This family-run hotel has a friendly atmosphere, created by its
charming proprietress. The bedrooms are all well equipped, with
the business guest in mind.*
21rm(4↪16↑1hc)(2fb)⊁in 4 bedrooms CTV in all bedrooms
® ⊁ ✻ sB&B↪↑£30-£48 dB&B↪↑£48-£60 LDO 8.30pm
Lic ⊞ CTV 18P
Credit Cards |1| |2| |3| ⓔ

GH |Q||Q||Q| *Oakwood Hotel* 69 Outram Rd CR0 6XJ
℡081-654 2835
rs Xmas & Boxing Day
*Near the town centre, this Victorian house provides comfortable
accommodation which is continually being improved.*
17rm(10↪7↑)(3fb) CTV in all bedrooms ® LDO 8pm
Lic ⊞ CTV 7P sauna solarium
Credit Cards |1| |2| |3| |5|

CUCKNEY Nottinghamshire Map **08** SK57

FH |Q||Q| Mrs J M Ibbotson **Blue Barn** *(SK539713)* NG20 9JD
℡Mansfield(0623) 742248
Closed Xmas Eve & Xmas Day
*Although within easy reach of all the country's attractions, this
farm is quite isolated and is reached by a private lane off the A616
out of Cuckney. As well as the comfortable rooms in the house,
there is a self-catering cottage in the grounds.*
3hc (1fb) ® ⊁ (ex guide dogs) ✻ sB&Bfr£14 dB&B£28
⊞ CTV 6P 2▩ 250 acres arable beef mixed
ⓔ

CULLEN Grampian *Banffshire* Map **15** NJ56

GH |Q||Q| *The Wakes Hotel* Seafield Place AB5 2TE
℡(0542) 40251
*This large, Victorian guesthouse, set in its own gardens in a
residential area, has modest bedrooms and a choice of comfortable
and relaxing lounges.*
23rm(22hc)(5fb) LDO 7.30pm
Lic CTV 20P

CULLODEN MOOR Highland *Inverness-Shire* Map **14** NH74

FH |Q||Q| Mrs E M C Alexander **Culdoich** *(NH755435)* IV1 2EP
℡Inverness(0463) 790268
Etr-Oct
*This 18th-century farmhouse stands near the historic battlefield of
Culloden and Clava Standing Stones.*
2hc (1fb) ® ⊁ ✻ dB&B£24-£25 LDO 5pm
CTV 0P 200 acres mixed
ⓔ

CWMBRAN Gwent Map **03** ST29

FH |Q||Q| Mrs B Watkins **Glebe** *(ST325965)* Croes Y Ceiliog
NP44 2DE (1.5m E unclass towards Llandedveth village)
℡Tredunnock(063349) 251 & 242
Closed 21 Dec-7 Jan

*Popular with guests using the Irish ferries, due to its proximity to
the M4, this modern bungalow stands in picturesque surroundings
and provides comfortable accommodation together with warm
hospitality.*
3hc (1fb)⊁in all bedrooms ⊁ ✻ sB&Bfr£14 dB&Bfr£26
⊞ CTV 6P 100 acres beef dairy

CWMDUAD Dyfed Map **02** SN33

⊢⟶**GH** |Q||Q| **Neuadd-Wen** SA33 6XJ
℡Cynwyl Elfed(026787) 438
*Standing at the centre of this little village, in a lovely wooded
valley, this friendly, family-run guesthouse features a comfortable
and relaxing lounge with a stone fireplace and well-furnished
bedrooms.*
7rm(6↪↑1hc)(2fb) sB&B£10-£11 sB&B↪↑£11-£12.50
dB&B↪£22-£25 WB&B£70-£75 WBDi£95-£105 LDO
10.30pm
Lic ⊞ CTV 12P ⚬
Credit Cards |1| |3| ⓔ

DALMALLY Strathclyde *Argyllshire*

See **Ardbecknish**

DARLINGTON Co Durham Map **08** NZ21

GH |Q||Q| **Woodland** 63 Woodland Rd DL3 7BQ
℡(0325) 461908
*A mid-terrace house, this hotel is situated just out of the town on
the A68, and is within easy reach of the A1(M). A comfortable
lounge complements the traditional bedrooms.*
8rm(1↪7hc)(2fb) CTV in 1 bedroom sB&Bfr£16 dB&Bfr£28
dB&B↪fr£34
⊞ CTV
ⓔ

FH |Q||Q||Q| Mr & Mrs D & A Armstrong **Clow Beck House**
(NZ281100) Monk End Farm, Croft on Tees DL2 2SW
℡(0325) 721075
*All facilities at this modern farmhouse are of the highest standard.
Meals are taken round the single table in the dining room. Heather
and David Armstrong provide a warm welcome to their home,
which is set in open countryside in Croft on Tees, just south of
Darlington.*
3rm(1↑2hc) ® ⊁ sB&B£20 sB&B↑£30 dB&B£30
dB&B↑£40
⊞ CTV 8P ✐ 90 acres mixed

DARTINGTON Devon Map **03** SX76

INN |Q||Q| **Cott** TQ9 6HE ℡Totnes(0803) 863777
FAX (0803) 866629
*This rambling, thatched inn dates back to 1324. Full of character,
it offers a high standard of catering and is ideally positioned for
touring the South Hams.*
7rm(5↪2hc)⊁in all bedrooms CTV in all bedrooms ®
⊁ (ex guide dogs) ✻
dB&B↪↑£55-£65 WB&B£160-£195 LDO 9pm
CTV 50P nc10yrs
Credit Cards |1| |2| |3|

DARTMOUTH Devon Map **03** SX84

SELECTED

GH |Q||Q||Q||Q| **Captains House** 18 Clarence St TQ6 9NW
℡(0803) 832133
*Built in 1780, this charming listed house is close to the shops
and the River Dart. Ann and Nigel Justico offer a high quality
bed and breakfast service in this cosy, intimate house.
Comfortable and richly furnished, the en suite bedrooms offer*
▶

many facilities – even hot water bottles. Home-produced ingredients go into the superb English breakfasts. Although there is no on-site parking, local car parks are close at hand.

5rm(3⇄2♠) CTV in all bedrooms ® ✠
dB&B⇄♠£28-£40 WB&B£90-£125
� nc5yrs

GH Q Q Sunny Banks 1 Vicarage Hill TQ6 9EN
☎(0803) 832766

Recently extended to provide 10 comfortable bedrooms together with a small lounge and dining room, this family establishment provides a set meal, and is within walking distance of the river front and town centre.

10rm(2⇄2♠4hc)(2fb)✕in 2 bedrooms CTV in all bedrooms ® sB&B£15-£17.50 dB&B£29-£32
dB&B⇄♠£33-£40 WB&B£95-£130 WBDi£140-£175 LDO 7.30pm
Lic ♦ CTV 3P 1🏆 (£2 per night)

DAVIOT Highland *Inverness-Shire* Map **14** NH73

FH Q Q Q Mrs E M MacPherson **Lairgandour** *(NH720376)*
IV1 2XH ☎(046385) 207
Apr-Sep

In a quiet location near to Culloden Moor, Loch Ness and the Cairngorms. Situated east of A9 at junction with B9154.

5hc (3fb) ® ✻ sB&B£11 dB&Bfr£22
♦ CTV 0P 1000 acres beef mixed sheep
£

DAWLISH Devon Map **03** SX97

⊢⊷**GH Q Q Broxmore Private Hotel** 20 Plantation Ter
EX7 9DR ☎(0626) 863602
7rm(1♠6hc)(2fb) ® ✠ (ex guide dogs) sB&B£12-£15
sB&B♠£15-£18 dB&B£24-£30
dB&B♠£30-£36 WB&B£81-£101 WBDi£113-£133 LDO 4.30pm
Lic ♦ CTV ⊁
Credit Cards 1 3 £

GH Q Mimosa 11 Barton Ter EX7 9QH ☎(0626) 863283
Close to the town centre and beaches, this holiday guesthouse is family run.
9rm(1♠)(4fb) ✠ ✻ sB&B£10-£11 dB&B£20-£22
dB&B♠£24-£26 WB&B£64-£71 WBDi£97-£103 LDO 3pm
Lic ♦ CTV 4P nc3yrs

GH Q Q Walton House Plantation Ter EX7 9DR
☎(0626) 862760
Apr-Oct

Recent refurbishment has emphasized the beauty of this Nash-style Edwardian house. The comfortable, well-equipped bedrooms have quality en suite facilities. With its attractive small garden, Walton House overlooks the town and is close to the beach.

6rm(2⇄4♠)(1fb) CTV in all bedrooms ® ✠ (ex guide dogs)
✻ dB&B⇄♠£33-£35 WB&B£207.90-£220.50
6P
Credit Cards 1 3

DEBDEN GREEN Essex Map **05** TL53

FH Q Mrs K M Low **Wychbars** *(TL579320)* CB11 3NA
☎Bishops Stortford(0279) 850362
Run by the cheerful Mrs Low, this moated farmhouse stands in 3.5 acres. It is approached by an unclassified road, off the B1051, which runs through Scott Farm.
2rm CTV in all bedrooms ® sB&B£16 dB&B£29-£30
lift ♦ CTV 10P 600 acres arable non-working
£

Book as early as possible for busy holiday periods.

DENBIGH Clwyd Map **06** SJ06

⊢⊷**GH Q Cayo** 74 Vale St LL16 2BW ☎(074571) 2686 due to change to (0745) 812686
Closed Xmas

Located just south of the town centre, this mid-Victorian house provides simple but well-maintained accommodation, and a friendly, hospitable atmosphere. Nearby street parking is available.

5hc (2fb) sB&B£11-£12.50
dB&B£22-£25 WB&B£77-£87.50 WBDi£115.50 LDO 2pm
Lic ♦ CTV ⊁
Credit Cards 3 £

DENNY Central *Stirlingshire* Map **11** NS88

FH Q Q Mrs J Morton **Lochend** *(NS759856)* Carronbridge
FK6 5JJ ☎(0324) 822778
rs Oct-Apr

Friendly and comfortable, this traditional farmhouse enjoys a secluded, scenic setting. Take the B818 west from Denny for 4 miles, then turn right at Carronbridge Hotel onto an unclassified road for 2 miles.

2hc CTV in 1 bedroom ® ✠ LDO 1pm
♦ CTV 0P nc3yrs 650 acres sheep
£

FH Q Q Q Mr Mrs Steel **The Topps** *(NS757843)* Fintry Rd
FK6 5JF ☎(0324) 822471

Secluded amid beautiful rolling countryside, this tastefully appointed modern bungalow offers comfortable accommodation with a friendly atmosphere. The Topps is found 4 miles west of Denny on the B818.

8rm(1⇄7♠)(1fb)✕in all bedrooms CTV in all bedrooms ® sB&B⇄♠fr£20 dB&B⇄♠fr£30 LDO 5pm
Lic ♦ CTV 12P ⊿ 300 acres cashmere goats sheep
£
See advertisement under STIRLING on page 341

DENT Cumbria Map **07** SD78

INN Q Q George & Dragon Main St LA10 5QL ☎(05875) 256
9rm(3♠6hc)(2fb) CTV in all bedrooms ® LDO 9pm
♦ 14P pony trekking
Credit Cards 1 3

DERBY Derbyshire Map **08** SK33

GH Q Q Dalby House Hotel 100 Radbourne St, off Windmill Hill Ln DE3 3BU (off Windmill Hill Ln) ☎(0332) 42353
Lovely old house in residential area. Popular with tourists and business travellers.
9hc (2fb) CTV in all bedrooms ® sB&B£17-£18
dB&B£30-£32 LDO 4pm
♦ CTV 9P 1🏆 ♒
£

GH Q Q Georgian House Hotel 32/34 Ashbourne Rd DE3 3AD
☎(0332) 49806
Beautifully maintained house offering a high standard of accommodation.
20rm(2⇄8♠10hc)(5fb) CTV in all bedrooms ® sB&B£20-£24
sB&B⇄♠£35-£40 dB&Bfr£34
dB&B⇄♠£45-£50 LDO 9.30pm
Lic ♦ CTV 24P
£

GH Q Rangemoor Hotel 67 Macklin St DE1 1LF
☎(0332) 47252
Simple accommodation in a terraced house near town centre.
12hc Annexe 8hc (3fb) CTV in all bedrooms ® ✠
sB&B£21-£23 dB&B£30-£34
♦ CTV 18P 2🏆

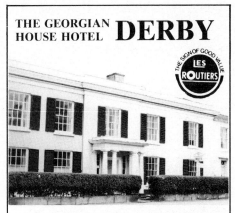

GH [Q] Rollz Hotel 684-8 Osmaston Rd DE2 8GT (on A514 2m S) ☎(0332) 41026
Two miles south of the city centre, on the A514, this large, well-maintained house provides simple and comfortable accomodation.
14hc (1fb) [R] 🐕 (ex guide dogs) ✱ sB&Bfr£18.40 dB&Bfr£36.80 WB&Bfr£128.80 WBDifr£169.05 LDO 9pm
Lic ♨ CTV 4🚗

DEVIL'S BRIDGE Dyfed Map **06** SN77

FH [Q][Q] Mrs E E Lewis **Erwbarfe** *(SN749784)* SY23 3JR ☎Ponterwyd(097085) 251
Etr-Oct
This traditional stone-built farmhouse is just off the A4120, and has a modern, comfortable lounge and 2 cosy bedrooms.
2hc [R] 🐕 dB&Bfr£26 WB&Bfr£90 WBDifr£125 LDO 4pm
♨ CTV 4P 400 acres beef sheep working farm

DEVIZES Wiltshire Map **04** SU06

GH [Q][Q] Pinecroft Potterne Rd SN10 5DA ☎(0380) 721433 FAX (0380) 728368
This substantial semi detached stone house is conveniently situated close to the town centre. The bedrooms are simply furnished and breakfast is taken around a large table. Smoking in bedrooms is discouraged.
4rm(1🛁3🚿)(1fb)🚭in 3 bedrooms CTV in all bedrooms [R] 🐕 sB&B🛁🚿£20-£24 dB&B🛁🚿£34-£36 WB&B£75-£100
♨ 6P 1🚗 ⌂
Credit Cards [1] [2] [3] [£]

GH [Q][Q][Q] Rathlin Wick Ln SN10 5DP ☎(0380) 721999
Quietly situated in a residential area, Rathlin has a relaxed, friendly atmosphere. The bedrooms are well equipped and contain antique art works. Peter and Barbara Fletcher serve breakfast around a large refectory table.
4🚿 CTV in all bedrooms [R] 🐕 ✱ sB&B🚿£17 dB&B🚿£30 WB&B£105
♨ 4P

DIBDEN Hampshire Map **04** SU40

GH [Q][Q][Q] Dale Farm Manor Rd, Applemore Hill SO4 5TJ ☎Southampton(0703) 849632
Closed Xmas
18th-century farmhouse on edge of the New Forest with modern bedrooms and fresh home-cooking.
6hc (2fb) TV in 1 bedroom [R] 🐕 (ex guide dogs) sB&B£15.50-£17.50
dB&B£28-£32 WB&B£85-£115 WBDi£135-£150 LDO 11am
♨ CTV 20P 🐎
[£]

DIDDLEBURY Shropshire Map **07** SO58

SELECTED

GH [Q][Q][Q][Q] The Glebe SY7 9DH
☎Munslow(058476) 221
Mar-Oct (closed 10 days early Jun)
A warm welcome awaits guests at this Elizabethan house, part of the Wilkes family's working farm. The dining room gleams with polished copper and oak and serves evening meals by prior arrangement.
3🚿 Annexe 3rm(1🚿2hc) CTV in 4 bedrooms [R] 🐕 (ex guide dogs) ✱ sB&B£18-£22 dB&B£40-£44 dB&B🚿£40-£52 LDO 6pm
Lic ♨ CTV 10P 2🚗 nc9yrs

DINDER Somerset Map **03** ST54

FH [Q][Q][Q] Mrs P J Keen ***Crapnell*** *(ST597457)* BA5 3HG ☎Shepton Mallet(0749) 2683
Mar-Oct
Pleasant farm with comfortable bedrooms and friendly atmosphere.
3hc (1fb) [R] 🐕 LDO noon
♨ CTV 0P 🏊snooker 300 acres dairy mixed

DINTON Buckinghamshire Map **04** SP71

FH [Q][Q][Q] Mrs J M W Cook **Wallace** *(SP770110)* HP17 8UF ☎Aylesbury(0296) 748660 FAX (0296) 748851
3rm(1🛁2🚿)(1fb) [R] 🐕 (ex guide dogs) sB&Bfr£20 dB&Bfr£28 dB&B🛁🚿fr£32
♨ CTV 6P 🎣 150 acres beef cattle & sheep
Credit Cards [1] [3] [£]

DIRLETON Lothian *East Lothian* Map **12** NT58

INN [Q][Q] Castle EH39 5EP ☎(062085) 221
Closed 21 Dec-5 Jan rs Nov-Apr
Plain but comfortable inn in attractive setting on village green.
4rm(3🛁1🚿)Annexe 4hc [R] sB&B£17 sB&B🛁🚿£20 dB&B£34 dB&B🛁🚿£40 WB&Bfr£98 Bar Lunch £1-£8&alc LDO 8.30pm
♨ CTV 20P
Credit Cards [1] [2] [3] [£]

DITCHLING East Sussex Map **04** TQ31

INN [Q][Q][Q] ***The Bull Hotel*** 2 High St BN6 8TA ☎Hassocks(07918) 3147
Once a coaching inn, this 14th-century village inn has a reputation for good wholesome meals, with a good selection of seafood. The comfortable, modern bedrooms are well furnished and the service is efficient.
3🛁🚿 CTV in all bedrooms [R] LDO 9.30pm
♨ 50P
Credit Cards [1] [2] [3] [5]

DOCKLOW Hereford & Worcester Map **03** SO55

🛏**FH [Q]** Mrs M R M Brooke **Nicholson** *(SO584581)* HR6 0SL ☎Steens Bridge(056882) 269
Closed Xmas & New Year
This 17th-century stone farmhouse is in a peaceful and picturesque area, approximately 5.5 miles east of Leominster. It is reached by way of a long private road from the A44. The accommodation is simple but comfortable.
2rm(1hc)(1fb) [R] sB&Bfr£11
dB&Bfr£22 WB&Bfr£75 WBDifr£120.50 LDO before 2pm
♨ CTV 0P 🎣 snooker 200 acres dairy mixed
Credit Cards [1] [3]

DODDISCOMBSLEIGH Devon Map **03** SX88

INN [Q][Q] Nobody EX6 7PS ☎Christow(0647) 52394
rs Sun, Mon & 8-15 Jan also Xmas Day pm
Full of character, with an inglenook fireplace and exposed beams, this popular inn provides accommodation with all modern facilities, 3 of the bedrooms being in a nearby annexe. Bar meals are available and the à la carte restaurant is open to non-residents.
4rm(2🚿2hc)Annexe 3🛁🚿 CTV in all bedrooms [R] 🐕 ✱ sB&B£20 sB&B🛁🚿£28
dB&B🛁🚿£47 WB&Bfr£161 Bar Lunch £5-£10alc Dinner £12-£15alc LDO 9.30pm
50P nc14yrs game fishing shooting
Credit Cards [1] [3]

DOLGELLAU Gwynedd Map **06** SH71

⊢⊸⊣**FH** Ⓠ Ⓠ Mrs E W Price **Glyn** *(SH704178)* LL40 1YA
☎(0341) 422286
Mar-Nov
*Situated approximately 1 mile west of Dolgellau this traditional
300-hundred-year-old farmhouse commands good views over the
Mawddach Estuary from its elevated position amidst wooded hills.*
4hc (2fb) TV in 3 bedrooms Ⓡ sB&B£12-£14
dB&B£24-£28 WB&B£65-£70 LDO previous day
🍴 CTV 6P 150 acres mixed
£

FH Ⓠ Mrs C Tudor Owen **Rhedyncochion** *(SH773207)*
Llanfachreth LL40 2DL (3m NE unclass)
☎Rhydymain(034141) 600
Etr-Oct
*This attractive 100-year-old farmhouse offers a warm and friendly
welcome. Standing in beautiful open countryside, about 3 miles
from the town, it has 2 pleasant bedrooms and a comfortable
lounge.*
2rm(1hc)(1fb) ✠ ✱ sB&Bfr£11 dB&Bfr£22
🍴 CTV 0P 120 acres mixed
£

DOLWYDDELAN Gwynedd Map **06** SH75

INN Ⓠ Ⓠ *Gwydyr* LL24 0EJ ☎(06906) 209
3hc CTV in all bedrooms Ⓡ LDO 9.30pm
🍴 CTV 5P

DONCASTER South Yorkshire Map **08** SE50

GH Ⓠ Ⓠ **Almel Hotel** 20 Christchurch Rd DN1 2QL
☎(0302) 365230
*Three town houses, close to the town centre, have been converted
and modernised to form a comfortable and friendly hotel. There is
a well-fitted lounge bar and an attractive, pine-clad dining room.*
22hc (8fb) CTV in all bedrooms Ⓡ ✱ sB&B£18-£25
dB&B£30-£32 LDO 8pm
Lic 🍴 CTV 8P
Credit Cards ① ③

DORCHESTER Dorset

See **Evershot & Winterbourne Abbas**
See advertisement on page 137

DORNOCH Highland *Sutherland* Map **14** NH78

GH Ⓠ Ⓠ Ⓠ **Evelix** IV25 3RE ☎(0862) 810271
Mar-Oct
*Set in peaceful woodland just off the A9, this Jacobean farmhouse
has a friendly atmosphere and offers comfortable, well-equipped
bedrooms. Non-smokers will appreciate the complete ban on
smoking.*
3hc ✗in all bedrooms CTV in all bedrooms Ⓡ ✠ sB&Bfr£18
dB&Bfr£26 WB&Bfr£87.50 WBDifr£150.50 LDO 4pm
🍴 CTV 4P nc6yrs

DORSINGTON Warwickshire Map **04** SP14

FH Ⓠ Ⓠ Mrs M J Walters **Church** *(SP132495)* CV37 8AX
☎Stratford-on-Avon(0789) 720471
*This pleasant Georgian house is situated on the outskirts of the
village.*
3hc Annexe 4⇆🐾 (2fb)✗in all bedrooms CTV in 4 bedrooms
Ⓡ ✠ (ex guide dogs) dB&B£22-£25 dB&B⇆🐾£28-£31
🍴 CTV 12P 3🐎 127 acres mixed

Visit your local AA Centre.

DOUGLAS

See MAN, ISLE OF

DOUGLAS WATER Strathclyde *Argyllshire* Map 11 NS83

FH Q Q Q Mrs J Tennant *Eastertown* (*NS874377*)
Sandilands ML11 9TX ☎(055588) 236
A substantial, stone-built house standing on the northern outskirts of the village. The accommodation is attractive and comfortable, and Mrs Tennant's 'Taste of Scotland' meals are a welcome bonus.
5rm(2♠3hc)(1fb) CTV in all bedrooms ® ✗ (ex guide dogs)
LDO 5pm
🏵 CTV 12P 300 acres sheep

DOVER Kent Map 05 TR34

GH Q **Beulah House** 94 Crabble Hill, London Rd CT17 0SA
☎(0304) 824615
Rooms, though compact, are cosy, and there are limited lounge facilities. There are extensive lawns and garden to the rear of the house, giving it an open aspect.
8hc (3fb) CTV in 1 bedroom ✗ (ex guide dogs) ✱
sB&B£18-£20 dB&B£34-£36 WB&Bfr£105
🏵 CTV 8P 2🐾 (£2)
£

GH Q Q Q **Castle House** 10 Castle Hill Rd CT16 1QW
☎(0304) 201656 FAX (0304) 210197
Closed Dec
Close to the castle, town centre and ferry ports, this friendly, family-run hotel has pretty bedrooms and a small cosy lounge together with an attractive dining room.
6rm(3♠3hc)(1fb) CTV in all bedrooms ® ✗ sB&B£18-£26
dB&B£24-£32 dB&B♠£26-£34
Lic 🏵 3P 1🐾 (£2.50) nc10yrs
Credit Cards [1][3] £

GH Q Q **Dell** 233 Folkestone Rd CT17 9SL ☎(0304) 202422
This is a pleasant establishment in a Victorian terraced house, which offers pretty and well-maintained accommodation, in addition to a friendly atmosphere. Breakfast is served in the nicely appointed dining room which extends from the lounge.
6hc (3fb) ® ✗ (ex guide dogs) sB&B£14-£16 dB&B£24-£28
🏵 CTV 6P
£

GH Q Q **Gateway Hovertel** Snargate St CT17 9BZ
☎(0304) 205479
Closed 23 Dec-Feb
Close to the ferry and hoverports, this family-run hotel offers modestly appointed rooms, all with en suite facilities.
27rm(4⇌23♠)(7fb) CTV in all bedrooms ✗ (ex guide dogs)
sB&B⇌♠£22-£28 dB&B⇌♠£37-£45 LDO 7pm
Lic 🏵 CTV 24P 2🐾
Credit Cards [1][3] £

GH Q Q Q **Number One** 1 Castle St CT16 1QH
☎(0304) 202007
Delightfully Victorian in style, this hotel offers a warm welcome and accommodation equipped for every need. Full breakfast is served in the bedrooms as required, and 'early riser' trays are available for those catching an early ferry.
5rm(3♠2hc)(3fb) CTV in all bedrooms ® ✗ ✱ dB&B£28-£32
dB&B♠£30-£35
🏵 2P 4🐾 (£1.50)
£

GH Q Q Q **Peverall House Hotel** 28 Park Av CT16 1HD
☎(0304) 202573 & 205088
Comfortable, well-appointed accommodation and a cheerful, pleasant welcome.

6rm(2⇌4hc)(2fb) CTV in all bedrooms ® ✗ sB&B£17-£20
dB&B£30-£35 LDO noon
Lic 🏵 CTV 8P

GH Q Q Q **St Martins** 17 Castle Hill Rd CT16 1QW
☎(0304) 205938
Closed Xmas
This charming Victorian house stands on the leas of Dover Castle and is ideally situated for the town and seaports. The pretty bedrooms are complemented by a pleasant lower ground floor dining room and a comfortable lounge.
8hc (2fb) CTV in all bedrooms ® ✗ ✱ sB&B£20-£25
dB&B£25-£35
Lic 🏵 1🐾 (£2 per night)

GH Q Q Q **Walletts Court Manor** West Cliffe, St Margarets-at-Cliffe CT15 6EW (1.5m NE of A2/A258 junct, off B2058)
☎(0304) 852424
Closed 24-27 Dec
A restored 17th-century farmhouse with large beamed bedrooms, inglenooks and oak staircase. Situated on the white cliffs of Dover, 3 miles from harbour.
3⇌♠ Annexe 4⇌♠ (1fb) CTV in all bedrooms ® ✗
sB&B⇌♠£34-£52 dB&B⇌♠£40-£60 LDO 8.30pm
Lic 🏵 16P 10🐾 games room
Credit Cards [1][3]

DOVERIDGE Derbyshire Map 07 SK13

GH Q Q *Ley Hill Farm* DE6 5PA ☎Uttoxeter(0889) 564252
Closed 21-31 Dec
5⇌♠ (4fb)✂in all bedrooms CTV in all bedrooms ®
✗ (ex guide dogs) LDO 5pm
🏵 15P ⛳ pitch & putt

Wallett's Court Country House Hotel

West Cliffe, St Margarets-at-Cliffe, Dover, Kent CT15 6EW.
Telephone: (0304) 852424

Chris & Lea Oakley invite you to stay at Wallett's Court a manor house restored in the 17th Century but with cellars dating back to Domesday. Reception rooms are large with carved oak beams, ornate fireplaces and antique furniture. All bedrooms have bathrooms en suite and are tastefully furnished. They have tea-making facilities, telephone and colour television.

Wine and dine in the Jacobean restaurant listed in "Egon Ronay". Take a trip across the Channel or within an hour's drive visit Leeds Castle and the many lovely houses, gardens and beauty spots of Kent. Wallett's Court is only a short drive from championship golf courses.

B.T.A. Commended

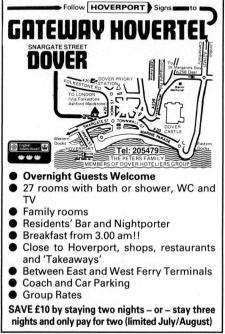

DOWNHAM MARKET Norfolk Map **05** TF60

GH Q Q Q **Crosskeys Riverside Hotel** Hilgay PE38 0LN
☎(0366) 387777
Standing in lovely gardens on the banks of the River Wissey, next to the A11, Crosskeys has been converted from 17th-century buildings to offer a high standard of accommodation. All rooms have en suite facilities and are very comfortable. Mr and Mrs Bulmer are the caring hosts.
3⇨ Annexe 2⇨ CTV in all bedrooms ® sB&B⇨fr£29.10 dB&B⇨£42.55-£54.25 WBDi£171-£242.75 LDO 8.30pm
Lic ⴲ 10P ✔
Credit Cards 1 3

DOWNTON Wiltshire Map **04** SU12

GH Q Q Q **Warren** 15 High St SP5 3PG ☎(0725) 20263
Closed 15 Dec-15 Jan
A charming period house, comfortably furnished, with a warm welcome.
6rm(1⇨5hc)(1fb) ® sB&B£16-£17.50 dB&B£32-£35.50 dB&B⇨£35-£38.50
ⴲ CTV 8P nc5yrs
£

DROXFORD Hampshire Map **04** SU61

GH Q Q **Coach House Motel** Brockbridge SO3 1QT
☎(0489) 877812
Annexe accommodation in a converted stable block is comfortable and well equipped here, a few yards from The Hurdles Public House. Restaurant and bar meals are served and there is a pine-furnished breakfast room.
8rm(6⇨2♟) CTV in all bedrooms ® ✗ (ex guide dogs) sB&B⇨♟£27.50-£31.50 dB&B⇨♟£37.50-£47.50
ⴲ 12P
Credit Cards 1 2 3 5

GH Q Q Q **Little Uplands Country Motel** Garrison Hill
SO3 1QL ☎(0489) 878507 FAX (0489) 877853
Closed 24 Dec-2 Jan
4⇨♟ Annexe 14rm(2⇨12♟) CTV in all bedrooms ®
✗ (ex guide dogs) LDO 9pm
Lic ⴲ CTV 25P ⌒(heated) ♟(hard)✔ sauna solarium gymnasium table tennis
Credit Cards 1 2 3 5

DRUMNADROCHIT Highland *Inverness-Shire*
Map **14** NH52

INN Q Q **Lewiston Arms Hotel** Lewiston IV3 6UN
☎(04562) 225
A comfortable and cosy old inn with a friendly relaxed atmosphere and a reputation for good food.
4rm(3hc)Annexe 4hc ® LDO 8.30pm
ⴲ CTV 30P
Credit Cards 3 £

DULVERTON Somerset

See Oakford

DUMFRIES Dumfries & Galloway

See Auldgirth & Clarencefield

DUNBAR Lothian *East Lothian* Map **12** NT67

GH Q Q Q **The Courtyard** Woodbush Brae EH42 1HB
☎(0368) 64169 & 62683
Closed 3wks Jan
This delightfully modernised guesthouse stands in a cobbled courtyard on the seafront. Bedrooms are well equipped and the home cooking is excellent.
7rm(2♟5hc) CTV in all bedrooms ® LDO 8.30pm

Lic ⴲ 7P
Credit Cards 1 3

⊷GH Q Q **Marine** 7 Marine Rd EH42 1AR ☎(0368) 63315
A friendly, comfortable, seaside guesthouse in a quiet, residential area on the west side of town.
10hc (3fb) sB&Bfr£12 dB&Bfr£24 LDO 4pm
ⴲ CTV ♟

GH Q **Overcliffe** 11 Bayswell Park EH42 1AE ☎(0368) 64004
5hc (2fb) CTV in all bedrooms ® ✳
dB&Bfr£28 WB&Bfr£98 WBDifr£168 LDO 5pm
Lic ⴲ CTV ♟

GH Q Q Q **St Beys** 2 Bayswell Rd EH42 1AB ☎(0368) 63571
Feb-Dec
Overlooking the sea and close to the town centre, this friendly hotel is in a residential area and has comfy bedrooms with many little extras. The first floor lounge takes advantage of the views.
6hc (3fb) CTV in all bedrooms ® LDO 6pm
ⴲ CTV ♟
Credit Cards 3

GH Q Q Q **Springfield** Edinburgh Rd EH42 1NH
☎(0368) 62502
Mar-Oct
Spacious, comfortable accommodation is offered at this attractive stone-built house. The resident proprietors provide home-cooked dinners and attentive service.
5hc (2fb) CTV in all bedrooms ® sB&Bfr£15
dB&Bfr£28 WB&Bfr£98 WBDifr£145 LDO 5pm
Lic ⴲ CTV 7P ⏶
Credit Cards 1 3

DUNDEE Tayside *Angus* Map **11** NO43

GH Q Q Q **Beach House Hotel** 22 Esplanade, Broughty Ferry
DD5 2EQ ☎(0382) 76614 FAX (0382) 480241
Pleasantly situated overlooking the River Tay, this popular business and tourist hotel is warmly welcoming. The bedrooms vary in size, but all are tastefully appointed and are well equipped with useful extras.
5⇨♟ (2fb) CTV in all bedrooms ® sB&B⇨♟£40-£44
dB&B⇨♟£44-£50 LDO 9pm
Lic ⴲ ♟
Credit Cards 1 3

DUNKELD Tayside *Perthshire* Map **11** NO04

⊷GH Q Q **Waterbury** PH8 0BG ☎(03502) 324
A popular base for the touring holidaymaker, this guesthouse offers traditional comforts and good value for money. It stands in the centre of Birmingham, just south of Dunkeld.
6hc (2fb) ® sB&B£10.50-£12
dB&B£21-£24 WB&B£73.50 WBDi£126 LDO 7pm
Lic ⴲ CTV 6P
£

DUNLOP Strathclyde *Ayrshire* Map **10** NS44

FH Q Q Q Mr & Mrs R B Wilson **Struther** *(NS412496)*
Newmill Rd KA3 4BA ☎Stewarton(0560) 84946
Closed 2wks spring & autumn rs Sun & Mon
Large farmhouse in its own gardens. On the outskirts of Dunlop village.
5hc (2fb) ✳ sB&B£12.50
dB&B£25 WB&B£80 WBDi£140 LDO 8.30pm
CTV 16P 16 acres non-working
£
See advertisement under STEWARTON see page 339

DUNOON Strathclyde *Argyllshire* Map **10** NS17

GH [Q][Q][Q] Cedars Hotel 51 Alexandra Pde, East Bay PA23 8AF ☎(0369) 2425 & 2066

This small family-run hotel stands on the promenade and has well-appointed and equipped bedrooms, several of which enjoy attractive views over the Firth of Clyde.

13rm(4🛁9🚿)(1fb) CTV in all bedrooms Ⓡ 🐕 sB&B🛁🚿fr£19 dB&B🛁🚿fr£34

Lic ♨ CTV P̸

Credit Cards [1] [2] [3] [5] [£]

DUNSTER Somerset

See **Minehead & Roadwater**

DUNSYRE Strathclyde *Lanarkshire* Map **11** NT04

FH [Q][Q][Q] Mrs L Armstrong **Dunsyre Mains** *(NT074482)* ML11 8NQ ☎(089981) 251

Two-storeyed, stone farmhouse dating from 1800 in courtyard-style with splendid views and small garden.

3hc (1fb)🚭in all bedrooms Ⓡ 🐕 (ex guide dogs) * sB&Bfr£13 dB&Bfr£24 WB&Bfr£84 WBDifr£126 LDO 7pm

♨ CTV 6P 400 acres beef sheep

[£]

DUNURE Strathclyde *Ayrshire* Map **10** NS21

FH [Q][Q][Q] Mrs R J Reid ***Lagg*** *(NS281166)* KA7 4LE ☎(029250) 647

May-Oct

Extensively renovated and modernised farmhouse overlooking the coast.

3hc Ⓡ

♨ CTV 6P 480 acres dairy sheep

DUNVEGAN

See **SKYE, ISLE OF**

DURHAM Co Durham Map **12** NZ24

See also Haswell Plough

GH [Q][Q] *Lothlorien* 48/49 Front St, Witton Gilbert DH7 6SY ☎091-371 0067

Set in the centre of a small village on the A691, this neat, 200-year-old house is 3 miles north west of Durham. A cooking range from an old miner's house is a particular feature of the comfortable lounge, and there is a small dining room.

4hc Ⓡ 🐕

♨ CTV 3P

INN [Q] Croxdale Croxdale DH6 5HX (3m S A167) ☎Spennymoor(0388) 815727

This roadside inn with its comfortable lounge bar has spacious bedrooms in the main building as well as four more compact rooms in the converted stone house at the rear.

9rm(1🛁4🚿4hc)Annexe 4🚿 (1fb) CTV in all bedrooms Ⓡ * sB&B£20 sB&B🛁🚿£25 dB&B£30 dB&B🛁🚿£35 Bar Lunch £2.50-£4.95 Dinner £9.50-£19.50alc LDO 10pm

♨ 30P

Credit Cards [1] [3] [£]

DURSLEY Gloucestershire Map **03** ST79

FH [Q][Q][Q] Mr & Mrs St John Mildmay **Drakestone House** *(ST734977)* Stinchcombe GL11 6AS (2.5m W off B4060) ☎(0453) 542140

Apr-Oct

Situated between Dursley and Wooton-under-Edge on the B4060, this fine country house retains many original features, which have been enhanced by the fine antiques and objects collected by hosts Hugh and Crystal St John Mildmay during their many years overseas.

3rm(1hc) TV available 🐕 * sB&B£17-£22 dB&B£34 WB&Bfr£119 WBDifr£206.50 LDO previous day

♨ 6P 10 acres sheep

[£]

DYLIFE Powys Map **06** SN89

INN [Q] Star SY19 7BW ☎Llanbrynmair(06503) 345

Slate floors and log fires add to the character of the bars at this inn which stands on the B4518 mountain road, in wild and rugged countryside. Ideally situated for activity holidays, the inn has its own pony trekking centre.

7rm(2🛁5hc)(1fb) Ⓡ * sB&B£14-£16 sB&B🛁£14-£16 dB&B£28 dB&B🛁£32 WB&B£95 WBDi£125 LDO 10.30pm

♨ CTV 30P 🐎 boat hire pony trekking

[£]

DYMCHURCH Kent Map **05** TR12

GH [Q][Q] Chantry Hotel Sycamore Gardens TN29 0LA ☎(0303) 873137

Enjoying a fine beach location, this hotel has bedrooms with interconnecting rooms for children. A 4-course meal is served in the basement restaurant, with a choice selection of wines. Children are provided with a large garden with swings, well away from the roads.

6rm(5🛁🚿1hc)(5fb) CTV in all bedrooms Ⓡ sB&B£15-£17 sB&B🛁🚿£18-£20 dB&B£30-£34 dB&B🛁🚿£33-£40 WB&B£84-£112 WBDi£135-£165 LDO 8.30pm

Lic ♨ CTV 9P

Credit Cards [1] [3] [£]

See advertisement under FOLKESTONE on page 157

GH [Q][Q] *Waterside* 15 Hythe Rd TN29 0LN ☎(0303) 872253

Standing on the main road into Dymchurch, this pretty detached building has views over pleasant rural countryside. The accommodation includes neat bedrooms and a small cosy lounge bar.

7hc (3fb) 🐕 LDO 3pm

Lic ♨ CTV 9P

EARDISLAND Hereford & Worcester Map **03** SO45

FH [Q][Q] Miss M Johnson **The Elms** *(SO418584)* HR6 9BN ☎Pembridge(05447) 405

This small, renovated farmhouse is set in the centre of the village and offers special interest holidays, such as photography or needlecraft. Guests are reminded that no smoking is permitted in the house.

4hc 🚭in all bedrooms 🐕 * sB&Bfr£13.50 dB&Bfr£26 WB&Bfr£101.50 WBDifr£140 LDO noon

6P nc10yrs 32 acres stock rearing

[£]

EARLSWOOD Gwent Map **03** ST49

FH [Q][Q][Q] Mrs G Powell **Parsons Grove** *(ST452943)* NP6 6RD ☎Shirenewton(02917) 382

Closed 20-31 Dec

Run by the friendly Powell family, this very comfortable farmhouse has good bedrooms and a spacious lounge. A swimming pool and self catering flats are also available.

2🛁🚿 Annexe 1🛁🚿 (3fb) CTV in 1 bedroom Ⓡ 🐕 (ex guide dogs) * dB&B🛁🚿£26-£30 WB&B£85-£100 LDO 11am

♨ CTV 10P 🏊(heated) 20 acres vineyards

[£]

[£] Remember to use the money-off vouchers.

EASTBOURNE East Sussex Map **05** TV69

See Town Plan Section

GH [Q][Q][Q] Bay Lodge Hotel 61 & 62 Royal Pde BN22 7AQ
☎(0323) 32515

Mar-Oct

This attractive double-fronted Victorian house overlooks the sea and has neatly appointed, comfortable accommodation and a cosy bar. There are pleasant sun lounges for smokers and non-smokers, and good home cooking is provided.

12rm(5🛁4🚿3hc) CTV in all bedrooms [R] 🐕 (ex guide dogs) ✻
sB&B£14-£23 dB&B£30-£40
dB&B🛁🚿£32-£46 WB&B£66-£118 WBDi£98-£151 (wkly only Jul & Aug) LDO 6pm
Lic 🍽 CTV 2🚗 (£2 per night) nc7yrs
Credit Cards [1] [3] [£]

GH [Q][Q][Q] Beachy Rise 20 Beachy Head Rd BN20 7QN
☎(0323) 639171

This friendly establishment has been carefully refurbished and offers accommodation of a good standard with a non-smoking dining room and a comfortable, well-appointed lounge. Set in a quiet residential area, it is close to local amenities.

6rm(1🛁3🚿2hc)(1fb) CTV in all bedrooms [R]
🐕 (ex guide dogs) dB&B£28-£34
dB&B🛁🚿£34-£40 WB&B£88-£120 WBDi£138-£170 LDO noon
Lic 🍽 🅿
Credit Cards [1] [3] [£]

GH [Q][Q][Q] ***Bourne House Private Hotel*** 16 Bourne St BN22 3ER
☎(0323) 21981

Bourne House offers guests a choice of modern bedrooms together with a comfortable lounge and a separate bar-dining room. The accommodation is complemented by good cooking and generous breakfasts. Car parking may be a little difficult.

▶

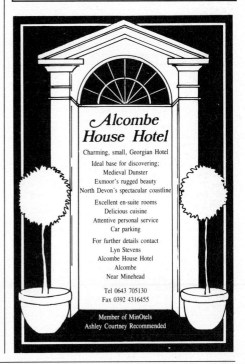

9rm(4♪ 5hc)(1fb) CTV in all bedrooms ® LDO noon
Lic ⊞ CTV ⊬ ✓

GH Q Q **Chalk Farm Hotel & Restaurant** Coopers Hill,
Willingdon BN20 9JD (2m NNE) ☎(0323) 503800
*This 17th-century, flint-built farmhouse overlooks the Sussex
Downs. Bedrooms are furnished with antiques and the lounges are
comfortable.*
9rm(2⇔5♪ 2hc)(1fb) CTV in all bedrooms ® ✱ sB&B£22-£29
sB&B⇔♪£22-£29 dB&B£44-£58
dB&B⇔♪£50-£58 WB&B£150-£190 LDO 9pm
Lic ⊞ CTV 30P
Credit Cards [1] [3] [5]

GH Q Q Q **Far End Hotel** 139 Royal Pde BN22 7LH
☎(0323) 25666
Apr-Oct
*This relaxing, family-run guesthouse stands beside Princes Park
within easy reach of the seafront amenities. The bright, modern,
comfortable bedrooms are complemented by a lounge and
residential bar.*
11rm(4♪7hc) CTV in all bedrooms ® sB&B£16 dB&B£32
dB&B♪£36 WB&B£106-£120 WBDi£123-£156 LDO 1pm
Lic ⊞ CTV 8P nc4yrs

GH Q Q Q **Flamingo Private Hotel** 20 Enys Rd BN21 2DN
☎(0323) 21654
Closed Nov
*This attractive period house retains many original features and
benefits from a quiet situation and unrestricted parking. A spacious
bar/lounge and a well-appointed, non-smoking dining room are
complemented by very well-equipped bedrooms.*
12rm(5⇔7♪) CTV in all bedrooms ® ✕ (ex guide dogs) ✱
sB&B⇔♪£19-£23
dB&B⇔♪£38 WB&B£114-£138 WBDifr£165 LDO 4.30pm
Lic ⊞ ⊬ nc8yrs
Credit Cards [1] [3] £

GH Q Q Q **Hotel Mandalay** 16 Trinity Trees BN21 3LE
☎(0323) 29222
*With its private car park and fully licensed restaurant 'Gatsby's',
this well-managed hotel has been upgraded by its present owners.
The bedrooms are well equipped and services are extensive.*
12rm(2⇔10♪)(1fb) CTV in all bedrooms ® ✕ (ex guide dogs)
✱ sB&B⇔♪£20-£23
dB&B⇔♪£40-£46 WB&B£135-£160 WBDi£155-£198 LDO
9pm
Lic ⊞ 15P
Credit Cards [1] [3] £

GH Q Q Q **Mowbray Hotel** Lascelles Tce BN21 4BJ
☎(0323) 20012
Apr-Dec
*Well placed for easy access to the seafront, shops and theatres, this
guesthouse has a basement dining room and a passenger lift to all
upper floors.*
15rm(6♪9hc) CTV in all bedrooms ® dB&Bfr£34
dB&B♪fr£40 WB&B£100-£114 WBDi£142-£156 LDO 5.30pm
lift CTV nc6yrs
Credit Cards [1] [3]

GH Q Q Q *Orchard House Private Hotel* 10 Old Orchard Rd
BN21 1DB ☎(0323) 23682
Apr-Oct
*Close to the station and with unrestricted car parking facilities,
Orchard House provides every comfort in a relaxing atmosphere.
The accommodation is generally spacious and well furnished with
a very comfortable lounge.*
6rm(5⇔1♪)(1fb) CTV in all bedrooms ® ✕
⊞ 3P nc5yrs

GH Q Q Q **Park View Hotel** Wilmington Gardens BN21 4JN
☎(0323) 21242
*Perfectly situated for the local amenities and opposite Devonshire
Park Theatre, this hotel has well-furnished and particularly well-
equipped rooms. There is a small bar lounge and a dining room
where the cooking and service are equally good.*
13rm(3⇔9♪1hc) CTV in all bedrooms ® ✕ LDO 8pm
Lic lift 10P nc2yrs

GH Q Q Q Q *Saffrons Hotel* 30-32 Jevington Gardens BN21 4HN
☎(0323) 25539
Etr-Oct
*This friendly hotel, situated quite close to the town centre and sea
front, has undergone some major improvements to offer a good
standard of modern accommodation. The attractive lower ground
floor restaurant and bar may be reached by a lift.*
25rm(7⇔6♪12hc)(2fb) CTV in all bedrooms ® LDO 7pm
Lic CTV ⊬
Credit Cards [1] [3]

GH Q Q Q **Stirling House Hotel** 5-7 Cavendish Place
BN21 3EJ ☎(0323) 32263
Closed 1st wk Nov, last wk Jan & 1st wk Feb
*This hotel is centrally situated with easy access to the sea front and
shops, and offers comfortable bedrooms, a lounge and a bar, with a
basement dining room. Good English cooking and friendly service
are provided.*
21rm(11♪10hc)(1fb) CTV in all bedrooms ®
✕ (ex guide dogs) sB&B£16-£17 dB&B£30-£32
dB&B♪£34-£36 WB&B£90-£115 WBDi£104-£135 LDO 9am
Lic CTV ⊬ nc10yrs
£

GH Q Q Q Q **Wynstay Private Hotel** Lewes Rd BN21 2BY
☎(0323) 21550
Apr-11 Oct
*This is a well-maintained guesthouse with pleasantly furnished
rooms. Service is friendly and helpful, and the house is
conveniently situated near to the A22.*
6rm(1⇔5♪)(2fb) CTV in all bedrooms ® ✕
sB&B⇔♪£18-£20
dB&B⇔♪£30-£34 WB&B£84-£112 WBDi£112-£140 LDO
10am
⊞ 7P nc3yrs

EAST CALDER Lothian *Midlothian* Map **11** NT06

FH Q Q Mr & Mrs D R Scott **Whitecroft** *(NT095682)*
EH53 0ET ☎Midcalder(0506) 881810
*Large roadside bungalow attached to smallholding half a mile east
on B7015.*
3hc (1fb)⅌in all bedrooms ® ✕ ✱ sB&Bfr£15
dB&Bfr£24 WB&Bfr£84
⊞ CTV 8P 5 acres mixed beef sheep
£

See advertisement under EDINBURGH on page 151

EAST GRINSTEAD West Sussex Map **05** TQ33

GH Q Q *Cranfield Lodge Hotel* Maypole Rd RH19 1HW
☎(0342) 321251 & 410371
*Standing in a residential area close to the town, this guesthouse has
a well-kept garden and provides neat, beautifully maintained
accommodation.*
11rm(4♪7hc)Annexe 9rm(1⇔6♪2hc)(1fb) CTV in all
bedrooms ® LDO 8pm
Lic ⊞ CTV 11P
Credit Cards [1] [3]

This guide is updated annually – make sure you
use an up-to-date edition.

EBBERSTON North Yorkshire Map **08** SE88

GH QQ Foxholm Hotel YO13 9NJ (on B1258)
☎Scarborough(0723) 85550

Mar-Nov & Xmas

Small, family-run country hotel in a peaceful setting. York, the moors, dales and sea all within easy reach.

9rm(2⌒4↑3hc)(1fb) ® LDO 7pm

Lic ♨ CTV 12P 2☎

£

EDINBURGH Lothian *Midlothian* Map **11** NT27

See **Town Plan Section**

GH QQ Adam Hotel 19 Lansdowne Crescent EH12 5EH
☎031-337 1148

This elegant Georgian house is set in a quiet location, and yet is convenient for the main road. The warm, traditional bedrooms each have a colour television set.

9hc (2fb) CTV in all bedrooms ✻ (ex guide dogs) sB&B£17 dB&B£32-£34

Lic ♨ CTV

£

See advertisement on page 145

GH QQQ The Adria Hotel 11-12 Royal Ter EH7 5AB
☎031-556 7875

Closed Nov-Dec

Part of a Georgian terrace close to Princes Street. Spacious, well-decorated accommodation.

28rm(2⌒4↑22hc)(7fb) ® ✻ ✳ sB&B£21.85-£28.75 sB&B⌒↑fr£28.75 dB&B£39.10-£41.40 dB&B⌒↑£48.30-£50.60

♨ CTV ₽

£

GH Q Q Q **Allison House** 15/17 Mayfield Gardens EH9 2AX
☎031-667 8049

*A conversion of 2 terraced houses to the south of the city centre.
Accommodation is comfortable and each bedroom well equipped.*
24rm(22♠2hc)(10fb) CTV in all bedrooms ®
✠ (ex guide dogs) sB&B♠£24-£28 dB&B£30-£40
dB&B♠£38-£50 WB&B£150-£180 WBDi£210-£250 LDO
7.30pm
Lic ⁋⁋ 12P
Credit Cards ⊡ ③ £

GH Q Q **Ashdene House** 23 Fountainhall Rd EH9 2LN
☎031-667 6026

Closed Nov

*The well-appointed bedrooms at this very comfortable house have
colour TVs, hairdryers and telephones.*
5rm(4♠1hc)(2fb) CTV in all bedrooms ® ✠ (ex guide dogs)
sB&B♠£20-£28 dB&B♠£30-£36
⁋⁋ 3P nc2yrs

GH Q Q **Avenue Hotel** 4 Murrayfield EH12 6AX
☎031-346 7270

*Part of a Victorian terrace, this friendly, family-run guesthouse
offers spacious, comfortable accommodation. It is located to the
west of the city with easy access to the A8.*
9rm(1⇆5♠3hc)(3fb) CTV in all bedrooms ®
⁋⁋ ⅌

GH Q **Ben Doran** 11 Mayfield Gardens EH9 2AX
☎031-667 8488

Closed 20-27 Dec

Situated in a terraced row, with modest bedrooms.
9rm(1⇆3♠5hc)(5fb) CTV in all bedrooms ® ✳ sB&B£16-£24
dB&B£27-£30 dB&B⇆♠£30-£37
⁋⁋ 6P 2🛞
£

GH Q Q **Boisdale Hotel** 9 Coates Gardens EH12 5LB
☎031-337 1134

*This pleasant terraced house is close to the city's West End, and is
a comfortable establishment, where the breakfasts are enjoyable
and the service friendly. Bedrooms have recently been refurbished
and there are neat bath and shower rooms.*
10rm(4⇆6♠)(5fb) CTV in all bedrooms ® ✳
sB&B⇆♠£22-£28 dB&B⇆♠£32-£56 LDO 7pm
Lic ⁋⁋ CTV ⅌
£

GH Q Q **Bonnington** 202 Ferry Rd EH6 4NW ☎031-554 7610
*Situated in the northern suburbs, this friendly, family-run
guesthouse offers neat, simple accommodation.*
6rm(1♠5hc)(3fb) CTV in all bedrooms ® sB&B£18-£22
dB&B£29-£34 dB&B♠£34-£39 LDO 10am
⁋⁋ CTV 9P
£

GH Q Q Q **Brunswick Hotel** 7 Brunswick St EH7 5JB
☎031-556 1238

*An attractively appointed and comfortable guesthouse situated
close to the city centre. It offers a high standard of housekeeping,
with pleasant bedrooms, all with bright, compact shower rooms.*
10♠ (1fb) CTV in all bedrooms ® ✠ sB&B♠£20-£30
dB&B♠£36-£50
⁋⁋ nc2yrs
£

GH Q Q Q **Buchan Hotel** 3 Coates Gardens EH12 5LG
☎031-337 1045

*Charming and well-maintained, this Victorian guesthouse is set in
a residential area close to the city centre. The attractive
accommodation is complemented by the warm and personal
attention of the owners.*
11rm(2♠9hc)(6fb) CTV in all bedrooms ® sB&B£18-£20
dB&B£30-£34 dB&B♠£40-£45

⁋⁋ CTV ⅌
£

SELECTED

GH Q Q Q Q **Dorstan Private Hotel** 7 Priestfield Rd
EH16 5HJ ☎031-667 6721

Closed 23 Dec-8 Jan

*Attentive, caring service and a high standard of
accommodation are offered at this family-run hotel which
stands in a quiet residential area to the south of the city.
Tastefully decorated and comfortable throughout, Dorstan
has bedrooms comprehensively equipped with telephones,
colour TV and beverage facilities. The menu of freshly cooked
dishes changes daily.*
14rm(12⇆♠2hc)(2fb) CTV in all bedrooms ® ✠ ✳
sB&B£16-£20 sB&B⇆♠£20-£26 dB&B£32
dB&B⇆♠£39 LDO 4pm
⁋⁋ 8P
Credit Cards ⊡ £

GH Q Q **Dunstane House** 4 West Coates EH12 5TQ
☎031-337 6169

Closed Xmas-4 Jan

*Sympathetically run, this detached house stands on the western
approach to the city centre. Accommodation is spacious and
comfortable, and all bedrooms have shower units.*
15hc (5fb) CTV in all bedrooms ®
Lic ⁋⁋ CTV 10P
Credit Cards ② ③

GH Q Q **Ellesmere House** 11 Glengyle Ter EH3 9LN
☎031-229 4823

*Overlooking open parkland and within walking distance of the city
centre, this small, friendly guesthouse enjoys a superb location.*
6hc (2fb) CTV in all bedrooms ® ✠ (ex guide dogs) ✳
sB&B£13-£17 dB&B£26-£34 WB&B£91-£119
⁋⁋ CTV ⅌

See advertisement on page 147

GH Q Q **Galloway** 22 Dean Park Crescent EH4 1PH
☎031-332 3672 Telex no 72165

*This cheerful, informally-run establishment forms part of a
handsome Victorian terrace. Most bedrooms are spacious and
tastefully appointed; those with private facilities are particularly
comfortable. Table sharing is sometimes unavoidable at breakfast
time.*
10rm(6⇆♠4hc)(6fb) CTV in all bedrooms ® sB&B£18-£28
sB&B⇆♠£25-£35 dB&B£28-£30
dB&B⇆♠£36-£38 WB&Bfr£90
⁋⁋
£

GH Q Q **Glenisla Hotel** 12 Lygon Rd EH16 5QB
☎031-667 4877 FAX 031-667 4098

*Most attractive and well-maintained house in a residential area on
the south side. The cheerful proprietors have extended the catering
facilities and are constantly making improvements throughout.*
8rm(5♠3hc)(2fb) ® LDO 8.15pm
Lic ⁋⁋ CTV 6P 1🛞

See advertisement on page 147

GH Q Q Q **Glenora Hotel** 14 Rosebery Crescent EH12 5JY
☎031-337 1186

*An attractively decorated and furnished compact hotel with well-
equipped bedrooms.*
10♠ (2fb) CTV in all bedrooms ® ✠ ✳ sB&B♠£25-£30
dB&B♠£45-£55
Lic ⁋⁋ CTV
Credit Cards ⊡ ③ £

See advertisement on page 147

Edinburgh

GH Q Q Q **Greenside Hotel** 9 Royal Ter EH7 5AB
☎031-557 0022
Closed Dec
This elegant, Regency house is neat and well maintained, with large bedrooms. Service is attentive and friendly, and the hearty breakfasts can be thoroughly recommended.
12rm(2⇆4♠6hc)(3fb) ✱ sB&Bfr£20.70 sB&B⇆♠fr£25.30 dB&Bfr£40 dB&B⇆♠fr£45
🍴 CTV ⊁

GH Q **Grosvenor** 1 Grosvenor Gardens EH12 5JU
☎031-337 4143 FAX 031-346 8732
A friendly welcome awaits guests at this Victorian town house. Spacious but modest accommodation in a peaceful atmosphere.
8rm(7⇆♠1hc) CTV in all bedrooms ® ✖ (ex guide dogs) sB&B£18-£20 sB&B⇆♠£20-£25 dB&B⇆♠£34-£40 🍴
Credit Cards ① ② ③

GH Q **Halcyon Hotel** 8 Royal Ter EH7 5AB ☎031-556 1033 & 031-556 1032
Part of a fine Georgian terrace close to the city centre, the upper floors of this establishment command fine views of the Firth of Forth. The proprietors are gradually upgrading the simply-equipped and pleasant accommodation.
16hc (6fb) ✱ sB&B£21-£27 dB&B£36-£48
🍴 CTV ⊁ ♪(hard)
£

GH Q **Haven** 180 Ferry Rd EH6 4MS ☎031-554 6559
Situated close to the town centre, this small guesthouse offers cosy accommodation and friendly service.
10rm(1♠9hc)(4fb) CTV in all bedrooms ® ✱ sB&B£18-£23 dB&B£30-£40 dB&B♠£36-£46
Lic 🍴 CTV 6P

GH Q Q **Heriott Park** 256 Ferry Rd EH5 3AN ☎031-552 6628
Smart, recently converted house on main road, north part of the city.
6rm(2♠4hc)(4fb) CTV in all bedrooms ® sB&B£15-£18 dB&B£24-£30 dB&B♠£30-£36
Lic 🍴 CTV ⊁
£

GH Q Q Q **International** 37 Mayfield Gardens EH9 2BX
☎031-667 2511
Managed by the friendly resident proprietors, this guesthouse has comfortable and spacious bedrooms. Guests will be well looked after.
7⇆♠ (3fb) CTV in all bedrooms ® ✖ (ex guide dogs) ✱ sB&B⇆♠£15-£22 dB&B⇆♠£30-£40 WB&B£100-£140 3P

GH Q Q **Kariba** 10 Granville Ter EH10 4PQ ☎031-229 3773
Small and cosy guesthouse.
9rm(2♠7hc)(2fb) CTV in all bedrooms ® dB&B£28-£31.00 dB&B♠£33-£35
🍴 CTV 4P
£

GH Q Q *Kildonan Lodge Hotel* 27 Craigmillar Park EH16 5PE
☎031-667 2793
A private hotel lying south of the city centre. Modest bedroom accommodation and attractive restaurant and cocktail lounge. Extensive à la carte menu offers value for money.
13rm(6♠7hc)(5fb) CTV in all bedrooms ® ✖ (ex guide dogs) LDO 9pm
Lic 🍴 20P
Credit Cards ② ③

Book as early as possible for busy holiday periods.

GH [Q][Q] Kingsley 30 Craigmillar Park, Newington EH16 5PS ☎031-667 8439
Mrs Hogg offers clean, well-maintained standards at Kingsley Guest House. The bedrooms, some with shower cabinets, are bright and cheery, and for a relaxing end to the day, the lounge has nice comfy sofas and chairs.
7hc (3fb) CTV in all bedrooms [R] 🐕
dB&B£25-£30 WB&Bfr£85
♨ CTV 7P nc6yrs
[£]

GH [Q] *Kirtle House* 8 Minto St EH9 1RG ☎031-667 2813
Neat, semidetached house to the south of the city centre.
7rm(4🚿3hc)(4fb) CTV in all bedrooms [R] 🐕
♨ CTV 5P nc4yrs
Credit Cards [1] [2] [3] [5]

GH [Q][Q] Lindsay 108 Polwarth Ter EH11 1NN ☎031-337 1580
Comfortable neatly appointed house with a relaxed and friendly atmosphere.
8rm(1🚿7hc)(2fb) CTV in all bedrooms [R] * sB&B£16 sB&B🚿£20 dB&B£32 dB&B🚿£40
♨ 6P
Credit Cards [2]

SELECTED

GH [Q][Q][Q][Q] The Lodge Hotel 6 Hampton Ter, West Coates EH12 5JD ☎031-337 3682
On the A8 just west of the city centre, this comfortable hotel is in an ideal location. Linda and George Jarron have tastefully decorated and furnished their establishment throughout, comfort being the main consideration. The quaint bedrooms contain many thoughtful and useful extras. Linda prepares the meals offered on the set menu, which is very good value, and includes dishes such as steak au poivre.
10🚿 (2fb) CTV in all bedrooms [R] 🐕 * sB&B🚿£35-£45 dB&B🚿£50-£60 LDO 7.45pm
Lic ♨ 10P
Credit Cards [1] [3] [£]

GH [Q][Q] *Marchhall Hotel* 14-16 Marchhall Crescent EH16 5HL ☎031-667 2743
This comfortable guesthouse is situated in a pleasant residential area close to swimming pool and University buildings. The attractive lounge bar is open to non-residents.
13rm(2🚿11hc)(3fb) CTV in all bedrooms [R] LDO 3pm
Lic ♨ CTV 🚫P

GH [Q][Q] Mardale 11 Hartington Place EH10 4LF ☎031-229 2693
Located in a quiet residential area, close to the town centre, this small guesthouse offers cosy, attractive bedrooms and friendly service.
6hc (3fb) CTV in 5 bedrooms TV in 1 bedroom [R] *
sB&B£13-£15 dB&B£26-£30
♨ CTV
[£]

GH [Q][Q] Marvin 46 Pilrig St EH6 5AL ☎031-554 6605
Closed Xmas
A friendly, family-run establishment with a cosy dining room and lounge. Bedrooms are comfortable and well appointed. Guests are offered a wide choice of breakfast dishes.
7rm(4🛁🚿3hc)(2fb) CTV in all bedrooms [R] 🐕 (ex guide dogs) dB&B£24-£26 dB&B🛁🚿£28-£32
♨ 6P
[£]

Visit your local AA Centre.

GH [Q][Q] Meadows 17 Glengyle Ter EH3 9LN ☎031-229 9559
Closed 18-28 Dec
This attractive, comfortable property to the south of the city centre overlooks Bruntsfield Links. The standard of housekeeping is high and the bedrooms are spacious and well equipped.
7rm(5🚿2hc)(3fb) CTV in all bedrooms [R] * sB&B£18 dB&B£34 dB&B🚿£42
♨
Credit Cards [1] [3] [£]

GH [Q][Q][Q] The Newington 18 Newington Rd EH9 1QS ☎031-667 3356
A house of character and appeal, well appointed and thoughtfully equipped.
8rm(3🚿5hc)(1fb) CTV in all bedrooms [R] sB&B£20-£24 dB&B£29-£31 dB&B🚿£37-£40
Lic ♨ 3P

GH [Q][Q][Q] Parklands 20 Mayfield Gardens EH9 2BZ ☎031-667 7184
An exceptionally well-maintained establishment, Parklands forms part of a terraced row south of the city centre. The bedrooms are comfortable, reflecting high standards of housekeeping. The cosy lounge is combined with the breakfast room.
6rm(3🚿3hc)(1fb) [R] dB&B£26-£28 dB&B🚿£36-£38
♨ CTV
[£]

GH [Q][Q] *Park View Villa* 254 Ferry Rd EH5 3AN ☎031-552 3456
Guests at this friendly, comfortable guesthouse can enjoy good views of the Edinburgh skyline, and the owners will arrange sightseeing tours of the city. Ample car parking space is available.
7rm(3🚿4hc)(4fb) CTV in all bedrooms [R]
♨ CTV 🚫P

149

GH [Q][Q] Ravensdown 248 Ferry Rd EH5 3AN ☎031-552 5438
Comfortable, well-appointed house with views over the city and its imposing castle.
7hc (5fb) CTV in all bedrooms [R] 🚫 ✱ dB&B£26-£30
Lic 🛋 4P

GH [Q][Q][Q] Ravensnuek 11 Blacket Av EH9 1RR
☎031-667 5347
Very comfortable, attractive accommodation is complemented here by the courteous service from the friendly resident proprietors.
6hc (2fb) [R] 🚫 ✱ sB&B£17-£18 dB&B£30-£32
🛋 CTV 0P

GH [Q][Q][Q] Rockville House Hotel Seaview Ter, Joppa EH15 2HA (2m E off A1) ☎031-669 5418
This small family run hotel is situated 3 miles from the city centre with panoramic views over the Firth of Forth. The hotel has a popular restaurant and provides courteous and attentive service.
4🛁🚿 (1fb)🚭in 1 bedroom CTV in all bedrooms [R] ✱
sB&B🛁🚿fr£38 dB&B🛁🚿fr£48
Lic 🛋 CTV 0P
Credit Cards [1] [2] [3] [5]

GH [Q][Q] St Margaret's 18 Craigmillar Park EH16 5PS
☎031-667 2202
Apr-Dec
Well-appointed Victorian house on main road south of city centre.
8hc (3fb) CTV in all bedrooms [R] 🚫 ✱ dB&B£22-£30
🛋 CTV 6P

GH [Q][Q][Q] Salisbury Hotel 45 Salisbury Rd EH16 5AA
☎031-667 1264
Closed Xmas-New Year
A neatly decorated combination of two Georgian town houses close to a shopping suburb.
13rm(10🛁🚿3hc)(3fb) CTV in 11 bedrooms [R] sB&B£15-£18
sB&B🛁🚿£18-£22 dB&B£30-£32
dB&B🛁🚿£32-£42 WB&B£120
Lic 🛋 CTV 12P
[£]

GH [Q][Q] Sherwood 42 Minto St EH9 2BR ☎031-667 1200
Closed Xmas & New Year
A friendly, well-maintained terraced house south of the city centre.
6hc (3fb) CTV in all bedrooms [R] dB&B£20-£30
🛋 3P
[£]

GH [Q][Q] Southdown 20 Craigmillar Park EH16 5PS
☎031-667 2410
This substantial, Victorian terraced house offers well-appointed rooms with showers, and very comfortable public areas. The service is friendly and breakfasts enjoyable, with homemade preserves a speciality.
6hc (2fb) CTV in all bedrooms [R] 🚫 (ex guide dogs) ✱
sB&Bfr£20 dB&Bfr£32 WB&Bfr£105
🛋 CTV 7P

GH [Q][Q][Q] Stra'ven 3 Brunstane Rd North, Joppa EH15 2DL
☎031-669 5580
Close to the beach, this handsome stone-built house offers attractive, modern bedrooms, a comfortable first floor lounge and friendly service from the owners.
7🛁🚿 CTV in all bedrooms [R] 🚫 (ex guide dogs) ✱
dB&B🛁🚿£30-£36
🛋 CTV P̸

GH [Q][Q][Q] Teviotdale House 53 Grange Loan, Grange EH9 2ER ☎031-667 4376
South of the city centre, this carefully renovated Victorian house is comfortably appointed with quality fabrics used to good effect in the attractive bedrooms. Superb breakfasts are offered in the neat dining room. Smoking is not permitted in the house.
7rm(5🛁🚿2hc)(3fb)🚭in all bedrooms CTV in all bedrooms [R]
🚫 (ex guide dogs) ✱ sB&B£18-£44 sB&B🛁🚿£33-£44
dB&Bfr£44
dB&B🛁🚿£44-£52 WB&B£140-£160 WBDi£210-£245
🛋 CTV
Credit Cards [1] [2] [3]

GH [Q][Q][Q] Thrums Private Hotel 14 Minto St, Newington EH9 1RQ ☎031-667 5545
Closed Xmas & New Year
Good value lunch and dinner menus offer a choice of dishes at this attractive, spacious house. The bedrooms are provided with many extras not normally found in the smaller hotel.
7rm(6🚿1hc)Annexe 7rm(2🛁4🚿1hc)(4fb) CTV in all bedrooms [R] sB&B£22-£40 sB&B🛁🚿£25-£40 dB&B£39-£50
dB&B🛁🚿£44-£52 LDO 7.45pm
Lic 🛋 12P

↦**GH [Q] Tiree** 26 Craigmillar Park EH16 5PS ☎031-667 7477
Tidy, well-decorated house with good bedroom facilities.
7rm(4🚿3hc)(2fb) CTV in all bedrooms [R] sB&B£11-£13
dB&B£22-£26 dB&B🚿£28-£36
🛋 7P
[£]

ELIE Fife Map 12 NO40

GH [Q][Q] The Elms 14 Park Place KY9 1DH ☎(0333) 330404
FAX (0333) 330115
Apr-Oct
A warm welcome awaits guests at this attractive house which is set back from the road, with well-tended walled gardens to the rear. The accommodation is individually decorated and fitted and the inviting lounge is on the first floor.
7rm(1🛁3🚿3hc)(3fb) CTV in 3 bedrooms [R] sB&B£20-£35
sB&B🛁🚿£35 dB&B£30
dB&B🛁🚿£36-£42 WBDi£150-£190 LDO 6.30pm
Lic 🛋 CTV P̸
[£]

ELSDON Northumberland Map 12 NY99

FH [Q] Mrs T M Carruthers **Dunns** *(NY937969)* NE19 1AL
☎Rothbury(0669) 40219
Set amidst moorland where sheep and cattle are reared, this farmhouse, 2 miles north east of the village on the Rotherbury road, has an attractive outlook.
3hc (1fb) [R] 🚫 (ex guide dogs)
CTV 6P nc4yrs 🎣 1000 acres mixed sheep working

ELTERWATER Cumbria Map 07 NY30

INN [Q][Q][Q] Britannia LA22 9HP ☎Langdale(09667) 210 & 382
FAX (09667) 311
Closed 25 & 26 Dec
9rm(6🚿3hc) CTV in all bedrooms [R] dB&B£37-£46
dB&B🚿£43-£52 Bar Lunch £2-£8alc Dinner £13.75-£15.75alc
LDO 7.30pm
10P ⌂
Credit Cards [1] [3]

ELY Cambridgeshire Map 05 TL58

GH [Q][Q] Castle Lodge Hotel 50 New Barns Rd CB7 4PW
☎(0353) 662276
Situated in a residential area, yet within walking distance of the cathedral and town centre, this family-owned and run hotel provides a range of accommodation, all well maintained and in good order. There is also a well-stocked bar.
10rm(1🛁2🚿7hc)(1fb) CTV in all bedrooms [R]
🚫 (ex guide dogs) sB&B£17.50-£22.50 sB&B🛁🚿£30-£32.50
dB&B£35-£40

dB&B⇨ᐱ£45-£48 WB&B£110-£142 WBDi£166-£198 LDO 7.30pm
Lic 鬥 8P
Credit Cards ①③

EMSWORTH Hampshire Map **04** SU70

GH ⑨⑨⑨ **The Chestnuts** 55 Horndean Rd PO10 7PU
☎(0243) 372233
This late Victorian house stands in its own grounds in a quiet residential area north west of the town. The bedrooms are cosy and the lounge is furnished with antiques.
4hc (2fb) dB&B£25-£27.50
鬥 CTV 6P ⇨

GH ⑨⑨ **Jingles Hotel** 77 Horndean Rd PO10 7PU
☎(0243) 373755
Just north of the town centre, this comfortable small hotel is privately owned and has compact adequately appointed bedrooms. The pleasant staff create a friendly, informal atmosphere.
13rm(4ᐱ9hc)(1fb) CTV in all bedrooms ⑧ ✱ sB&Bfr£21 sB&Bᐱfr£28 dB&Bfr£38 dB&Bᐱfr£44 (wkly only Oct-Mar) LDO 7pm
Lic 鬥 CTV 14P
Credit Cards ①③£

GH ⑨⑨ **Merry Hall Hotel** 73 Horndean Rd PO10 7PU
☎(0243) 372424
Closed 25 Dec-3 Jan
An attractive well-appointed hotel with large garden. Ideally situated for yachting centres.
10rm(7⇨3ᐱ)(2fb) CTV in all bedrooms ⑧ ✕ ✱
sB&B⇨ᐱ£32 dB&B⇨ᐱ£52 LDO 7.30pm
Lic 鬥 CTV 12P ♣ putting green
Credit Cards ①③£

GH [Q][Q] **Queensgate Hotel** 80 Havant Rd PO10 7LH
☎(0243) 371960 & 377766
Most of the bedrooms of this comfortable guesthouse are equipped with showers. Mrs Nasir cooks delicious Indian dishes using recipes from the royal kitchens of northern India's great Mogul emperors.
10hc (1fb) CTV in 9 bedrooms Ⓡ LDO 6pm
Lic 🍴 CTV 12P
Credit Cards [1] [2] [3] [5] (£)
See advertisement under HAVANT on page 177

EPSOM Surrey Map **04** TQ26

GH [Q][Q][Q] ***Epsom Downs Hotel*** 9 Longdown Rd KT17 3PT
☎(0372) 740643
This charming hotel is located in a peaceful residential area, with bedroom accommodation which is modern and well equipped. In addition to the pleasant bar, there is a comfortable lounge and an attractive dining room.
17rm(14🛁3hc) CTV in all bedrooms Ⓡ LDO 8.30pm
Lic 🍴 CTV 25P 🏠
Credit Cards [1] [2] [3] [5]

ERLESTOKE Wiltshire Map **03** ST95

FH [Q][Q][Q] Mrs P Hampton **Longwater Park** *(ST966541)* Lower Rd SN10 5UE ☎Devizes(0380) 830095
Closed Xmas & New Year
Close to Salisbury Plain, this modern, red-brick farmhouse overlooks water. The furnishings and displays of china add charm to the comfortable accommodation. The well-equipped bedrooms have private facilities.
3🛁🚿 (1fb) CTV in 1 bedroom TV in 2 bedrooms Ⓡ ✱ dB&B🛁🚿£32-£40 WB&B£112-£140 WBDi£182-£210 LDO 5pm
🍴 CTV 6P 🎣 166 acres beef waterfowl
(£)

ETTINGTON Warwickshire Map **04** SP24

FH [Q][Q] Mrs B J Wakeham **Whitfield** *(SP265506)* Warwick Rd CV37 7PN ☎Stratford on Avon(0789) 740260
Closed Dec
Pleasant house set in active farm with a wide variety of animals for interest.
3hc (2fb) Ⓡ 🐕 (ex guide dogs) ✱ sB&B£12.50-£13.50 dB&B£22-£33
🍴 CTV 3P 220 acres mixed
(£)

EVERSHOT Dorset Map **03** ST50

GH [Q][Q][Q] **Rectory House** Fore St DT2 0JW ☎(093583) 273
Closed Xmas
Standing in the centre of the peaceful village, this charming stone house offers well-equipped accommodation, some in a converted stable, together with a cosy lounge. Guests will enjoy English-style cooking and a friendly atmosphere.
6🛁🚿 CTV in all bedrooms Ⓡ 🐕 (ex guide dogs) ✱ sB&B🛁🚿£30-£40
dB&B🛁🚿£50-£55 WBDi£195-£200 LDO 6.30pm
Lic 🍴 TV 6P nc12yrs
(£)
See advertisement under DORCHESTER on page 137

EVESHAM Hereford & Worcester Map **04** SP04

GH [Q][Q] **Lyncroft** 80 Greenhill WR11 4NH ☎(0386) 442252
Feb-Nov
The accommodation at Lyncroft is comfortable and well equipped with an attractive dining room and comfortable lounge. Mrs. McLean is friendly and helpful and is sure to make guests welcome.
5rm(1🛁4🚿) CTV in all bedrooms Ⓡ 🐕 ✱ sB&B🛁🚿£20-£25 dB&B🛁🚿£32-£40
10P nc5yrs

EXBOURNE Devon Map **02** SS60

FH [Q][Q][Q] Mrs S J Allain **Stapleford** *(SS580039)* EX20 3RA
☎(083785) 277
Closed Dec & New Year
This 17th-century longhouse, in a peaceful location with views of north Devon has been modernised to offer a high standard of comfort. The menus offer home produced food and a warm, friendly welcome is assured.
2rm(1hc) Ⓡ 🐕 ✱ sB&B£15
dB&B£25 WB&B£80 WBDi£120-£124 LDO 5pm
CTV 4P 2🚗 nc12yrs 🎣 games room croquet lawn 80 acres sheep
(£)

EXETER Devon Map **03** SX99

See **Town Plan Section**

GH [Q] **Braeside** 21 New North Rd EX4 4HF ☎(0392) 56875
Closed 25-26 Dec
7rm(3🚿4hc)(1fb) CTV in all bedrooms Ⓡ ✱ sB&Bfr£14 dB&Bfr£28 LDO 4pm
🍴 P̸

GH [Q][Q] **Hotel Gledhills** 32 Alphington Rd EX2 8HN
☎(0392) 430469
Closed 2 wks Xmas
Friendly, traditional, small hotel standing in own grounds, close to city and St Thomas' Station.
12rm(9🚿3hc)(3fb) CTV in all bedrooms Ⓡ 🐕
sB&B£16.50-£17.50 sB&B🚿£19.50-£23 dB&B£38-£40 dB&B🚿£38-£40 WB&B£115.50-£161 WBDi£168-£213.50 LDO 6pm
Lic 🍴 CTV 11P 2🚗
Credit Cards [1] [2] [3]

GH [Q][Q] **Park View Hotel** 8 Howell Rd EX4 4LG
☎(0392) 71772 & 53047
Closed Xmas
This bed and breakfast establishment is within walking distance of the station and city centre. The bedrooms have good facilities including colour TV and direct dial telephones, and some have en suite shower rooms.
10rm(2🛁2🚿6hc)Annexe 6rm(4🚿2hc)(1fb)🚭in 1 bedroom CTV in all bedrooms Ⓡ sB&Bfr£16 sB&B🛁🚿fr£28 dB&Bfr£32 dB&B🛁🚿fr£40
🍴 CTV 6P
Credit Cards [1] [3] (£)

GH [Q][Q] **Sunnymede** 24 New North Rd EX4 4HF
☎(0392) 73844
Closed 24 Dec-1 Jan
Georgian property, recently refurbished, close to shopping area. Comfortable, modern bedrooms and welcoming atmosphere.
9rm(5🚿4hc)(1fb) CTV in all bedrooms 🐕 sB&B£18 sB&B🚿£20 dB&B£28 dB&B🚿£30 LDO 9pm
🍴 CTV P̸

GH [Q] **Telstar Hotel** 77 St Davids Hill EX4 4DW
☎(0392) 72466
Closed 2 wks Xmas
Friendly, family-run guesthouse with cosy bedrooms. Close to colleges and central station.
9hc (1fb)
🍴 CTV 5P
(£)

GH |Q||Q| **Trees Mini Hotel** 2 Queen's Crescent, York Rd
EX4 6AY ☎(0392) 59531
*Comfortable accommodation and a relaxed atmosphere are found
at this semi detached house which stands opposite the park and
close to the city centre.*
10rm(1⇔9hc)(1fb) CTV in all bedrooms ® ✖ ✱ sB&B£14-£16
dB&B£24-£26 dB&B⇔£32-£34 LDO 10am
♨ CTV 1🏠 nc3yrs
Credit Cards |1| |3|

GH |Q| **Trenance House Hotel** 1 Queen's Crescent, York Rd
EX4 6AY ☎(0392) 73277
Closed Xmas
*This family guesthouse has compact bedrooms which are simply
furnished, and comfortable public rooms. It is conveniently sited
for the city.*
15rm(1⇔1🏳13hc)(2fb) CTV in all bedrooms ® LDO noon
♨ CTV 7P
Credit Cards |1| |3|

EXMOUTH Devon Map **03** SY08

GH |Q||Q| **Blenheim** 39 Morton Rd EX8 1BA ☎(0395) 264230
Closed 24-26 Dec
6hc (2fb) CTV in all bedrooms ® ✖ (ex guide dogs) ✱
sB&B£11-£12
dB&B£22-£24 WB&B£75-£78 WBDi£95-£105 LDO 4.30pm
Lic ♨ CTV 1P
Credit Cards |1| |3| £

GH |Q||Q||Q| **Carlton Lodge Hotel** Carlton Hill EX8 2AJ
☎(0395) 263314
*Pleasant, fully licensed hotel just off the seafront. Bedrooms are
comfortable and well maintained and staff are friendly.* ▶

Lyme Bay House Hotel

Warm comfortable house in quiet situation
on level sea front at the Dorset end of
Teignmouth's Promenade. Sea Sports —
Busy Shipping Lane. All the fascination of
the sea's everchanging colours and mood
can be absorbed in comfort through our
windows.

*Directions — Go to the seafront
and turn left*

**Den Promenade, Teignmouth
South Devon. Telephone: 0626 772953**

Lift — No steps — En suite facilities
Midweek bookings — Licensed
Adjacent rail/coach stations

Park View Hotel
Exeter
8 Howell Rd, Exeter
tel **(0392) 71772 & 53047**

This charming small hotel is noted for its
peace and quiet. Overlooking park. Near
city centre and university. Lounge. All
bedrooms with Colour T.V., tea & coffee
making facilities and telephone, some with
private bathrooms and toilets. Full central
heating. Exceptionally high standard of
comfort. Pets welcome. Car Park.

Lyncroft

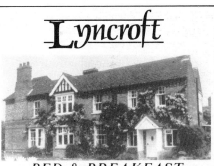

BED & BREAKFAST

All bedrooms have en-suite facilities, colour
T.V. and tea and coffee making. Private
parking, full central heating, guests own
quiet lounge.

LYNCROFT is a large Edwardian family
house standing in grounds of one acre and is
within walking distance of Evesham.

Mrs. CHRISTINE McLEAN,
"Lyncroft", 80 Greenhill, Evesham,
Worcestershire WR11 4NH.
Telephone: (0386) 442252

6rm(2⇔2♠)(3fb) CTV in all bedrooms ® ✳ sB&B£21
sB&B⇔♠£25 dB&B£32
dB&B⇔♠£38 WB&B£107.50-£135 WBDi£145-£175 LDO
9pm
Lic ⑭ 14P
Credit Cards ⬛1 ⬛3 ⓔ

FAIRBOURNE Gwynedd Map 06 SH61

⊢⊶GH ⓠ **Sea View** Friog LL38 2NX ☎(0341) 250388
Closed 24-26 Dec
*Located in the tiny hamlet of Friog, on the A439, 9 miles south
west of Dolgellau, this stone-built house has pleasant gardens. The
accommodation is simple and comfortable and within a few
minutes' walk of the picturesque mountains and sandy beaches.*
6hc (2fb)✄in 1 bedroom CTV in 5 bedrooms TV in 1 bedroom
® ✈ sB&B£13-£14.50
dB&B£26-£29 WB&B£77-£87 WBDi£120-£130 LDO 8pm
Lic ⑭ CTV
ⓔ

FAKENHAM Norfolk

See **Barney**

FALFIELD Avon Map 03 ST69

GH ⓠⓠ **Green Farm** GL12 8DL ☎(0454) 260319
*14th-century, former farmhouse, carefully modernised, with tennis
court and swimming pool in grounds. Extensive dinner menu.*
8rm(1⇔7hc) ® ✳ sB&Bfr£16 sB&B⇔fr£27 dB&Bfr£25
dB&B⇔fr£36 LDO 8.30pm
⑭ CTV 10P ⊇ ♪(hard)

FALMOUTH Cornwall & Isles of Scilly Map 02 SW83

See **Town Plan Section**
GH ⓠⓠⓠ **Cotswold House Private Hotel** 49 Melvill Rd
TR11 4DF ☎(0326) 312077
*Maintained to very high standards, this hotel is both modern and
relaxing. The lounge is comfortable and spacious, and there is also
a 'Saints and Sinners' bar. The food is home cooked and there is a
choice of bright bedrooms.*
10rm(4⇔4♠2hc)(2fb) CTV in all bedrooms ® ✈ sB&Bfr£16
dB&Bfr£30
dB&B⇔♠fr£32 WB&B£100-£112 WBDi£128-£140
Lic 10P nc3yrs
ⓔ

GH ⓠⓠⓠ **Gyllyngvase House Hotel** Gyllyngvase Rd
TR11 4DJ ☎(0326) 312956
Mar-Oct
*Benefiting from a rear garden and good car parking, this small
private hotel offers a good standard of housekeeping and very
friendly service. Together with good home cooking, this makes
Gyllyngvase House an ideal base from which to tour Cornwall.
There is an excellent lounge and an attractive open plan dining
room, complemented by well-equipped bedrooms.*
15rm(12⇔♠3hc)(2fb) CTV in all bedrooms ✳ sB&B£15.50
sB&B⇔♠£17.50-£29
dB&B⇔♠£35 WBDi£142-£159 LDO 7pm
Lic ⑭ CTV 15P
ⓔ

GH ⓠ **Harbour Hotel** 1 Harbour Ter TR11 2AN
☎(0326) 311344
*This guesthouse occupies an elevated position with a picturesque
view overlooking the harbour. It has modestly furnished and
equipped bedrooms, a cosy lounge with a bar, and a separate front
dining room.*
6rm(2♠4hc)(2fb) ® ✳ sB&B£11-£12 dB&B£22-£24
dB&B♠£26-£28 WB&B£77-£81.40 WBDi£93.50-£118.80 LDO
6pm
Lic ⑭ CTV ⚥
ⓔ

GH ⓠⓠⓠ **Penmere** "Rosehill", Mylor Bridge TR11 5LZ
☎(0326) 74470
Mar-Oct
*Standing in attractive gardens, this traditional Cornish house has
been tastefully renovated by Ann and Ron Thomas. Particularly
well equipped, some of the pine-furnished bedrooms have splendid
views. A Victorian fireplace graces the lounge.*
6rm(1⇔1♠4hc)(2fb) CTV in all bedrooms ®
✈ (ex guide dogs) sB&B£16.50-£19.50
sB&B⇔♠£19.25-£22.25 dB&B£33 dB&B⇔♠£38.50
⑭ 7P
ⓔ

GH ⓠⓠⓠ **Penty Bryn Hotel** 10 Melvill Rd TR11 4AS
☎(0326) 314988
Etr-Oct
*The modern bedrooms at this small licensed hotel are particularly
well equipped, and most have sea views. There is a small, old
fashioned lounge and bar/breakfast room. Mrs Jane Wearne
provides friendly, personal service.*
7rm(5♠2hc)(3fb) CTV in all bedrooms ® ✳ sB&B£14-£14.50
dB&B♠£28-£29
Lic ⑭ CTV 2P 1🚗
Credit Cards ⬛1 ⬛3

GH ⓠⓠⓠ **Rathgowry Hotel** Gyllyngvase Hill TR11 4DN
☎(0326) 313482
Mar-Oct
*This spacious Edwardian house overlooking the beach has
comfortable public rooms and well-equipped bedrooms.*
10rm(2⇔8♠)(4fb) CTV in all bedrooms ® sB&B⇔♠fr£14
dB&B⇔♠fr£28 WB&B£85-£118 WBDi£115-£148 LDO 5pm
Lic ⑭ 10P
ⓔ

⊢⊶GH ⓠⓠⓠ **Westcott Hotel** Gyllyngvase Hill TR11 4DN
☎(0326) 311309
3 Jan-Oct rs Jan-Mar
*Friendly, attentive service is provided by conscientious owners of
this cosy hotel. Standing in a quiet position, with view of the bay, it
offers bright bedrooms, most with en suite facilities.*
11rm(4⇔4♠3hc)(2fb) CTV in all bedrooms ® ✈
sB&B£13-£17 dB&B£25-£29
dB&B⇔♠£26-£34 WB&B£84-£119 WBDi£114-£149 LDO
6.30pm
⑭ CTV 9P nc2yrs

FALSTONE Northumberland Map 12 NY78

INN ⓠⓠⓠ **Pheasant** Stannersburn NE48 1DD
☎Bellingham(0434) 240382
*A cosy, stone-built inn situated at the eastern tip of Keilely Water.
The accommodation is attractive and comfortable. Service is
friendly and especially recommended are the delicious home-
cooked evening meals.*
Annexe 11rm(5♠6hc) CTV in 5 bedrooms ® sB&B£17-£22
dB&B£34-£38
dB&B♠£40-£44 WB&B£107-£138.60 WBDi£176.40-£207.90
Lunch £7.50-£8.50&alc Dinner £10.50-£14alc LDO 9pm
⑭ 40P pool room darts
ⓔ

FAREHAM Hampshire Map 04 SU50

GH ⓠ *Catisfield Hotel* Catsfield Ln, Catisfield PO15 5NN (2m
W A27) ☎Titchfield(0329) 41851
*Occupying the first and second floors above Catsfield Wine Stores
in a quiet residential area, with green belt to the rear, this hotel
offers well-equipped and simply furnished bedrooms.*
20rm(16⇔2♠2hc)(7fb) CTV in all bedrooms ® LDO 6pm
Lic ⑭ CTV 100P

FARINGDON Oxfordshire Map **04** SU29

GH Q Q Q **Faringdon Hotel** Market Place SN7 7HL
☎(0367) 20536
Standing in this market town's centre, this hotel provides
comfortable, well-equipped en suite rooms, five of which are in
annexe cottages. À la carte meals and bar snacks are served in the
relaxing restaurant.
17rm(11⇌6↑)Annexe 5rm(1⇌4↑)(3fb) CTV in all bedrooms
® ✱ sB&B⇌↑fr£40 dB&B⇌↑fr£50 LDO 9pm
Lic ♛ 5P
Credit Cards [1] [2] [3] [5]

FARMBOROUGH Avon Map **03** ST66

GH Q Q Q **Streets Hotel** The Street BA3 1AR
☎Timsbury(0761) 71452 FAX (0761) 52695
Closed 23 Dec-1 Jan
An attractive 17th-century house set in a picturesque village, this
small private hotel offers some of its accommodation in a converted
coaching house. Rooms are well furnished and decorated and have
some good modern facilities. An acre of garden is the perfect
setting for the swimming pool.
3⇌↑ Annexe 5⇌↑ CTV in all bedrooms ® ✖ ✱
sB&B⇌↑£39-£63 dB&B⇌↑£46-£53 LDO 8.50pm
Lic ♛ CTV 8P nc6yrs ⇌(heated) solarium

FARNHAM Surrey Map **04** SU84

INN Q **The Eldon Hotel** 43 Frensham Rd, Lower Bourne
GU10 3PZ ☎Frensham(025125) 2745
Popular, privately-managed hotel with modern, well-equipped
bedrooms, good leisure facilities plus restaurant.
14rm(10⇌2↑2hc)(2fb) CTV in all bedrooms ® ✱ sB&Bfr£30
sB&B⇌↑fr£42 dB&Bfr£58 dB&B⇌↑fr£58 LDO 9.30pm
♛ CTV 65P squash solarium pool table
Credit Cards [1] [2] [3]

FAR SAWREY Cumbria Map **07** SD39

GH Q Q Q **West Vale Country** LA22 0LQ
☎Windermere(09662) 2817

Enjoying a fine outlook from its own gardens on the edge of the village, this detached house provides accommodation in well-proportioned bedrooms, a comfortable lounge with board games and a spacious dining room.

8rm(7 1hc)(3fb) ® ✖ (ex guide dogs) sB&B£15 sB&B£17 dB&B£30
dB&B£34 WB&B£105-£119 WBDi£147-£161 LDO noon
Lic ₩ CTV 8P nc7yrs
£

FAZELEY Staffordshire Map **04** SK20

GH Q **Buxton Hotel** 65 Coleshill St B78 3RG
☎Tamworth(0827) 285805 & 284842
Closed 25-26 Dec rs 1 Jan

Conveniently situated for a visit to Drayton Manor Park, this large house has a snooker table and an oak-panelled bar.

15rm(3 9 3hc)(4fb) CTV in all bedrooms ® ✱ sB&B£24
sB&B£25-£30 dB&B£30-£34
dB&B£35-£40 LDO 8.45pm
Lic ₩ CTV 16P
Credit Cards 1 3 £

FELINDRE (nr Swansea) West Glamorgan Map **02** SN60

FH Q Q Q Mr F Jones **Coynant** *(SN648070)* FELINDRE
SA5 7PU (4m N of Felindre off unclass rd linking M4 j unc 46 and Ammanford) ☎Ammanford(0269) 595640 & 592064
Secluded house in elevated position at head of valley.

5rm(3 2hc)(2fb) CTV in all bedrooms ® ✖ (ex guide dogs)
sB&B£15.50-£16 sB&B£15.50-£16 dB&B£31-£32
dB&B£31-£32 WB&Bfr£112 WBDi£126-£133 (wkly only Jul-Aug) LDO 7pm
Lic ₩ 10P ✈ ∪ games room 150 acres mixed
£

FENITON Devon Map **03** ST10

SELECTED

GH Q Q Q Q **Colestocks House** Colestocks EX14 0JR (1m N unclass rd) ☎Honiton(0404) 850633
Closed 21 Nov-22 Dec

Standing in 2 acres of delightful gardens this 16th-century thatched house is owned by Jacqueline and Henri Yot who bring a French influence to quality meals served here. The charm and character of Colestocks is enhanced by a four-poster and a canopied bed in 2 of the rooms, all of which have private bathrooms.

9 (1fb) CTV in all bedrooms ® ✖ (ex guide dogs)
sB&B£22.95-£27.50
dB&B£39.90-£55 WBDi£189-£218 LDO 8pm
Lic ₩ 9P nc10yrs putting green
Credit Cards 1 3

FILEY North Yorkshire Map **08** TA18

GH Q Q **Abbots Leigh** 7 Rutland St YO14 9JA
☎Scarborough(0723) 513334
Delightful and friendly, this small guesthouse is set in a quiet side road close to the sea. Good facilities are provided and the bedrooms are furnished and equipped to a high standard.

6 (3fb)✂in all bedrooms CTV in all bedrooms ®
✖ (ex guide dogs) sB&B fr£16
dB&Bfr£28 WB&B£88-£150 WBDi£126-£185 LDO 2pm
Lic ₩ 4P
£

GH Q Q **Downcliffe Hotel** The Beach YO14 9LA
☎Scarborough(0723) 513310
Apr-Oct
This detached hotel on the seafront offers a special welcome to families.

17rm(1 6 10hc)(9fb) CTV in all bedrooms ® ✱
sB&B£15.50-£17.50 sB&B fr£17.50 dB&Bfr£31
dB&Bfr£35 WB&B£108.50-£122.50
WBDi£139.65-£153.65 LDO 6pm
Lic ₩ CTV 8P 2🐾
Credit Cards 1 3 £

GH Q Q **Seafield Hotel** 9/11 Rutland St YO14 9JA
☎Scarborough(0723) 513715
Comfortable, bright, pretty bedrooms and with an attractive dining room.

13rm(3 6 4hc)(7fb) CTV in all bedrooms ® ✖
sB&B£15-£16.50 sB&B fr£17-£18.50 dB&B£30-£33
dB&B£34-£37 (incl dinner) WB&B£100-£110
WBDi£128-£138 LDO 4pm
Lic ₩ CTV 8P
£

FIR TREE Co Durham Map **12** NZ13

GH Q Q Q **Greenhead Country House Hotel** DL15 8BL
☎Bishop Auckland(0388) 763143
A tasteful and interesting conversion of traditional farmhouses, this is now a small, beautifully appointed establishment. The stone-arched lounge has a woodburning stove in the centre and the bedrooms are attractively modern.

8 (1fb) CTV in 7 bedrooms ® ✖ (ex guide dogs)
sB&B£25-£28 dB&B£35-£38 WB&B£133 LDO 5pm
Lic ₩ CTV 18P 2🐾 (£2 per night) nc13yrs
Credit Cards 1 3 £

FLAX BOURTON Avon Map **03** ST56

INN Q Q Q **Jubilee** Main Rd BS19 3QX ☎(027583) 2741
Closed 25 Dec evening
Located on the A370, at the edge of the village, this inn offers 3 comfortable bedrooms and a spacious, relaxing residents' lounge. The public areas have character, and the food offered is cooked with both skill and imagination.

3hc ✱ sB&B£24-£26 LDO 10pm
CTV 51P nc14yrs

FOLKESTONE Kent Map **05** TR23

See **Town Plan Section**

GH Q Q Q **Belmonte Private Hotel** 30 Castle Hill Av
CT20 2RE ☎(0303) 54470 Telex no 94070815
Pleasant accommodation and a warm welcome are to be found at this large, attractive Victorian house. The attractive dining room is complemented by a conservatory and a cosy, relaxing lounge. Plants and dried flowers abound here.

10rm(4 6hc)(2fb) CTV in all bedrooms ® ✱ sB&Bfr£20
sB&Bfr£24 dB&Bfr£40
dB&Bfr£44 WB&B£120-£132 WBDi£192-£216 LDO 6pm
Lic ₩ 4P
Credit Cards 1 2 3 5 £

FONTMELL MAGNA Dorset Map **03** ST81

GH Q Q **Estyard House Hotel** SP7 0PB ☎(0747) 811460
Closed Nov-Dec
This attractive house has large gardens which supply many of the fruits and vegetables which are served for dinner. Mr and Mrs Jones cater for an older clientele, and offer a comfortable lounge with books and games. The 6 comfortable bedrooms share 1 bathroom and 2 toilets. This is a non-smoking house.

6hc ✂in all bedrooms ✖ ✱ sB&B£15-£20
dB&B£30-£40 WB&B£95-£115 WBDi£140-£160 LDO 7pm
₩ 8P nc10yrs

FORDOUN Grampian *Kincardineshire* Map **15** NO77

FH QQQ Mrs M Anderson **Ringwood** *(NO743774)* AB3 1JS
(1.5m off A94 on B966) ☎Auchenblae(05612) 313
Apr-Oct
*Small, modernised villa in open setting amidst farmland, with its
own neat garden and outhouse. Very high standard of décor and
furnishings.*
4hc (1fb) ® ✠ sB&B£15 dB&B£25-£26 WB&B£84-£98
⊞ CTV 4P 16 acres arable
£

FORGANDENNY Tayside *Perthshire* Map **11** NO01

┠┈┤**FH** QQQ Mrs M Fotheringham **Craighall** *(NO081176)*
PH2 9DF (0.5m W off B935 Bridge of Earn-Forteviot Rd)
☎Bridge of Earn(0738) 812415
*A friendly atmosphere prevails at Mrs Fotheringham's tastefully
furnished bungalow. It has an attractive lounge/dining room, and
the bedrooms, 2 of which have en suite facilities, are comfortably
appointed.*
3rm(2♠1hc)(1fb)✍in all bedrooms ® ✠ sB&B£12-£14
dB&Bfr£23 dB&B♠fr£26 WB&Bfr£80.50
⊞ CTV 4P ✈ 1000 acres beef mixed sheep
£

FORRES Grampian *Morayshire* Map **14** NJ05

SELECTED

GH QQQQ **Parkmount House Hotel** St Leonards Rd
IV36 0DW ☎(0309) 73312
Closed Xmas & New Year
*A charming mid 19th-century town house, with well-kept
gardens, has been tastefully converted to offer comfortable,
modern accommodation. The bedrooms are well equipped, and
there is a cosy sitting room with a welcoming log fire. A choice
of dishes is offered at dinner, the cooking being simple and
honest. Mr and Mrs Steer create a warm, friendly atmosphere
and ensure that their guests have an enjoyable stay.*
6⇨♠ (1fb) CTV in all bedrooms ® sB&B⇨♠£29-£34
dB&B⇨♠£40-£46 WB&B£190-£220 WBDi£285-£315
LDO 5pm
Lic ⊞ 25P ⚲ ▶ 18 special rate car hire is available to
guests
Credit Cards ⒈⒊ £

FORT WILLIAM Highland *Inverness-Shire* Map **14** NN17

GH QQ **Benview** Belford Rd PH33 6ER ☎(0397) 2966
Mar-Nov
*This friendly, family-run guesthouse stands on the main road north
of the town centre overlooking Ben Nevis. It offers good value
holiday accommodation.*
13rm(3⇨3♠7hc) CTV in 6 bedrooms ® ✠ (ex guide dogs) ✱
sB&B£12.65-£15 dB&B£27.60-£30
dB&B⇨♠£32.20-£34.50 WB&B£88.55-£105 WBDi£119-£147
LDO 5pm
⊞ CTV 20P
£

GH QQ **Glenlochy** Nevis Bridge PH33 6PF ☎(0397) 2909
*An attractive house standing in its own grounds opposite the
Distillery. The accommodation is clean and modern and an ideal
base for touring and fishing.*
10rm(8♠2hc)(2fb)✍in 2 bedrooms ® ✠ (ex guide dogs) ✱
sB&B£14.50-£17.50 sB&B♠£17.50-£18.50 dB&B£25-£30
dB&B♠£27-£35
⊞ CTV 12P
£

GH [Q][Q] Guisachan Alma Rd PH33 6HA ☎(0397) 3797
Closed 23 Dec-3 Jan
Comfortable, well-maintained house in an elevated, residential area.
15rm(1🛁6🚿8hc)(3fb) [R] 🚫🐕 * sB&B£16-£24
dB&B£32-£44 LDO 5.30pm
Lic ♨ CTV 15P

GH [Q][Q][Q] Lochview Heathercroft, Argyll Rd PH33 6RE
☎(0397) 3149
Etr-Oct
Well-appointed, modern house offering comfortable accommodation amid peaceful surroundings. Elevated position with panoramic views across Loch Linnhe.
8🛁🚿 CTV in all bedrooms [R] dB&B🛁🚿£32-£35
♨ 8P

GH [Q][Q] *Orchy Villa* Alma Rd PH33 6HA ☎(0397) 2445
This friendly, family-run guesthouse, set in an elevated position above the town, offers accommodation in bedrooms which, though compact, are cheerfully decorated and comfortable.
6hc (4fb)🚭in all bedrooms [R] 🚫🐕
♨ CTV 6P

↦**GH [Q] Rhu Mhor** Alma Rd PH33 6BP ☎(0397) 2213
Etr-Sep
A traditional-style guesthouse in a quiet residential area.
7hc (2fb) sB&B£11-£11.50 dB&B£22-£23 LDO 5pm
♨ CTV 7P
[£]

FOVANT Wiltshire Map **04** SU02

INN [Q][Q][Q] *Cross Keys* SP3 5JH ☎(072270) 284
Built in 1845, this old coaching inn nestles in the village of Fovant and has tastefully appointed bedrooms and comfortable lounges. Homemade food is served in a warm, welcoming atmosphere.
4hc (1fb) 🚫🐕 (ex guide dogs) LDO 9.30pm
♨ CTV 30P
Credit Cards [1] [3]

FOWEY Cornwall & Isles of Scilly Map **02** SX15

GH [Q][Q][Q] *Ashley House Hotel* 14 Esplanade PL23 1BJ
☎(072683) 2310
Etr-Oct
Extensively improved, Ashley House has spacious bedrooms, three en suite, and two with exclusive use of a bath or shower. Two have views of the river. Mrs Anne Holden cooks for her guests, who will find the hotel convenient for local amenities.
8rm(1🚿7hc)(4fb) [R] LDO 6pm
Lic ♨ CTV 🚫P

SELECTED

GH [Q][Q][Q][Q] Carnethic House Lambs Barn PL23 1HQ
☎(0726) 3336
Closed Dec-Jan
The beautiful gardens of this welcoming house contain a heated swimming pool. The bedrooms are comfortable and well equipped. Guests can relax in the lounge bar and enjoy home cooked dishes, including fresh fish, from the table d'hôte menu.
8rm(5🚿)(2fb)🚭in 1 bedroom CTV in all bedrooms [R]
🚫🐕 (ex guide dogs) sB&B£24-£30 sB&B🚿£27-£35
dB&B£36-£40
dB&B🚿£40-£48 WB&B£115-£160 WBDi£175-£220 LDO 8pm
Lic ♨ 20P ⚘ 🏊(heated) 🎾(grass)badminton, putting, pool table & short tennis
Credit Cards [1] [2] [3] [5] [£]

↦**GH [Q][Q][Q] Wheelhouse** 60 Esplanade PL23 1JA
☎(0726) 832452
Mar-Oct rs Nov-Feb
Set in an elevated position with stunning views of the Favey estuary. The Wheelhouse has well-equipped old-style bedrooms some with splendid river views. The lounge is comfortable and there is a compact dining room.
6hc (1fb) CTV in 4 bedrooms [R] 🚫🐕 sB&B£12-£15
dB&B£24-£30 WB&B£84-£105 WBDi£120-£145 LDO noon
Lic ♨ CTV 🚫P
[£]

FOWNHOPE Hereford & Worcester Map **03** SO53

GH [Q][Q][Q] Bowens Country House HR1 4PS ☎(043277) 430
rs Xmas & New Year
Beautifully preserved, this 17th-century house is set in attractive gardens in this pleaesant village. The comfortable, well-equipped accommodation includes 2 rooms specifically designed and equipped for disabled and wheelchair-bound guests.
8rm(3🛁🚿1hc)Annexe 4🛁🚿 (2fb) CTV in all bedrooms [R]
🚫🐕 (ex guide dogs) dB&Bfr£34
dB&B🛁🚿fr£36.50 WB&Bfr£101.75 WBDifr£168.25 LDO 8pm
Lic ♨ 15P nc10yrs 🎾(grass)putting
Credit Cards [1] [3] [£]

FRESHWATER

See **WIGHT, ISLE OF**

[Q] is for quality. For a full explanation of this AA quality award, consult the Contents page.

FRINTON-ON-SEA Essex Map **05** TM21

GH [Q][Q] Forde 18 Queens Rd CO13 9BL ☎(0255) 674758
Closed Dec
Traditional-style seaside guesthouse run by friendly proprietors.
6hc (1fb) * sB&B£16.50 dB&B£27 WB&B£94.50
♨ CTV 1P nc5yrs
[£]

FRITH COMMON Hereford & Worcester Map **07** SO66

FH [Q][Q][Q] J M Keel **Hunt House** *(SO698702)* WR15 8JY (S of A456 and N of A443 on unclass rd) ☎Clows Top(029922) 277 due to change to (0299) 892277
Situated in an elevated position this lovely listed farmhouse has breathtaking views across the surrounding countryside. A policy of non-smoking applies to all of the comfortable and well-kept rooms. Hunt House Farm is friendly and welcoming and you are assured of a warm welcome.
3rm(1🛁2🚿)(1fb) [R] 🚫🐕 * dB&B🛁🚿fr£28
♨ CTV 4P 2🚗 nc6yrs 180 acres arable sheep
[£]

FROGMORE Devon Map **03** SX74

INN [Q][Q] Globe TQ7 2NR ☎Kingsbridge(0548) 531351
Three miles from Kingsbridge on the A379, the Globe is in an excellent position from which to tour picturesque South Devon. With a good reputation for food it has comfortable rooms and many facilities for children.
6rm(2🚿4hc)(1fb) CTV in all bedrooms [R] dB&Bfr£30
dB&B🚿fr£34 WB&Bfr£100 Lunch £5-£10 Dinner £5-£10 LDO 9.45pm
♨ CTV 20P

Credit Cards [1] [2] [3] [5] [£]
See advertisement under KINGSBRIDGE

GAIRLOCH Highland *Ross & Cromarty* Map **14** NG87

GH [Q][Q][Q] Birchwood IV21 2AH ☎(0445) 2011
Apr-mid Oct
Set in its own gardens overlooking the old harbour and towards Skye and the outer Isles, the guesthouse has a friendly atmosphere and provides comfortable bed and breakfast accommodation.
6🚿 (1fb)🚭in all bedrooms ® ✱
dB&B🚿£38-£42 WB&B£140-£147
♨ CTV 8P

GH [Q][Q][Q] *Eilean View* IV21 2BH ☎(0445) 2272
There are fine views over Gairloch Bay from this modern, timber-clad bungalow.
3hc ® LDO 6.30pm
♨ CTV 5P

SELECTED

⊢→**GH [Q][Q][Q][Q] Horisdale House** Strath IV21 2DA
☎(0445) 2151
May-Sep
Non-smokers are especially welcome at this delightful modern villa, which enjoys a splendid outlook over the bay. Comfortably appointed and with caring owners, it is an ideal base from which to explore Wester Ross.
9hc (3fb)🚭in all bedrooms ® 🐕 sB&B£11-£13.50 dB&B£20-£25 LDO 9am
♨ 10P nc7yrs

GALSTON Strathclyde *Ayrshire* Map **11** NS53

FH [Q][Q] Mrs J Bone **Auchencloigh** *(NS535320)* KA4 8NP (5m S off B7037-Scorn Rd) ☎(0563) 820567
Apr-Oct
A comfortable, traditional farmhouse with a friendly atmosphere.
2rm (1fb)🚭in all bedrooms TV available ® 🐕 ✱
sB&B£11-£12 dB&B£22-£24
♨ CTV 4P 4🚗 sauna 240 acres beef mixed sheep

GARBOLDISHAM Norfolk Map **05** TM08

GH [Q][Q] Ingleneuk Lodge Hopton Rd IP22 2RQ
☎(095381) 541
rs late Oct-early Nov & Xmas
Modern bungalow set in 10 acres of quiet wooded countryside.
11rm(10🛁🚿1hc)(2fb)🚭in 4 bedrooms CTV in all bedrooms ® sB&B£18 sB&B🛁🚿£26 dB&B£29.50 dB&B🛁🚿£39.50 WB&B£95-£130 WBDi£166-£199 LDO 1pm
Lic ♨ 20P
Credit Cards [1] [3] [£]

GARGRAVE North Yorkshire Map **07** SD95

GH [Q][Q][Q] Kirk Syke 19 High St BD23 3RA
☎Skipton(0756) 749356
Closed 16 Dec-Jan
Large stone house in village, with pleasant modern bedrooms.
6rm(3🛁3hc)Annexe 6🛁🚿 CTV in all bedrooms ® 🐕
sB&B£23 sB&B🛁🚿£24 dB&B£34
dB&B🛁🚿£36 WB&B£120-£160 WBDi£180-£220 LDO 10am
Lic ♨ CTV 12P

See advertisement on page 161

Street plans of certain towns and cities will be found in a separate section at the back of the book.

The Bowens Country House

Fownhope, Hereford. Telephone: (043277) 430

Intimate comfortable 17th C farmhouse providing tastefully furnished high standard accommodation. 12 bedrooms — 7 fully en suite, 4 with shower and basin. 2 single, double, twin, family and 4 ground floor rooms available, all have TV and tea tray. Oak beamed dining room and lounge with log fires. Highly recommended for traditional cooking using own and local produce. Vegetarians welcome. Peaceful village setting with large attractive garden with tennis court and putting green. Superb views. Excellent centre for walking and touring Wye Valley, Welsh Marches, Malverns. Bicycles for hire. Bargain breaks Oct-May. Licensed. Not suitable for children under 10 yrs. On B4224 Ross-Hereford. Access & Visa accepted. **Resident owner: Mrs Carol Hart.**

CARNETHIC

HOUSE

Lambs Barn · Fowey · Cornwall
Tel: (0726) 833336
David & Trisha Hogg

This delightful Regency house, situated in tranquil countryside close to the sea at Fowey, provides gracious accommodation and excellent food. Licensed bar & heated outdoor swimming pool.
1½ acres mature gardens.
AA selected in 1990.
For FREE brochure write or telephone.

Ashley Courtenay Recommended

English Tourist Board COMMENDED — MEMBER — AA SELECTED — BTA COMMENDED

GARSTANG Lancashire Map **07** SD44

FH Q Q Q Mrs J Higginson *Clay Lane Head* (*SD490474*)
Cabus, Preston PR3 1WL (2m N on A6) ☎(09952) 3132
Mar-23 Dec
*Two miles north of Garstang, this ivy-clad farmhouse stands in
front of meadowland on the A6 at Cabus.*
3hc ® ✻ (ex guide dogs)
CTV 4P 1🐎 30 acres beef

GATEHEAD Strathclyde *Ayrshire* Map **10** NS33

INN Q Q **Old Rome** KA2 9AJ ☎Drybridge(0563) 850265
*Situated 2.5 miles west of Kilmarnock, off the A759, this inn has 3
bedrooms and a nice lounge. A good range of bar meals is served in
the cosy lounge bar.*
3hc ® ✻ ✳ dB&B£27 LDO 9.30pm
💷 CTV 25P
£

GATEHOUSE OF FLEET Dumfries & Galloway
Kirkcudbrightshire Map **11** NX55

GH Q Q **Bobbin** 36 High St DG7 2HP ☎(05574) 229 due to
change to (0557) 814229
*This smart little guesthouse is part of a terraced row in the town's
main street. The bright accommodation is comfortable and neat.
After breakfast the dining room is used as a coffee shop.*
7rm(1🛦6hc)(3fb) ® ✻ sB&B£14-£15 dB&B£28-£30
dB&B🛦£31-£34 WB&B£98-£112 LDO 5pm
💷 CTV 8P
Credit Cards 1 3

GATWICK AIRPORT (LONDON) West Sussex
Map **04** TQ24

GH Q Q Q **Barnwood Hotel** Balcombe Rd, Pound Hill
RH10 4RU ☎Crawley(0293) 882709 Telex no 877005
Closed Xmas-New Years Day
*This popular hotel is situated on the B2036 S of the airport. There
is a choice of very well-equipped bedrooms, a residential bar and
lounge. The Barn Restaurant is open in the evening and 2
conference rooms are available.*
35rm(3🛦32🛦)(7fb) CTV in all bedrooms ® ✻ (ex guide dogs)
✻ sB&B🛦fr£50 dB&B🛦fr£60 LDO 9pm
Lic 💷 50P
Credit Cards 1 2 3 5

GH Q Q Q *Gainsborough Lodge* 39 Massetts Rd RH6 7DT (2m
NE of airport adjacent A23) ☎Horley(0293) 783982
*An attractive detached residence with a modern extension,
Gainsborough Lodge offers well-equipped accommodation. There
is a cosy lounge and a pleasant dining room which overlooks the
rear garden.*
13🛦🛦 (3fb) CTV in all bedrooms ® ✻
💷 16P
Credit Cards 1 3

GH Q Q **Gatwick Skylodge** London Rd, County Oak
RH11 0PF (2m S of airport on A23) ☎Crawley(0293) 544511
Telex no 878307
Closed 25-29 Dec
*Conveniently close to the airport, this purpose-built hotel has been
extensively refurbished to offer a good standard of
accommodation. Dinner and breakfast are available, for residents
only, in the bar-cum-lounge dining-room.*
51🛦 (7fb) CTV in all bedrooms ® ✻ (ex guide dogs) ✻
sB&B🛦£38-£48 dB&B🛦£45-£55 LDO 9.15pm
Lic 💷 60P (£1.90 nightly)
Credit Cards 1 2 3 £

GH Q Q Q **The Lawn** 30 Massetts Rd RH6 7DE
☎Horley(0293) 775751
Closed Xmas
*A warm welcome is offered by the proprietors of this well-kept
hotel. The comfortable accommodation has modern facilities and
fresh decor. Many original fireplaces have been retained, lending
character to most rooms.*
7🛦 CTV in all bedrooms ® dB&B🛦£39
💷 10P
Credit Cards 1 3 £

GH Q Q Q **Little Foxes** Ifield Woods, Ifield Rd RH11 0JY
☎Crawley(0293) 552430
*Set within 5 acres of grounds, this large modern bungalow has
spacious bedrooms, a lounge and a large breakfast room. Car
parking, airport transport and 24 hour service is readily available.*
10rm(7🛦🛦3hc)(2fb) CTV in all bedrooms ® ✻
sB&B£34.50-£55 sB&B🛦🛦£34.50-£55 dB&B£46-£55
dB&B🛦🛦£46-£55
💷 CTV 150P
Credit Cards 1 2 3 £

GH Q Q **Massetts Lodge** 28 Massets Rd RH6 7DE
☎Crawley(0293) 782738
*This small, friendly establishment has cosy bedrooms, well
equipped with colour TV, coffee facilities and modern en suites.
Convenient for Gatwick airport, it has limited public areas and a
pleasant dining room.*
8rm(5🛦🛦3hc)(2fb) CTV in all bedrooms ® ✻ (ex guide dogs)
sB&B£22 sB&B🛦🛦£32 dB&B£32
dB&B🛦🛦£40 WB&B£112-£224 WBDif142-£254 LDO
7.45pm
💷 10P ♨(heated)
Credit Cards 1 2 3

See advertisement on page 163

GH [Q][Q] Woodlands 42 Massetts Rd RH6 7DS
☎Horley(0293) 782994 & 776358
The cosy, well-furnished and equipped accommodation at this small guesthouse is ideal for travellers using Gatwick Airport. It has a friendly atmosphere and offers bed and breakfast.
5🚿 (2fb)🚭in all bedrooms CTV in all bedrooms Ⓡ 🚫
sB&B🚿£25-£26 dB&B🚿£35-£37.50
🍴 20P (£10 per wk) 2🚗 (£15 per wk) nc5yrs
[£]

GAYHURST Buckinghamshire Map **04** SP84

FH [Q][Q] Mrs K Adams **Mill** *(SP852454)* MK16 8LT (1m S off B526 unclass rd to Haversham)
☎Newport Pagnell(0908) 611489
The River Ouse runs through the grounds of this 17th-century farmhouse and fishing is available.
3hc (1fb)🚭in 1 bedroom CTV in all bedrooms Ⓡ ✱
sB&B£15-£20 dB&B£25-£35 LDO 4pm
🍴 CTV 10P 3🚗 🎾(hard)🎣 🐎 550 acres mixed
[£]

GEDNEY HILL Lincolnshire Map **09** TF31

FH [Q] Mrs C Cave **Sycamore** *(TF336108)* PE12 0NP (on B1166) ☎Holbeach(0406) 330445
Situated on the B1166 in the village the farmhouse is over 100 years old.
3rm (2fb) TV in 1 bedroom sB&B£15-£20 dB&B£30
🍴 CTV 6P 80 acres beef dairy mixed
[£]

CLOSED

GIGGLESWICK North Yorkshire Map **07** SD86

INN [Q][Q] Black Horse Hotel Church St BD24 0BE
☎Settle(07292) 2506
A secluded village inn dating back to 1663 with well-furnished bedrooms and good home-cooking.
3rm(1🛁2🚿)(1fb) CTV in all bedrooms Ⓡ 🚫
dB&B🛁🚿£34 WB&B£105 WBDi£110.80 Lunch £5.80-£9.90alc Dinner £5.80-£9.90alc LDO 8.45pm
🍴 CTV 20P
Credit Cards [1] [3] [5]

GILWERN Gwent Map **03** SO21

FH [Q][Q][Q] Mr B L Harris **The Wenallt** *(SO245138)* NP7 0HP (Three quarters of a mile S of A465 Gilwern b y pass)
☎(0873) 830694
Situated three quarters of a mile south of the A465 Gilwern bypass, this 16th-century Welsh longhouse has lovely views of the Usk Valley. Spacious comfortable bedrooms are provided together with good public rooms.
3rm(1🛁2hc)Annexe 4rm(1🛁3🚿) Ⓡ 🚫 (ex guide dogs)
sB&B£14.38-£17.83 sB&B🛁🚿£20.70 dB&B£28.76
dB&B🛁🚿£34.50 WB&B£92.58-£136.85
WBDi£144.90-£189.18 LDO 6pm
Lic 🍴 CTV 10P 50 acres sheep

GISLINGHAM Suffolk Map **05** TM07

SELECTED

GH [Q][Q][Q][Q] ***The Old Guildhall*** Mill St IP23 8JT
☎Mellis(037983) 361
Closed Jan
Formerly a 15th-century guildhall, this timber-framed house enjoys a peaceful village location, enclosed in its own gardens. Its distinct thatched roof belies the fact that inside, every modern convenience is blended with good quality furnishings and fittings. Each room is quite spacious and attractive, each having its own bathroom. Mr and Mrs Tranter offer a small à la carte menu, which changes every week.
4🛁 CTV in all bedrooms Ⓡ LDO 6pm
Lic 🍴 5P

GLAN-YR-AFON (nr Corwen) Gwynedd Map **06** SJ04

FH [Q][Q] Mrs G B Jones **Llawr-Bettws** *(SJ016424)* Bala Rd
☎Maerdy(049081) 224
This small farmhouse is friendly and warm, and offers good home comforts. It is found off the Bala road, 2 miles from the Druid traffic lights.
4hc (2fb) 🚫 LDO 7pm
CTV 3P 18 acres mixed beef sheep
[£]

GLASBURY Powys Map **03** SO13

FH [Q][Q] Mrs B Eckley ***Fforddfawr*** *(SO192398)* HR3 5PT
☎(04974) 332
Apr-Oct
On the Brecon road just 3 miles from Hay-on-Wye, this 17th-century stone-built farmhouse is bordered by the river Wye. Very much a working farm, it provides spacious accommodation.
2hc Ⓡ 🚫
CTV 4P 280 acres mixed

GLASGOW Strathclyde *Lanarkshire* Map **11** NS56

GH [Q][Q][Q] Dalmeny Hotel 62 St Andrews Dr, Nithsdale Cross G41 5EZ ☎041-427 1106 & 6288
Closed 1 wk New Year
The bedrooms are comfortable and thoughfully equipped at this small, family-run hotel, situated in a residential area on the city's southern side. The attractive public rooms, including a restaurant open to non-residents, highlight the house's period features.
8rm(2🛁1🚿5hc) CTV in all bedrooms Ⓡ sB&B£27
sB&B🛁🚿£42.50 dB&B£42.50 dB&B🛁🚿£52
Lic 🍴 CTV 20P
Credit Cards [1] [2] [3]

GH [Q][Q] Kelvin Private Hotel 15 Buckingham Ter, Hillhead G12 8EB ☎041-339 7143
A terraced house in the West End area of the city, close to the Botanical Gardens.
15hc (3fb) CTV in all bedrooms Ⓡ sB&B£21-£24 sB&B£28-£32
dB&B£36-£42 dB&B£44-£48 WB&B£125-£147
🍴 5P
[£]

GLASTONBURY Somerset Map **03** ST53

SELECTED

FH [Q][Q][Q][Q] Mrs J I Nurse **Berewall Farm Country Guest House** *(ST516375)* Cinnamon Ln BA6 8LL
☎(0458) 31451
A short drive from the town brings you to the tranquil, rural surroundings of this former farmhouse. Mr and Mrs Nurse and their daughter provide a warm and friendly atmosphere and unique hospitality. The simply furnished and well-equipped bedrooms are en suite. Excellent home cooking is, however, the main feature of this house, lovingly prepared by Mrs Nurse and offering a varied choice.
9🛁🚿 (3fb) CTV in all bedrooms Ⓡ 🚫 (ex guide dogs)
sB&B🛁🚿£21-£23
dB&B🛁🚿£37-£39 WBDi£155-£165 LDO 9.30pm
Lic 🍴 12P 🏊 🎾(hard)🐎 30 acres dairy
Credit Cards [1] [3]

[£] Remember to use the money-off vouchers.

FH **Q Q Q** Mrs H T Tinney **Cradlebridge** *(ST477385)*
BA16 9SD ☎(0458) 31827
Closed Xmas
Under the expert care of Mrs Tinney, the accommodation here is in a purpose-built bungalow next to the farmhouse. The 2 lovely bedrooms have en suite facilities and each has a sitting area and patio.
2🛏 Annexe 3hc (2fb) CTV in 2 bedrooms ® ✖
sB&B£17.50-£20 sB&B🛏£17.50-£20 dB&B£30-£35
dB&B🛏£30-£35 WB&B£90-£120
🍴 6P 200 acres dairy
£

GLENCOE Highland *Argyllshire* Map **14** NN15

GH **Q Q** **Scorrybreac** PA39 4HT ☎Ballachulish(08552) 354
Set in mature woods above the village, this modern guesthouse is comfortable and well appointed.
5hc (2fb)✄in all bedrooms CTV in 1 bedroom TV in 1 bedroom ® ✖ (ex guide dogs) ✱
dB&B£23-£26 WB&B£76-£80 WBDi£125-£129 LDO 10am
🍴 CTV 8P
£

GLENFARG Tayside *Perthshire* Map **11** NO11

FH **Q Q** Mrs W E A Lawrie **Candy** *(NO118098)* P42 9QL
☎(05773) 217
Apr-Oct
Peacefully set beside the Ochil Hills amid picturesque countryside, this welcoming farmhouse offers traditional hospitality and comfortably appointed accommodation.
2hc (1fb)✄in all bedrooms ® ✖ LDO 10am
🍴 CTV 6P nc5yrs ✔ 520 acres beef sheep

GLENMAVIS Strathclyde *Lanarkshire* Map **11** NS76

FH Ⓠ Mrs M Dunbar **Braidenhill** *(NS742673)* ML6 0PJ
☎Glenboig(0236) 872319
The friendly, welcoming attention of Mrs Dunbar awaits guests at her 300-year-old farmhouse. The comfortable, modest accommodation includes a lounge and dining-room.
3hc (1fb) Ⓡ ⊁ ✳ sB&B£11 dB&B£22
ᵐᵐ CTV 4P 50 acres arable mixed

GLOUCESTER Gloucestershire Map **03** SO81

GH Ⓠ **Claremont** 135 Stroud Rd GL1 5LJ ☎(0452) 29540 & 29270
7hc (2fb) CTV in all bedrooms ⊁ ✳ sB&B£14-£16 dB&B£27-£30
ᵐᵐ CTV 6P
Ⓔ

GH Ⓠ **Lulworth** 12 Midland Rd GL1 4UF ☎(0452) 21881
8rm(1⇨1❧6hc)(2fb) CTV in all bedrooms Ⓡ ✳ sB&B£13-£16 sB&B⇨❧fr£16 dB&B£26-£32 dB&B⇨❧£28-£32
ᵐᵐ CTV 14P

GOATHLAND North Yorkshire Map **08** NZ80

GH ⓆⓆⓆ **Heatherdene Hotel** YO22 5AN
☎Whitby(0947) 86334
Apr-Dec
Comfortably furnished accommodation on the outskirts of the village with fine views over the moors.
6rm(2⇨2❧2hc)(3fb)⊁in 1 bedroom CTV in all bedrooms Ⓡ ✳ sB&Bfr£15.50 sB&B⇨❧fr£19 dB&Bfr£31 dB&B⇨❧fr£38 LDO 4pm
Lic ᵐᵐ CTV 10P solarium

GOREY

See **JERSEY** under **CHANNEL ISLANDS**

GORRAN HAVEN Cornwall & Isles of Scilly Map **02** SX04

INN ⓆⓆ *Llawnroc* PL26 6NU ☎Mevagissey(0726) 843461
Closed Xmas & Boxing Day
Pleasant inn with large garden and modern bedrooms in new extension.
6rm(3⇨3❧)(2fb) CTV in all bedrooms Ⓡ LDO 9pm
ᵐᵐ CTV 40P table tennis pool
Credit Cards ❘1❘❘2❘❘3❘❘5❘
See advertisement under MEVAGISSEY on page 261

GRAMPOUND Cornwall & Isles of Scilly Map **02** SW94

⊶**GH** ⓆⓆ **Perran House** Fore St TR2 4RS
☎St Austell(0726) 882066
This semi detached residence stands beside the A390 and offers friendly service and compact, well-equipped bedrooms. Cream teas may be taken on the patio during the summer.
5rm(2⇨1❧2hc)(1fb)⊁in all bedrooms CTV in all bedrooms Ⓡ ⊁ (ex guide dogs) sB&B£11.50-£13.50 dB&B£23-£27 dB&B⇨❧£25-£33 WB&B£80-£102
ᵐᵐ 8P
Credit Cards ❘1❘❘3❘ Ⓔ

GRANDES ROCQUES

See **GUERNSEY** under **CHANNEL ISLANDS**

GRANGE-OVER-SANDS Cumbria Map **07** SD47

GH ⓆⓆⓆ **Elton Private Hotel** Windermere Rd LA11 6EQ
☎(05395) 32838
A short distance from the shops and railway station, this family-run house has very well-appointed bedrooms, most with en suite facilities, and all with colour television and tea-making facilities. There is a cosy first floor lounge and a comfortable dining room.

7rm(5⇨❧2hc)(3fb) CTV in all bedrooms Ⓡ ⊁ ✳ sB&B⇨❧£18-£20 dB&B£30-£34 dB&B⇨❧£30-£34 LDO 2pm
Lic ᵐᵐ CTV ⊁

GH ⓆⓆⓆ *Greenacres* Lindale LA11 6LP (2m N)
☎(05395) 34578
Closed 15 Nov-Dec
This 19th-century roadside cottage has been tastefully modernised to a very high standard, with lovely bedrooms, a comfy lounge, cosy dining room and sun lounge. A separate outside door gives access to the annexe bedroom.
5rm(4⇨1❧)Annexe 1⇨ (1fb) CTV in all bedrooms Ⓡ ⊁ LDO 3pm
Lic ᵐᵐ CTV 6P

GRANTOWN-ON-SPEY Highland *Morayshire* Map **14** NJ02

SELECTED

GH ⓆⓆⓆⓆ **Culdearn House** Woodlands Ter PH26 3JU
☎(0479) 2106
Feb-Oct
Recently refurbished by Alasdair and Isobel Little, this delightful house has comfortable, thoughtfully equipped bedrooms, many with en suite facilities. A 'house party' atmosphere prevails in the comfortable, attractive lounge and a pleasurable 3-course dinner is served.
8rm(1⇨3❧4hc)(2fb) CTV in all bedrooms Ⓡ ⊁ (ex guide dogs) sB&B⇨❧£19.95-£25 dB&B⇨❧£39.90-£50 WB&B£129.95-£160 WBDif£194.65-£265 LDO 6pm
Lic ᵐᵐ 9P ⚗
Credit Cards ❘1❘❘3❘ Ⓔ

⊶**GH** ⓆⓆⓆ **Dar-Il-Hena** Grant Rd PH26 3LA
☎(0479) 2929
Etr-Oct
Surrounded by attractive gardens and enjoying an elevated position in a quiet residential road, this well-maintained house is close to the centre of town. Wood panelling is a feature of the public areas of the spacious, comfortable accommodation.
7hc (3fb) Ⓡ sB&Bfr£12 dB&Bfr£24 WB&Bfr£84 WBDifr£128
ᵐᵐ CTV 10P

⊶**GH** ⓆⓆ **Dunallan** Woodside Av PH26 3JN ☎(0479) 2140
May-Nov
This detached house is situated in a residential area and offers good value tourist accommodation together with traditional comforts.
6hc (2fb)⊁in 3 bedrooms Ⓡ ⊁ (ex guide dogs) sB&B£10 dB&B£20 LDO 4pm
ᵐᵐ CTV 5P

SELECTED

GH ⓆⓆⓆⓆ **Dunstaffnagie House** Woodside Av
PH26 3JR ☎(0479) 2000
A strict 'no-smoking' policy is enforced at this charming Victorian house, set in an acre of grounds. David and Martha Hunt have thoughtfully equipped the cheery bedrooms, and Martha's Cordon Bleu cooking is served in the candlelit dining room.
6rm(4⇨❧2hc)⊁in all bedrooms CTV in all bedrooms Ⓡ sB&B⇨❧fr£25 dB&B⇨❧fr£42 WB&Bfr£145 WBDifr£210 LDO 6.30pm
Lic ᵐᵐ 6P 2☙
Credit Cards ❘1❘❘3❘ Ⓔ

SELECTED

GH 🔘🔘🔘🔘 **Garden Park** Woodside Av PH26 3JN
☎(0479) 3235

Frank and Dee Sloan are the hospitable hosts of this Victorian house featuring a dovecote in its attractive gardens. In an elevated site just off the main high street, the house has many rooms with lovely views over pine forests to the Cromdale Hills. Guests may choose from 2 comfy lounges – one with colour TV and the other well stocked with books, and the bedrooms are cosy, comfortable and nicely decorated. Mrs Sloan uses fresh ingredients in her meals which are of excellent value.

6rm(2⇔4🛏)(1fb) ® ✠
dB&B⇔🛏£35-£37 WB&B£115-£120 WBDi£165-£174
LDO 7pm
Lic ♀ CTV 8P
£

GH 🔘🔘🔘 **Kinross House** Woodside Av PH26 3JR
☎(0479) 2042
Mar-Oct

Close to pine woods and the river Spey, this late Victorian house offers comfortable, traditional bedrooms and public areas. David and Katherine Elder provide personal and attentive service. There is a lovely lounge, complete with open log fire in the winter, and David serves dinner in full Highland dress.

7rm(4🛏3hc)(2fb)⊬in all bedrooms CTV in all bedrooms ®
✠ (ex guide dogs) sB&B£13.50-£14 dB&B£26-£27
dB&B🛏£31-£32 WB&B£91-£109 WBDi£150-£164 LDO 4pm
Lic ♀ CTV 6P nc5yrs
£

⊷GH 🔘 **Pines Hotel** Woodside Av PH26 3JR ☎(0479) 2092

Standing on the edge of a pine wood, and with extensive views, this secluded house offers comfortable, traditional accommodation. The owners give friendly attention to guests. Run by a cheerful young couple, this friendly guesthouse is ideal for families.

9rm(2🛏7hc)(3fb) ® sB&B£11.50-£18.50 dB&B£23-£37
dB&B🛏£30-£43 WB&B£80.50-£105 WBDi£118-£140 LDO
5pm
Lic ♀ CTV 9P putting
£

GH 🔘🔘🔘 **Umaria** Woodlands Ter PH26 3JU ☎(0479) 2104
Closed Nov-Dec

Set in its well-tended garden on the town's southern fringe, this attractive Victorian house provides a warm welcome with attractive, comfortable bedrooms and a cosy lounge with a log fire.

8hc (3fb) ® sB&B£13.50-£14.50
dB&B£27-£29 WB&B£94.50-£109 WBDi£135-£150 LDO
4.30pm
Lic ♀ CTV 9P croquet

GRASMERE Cumbria Map **11** NY30

GH 🔘🔘🔘 **Bridge House Hotel** Stock Ln LA22 9SN
☎(09665) 425
mid Mar-mid Nov

Comfortable, spacious and tastefully furnished, this detached house stands in secluded gardens in the village centre. All the bedrooms have colour TV and most have modern en suite facilities. Bridge House is family-owned and managed to a high standard.

12rm(10⇔🛏2hc) CTV in all bedrooms ® ✠
sB&B⇔🛏£33-£38 dB&B£60-£66
dB&B⇔🛏£66-£76 (incl dinner) WBDi£200-£230 LDO 7pm
Lic ♀ 20P nc5yrs
Credit Cards [1][3]

GH 🔘🔘 **Lake View** Lake View Dr LA22 9TD ☎(09665) 384
Mar-Nov

This small guesthouse, positioned close to the village centre yet overlooking meadowland towards the lake and fells, has a friendly and relaxing atmosphere and also gardens in which to enjoy the peaceful surrounds.

6rm(2🛏4hc) ® sB&B£18 dB&B£36
dB&B🛏£42 WB&B£120 WBDi£177 LDO noon
CTV 11P nc12yrs
£

⊷GH 🔘🔘🔘 **Raise View** Whitebridge LA22 9RQ
☎(09665) 215
Apr-Oct

This attractive and immaculate Lakeland house is situated on the edge of the village and enjoys delightful views of the surrounding countryside. It is reached by turning off at the Swan Hotel on the A591.

6rm(1🛏5hc)(1fb) ® ✠ dB&B£12-£14 dB&B🛏fr£28
♀ CTV 6P nc5yrs

GH 🔘🔘 **Titteringdales** Pye Ln LA22 9RQ ☎(09665) 439
Feb-Nov

A pleasant house in 2.5 acres of gardens with good views over the surrounding fells.

6rm(5⇔🛏1hc) CTV in all bedrooms ® dB&B£28-£32
dB&B⇔🛏£32-£36 WB&B£98-£112 WBDi£143.50-£164.50
LDO 1pm
Lic ♀ 6P nc10yrs
£

GRASSINGTON North Yorkshire Map **07** SE06

GH 🔘🔘🔘 **Ashfield House Hotel** BD23 5AE ☎(0756) 752584
Mar-end Oct

Secluded, comfortable, 17th-century house, offering splendid food.

7rm(5🛏2hc) CTV in all bedrooms ® ✠ ✳ sB&B£31.50
dB&B£55-£60
dB&B🛏£62.50-£67 (incl dinner) WBDi£167-£189 LDO
5.30pm
Lic ♀ 7P nc5yrs

GH 🔘🔘 **The Lodge** 8 Wood Ln BD23 5LU ☎(0756) 752518
Mar-Oct rs Dec

Home-cooked dinners are served at this cosy house, which is just one minute's walk from the charming village centre. The lounge is large and well furnished.

8rm(1⇔7hc)(1fb) TV in 1 bedroom ® ✳ dB&B£28-£32
dB&B⇔🛏£32 WB&B£95-£123 WBDi£150-£178 LDO 2pm
♀ CTV 7P

GRAVESEND Kent Map **05** TQ67

GH 🔘🔘 **The Cromer** 194 Parrock St DA12 1EW
☎(0474) 361935
Closed 24 Dec-2 Jan

This friendly, Victorian-style establishment has well-maintained accommodation and a delightful, well-appointed dining room. There is also a cosy, comfortable lounge.

11rm(1⇔10hc)(3fb) CTV in all bedrooms ✠ sB&B£13.50-£15
dB&B£25-£26 dB&B⇔£30
♀ CTV 15P nc9yrs
Credit Cards [3]

GH 🔘🔘🔘 *Overcliffe Hotel* 15-16 The Overcliffe DA11 0EF
☎(0474) 322131 Telex no 965117

This well-run hotel offers a good standard of well-equipped accommodation which includes nicely appointed annexe rooms. There is a pleasant restaurant and bar.

19🛏 (1fb) CTV in all bedrooms ® LDO 9.30pm
Lic ♀ 45P
Credit Cards [1][2][3][5]

GREAT

Placenames incorporating the word 'Great', such as Gt Yarmouth, will be found under the actual placename, ie Yarmouth.

GREENHEAD Northumberland Map 12 NY66

FH 🅠🅠 Mrs P Staff **Holmhead** *(NY659661)* Hadrians Wall CA6 7HY ☎Gilsland(06972) 402 due to change to (06977) 47402 Closed 19 Dec-9 Jan
A traditional Northumbrian farmhouse offering warmth and comfort and an excellent selection of breakfast dishes. The Roman Wall runs beneath the house and Thirlwell Castle is behind.
4🏠 (1fb)⊬in all bedrooms ® ⊀
dB&B🏠£35 WB&B£105 WBDi£175 LDO 3pm
Lic ᵐ CTV 6P ♪ table tennis 300 acres breeding sheep cattle
Credit Cards 1 2 3

GRETNA Dumfries & Galloway *Dumfriesshire* Map 11 NY36

GH 🅠🅠🅠 *Surrone House* Annan Rd CA6 5DL
☎(0461) 38341
Managed by the friendly resident proprietors, this small hotel offers well-appointed bedrooms, comfortable lounges and good-value evening meals.
6⇆🏠 (4fb) CTV in all bedrooms ® LDO 8pm
Lic ᵐ CTV 16P

GRETNA GREEN Dumfries & Galloway *Dumfriesshire* Map 11 NY36

GH 🅠🅠 **Greenlaw** CA6 5DU ☎Gretna(0461) 38361
A cosy house situated on the edge of the village with fresh, compact bedrooms.
8hc (1fb) CTV in 6 bedrooms ® ✱ sB&Bfr£12 dB&B£21-£23
ᵐ CTV 12P 1🛏
£

GREVE DE LECQ BAY

See **JERSEY under CHANNEL ISLANDS**

GRINDON Staffordshire Map 07 SK05

GH 🅠🅠🅠 **Porch Farmhouse** ST13 7IP ☎Onecote(05388) 545
Overlooking the Manifold valley, this charming 400-year-old stone cottage provides a warm welcome and home-cooked country fayre. The proprietors are keen walkers and have many guidebooks to peruse in the comfortable lounge.
3rm(2🏠1hc) CTV in all bedrooms ® ✱ sB&B🏠fr£16.50
dB&B🏠fr£33
3P nc5yrs

See advertisement on page 169

GROUVILLE

See **JERSEY under CHANNEL ISLANDS**

GUERNSEY

See **CHANNEL ISLANDS**

GUILDFORD Surrey Map 04 SU94

GH 🅠🅠 **Blanes Court Hotel** Albury Rd GU1 2BT
☎(0483) 573171 FAX (0483) 32780
Closed 1wk Xmas
Quietly situated, elegant accommodation, with well-equipped bedrooms and welcoming atmosphere.
20rm(4⇆10🏠6hc)(3fb) CTV in all bedrooms ® sB&B£30
sB&B⇆🏠£40-£45 dB&Bfr£45
dB&B⇆🏠£55-£60 WB&B£135-£360
Lic ᵐ CTV 22P
Credit Cards 1 2 3 £

See advertisement on page 169

GH [Q][Q][Q] **Quinns Hotel** 78 Epsom Rd GU1 2BX
☎(0483) 60422 Telex no 859754
A fine Victorian house, close to all the main routes through the busy town centre. Managed privately, service is limited but there is a choice of well-furnished bedrooms.
10rm(3🛁4🚿3hc)(2fb) CTV in all bedrooms [R] 🐕 ✱ sB&B£35 sB&B🛁🚿£45 dB&B£46 dB&B🛁🚿£56 LDO 6pm
♨ CTV 14P
Credit Cards [1] [2] [3] [5] [£]

GUNNISLAKE Cornwall & Isles of Scilly Map **02** SX47

GH [Q][Q][Q] **Hingston House Country Hotel** St Anns Chapel PL18 9HB ☎Tavistock(0822) 832468
This charming Victorian country house has splendid views down the Tamar to the sea. There is a large lounge with comfortable chairs and a woodburning stove, a delightful dining room and a cosy bar. The bedrooms are well equipped.
10rm(8🚿2hc)(1fb) CTV in all bedrooms [R] ✱
sB&B£22.50-£23.50 sB&B🚿£28.50-£29.50 dB&B£37-£39 dB&B🚿£46-£48 WB&B£122.50-£192.50
WBDi£204.75-£274.75 LDO 7pm
Lic ♨ CTV 12P croquet, putting green
Credit Cards [1] [3] [£]

GWAUN VALLEY Dyfed Map **02** SN03

SELECTED

FH [Q][Q][Q][Q] Mr P Heard & M J Cox **Tregynon Country Farmhouse Hotel** *(SN054345)* SA65 9TU (4m E of Pontfaen, off unclass road joining B 4313)
☎Newport(0239) 820531
Closed 2wks winter
Lying in the Preseli foothills, this secluded 16th-century farmhouse has 3 bedrooms of a very high standard in newly converted outbuildings. The restaurant enjoys an excellent local reputation, with wholefood and vegetarian dishes a speciality.
3🚿 Annexe 5🛁 (4fb) CTV in all bedrooms [R] 🐕
dB&B🛁🚿£37-£55 WBDi£190-£250 LDO 6pm
Lic ♨ 10P 10 acres sheep

HADDINGTON Lothian *East Lothian* Map **12** NT57

↔**FH** [Q][Q] Mrs K Kerr **Barney Mains** *(NT523764)* Barney Mains EH41 3SA (off A1, 1m S of Haddington)
☎Athelstaneford(062088) 310
May-Sep
3rm 🚭in all bedrooms 🐕 sB&B£12-£15
dB&B£24-£30 LDO noon
CTV 0P 580 acres arable beef sheep

HALFORD Warwickshire Map **04** SP24

INN [Q][Q] **Halford Bridge** Fosse Way CV36 5BN
☎Stratford on Avon(0789) 740382
This spacious Cotswold stone road-house, situated on the A429, offers pretty, well-equipped bedrooms and public areas that have character. A wide choice of food is available in either the bars or the dining room.
6hc (1fb) CTV in all bedrooms [R] 🐕 (ex guide dogs) ✱
sB&B£25-£36
dB&B£35-£46 Sunday Lunch fr£4.95&alc Dinner £8.80-£12.50alc LDO 9pm
50P
Credit Cards [1] [3]

HALLWORTHY Cornwall & Isles of Scilly Map **02** SX18

INN [Q] **Wilsey Down** PL32 9SH ☎Camelford(08406) 205
This fully licensed free house stands on the A395, 10 miles from Launceston. The accommodation is comfortable and bar meals are served.
6hc (1fb)🚭in all bedrooms TV in 1 bedroom [R] 🐕 ✱
sB&B£11-£17
dB&B£25-£27 WB&Bfr£80.50 Lunch £1.80-£7.50 Dinner £1.80-£7.50&alc
CTV 10P nc12yrs pool table
[£]

HALSTOCK Dorset Map **03** ST50

GH [Q][Q][Q] ***Halstock Mill*** BA22 9SJ ☎Corscombe(093589) 278
mid Mar-Oct
This 17th-century cornmill has been tastefully converted to provide en suite rooms with colour TV and central heating. The public rooms retain many original features. Evening meals are available by arrangement.
5🛁 (1fb) CTV in all bedrooms [R] 🐕 (ex guide dogs) LDO am
♨ 6P 3🚗 nc10 yrs games room bikes for hire
Credit Cards [1] [3]

HALTWHISTLE Northumberland Map **12** NY76

GH [Q][Q] **Ashcroft** NE49 0DA ☎(0434) 320213
Closed 23 Dec-2 Jan
Carefully-modernised former Victorian vicarage with spacious rooms and tranquil atmosphere.
6hc (3fb)🚭in 1 bedroom 🐕 ✱ dB&B£24-£28
♨ CTV 15P croquet lawn
[£]

FH [Q][Q][Q] Mrs J I Laidlow ***Ald White Craig*** *(NY713649)* Shield Hill NE49 9NW ☎(0434) 320565
Apr-Sep
Modernised, croft-style farmhouse, with well-appointed bedrooms but retaining an olde worlde atmosphere in the comfortable lounge.
3rm(1🛁2🚿) CTV in all bedrooms [R] 🐕 (ex guide dogs)
♨ 3P nc 60 acres stock rearing rare breeds

SELECTED

FH [Q][Q][Q][Q] Mrs J Brown **Broomshaw Hill** *(NY706654)* Willia Rd NE49 9NP ☎(0434) 320866
Apr-Oct
Secluded in its own small vale behind the town, this farm is approached by the military road running alongside Hadrian's Wall, and the effort spent on seeking is out is well rewarded. The stone-built house stands on raised ground and provides spacious and well-furnished accommodation.
3hc (1fb) CTV in all bedrooms [R] sB&B£15-£16
dB&B£28-£30 WB&B£92-£95 WBDi£135-£145 LDO 10am
♨ CTV 4P 2🚗 7 acres livestock horses
[£]

HALWELL Devon Map **03** SX75

GH [Q] **Stanborough Hundred Hotel** TQ9 7JG
☎East Allington(054852) 236
20 Mar-15 Oct
This charming, small hotel stands in sheltered gardens in an elevated position between Totnes and Kingsbridge, near a Bronze Age campsite. A friendly welcome awaits the visitor, who will enjoy splendid views of Dartmoor and the coast.

5rm(3⇆2hc)Annexe 1⇆ (2fb) CTV in 4 bedrooms ®
✠ (ex guide dogs) sB&B£27-£29 dB&B£54-£58
dB&B⇆£58-£63 WB&B£95-£105 WBDi£140-£171 LDO
6.30pm
Lic ⌘ CTV 10P nc5yrs

HAMBLETON Lancashire Map **07** SD34

FH ⓆⓆ Mrs B Jenkinson *White Lodge (SD382435)* Sower
Carr Ln FY6 9DJ ☎(0253) 700342
*An attractive, modern farmhouse with accommodation of a very
high standard, ideally located between Blackpool and Lancaster.*
3♘ (1fb)⚹in all bedrooms ✠
⌘ CTV 6P nc5yrs ✎ 220 acres arable dairy sheep pigs

HAMSTERLEY Co Durham Map **12** NZ13

GH ⓆⓆⓆ **Grove House** Hamsterley Forest DL13 1NL
☎Witton-Le-Wear(038888) 203
Closed Aug & Xmas & New Year
*Situated in the heart of Hamsterley Forest, this charming house,
once a shooting lodge, will appeal to those seeking peace and
tranquillity and will appeal to lovers of wild life. Now the home of
Helene and Russell Close, Grove House offers comfortable,
attractive accommodation in which to relax. From Hamsterley
Village follow the signs to Hamsterley Forest and Redburn, and
then take the forest road for about 3 miles to Grove House.*
4hc ⚹in all bedrooms ® ✠ ✳ sB&B£17-£22
dB&B£34 WB&B£119 WBDi£175 LDO 7.30pm
⌘ CTV 8P nc6yrs
£

This guide is updated annually – make sure you
use an up-to-date edition.

HANLEY CASTLE Hereford & Worcester Map **03** SO84

SELECTED

GH ⓠⓠⓠⓠ **Old Parsonage Farm** WR8 0BU
☎Hanley Swan(0684) 310124
Closed 11 Dec-12 Jan

Old Parsonage farm is an 18th-century guesthouse which treats visitors as guests of the family. Surrounded by beautiful countryside it is situated close to many places of interest. Accommodation is spacious and comfortable with private facilities for each of the bedrooms and 2 delightful sitting rooms. Ann Addison's meals are a highlight of the stay and as Tony Addison runs his own wine business, there is an interesting and extensive wine list.

3⇩ (1fb) TV in 1 bedroom ✖ ✳ sB&B⇩£25-£27.50
dB&B⇩£39.50-£43 WB&B£138-£150 WBDif£238-£250
Lic ⁽ᵐ⁾ CTV 6P 1🐾 nc8yrs
Credit Cards ② ⓔ

HANMER Clwyd Map **07** SJ44

FH ⓠ C Sumner & F Williams-Lee **Buck** *(SJ435424)*
SY14 7LX ☎(094874) 339
This 16th-century, timber-framed farmhouse stands on the A525, midway between Wrexham and Whitchurch, amid 8 acres of gardens and woodland. The cuisine served here reflects the international travels of the proprietors.

4hc (1fb)⤢in all bedrooms ✖ (ex guide dogs) ✳ sB&B£15
dB&B£30 WB&B£91 WBDif£154 LDO previous day
⁽ᵐ⁾ CTV 12P 8 acres non-working
ⓔ

HARBERTON Devon Map **03** SX75

FH ⓠⓠⓠ Mrs I P Steer **Preston** *(SX777587)* TQ9 7SW
☎Totnes(0803) 862235
Apr-Oct
Built before 1680, this attractive Devonshire Farmhouse has 3 tastefully furnished bedrooms and both lounge and dining room offer quality and comfort. Mrs Steer takes a pride in her cooking and provides a set meal.

3hc (1fb) Ⓡ ✖ ✳ dB&B£26-£30 LDO 6.45pm
CTV 3P nc3yrs 250 acres mixed
ⓔ

FH ⓠⓠ Mr & Mrs Rose **Tristford** *(SX775587)* TQ9 7SP
☎Totnes(0803) 862418
This charming house with its olde worlde atmosphere makes a good centre for touring the coast between Plymouth and Torbay.

3hc ✖ (ex guide dogs)
⁽ᵐ⁾ CTV 5P nc 150 acres arable beef mixed sheep

HARLECH Gwynedd Map **06** SH53

SELECTED

GH ⓠⓠⓠⓠ **Castle Cottage Hotel** Pen Llech LL46 2YL
☎(0766) 780479
Recently taken over by the Roberts family, this quaint little hotel lies a stone's throw away from the famous castle. Bedrooms are a little compact, but in the cottage tradition, and are comfortable. En suite rooms are modern, and there is a bowl of fresh fruit for each guest. There are two comfortable lounges, each one with a colour television and a small collection of books. The restaurant is a feature in its own right, with the chef proprietor making good use of fresh local produce. Food is imaginative and very attractively presented. This is a good base from which to tour North Wales, and convenient for the local championship golf course.

6rm(4⇩🯁2hc) Ⓡ sB&B£14-£17 sB&B⇩🯁£34 dB&B£37
dB&B⇩🯁£37 LDO 9pm

Lic ⁽ᵐ⁾ CTV
Credit Cards ① ③ ⓔ

GH ⓠⓠⓠ **Gwrach Ynys Country** Ynys, Talsarnau LL47 6TS
☎(0766) 780742
Feb-Nov
Beautifully restored Edwardian country house situated in own grounds, close to Harlech.

7rm(1⇩5🯁1hc)(2fb) CTV in all bedrooms Ⓡ sB&B£15
dB&B⇩🯁£30-£34 WB&B£100-£115 WBDif145-£165 LDO noon
⁽ᵐ⁾ CTV 10P
ⓔ

FH ⓠ Mrs E A Jones **Tyddyn Gwynt** *(SH601302)* LL46 2TH
(2.5m off B4573 (A496)) ☎(0766) 780298
A traditional farmhouse, Tyddyn Gwynt is approximately 1.5 miles south east of Harlech and surrounded by spectacular mountain scenery. The accommodation is pleasant and well maintained.

4rm(3hc)(1fb) Ⓡ ✳ sB&Bfr£12
dB&Bfr£22 WB&Bfr£70 WBDifr£100
CTV 6P 3 acres small holding
ⓔ

INN ⓠ **Rum Hole Hotel** Ffordd Newydd LL46 2UB
☎(0766) 780477
Closed 23 Dec-2 Jan
Modern accommodation and a good range of bar meals are available at this roadside inn which stands at the lower end of the village.

8rm(2⇩3🯁3hc)(5fb) CTV in all bedrooms Ⓡ
✖ (ex guide dogs) ✳ sB&B£15
dB&B⇩🯁£36 Lunch £7.20-£10.40 LDO 9.30pm
CTV 25P

HARROGATE North Yorkshire Map **08** SE35

GH ⓠ **Abbey Lodge Hotel** 31 Ripon Rd HG1 2JL
☎(0423) 569712
Smart, stylish house with very comfortable bedrooms and pleasant public areas.

17rm(3⇩11🯁3hc)(3fb) CTV in all bedrooms Ⓡ
✖ (ex guide dogs) LDO 8pm
Lic ⁽ᵐ⁾ 18P 2🐾

GH ⓠⓠⓠ **Acacia Lodge** 21 Ripon Rd HG1 2JL
☎(0423) 560752
Closed Xmas & New Year
Conveniently located for all of Harrogate's conference facilities, this is a comfortable guesthouse with well-appointed and attractively decorated bedrooms. Peter Bateson is a welcoming host and guests here are well cared for.

5rm(1⇩4🯁)(1fb) CTV in all bedrooms Ⓡ ✖ (ex guide dogs)
sB&B⇩🯁fr£20 dB&B⇩🯁fr£38
⁽ᵐ⁾ CTV 5P 1🐾

SELECTED

GH ⓠⓠⓠⓠ **Alexa House & Stable Cottages** 26 Ripon
Rd HG1 2JJ ☎(0423) 501988
Closed 21 Dec-4 Jan
Built in 1830 for Baron de Ferrier, this attractive house is now a short walk from the town centre. Marilyn Bateson provides a warm welcome and ensures her guests are well looked after. All bedrooms are well equipped and range from compact, modern rooms to spacious, traditional accommodation. Some are situated in a converted stable block. There is also a spacious dining room and cosy bar lounge.

9rm(2⇨5♪2hc)Annexe 4♪ (1fb) CTV in all bedrooms ®
✗ sB&Bfr£21 sB&B⇨♪fr£21
dB&B⇨♪fr£42 WB&Bfr£132.30
Lic ♔ CTV 14P
£

GH Ⓠ *Argyll House* 80 Kings Rd HG1 5JX ☎(0423) 562408
*This attractive Victorian terraced house is close to the exhibition
centre and within easy walking distance of the town centre.
Bedrooms are simply furnished and are neat and clean. Good
breakfasts are served in the cosy dining room.*
6hc (1fb) ® LDO 4pm
♔ CTV 6P

GH ⓆⓆⓆ *Ashley House Hotel* 36-40 Franklin Rd HG1 5EE
☎(0423) 507474 & 560858
*Three town houses have been combined to provide well-equipped
accommodation, a spacious dining room, 2 lounges and a cosy bar.*
17rm(2⇨9♪6hc)(2fb) CTV in all bedrooms ® ✳ sB&B£18.75
sB&B⇨♪£23.50-£25 dB&B£32
dB&B⇨♪£39-£46 WB&B£122.50-£168 LDO noon
Lic ♔ CTV 6P
Credit Cards ①③

GH ⓆⓆⓆ *Ashwood House* 7 Spring Grove HG1 2HS
☎(0423) 560081
Closed 24 Dec-1 Jan
*This well-maintained Edwardian house stands in a quiet cul-de-sac
just off the Ripon road, close to the town centre. The bedrooms are
well appointed and there is a cosy lounge and a most attractive
dining room.*
▶

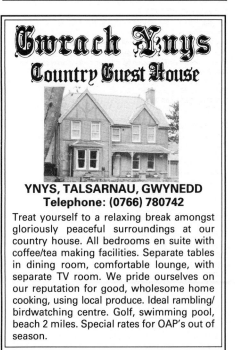

10rm(8🛁🚿2hc)(2fb)🚭in 1 bedroom CTV in all bedrooms ® 🐕 sB&B£16.20-£18 sB&B🛁🚿£22.50-£25 dB&B£32.40-£36 dB&B🛁🚿£36-£44 WB&B£113.40-£154
Lic ♨ CTV 5P
[£]

GH [Q][Q][Q] **Aston Hotel** 7-9 Franklin Mount HG1 5EJ
☎(0423) 564262
Situated close to the town centre and Exhibition Centre, the Aston Hotel is comfortable and well appointed with a welcoming and relaxed atmosphere. Bedrooms are nicely decorated and there is a comfortable lounge.
16🚿 (1fb) CTV in all bedrooms ® 🐕 (ex guide dogs) sB&B🚿£20-£24
dB&B🚿£40-£44 WB&B£140-£168 WBDi£210-£238 LDO noon
Lic ♨ CTV 10P 1🚗
Credit Cards [1] [3] [£]

GH [Q][Q][Q] **The Cavendish Hotel** 3-5 Valley Dr HG2 0JJ
☎(0423) 509637 FAX (0423) 504429
Conveniently placed guesthouse with nicely equipped bedrooms.
12rm(3🛁9🚿) CTV in all bedrooms ® sB&B🛁🚿£25-£30 dB&B🛁🚿£48-£60 WB&B£140-£200 WBDi£200-£250 LDO 6pm
Lic
Credit Cards [1] [3]

GH [Q][Q] **The Dales Hotel** 101 Valley Dr HG2 0JP
☎(0423) 507248
This friendly guesthouse stands opposite the beautiful Valley Gardens close to the town centre. Mrs Burton is a welcoming hostess and provides very well-equipped, pretty bedrooms and a comfortable lounge.
8rm(3🚿5hc)(2fb) CTV in all bedrooms ® * sB&B£18-£19 sB&B🚿£28-£30 dB&B£34-£38 dB&B🚿£40 LDO 9am
Lic ♨ CTV 1P
Credit Cards [1] [3] [£]

GH [Q][Q][Q] **Delaine Hotel** 17 Ripon Rd HG1 2JL
☎(0423) 567974
Rupert and Marian Viner are the friendly hosts at this hotel which is on the A61 Ripon road. It has comfortable, attractive bedrooms, a lovely lounge and a small bar. A home-cooked meal is available upon request.
9rm(1🛁3🚿5hc)Annexe 2rm(1🛁1🚿) CTV in all bedrooms ® 🐕 * sB&B£20-£25 dB&B£36-£44
dB&B🛁🚿£40-£48 WB&Bfr£130 LDO 2pm
Lic ♨ CTV 12P nc2yrs
Credit Cards [1] [3] [£]

GH [Q] **Gillmore Hotel** 98 Kings Rd HG1 5HH ☎(0423) 503699
An imaginative and well-organised conversion of 2 terraced houses.
22rm(2🛁4🚿16hc)(8fb) CTV in 9 bedrooms ®
sB&B£17.50-£20 dB&B£23-£26
dB&B🛁🚿£36 WB&Bfr£105 WBDifr£154 LDO 4pm
Lic ♨ CTV 20P snooker
[£]

GH [Q][Q] **Glenayr** 19 Franklin Mount HG1 5EJ
☎(0423) 504259
6rm(5🚿1hc) CTV in all bedrooms ® 🐕 (ex guide dogs)
sB&B£17.50-£19.50
dB&B🚿£41-£45 WB&B£110-£145 WBDi£175-£210 LDO 4.30pm
Lic ♨ 3P
[£]

[Q] is for quality. For a full explanation of this AA quality award, consult the Contents page.

GH [Q][Q][Q] ***Grafton Hotel*** 1-3 Franklin Mount HG1 5EJ
☎(0423) 508491
Situated in a quiet residential area close to the town centre, this cosy little hotel has a warm atmosphere. Monika and Les Mitchell provide good home cooking and attractive, well-appointed accommodation.
17rm(1🛁11🚿5hc)(1fb) CTV in all bedrooms ® 🐕 LDO 4pm
Lic ♨ CTV 3P
Credit Cards [1] [2] [3] [5]

GH [Q][Q][Q] **Knox Mill House** Knox Mill Ln, Killinghall HG3 2AE ☎(0423) 560650
Situated in the picturesque hamlet of Knox, this old house is full of character, with many original features. Two of the bedrooms are en suite. Mr and Mrs Thompson are welcoming hosts and serve breakfast around a communial dining table.
3rm(2🚿1hc) ® 🐕 dB&Bfr£28 dB&B🚿fr£32
♨ CTV 4P

GH [Q][Q] **Lamont House** 12 St Mary's Walk HG2 0LW
☎(0423) 567143
Closed Xmas
Set in a quiet area, just a few minutes' walk from the centre of this spa town, this family-run guesthouse offers bright and tastefully furnished accommodation.
9rm(2🚿7hc)(2fb) CTV in all bedrooms ® * sB&Bfr£16 dB&Bfr£30 dB&B🚿fr£50 LDO 6pm
Lic ♨ CTV
[£]

GH [Q][Q] ***Oakbrae*** 3 Springfield Av HG1 2HR ☎(0423) 567682
Closed Xmas
Small, picturesque semidetached house, near Conference Centre, with well-proportioned lounge and breakfast room, and pleasant bedrooms.
▶

GLENAYR

19 Franklin Mount, Harrogate HG1 5EJ
Telephone: (0423) 504259

Set in a peaceful tree lined avenue of Harrogate, an elegant town which became fashionable in the 19th century as a Spa. The six light and pleasantly furnished bedrooms have en suite bathroom, colour TV, tea & coffee tray, clock radio and central heating. A substantial English breakfast and an excellent home cooked dinner are available carefully chosen for quality and to please the palate. Relax in comfortable sofas with a drink before dinner or as a night cap. A warm welcome and genuine hospitality await you at this comfortable Victorian home.

173

6rm(1⇌4⌐1hc)(1fb) CTV in all bedrooms ® LDO 4pm
🍽 CTV 4P nc2yrs

GH QQQ Prince's Hotel 7 Granby Rd HG1 4ST
☎(0423) 883469
This charming Victorian house is full of character and has individually styled, comfortable bedrooms, many of which contain antique furniture.
8rm(2⇌2⌐4hc)(1fb)⅟in 1 bedroom CTV in all bedrooms ®
✗ ✱ sB&B£15-£17 dB&B£30-£50
dB&B⇌⌐£30-£50 LDO 9am
Lic 🍽 CTV ⁄P nc3yrs

GH QQ The Richmond 56 Dragon View, Skipton Rd
HG1 4DG ☎(0423) 530612
Set just off the A59 at the northern tip of the Stray, the Richmond is comfortable and friendly, with a cosy lounge and well-appointed bedrooms.
6rm(5⌐1hc)(1fb) CTV in all bedrooms ® ✗ (ex guide dogs) ✱
sB&B£18 sB&B⌐£18 dB&B⌐£36 WB&B£126
🍽 CTV 3P
£

GH QQ Roan 90 Kings Rd HG1 5JX ☎(0423) 503087
Closed 25-26 Dec
This attractively converted Victorian town house is situated close to the town's conference centre and exhibition centre. The compact bedrooms are well kept and comfortable, and there is a cosy lounge with a colour television for guests' use.
7rm(3⌐4hc)(1fb) ® ✗ sB&Bfr£15 dB&Bfr£28
dB&B⌐fr£33 LDO 4.30pm
🍽 CTV ⁄P nc7yrs
£

GH QQQ Scotia House Hotel 66/68 Kings Rd HG1 5JR
☎(0423) 504361
Immediately opposite the conference centre, this small family-run hotel has a lounge, cocktail bar and well-appointed dining room. Most bedrooms are en suite and are all well furnished, comfortable and well equipped.
14rm(1⇌10⌐3hc)(1fb) CTV in all bedrooms ® ✱
sB&B£20-£22 sB&B⇌⌐£22-£25
dB&B⇌⌐£44-£50 WB&B£150-£154 WBDi£190-£195 LDO 6pm
Lic 🍽 CTV 8P nc7yrs

GH Q *Shelbourne* 78 Kings Rd HG1 5JX ☎(0423) 504390
This neat guesthouse is set in the town centre and has very friendly, resident proprietors.
7hc (2fb) ® LDO noon
Lic 🍽 CTV 1P

GH QQQ Wharfedale House 28 Harlow Moor Dr HG2 0JY
☎(0423) 522233
Hospitable hosts Tricia and Howard Quinn have made Wharfedale House into a most welcoming small hotel. Situated in a quiet area overlooking Valley Gardens it provides comfortable, well-equipped accommodation and good home cooking.
8rm(1⇌7⌐)(2fb) CTV in all bedrooms ® sB&B⇌⌐£24
dB&B⇌⌐£44 WB&B£132-£144 WBDi£191.50-£203.50 LDO 4pm
Lic 🍽 3P
£

Street plans of certain towns and cities will be found in a separate section at the back of the book.

HARROP FOLD Lancashire Map **07** SD74

SELECTED

FH QQQQ Mr & Mrs P Wood ***Harrop Fold Country Farmhouse Hotel*** *(SD746492)* BBY 4PJ
☎Bolton-by-Bowland(02007) 600 Telex no 635562
Closed Jan
The experienced Wood family are dedicated to ensuring that guests are well looked after in their delightful 17th-century farmhouse, situated in attractive countryside. The bedrooms are most comfortably furnished, and are equipped with modern facilities and many thoughtful extras. The public areas are full of character, and there is a most inviting and relaxing first floor lounge. The cosy dining room serves excellent dinners, carefully prepared from local produce.
5⇌ Annexe 2⇌ CTV in all bedrooms ® ✗ LDO 8.45pm
Lic 🍽 16P nc 280 acres sheep
Credit Cards [1] [3]

HARROW Greater London

London plan **4** B5 (pages 000-000)

GH QQ Central Hotel 6 Hindes Rd HA1 1SJ ☎081-427 0893
Ideally situated in a residential area near the town centre, this small, simply appointed hotel is under the personal supervision of the owners.
10rm(3⌐7hc)(3fb) CTV in all bedrooms ® ✗ ✱ sB&Bfr£28
sB&B⌐fr£36 dB&Bfr£38 dB&B⌐fr£46
🍽 CTV 12P
Credit Cards [1] [3]

GH QQ Crescent Lodge Hotel 58/62 Welldon Crescent
HA1 1QR ☎081-863 5491 & 081-863 5163 FAX 081-427 5965
Small and friendly, this commercial style establishment has compact well-equipped bedrooms, a comfortable, bright lounge and breakfast room.
21rm(10⌐11hc)(2fb) CTV in all bedrooms ®
✗ (ex guide dogs) ✱ sB&Bfr£26 sB&B⌐fr£42 dB&Bfr£44
dB&B⌐fr£54 LDO 8.30pm
🍽 CTV 8P 1🚗 (£2 per night) 🏠
Credit Cards [1]

GH Q Hindes Hotel 8 Hindes Rd HA1 1SJ ☎081-427 7468
Hindes Hotel provides functional accommodation with an open plan breakfast room, and bedrooms with colour TV and beverage facilities. There is a small forecourt car park and metered street parking close by.
13rm(1⌐12hc)(2fb) CTV in all bedrooms ® ✗ ✱ sB&Bfr£28
dB&Bfr£38 dB&B⌐fr£48
🍽 CTV 5P
Credit Cards [1] [3] £

GH QQ Kempsford House Hotel 21-23 St Johns Rd HA1 2EE
☎081-427 4983
Closed Xmas 2 wks
Family-run private hotel offering basic but comfortable accommodation.
32rm(10⌐22hc)(6fb) CTV in 30 bedrooms TV in 2 bedrooms
✗ (ex guide dogs) sB&B£26.45-£29.90 sB&B⌐£36.80-£41.40
dB&B£36.80-£41.40 dB&B⌐£46-£52.90
Lic 🍽 30P
Credit Cards [1] [3] £

See advertisement on page 177

GH QQQ *Lindal Hotel* 2 Hindes Rd HA1 1SJ ☎081-863 3164
This welcoming, family-run hotel has been completely refurbished to offer high standards of accommodation. The bedrooms are modern and well equipped and complemented by a comfortable lounge-cum-bar and a pretty restaurant.
20rm(3⇌14⌐3hc)(1fb) CTV in all bedrooms ®
✗ (ex guide dogs) LDO 8.30pm

▶

Lic ♨ 20P
Credit Cards [3]

HARTFIELD East Sussex Map **05** TQ43

FH [Q][Q][Q] Mrs C Cooper **Bolebroke Watermill** *(TQ481373)* Perry Hill, Edenbridge Rd TN7 4JP (off B2026 1m N of Hartfield) ☎(0892) 770425
Mar-Nov
This charming and quite unique watermill is set in 6.5 acres of secluded woodlands, with an ancient history dating back to King William in 1086. The tools and machinery are still much in evidence. The bedrooms are reached by very steep staircases and are hence completely unsuitable for anybody with restricted mobility. The bedrooms are comfortable and well appointed, and all have private facilities. There is a comfortable lounge, and dinner, available by prior arrangement, is served in the adjoining mill house.
2🛁 🚭in all bedrooms CTV in all bedrooms Ⓡ 🐕 sB&B🛁£35 dB&B🛁£40 LDO 10am
♨ CTV 16P nc7yrs supervised rough shooting 6 acres smallholding

HARTLAND Devon Map **02** SS22

GH [Q][Q] Fosfelle EX39 6EF ☎(0237) 441273
Well-kept gardens surround this 17th-century manor which now offers comfortable accommodation. The spacious bar and TV lounge are popular with non-residents for coffee and afternoon tea. Resident proprietors provide simple home-cooked meals and personal service.
7rm(1🛁1🚿5hc)(2fb) CTV in 3 bedrooms TV in 2 bedrooms Ⓡ 🐕 sB&B£16-£17.50 dB&B£30-£32 dB&B🛁🚿£35-£37 WB&B£95-£100 WBDi£135-£155 LDO 9pm
Lic ♨ CTV 20P ⌂ 🎣 snooker
Credit Cards [1] [3] [£]

HASTINGS & ST LEONARDS East Sussex Map **05** TQ80

GH [Q][Q] Argyle 32 Cambridge Garden TN34 1EN ☎(0424) 421294
Closed Xmas
Comfortable and well situated guesthouse near the seafront and local amenities.
8rm(3🚿5hc)(1fb) Ⓡ 🐕 ✱ sB&Bfr£13 sB&B🚿fr£18 dB&Bfr£24 dB&B🚿fr£28 WB&Bfr£77
♨ CTV P̸ nc4yrs

GH [Q][Q][Q] Eagle House 12 Pevensey Rd TN38 0JZ ☎(0424) 430535 & 441273
Quietly situated away from the crowds, this friendly privately run hotel has a choice of very well-equipped bedrooms, a beautifully furnished restaurant, a lounge and bar facilities. Service is extensive and helpful, and reflects the individuality and personal style of the proprietors.
23rm(20🛁🚿3hc)(2fb) CTV in all bedrooms Ⓡ ✱ sB&B£27 sB&B🛁🚿£31 dB&B£38 dB&B🛁🚿£45 LDO 8.30pm
Lic ♨ 13P
Credit Cards [1] [2] [3] [5] [£]

🛏**GH [Q] Gainsborough Hotel** 5 Carlisle Pde TN34 1JG ☎(0424) 434010
Closed 24-26 Dec
Well-maintained seafront house with modern well-equipped bedrooms and comfortable public rooms.
12rm(3🛁5🚿4hc)(3fb) CTV in all bedrooms Ⓡ sB&B£13-£16 sB&B🛁🚿£15-£19 dB&B£26-£32 dB&B🛁🚿£30-£38 WB&B£91-£133 WBDi£136.50-£178.50 LDO 4.30pm
Lic ♨
[£]

SELECTED

GH [Q][Q][Q][Q] Parkside House 59 Lower Park Rd TN34 2LD ☎Hastings(0424) 433096
Enjoying a magnificent location overlooking Alexandra Park, this charming house is the home of Janet and Brian Kent. They offer comfortable rooms, one with a Louis XVI bed, and well-appointed public rooms together with well-prepared food.
4rm(2🚿2hc)(1fb)🚭in all bedrooms CTV in all bedrooms Ⓡ 🐕 (ex guide dogs) sB&B🚿£22-£28 dB&B£28-£32 dB&B🚿£32-£36 WB&B£95-£125 WBDi£130-£165 LDO 3pm
♨ CTV P̸
[£]

GH [Q][Q][Q] Tower Hotel 28 Tower Rd West TN38 0RG ☎(0424) 427217
This welcoming Victorian hotel, half a mile from the seafront and convenient for local amenities, has comfortable and individually decorated bedrooms. There is a lounge and a cosy bar, soon to include a new conservatory.
10rm(6🛁🚿4hc)(2fb) CTV in all bedrooms Ⓡ sB&B£16-£20 sB&B🛁🚿£18-£22 dB&B£32-£40 dB&B🛁🚿£36-£44 WB&B£96-£120 WBDi£143-£167 LDO 4pm
Lic ♨ CTV P̸
[£]

GH [Q][Q] ***Waldorf Hotel*** 4 Carlisle Pde TN34 1JG ☎(0424) 422185
This friendly, family-run hotel is conveniently located for all amenities and has a prime seafront situation. There is a pleasant dining room and adjoining lounge with a bar. Many of the neat bedrooms have good sea views.
12rm(3🛁1🚿8hc)(3fb) CTV in all bedrooms Ⓡ 🐕 LDO 11.30am
Lic CTV P̸

FH [Q][Q][Q] Mrs B Yarker **Filsham** *(TQ784096)* 111 Harley Shute Rd TN38 8BY ☎(0424) 433109
Closed Xmas & New Year
Now in a residential area, this listed Sussex farmhouse offers a wealth of rural charm, in addition to pretty bedrooms richly furnished with antiques, combined with television, central heating and tea and coffee-making facilities. One bedroom has private facilities as well.
3rm 🚭in all bedrooms CTV in all bedrooms Ⓡ 🐕 ✱ dB&B£25-£40 WB&B£80-£140 WBDi£150-£185
♨ CTV 4P 1 acres non-working
[£]

INN [Q][Q][Q] Highlands 1 Boscobel Rd TN38 0LU ☎Hastings(0424) 420299
Quietly situated on a steep hillside behind the Royal Victorian Hotel, this friendly, well-managed inn has modern, well-equipped bedrooms, a small old-fashioned lounge, public bar and a good restaurant. Craig O'Brien, the young chef, uses fresh ingredients in his cooking for the à la carte and table d'hôte menus. Fish is his speciality.
9🛁🚿 (1fb) CTV in all bedrooms Ⓡ 🐕 (ex guide dogs) LDO 9.30pm
♨ CTV 8P
Credit Cards [1] [3] [£]

HASWELL PLOUGH Co Durham Map **12** NZ34

GH [Q] The Gables Front St DH6 2EW ☎091-526 2982
This is a licensed property situated on the B1283, 6 miles east of Durham. The bar and the dining room are particularly attractive, and there are ample car parking facilities.
5hc (3fb) CTV in all bedrooms Ⓡ sB&B£22-£25 dB&B£35-£50 LDO 9.30pm

Lic 20P
£

HATHERSAGE Derbyshire Map **08** SK 28

FH QQQ Mrs T C Wain *Highlow Hall (SK219802)* S30 1AX
☎Hope Valley(0433) 50393
mid Mar-Oct
*Surrounded by farmland, this 16th-century manor house stands in
the heart of the Peak District National Park and has superb views
of the countryside. It is found by taking the B6001 to Bakewell
and then following signs to Abney.*
6hc (2fb) ®
Lic CTV 12P 900 acres mixed sheep

HATTON Warwickshire Map **04** SP26

SELECTED

GH QQQQ **Northleigh House** Five Ways Rd CV35 7HZ
☎Warwick(0926) 484203
Closed 17 Dec-5 Jan
*An ideal base for touring historic Warwickshire, this house is
surrounded by beautiful gardens. All bedrooms are well
equipped with en suite facilities, and the attractive dining
room opens on to a patio, where Sylvia Fenwick is pleased to
serve breakfast on warm mornings.*
6⇨↑ ⨉in all bedrooms CTV in all bedrooms ®
sB&B⇨↑fr£26 dB&B⇨↑£39-£45
 CTV 8P
£
See advertisement under **WARWICK** on page 372

HAVANT Hampshire

See **Emsworth**

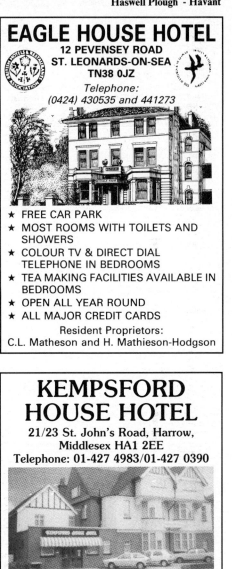

HAVERFORDWEST Dyfed

See **Broad Haven**

HAVERIGG Cumbria Map **07** SD17

GH [Q][Q][Q] **Dunelm Cottage** Main St LA18 4EX
☎Millom(0229) 770097
Two charming cottages have been converted into one tastefully decorated to provide 3 bedrooms, a cosy lounge with TV, and a small dining room with 1 large table. A free public car park is opposite.
3hc [R] ✱ dB&B£44-£48 (incl dinner) LDO 6.30pm
♨ CTV nc10yrs

HAWES North Yorkshire Map **07** SD88

GH [Q][Q][Q] **Steppe Haugh** Town Head DL8 3RJ
☎Wensleydale(0969) 667645
One of the oldest houses in Hawes, this 17th-century stone house stands on the edge of the village. The bedrooms are small and cosy and have lovely views. The pleasant, comfortable lounge has a log fire and colour television.
6rm(2🚿4hc) CTV in 1 bedroom [R] 🐕 ✱ sB&B£14-£20 sB&B🚿£25 dB&B£25 dB&B🚿£30-£35 WB&B£87.50 WBDi£161 LDO 5pm
Lic ♨ CTV 8P nc10yrs

HAWKSHEAD Cumbria Map **07** SD39

GH [Q][Q] ***Greenbank Country House Hotel*** Main St LA22 0NS
☎(09666) 497
Charming and friendly little hotel in 17th-century former farmhouse.
10rm(2🚿8hc)(1fb) [R] LDO 4.30pm
Lic ♨ CTV 12P

GH [Q][Q] **Ivy House** LA22 0NS ☎(09666) 204
Mar-Oct
Attractive, well-furnished Georgian house.
6rm(3🛁3🚿)Annexe 5hc (2fb) [R] ✱ sB&B£20.25-£24.75 sB&B🛁🚿£24-£27.50 dB&B£40.50-£49.50 dB&B🛁🚿£48-£55 (incl dinner) WB&B£110.25-£140 WBDi£141.75-£171.50 LDO 6pm
Lic ♨ CTV 14P 🎣 bicycles & windsurfers available
[£]

GH [Q][Q][Q] **Rough Close Country House** LA22 0QF
☎(09666) 370
Apr-Oct rs Mar
A fine country house overlooking Esthwaite Water and set in lovely gardens. Guests are assured of a friendly welcome and very comfortable accommodation, including a cosy little residents' bar. Excellent, home cooked dinner of 5 courses.
6rm(3🛁🚿3hc)🚭in all bedrooms [R] 🐕 (ex guide dogs) sB&B£28.50 dB&B£53 dB&B🛁🚿£59 (incl dinner) WBDi£175-£196 LDO 7pm
Lic ♨ CTV 10P nc5yrs
Credit Cards [1] [3] [£]

FH [Q][Q][Q] Wendy & Dennis Chandler ***Walker Ground Manor*** *(SD349981)* LA22 0PD ☎(09666) 219
More of a smallholding than a farmhouse, this historic manor is furnished with antiques and items collected by Mr and Mrs Chandler. Guests dine house party-style, more often than not in the company of their affable hosts.
3rm(2🛁) [R] 🐕
♨ CTV 6P nc9yrs 18 acres sheep cattle

INN [Q] **Kings Arms Hotel** LA22 0NZ ☎(09666) 372
16th-century inn with oak beams and open fire, overlooking the village square.
8rm(4🚿4hc)(2fb) CTV in all bedrooms [R] ✱ sB&B£20.50 sB&B🚿£23 dB&B£34 dB&B🚿£42 Lunch £6-£8.55 Dinner £6-£8.55&alc LDO 9pm
♨
Credit Cards [1] [3] [£]

INN [Q][Q][Q] **Red Lion** The Square LA22 0HB ☎(09666) 213
Closed Xmas Day
An inn at the centre of the village serves real ale to accompany its generously portioned bar meals and offers an à la carte menu in the evenings.
8🚿 (2fb) CTV in all bedrooms [R] 🐕 ✱ sB&B£25 sB&B🚿£25 dB&B🚿£48 WB&Bfr£150 WBDifr£220 Bar Lunch £3-£8 High tea £2.50-£4 Dinner £8.50&alc LDO 9pm
♨ 8P
Credit Cards [1] [3] [£]

HAWORTH West Yorkshire Map **07** SE03

GH [Q][Q] **Ferncliffe Hotel** Hebden Rd BD22 8RS
☎(0535) 43405
This is a small and comfortable hotel that stands in an elevated position overlooking the valley. A good range of home-cooked food is available from the extensive menu.
6🚿 (1fb) CTV in all bedrooms [R] sB&B🚿£18-£20 dB&B🚿£36-£40 WB&B£126-£140 WBDi£182-£196 LDO 8.30pm
Lic ♨ CTV 12P
Credit Cards [3]

HAYDON BRIDGE Northumberland Map **12** NY86

SELECTED

GH [Q][Q][Q][Q] **Langley Castle** Langley-on-Tyne NE4 5LU
☎(0434) 688888
This hotel has been splendidly modernised and yet still retains the ambience of a genuine small castle. Each of the spacious bedrooms has its own, individual qualities, and their luxury has been extended to the bathrooms. The first floor lounge is most impressive in its elegance and comfort, as is the restaurant which offers interesting menus. For travellers looking for the unusual, this is the ideal place to stay.
8🛁 (3fb) CTV in all bedrooms ✱ sB&B🛁£39-£72 dB&B🛁£50-£94 LDO 9pm
Lic lift CTV 50P
Credit Cards [1] [2] [3] [5] [£]

HAYFIELD Derbyshire Map **07** SK08

INN [Q] **Sportsman** Kinder Rd SK12 5EL
☎New Mills(0663) 742118
Traditional country inn, with well-furnished, modern bedrooms, in valley of the River Set on the approach to Kinder Scout.
7rm(5🚿2hc)(1fb) CTV in all bedrooms [R] sB&B£24.50-£29.50 sB&B🚿£24.50-£29.50 dB&B£39-£49 dB&B🚿£39-£49 WB&B£136.50 WBDi£206.50 Lunch £5.50-£14.50alc Dinner £5.50-£14.50alc LDO 9.30pm
♨ 20P
Credit Cards [1] [3] [£]

HAYLING ISLAND Hampshire Map **04** SU70

SELECTED

GH [Q][Q][Q][Q] **Cockle Warren Cottage Hotel** 36 Seafront PO11 9HL ☎(0705) 464961
Mr and Mrs Skelton have created an appealing, comfortable hotel in this seafront, tile-hung house. The bedrooms have many useful extras, pine furnishings and beautifully kept shower rooms. The lounge has an open fire, and Mrs Skelton's excellent French country cooking, produced from fresh ingredients, is served in a cool, tiled conservatory with marble topped tables. With Mr Skelton's natural hospitality, this makes for a most enjoyable stay.

4🛁🚿 Annexe 1🛁🚿 🚭in all bedrooms CTV in all bedrooms 🚫🐕 (ex guide dogs) ✱ sB&B🛁🚿£30-£45 dB&B🛁🚿£44-£68 WB&B£154-£238 WBDi£283.50-£367.50 LDO 4.30pm
Lic 🍴 7P 2🚗 nc10yrs 🏊(heated) ⛳ 18
Credit Cards [1] [3]

GH [Q][Q][Q] The Rook Hollow Hotel 84 Church Rd PO11 0NX ☎(0705) 467080 & 469620
Wendy Prior creates a friendly, relaxed atmosphere, and provides attentive service at this centrally situated Edwardian building. The bedrooms are comfortable and well equipped.
7rm(4🚿3hc)🚭in 1 bedroom CTV in all bedrooms ® sB&B£20-£23 dB&B£30-£36
dB&B🚿£38-£48 WB&B£140-£161 WBDi£170-£200 LDO 9pm
Lic 🍴 CTV 9P
Credit Cards [1] [3] [5] [£]

HAY-ON-WYE Powys Map **03** SO24

GH [Q][Q][Q] York House Hardwick Rd, Cusop HR3 5QX (1m SE in England) ☎(0497) 820705
rs Xmas
This pleasant guesthouse has attractive gardens and is a short walk from the town centre on the Peterchurch road. The bedrooms are pretty and well maintained, and there is a comfortable lounge.
6rm(1🚿5hc)(1fb)🚭in all bedrooms CTV in 3 bedrooms ®
sB&B£15.50-£19.50 sB&B🚿£25 dB&B£31-£33
dB&B🚿£36-£40 WB&B£97.65-£126 WBDi£157.50-£185.85
LDO 5pm
🍴 CTV 8P nc8yrs [£]

HEASLEY MILL Devon Map **03** SS73

GH [Q][Q] Heasley House EX36 3LE ☎North Molton(05984) 213
Closed Feb
A Georgian-style building, full of atmosphere and furnished with antiques, Heasley House overlooks a mill stream.
8rm(2🛁3🚿3hc) sB&Bfr£16 sB&B🛁🚿fr£17.50 dB&Bfr£32
dB&B🛁🚿fr£35 WB&Bfr£110 WBDifr£170 LDO 5pm
Lic 🍴 CTV 11P
Credit Cards [1] [3] [£]

HEATHROW AIRPORT Greater London

London plan **4** A3 (pages 230-231)
See also Slough
GH [Q][Q] *The Cottage* 150 High St, Cranford TW5 9PD
☎081-897 1815
Set in a quiet cul-de-sac close to Heathrow, The Cottage offers comfortable accommodation in a relaxed, informal atmosphere, under the proprietors' personal supervision.
6hc (1fb) CTV in all bedrooms 🚫🐕 (ex guide dogs) 🍴 20P

HEBDEN BRIDGE West Yorkshire Map **07** SD92

GH [Q][Q][Q] Redacre Mill Redacre, Mytholmroyd HX7 5DQ
☎Halifax(0422) 885563
Feb-Nov
Standing beside the tranquil Rochdale canal, this tastefully converted mill has exceptionally well-furnished and equipped bedrooms. The resident owners give a warm and friendly welcome.
5🛁🚿 (1fb)🚭in all bedrooms CTV in all bedrooms ®
🚫🐕 (ex guide dogs) sB&B🛁🚿£30 dB&B🛁🚿£40 LDO 8pm
Lic 🍴 8P
Credit Cards [1] [3]

HELENSBURGH Strathclyde *Dunbartonshire*

See **Cardross**

See advertisement on page 181

HELMSLEY North Yorkshire Map **08** SE68

GH [Q][Q] Beaconsfield Bondgate YO6 5BW ☎(0439) 71346
Centrally situated in this attractive market town, this comfortable guesthouse has pleasantly decorated bedrooms with colour TV and tea/coffee making facilities. Mrs Meadows provides a good home-cooked breakfast with plenty of choice.
6hc CTV in all bedrooms [R] 🐕 ✱ sB&Bfr£23 dB&Bfr£38
♨ 8P nc12yrs

HELTON Cumbria Map **12** NY52

GH [Q][Q] Holywell Country CA10 2QA
☎Hackthorpe(09312) 231
Closed 20 Dec-2 Jan
Four miles from Penrith, this establishment is situated in a beautiful location overlooking the village of Helton. The house, set in its own grounds, is comfortably furnished and offers a warm and friendly welcome.
4rm(2🚿2hc) [R] sB&Bfr£20 dB&Bfr£28
dB&B🚿fr£32 WB&B£93-£107 WBDi£150.50-£174.50 LDO 10am
Lic ♨ CTV 6P
[£]

HENFIELD West Sussex Map **04** TQ21

FH [Q][Q] Mrs M Wilkin **Great Wapses** *(TQ242192)* Wineham BN5 9BJ ☎(0273) 492544
This appealing farmhouse is about half a mile off the road in lovely surroundings. Dating back to the 16th century, with a Georgian extension, the house has spacious rooms with private facilities.
3rm(2🛁1🚿)(1fb) CTV in all bedrooms [R] sB&B🛁🚿£20-£25
dB&B🛁🚿£32-£35
♨ 7P 🎾(hard)33 acres mixed

HENLEY-IN-ARDEN Warwickshire Map **07** SP16

GH [Q][Q][Q] *Ashleigh House* Whitley Hill B95 5DL
☎(05642) 2315
Comfortable and welcoming hotel in peaceful area. Interesting gardens.
6rm(2🛁4🚿)Annexe 4🚿 CTV in all bedrooms [R]
♨ CTV 11P nc5yrs
Credit Cards [1] [3]

HENLEY-ON-THAMES Oxfordshire Map **04** SU78

GH [Q] *Flohr's Hotel & Restaurant* Northfield End RG9 2JG
☎(0491) 573412
Simply furnished modern bedrooms together with a high quality formal restaurant.
9rm(1🛁2🚿6hc)(4fb) CTV in all bedrooms [R] LDO 10pm
Lic ♨ 6P
Credit Cards [1] [2] [3] [5]

HENSTRIDGE Somerset Map **03** ST71

FH [Q][Q][Q] Mrs P J Doggrell **Toomer** *(ST708192)*
Templecombe BA8 0PH ☎Templecombe(0963) 250237
200-year-old, stone-built farmhouse with large, walled garden with an Elizabethan dovecote. 1.5 miles west then south off A30.
3rm(1🚿2hc)(2fb) CTV in all bedrooms [R] 🐕 (ex guide dogs) ✱
sB&B£12-£15 sB&B🚿fr£16 dB&B£24-£30
dB&B🚿fr£30 WB&B£84-£180
♨ CTV 6P 🎣 400 acres arable dairy
[£]

This is one of many guidebooks pubished by the AA. The full range is available at any AA Centre or good bookshop.

HEREFORD Hereford & Worcester Map **03** SO54

See also Bodenham, Kingstone & Little Dewchurch
GH [Q][Q] Ferncroft Hotel 144 Ledbury Rd HR1 2TB
☎(0432) 265538
Closed mid Dec-2 Jan
Standing in pleasant gardens in a residential area, yet conveniently close to the town centre, Ferncroft provides comfortable accommodation and is suitable for tourists and commercial visitors.
11rm(6🚿5hc)(2fb) CTV in all bedrooms [R] 🐕 ✱ sB&B£20-£22
sB&B🚿£25-£30 dB&B£35-£40 dB&B🚿£40-£50 LDO 7pm
Lic ♨ CTV 8P
Credit Cards [1] [3]

SELECTED

GH [Q][Q][Q][Q] *Hermitage Manor* Canon Pyon HR4 8NR
(3.5m NW off A4110 towards Canon Pyon)
☎(0432) 760317
Mar-mid Dec
This elegant manor house is set in 11 acres overlooking beautiful countryside and fruit orchards. Mrs Hickling is an excellent hostess, as comments in her visitors' book verify. There are 3 separate lounge areas, including a very impressive oak-panelled lounge. There is also a delightful non-smoking lounge and a smaller TV lounge. The sweeping staircase leads to the 5 well-furnished rooms, all with private facilities. A substantial English breakfast is served, although dinner is not available. A peaceful haven where guests can relax and get away from it all.
3rm(2🛁1🚿) [R] 🐕
♨ CTV 12P 2🚗 nc9yrs

GH [Q] Hopbine Hotel Roman Rd HR1 1LE ☎(0432) 268722
Standing on the A4103, on the northern outskirts of the city, this guesthouse has simple, compact accommodation and is popular because of the friendly, welcoming atmosphere created by the proprietors.
10rm(3🛁7hc)(1fb) CTV in all bedrooms [R] 🐕 (ex guide dogs)
sB&B£17.50-£19.50 sB&B🛁£21-£23 dB&B£30-£35
dB&B🛁£33.50-£38.50 WB&B£122.50-£134 WBDi£178-£192
LDO before noon
CTV 20P
[£]

GH [Q][Q] White Lodge Hotel 50 Ledbury Rd HR1 2SY
☎(0432) 273382
Closed Xmas
Situated on the A368, this small private hotel is only a short walk from the town centre. The rooms are comfortable and well equipped, and the attractive dining room has a very impressive, carved mantlepiece.
7🛁🚿 CTV in all bedrooms [R] 🐕 ✱ sB&B🛁🚿£22
dB&B🛁🚿£38.50 WB&B£134.75-£154 WBDi£182-£203 LDO 5.30pm
Lic ♨ CTV 14P
[£]

↔**FH [Q][Q]** Mrs R A Price **Dinedor Court** *(SO545368)*
Dinedor HR2 6LG (3m SE B4399)
☎Holme Lacy(043273) 481 Due to change to (0432) 870481
Etr-4 Nov
A long drive leads to this peacefully located, 16th-century farmhouse that has attractive, well-kept gardens and access to the River Wye.
3rm(2hc)(1fb) [R] sB&B£12.50-£15.50 dB&B£25-£27
CTV 6P 200 acres mixed
[£]

FH 🅠 Mrs M J Barrell **Orchard** *(SO575384)* Mordiford
HR1 4EJ (Mordiford 3m E off B4224)
☎Holme Lacey(043273) 253 due to change to (0432) 870253
Closed Xmas
Comfortable accommodation is provided at this 17th-century,
stone-built farmhouse, which is set in a quiet location with fine
views of the surrounding countryside.
3hc ⌀in all bedrooms Ⓡ ✳ sB&Bfr£15
dB&B£25-£30 WBDifr£140 LDO 7pm
Lic ⍖ CTV 0P ↗ 57 acres mixed sheep
⊕

HERMITAGE Dorset

see **Holnest**

HERSTMONCEUX East Sussex Map 05 TQ61

GH 🅠🅠 **Cleavers Lyng Country Hotel** Church Rd BN27 1QJ
☎(0323) 833131
Closed 24 Dec-1 Jan
Set in attractive grounds amid peaceful countryside, this charming
16th-century house has comfortable bedrooms complemented by a
TV lounge and an appealing low-beamed dining room with a large
fireplace.
8hc Ⓡ sB&B£15.25-£17.25
dB&B£30.50-£34.50 WB&B£105-£110 WBDi£150-£172.50
LDO 6pm
Lic ⍖ CTV 15P
⊕

HEXHAM Northumberland Map 12 NY96

GH 🅠🅠 **Westbrooke Hotel** Allendale Rd NE46 2DE
☎(0434) 603818
Detached Victorian house with a pretty little garden. Well-
appointed and comfortable bedrooms.

▶

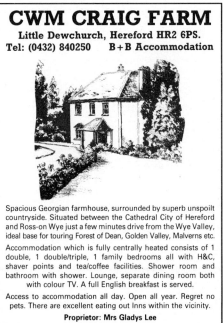

11rm(5🚿6hc)(2fb)🚭in 2 bedrooms CTV in all bedrooms ® *
sB&B£17-£18 dB&B£30 dB&B🚿£40
Lic CTV 3P snooker
Credit Cards [1] [3] [£]

FH [Q][Q][Q] Elizabeth Anne Courage **Rye Hill** *(NY958580)*
Slaley NE47 0AH (5m S off B6306) ☎Slayley(0434) 673259

7rm(4🛁3hc)(2fb) CTV in all bedrooms ® * sB&Bfr£13
sB&B🛁fr£16 dB&Bfr£26
dB&B🛁fr£28 WB&B£82-£100 WBDi£145-£163 LDO 6pm
Lic ♨ CTV 6P games room 30 acres sheep
[£]

HEYSHAM Lancashire Map **07** SD46

⟷**GH** [Q] **Carr-Garth** Bailey Ln LA3 2PS ☎(0524) 51175
Etr-mid Oct
Set within its walled garden in a quiet residential area, this small hotel offers comfortable accommodation.
10hc (2fb) ® sB&B£10.50-£12
dB&B£21-£22 WB&B£67-£76 WBDi£88-£97 LDO 4pm
CTV 8P

HIGHAM Suffolk Map **05** TM03

SELECTED

GH [Q][Q][Q][Q] **The Old Vicarage** CO7 6JY ☎(020637) 248
Set in a tranquil and picturesque village adjacent to St Mary's church. The old vicarage is situated 1.5 miles from the A12, south of Ipswich. The house with it's Elizabethan Tudor exterior has much character dating back to the 15th century with more recent Victorian and Georgian additions. Furnished with quality period and antique pieces and adorned by floral arrangements. The bedrooms are light and spacious offering a high degree of comfort.
3🛁 Annexe 2rm(1🚿1hc)(1fb) CTV in all bedrooms ® *
sB&B£20-£24 sB&B🛁🚿£24-£30 dB&B£36-£40
dB&B🛁🚿£40-£48 WB&B£120-£180
♨ CTV 10P 🏊🎾(hard)🎣 boats
[£]

HIGH CATTON North Yorkshire Map **08** SE75

FH [Q][Q] Mr & Mrs Foster **High Catton Grange** *(SE128541)*
YO4 1EP ☎Stamford Bridge(0759) 71374
Closed Xmas & New Year
One mile east of High Catton crossroads towards Pocklington, this farmhouse is part of a mixed farm. There is a well-maintained garden and a large duckpond to the rear, and the accommodation is of a good standard.
3rm(1hc)(1fb) sB&Bfr£15 dB&Bfr£25
♨ CTV 6P 🏠 300 acres arable beef dairy sheep
[£]

HIGHER BURWARDSLEY Cheshire Map **07** SJ45

INN [Q][Q][Q] **Pheasant** CH3 9PF ☎Tattenhall(0829) 70434
FAX (0829) 71097
Full of character, this 300-year-old beamed inn is situated in delightful rural surroundings on a hilltop, with panoramic views towards Chester and the mountains of north Wales. The excellent modern bedrooms are in a converted barn; each has en suite bathroom, television, radio and tea-making facilities. Meals are served in the Bistro Restaurant, and there is also a wide choice of bar meals and snacks available in the lounge bar.
2🛁🚿 Annexe 6🛁🚿 CTV in all bedrooms ® * sB&B🛁🚿£35
dB&B🛁🚿£45 WB&B£150 WBDi£200 Bar Lunch £1.40-£6alc
Dinner £10-£15alc LDO 9.30pm
♨ 60P nc14yrs
Credit Cards [1] [2] [3] [5] [£]
See advertisement under CHESTER

HIGH WYCOMBE Buckinghamshire Map **04** SU89

GH [Q][Q][Q] ***Amersham Hill*** 52 Amersham Hill HP13 6PQ
☎(0494) 20635
Closed Xmas & New Year
Small, friendly place in which to stay.
8rm(1🚿7hc) CTV in all bedrooms ® 🐕
♨ CTV 9P

GH [Q][Q][Q] **Clifton Lodge Hotel** 210 West Wycombe Rd
HP12 3AR ☎(0494) 440095 & 29062
rs 25 & 26 Dec
This small hotel is undergoing further improvements to its public areas, and the accent is on comfort and modern facilities. Many of the bedrooms have en suite facilities. Clifton Lodge is personally supervised by the proprietor, assisted by friendly, helpful staff.
31rm(12🛁7🚿12hc)(2fb) CTV in all bedrooms ®
🐕 (ex guide dogs) sB&Bfr£28 sB&B🛁🚿fr£44 dB&Bfr£48
dB&B🛁🚿fr£62 WB&Bfr£196 WBDifr£294 LDO 8.45pm
Lic ♨ CTV 28P sauna jacuzzi
Credit Cards [1] [2] [3] [5] [£]

HIMBLETON Hereford & Worcester Map **03** SO95

FH [Q][Q] Mrs P Havard **Phepson** *(SO941599)* WR9 7JZ
☎(090569) 205
Closed Xmas & New Year
The rooms in this 17th-century farmhouse are quite simple in furnishings and décor. The Granary annexe provides en suite rooms of good quality. Set in the heart of the country, yet only 5 miles from the N5 motorway.
5rm(3hc)(1fb) CTV in 2 bedrooms ® sB&B£16-£18
sB&B£17-£20 dB&B£26-£30 dB&B£30-£32 LDO noon
♨ CTV 6P 170 acres beef sheep
[£]

HINCKLEY Leicestershire Map **04** SP49

GH [Q][Q][Q] **Ambion Court Hotel** The Green, Dadlington
CV13 6JB 3m NW ☎(0455) 212292 FAX (0455) 213141
About two miles north of Hinkley, this small hotel is set in a quiet village overlooking the green. Comfortably appointed public rooms and bedrooms (all with en suite facilities) are clean and well maintained.
2🚿 Annexe 5rm(1🛁4🚿) CTV in all bedrooms ® *
sB&B🛁🚿£30-£45
dB&B🛁🚿£40-£60 WB&B£190-£280 WBDi£250-£350 LDO 8.30pm
Lic ♨ CTV 8P nc5yrs
Credit Cards [1] [3] [£]
See advertisement under NUNEATON on page 279

HINTON CHARTERHOUSE Avon Map **03** ST75

GH [Q][Q][Q] **Green Lane House** 1 Green Ln BA3 6BL
☎Limpley Stoke(0225) 723631
Feb-Nov
John and Lucille Baxter have tastefully converted this property, which was once 2 early 18th-century cottages, into a cosy and comfortable guest house situated close to the village centre.
4rm(2🚿2hc) ® 🐕 sB&B£23-£28 sB&B🚿£30-£39
dB&B£34-£43 dB&B🚿£40-£52
♨ CTV 2P 2🚗 🏠
Credit Cards [1] [3] [£]

See the regional maps of popular holiday areas at the back of the book.

HITCHAM Suffolk Map **05** TL95

FH **Q** Mrs B Elsden **Wetherden Hall** *(TL971509)* IP7 7PZ
☎Bildeston(0449) 740412
Feb-Nov
Part Tudor-style farmhouse close to the ruins of a former hall,
offering friendly accommodation. 1 mile west of unclassified road
to Kettlebaston.
3rm (1fb) ⴎ ✱ sB&B£12.50-£14 dB&B£24-£25 WB&B£80-£84
⫭ CTV 6P nc9yrs ✦ 300 acres mixed
£

HITCHIN Hertfordshire Map **04** TL12

GH **Q|Q|Q** **Firs Hotel** 83 Bedford Rd SG5 2TY
☎(0462) 422322
rs 25 Dec-2 Jan
This pleasant family run hotel offers varied accommodation with
some compact, and some newly built, more spacious, bedrooms. All
have modern facilities. There is a comfortable lounge bar and the
appealing Ristorante Classico, which specialises in authentic
Italian cuisine.
30rm(24⇌ℕ6hc)(2fb) CTV in all bedrooms ® sB&B£29-£46
sB&B⇌ℕ£35-£46 dB&B£r£45
dB&B⇌ℕ£51-£56 WB&B£203-£322 LDO 9.30pm
Lic ⫭ CTV 30P
Credit Cards [1][2][3][5] £

HOARWITHY Hereford & Worcester Map **03** SO52

FH **Q|Q** Mrs C Probert **The Old Mill** *(SO546294)* HR2 6QH
☎Carey(043270) 602
Small, white, cottage-style farmhouse in village centre with a
traditional country garden at the front of the house.
6hc ⴤin 1 bedroom ✱ sB&B£11-£15
dB&B£22-£30 WB&B£80-£85 WBDi£115-£120 LDO 7pm
CTV 6P

HOCKHAM, GREAT Norfolk Map **05** TL99

FH **Q** Mrs E M Morfoot *Church Cottage* *(TL957946)*
NR17 1EW (1m N A1075) ☎(095382) 286
4 Jan-20 Dec
Farmhouse-style accommodation set in 2 acres of smallholding,
gardens and paddock with an outdoor heated swimming pool.
There is access to a 2-acre coarse fishing lake 1 mile from the
cottage.
4rm(3hc)ⴤin 6 bedrooms ⴎ (ex guide dogs) LDO noon
⫭ CTV 10P nc9yrs ⌁(heated) ✦ 2 acres non-working

HOLBEACH Lincolnshire Map **09** TF32

GH **Q|Q|Q** **Pipwell Manor** Washway Rd, Saracens Head
PE12 8AL ☎(0406) 23119
Just off the A17 at Saracens Head, this period house is surrounded
by gardens and farmland. Mrs Honnor has recently renovated her
guesthouse with the comfort of her guests a priority. All rooms are
spacious and comfortable.
4rm ⴤin all bedrooms ® ⴎ
⫭ CTV 4P
£

HOLLYBUSH Strathclyde *Ayrshire* Map **10** NS31

FH **Q|Q|Q** Mrs A Woodburn **Boreland** *(NS400139)* KA6 7ED
☎Patna(0292) 531228
Jun-Sep
Two-storeyed farmhouse with roughcast exterior, situated on the
banks of the River Doon. West off A713 south of village.
3rm (2fb) ® ⴎ sB&B£14-£16 dB&B£24-£26
⫭ CTV 6P ✦ 190 acres dairy
£

HOLMFIRTH West Yorkshire Map **07** SE10

INN **Q|Q** **White Horse** Scholes Road, Jackson Bridge
HD7 7HF ☎(0484) 683940
Closed 24-25 Dec & 31 Jan
Featured in 'Last of the Summer Wine' this typical Yorkshire pub
offers typical Yorkshire hospitality. It is 2 miles from the town, just
off the A616 and has well-equipped bedrooms and a collection of
photographs of the television series.
5hc (3fb) CTV in 2 bedrooms TV in 3 bedrooms ®
ⴎ (ex guide dogs) ✱ sB&B£18
dB&B£32 Lunch £1.45-£5.75alc Dinner £1.65-£7.25alc LDO
9.30pm
⫭ 12P 2⛟
Credit Cards [3] £

HOLMROOK Cumbria Map **06** SD09

GH **Q|Q|Q** *Carleton Green* Saltcoats Rd CA19 1YX
☎(09404) 608
Mar-Nov
Set in extensive gardens just off the A595, this charming country
house is ideally situated for touring Eskdale, Wasdale and the
western lakes. The accommodation is well maintained and the
public rooms are comfortable and roomy.
7rm(2⇌1ℕ4hc)(2fb)ⴤin all bedrooms CTV in 2 bedrooms ®
Lic ⫭ CTV 7P

'Selected' establishments, which have the highest
quality award, are highlighted by a tinted panel.
For a full list of these establishments, consult the
Contents page.

Clifton Lodge Hotel

210 West Wycombe Road, High Wycombe, Bucks HP12 3AR
Telephone: 0494 440095 & 29062

Situated on the A40 West Wycombe approximately one
mile from the M40 London to Oxford motorway and
close to the centre of historic High Wycombe, the
principal town of the Chilterns. Ideal for touring the
Thames Valley, Oxford, Cotswold etc. There are ample
car parking facilities and pleasant gardens. Good
English breakfast, lunches and dinner available. All
rooms have central heating, wash basin, colour TV and
direct dial telephone. Small functions catered for.
Licensed.
**Under the personal supervision of the resident
proprietors Jane & Brian Taylor**

HOLNE Devon Map **03** SX76

SELECTED

FH Ⓠ Ⓠ Ⓠ Ⓠ Mrs S Townsend **Wellpritton** *(SX716704)*
TQ13 7RX ☎Poundsgate(03643) 273
Closed 25-26 Dec
Peacefully situated on the edge of Dartmoor, this farmhouse provides popular family holiday accommodation. The bedrooms are equipped with radio/alarms, tea facilities, biscuits and fruit juices, and most are en suite. The cosy lounge has a colour TV, and good home-cooked meals are served in the dining room.
4rm(1⇔2🛏)(1hc)(2fb)✠in all bedrooms Ⓡ
🎄 (ex guide dogs) ✳ sB&B£13-£15 sB&B⇔🛏£13-£15 dB&B£26-£30
dB&B⇔🛏£26-£30 WB&B£91 WBDi£119 (Wkly only Jul-Aug) LDO 6pm
🍴 CTV 6P ⇰games room with snooker table tennis & skittles 15 acres mixed
Ⓔ

INN Ⓠ Ⓠ **Church House** TQ13 7SJ ☎Poundsgate(03643) 208
An inn of great character standing in the centre of this moorland village, Church House has comfortable bedrooms, some with en suite facilities, and colour TV. The bars have a cheerful atmosphere and interesting home-cooked dishes are included on the menus.
7rm(1⇔3🛏3hc)(1fb) CTV in all bedrooms Ⓡ ✳
sB&B£15-£17.50 sB&B⇔🛏£19.50-£25 dB&B£30-£35
dB&B⇔🛏£39-£50 WB&B£90-£150 Sunday Lunch fr£5.95 Dinner fr£7.50 LDO 9pm
🍴 5P
Credit Cards ①③

HOLNEST Dorset Map **03** ST60

FH Ⓠ Ⓠ Mrs J Mayo **Almshouse** *(ST651082)* DT9 6HA (S off A352 on unclass road towards Hermitage) ☎(096321) 296
Mar-Oct
Set in the peaceful rural surroundings of a large dairy farm, this homely, comfortable house provides simple, clean accommodation and extends a warm welcome to guests.
3hc Ⓡ 🎄 ✳ sB&B£12-£14 dB&B£24-£28 LDO 2pm
CTV 4P 140 acres dairy
Ⓔ

HOLSWORTHY Devon Map **02** SS30

GH Ⓠ Ⓠ **Coles Mill** EX22 6LX ☎(0409) 253313
Apr-mid Oct rs Mar
The lounge and dining room of this attractive 18th-century mill still retain some original features. Just out of Holsworthy's centre, the accommodation includes 5 well equipped bedrooms and guests will enjoy home-cooked meals and a warm welcome.
5🛏 TV in all bedrooms Ⓡ 🎄 (ex guide dogs)
sB&B🛏£15-£16.50
dB&B🛏£25-£29 WB&B£87.50-£101.50 WBDi£138-£150 LDO 5pm
Lic CTV 12P nc6yrs coarse fishing lake

FH Ⓠ Mr & Mrs E Cornish *Leworthy (SS323012)* EX22 6SJ ☎(0409) 253488
This low, white-fronted farmhouse has an attractive garden facing open country.
10rm(3🛏5hc)(5fb) Ⓡ 🎄 (ex guide dogs) LDO 6pm
Lic CTV 20P 2🎾 ⚬ ♟(hard)⤸ ♪ badminton skittles archery shooting pitch & putt 235 acres mixed

---

HOLT Norfolk Map **09** TG03

GH Ⓠ Ⓠ Ⓠ **Lawns Private Hotel** Station Rd NR25 6BS
☎(0263) 713390
Built as a Georgian farmhouse and later used as a dormitory for Gresham Public School, The Lawns is now a highly recommended hotel. The accommodation has been attractively refurbished by Roger and Jackie Tuck.
11⇔🛏 (2fb)✠in all bedrooms CTV in all bedrooms Ⓡ
sB&B⇔🛏fr£30
dB&B⇔🛏fr£50 WB&B£165-£200 WBDi£250-£265 LDO 8.30pm
Lic 🍴 12P
Credit Cards ①②③Ⓔ

HOLYHEAD Gwynedd Map **06** SH28

GH Ⓠ Ⓠ **Offaly** 20 Walthew Av LL65 1AF ☎(0407) 762426
Conveniently placed for the ferry terminal, this well-maintained, detached house is close to the harbour and provides comfortable accommodation and friendly hospitality.
5rm(1🛏4hc)(2fb) Ⓡ 🎄 ✳ sB&B£10-£12 sB&B🛏£12
dB&B£20-£24 dB&B🛏£24 LDO 3pm
🍴 CTV 3P (charged)

HOLYWELL Clwyd Map **07** SJ17

FH Ⓠ Ⓠ Ⓠ Mrs M D Jones **Green Hill** *(SJ186776)* CH8 7QF ☎(0352) 713270
Mar-Nov
15th-century farmhouse completely modernised to provide comfortable accommodation, overlooking the Dee estuary.
4rm(1⇔3hc)(3fb) Ⓡ 🎄 dB&Bfr£22 LDO 9am
CTV 6P ⚬ snooker table childrens play area 120 acres dairy mixed
Ⓔ

HONITON Devon Map **03** ST10

See also Feniton

↦FH Ⓠ Ⓠ Mrs I J Underdown **Roebuck** *(ST147001)*
EX14 0PB (western end of Honiton-by-pass) ☎(0404) 42225
Modern farm 8 miles from the coast.
4rm(3hc)(1fb) CTV in 1 bedroom Ⓡ sB&B£11 dB&Bfr£22
🍴 CTV 0P 180 acres dairy mixed

INN Ⓠ Ⓠ Ⓠ **The Heathfield** Walnut Rd EX14 8UG
☎(0404) 45321 or 45322
Beautifully restored, this 16th-century thatched Devon long house has attractive bedrooms, well equipped with private bathrooms, colour TV, direct dial telephones and other thoughtful extras. Interesting dishes are offered on the bar menu together with home-baked bread.
5⇔🛏 CTV in all bedrooms Ⓡ 🎄 (ex guide dogs) LDO 10pm
🍴 50P nc14yrs pool table skittle alley
Credit Cards ①②③Ⓔ

INN Ⓠ Ⓠ **Monkton Court** Monkton EX14 9QH (2m E A30)
☎(0404) 42309
A cosy bar and restaurant complement the comfortable modern bedrooms at this friendly establishment. The Taylors have furnished and equipped the inn very well, and serve wholesome food. Monkton Court Inn stands next to the A30, east of Honiton.
8rm(2⇔4🛏2hc)(1fb) CTV in all bedrooms Ⓡ
🎄 (ex guide dogs) sB&B£19.50 sB&B⇔🛏£29.50 dB&B£36
dB&B⇔🛏£45 WB&B£107.50-£135 WBDi£165-£239 Lunch £6-£10alc Dinner £10&alc LDO 9.30pm
🍴 100P
Credit Cards ①③Ⓔ

Book as early as possible for busy holiday periods.

Visit your local AA Centre.

HOOK Hampshire Map **04** SU75

GH Q Q *Oaklea* London Rd RG27 9LA ☎(0256) 762673
Detached Victorian house with large walled garden and good home cooking.
10rm(4↟6hc)(1fb)⊁in 3 bedrooms CTV in 5 bedrooms ®
LDO noon
Lic CTV 11P
See advertisement under BASINGSTOKE on page 49

HOPE COVE Devon Map **03** SX63

GH Q Q *Fern Lodge* TQ7 3HF ☎Kingsbridge(0548) 561326
Apr-Sep rs Mar
Enjoying views of the sea and countryside, this modern detached house is in an elevated position, 3 minutes walk from the sea. It provides comfortable bedrooms, peaceful public rooms together with interesting menus and friendly service.
5rm(1⇨4↟)Annexe 3hc (2fb) ® LDO 5pm
Lic ᠁ CTV 8P 1🛋 nc3yrs ♨

HOPTON Derbyshire Map **08** SK25

GH Q Q Q **Henmore Grange** DE4 4DF
☎Carsington(062985) 420
Standing in a natural butterfly garden of 2.5 acres, this charming house has been fully extended and now incorporates a popular restaurant serving English fruit wines and afternoon cream teas.
14rm(12⇨↟2hc)(4fb) ® ✳ sB&Bfr£20 sB&B⇨↟£30
dB&Bfr£40
dB&B⇨↟£55 WB&B£192.50 WBDi£262.50 LDO 6pm
Lic ᠁ CTV 14P
Credit Cards ① ② ③ ⓔ

HORLEY Surrey

For accommodation details see under **Gatwick Airport, London**

HORNSEA Humberside Map **08** TA24

GH Q *Hotel Seaforth* Esplanade HU18 1NQ ☎(0964) 532616
A large house overlooking the bowling green with seafront views. Cosy atmosphere.
6hc (2fb) CTV in all bedrooms ® LDO 4pm
Lic ᠁ CTV 4P
Credit Cards ① ③

HORSHAM West Sussex Map **04** TQ13

GH Q Q **Blatchford House** 52 Kings Rd RH13 5PR
☎(0403) 65317
Closed Xmas
This converted Georgian house offers comfortable bedrooms with modern shower rooms. Proprietor-run, the guest house offers a warm welcome to all guests at Blatchford House which is popular with business people and tourists alike.
11↟ CTV in all bedrooms ® sB&B↟fr£32.50 dB&B↟fr£48
᠁ 14P
Credit Cards ① ③

GH Q Q Q **Horsham Wimblehurst Hotel** 6 Wimblehurst Rd
RH12 2ED ☎(0403) 62319
Quietly situated in mature grounds, this fine Victorian residence has been skilfully modernised to provide well-equipped, compact bedrooms, 2 lounges and a comfortable dining-room. Location directions are advisable.
14rm(11⇨↟2hc)(2fb)⊁in all bedrooms CTV in all bedrooms
® 🐾 (ex guide dogs) sB&Bfr£37.50 sB&B⇨↟£39.50-£49.50
dB&B£44.50-£49.50 dB&B⇨↟£49.50-£59.50 LDO 6.45pm
᠁ CTV 14P ♨
Credit Cards ① ③ ⓔ

HORSHAM ST FAITH Norfolk Map 09 TG21

GH 🔾🔾🔾 **Elm Farm Chalet Hotel** Norwich Rd NR10 3HH
☎Norwich(0603) 898366
rs 25-26 Dec
Set in the middle of this picturesque village, this former farmhouse
has well-equipped, comfortable barn conversions with a lovely
lounge. The Parker family extend a warm welcome to all their
guests.
4rm(1⇨1♠2hc)Annexe 21⇨♠ CTV in all bedrooms ®
✕ (ex guide dogs) sB&B£25-£33 sB&B⇨♠£25-£33
dB&B⇨♠£42.35-£49.50 WB&B£168-£224 WBDi£238-£294
LDO 6.30pm
Lic 🕮 CTV 20P
Credit Cards 1️⃣ 2️⃣ 3️⃣ £

HORSMONDEN Kent Map 05 TQ74

FH 🔾 Mrs S M Russell **Pullens** *(TQ689389)* Lamberhurst Rd
TN12 8ED ☎Brenchley(089272) 2241
Mar-Nov
Part of a busy arable farm, this attractive timbered farmhouse has
an abundance of charm and character. Bedrooms are spacious and
the large lounge/dining room offers unpretentious comfort.
3hc (1fb)✕in all bedrooms ® ✕ ✳ dB&B£29-£32
🕮 CTV 3P 🖈 200 acres arable

HORTON Dorset Map 04 SU00

SELECTED

GH 🔾🔾🔾🔾 **Northill House** BH21 7HL
☎Witchampton(0258) 840407
Closed 20 Dec-mid Feb
This attractive farmhouse with rural surroundings offers
carefully modernised, comfortable bedrooms which provide en
suite facilities and niceties such as fresh flowers, books and
toiletries. The dining room is cool and spacious and overflows
into a new conservatory. There is an elegant lounge and cosy
bar. The Garnsworthy family take great care of their guests,
providing warm hospitality.
9rm(7⇨2♠)(1fb) CTV in all bedrooms ®
✕ (ex guide dogs) sB&B⇨♠£28
dB&B⇨♠£52 WB&B£163.80-£176.40
WBDi£233.10-£245.70 LDO 7pm
Lic 🕮 9P nc8yrs
Credit Cards 1️⃣ 3️⃣
See advertisement under **WIMBORNE MINSTER** on
page 391

INN 🔾🔾🔾 **Horton** Cranborne Rd BH21 5AD
☎Witchampton(0258) 840252
Large, detached inn on crossroads. Good food and very well-
equipped bedrooms.
5rm(2⇨3hc)✕in 1 bedroom CTV in all bedrooms ®
✕ (ex guide dogs) ✳ sB&B£30-£35 sB&B⇨£35-£40
dB&B£40-£45
dB&B⇨£50-£55 WB&B£240-£280 Bar Lunch £4-£10 Dinner
£8.95-£12.95alc LDO 10pm
🕮 100P
Credit Cards 1️⃣ 3️⃣

HORTON IN RIBBLESDALE North Yorkshire
Map 07 SD87

INN 🔾🔾 **Crown Hotel** BD24 0HF ☎(07296) 209
A good range of home-cooked bar meals is available at this
popular village inn. On fine days, you can eat in the pleasant
garden. Dinner is served in the attractive dining room.
10rm(1⇨9hc)(4fb) sB&B£15.75-£21.50 dB&B£31.50-£35.30
dB&B⇨£39.10-£43 WB&B£107.50-£126.50
WBDi£164.50-£183.50 LDO 6pm

🕮 CTV 15P
£

HOUNSLOW Greater London

London plan **4** D3 (pages 000-000)
GH 🔾🔾 *Shalimar Hotel* 219-221 Staines Rd TW3 3JJ
☎081-577 7070 & 081-572 2816
Modest and informal guesthouse offering friendly personal service.
14rm(4♠10hc)(4fb) CTV in all bedrooms ® ✕ LDO noon
🕮 CTV 8P
Credit Cards 1️⃣ 2️⃣ 3️⃣ 5️⃣

HOUSESTEADS Northumberland Map 12 NY87

SELECTED

FH 🔾🔾🔾🔾 Mrs B Huddleston **Beggar Bog**
(NY797686) NE47 6NN ☎Haydon Bridge(0434) 344320
Standing beside the Roman military road (now the B6318)
which runs beside Hadrian's Wall, this farm overlooks
Housesteads Roman fort. The farmhouse has been
sympathetically restored to provide a lovely first floor lounge
and ground floor bedrooms in a carefully designed extension
featuring a conservatory which has proved a real suntrap. The
farmhouse is now open all year.
3hc (1fb) ✕ sB&B£18-£20 dB&B£28-£30 LDO 6pm
🕮 CTV 6P 2🐾 38 acres stock

HOVE East Sussex

See **Brighton & Hove**

HUBBERHOLME North Yorkshire Map 07 SD97

GH 🔾🔾🔾 **Kirkgill Manor** BD23 5JE
☎Kettlewell(075676) 800
John and Lesley Robinson run a relaxing and well-appointed
guesthouse in this peaceful part of Upper Wharfedale, within the
Yorkshire Dales National Park. Kirkgill Manor is an ideal centre
for a walking or touring holiday, and guests are sure of a
comfortable, beautifully decorated and furnished bedroom and
enjoyable evening meals taken house party-style around a large
dining table. This was the North of England winner of the 1988/9
Best Newcomer Award.
6rm(5⇨1♠) CTV in all bedrooms ® ✳
dB&B⇨♠£37-£40 WB&Bfr£127.50 LDO 6pm
Lic 🕮 12P
£

HUGHLEY Shropshire Map 07 SO59

FH 🔾🔾 Mrs E Bosworth **Mill** *(SO565978)* SY5 6NT
☎Brockton(074636) 645
Lovely old house in pleasant rural area beneath Wenlock Edge.
2♠ (1fb) CTV in 1 bedroom ✕ sB&B♠£18-£25
dB&B♠£30-£36
CTV 6P 🖈 ♿ own riding centre 250 acres arable beef
£

HULL Humberside Map 08 TA02

GH 🔾🔾 **Earlesmere Hotel** 76/78 Sunny Bank, Spring Bank
West HU3 1LQ ☎(0482) 41977 Telex no 592729
FAX (0482) 214121
Closed Xmas rs wknds
15rm(7♠8hc)(4fb) CTV in all bedrooms ® ✳
sB&B£18.40-£19.55 sB&B♠fr£26.45
dB&B♠£40.25-£51.75 WB&B£128.80-£136.85
WBDi£184.80-£249.55 LDO 6pm
Lic 🕮 CTV
£

GH Q Parkwood Hotel 113 Princes' Av HU5 3JL
☎(0482) 445610
Terraced town house on bus route with well-fitted, comfortable bedrooms.
9rm(6🟍3hc)(1fb) CTV in all bedrooms ® ✳ sB&B£19.50-£21 sB&B🟍£25-£29
dB&B🟍£35-£40 WB&B£136-£175 WBDi£206-£245 LDO 9.30pm
Lic 🚪 CTV 4P
Credit Cards 1 3 £

HUNGERFORD Berkshire Map **04** SU36

GH QQQ Marshgate Cottage Marsh Ln RG17 0QX
☎(0488) 682307
Closed 25 Dec-Jan
A sympathetically designed extension provides modern bedrooms at this delightful 17th-century thatched cottage. Most of the accommodation, many with en suite facilities, is on the ground floor. The friendly proprietors serve imaginative meals with their unique style of hospitality.
9rm(1⇆6🟍2hc)(2fb)⊁in 3 bedrooms CTV in all bedrooms ®
✖ (ex guide dogs) sB&Bfr£23.50 sB&B⇆🟍fr£33 dB&Bfr£33
dB&B⇆🟍fr£45.50 LDO 8.30pm
Lic 🚪 7P 2🐾 nc5yrs bike hire
Credit Cards 1 3 £

HUNSTANTON Norfolk Map **09** TF64

GH QQQ Claremont 35 Greevegate PE36 6AF
☎(0485) 533171
A few minutes from the town centre and seafront, this guesthouse has been totally refurbished by Mr and Mrs Parsons. Each pine-furnished bedroom has a good armchair and a quality en suite bathroom. The lounge, bar and dining room are comfy and cheerful.
7rm(4⇆3🟍)(1fb)⊁in all bedrooms CTV in all bedrooms ®
sB&B⇆🟍£16-£20
dB&B⇆🟍£32-£40 WB&B£105-£140 WBDi£156-£219 LDO 6pm
Lic 🚪 CTV 3P
Credit Cards 1 3 £

GH QQQ Pinewood Hotel 26 Northgate PE36 6AP
☎(0485) 533068
Closed Xmas
The elevated position of this hotel provides many rooms with a sea view. Mrs Porter is an excellent hostess, and offers prettily furnished bedrooms, some with en suite facilities. The restaurant serves a well-chosen menu and uses fresh ingredients.
8rm(4🟍4hc)(4fb)⊁in all bedrooms CTV in all bedrooms ® ✳
sB&B£14-£28 sB&B🟍£18-£36 dB&B£28-£30
dB&B🟍£32-£36 WB&B£88-£116 WBDi£144-£172 LDO 9pm
Lic 🚪 6P
Credit Cards 1 3 £

GH QQQ Sutton House Hotel 24 Northgate PE36 6AP
☎(0485) 532552
This large stone-built house enjoys an elevated position, providing many rooms with good sea views. Most rooms are en suite. There is a well-stocked bar and a variety of dishes on the well-chosen menu. The hotel provides good value for money.
7rm(5⇆🟍2hc) CTV in all bedrooms ® sB&B£17-£25
sB&B⇆🟍£19-£27 dB&B£34-£50
dB&B⇆🟍£38-£54 WB&B£115-£185 WBDi£180-£235 LDO 7.30pm
Lic 🚪 CTV 5P
Credit Cards 1 3 £

This guide is updated annually – make sure you use an up-to-date edition.

HUNTON North Yorkshire Map **07** SE19

INN QQQ The Countryman's DL8 1PY ☎Bedale(0677) 50554
A lovely, renovated, stone-built inn full of charm and character offering pleasant accommodation.
6rm(1⇆5🟍)⊁in all bedrooms CTV in all bedrooms ® ✖
sB&B⇆🟍£25
dB&B⇆🟍£36-£38 Bar Lunch £2.75-£5.75alc Dinner £3-£9alc
LDO 9.30pm
🚪 20P nc14yrs ▶ 9 pool table
Credit Cards 1 3 £

HURSLEY Hampshire Map **04** SU42

INN QQ Kings Head Hotel SO21 2JW
☎Winchester(0962) 75208
Closed Xmas Day
Popular roadside Charrington's house with good-size bedrooms and cosy lounge. Bar serves bistro-type food.
5hc (1fb) ® ✖ (ex guide dogs) ✳ sB&B£17.50-£20
dB&B£30-£35 Bar Lunch £2-£5alc Dinner £5-£9alc LDO 9.30pm
🚪 CTV 30P nc1yr
Credit Cards 1 3

HUTTON-LE-HOLE North Yorkshire Map **08** SE79

GH QQQ The Barn Hotel YO6 6UA
☎Lastingham(07515) 311
Mar-Dec
This converted barn is set in the centre of this charming village, overlooking the green. The interior has been attractively renovated while maintaining the character, with stone walls, flagged floors and beamed ceilings. There is a busy tea room, and guests can dine in the attractive small restaurant. Bedrooms are small but comfortable.

▶

8rm(3🛁🚿5hc) CTV in 2 bedrooms Ⓡ ✖ sB&B£16 dB&B£32-£40 dB&B🛁🚿fr£40 WB&B£100-£126 WBDi£170-£195 LDO 10am
Lic 🍴 CTV 15P nc12yrs
Credit Cards [1] [3] [£]

HYDE Greater Manchester Map **07** SJ99

FH [Q][Q][Q] Mr & Mrs I Walsh **Needhams** *(SJ968925)* Uplands Rd, Werneth Low, Gee Cross SK14 3AQ
☎061-368 4610 FAX 061-367 9106
This modernised, 16th-century farmhouse, close to a golf course, is set on a smallholding specialising in cows, goats and poultry.
6rm(5🚿1hc)(1fb) CTV in all bedrooms Ⓡ sB&B£16-£18 sB&B🚿fr£18 dB&B£32-£36 dB&B🚿£34-£38 LDO 9.30pm
Lic 🍴 CTV 12P 2🚗 ⛳9 U 30 acres beef
[£]

ILFORD Greater London

London plan **4F4** (pages 000-000)
GH [Q][Q] Cranbrook Hotel 24 Coventry Rd IG1 4QR
☎081-554 6544 & 4765 FAX 081-518 1463
A few minutes from the town centre, this hotel has functional, well-equipped bedrooms, some on the ground floor. The combined dining room and bar has a pool table and 'space invader' machines. Dinner must be pre-arranged.
16rm(13🚿3hc)(7fb) CTV in all bedrooms Ⓡ ✱ sB&B£24-£28.50 sB&B🚿£33.35 dB&B£32-£39 dB&B🚿£43.60 LDO 7.30pm
Lic 🍴 CTV 11P 2🚗
Credit Cards [1] [2] [3] [£]
See advertisement under LONDON on page 235

GH [Q][Q] Park Hotel 327 Cranbrook Rd IG1 4UE
☎081-554 9616 & 7187 FAX 081-518 2700
Good family accommodation is offered at this private, family-run hotel. Overlooking Valentines Park, it has the benefit of good parking facilities.
21rm(6🛁6🚿9hc)(3fb) CTV in all bedrooms Ⓡ sB&B£27.50 sB&B🛁🚿£37 dB&B£37.30 dB&B🛁🚿£48 LDO 8pm
Lic 🍴 CTV 23P
Credit Cards [1] [3]

ILFRACOMBE Devon Map **02** SS54

See **Town Plan Section**
See also West Down
GH [Q] Avenue Private Hotel Greenclose Rd EX34 8BT
☎(0271) 863767
22rm(4🛁5🚿13hc)(4fb) Ⓡ ✖ (ex guide dogs) sB&Bfr£14 sB&B🛁🚿fr£17 dB&Bfr£28 dB&B🛁🚿fr£31 WB&B£95-£108.50 WBDi£140-£152 LDO 6.45pm
Lic 🍴 CTV 0P
Credit Cards [1] [3] [£]

GH [Q][Q][Q] ***Avoncourt Hotel*** 6 Torrs Walk Av EX34 8AU
☎(0271) 862543
Mar-Oct & Xmas
A purpose-built, modern hotel situated in an elevated position with views over the town.
13rm(6🛁7hc)(3fb) Ⓡ LDO 6pm
Lic CTV 10P
Credit Cards [3]

GH [Q][Q] Cairngorm Hotel 43 St Brannocks Rd EX34 8EH
☎(0271) 863911
Feb-Nov
8🛁 (3fb) CTV in all bedrooms Ⓡ sB&B🛁£25-£29 dB&B🛁£50-£58 (incl dinner) WB&B£126-£147 WBDi£168-£196 LDO 6.30pm
Lic 🍴 10P
Credit Cards [1] [3] [£]

GH [Q][Q] Cavendish Hotel 9-10 Larkstone Ter EX34 9NU
☎(0271) 863994
Etr-Oct
This family hotel enjoys an elevated position with panoramic views. The bedrooms are comfortable and the service friendly.
23rm(15🚿8hc)(5fb) CTV in all bedrooms Ⓡ sB&B£16.50-£20 dB&B£26-£33 dB&B🚿£33-£40 WB&B£82-£135 WBDi£105-£150 LDO 5pm
Lic CTV 20P snooker
Credit Cards [1] [2] [3] [£]

GH [Q] Chalfont Private Hotel 21 Church Rd EX34 8BZ
☎(0271) 862224
Mar-Oct rs Feb & Nov
Close to the beach and town centre, this family-run establishment offers bright bedrooms and warm, comfortable public rooms, together with personal service.
8rm(6🚿2hc)(2fb) Ⓡ ✱ dB&B£22-£25 dB&B🚿£26-£29 WB&B£66-£75 WBDi£99-£120 LDO 4pm
Lic 🍴 CTV P̸
Credit Cards [1] [3]

GH [Q][Q] Collingdale Hotel Larkstone Ter EX34 9NU
☎(0271) 863770
Mar-Oct
This family-run guesthouse enjoys an elevated position with fine sea views. It is close to the town centre, all amenities and beaches.
9rm(3🚿6hc)(6fb) Ⓡ sB&Bfr£16.50 sB&B🚿fr£19 dB&Bfr£33 dB&B🚿fr£38 WBDi£125-£140 (Mar-Oct) LDO 5.30pm
Lic CTV P̸

GH [Q] ***Cresta Private Hotel*** Torrs Park EX34 8AY
☎(0271) 863742
mid May-Sep
24rm(15🚿9hc)(10fb) TV available Ⓡ LDO 6.30pm
Lic lift 🍴 CTV 30P putting green
Credit Cards [1]

GH [Q][Q] ***Dedes Hotel*** 1-3 The Promenade EX34 9BD 9637
☎(0271) 862545
rs Nov-Etr
17rm(7🛁10hc)(6fb) CTV in 5 bedrooms Ⓡ LDO 10pm
Lic CTV 6P
Credit Cards [1] [2] [3] [5]

GH [Q] Earlsdale Hotel 51 St Brannocks Rd EX34 8EQ
☎(0271) 862496
This family-run establishment is close to all the amenities of the town, and guests will receive friendly service. Earlsdale has a lively bar.
10rm(5🚿5hc)(4fb) CTV in 5 bedrooms ✖ (ex guide dogs) sB&B£16-£17 sB&B🚿£17.50-£18.50 dB&B£32-£34 dB&B🚿£35-£37 (incl dinner) WB&B£70-£75 WBDi£110-£115 LDO 6.30pm
Lic 🍴 CTV 10P darts miniature snooker table board games
[£]

GH [Q] Lympstone Private Hotel Cross Park EX34 8BJ
☎(0271) 863038
Mar-Oct rs Mar-May
15rm(9🚿6hc)(3fb) CTV in all bedrooms Ⓡ ✱ sB&B£13-£14 sB&B🚿£13.50-£14.50 dB&B£26-£28 dB&B🚿£30-£32 WB&B£83-£87 WBDi£120-£125 LDO 5pm
Lic CTV 10P
[£]

GH [Q][Q][Q] Merlin Court Hotel Torrs Park EX34 8AY
☎(0271) 862697
Mar-Nov

14rm(2➪9🛏3hc)(4fb) CTV in all bedrooms ® ✖ sB&Bfr£19
sB&B➪🛏fr£21 dB&Bfr£38
dB&B➪🛏fr£42 WBDi£168-£182 LDO 6.30pm
Lic ♨ 14P skittle alley
Credit Cards ① ③

GH Ⓠ Queens Court Hotel Sea Front, Wilder Rd EX34 9AJ
☎(0271) 863789
Apr-Oct
*This centrally located house facing the sea and gardens offers
clean, bright bedrooms, comfortable public areas and helpful
service.*
12rm(4➪6🛏2hc)(7fb) CTV in 10 bedrooms TV in 2 bedrooms
® sB&B£21-£22 sB&B➪🛏£23-£24 dB&B£42-£44
dB&B➪🛏£46-£48 (incl dinner) WB&B£119-£126
WBDi£161-£168 LDO 4.30pm
Lic CTV 14P
Credit Cards ① ③ ⓔ

GH ⓆⓆ Seven Hills Hotel Torrs Park EX34 8AY
☎(0271) 862207
Apr-Oct
*Standing in well-kept gardens, this semidetached Victorian house
occupies an elevated position with some sea views. The service is
friendly.*
15rm(5➪10hc)(4fb) ® LDO 7pm
Lic ♨ CTV 10P nc3yrs

GH ⓆⓆ Southcliffe Hotel Torrs Park EX34 8AZ
☎(0271) 862958
Spring BH-17 Sep rs Oct-Nov & Mar-Apr
*A small family-run hotel offering friendly service and attractive
bedrooms.*
13🛏 (8fb) ® ✖ ✳ WBDi£145-£152 (wkly only) LDO 6pm
Lic CTV 10P 🐾 games room childrens play area

GH QQQ South Tor Hotel Torrs Park EX34 8AZ
☎(0271) 863750
Etr-Oct
This Victorian house is situated in a quiet location half a mile from the town centre and beaches. Bedrooms are comfortable and have en suite facilities. Public areas provide attractive surroundings in which to relax; a stone well is near the pool and skittle room on the lower ground floor. Mr and Mrs Moor extend a warm welcome to all guests, and provide a choice of table d'hôte menus.
12↱ (3fb) Ⓡ ✱ sB&B↱£20-£24
dB&B↱£40-£48 (incl dinner) WBDi£120-£150 LDO 6pm
Lic CTV 14P nc6yrs snooker games room

GH QQ Strathmore Private Hotel 57 St Brannocks Rd EX34 8EQ ☎(0271) 862248
Apr-Sep
This comfortable, family-run guesthouse is conveniently placed for all the amenities of Ilfracombe. Most rooms have en suite facilities and interesting menus are offered.
9rm(2⇌6↱1hc)(2fb) CTV in all bedrooms Ⓡ ✱ sB&B£15
sB&B⇌↱£16.50 dB&B£30
dB&B⇌↱£33 WB&B£99.75 WBDi£159.50 LDO 5pm
Lic 7P
Credit Cards 1 2 3 5

GH QQQ *Sunny Hill* Lincombe EX34 8LL ☎(0271) 862953
Jan-Nov
Brightly decorated bedrooms are offered at this detached 1930s country house which is approximately 2 miles from Ilfracombe. The public areas are cosy and interesting, freshly prepared meals are taken in the dining room.
6rm(2↱4hc)(1fb) LDO 8.30pm
Lic CTV 6P nc10yrs

GH QQQ Varley House 13 Chambercombe Ter, Chambercombe Park EX34 9QW ☎(0271) 863927
A high standard of comfort and a particularly friendly atmosphere are provided by Roy and Barbara Gable who also serve well cooked English dishes accompanied by a wine list of excellent value for money. The luxurious bedrooms all have modern en suite facilities.
9rm(8⇌↱1hc)(3fb) CTV in all bedrooms Ⓡ sB&B£13.50-£15
dB&B⇌↱£30-£32 WB&B£94.50-£100.80 WBDi£138-£148
LDO 5.30pm
Lic CTV 7P nc5yrs
Credit Cards 1 3 £

GH QQQ Westwell Hall Hotel Torrs Park EX34 8AZ
☎(0271) 862792
An elegant, detached Victorian property with lovely views of the town and coastline, Westwell Hall has spacious bedrooms with en suite facilities. Within the intimate dining room, imaginative home cooked meals are served, and a warm welcome awaits all guests.
14rm(7⇌7↱)(2fb) CTV in all bedrooms Ⓡ ✱
sB&B⇌↱£23-£27.50
dB&B⇌↱£46-£55 (incl dinner) WB&B£126 WBDi£154-£168
LDO 7pm
Lic 14P nc6yrs snooker croquet table tennis
Credit Cards 3 £

ILKLEY West Yorkshire Map 07 SE14

GH QQ Moorview House Hotel 104 Skipton Rd LS29 9HE
☎(0943) 600156
Closed Xmas & New Year
Situated on the Skipton road, just on the edge of the town, this is a spacious and well-furnished house offering good all round comforts and service. There are good moor and river views from the rear of the house.
11rm(1⇌8↱2hc)(6fb) CTV in 10 bedrooms TV in 1 bedroom Ⓡ sB&B£26-£30 sB&B⇌↱£32-£36 dB&B£34-£40
dB&B⇌↱£44-£50 LDO 5pm
Lic CTV 12P
£

INGHAM Suffolk Map 05 TL87

INN Q *Cadogan Arms* The Street IP31 1NG
☎Culford(028484) 226
Standing on the main street, with a garden and ample parking space, this flint-faced Inn offers good bar food and home-cooked beef and ham dishes. There is also an attractive lounge and dining area.
4hc (2fb) CTV in 3 bedrooms TV in 1 bedroom Ⓡ LDO 9.30pm
80P
See advertisement under BURY ST EDMUNDS on page 95

INGLEBY GREENHOW North Yorkshire Map 08 NZ50

FH QQQ Mrs M Bloom **Manor House** *(NZ586056)* TS9 6RB
☎Great Ayton(0642) 722384
Closed 24-29 Dec
This working farm provides comfortable accommodation in the superb setting of the North Yorkshire National Park. Ideal for walking, the farm also provides rough shooting, and stabling and grazing for visitors bringing their own horses. Visitors enjoy the good cooking here and dinner is served by candlelight. Price per night includes a 3-course dinner. Dogs may be accepted by prior arrangement.
3hc (1fb) in all bedrooms Ⓡ ✱
dB&B£55-£59 (incl dinner) WBDi£182-£196 LDO 5pm
Lic CTV 40P 10 nc12yrs rough shooting & stabling for guest horses 164 acres mixed

INGLETON North Yorkshire Map 07 SD67

GH QQ Langber Country LA6 3DT ☎(05242) 41587
2 Jan-23 Dec
A large, detached property in open countryside. Occupies an elevated position situated in a quiet country lane about one mile south of Ingleton village. Turn off A65 at 'Masons Arms'.
7rm(2⇌1↱4hc)(3fb) in all bedrooms Ⓡ sB&B£12-£15
sB&B⇌↱£15-£18 dB&B£23-£29
dB&B⇌↱£29-£35 WB&B£79-£89 WBDi£104-£118 LDO 5.15pm
CTV 6P
£

GH QQQ Oakroyd Hotel Main St LA6 3HJ ☎(05242) 41258
Peter and Ann Hudson are a charming, hospitable couple who enjoy looking after guests at this attractive former rectory. Peter cooks good wholesome meals. The bedrooms are comfortable and simply equipped and there is also a lounge and residents' bar.
8rm(4↱4hc)(2fb) CTV in all bedrooms Ⓡ (ex guide dogs) ✱
sB&B£15-£16 dB&B£30-£34
dB&B↱£34-£36 WB&Bfr£100 WBDifr£149
Lic CTV 9P
£

GH QQQ Pines Country House Hotel LA6 3HN
☎(05242) 41252
Set in three-quarters of an acre of gardens this neat hotel provides attractive accommodation and good food.
4rm(2⇌2↱)(1fb) CTV in all bedrooms Ⓡ ✱
sB&B⇌↱£20-£22
dB&B⇌↱£32-£36 WB&B£112-£126 WBDi£178-£192 LDO 7.30pm
Lic CTV 10P 3

GH QQ Springfield Private Hotel Main St LA6 3HJ
☎(05242) 41280
Jan-Oct
Large Victorian villa. Family-run hotel with friendly atmosphere and panoramic views at rear.

6rm(4♠2hc)(3fb) CTV in all bedrooms ® ✻ sB&B£14-£16
sB&B♠£16-£18 dB&B£28-£36
dB&B♠£32-£36 WB&B£90-£104 WBDi£138-£152 LDO 5pm
Lic ♨ CTV 12P
£

INGLEWHITE Lancashire Map **07** SD54

FH Q Q Mrs R Rhodes **Park Head** *(SD542395)* Bilsborrow
Ln PR3 2LN ☎Brock(0995) 40352
*A well-furnished farmhouse with old oak beams and offering true
Lancashire hospitality.*
3hc (1fb) CTV in all bedrooms ® ✕ sB&B£15
dB&B£30 WB&B£100
♨ 10P 255 acres dairy sheep
£

INSTOW Devon Map **02** SS43

GH Q Q *Anchorage Hotel* The Quay EX39 4HX
☎(0271) 860655
Mar-Dec
Private hotel on quay, facing river and beach. Excellent views.
9rm(7♠2hc)(6fb) ®
Lic CTV 9P
Credit Cards ① ③

INVERGARRY Highland *Inverness-Shire* Map **14** NH30

GH Q Q Q **Craigard** PH35 4HG ☎(08093) 258
*Under the caring ownership of Barbara and David Withers, this
tastefully appointed guesthouse is just west of the village on the
main route to the Isle of Skye ferry. It offers attractive bedrooms
which are spacious and very comfortable.*
7hc ® ✻ sB&Bfr£12 dB&Bfr£24 WB&Bfr£84 WBDifr£140
Lic CTV 6P

GH Q Q **Forest Lodge** South Laggan PH34 4EA (3m SW A82)
☎(08093) 219
*Spacious and comfortable, this purpose-built property stands back
from the A82, 3 miles south west of Invergarry.*
7rm(2♠5hc)(2fb) ® dB&Bfr£24
dB&B♠fr£27 WBDifr£122.50 LDO 6.30pm
♨ CTV 10P

FH Q Mr & Mrs R Wilson **Ardgarry Farm Guest House**
(NH286015) Faichem PH35 4HG (1m from Invergarry off A87
signs Faichem) ☎(08093) 226
*A comfortable and pleasant, traditional farmhouse with a
smallholding attached.*
1hc Annexe 3hc (1fb) ®
dB&B£21 WB&B£73 WBDi£112 (wkly only Jul & Aug) LDO
4pm
♨ CTV 10P nc5yrs 10 acres mixed

FH Q Q Mr & Mrs O'Connell *Faichem Lodge* *(NH286014)*
PH35 4HG ☎(08093) 314
Mar-Oct
*Attractively modernised, with cosy accommodation, this stone
farmhouse is now an alpine plant nursery. There is access to a
working farm.*
4hc (1fb)✕in all bedrooms ® LDO 4pm
♨ CTV 5P 1 acres non-working

INVERKEITHING Fife Map **11** NT18

GH Q Q Q **Forth Craig Private Hotel** 90 Hope St KY11 1LL
☎(0383) 418440
*A smart, modern hotel with comfortable well-equipped bedrooms,
popular with business people.*
5♠ CTV in all bedrooms ® ✻ sB&B♠£17-£18
dB&B♠£30-£32 LDO 6pm
Lic ♨ 8P
£

INVERNESS Highland *Inverness-Shire* Map **14** NH64

See **Town Plan Section**

GH Q Q Q **Aberfeldy Lodge** 11 Southside Rd IV2 3BG
☎(0463) 231120
*Set in a residential area, this friendly small hotel offers attractive,
comfortable accommodation with spacious, well-equipped
bedrooms and a separate lounge for non-smokers. Mr and Mrs
Hayes provide good friendly service.*
9♠ (4fb) CTV in all bedrooms ® ✕
dB&B♠£32-£40 WBDi£175-£203 LDO 4pm
♨ 9P

GH Q Q *Ardmuir House* 16 Ness Bank IV2 4SF
☎(0463) 231151
*Standing on the banks of the River Ness, this comfortable
guesthouse offers good all round comfort and service.*
8♠ (2fb) CTV in all bedrooms ® LDO 7pm
Lic ♨ 4P

See advertisement on page 193

GH Q Q **Ardnacoille House** 1A Annfield Rd IV2 3HP
☎(0463) 233451
Apr-Oct
*This attractive Victorian house is set in a residential area and
offers good accommodation and service.*
6hc (2fb) ✕ sB&B£14 dB&B£24-£26
♨ CTV 8P nc7yrs

GH Q Q **Brae Ness Hotel** 16-17 Ness Bank IV2 4SF
☎(0463) 231732 due to change to 712266
rs Dec-Feb
*Standing on the River Ness only a few minutes' walk from the town
centre, this small, family-owned hotel is comfortable and provides
good value for money.*
▶

10rm(9⇨🟢1hc)(2fb)✒in 2 bedrooms CTV in all bedrooms ®
sB&B£17-£26 sB&B⇨🟢£22-£26
dB&B⇨🟢£34-£47 WB&B£119-£165 WBDi£173-£215 LDO
7pm
Lic ᵚᵚ 6P
ⓔ

GH 🅀🅀🅀 Craigside 4 Gordon Ter IV2 3HD ☎(0463) 231576
*Occupying an elevated site from which it overlooks the castle.
Craigside is an attractive Victorian house providing comfortable
and well-equipped accommodation.*
6rm(4⇨🟢2hc) CTV in all rooms ® ✇ (ex guide dogs) ✳
sB&Bfr£13 sB&B⇨🟢fr£16 dB&Bfr£26
dB&B⇨🟢fr£32 WB&Bfr£150 LDO 2.30pm
ᵚᵚ 4P nc9yrs
ⓔ

GH 🅀🅀🅀 Culduthel Lodge 14 Culduthel Rd IV2 4AG
☎(0463) 240089
*This attractive Georgian house is set in its own garden with views
over the town. The public rooms are comfortably appointed and the
individually decorated bedrooms have been thoughtfully equipped.*
7rm(1⇨🟢5🟢1hc)(2fb) CTV in all bedrooms ®
✇ (ex guide dogs) ✳ sB&B⇨🟢£25-£30
dB&B⇨🟢£40-£48 WB&B£135-£165 WBDi£205-£275 LDO
7.30pm
Lic ᵚᵚ 9P nc5yrs
Credit Cards ①③

GH 🅀🅀 Four Winds 42 Old Edinburgh Rd IV2 3PG
☎(0463) 230397
Closed Xmas wk & New Year
*This Victorian villa stands in its own grounds and offers
accommodation of a good standard. Family owned and run, it
offers friendly, attentive service.*
7rm(4🟢3hc)(2fb) CTV in all bedrooms ® ✳
sB&B🟢£15-£16.50 dB&B£28-£31
dB&B🟢£30-£33 WB&B£95-£105
ᵚᵚ 16P

⊢◄GH 🅀 Leinster Lodge 27 Southside Rd IV2 4XA
☎(0463) 233311
Closed Xmas & New Year
*Family owned and run, this comfortable guesthouse is in a
residential area and offers good all-round value.*
6hc (2fb) ® sB&Bfr£11.50 dB&Bfr£23 WB&Bfr£80.50
ᵚᵚ CTV 8P
ⓔ

GH 🅀🅀🅀 The Old Rectory 9 Southside Rd IV2 3BG
☎(0463) 220969
Closed 21 Dec-5 Jan
*Quietly set a few minutes' walk from the town centre, this is a
popular base for the touring holidaymaker. Tastefully appointed
throughout, it has comfortable bedrooms. Non-smokers are
especially welcome.*
4rm(2🟢2hc)(1fb)✒in all bedrooms ® ✇ (ex guide dogs) ✳
sB&B£12-£20 sB&B🟢£15-£25 dB&B£24-£26 dB&B🟢£35
ᵚᵚ CTV 5P nc7yrs

GH 🅀🅀🅀 *Riverside House Hotel* 8 Ness Bank IV2 4SF
☎(0463) 231052
*On the picturesque banks of the River Ness, this elegant
guesthouse is tastefully furnished and well equipped. The service is
extensive and the good cooking is undertaken by the friendly
proprietor.*
11rm(5⇨🟢5🟢1hc)(3fb) CTV in all rooms ® LDO 7pm
Lic ᵚᵚ CTV ✗

ⓔ Remember to use the money-off vouchers.

⊢◄GH 🅀🅀🅀 St Ann's Hotel 37 Harrowden Rd IV3 5QN
☎(0463) 236157
*Set in a quiet side road, this stone-built Victorian house is
attractively furnished with modern, well-equipped bedrooms. The
owners, Mr and Mrs Coleman provide friendly, personal service.*
6rm(5⇨🟢1hc)(3fb) CTV in all rooms ® sB&B£11-£12
sB&B⇨🟢£13.75-£15
dB&B⇨🟢£27.50 WB&B£105 WBDi£152 LDO 3.30pm
Lic ᵚᵚ CTV 3P
ⓔ

GH 🅀🅀🅀 Villa Fontana 13 Bishops Rd IV3 5SB
☎(0463) 232999
*Close to the cathedral, theatre and river, this detached house offers
bed and breakfast accommodation in comfortable surroundings.
Mrs Gander has tastefully decorated the house and furnished it
with antiques.*
4hc (2fb) CTV in all rooms ® ✳ sB&B£13-£14
dB&B£26-£28 WB&B£91-£98 (wkly only Nov-1 Mar)
ᵚᵚ 4P

See advertisement on page 195

INN 🅀🅀 Smithton Hotel Smithton IV1 2NL ☎(0463) 791999
*Standing on the edge of the village of Smithton, 3.5 miles from
Inverness, this modern hotel is well furnished and has very well-
equipped bedrooms. Friendly service is provided.*
10rm(2⇨🟢8🟢)(1fb) CTV in all rooms ® ✇ (ex guide dogs)
✳ sB&B⇨🟢£25-£27.50
dB&B⇨🟢£45-£50 WB&B£140-£157.50 WBDi£182-£213.50
LDO 8.30pm
CTV 50P pool tables
Credit Cards ①③ⓔ

Book as early as possible for busy holiday periods.

IPSWICH Suffolk Map **05** TM14

GH QQQ **Bentley Tower Hotel** 172 Norwich Rd IP1 2PY
☎(0473) 212142

Closed 24 Dec-4 Jan

*Set back from the A1156 with a car park to the fore, this
attractively furnished hotel has well-equipped en suite rooms. A
caring host welcomes guests, and a well-stocked bar, cosy lounge
and pleasant dining room complete Bentley Tower.*

11🜚 (2fb) CTV in all bedrooms ® 🛏 ✻ sB&B🜚£35-£38
dB&B🜚£45-£48 WB&B£245 WBDi£339 LDO 8.45pm
Lic 🏨 12P
Credit Cards [1] [3] £

ISLE OF

Places incorporating the words 'Isle of' or 'Isle' will be found
under the actual name, eg Isle of Wight is listed under Wight,
Isle of.

ISLE ORNSAY

See **SKYE, ISLE OF**

ISLEWORTH Greater London

London plan **4** B3 (pages 000-000)
GH QQ **Kingswood Hotel** 33 Woodlands Rd TW7 6NR
☎081-560 5614

14rm(5🜚9hc)(3fb) CTV in 10 bedrooms ® 🛏 ✻ sB&B£25-£35
dB&B£30-£40 dB&B🜚£35-£45
Lic 🏨 CTV 5P nc8yrs
£

IVER HEATH Buckinghamshire Map **04** TQ08

GH QQ **Bridgettine Convent** Fulmer Common Rd SL0 0NR
☎Fulmer(0753) 662073 & 662645

*Primarily a nunnery, this is a popular guesthouse run by nuns. The
accommodation is comfortable and, as can be expected, the
atmosphere is friendly and relaxed. A warm welcome is
guaranteed.*

13hc (3fb) 🛏 ✻ sB&Bfr£16 dB&Bfr£32 LDO 2pm
🏨 CTV
£

JACOBSTOWE Devon Map **02** SS50

FH QQ Mrs J King **Higher Cadham** *(SS585026)* EX20 3RB
☎Exbourne(083785) 647

Mar-Oct rs Nov & Feb

*Well-decorated and comfortably furnished 16th-century
farmhouse. Ideal base for touring.*

4hc (1fb) ® 🛏 ✻ sB&B£10.50-£11
dB&B£21-£22 WB&B£70 WBDi£100 (wkly only Aug) LDO
5pm
Lic 🏨 CTV 6P nc3yrs ✔ pool table darts 139 acres beef sheep
£

JEDBURGH Borders *Roxburghshire* Map **12** NT62

GH QQ **Ferniehirst Mill Lodge** TD8 6PQ ☎(0835) 63279

*A modern, purpose-built lodge in a secluded location, with compact
bedrooms and a spacious, comfortable lounge. Designed for those
going pony-trekking or horse-riding.*

11rm(5🜚3🜚3hc) ® sB&B£15 sB&B🜚🜚£18.50 dB&B£30
dB&B🜚🜚£37 WB&B£90-£110 WBDi£165-£185 LDO 8.30pm
Lic 🏨 CTV 16P 2🜚 ✔ ◡ clay pigeon shooting
Credit Cards [1] [3] £

GH QQQ **'Froylehurst'** Friars TD8 6BN ☎(0835) 62477
Mar-Nov

*Enjoying an elevated position above the town, this Victorian house
has spacious, comfortable and well-appointed bedrooms. To find
Froylehurst leave the Market Place by Exchange Street, take the
first right into Friars and the third drive on the left.*

5hc (3fb) CTV in all bedrooms ® 🛏 sB&Bfr£13.50
dB&Bfr£23 WB&Bfr£75
🏨 CTV 5P nc5yrs

GH QQ **Kenmore Bank** Oxnam Rd TD8 6JJ ☎(0835) 62369

*Enjoying an elevated position overlooking the abbey and river, this
detached house, with adjacent garden, is conveniently placed for
the town centre, and provides a good base from which to explore
the historic border country.*

6rm(2🜚4hc)(2fb) CTV in all bedrooms ® 🛏 (ex guide dogs)
LDO 8pm
Lic 6P ✔
Credit Cards [1] [3]

SELECTED

GH QQQQ **The Spinney** Langlee TD8 6PB (2m S on
A68) ☎(0835) 63525

mid Mar-Oct

*Modern, well-appointed and tasteful bedrooms, comfortable
lounge and most attractive lawns and gardens are features of
this charming house. Formerly 2 country cottages, it stands on
the A68 2 miles south of Jedburgh. With the personal
supervision of a warm welcome in very congenial
surroundings.*

3rm(2🜚) ® 🛏 (ex guide dogs) dB&B🜚fr£30
🏨 CTV 0P

JERSEY

See **CHANNEL ISLANDS**

KEITH Grampian *Banffshire* Map **15** NJ45

SELECTED

FH QQQQ Mrs J Jackson **The Haughs** *(NJ416515)*
AB5 3QN (1m from Keith off A96) ☎(05422) 2238

Apr-Oct

*This welcoming traditional farmhouse is situated west of the
village and is an ideal base for the touring holidaymaker with
easy access to the popular 'Whisky and Castle' trails. It has a
friendly atmosphere, relaxing lounge and comfortable, well-
equipped bedrooms, some of which have en suite facilities.
Enjoyable home cooking is served in the small dining room.*

5rm(3🜚🜚2hc)(1fb)🜚in all bedrooms CTV in all
bedrooms ® 🛏 (ex guide dogs) dB&B£24-£25
dB&B🜚🜚£28-£30 LDO 3pm
🏨 10P 2🜚 165 acres beef mixed sheep
£

KELMSCOT Oxfordshire Map **04** SU29

FH QQ Mrs A Amor **Manor Farm** *(SU253995)* GL7 3HJ
☎Faringdon(0367) 52620

*Set on the edge of the attractive and peaceful village, Manor Farm
offers typical comfortable farmhouse accommodation, together
with a warm, friendly atmosphere and attentive, helpful service.*

2hc (2fb)🜚in all bedrooms ® 🛏
🏨 CTV 4P 315 acres arable dairy

KENDAL Cumbria Map **07** SD59

See also **Brigsteer**

SELECTED

GH QQQQ **Lane Head Country House Hotel**
Helsington LA9 5RJ (0.5m S off A6) ☎(0539) 731283 &
721023

Closed Nov

*This charming 17th-century house, situated in peaceful rural
surroundings just outside Kendal, is well signposted from the*

A6 southern approach, and is convenient for the M6. Tastefully decorated and furnished throughout, this comfortable hotel has very well-equipped bedrooms, all with en suite facilities. A 3 or 4-couse set menu is served each evening, prepared and cooked to the highest standard, by the proprietress, Mrs Craig.

7rm(4⇌3♠)(1fb) CTV in all bedrooms ® ✖ (ex guide dogs) sB&B⇌♠£33-£38 dB&B⇌♠£50-£58 LDO 5pm
Lic ⁴⁰ 10P nc5yrs
Credit Cards ① ③ ⓔ

See advertisement on page 197

GH **Q Q Q Martindales** 9-11 Sandes Av LA9 4LL
☎(0539) 724028
Good standards are maintained at this attractive small guesthouse which is conveniently situated for the town centre. The thoughtfully equipped bedrooms are fairly compact and there is a separate lounge for smokers.

8♠ (1fb) CTV in all bedrooms ® ✖ (ex guide dogs) ✱
sB&B♠£25-£28
dB&B♠£35-£38.50 WB&B£122.50-£175 WBDi£171.50-£245 LDO 1pm
Lic ⁴⁰ 6P 1🐾 nc

See advertisement on page 197

FH **Q Q** Mrs S Beaty *Garnett House* *(SD500959)* Burneside
LA9 5SF ☎(0539) 724542
Closed Xmas & New Year
This stone-built 15th-century house features old oak panelling and a former peel tower. The accommodation is comfortable and a pleasant atmosphere prevails. It is located in the village of Burneside, 2 miles from Kendal.

▶

5hc (2fb) CTV in all bedrooms ® ✖ LDO 5pm
CTV 6P 750 acres dairy sheep

FH Ⓠ Ⓠ Mrs J Ellis **Gateside** *(NY494955)* Windermere Rd
LA9 5SE ☎(0539) 722036
*This attractive, white-painted farmhouse is situated 2 miles from
Kendal on the A591 towards Windermere. The bedrooms all have
a colour television and tea-making facilities, and there is a cosy
lounge and an attractive dining room.*
4hc (1fb) CTV in all bedrooms ® ✳
dB&B£22-£23 LDO 4.30pm
🛲 6P 280 acres dairy sheep
£

FH Ⓠ Ⓠ Mrs E M Gardner **Natland Mill Beck** *(SD520907)*
LA9 7LH (1m from Kendal on A65) ☎(0539) 721122
Mar-Oct
*17th-century, local stone-built farmhouse with original beams,
doors and cupboards. Large well-furnished rooms and homely
atmosphere. Attractive, walled gardens.*
3rm(2hc) ® ✖ ✳ dB&B£22-£25
🛲 CTV 3P 100 acres dairy
£

↦↦**FH** Ⓠ Ⓠ Ⓠ Mr & Mrs Bell **Oxenholme** *(SD529905)*
Oxenholme Rd LA9 7HG ☎(0539) 727226
Closed Jan
*A delightfully furnished farmhouse dating back to 1540. Many
natural beams and an inglenook fireplace. 2 miles south east of the
B6254.*
3hc ✖ sB&B£11-£12 dB&B£22-£24 WB&Bfr£75
🛲 CTV 3P nc5yrs 180 acres dairy sheep soft fruit
£

KENILWORTH Warwickshire Map **04** SP27

GH Ⓠ Ⓠ Ⓠ **Castle Laurels Hotel** 22 Castle Rd CV8 7NG
☎(0926) 56179
Closed 24 Dec-2 Jan
*Overlooking the castle and Abbey Fields, this delightful little
guesthouse provides warm hospitality in cosy, well-appointed
accommodation. It is perfect for business or pleasure.*
12♠ (1fb)⚡in all bedrooms CTV in all bedrooms ®
✖ (ex guide dogs) ✳ sB&B♠fr£24 dB&B♠fr£39 LDO noon
Lic 🛲 CTV 14P
£

GH Ⓠ Ⓠ **Ferndale** 45 Priory Rd CV8 1LL ☎(0926) 53214
8⇨♠ (2fb) CTV in all bedrooms ® ✳ sB&B£15
sB&B⇨♠£17-£18 dB&B⇨♠£30-£34 LDO 6pm
Lic 🛲 CTV 8P
£

GH Ⓠ Ⓠ **Hollyhurst** 47 Priory Rd CV8 1LL ☎(0926) 53882
Closed 24 Dec-2 Jan
*Large semi detached house with well-decorated bedrooms and
comfortable lounge.*
8rm(3♠5hc)(3fb) CTV in all bedrooms ® sB&B£14-£17
sB&B♠£18 dB&B£28
dB&B♠£33 WB&B£90-£115 WBDi£114.50-£170 LDO noon
Lic 🛲 CTV 8P
£

KENTALLEN Highland *Argyllshire* Map **14** NN05

FH Ⓠ Ⓠ Ⓠ Mrs D A MacArthur *Ardsheal Home* *(NN996574)*
PA38 4DZ ☎Duror(063174) 229
Apr-Oct
*This farmhouse has a pretty garden with lovely views of Loch
Linnhie and the mountains. One of the 3 bedrooms is on the ground
floor. Breakfast is served around a stripped wood table in the old
living room.*
3rm(1hc)(1fb) ®
🛲 CTV 5P 1000 acres beef dairy sheep mixed

KESWICK Cumbria Map **11** NY22

See **Town Plan Section**

GH Ⓠ Ⓠ **Acorn House Hotel** Ambleside Rd CA12 4DL
☎(07687) 72553
Feb-Nov
Large, detached house with pleasant garden in quiet part of town.
10rm(9⇨♠1hc)(4fb)⚡in all bedrooms CTV in all bedrooms
® ✖ (ex guide dogs) sB&B£15-£20 sB&B⇨♠£17-£20
dB&B£30-£34 dB&B⇨♠£32-£40 WB&B£110
Lic 🛲 CTV 9P 1☎ nc5yrs
Credit Cards ① ③ £

GH Ⓠ Ⓠ **Allerdale House** 1 Eskin St CA12 4DH
☎(07687) 73891
Closed Nov-Dec
*The bedrooms of this Lakeland slate house all have en suite
facilities, and the tastefully furnished, comfortable lounge and
dining room really catch the eye. The neat and colourful flower
borders are appealing.*
6⇨♠ (2fb)⚡in all bedrooms CTV in all bedrooms ®
dB&B⇨♠£50 (incl dinner) WB&B£122.50 WBDi£175 LDO
4.30pm
Lic 🛲 2P 4☎ nc5yrs

GH Ⓠ **Brierholme** 21 Bank St CA12 5JZ ☎(07687) 72938
*This pleasant, family-run Victorian house is on the end of a terrace
close to the town centre. Most of the bedrooms have en suite
facilities, colour TV and tea-making facilites. A selection of
inexpensive wines is available.*
6rm(1⇨4♠1hc)(2fb) CTV in all bedrooms ® dB&B£27-£35
dB&B⇨♠£33-£38 LDO 4pm
Lic 🛲 6P
£

GH Ⓠ Ⓠ Ⓠ **Charnwood** 6 Eskin St CA12 4DH (0.5m S off A6)
☎(07687) 74111
rs Nov-Mar wknds only
*An attractive, comfortable and well-maintained guesthouse.
Bedrooms are spacious, and the lounge features a selection of
books and a living flame fire set in an unusual carved fireplace.*
6rm(4♠1hc)(2fb) CTV in all bedrooms ® ✖ ✳ dB&B£24-£28
dB&B♠£32 WB&B£80-£108 WBDi£124-£152 LDO 4pm
Lic 🛲 nc5yrs
£

GH Ⓠ Ⓠ Ⓠ **Claremont House** Chestnut Hill CA12 4LT
☎(07687) 72089
*Situated on the A591, a mile from the town towards Windermere,
this establishment was once a lodge for a manor house. It has well-
appointed, pretty bedrooms, and serves 5-course dinners.*
5rm(3♠1hc)(1fb) ® ✖ ✳ sB&B£20 dB&B£40
dB&B♠£40 WBDi£200 LDO 4pm
Lic 🛲 CTV 8P

See advertisement on page 199

GH Ⓠ Ⓠ **Clarence House** 14 Eskin St CA12 4DQ
☎(07687) 73186
*This neatly-appointed Lakeland guesthouse has some spacious
bedrooms. This is a 'no-smoking' establishment.*
8rm(7♠1hc)(3fb)⚡in all bedrooms CTV in all bedrooms
sB&B£13.50-£14.50
dB&B♠£32-£34 WB&B£112-£119 WBDi£156-£163 LDO 3pm
Lic 🛲 CTV ⚡

See advertisement on page 199

GH Ⓠ Ⓠ Ⓠ **Dalegarth House Country Hotel** Portinscale
CA12 5RQ ☎(07687) 72817
*Spacious, comfortable lounges and very well-appointed en suite
bedrooms feature at this hotel which commands fine views of
Derwentwater. 6-course dinners are served in the dining room each
evening.*

▶

6rm(3⇨3♪)⊁in all bedrooms CTV in all bedrooms ®
✗ (ex guide dogs) ✳ sB&B⇨♪£29.50-£32
dB&B⇨♪£59-£64 (incl dinner) WB&Bf£130-£140
WBDif£190-£210 LDO 5.30pm
Lic ♔ CTV 12P nc5yrs
Credit Cards ⓵ ⓷ ⓔ

├─GH ®®® Fell House 28 Stanger St CA12 5JU
☎(07687) 72669
*Situated close to the town centre, this attractive Victorian terraced
house offers very well-maintained accommodation. A friendly
atmosphere prevails throughout.*
6rm(2♪4hc)(1fb) CTV in all bedrooms ® ✗ (ex guide dogs)
sB&Bf£11.50-£14.25 dB&Bf£22-£26.50
dB&B♪£27-£32.50 WB&Bf£72-£96 WBDif£110-£138 LDO
10am
♔ CTV 4P

GH ® Foye House 23 Eskin St CA12 4DQ ☎(07687) 73288
*A 'no-smoking' rule applies throughout this house which has bright
well-maintained bedrooms with colour TV, but no lounge.*
7hc (2fb)⊁in all bedrooms CTV in all bedrooms ®
✗ (ex guide dogs) sB&Bf£13.25-£14.25
dB&Bf£26.50-£28.50 WB&Bf£90 WBDif£142.50 LDO 4pm
Lic ♔ ⚲ nc5yrs
ⓔ

SELECTED

GH ®®®® The Gales Country House Hotel
Applethwaite, Underskiddaw CA12 4PL ☎(07687) 72413
Mar-Nov
*Standing in 2 acres with panoramic views across Keswick to
Borrowdale, this splendid Victorian house has particularly
impressive public areas including a residents' bar and the new
Garden Room with its attractive tented ceiling. Most of the
individually designed bedrooms have en suite facilities. The
English food is cooked with flair, and a choice of main course
is offered at dinner. Bowls, putting and croquet may be played
on the lawns.*
13rm(7⇨5♪1hc)(2fb) ® ✗ (ex guide dogs) sB&Bf£20-£24
sB&B⇨♪£20-£24 dB&Bf£40-£48
dB&B⇨♪£40-£48 WBDif£190-£220 LDO 6pm
Lic ♔ CTV 10P bowling green putting
Credit Cards ⓵ ⓷ ⓔ

GH ®®® Greystones Ambleside Rd CA12 4DP
☎(07687) 73108
Closed 1-27 Dec
*This attractive and spacious end terrace house is set in a quiet
location and is enthusiastically managed to provide stylish and
comfortable accommodation and a friendly atmosphere, together
with traditional home cooking. It's an ideal base for touring or
walking.*
9⇨♪ (2fb) CTV in all bedrooms ® ✗ (ex guide dogs)
sB&Bf£17.50-£18.50 dB&B⇨♪£31-£34 LDO 2pm
Lic ♔ 7P 2🐾 nc8yrs
ⓔ

GH ®® Hazeldene Hotel The Heads CA12 5ER
☎(07687) 72106
Mar-Nov
*Good views of Derwent Water can be enjoyed from this large
stone-built house a few minutes' walk from the town centre.
Generally spacious and well equipped, the bedrooms have well-
stocked mini bars and there are ample lounge areas.*
22rm(16♪6hc)(5fb) CTV in all bedrooms ® ✳
sB&Bf£15.50-£18 sB&Bf£18-£20.50 dB&Bf£31-£36
dB&Bf£36-£41 WB&Bf£102-£139 WBDif£182.50-£219.50
LDO 4pm

Lic ♔ CTV 18P
ⓔ

GH ®®® Holmwood House The Heads CA12 5ER
☎(07687) 73301
mid Mar-mid Nov
*This well-appointed Victorian house has views towards
Derwentwater and the Borrowdale Valley. The bedrooms are
comfortable, and guests can enjoy the beautiful view from the first
floor lounge.*
7hc (1fb) ✗ (ex guide dogs) sB&Bf£14.50-£16
dB&Bf£29-£32 WB&Bf£97 WBDif£146.50 LDO 2pm
Lic ♔ CTV 3P nc5yrs

GH ®® Leonards Field 3 Leonards St CA12 4EJ
☎(07687) 74170
Closed 23 Dec-Jan
*Set in this popular Lake District town, Leonards Field offers
bright and comfortable accommodation.*
8rm(3♪5hc)(1fb) CTV in all bedrooms ® ✳
sB&Bf£11.50-£12.50 dB&Bf£22-£23.50
dB&Bf£28-£31 WB&Bf£77-£108.50 WBDif£126-£157.50 LDO
4.30pm
Lic ♔ nc3yrs
ⓔ

GH ®® *Lincoln House* Stanger St CA12 5JU ☎(07687) 72597
Closed Dec
*Enjoying an elevated position, not far from the centre of town, this
semi detached Victorian house has views of the surrounding fells
from every bedroom.*
6hc (1fb) ® ✗ LDO 3pm
Lic ♔ CTV 5P

├─GH ®® Lynwood 12 Ambleside Rd CA12 4DL
☎(07687) 72081
*Set in a residential area close to the town centre, this mid-terrace
Victorian house has a lounge and lounge/bar. Several bedrooms
have en suite facilities.*
9rm(5♪4hc)⊁in all bedrooms CTV in all bedrooms ® ✗
sB&Bf£13-£14.50 dB&Bf£26-£28
dB&Bf£31-£35 WB&Bf£91-£122.50 WBDif£143.50-£175 LDO
10.30am
Lic ♔ ⚲ nc3yrs
Credit Cards ⓵ ⓷ ⓔ

See advertisement on page 201

GH ®®® Ravensworth Private Hotel 29 Station St CA12 5HH
☎(07687) 72476
Closed 7-31 Jan rs Feb
*High standards of housekeeping are evident at this attractive town
centre hotel. Friendly proprietors offer comfortable, modern
accommodation and good home-cooked meals which are taken in
the pleasant dining room. There is a separate lounge bar.*
8rm(1⇨7♪)(2fb) CTV in 4 bedrooms ® ✗ (ex guide dogs)
sB&B⇨♪£24
dB&B⇨♪£35-£38 WB&Bf£115-£125 WBDif£160-£168 LDO
6pm
Lic ♔ CTV 5P
Credit Cards ⓵ ⓶ ⓷ ⓹ ⓔ

GH ®® Richmond House 37-39 Eskin St CA12 4DG
☎(07687) 73965
*A comfortable guesthouse set in a residential area close to town
centre.*
10rm(6♪4hc)(1fb)⊁in all bedrooms ® ✗ (ex guide dogs) ✳
sB&Bf£12-£12.50 dB&Bf£24-£25
dB&Bf£29-£30 WBDif£125-£140 LDO 5pm
Lic ♔ CTV ⚲ nc8yrs
Credit Cards ⓵ ⓷ ⓔ

See advertisement on page 201

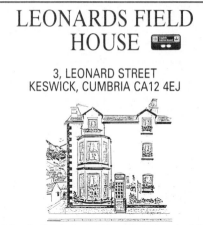

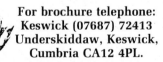

GH [Q][Q][Q] **Rickerby Grange** Portinscale CA12 5RH
☎(07687) 72344
Closed 23-28 Dec
The new proprietors of this well-maintained property assure a warm and relaxing atmosphere. There is a spacious, well-appointed restaurant, and the bedrooms are well equipped, most having en suite facilities.
14rm(2⇔9♠3hc)(3fb) CTV in 2 bedrooms ® sB&Bfr£19.50 dB&Bfr£39
dB&B⇔♠fr£46 WB&B£125-£149 WBDi£193-£214 LDO 5pm
Lic ᵐ CTV 20P

See advertisement on page 203

GH [Q][Q][Q] **Skiddaw Grove Hotel** Vicarage Hill CA12 5QB
☎(07687) 73324
Closed Dec-Jan
This comfortable, detached period house is peacefully situated on the edge of the town, in well tended gardens, and has a swimming pool to the rear. It commands fine views of Skiddaw, and is easily reached from the A66 bypass.
10rm(5⇔2♠3hc) ® ✖ (ex guide dogs) ✱ sB&B£14 dB&B£28
dB&B⇔♠£34 WB&B£90.65-£110 WBDi£146.65-£166.11 LDO 4.30pm
Lic ᵐ CTV 11P nc8yrs ⌂
£

GH [Q][Q] **Squirrel Lodge** 43 Eskin St CA12 4DG
☎(07687) 73091
Equally attractive bedrooms and dining room are features of this small, well-appointed guesthouse. A cosy residents' lounge is on the first floor.
7hc ⅝in all bedrooms CTV in all bedrooms ®
✖ (ex guide dogs) ✱ sB&Bfr£12.50
dB&Bfr£25 WB&Bfr£82 WBDifr£125 LDO 5pm
Lic ᵐ CTV ✗ nc6yrs
Credit Cards [1][3] £

⊷**GH** [Q][Q][Q] **Stonegarth** 2 Eskin St CA12 4DH
☎(07687) 72436
Feb-Nov rs Jan
Stonegarth is a family-run guesthouse with well-equipped bedrooms, an attractive dining room and a comfortable lounge. There is also a private car park. The Victorian building itself is of special architectural interest.
9rm(4⇔3♠2hc)(3fb) CTV in all bedrooms ®
✖ (ex guide dogs) sB&B£13-£14.50
dB&B⇔♠£31-£35 WBDi£130-£169.75 LDO 6pm
Lic ᵐ 9P nc3yrs

GH [Q][Q] **Sunnyside** 25 Southey St CA12 4EF ☎(07687) 72446
Closed 15 Nov-15 Jan
Within walking distance of the town centre in a residential area, this deceptively spacious house is under the personal supervision of the resident proprietors.
8hc (2fb) CTV in all bedrooms ® ✖ (ex guide dogs) ✱
sB&B£12.50-£13.50 dB&B£25-£27 WB&B£75-£85
ᵐ 8P
Credit Cards [1][3]

See advertisement on page 203

GH [Q][Q] *Swiss Court* 25 Bank St CA12 5JZ ☎(07687) 72637
Part of a Victorian terrace, this neat and pleasant house has a profusion of house plants.
7hc ✖
ᵐ CTV 3P nc6yrs

GH [Q][Q][Q] **Thornleigh** 23 Bank St CA12 5JZ ☎(07687) 72863
Friendly and welcoming, this centrally situated guesthouse has well-appointed en suite bedrooms, a comfortable first floor lounge and attractive little dining room. The pretty frontage, with flowers and walls makes Thornleigh particularly inviting.
6⇔♠ ⅝in 2 bedrooms CTV in all bedrooms ®
dB&B⇔♠£34-£38 WB&B£112-£126 WBDi£165-£185 LDO 4.30pm

ᵐ 3P nc14yrs
Credit Cards [1][3] £

See advertisement on page 205

GH [Q][Q] **Twa Dogs** Penrith Rd CA12 4JU ☎(07687) 72599
Built on the site of a much older inn, associated with the dogs of Robbie Burns, this inn offers fresh bedrooms and an attractive dining room on the first floor, with a spacious bar providing bar meals on the ground floor.
5hc (2fb) CTV in all bedrooms ✖ (ex guide dogs)
dB&B£30-£40 WB&B£200-£250 LDO 8.30pm
Lic ᵐ 20P nc5yrs games room
£

See advertisement on page 203

KETTLEWELL North Yorkshire Map **07** SD97

GH [Q][Q][Q] **Dale House** BD23 5QZ ☎(075676) 836
Charming, stone-built village house close to the River Wharfe.
8rm(3⇔5♠) CTV in all bedrooms ® sB&B⇔♠fr£42
dB&B⇔♠fr£84 (incl dinner) LDO 8.15pm
Lic ᵐ ✗ nc8yrs
Credit Cards [1][3]

GH [Q][Q][Q] **Langcliffe House** BD23 5RJ ☎(075676) 243
Closed Jan
Charming, relaxed house on the edge of the village.
6rm(2⇔4♠)Annexe 1⇔♠ (1fb) CTV in all bedrooms ®
sB&B⇔♠fr£33
dB&B⇔♠fr£60 (incl dinner) WB&Bfr£135 WBDifr£185 LDO 7pm
Lic ᵐ 7P
Credit Cards [1][3] £

KEXBY North Yorkshire Map **08** SE75

FH [Q] Mrs K R Daniel **Ivy House** *(SE691511)* YO4 5LQ
☎York(0904) 489368
Brick-built farmhouse adjacent to A1079 York-Pocklington road. Snug accommodation of neat and modest proportions.
3hc (1fb) CTV in all bedrooms ✖ sB&Bfr£14 dB&Bfr£24
ᵐ CTV 5P 132 acres mixed
£

KEYNSHAM Avon Map **03** ST66

GH [Q][Q][Q] **Grasmere Court Hotel** 22/24 Bath Rd BS18 1SN
☎Bristol(0272) 862662
Situated on the edge of the town, this hotel has been totally refurbished to a good standard. It offers public areas of quality, and well-equipped bedrooms, many of which have good, modern en suite facilities.
18rm(15⇔♠3hc)(4fb)⅝in all bedrooms CTV in all bedrooms ® ✖ ✱ sB&B£27-£30 sB&B⇔♠£35-£45
dB&B⇔♠£40-£54 LDO 7.30pm
Lic ᵐ CTV 18P 1🚗 ⌂
Credit Cards [1][3] £

FH [Q] Mrs L Sparkes **Uplands** *(ST663664)* Wellsway BS18 2SY
☎Bristol(0272) 865764 & 865159
Closed Dec
Conveniently situated for touring this beautiful part of the country, this 19th-century stone farmhouse has simple accommodation with large, airy rooms. Mrs Sparkes is providing bed and breakfast this year.
9rm(2♠7hc)(4fb) CTV in all bedrooms ® ✖ ✱
sB&B£17.50-£21 sB&B♠£21-£23.50 dB&B£30-£35
dB&B♠£35-£40 WB&Bfr£140
ᵐ CTV 20P 200 acres dairy
£

INN [Q][Q][Q] ***Grange Hotel*** 42 Bath Rd BS18 1SN
☎Bristol(0272) 869181
On the outskirts of the town centre, this hotel has been upgraded to provide well-equipped, comfortable bedrooms, all with en suite facilities. There are public areas, and a good range of meals is offered in the dining room.
11rm(8🛁3🚿)(4fb)🚭in all bedrooms CTV in all bedrooms Ⓡ
🐕 LDO 8.45pm
CTV 29P
Credit Cards [1] [3]

KIDLINGTON Oxfordshire Map **04** SP41

SELECTED

GH [Q][Q][Q][Q] **Bowood House** 238 Oxford Rd OX5 1EB
☎Oxford(0865) 842288
Closed 24 Dec-1 Jan
Friendly and welcoming with well-appointed accommodation, some of which is in a rear annexe, this hotel has a comfortable lounge and attractive bar. The dining room, which offers an à la carte menu, overlooks the patio and small fountain.
10rm(8🛁🚿2hc)Annexe 12🛁🚿 (4fb) CTV in all bedrooms Ⓡ 🐕 sB&B£30-£35 sB&B🛁🚿£45-£50
dB&B🛁🚿£60-£65 LDO 8.30pm
Lic ♨ 25P
Credit Cards [1] [3]
See advertisement under OXFORD on page 281

KILBARCHAN Strathclyde *Renfrewshire* Map **10** NS46

GH [Q][Q] **Ashburn** Milliken Park Rd PA10 2DB ☎(05057) 5477
A detached Victorian house, Kilbarchan has oak-panelled stairways and hall and attractive stained glass windows. It has well-equipped bedrooms and a children's play area within the acre of grounds.
6rm(2🚿4hc)(3fb) CTV in all bedrooms Ⓡ sB&B£19
sB&B🚿£27 dB&B£32
dB&B🚿£45 WB&B£130-£185 WBDi£190-£235 LDO 11am
Lic ♨ CTV 8P
Credit Cards [5] [£]

KILBURN North Yorkshire Map **08** SE57

INN [Q][Q][Q] **Forresters Arms Hotel** YO6 4AH
☎Coxwold(03476) 386
Next door to the 'Mouseman' furniture workshops, this 12th-century inn is run by the friendly Cussons family. Home-cooked food is served in the bars and restaurant, and the pretty en suite bedrooms are well equipped.
8🛁 (2fb) CTV in all bedrooms Ⓡ
dB&B🛁£46-£56 Bar Lunch £1.95-£5 High tea £1.50-£3 Dinner £10-£20alc LDO 9.30pm
♨ 40P
Credit Cards [1] [3] [£]
See advertisement under YORK on page 414

KILCHRENAN Strathclyde *Argyllshire* Map **10** NN02

GH [Q][Q] ***Cuil-na-Sithe*** PA35 1HF ☎(08663) 234
This period mansion is set in gardens close to Loch Awe, and is now a small hotel popular with fishermen. A small bar lounge caters for residents and diners.
5rm(1🛁1🚿3hc)(3fb) CTV in all bedrooms Ⓡ LDO 9pm
Lic CTV 10P 🏠 🎾(grass)🎣 boat hire
Credit Cards [1] [3]

[Q] is for quality. For a full explanation of this AA quality award, consult the Contents page.

KILLIECRANKIE Tayside *Perthshire* Map **14** NN96

GH [Q][Q] **Dalnasgadh House** PH16 5LN ☎Pitlochry(0796) 3237
Etr-Oct
Set in 2 acres of well tended grounds, this attractive Victorian house is an ideal base for the touring holidaymaker seeking peaceful relaxation. The house offers traditional comforts and Mrs McDougall maintains high standards throughout.
5hc 🚭in 2 bedrooms Ⓡ 🐕 (ex guide dogs) ✱ sB&B£14.50-£15
dB&B£26-£27
♨ CTV 10P nc5yrs
[£]
See advertisement under PITLOCHRY on page 297

KILVE Somerset Map **03** ST14

SELECTED

INN [Q][Q][Q][Q] **Hood Arms** TA5 1EA
☎Holford(027874) 210
Closed 25 Dec
This popular inn stands beside the A39 between Bridgewater and Minehead, and the resident proprietors have a reputation for their friendly hospitality. The bedrooms are equipped with many thoughtful extras such as colour TVs, sewing kits, chilled water and fresh flowers, and most are en suite. Interesting home-prepared dishes are served in the bar.
5rm(3🛁2🚿) CTV in all bedrooms Ⓡ sB&B🛁🚿£33-£38
dB&B🛁🚿£54-£60 WB&B£160-£180 WBDi£230-£250
Lunch £6-£9alc Dinner £6-£12alc LDO 10pm
♨ 12P nc7yrs
Credit Cards [1] [3] [£]

KINCRAIG Highland *Inverness-Shire* Map **14** NH80

GH [Q][Q] **March House** Lagganlia, Feshie Bridge PH21 1NG
☎(05404) 388
Closed 21 Oct-26 Dec
Secluded in the tree-studded Glen Feshie, this modern house, with its timber upper floor offers modern facilities throughout. Magnificent views are to be had, together with friendly service and interesting meals.
6rm(5🛁🚿1hc)(1fb)🚭in all bedrooms Ⓡ dB&B£26-£28
dB&B🛁🚿£30-£32 WB&B£84-£105 WBDi£133-£161 LDO 6pm
♨ 8P
[£]

KINGHAM Oxfordshire Map **04** SP22

GH [Q][Q][Q] **Conygree Gate** Church St OX7 6YA
☎(060871) 389 due to change to (0608) 658389
Closed 25 Dec-Jan
Surrounded by pretty gardens in a peaceful village setting, this attractive stone-built house has well-equipped accommodation and serves good home-cooked food. The hotel is complemented by 2 self-catering cottages.
8rm(1🛁5🚿2hc)(2fb) CTV in all bedrooms Ⓡ ✱ sB&B£22-£26
dB&B£40
dB&B🛁🚿£42 WB&B£114-£154 WBDifr£224 LDO 5pm
Lic ♨ 12P 2🚗
Credit Cards [1] [3] [£]

KINGHORN Fife Map **11** NT28

INN [Q][Q][Q] **Long Boat** 107 Pettycur Rd KY3 9RU
☎(0592) 890625
Large modern villa looking out across the Firth of Forth, decorated and furnished to the highest standard.
6🛁🚿 CTV in all bedrooms Ⓡ sB&B🛁🚿£29.95-£39.95
dB&B🛁🚿£32.95-£39.95 Lunch fr£5.95&alc Dinner fr£7.95&alc LDO 9.30pm

▶

♨ CTV 10P
Credit Cards [1] [2] [3] [5] [£]

KINGSBRIDGE Devon Map **03** SX74

GH [Q] [Q] [Q] ***Ashleigh House*** Ashleigh Rd, Westville TQ7 1HB ☎(0548) 2893
rs Nov-Mar
Bright modern accommodation is offered at this small friendly guesthouse. The public rooms are cosy and the sun lounge is an attractive feature. Michael Taylor, a professional toastmaster, and his wife, create a relaxed atmosphere and provide good food.
8hc (1fb) 🚭 in all bedrooms ® LDO 4pm
Lic CTV 5P nc5yrs
Credit Cards [1] [3]

KINGSDOWN Kent Map **05** TR34

GH [Q] [Q] **Blencathra Country** Kingsdown Hill CT14 8EA ☎Deal(0304) 373725
Friendly, modern, country guesthouse with use of a croquet lawn.
7rm(3🚿4hc)(3fb) CTV in all bedrooms ® 🐕 (ex guide dogs) ✱ sB&B£14-£16 dB&B£15-£16 dB&B🚿£36-£38
Lic CTV 7P croquet lawn

KINGSEY Buckinghamshire Map **04** SP70

FH [Q] [Q] [Q] Mr & Mrs N M D Hooper **Foxhill** *(SP748066)* HP17 8LZ ☎Haddenham(0844) 291650
Feb-Nov
This 17th-century farmhouse with spacious, comfortable bedrooms has a delightful garden with pool and pond. The farmhouse is 'no smoking' throughout.
3hc 🚭 in all bedrooms CTV in all bedrooms ®
🐕 (ex guide dogs) dB&B£30-£34
♨ CTV 40P nc5yrs 🏊(heated) 4 acres non-working
[£]

KINGSGATE Kent Map **05** TR37

GH [Q] [Q] **Marylands Hotel** Marine Dr CT10 3LG ☎Thanet(0843) 61259
Apr-Oct
This small privately owned hotel has a warm, friendly atmosphere and simple, comfortable accommodation. Overlooking the sea, it has easy access to the beach.
9rm(1🛁5🚿3hc)(3fb) CTV in 6 bedrooms ® sB&B£17.50 sB&B🛁🚿£20 dB&B£30 dB&B🛁🚿£35 WB&B£89.50-£99.50 WBDi£124.50-£139 LDO noon
Lic CTV 12P snooker
[£]

KING'S LYNN Norfolk Map **09** TF62

GH [Q] **Havana** 117 Gaywood Rd PE30 2PU ☎(0553) 772331
This is a family-run guesthouse offering simple, good-value accommodation.
6rm(1🚿5hc)(2fb) 🚭 in 1 bedroom CTV in all bedrooms ® 🐕 ✱ sB&B£15 dB&B£24 dB&B🚿£30 WB&B£72-£90
♨ CTV 8P
[£]

GH [Q] ***Maranatha*** 115 Gaywood Rd PE30 2PU ☎(0553) 774596
This small, family-run guesthouse, on the outskirts of the town, provides simple accommodation.
6rm(1🚿5hc)(2fb) CTV in all bedrooms LDO 6pm
Lic ♨ CTV 6P

See the regional maps of popular holiday areas at the back of the book.

SELECTED

GH [Q] [Q] [Q] [Q] **Russet House Hotel** Vancouver Ave, 53 Goodwins Rd PE30 5PE ☎(0553) 773098
Closed Xmas & New Year
Set in attractive gardens in a quieter residential area of Kings Lynn, this detached Victorian house provides excellent service, food and accommodation, complemented by genuine warmth and hospitality from Rae and Barry Muddle, the proprietors.
12rm(6🛁4🚿2hc)(1fb) 🚭 in 1 bedroom CTV in all bedrooms ® 🐕 (ex guide dogs) LDO 7.30pm
Lic ♨ CTV 16P nc4yrs
Credit Cards [1] [2] [3] [5]

FH [Q] [Q] Mr N Olesen **Lodge** *(TF824172)* Castle Acre PE32 2BS ☎Castle Acre(0760) 755206
Simple accommodation is offered at this relaxing farm in peaceful surroundings.
3rm(2🛁1hc)(1fb) CTV in all bedrooms ® 🐕 (ex guide dogs) ✱ sB&B🛁fr£17 dB&Bfr£28 dB&B🛁£30-£32 WB&B£98-£105 WBDi£168-£175 LDO 5pm
♨ CTV 20P 1000 acres mixed

Every effort is made to provide accurate information, but details can change after we go to print. It is advisable to check prices etc. before you make a firm booking.

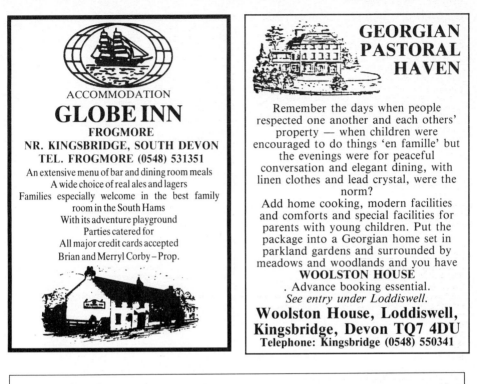

KINGSTON Devon Map 02 SX64

SELECTED

GH **Q Q Q Q** **Trebles Cottage Hotel** TQ7 4PT
☎Bigbury-on-Sea(0548) 810268
*This comfortable, personally-managed small hotel enjoys an
unspoilt village setting and stands in 1.25 acres of attractively
wooded grounds. Its proprietors offer a good standard of
service and traditional home cooking. All bedrooms are
spotless and well equipped, and there are cosy public rooms.*
5⇄ CTV in all bedrooms ®
dB&B⇄£42-£48 WBDi£210-£224 LDO 4pm
Lic ∰ 10P nc12yrs
Credit Cards [1] [3] ⓔ

KINGSTON BAGPUIZE Oxfordshire Map 04 SU49

SELECTED

FH **Q Q Q Q** Mrs A Y Crowther **Fallowfields**
(SU393979) Southmoor OX13 5BH
☎Longworth(0865) 820416 Telex no 83388
FAX (0865) 820629
Apr-Sep rs Wed
*More than 300 years old, this lovely country house, with its
magnificent Victorian façade, sits in 2 acres of tranquil
gardens. The spacious bedrooms are well appointed and
comfortable, as are the lounge and the dining room.*
4⇄♠ CTV in all bedrooms ® ✱ sB&B⇄♠fr£34
dB&B⇄♠£50-£54 WB&Bfr£238 WBDifr£350 LDO
6.30pm
Lic ∰ CTV 15P nc10yrs ⌿(heated) ℘(hard)table tennis
croquet 12 acres sheep
Credit Cards [1] [3] ⓔ

KINGSTONE Hereford & Worcester Map 03 SO43

FH **Q** Mrs G C Andrews *Webton Court (SO421365)* HR2 9NF
☎Golden Valley(0981) 250220
Closed 25 Dec
*Set in 280 acres of mixed farmland, this large black and white
Georgian farmhouse uses home produced food for most meals.*
6hc (2fb) ® LDO 8pm
CTV 10P snooker 300 acres arable beef horse mixed

KINGSWELLS Grampian *Aberdeenshire* Map 15 NJ80

FH **Q Q Q** Mrs M Mann *Bellfield (NJ868055)* AB1 8PX
☎Aberdeen(0224) 740239
Closed Dec
*Situated 4 miles from Aberdeen beside the A944, this friendly
farmhouse is surrounded by gentle rolling countryside. It has an
attractive lounge, and offers tastefully appointed, spacious and
comfortable bed and breakfast accommodation.*
3hc (2fb) CTV in 1 bedroom
∰ CTV 200 acres arable beef

KINGUSSIE Highland *Inverness-Shire* Map 14 NH70

GH **Q Q Q** **Homewood Lodge** Newtonmore Rd PH21 1HD
☎(0540) 661507
Closed Xmas
*This attractively appointed house stands just south of the village,
its position above the Newtonmore road commanding views over
the Spey Valley.*
4♠ (2fb)⊁in all bedrooms ® sB&B♠fr£20.50
dB&B♠fr£35 LDO 9pm
Lic ∰ CTV 6P

GH **Q Q** *Sonnhalde* East Ter PH21 1JS ☎(05402) 266
Closed Nov & Dec
*A large Victorian house in an elevated position above the town
offers fine views over the surrounding hills.*
8hc (3fb) CTV in 1 bedroom LDO 2pm
∰ CTV 8P

KINVER Staffordshire Map 07 SO88

INN **Q Q** **Kinfayre Restaurant** 41 High St DY7 6HF
☎(0384) 872565 FAX (0384) 877724
11♠ (1fb) CTV in all bedrooms ® ✖ (ex guide dogs) ✱
sB&B♠£30
dB&B♠£50 WB&B£175 Lunch £3.95-£6.35 High tea £2-£5.95
Dinner £10-£15alc LDO 10pm
∰ CTV 17P ⌿(heated)

KIRKBEAN Dumfries & Galloway *Dumfriesshire*
Map 11 NX95

SELECTED

GH **Q Q Q Q** **Cavens House** DG2 8AA ☎(038788) 234
*Set in 11 acres of gardens and woodland on the Solway Coast,
this converted licensed mansion house has a tranquil
atmosphere. The bedrooms are spacious and well appointed,
each with views across the attractive gardens. Nothing is too
much trouble for the friendly proprietors, and the freshly
cooked 4-course dinners offer a choice of dishes of good value.*
6rm(4⇄2♠)(1fb) CTV in all bedrooms ® ✱
sB&B⇄♠£28 dB&B⇄♠£40 LDO 7pm
Lic ∰ CTV 10P
Credit Cards [1] [3]

KIRKBY LONSDALE Cumbria Map 07 SD67

GH **Q Q Q** **Abbot Hall** LA6 2AB ☎(05242) 71406
Mar-Oct
*This former farmhouse with its colourful windowboxes offer
pleasant accommodation. Oak beams and flagstone floors add to
the character and enjoyable home-cooked meals are served on an
impressive antique oak table.*
4♠ Annexe 3♠ (1fb)⊁in all bedrooms CTV in 3 bedrooms ®
✖ (ex guide dogs) sB&B♠£18
dB&B♠£32-£34 WB&B£101-£108 WBDi£160.50-£167.50
LDO 6pm
∰ CTV 10P nc12yrs
ⓔ

SELECTED

GH **Q Q Q Q** **Cobwebs Country House** Leck, Cowan
Bridge LA6 2HZ ☎Kirby Lonsdale(05242) 72141
Mar-Dec rs Sun
*Best Newcomer award winner (North of England) 1990–91.
See page 10 for fuller details.*
5⇄♠ CTV in all bedrooms ® ✖ ✱ sB&B⇄♠£30
dB&B⇄♠£50 WB&B£175 WBDi£290 LDO 7.30pm
Lic ∰ 20P nc12yrs ✔
Credit Cards [1] [3] ⓔ

SELECTED

GH **Q Q Q Q** **Hipping Hall Hotel** Cowan Bridge LA6 2JJ
☎(05242) 71187
Mar-Nov
*This charming small hotel is just off the A65 east of Kirkby
Lonsdale. Ian Beyant and Jocelyn Ruffle serve excellent
meals in the great hall under the minstrels gallery. Taken
around a communal table, they are accompanied by wine*

which is included in the price. The pretty bedrooms are complemented by the lounges – one of which is in a conservatory built around a well and looking out on to the stream which runs through the gardens.

7rm(6⇌1♠) CTV in all bedrooms ® ✕ (ex guide dogs)
sB&B⇌♠£46 dB&B⇌♠£58 LDO 5pm
Lic ♨ CTV 7P nc12yrs croquet
Credit Cards ①③

INN ◗◗ **Red Dragon** Main St LA6 2AH ☎(05242) 71205
This attractive inn has old oak beams, a huge log fire in season, a friendly atmosphere and serves good bar meals.
8rm(2⇌6hc)(1fb) ® LDO 9pm
CTV 3P

INN ◗◗◗ **Whoop Hall** Skipton Rd LA6 2HP
☎(05242) 71284 FAX (05242) 72154
Farm buildings of 1618 provide the shell for this attractive modern inn. It has a spacious lounge bar and a pleasant split-level restaurant with a comfortable gallery coffee lounge. The bedrooms are pleasant and well equipped with many thoughtful extras.
5rm(4⇌1♠)(1fb)✕in 4 bedrooms CTV in all bedrooms ®
✕ (ex guide dogs) sB&B⇌♠fr£35
dB&B⇌♠£50-£55 WBDifr£227.50 LDO 10pm
♨ 120P
Credit Cards ①③ ⓔ

KIRKBYMOORSIDE North Yorkshire Map **08** SE68

GH ◗◗◗◗ **Appletree Court** Town Farm, 9 High Market Place YO6 6AT ☎(0751) 31536
Delightfully located in the village centre, Appletree Court was once a working farm. It is now an attractive small hotel offering warm and comfortable accommodation. The original character of the building has been preserved and there is a charming, pretty lounge with lots of books and flowers. Bedrooms are thoughtfully designed, and equipped with little extras. Traditional farmhouse meals are provided, and the hosts ensure that all guests are well looked after at all times.
6rm(4⇌♠2hc)(2fb)✕in all bedrooms CTV in all bedrooms ✕ ✱ sB&Bfr£17.50 dB&Bfr£32
dB&B⇌♠fr£35 WB&Bfr£115 LDO noon
♨ 2P nc12yrs

KIRKBY STEPHEN Cumbria Map **12** NY70

GH ◗◗◗◗ **The Town Head House** High St CA17 4SH
☎(07683) 71044 FAX (07683) 72128
Situated within its own walled garden, this elegant 18th-century house has been tastefully modernised to offer comfortable accommodation with good service. The bedrooms have well-appointed en suite facilities, some having impressive four-poster beds. All rooms are furnished in keeping with the house. There are two cosy lounges and a quaint restaurant which offers good home-cooked food. Non residents would be wise to make reservations for dinner to avoid disappointment.
6rm(2⇌4♠)✕in 2 bedrooms CTV in all bedrooms ® ✱
sB&B⇌♠£29-£35
dB&B⇌♠£46-£52 WB&B£180-£225 WBDif£270-£320
LDO 4pm
Lic ♨ 8P nc12yrs
Credit Cards ①③

KIRKCAMBECK Cumbria Map **12** NY56

FH ◗◗◗◗ Mrs M Stobart **Cracrop** *(NY521697)*
CA8 2BW ☎Roadhead(06978) 245
Jan-Nov
Part of a 425-acre working mixed farm, this early Victorian farmhouse has 3 spacious and comfortable bedrooms, all with en suite facilities, colour TV and other extras. Downstairs there is a relaxing lounge and a games room. Dinners, which should be requested in advance, are taken around one large table and are highly acclaimed. Mrs Stobart's breakfasts are enormous, and afterwards there are lots of marked farm trails to explore.
3♠ (2fb)✕in all bedrooms CTV in all bedrooms ®
✕ (ex guide dogs) ✱ sB&B♠£20
dB&B♠£25-£26 WB&Bfr£85 LDO 1pm
♨ CTV 3P sauna 425 acres arable beef dairy mixed sheep
See advertisement under CARLISLE on page 105

KIRKHILL Highland *Inverness-Shire* Map **14** NH54

GH ◗◗◗◗ **Moniack View** IV5 7PQ
☎Drumchardine(046383) 757
Apr-Oct
Mrs Munro has moved from Tomich House, Beauly, to this delightful modern ranch style bungalow, which is set in pastureland overlooking the gentle wooded slopes which rise above Moniack. The attractive bedrooms are small and comfortably furnished and the lounge is especially inviting and tastefully appointed. The atmosphere is friendly and informal. ▶

3hc * dB&B£22 WB&Bfr£77
🛗 CTV 3P nc12yrs
[£]

⊢⊣**FH** [Q][Q][Q] Mrs C Munro **Wester Moniack** *(NH551438)* IV5 7PQ ☎Drumchardine(046383) 237
Situated beside the Highland winery at Castle Fraser, this well-maintained traditional farmhouse offers attractive, decorative accommodation at very reasonable prices. Although the 2 bedrooms are not very spacious, they are comfortably furnished. There is a pleasant lounge in which guests may relax. Home-cooked meals are served in farmhouse fashion around a communal table in the small dining room.
2hc (1fb) sB&B£11-£12
dB&B£20-£22 WB&B£70-£77 WBDi£105-£112 LDO 8pm
🛗 CTV 4P 600 acres arable beef mixed sheep
[£]

KIRKMUIRHILL Strathclyde *Lanarkshire* Map 11 NS74

FH [Q] Mrs I H McInally **Dykecroft** *(NS776419)* ML11 0JQ
☎Lesmahagow(0555) 892226
Compact and cosy accommodation can be found at this cheerful, modern bungalow situated 1.5 miles west of Kirkmuirhill on an unclassified road to Strathaven.
3rm Ⓡ * sB&B£11-£11.50 dB&B£21-£22 WB&B£70-£75
🛗 CTV 4P 60 acres sheep
[£]

KIRKOSWALD Cumbria Map 12 NY54

SELECTED

GH [Q][Q][Q][Q] **Prospect Hill Hotel** CA10 1ER
☎Lazonby(076883) 500
Closed 25-26 Dec & Feb
Set in open countryside, a mile north of the village, Prospect Hill has been converted from a group of 18th-century farm buildings by Isa and John Henderson, and many artifacts and features remain, lending charm and character. Many of the bedrooms have brass bedsteads and there are cosy lounges. Dinner is served from 7.15pm to 8.30pm and is highly acclaimed.
9rm(2🛁1🚿6hc)(1fb) Ⓡ 🚫🐕 * sB&B£18-£25
sB&B🛁🚿£33-£35 dB&B£38-£40
dB&B🛁🚿£50-£55 LDO 8.45pm
Lic 🛗 CTV 30P 1🚗 (charge) croquet clock golf barbecue patio
Credit Cards [1] [2] [3] [5] [£]
See advertisement under PENRITH on page 293

KIRKWHELPINGTON Northumberland Map 12 NY98

SELECTED

FH [Q][Q][Q][Q] Mrs C Robinson-Gay **Shieldhall** *(NZ026827)* Wallington, Cambo NE16 4AQ (0.75m E of B6342/A696 jct) ☎Otterburn(0830) 40387
rs Nov-Feb
Although only 300 yards from the A696 north of the village, this delightful stone-built house enjoys a tranquil setting. The bedrooms stand around an attractive courtyard and are furnished with quality reproduction pieces made on the premises by Mr. Robinson-Gay. In the main house, the dining room and lounge are both impressive and inviting, the dining room featuring a wealth of bric-a-brac. A separate TV lounge is available.
6rm(5🛁🚿1hc)(1fb) Ⓡ 🚫🐕 (ex guide dogs) *
sB&B🛁🚿£14-£21 dB&B🛁🚿£28-£46 LDO 10am
Lic 🛗 CTV 10P croquet 10 acres horses

KIRTLING Cambridgeshire Map 05 TL65

FH [Q][Q] Mrs C A Bailey **Hill** *(TL685585)* CB8 9HQ
☎Newmarket(0638) 730253
Situated just south of Newmarket, between the villages of Saxon Street and Kirtling, this old farmhouse, with its massive beams and old timbers, is full of character, and the farmyard and buildings, with ducks and chickens, add to the atmosphere of farm life. Moving here from running an old inn nearby, Mr and Mrs Bailey have used their collection of pub memorabilia to create a games room with bar billiards and darts.
3rm(2🚿1hc) CTV in 1 bedroom Ⓡ * sB&Bfr£20 sB&B🚿fr£20
dB&B£40 LDO 8.30pm
Lic 🛗 CTV 15P games room 500 acres arable
[£]
See advertisement under NEWMARKET on page 271

KIRTON Nottinghamshire Map 08 SK66

GH [Q][Q] ***Old Rectory*** Main St NG22 9LP
☎Mansfield(0623) 861540 Telex no 378505
Closed Xmas & New Year
This attractive detached Georgian house stands in well-maintained grounds in a rural setting between Ollerton and Tuxford.
10rm(2🚿8hc)(1fb) 🚫🐕 (ex guide dogs) LDO 7pm
Lic CTV 18P
Credit Cards [1] [3]

KNARESBOROUGH North Yorkshire Map 08 SE35

GH [Q][Q][Q] **Newton House Hotel** 5/7 York Place HG5 0AD
☎Harrogate(0423) 863539 FAX (0423) 869614
Len and Jackie Cohen make charming hosts at this lovely Grade II listed building that they have carefully restored. The house has been decorated throughout in rich prints and stripped pine, complemented by arrangements of dried flowers. Rooms are very well equipped, and have mini bars, colour televisions and radio alarms.
10rm(3🛁7🚿)Annexe 2rm(1🛁1🚿)(3fb) CTV in all bedrooms Ⓡ * sB&B🛁🚿£27.50-£30
dB&B🛁🚿£45-£55 LDO by arrangment
Lic 🛗 CTV 8P
Credit Cards [1] [2] [3] [£]
See advertisement under HARROGATE on page 173

GH [Q][Q][Q] **The Villa** The Vill Hotel, 47 Kirkgate HG5 8BZ
☎Harrogate(0423) 865370
A short walk from the historic market square, The Villa overlooks the River Nidd. Four bedrooms are en suite and all are very well equipped. A pretty conservatory breakfast room overlooks the patio, and friendly Mrs Nicholson provides breakfast only.
6rm(4🚿2hc)(1fb) CTV in all bedrooms Ⓡ * sB&B£10-£16.50
dB&B£30-£34 dB&B🚿£32-£38 WB&B£200
🛗 CTV 🚫🅿

INN [Q][Q] **Mitre Hotel** Station Rd HG5 9AA
☎Harrogate(0423) 863589
9rm(4🛁5🚿) CTV in all bedrooms Ⓡ 🚫🐕 (ex guide dogs) *
sB&B🛁🚿fr£30
dB&B🛁🚿fr£40 WB&Bfr£124 Lunch £4.95-£14alc Dinner £4.95-£14alc LDO 10pm
🛗 CTV
Credit Cards [1] [2] [3] [5] [£]

KNIGHTON Powys Map 07 SO27

FH [Q][Q] R Watkins ***Heartsease*** *(SO343725)* LD7 1LU
☎Bucknell(05474) 220
Apr-Oct
Standing on the A4113 east of the town, this Georgian stone-built farmhouse offers spacious accommodation, and guests can use the conservatory as well as the large lounge.
3rm(1🛁1hc)(1fb) LDO 9am

뽕 CTV 6P 3⮐ ✒ snooker 800 acres mixed
Credit Cards 3

KNUTSFORD Cheshire Map **07** SJ77

GH Q Q **Pickmere House** Park Ln, Pickmere WA16 0JX
☎(0565) 893433
Closed Xmas
*Recently modernised, this 3-storeyed Georgian farmhouse is in the
heart of the village. No smoking is allowed here. The lounge areas
are comfortable and the bedrooms have most modern amenities.*
9rm(5⋔2hc)(3fb)⤦in all bedrooms CTV in all bedrooms ⓡ ✳
sB&Bfr£15.50 sB&B⋔fr£21.50 dB&B⋔fr£31
뽕 CTV 9P

LACOCK Wiltshire Map **03** ST96

GH Q Q Q **At the Sign of the Angel** 6 Church St SN15 2LA
☎(024973) 230
Closed 23 Dec-5 Jan
*The Levis family have run this inn since 1953 and manage to retain
its old world charm while providing all modern facilities including
private bathrooms. Some rooms are in an annexe on the other side
of the garden and are reached via a footbridge.*
6⇌ Annexe 4⇌ (1fb) CTV in all bedrooms ⓡ sB&B⇌£65
dB&B⇌£90 LDO 8.15pm
Lic 뽕 2P 1⮐ nc10yrs
Credit Cards 1 2 3

LADYBANK Fife Map **11** NO31

GH Q Q Q **Redlands Country Lodge** KY7 7SH ☎(0337) 31091
Closed last wk Feb 1st wk Mar
*A splendid pine-clad lodge with smart, well-appointed bedrooms
and lounge. Meals are taken in the attractive stone-built house
surrounded by a pretty garden and patio.*

▶

4⋔ CTV in all bedrooms ® ⊁ ✻
dB&B⋔£39 WBDi£206.50 LDO 5pm
Lic ⁂ 6P ◢

LAMBERHURST Kent Map **05** TQ63

INN 🆀🆀 **George & Dragon** High St TN3 8DQ
☎(0892) 890277
Closed 26-27 Dec
*Almost two hundred years old, this friendly and welcoming
roadside inn has warmth and charm. The bedrooms are freshly
decorated and quite well equipped, while the staff are cheerful and
helpful, and serve good home cooking.*
6rm(2⇄2⋔2hc)(2fb) CTV in all bedrooms ® ✻
sB&B£25-£29.50 sB&B⇄⋔£27.50-£32.50 dB&B£35-£42.50
dB&B⇄⋔fr£42.50 Lunch £3-£5&alc Dinner £4.50-£7.50&alc
LDO 9.30pm
⁂ 25P snooker
Credit Cards 1 2 3 5 ⓔ

LANCASTER Lancashire Map **07** SD46

SELECTED

GH 🆀🆀🆀 **Edenbreck House** Sunnyside Ln LA1 5ED
☎(0524) 32464
*Peacefully situated on the edge of town, with an open rural
aspect, this house incorporates several Victorian architectural
features. Furnished in keeping with that era, great attention
has been paid to detail and quality. The bedrooms are most
comfortable and the bathrooms are particularly impressive.
The friendly proprietors, Mr and Mrs Houghton will provide a
courtesy car to and from the nearby bus and railway station.*
5rm(4⇄1⋔) CTV in all bedrooms ® ✻
dB&B⇄⋔£35-£40
⁂ 6P

GH 🆀🆀🆀 **Lancaster Town House** 11/12 Newton Ter, Caton
Rd LA1 3PB ☎(0524) 65527
*This small bed and breakfast establishment offers pleasant well-
maintained accommodation. With friendly proprietors, it is on the
town centre road from jucntion 34 of the M6.*
6rm(3⇄3⋔)(2fb) CTV in all bedrooms ® ⊁ (ex guide dogs)
sB&B⇄⋔£20-£25 dB&B⇄⋔£30 WB&B£200-£210
⁂ nc4yrs

LANCING West Sussex Map **04** TQ10

INN 🆀🆀🆀 **Sussex Pad Hotel** Old Shoreham Rd BN15 0RH
☎Shoreham(0273) 454647
Closed Xmas & New Years Day
*Nestling at the foot of the South Downs looking across the Adur
Valley, this friendly free house has a spacious bar and a well-
appointed restaurant which serves good food, including fresh sea
food, and has a good wine list. The hotel offers spacious, modern
accommodation.*
6⇄⋔ (1fb) CTV in all bedrooms ® ✻ sB&B⇄⋔£41
dB&B⇄⋔£54 Lunch £11.50-£25alc Dinner £11.50-£25alc
LDO 10pm
⁂ 150P
Credit Cards 1 2 3 5

LANGLAND BAY West Glamorgan Map **02** SS68

See also Bishopston and **Mumbles**
GH 🆀🆀🆀 **Wittemberg Hotel** SA3 4QN
☎Swansea(0792) 369696
Closed 24 Dec-4 Jan
*The sea is just a short walk away from this family run holiday
hotel, set in a quiet area of the town. In an ideal centre from which
to tour the Gower, the hotel provides bright, well-equipped
accommodation.*

12rm(10⋔2hc)(2fb)⊬in 5 bedrooms CTV in all bedrooms ®
⊁ sB&B⋔£28-£30 dB&B£40
dB&B⋔£45 WB&B£130-£150 WBDi£190-£210 LDO 7pm
Lic ⁂ CTV 11P nc5yrs
Credit Cards 1 3 ⓔ

LANGPORT Somerset Map **03** ST42

SELECTED

GH 🆀🆀🆀🆀 **Hillards** High St, Curry Rivel TA10 0EY
☎(0458) 251737
*It is a treat to return to Hillards and feel the warmth of
welcome always given by Jeannie Wilkens and Mike Carter in
their beautiful Grade II listed farmhouse. The fine antique
pieces of furniture and beautiful drapes have been carefully
chosen to enhance the building's graceful elegance, including
oak and elm panelled walls and beamed ceilings. Two of the
very comfortable bedrooms have access from the rose garden.*
4rm(1⇄⋔3hc)Annexe 2⇄⋔ ⊬in all bedrooms
⊁ (ex guide dogs) ✻ sB&B£15-£25 sB&B⇄⋔£25-£30
dB&Bfr£35 dB&B⇄⋔£44-£50
⁂ CTV 25P 3🚗 nc
ⓔ

LAPWORTH Warwickshire Map **07** SP17

FH 🆀🆀🆀 Mr & Mrs Smart **The Old Barn** *(SO164714)*
Mountford Farm, Church Ln B94 5NU ☎(05643) 3283
Tudor house with outdoor swimming pool and duck pond.
2⇄⋔in all bedrooms TV in all bedrooms ® ⊁
sB&B⇄⋔£25-£27
⁂ 3P nc9yrs 30 acres arable mixed water fowl

LARGS Strathclyde *Ayrshire* Map **10** NS25

⊢⊷**GH** 🆀 **Carlton** 10 Aubery Crescent KA30 8PR
☎(0475) 672313
Apr-Oct
*Standing on the sea-front overlooking the Firth of Clyde, this
stone-built, terraced house offers simple and pleasant bedrooms
and a comfortable first floor lounge with open views.*
6hc (2fb) ® sB&B£13-£14
dB&B£24-£26 WB&B£168-£182 WBDi£210-£224
⁂ CTV 6P

FH 🆀🆀 Mrs M Watson **South Whittlieburn** *(NS218632)*
Brisbane Glen KA30 8SN ☎(0475) 675881
Mar-Nov
*One of the bright airy bedrooms at this small, friendly farmhouse
has an adjoining family room. The house stands beside a country
park 2 miles north east of Largs, and is signposted from the main
road.*
3hc (1fb) TV in 1 bedroom ® ✻ sB&Bfr£12
dB&Bfr£23 WB&Bfr£79.50
⁂ CTV 10P 155 acres sheep

LATHERON Highland *Caithness* Map **15** ND13

⊢⊷**FH** 🆀 Mrs C B Sinclair **Upper Latheron** *(ND195352)*
KW5 6DT ☎(05934) 224
May-Oct
*Two-storeyed farmhouse in elevated position with fine views across
the North sea. The farm runs its own Ponies of Britain Pony
Trekking Centre.*
3rm (1fb)⊬in 2 bedrooms TV in 1 bedroom ®
⊁ (ex guide dogs) sB&B£10-£12 dB&B£18-£20
CTV 6P ☾ 200 acres arable beef mixed sheep
ⓔ

LAUNCESTON Cornwall & Isles of Scilly Map **02** SX38

⊢⊷**FH** Q Q Q Mrs Margaret Smith **Hurdon** *(SX333828)*
PL15 9LS ☎(0566) 772955
May-Oct
*Friendly service and home cooking are features of this gracious,
18th-century, stone farmhouse which has comfortable bedrooms
and public areas. There is a pony for children to ride free of
charge.*
6rm(4⇨2hc)(1fb)⚹in all bedrooms 🐾 (ex guide dogs)
sB&B£12 sB&B⇨£14.50 dB&B£24
dB&B⇨£29 (incl dinner) WB&B£90 WBDi£110-£127 LDO
4.30pm
CTV 10P 400 acres mixed

LAVENHAM Suffolk Map **05** TL94

INN Q Q Q **The Angel** Market Place CO10 9QZ
☎Sudbury(0787) 247388
*Situated by the market place, this sympathetically modernised
14th-century inn offers freshly furnished and decorated rooms, all
equipped with good quality en suite facilities, helpful, friendly staff,
parking and a popular menu cooked by the Whitworths.*
7⇨🏠 (1fb) CTV in all bedrooms ® 🐾 (ex guide dogs) ✳
sB&B⇨🏠£30-£35
dB&B⇨🏠£50-£60 WB&B£150-£200 WBDi£200-£260 Lunch
£7.50-£9&alc Dinner £8-£16&alc LDO 9.15pm
🍴 ⚓
Credit Cards 1 3 £

Book as early as possible for busy holiday periods.

LAVERTON Gloucestershire Map **04** SP03

SELECTED

GH QQQQ Leasow House WR12 7NA (2m SW of Broadway off A46) ☎Stanton(038673) 526

Standing in meadows below the Cotswold escarpment outside of the village, this traditional stone farmhouse has been imaginatively modernised to provide comfortable accommodation. The spacious bedrooms are well equipped, and the 'Bull Pen' and 'Hay Loft' are two recently completed rooms, converted from a barn. The hospitality of Gordon and Barbara Meeking, and the peaceful atmosphere and location make a visit here memorable.

5⇔🚿 Annexe 2⇔ (2fb) CTV in all bedrooms ® ✱
dB&B⇔🚿£40-£50
♨ 10P
Credit Cards [1] [2] [3] (£)
See advertisement under BROADWAY on page 91

LAXTON Nottinghamshire Map **08** SK76

FH Q Mrs L S Rose **Moorgate** *(SK726665)* NG22 0NU
☎Tuxford(0777) 870274
Closed Xmas Day
This small, family-run mixed farm stands on the edge of the Medieval village of Laxton, and is found by following the signs to Moorhouse.
3rm (1fb)🚭in all bedrooms ✖ (ex guide dogs) ✱
dB&B£24-£26 WB&B£82-£86 LDO 8.30pm
CTV 6P 145 acres mixed
(£)

LEAMINGTON SPA (ROYAL) Warwickshire Map **04** SP36

GH QQ Buckland Lodge Hotel 35 Av Rd CV31 3PG
☎(0926) 423843
The Chandler family provide friendly service and good accommodation with colour TV, radio-alarms and beverage facilities. Six have en suite facilities. Guests may enjoy a drink in the comfy lounge or with their evening meal – served Monday to Thursday.
10rm(6⇔4hc)(2fb) CTV in all bedrooms ® ✱ sB&Bfr£18
sB&B⇔fr£26 dB&Bfr£30 dB&B⇔fr£38 LDO noon
Lic ♨ 16P
Credit Cards [1] [2] [3] [5] (£)

GH QQ Charnwood 47 Av Rd CV31 3PF ☎(0926) 831074
Close to the town centre, this late Victorian semidetached house offers modern, well-equipped, pretty bedrooms and a comfortable and attractive dining room.
6rm(1⇔1🚿4hc)(1fb) CTV in all bedrooms ® ✖ sB&B£14-£16
sB&B⇔🚿£25-£30 dB&B£28-£32
dB&B⇔🚿£34-£38 WB&B£98-£133 WBDi£136.50-£175 LDO 4pm
♨ CTV 5P
Credit Cards [1] [3] (£)

GH QQQ Coverdale Private Hotel 8 Portland St CV32 5HE
☎(0926) 330400 FAX (0926) 833388
This Georgian house stands off Regent Street and has been carefully modernised to retain many original features while catering for the modern tourist. It is a frequent winner of prizes for its summer floral displays.
8rm(2⇔2🚿4hc)(2fb) CTV in all bedrooms ® ✱ sB&B£21-£23
sB&B⇔🚿£25-£28 dB&B£32-£35 dB&B⇔🚿£35-£38
♨ 3P
Credit Cards [1] [3] (£)

(£) Remember to use the money-off vouchers.

GH QQQ Flowerdale House 58 Warwick New Rd CV32 6AA
☎(0926) 426002
Beautifully converted Victorian house offering a high standard of accommodation with well-equipped bedrooms and a comfortable lounge. The dining room/conservatory opens onto a delightful walled garden.
6rm(4⇔2🚿)(1fb) CTV in all bedrooms ® ✖ (ex guide dogs)
✱ sB&B⇔🚿£19-£21 dB&B⇔🚿£34-£38
Lic ♨ 6P
Credit Cards [1] [3]

GH QQ Glendower 8 Warwick Place CV32 5BJ
☎(0926) 422784
This is a late Victorian end-of-terrace house, situated on the old Warwick road. The bedrooms are modern and well equipped, while the spacious public rooms retain many original features.
9rm(2⇔7hc)(3fb) ® ✱ sB&B£14-£30 dB&B£30 dB&B⇔£36
♨ CTV P̸

GH QQQ Milverton House Hotel 1 Milverton Ter CV32 5BE
☎(0926) 428335
The owners, Mr and Mrs Boyd, have enhanced the interior of this large Victorian brick house with tasteful decoration and occasional antiques. Many of the comfortable, well-equipped bedrooms have en suite facilities and the public areas retain original features.
11rm(3⇔4🚿4hc)(1fb) CTV in all bedrooms ®
✖ (ex guide dogs) ✱ sB&Bfr£20 sB&B⇔🚿fr£32 dB&Bfr£32
dB&B⇔🚿£40-£48 LDO 5pm
Lic ♨ 5P
Credit Cards [1] [3]

GH QQQ York House Hotel 9 York Rd CV31 3PR
☎(0926) 424671
Closed 24-31 Dec
Close to the main shopping centre and overlooking the Royal Pump Room and the River Leam, this imposing Victorian house offers quality public rooms and well-equipped bedrooms, some with good en suite facilities.
8rm(4⇔🚿4hc)(2fb) CTV in all bedrooms ® ✱ sB&B£17-£20
sB&B⇔🚿£28-£35 dB&B£30-£35
dB&B⇔🚿£40-£45 WB&B£115-£225 WBDi£185-£295 LDO 7.30pm
Lic ♨ 3P
Credit Cards [1] [2] [3] (£)

FH QQQ Mrs R Gibbs **Hill** *(SP343637)* Lewis Rd, Radford Semele CV31 1UX ☎(0926) 337571
Closed Xmas & New Year
Hill Farm is situated in a large attractive garden 2.5 miles south east of the A425.
6rm(3🚿3hc)(1fb)🚭in all bedrooms ® ✖ ✱ sB&B£15
sB&B🚿£15 dB&B£22-£26 dB&B🚿£22-£26
♨ CTV 6P 4🚗 350 acres arable beef mixed sheep

⊢⊣**FH QQ** Mrs N Ellis **Sharmer** *(SP359624)* Fosse Way, Radford Semele CV31 1XH (3m E A425 then 0.5m S on Fosse Way) ☎Harbury(0926) 612448
Closed Xmas & New Year
Sharmer Farm is situated half a mile south of the A425 on Fosse Way. This large farmhouse offers modern well-equipped bedrooms and a comfortable lounge with fine views of the surrounding countryside. Home cooking and friendly services are provided by Nora Ellis.
5rm(1🚿4hc)(1fb)🚭in all bedrooms ✖ sB&B£13-£20
dB&B£26-£30 dB&B🚿£30-£35 WB&B£91-£122.50
♨ CTV 5P 120 acres arable

Street plans of certain towns and cities will be found in a separate section at the back of the book.

LEEDS West Yorkshire Map **08** SE33

GH 🅠🅠🅠 **Aragon Hotel** 250 Stainbeck Lane, Meanwood
LS7 2PS ☎(0532) 759306
Closed Xmas
*This small hotel is well furnished and comfortable and has a good
range of facilities including a cocktail bar and small conference
room. The quiet residential area is only 2 miles from the city
centre.*
14rm(8⇄2🏠4hc)(1fb) CTV in all bedrooms ® sB&B£23.40
sB&B⇄🏠£33.92 dB&B£35.30 dB&B⇄🏠£44.27 LDO 6pm
Lic ⁂ 25P
Credit Cards 1 2 3 5 £

GH 🅠🅠 **Ash Mount Hotel** 22 Wetherby Road, Oakwood
LS8 2QD ☎(0532) 658164
Closed Xmas wk
*With gardens in front and a car park to the rear, this comfortable,
pleasantly furnished stone-built house is family run and offers
friendly hospitality.*
13rm(3🏠10hc)(1fb) CTV in all bedrooms ® sB&Bfr£17
sB&B🏠fr£24 dB&Bfr£31 dB&B🏠£34-£36 LDO am
Lic ⁂ CTV 10P
£

GH 🅠 **Highfield Hotel** 79 Cardigan Road, Headingley LS6 1EB
☎(0532) 752193
*Set well back from the road, and close to the county cricket
ground, this large semidetached house has modern bedrooms with
good furnishings. It is family owned and offers good value.*
10hc (1fb) ✱ sB&B£20 dB&B£32 LDO 7pm
⁂ CTV 7P

GH 🅠🅠🅠 **Trafford House Hotel** 18 Cardigan Road,
Headingley LS6 3AG ☎(0532) 752034
Closed Xmas
*Situated close to the county cricket ground, this is a small hotel
personally run by the resident owner. The accommodation is well
furnished and comfortable.*
18rm(4🏠14hc)(4fb) CTV in all bedrooms ® 🐕 (ex guide dogs)
✱ sB&B£17-£23.35 sB&B🏠£29-£35 dB&B£28-£32
dB&B🏠£41-£49 WB&B£100-£203 LDO noon
Lic ⁂ CTV 30P
Credit Cards 3 £

LEEK Staffordshire Map **07** SJ95

GH 🅠 **Peak Weavers Hotel** King St ST13 5NW
☎(0538) 383729
*Once a convent, this large Georgian house with well-kept front
gardens stands in a side street minutes from the town centre,
backing on to the Catholic church.*
11rm(3⇄1🏠7hc)(2fb) TV in all bedrooms ®
🐕 (ex guide dogs) sB&B£16-£20 sB&B⇄🏠£26 dB&B£30
dB&B⇄🏠£32-£34 LDO 8.30pm
Lic ⁂ CTV 8P 4🅿
Credit Cards 1 2 3 £

INN 🅠🅠 **Abbey** Abbey Green Rd ST13 8SA ☎(0538) 382865
*Located off the A523 Leek-Macclesfield road, this tall, sandstone-
built inn is found by following the signs off to Meerbrook. The
letting rooms are in an annexe, created from a converted barn, and
they have most modern facilities.*
Annexe 7🏠 CTV in all bedrooms ® 🐕 (ex guide dogs) ✱
sB&B🏠£24.50
dB&B🏠£38 WB&B£133-£171.50 Bar Lunch £1-£4.50 Dinner
£2.50-£5.25 LDO 8.30pm
⁂ 60P nc14yrs
Credit Cards 1 3

Book as early as possible for busy holiday periods.

LEICESTER Leicestershire Map **04** SK50

GH 🅠🅠 **Burlington Hotel** Elmfield Av LE2 1RB
☎(0533) 705112
Closed Xmas
16rm(4⇄5🏠7hc)(1fb) CTV in all bedrooms ® 🐕
sB&B£20-£30 sB&B⇄🏠£30 dB&B£33-£40
dB&B⇄🏠£40 LDO 7.30pm
Lic ⁂ CTV 23P
Credit Cards 1 3 £

GH 🅠 **Croft Hotel** 3 Stanley Rd LE2 1RF ☎(0533) 703220
FAX (0533) 543788
*This large, detached Victorian house is to be found just off the A6,
1 mile south of the city centre. Catering mainly for commercial
guests it provides simple and comfortable accommodation.*
26rm(1⇄2🏠23hc)(1fb) CTV in all bedrooms ®
🐕 (ex guide dogs) sB&B£20 sB&B⇄🏠fr£30 dB&B£30
dB&B⇄🏠fr£36 WB&Bfr£140 WBDifr£182 LDO 5pm
Lic ⁂ CTV 26P
Credit Cards 1 3 £

GH 🅠 **Daval Hotel** 292 London Road, Stoneygate LE2 2AG
☎(0533) 708234
*Popular with commercial guests, this large house stands at the end
of a Victorian terrace, 1 mile south of the city centre, on the A6.*
14rm(1⇄13hc)(2fb) CTV in all bedrooms ✱ sB&B£18.50-£25
sB&B⇄£35-£40 dB&B£30-£35 dB&B⇄£40-£45 LDO 7pm
Lic ⁂ CTV 20P

GH 🅠🅠 **Scotia Hotel** 10 Westcotes Dr LE3 0QR
☎(0533) 549200
Closed Xmas & New Year
*This popular, value-for-money hotel offers comfortable
accommodation and is convenient for access to the M1/M69
junction and city centre. Six bedrooms are located in an annexe
across the road from the main house.*
10hc Annexe 6hc (2fb) CTV in all bedrooms ® ✱
sB&B£19.50-£21 dB&B£34-£35 LDO 5pm
Lic ⁂ 5P

GH 🅠 **The Stanfre House Hotel** 265 London Rd LE2 3BE
☎(0533) 704294
Closed 24 Dec-2 Jan
*This simple, well-maintained and friendly guesthouse stands on the
A6 approximately one mile south of the city centre. Particularly
popular with commercial guests, it is equally suitable for
holidaymakers.*
12hc (1fb) ✱ sB&B£18 dB&B£29
Lic ⁂ CTV 6P
£

GH 🅠 **Stoneycroft Hotel** 5/7 Elmfield Av LE2 1RB
☎(0533) 706067 & 707605 FAX (0533) 543788
*In a residential area just a few minutes from city centre, the hotel is
large with a high proportion of single rooms.*
46rm(5⇄🏠41hc)(2fb) CTV in all bedrooms ®
🐕 (ex guide dogs) sB&Bfr£23 sB&B⇄🏠fr£33 dB&Bfr£33
dB&B⇄🏠fr£40 WB&Bfr£160 WBDifr£220 LDO 9pm
Lic ⁂ CTV 20P pool table
Credit Cards 1 3 £

LEIGH Hereford & Worcester Map **03** SO75

FH 🅠🅠 Mrs F S Stewart **Leigh Court** *(SO784535)* WR6 5LB
☎Leigh Sinton(0886) 32275
28 Mar-6 Oct
*Set in a quiet, rural area, this beautifully preserved example of a
17th-century farmhouse offers simple and spacious
accommodation, a billiard room and a library. Next to the farm is
a cruck-built tithe barn.*
3rm(1🏠2hc) ® sB&B£18-£19 sB&B🏠£21-£22 dB&B£28-£30
dB&B🏠£31-£33 WB&B£95 LDO 9am

▶

🏠 CTV 6P ♪ billiard room library 270 acres arable sheep
£

LEOMINSTER Hereford & Worcester Map **03** SO45

See also Bodenham

SELECTED

GH Ⓠ Ⓠ Ⓠ Ⓠ **Withenfield** South St HR6 8JN
☎(0568) 2011

*Jim and Pamela Cotton bring northern warmth and
hospitality to this well-proportioned Georgian and Victorian
house which is on the B4316 (the old A49) within easy
walking distance of the shops. Victorian furniture graces the
large rooms which also have colour TVs, direct dial telephones
and particularly good bathrooms. The carefully prepared food
deserves special praise, with lightly cooked vegetables and
featherlight pastry.*
4⇨🏠 (1fb)⊁in all bedrooms CTV in all bedrooms Ⓡ
🏃 (ex guide dogs) sB&B⇨🏠£39-£45
dB&B⇨🏠£56-£62 WB&B£175-£245 WBDi£263-£335
LDO 8.30pm
Lic 🏠 5P 🐾
Credit Cards ①③ £

FH Ⓠ Ⓠ Mrs E M Morris **Park Lodge** *(SO502643)* Eye
HR6 0DP (3m N between B4361 & A49) ☎(0568) 5711
*Set in a quiet, fairly remote location yet within easy reach of the
A49 between Leominster and Ludlow, this small 200-year-old
farmhouse has simple, cosy accommodation. Mr and Mrs Morris
are extremely friendly hosts.*
2hc (1fb) TV in 1 bedroom Ⓡ LDO 6pm
🏠 CTV 6P 2🐴 snooker 200 acres mixed working
£

⊷FH Ⓠ Ⓠ Mr & Mrs Black **Wharton Bank** *(SO508556)*
HR6 0NX ☎(0568) 2575
*This stone-built, hill-top farmhouse, which dates back to the 18th
century, is surrounded by attractive Herefordshire countryside.*
4rm(1⇨3hc) Ⓡ sB&Bfr£12.50 dB&Bfr£25
🏠 CTV 0P ⌂ ₽(grass)174 acres dairy

LERWICK

See SHETLAND

LEVENS Cumbria Map **07** SD48

INN Ⓠ Ⓠ Ⓠ **Gilpin Bridge Hotel & Restaurant** Bridge End
LA8 8EP ☎(044852) 206
*Just off the A590, this popular inn has well-furnished bedrooms
and attractive bars. A good range of food is available in bar and
restaurant.*
10rm(6⇨4🏠) CTV in all bedrooms Ⓡ 🏃 (ex guide dogs) ✳
sB&B£27.50
dB&B£42-£50 Bar Lunch £1.25-£10alc Dinner £6.25-£13.65alc
LDO 9.00pm
🏠 100P pool table darts board
Credit Cards ①③ £

LEW Oxfordshire Map **04** SP30

SELECTED

FH Ⓠ Ⓠ Ⓠ Ⓠ Mrs M J Rouse **The Farmhouse Hotel &
Restaurant** *(SP322059)* University Farm OX8 2AU
☎Bampton Castle(0993) 850297 & 851480 Telex no 83243
Closed Xmas & New Year rs Sun
*Tastefully and sympathetically modernised, this delightful
17th-century farmhouse offers comfortable and well-appointed
accommodation. Each room has been individually furnished
and decorated to retain much of the original charm. The*

---

*popular, cosy restaurant has a conservatory extension and
there is a comfy lounge and pleasant bar. The Rouse family
create a warm, hospitable atmosphere.*
6⇨🏠 (2fb)⊁in all bedrooms CTV in all bedrooms Ⓡ
🏃 (ex guide dogs)
dB&B⇨🏠£40-£60 WB&B£140-£199.50
WBDi£221-£278.50 LDO 7.30pm
Lic 🏠 25P nc5yrs 216 acres dairy
Credit Cards ①③

LEWDOWN Devon Map **02** SX48

GH Ⓠ Ⓠ **Stowford House Hotel** EX20 4BZ ☎(056683) 415
Mar-Oct
*Approximately a quarter of a mile from the A30, this beautifully
positioned house has great character and stands in mature,
secluded gardens. It provides comfortable accommodation in
pleasant surroundings.*
6rm(2⇨2🏠2hc) CTV in 4 bedrooms Ⓡ 🏃 sB&B£17-£24.50
sB&B⇨🏠£24.50 dB&Bfr£34
dB&B⇨🏠fr£39 WB&B£110-£140 WBDi£175-£210 LDO
8.30pm
Lic 🏠 CTV 8P nc5yrs croquet
£

FH Ⓠ Ⓠ Ⓠ Mrs M E Horn **Venn Mill** *(SX484885)* EX20 4EB
☎Bridestowe(083786) 288
Etr-Oct
*This large modern bungalow is set in peaceful surroundings with
river fishing and private trout lake. It is 400 yards from the A30.*
3rm(2hc)(1fb) CTV in 1 bedroom Ⓡ 🏃 ✳ sB&B£11-£12
dB&B£22-£24 LDO 4pm
CTV 4P 4🐴 ♪ 160 acres beef sheep

LEWIS, ISLE OF Western Isles *Ross & Cromarty* Map **13**

STORNOWAY Map **13** NB43

GH Ⓠ Ⓠ **Ardlonan** 29 St Francis St PA87 2PH ☎(0851) 3482
Closed Xmas & New Year
*A pleasantly-appointed house just off town centre. Communal
breakfast tables.*
5hc (1fb) TV in 2 bedrooms 🏃 ✳ sB&B£13-£15 dB&B£26
🏠 CTV
£

LEYBURN North Yorkshire Map **07** SE19

GH Ⓠ **Eastfield Lodge Private Hotel** 1 St Matthews Ter
DL8 5EL ☎Wensleydale(0969) 23196
*On the outskirts of this Dales town, Eastfield Lodge provides
simple accommodation and a bar for guests' use. It is an ideal base
for touring the area.*
8hc Annexe 2rm (2fb) CTV in 9 bedrooms TV in 1 bedroom Ⓡ
sB&B£15-£18 dB&B£24-£30 LDO 8.30pm
Lic 🏠 10P
Credit Cards ①③ £

LICHFIELD Staffordshire Map **07** SK10

GH Ⓠ Ⓠ **Coppers End** Walsall Rd, Muckley Corner WS14 0BG
☎Brownhills(0543) 372910
*This one-time police station now has bright, cheerful
accommodation with 2 bedrooms on the ground floor and a large
rear garden. It is situated 3 miles south of Lichfield on the A461.*
6hc CTV in all bedrooms Ⓡ ✳ sB&Bfr£18.40
dB&Bfr£32.20 WB&B£101.43-£105.05 WBDi£161.81-£169.45
LDO noon
Lic CTV 10P 2🐴 (£1)

GH QQQ *The Oakleigh House Hotel* 25 St Chads Rd
WS13 7LZ ☎(0543) 262688
rs Sun & Mon
*The bedrooms in this small private hotel are excellently decorated
and furnished, with good modern facilities. Some rooms are in the
adjoining annex. An attractive conservatory houses a well-
appointed restaurant, and the residents' meal is offered, as well as
an à la carte menu with some unusual and enjoyable dishes.*
10rm(4⇔4♠2hc) CTV in all bedrooms ® ✗ (ex guide dogs)
LDO 9.30pm
Lic ♨ 30P nc5yrs
Credit Cards ① ③

LIFTON Devon Map **02** SX38

GH QQ **Mayfield House** PL16 0AN ☎(0566) 84401
*A detached house in good-sized gardens off main A30, Mayfield
provides a friendly, informal atmosphere, and good food.*
6rm(1♠5hc)(2fb)✗in all bedrooms CTV in all bedrooms ®
sB&B£14.50 dB&B£23-£27 WB&B£80.50 LDO 4.30pm
Lic CTV 9P 1🎱 ⚽
See advertisement under LAUNCESTON on page 211

GH QQQ **Thatched Cottage Restaurant & Hotel** Sprytown
PL16 0AY ☎(0566) 84224
*This 16th-century cottage stands in peaceful grounds and a barn
conversion annexe provides 4 en suite bedrooms with colour TVs.
Interesting meals are served in the restaurant and morning coffee
and delicious afternoon teas are also offered.*
4♠ (2fb) CTV in all bedrooms ® ✗ ✱
dB&B♠£55 WB&B£173.80 LDO 9.30pm
Lic ♨ CTV 10P nc2yrs

LIGHTHORNE Warwickshire Map **04** SP35

⊢⊣**FH** QQ Mrs J Stanton **Redlands** *(SP334570)* Banbury Rd
CV35 0AH (on A41, 5m S of Warwick)
☎Warwick(0926) 651241
Closed Xmas
*A long drive leads from the A41 to this carefully preserved 16th-
century house. The pretty gardens and open-air swimming pool are
available to guests, and Mrs Stanton cooks wholesome dishes using
home-grown produce where possible.*
3rm(1⇔2hc)(1fb)✗in all bedrooms ✗ (ex guide dogs)
sB&B£12.50-£14 dB&B£25-£27
dB&B⇔£26-£28 WB&B£87.50-£98 LDO 3pm
♨ CTV 6P ⇋100 acres arable
£
See advertisement under WARWICK on page 375

LINCOLN Lincolnshire Map **08** SK97

GH QQ **Brierley House Hotel** 54 South Park LN5 8ER
☎(0522) 526945
Closed Xmas & following 2 wks
*Family run, this large house has good quality accommodation. It is
located in a quiet cul-de-sac overlooking the park.*
11rm(2⇔4♠5hc)(1fb) CTV in 9 bedrooms TV in 2 bedrooms
✗ ✱ sB&B£16-£18 sB&B⇔♠£18 dB&B£28-£32
dB&B⇔♠£32 LDO Breakfast
Lic ♨ CTV adjacent 18 hole golf course
£

This is one of many guidebooks pubished by
the AA. The full range is available at any
AA Centre or good bookshop.

**The Farmhouse
Hotel & Restaurant**

**University Farm, Lew, Bampton, Oxford OX8 2AU
Tel: Bampton Castle (0993) 850297**

A warm and friendly welcome awaits you at this tastefully
modernised 17th-century farmhouse. Situated on the
A4095 twixt Bampton and Witney. We are in an ideal
position for touring The Cotswolds and visiting Oxford –
city of spires. Superb country cooking, homemade bread
and preserves. Oak beamed restaurants. Sitting room
with inglenook fireplace. Tastefully furnished bedrooms
with bathrooms/shower rooms en suite
and Colour T.V. Honeymoon suite.
Ground floor rooms with facilities for
disabled guests. Central heating. Large
garden with sun terrace.
Award winner 1980

**Halfway Farm,
Motel and Guest House**
Swinderby, Lincoln LN6 9HN
Telephone: Swinderby (052 286) 749

This elegant Georgian farmhouse clad in
Virginia creeper provides excellent accommodation in 18 rooms split between the
main house and the single-storey outbuildings, modernised to a high standard
providing character rooms at a reasonable
price. Car parking is unlimited. Full English
breakfast is served in the farmhouse.

SELECTED

GH [Q][Q][Q][Q] D'Isney Place Hotel Eastgate LN2 4AA ☎(0522) 538881 FAX (0522) 511321

This small luxury hotel is ideally situated for guests who wish to explore the Minster Yard, Castle, Cathedral and the Bailygate shops. All bedrooms are individually designed and appointed – some with four-poster beds and spa baths. A popular recent addition is a steam shower. Substantial, well-presented breakfasts are served in the bedrooms.

18rm(15🛁3🚿)(2fb) CTV in all bedrooms [R] ✱
sB&B🛁🚿£38-£51 dB&B🛁🚿£59-£68
♨ 7P
Credit Cards [1] [2] [3] [5]

GH [Q][Q][Q] Minster Lodge Hotel 3 Church Ln LN2 1QJ ☎(0522) 513220

Very good accommodation is available at the delightful small hotel. Exceptionally clean and well-maintained bedrooms offer a good range of facilities, and all have quality bathrooms. A good choice is available at breakfast, which is served in the attractive dining room.

6🛁🚿 (2fb) CTV in all bedrooms [R] 🐕 (ex guide dogs) ✱
sB&B🛁🚿fr£42 dB&B🛁🚿fr£48
Lic ♨ CTV 6P
Credit Cards [1] [3]

GH [Q][Q][Q] Tennyson Hotel 7 South Park LN5 8EN ☎(0522) 521624
Closed Xmas

This pair of Victorian houses have been extensively modernised to provide good accommodation.

8rm(2🛁6🚿)(1fb) CTV in all bedrooms [R] 🐕 sB&B🛁🚿£27
dB&B🛁🚿£40 LDO 7.45pm
Lic ♨ 8P
Credit Cards [1] [2] [3] [£]

LINLITHGOW Lothian *West Lothian* Map **11** NS97

⊢⊣**FH [Q][Q]** Mrs A Hay **Belsyde House** *(NS976755)* Lanark Rd EH49 6QE ☎(0506) 842098
Closed Xmas

Situated 1.5 miles south west of the A706, this well-maintained Georgian farmhouse is located in tree-studded grounds above town.

4hc (1fb) CTV in all bedrooms [R] 🐕 (ex guide dogs)
sB&B£12-£15 dB&B£24-£30
dB&B£30-£36 WB&B£80-£100 LDO noon
♨ CTV 10P ⌂ 106 acres beef sheep [£]

LISKEARD Cornwall & Isles of Scilly Map **02** SX26

⊢⊣**GH [Q][Q] Elnor** 1 Russell St PL14 4BP ☎(0579) 42472
Closed Xmas

Proprietors Nancy and Gordon Strudwick provide a warm welcome at this 19th-century town house, which is close to the town centre and the railway station. The bedrooms are bright, with modern furnishings, complemented by a cosy television lounge.

6rm(1🚿5hc)(1fb) [R] 🐕 sB&B£13-£16 dB&B£26-£32
dB&B🚿£32-£36 WB&B£84-£105 WBDi£140-£161 LDO 5pm
Lic ♨ CTV 6P [£]

FH [Q][Q][Q] Mrs S Rowe **Tregondale** *(SX294643)* Menheniot PL14 3RG (E of Liskeard 1.5m N of A38) ☎(0579) 42407
Closed 25-26 Dec

Carefully modernised to retain its original character, this Cornish farmhouse, off the beaten track, provides a warm welcome. There are 3 comfortable bedrooms, attractive lounges, and guests are treated to farmhouse cooking.

3hc (1fb) [R] 🐕 sB&B£15-£16.50
dB&B£25-£27 WB&Bfr£84 WBDifr£133 LDO 6pm
CTV 3P shooting pony rides 180 acres arable beef mixed sheep
[£]

LITTLE DEWCHURCH Hereford & Worcester Map **03** SO53

FH [Q][Q] Mrs G Lee **Cwm Craig** *(SO535322)* HR2 6PS ☎Carey(043270) 250 due to change to (0432) 840250

Situated 7 miles north west of Ross-on-Wye and 6 miles south east of Hereford, this large Georgian farmhouse is an ideal base for touring the Wye Valley. Spacious and comfortable, it has lounges for smokers and non-smokers, and a games room with a snooker table.

3hc (1fb) [R] 🐕 (ex guide dogs) ✱ sB&B£14
dB&B£24-£28 WB&Bfr£77
♨ CTV 5P 190 acres arable beef
[£]

See advertisement under HEREFORD on page 181

LITTLE HAVEN Dyfed Map **02** SM81

GH [Q][Q] Pendyffryn Private Hotel SA62 3LA ☎Broad Haven(0437) 781337
Etr-Sep

Small and friendly, this hotel stands just above the harbour and has lovely views. It provides good, modern bedrooms and comfortable public areas.

7rm(2🛁5hc)(6fb) CTV in all bedrooms [R] 🐕 sB&B£16-£17
dB&B£27-£28 dB&B🛁£33-£34
Lic ♨ 6P nc4yrs

LITTLE MILL Gwent Map **03** SO30

FH [Q][Q][Q] Mrs A Bradley ***Pentwyn*** *(SO325035)* NP4 0HQ (off A472, 0.5m E of junct with A4042) ☎(049528) 249
Etr-Oct rs Dec & Jan

This 16th-century, traditional Welsh longhouse provides bright, modern bedrooms and a large, comfortable lounge. It is set in large gardens and lawns which also contain a swimming pool.

4rm(2🚿2hc)(1fb) [R] 🐕 LDO 6pm
Lic ♨ CTV nc4yrs 🏊(heated) 120 acres arable

LITTLE PETHERICK Cornwall & Isles of Scilly Map **02** SW97

GH [Q][Q][Q] The Old Mill Country House Hotel PL27 7QT ☎Rumford(0841) 540388
rs Nov-Etr

This unique old mill house has attractive, cosy bedrooms, a spacious beamed dining/sitting area, television lounge, foyer lounge and a sunny slate-paved patio. There is a set menu and a short alternative à la carte. Cream teas are available.

6rm(1🛁4🚿1hc)🚭in 1 bedroom [R] 🐕 (ex guide dogs)
sB&B£20.50-£34.50 sB&B🛁🚿£25-£40.25 dB&B£37
dB&B🛁🚿£46 WB&B£129.50-£161 WBDi£188-£219.50 LDO 6pm
Lic ♨ CTV 10P nc14yrs [£]

LITTON Derbyshire Map **07** SK17

FH [Q][Q] Mrs A Barnsley ***Dale House*** *(SK160750)* SK17 8QL ☎Tideswell(0298) 871309
Closed Xmas

Situated on the outskirts of the village, this is a simple Edwardian stone farmhouse. To the front is a mature garden, and the farmyard is nearby, while rolling hillsides and grazing sheep abound.

3rm(1hc)(1fb) 🐕
♨ CTV 6P nc5yrs 100 acres sheep

[£] Remember to use the money-off vouchers.

LIVERPOOL Merseyside Map **07** SJ39

GH Q Q **Aachen Hotel** 91 Mount Pleasant L3 5TB
☎051-709 3477 & 1126
rs 20 Dec-7 Jan
*Dating back to the 18th century, this mid-terrace house stands in
the city centre and offers compact, well-equipped bedrooms. The
staff here are very friendly.*
17rm(1➪6↟10hc)(6fb) CTV in all bedrooms ®
✖ (ex guide dogs) sB&B➪↟£18-£26 dB&B£32-£40
dB&B➪↟£38-£40 WB&B£126-£280 WBDif168-£224 LDO
8.30pm
Lic ♨ CTV 2P (£3) 3🎱 (£3) pool room
Credit Cards ⓵ ⓶ ⓷ ⓹ ⓺

⊢↞GH Q **New Manx Hotel** 39 Catherine St L8 7NE
☎051-708 6171
*This friendly bed and breakfast establishment is close to the
Anglican cathedral and offers modest accommodation at
reasonable rates. The dining room houses a collection of paintings
of actors and popular musicians – including The Beatles.*
11hc (2fb) CTV in all bedrooms ® sB&B£12.50-£15
dB&B£25-£28 WB&B£70-£75
♨ 20P
Credit Cards ⓵ ⓶ ⓷ ⓹ ⓺

LIZARD Cornwall & Isles of Scilly Map **02** SW71

GH Q Q **Mounts Bay House Hotel** Penmenner Rd TR12 7NP
☎(0326) 290305 & 290393
Closed Nov
*Set on the edge of the village with uninterrupted views across fields
to Kynance Cove, this Victorian house offers modern facilities and
comfort. The friendly owners look after their guests well.*
7rm(2↟5hc)(1fb) ® sB&B£16-£19.50 sB&B↟£17.50-£21
dB&B£32-£39
dB&B↟£35-£42 WB&B£92-£135 WBDif155-£198 LDO
6.30pm
Lic ♨ CTV 10P
Credit Cards ⓵ ⓷ ⓺

GH Q Q *Parc Brawse House* Penmenner Rd TR12 7NR
☎(0326) 290466
rs Dec-Feb
*This comfortable house enjoys views across farmland to the sea.
Friendly, family service is provided by the owners, whose
refurbished property provides a good base for touring south
Cornwall.*
6rm(2↟4hc) ® LDO 6pm
Lic CTV 6P
Credit Cards ⓵ ⓷

GH Q Q Q **Penmenner House Hotel** Penmenner Rd TR12 7NR
☎(0326) 290370
*This hotel has been transformed into a very comfortable and
welcoming retreat. Standing in its own grounds, Penmenner House
has panoramic views of the coastline and lighthouse. The excellent
accommodation is complemented by fine home cooking using fresh
local produce.*
8rm(5↟3hc)(2fb) CTV in all bedrooms ® ✖ (ex guide dogs)
sB&B£18.85-£20.65 sB&B↟£19.85-£22 dB&B£33.70-£37.30
dB&B↟£37.30-£41.30 WB&B£122.50-£134.05
WBDif168-£185.50 LDO 6pm
Lic ♨ CTV 10P
Credit Cards ⓵ ⓷ ⓺

Visit your local AA Centre.

LLANABER Gwynedd Map **06** SH61

FH [Q][Q] Mr P Thompson **Llwyndu** *(SH599185)* Llwyndu LL42 1RR ☎Barmouth(0341) 280144
Closed Dec-Jan
This well-furnished house is set on a hillside overlooking the sea. Built of stone in the 17th century, it has been restored to offer comfortable accommodation.
4rm(2🛁1🚿)(2fb)🚭in all bedrooms Ⓡ 🐕 *
dB&B🛁🚿£45-£49 (incl dinner) WBDi£150-£165 (wkly only Jul & Aug) LDO 6.30pm
Lic 🍴 CTV 10P 4 acres non-working

LLANBEDR Gwynedd Map **06** SH52

INN [Q][Q][Q] Victoria LL45 2LD (Frederic Robinson) ☎(034123) 213
This busy and popular stone-built former coaching inn dates back to the 17th century and is situated in the pleasant village of Llanbedr. All of the attractively decorated and well-furnished bedrooms are well equipped including en suite facilities.
5🛁🚿 CTV in all bedrooms Ⓡ * sB&B🛁🚿£20.50 dB&B🛁🚿£38 WB&B£123 Lunch £6.50&alc High tea £3.25-£7.50alc Dinner £6.50&alc LDO 9.30pm
🍴 CTV 75P 7🚗
Credit Cards [1] [2] [3]

LLANBERIS Gwynedd Map **06** SH56

GH [Q][Q] Lake View Hotel Tan-y-Pant LL55 4EL ☎(0286) 870422
Lake view is an old stone-built property which has recently been much extended and stands on the western edge of Llanberis, overlooking the lake. All except one of the well-equipped bedrooms have en suite facilities and the cottage style restaurant is popular with non-residents.
10rm(9🚿1hc)(3fb) CTV in all bedrooms Ⓡ 🐕 (ex guide dogs) sB&B🚿fr£20
dB&B🚿fr£34 WB&Bfr£110 WBDifr£180 LDO 9.30pm
Lic 🍴 CTV 10P
Credit Cards [1] [3]

LLANBOIDY Dyfed Map **02** SN22

FH [Q] Mrs B Worthing ***Maencochyrwyn*** *(SN181243)* Login SA34 0TN (3.5m WNW of Llanboidy) ☎Hebron(09947) 283 due to change to (0994) 419283
Apr-Oct
Small isolated farmhouse in elevated position overlooking its own farmland and hills.
3rm(1hc)(1fb)🚭in 2 bedrooms 🐕 LDO 4pm
CTV 80 acres dairy

LLANDDEINIOLEN Gwynedd Map **06** SH56

FH [Q][Q][Q] Mr & Mrs Pierce ***Ty-Mawr*** *(SH553664)* LL55 3AD ☎Port Dinorwic(0248) 670147
This traditional working Welsh farm dates back to 1740 and is very well furnished. All the bedrooms have en suite facilities and 2 comfortable rooms are available to guests.
4rm(1🛁3🚿)(1fb)🚭in 1 bedroom CTV in 1 bedroom Ⓡ 🐕 (ex guide dogs) LDO 6pm
🍴 CTV 20P 87 acres beef sheep

SELECTED

FH [Q][Q][Q][Q] Mrs Kettle **Ty'n-Rhos** *(SH548672)* Seion LL55 3AE ☎Port Dinorwic(0248) 670489
Closed 20 Dec-6 Jan
This farm has been extended to provide modern hotel comforts, while retaining its farm atmosphere. Imaginative country cooking, using fresh produce, is provided. The farm is half a mile north on an unclassified road.
11🛁🚿 (3fb) CTV in all bedrooms Ⓡ 🐕 (ex guide dogs) * sB&B🛁🚿£25
dB&B🛁🚿£36-£50 WB&B£120-£155 WBDi£192-£227 LDO 6.30pm
Lic 🍴 12P nc5yrs 🎣 72 acres mixed

LLANDEILO Dyfed Map **02** SN62

↔**GH [Q][Q][Q] Brynawel** 19 New Rd SA19 6DD ☎(0558) 822925
rs 25 & 26 Dec
This family-run hotel has been recently modernised and offers good quality accommodation with well-equipped bedrooms. A wide range of food is served in the popular restaurant. Brynawel stands on the A40.
5rm(2🛁1🚿2hc)(1fb) CTV in all bedrooms Ⓡ 🐕 (ex guide dogs) sB&Bfr£13 sB&B🛁🚿fr£21 dB&Bfr£24 dB&B🛁🚿fr£30 LDO 5pm
Lic 🍴 6P
Credit Cards [1] [3]

LLANDELOY Dyfed Map **02** SM82

FH [Q][Q][Q] K & C Shales **Upper Vanley** *(SM862245)* SA62 6LJ ☎Croesgoch(0348) 831418 837728
Closed Dec-Jan
Friendly Welsh farmhouse where good home cooking is a speciality. Vegetarians are well-catered for. There is a useful play area for children.
8🛁 (5fb) CTV in all bedrooms Ⓡ * sB&B£13.50-£16.50 dB&B🛁£27-£33 WBDi£132.50-£165 (wkly only Whit-Sep) LDO 5pm
Lic 🍴 CTV 0P

LLANDOGO Gwent Map **03** SO50

GH [Q] *Brown's Hotel & Restaurant* NP5 4TW ☎Dean(0594) 530262
Feb-Nov
Set in the beautiful Wye Valley, this guesthouse is also a shop and cafe which serves snacks all day. The bedrooms are modestly furnished but have good en suite facilities.
7rm(1🚿6hc) LDO 7.30pm
Lic CTV 20P nc

INN [Q][Q][Q] The Sloop NP5 4TW ☎Dean(0594) 530291
This roadside inn stands beside a river and was once a mill, and has fine views of the Wye Valley. The bedrooms are well furnished and comfortable and the bars are cosy. A good choice of food is offered.
4🛁🚿 CTV in all bedrooms Ⓡ *
dB&B🛁🚿£36-£44 Lunch £5-£10 High tea £5-£10 Dinner £5-£10 LDO 10pm
🍴 40P nc9yrs
Credit Cards [1] [2] [3] [5] [£]

LLANDOVERY Dyfed Map **03** SN73

GH [Q][Q] Llwyncelyn SA20 0EP ☎(0550) 20566
Closed Xmas
Alongside the river and the A40 road, just on the Llandeilo side of the town, this pleasant establishment has been run by the Griffiths family for twenty-one years. Their hospitality is warm and the accommodation is of good quality.
6hc (3fb) 🐕 (ex guide dogs) sB&B£16.80-£19.80 dB&B£29.60-£31.60 WB&B£82.80-£110.80 WBDi£152.80-£180.80 LDO 7.30pm
Lic 🍴 CTV 12P 🎣

[£] Remember to use the money-off vouchers.

LLANDRINDOD WELLS Powys Map **03** SO06

See also Penybont
GH 🄠🄠 *Griffin Lodge Hotel* Temple St LD1 5HF
☎(0597) 822432
The friendly and experienced Jones family run this Victorian
house, situated in the town centre, providing a spacious and
comfortable lounge and dining room, and well-equipped bedrooms.
8rm(5🜙3hc) ® LDO 6pm
Lic 🏵 CTV 8P
Credit Cards 1 3

GH 🄠🄠🄠 **Guidfa House** Crossgates LD1 6RF
☎Penybont(059787) 241
Hospitality proprietors welcome guests to this stone-built house and
will provide individual scenic routes of the surrounding
countryside. Guidfa House stands at the junction of the A483 and
the A44.
9rm(1⇆2🜙6hc)(3fb) ® ✱ sB&B£17.50 dB&B£32
dB&B⇆🜙£37 WB&B£115.50-£122.50 WBDi£178.50-£185.50
Lic 🏵 CTV 10P

FH 🄠 Mrs M A Davies *Bryn Nicholas (SJ075658)* Crossgates
LD1 6RW (Gwystre 2m W A44) ☎Penybont(059787) 447
May-Oct
This guesthouse is located off the A44 at Crossgates, just 4 miles
north west of the spa town. A relaxing, welcoming atmosphere is
provided in the cosy farmhouse.
3hc ® LDO 4pm
🏵 CTV 6P 161 acres beef sheep

FH 🄠🄠 Mrs D Evans *Dolberthog (SO048602)* Dolberthog
Ln LD1 5PH ☎(0597) 822255
Apr-Sep
This is a Victorian stone farmhouse on the outskirts of town.
3rm(1🜙2hc)(2fb) ® ✙ LDO 2pm
🏵 CTV 3P ⚓ 250 acres mixed

FH 🇶🇶 Mrs S A Evans **Highbry** *(SO044628)* Lanyre
LD1 6EA (1m W off A4081) ☎(0597) 822716
Apr-Sep
3rm(2hc)(1fb) ® ✱ ✱ sB&B£10.50-£12.50
dB&B£21-£25 WB&B£73-£85 WBDi£105-£120 LDO 3pm
⊮ CTV 3P 1🐾 20 acres sheep
£

↦↤**FH** 🇶🇶 Mrs R Jones **Holly** *(SJ045593)* Howey LD1 5PP
(Howey 2m S A483) ☎(0597) 822402
Apr-Nov
At Howley, just off the A483, this stone farmhouse has 3 cosy
bedrooms, and a comfortable lounge. The Jones family are very
friendly hosts.
3rm(1🌙2hc)(1fb) ® ✱ sB&B£11.50-£14 dB&B£23-£28
dB&B🌙£23-£28 WB&Bfr£80 WBDi£110-£125 LDO 5pm
⊮ CTV 4P 70 acres beef sheep

FH 🇶🇶🇶 Mr & Mrs R Bufton **Three Wells** *(SO062586)*
Chapel Rd, Howey LD1 5PB (Howey 2m S A483 then unclass
rd, E 1m) ☎(0597) 824427 & 822484
Three Wells stands east of the A483 at Howley and overlooks a
duck pond. An excellent standard of accommodation is maintained
and the Bufton family have run this relaxing 'Farm Hotel' for
many years. Good food is served and fishing is available.
14🌙🌙 CTV in all bedrooms ® ✱ ✱ sB&B🌙🌙fr£14
dB&B🌙🌙£28-£38 WB&B£95-£128 WBDi£130-£172 LDO
5pm
Lic lift ⊮ CTV 20P nc10yrs ⏎ ⏝ 50 acres beef mixed sheep

LLANDRINIO Powys Map **07** SJ21

FH 🇶🇶🇶 Mrs G M Wigley **New Hall** *(SJ296171)* SY22 6SG
☎Llanymynech(0691) 830384
Etr-Sep
Polished floorboards, beamed ceilings and a lounge with inglenook
fireplace characterise this friendly and spacious farmhouse, partly
dating from the 16th century. At the heart of a very busy farm, it is
run by the Whisley family.
2rm(1🌙1🌙)(2fb) ✱ dB&B🌙🌙£26-£30 WB&B£91-£105
⊮ CTV 0P 265 acres arable beef dairy mixed sheep

LLANDUDNO Gwynedd Map **06** SH78

See **Town Plan Section** During the currency of this publication
Llandudno telephone numbers are liable to change.

↦↤**GH** 🇶🇶 **Brannock Private Hotel** 36 St Davids Rd
LL30 2UH ☎(0492) 77483
Closed Xmas & New Year
This small, well-maintained, family-run hotel is situated in a quiet
road convenient for access to the town centre and beaches and has
the additional advantage of its own small car park.
8rm(3🌙5hc)(1fb) CTV in all bedrooms ® sB&B£11-£12
sB&B🌙£13-£14 dB&B£22-£24
dB&B🌙£26-£28 WB&B£70-£77 WBDi£94-£102 LDO 5pm
⊮ 5P nc3yrs
Credit Cards 1 3 £

↦↤**GH** 🇶🇶🇶 **Brigstock Private Hotel** 1 St David's Close
LL30 2UG ☎(0492) 76416 Due to change to 876416
Quietly situated, this friendly establishment has its own car park
and is within easy reach of the town centre and other amenities.
The accommodation is comfortable and well equipped, including
several en suite facilities, and is well maintained throughout.
10rm(1🌙2🌙7hc)(1fb)✁in all bedrooms CTV in all bedrooms
® ✱ sB&B£12-£13.50 dB&B£24-£27
dB&B🌙🌙£26-£29 WB&B£84-£94.50 WBDi£116-£124 LDO
5.30pm
Lic ⊮ CTV 7P nc4yrs
£

GH 🇶🇶 **Britannia Hotel** Promenade, 15 Craig-y-Don Pde
LL30 1BG ☎(0492) 77185
Closed Xmas
This small family-run hotel is situated on the promenade and
enjoys good views of the bay. The accommodation is nicely
maintained and many of the bedrooms have en suite facilities.
9rm(1🌙3hc)(5fb) CTV in all bedrooms ®
✱ (ex guide dogs) dB&B£23
dB&B🌙🌙£28 WB&B£80.50-£98 WBDi£108.50-£126 LDO
5pm
⊮ CTV
£

GH 🇶🇶 *Bryn Rosa* 16 Abbey Rd LL30 2EA ☎(0492) 78215
Standing in a quiet side road a short distance from the promenade
and shops, this pleasant family-run hotel is attractively furnished
throughout.
7rm(2🌙5hc)(2fb) CTV in all bedrooms ® LDO 4.30pm
⊮ CTV 4P nc2yrs
Credit Cards 1 3

GH 🇶🇶 **Bryn-y-Mor Private Hotel** North Pde LL30 2LP
☎(0492) 76790 FAX (0492) 860825
This large and beautifully maintained early 18th-century house,
standing close to the pier, commands excellent views of the bay, the
beach and the promenade, from its elevated position. Nearby street
parking is available.
19rm(7🌙🌙12hc)(5fb) CTV in all bedrooms ®
✱ (ex guide dogs) sB&B£15-£20 sB&B🌙🌙£26.50-£30
dB&B£28-£38
dB&B🌙🌙£37-£47 WB&B£97-£175 WBDi£145-£223 LDO
2.30pm
Lic ⊮ CTV 1P
Credit Cards 1 2 3 5 £

GH 🇶🇶🇶 **Buile Hill Private Hotel** 46 St Mary's Rd LL30 2UE
☎(0492) 76972
Mar-Nov & Xmas
This large, well maintained private hotel is centrally situated and
provides easy access to the centre of the town and other amenities.
Several of the bedrooms here are equipped with en suite facilities.
13rm(3🌙4🌙6hc) ® sB&B£13.50-£15 dB&B£27-£30
dB&B🌙🌙£38-£42 WB&B£95-£125 WBDi£113-£155 LDO
4pm
Lic ⊮ CTV 6P nc5yrs
£

↦↤**GH** 🇶🇶 **Capri Hotel** 70 Church Walks LL30 2HG
☎(0492) 879177
Situated in a quiet side-street this pleasant guesthouse offers
convenient accommodation, with easy access to the shops, the pier,
the beach and other amenities.
8hc (7fb) ® sB&B£12.50-£15
dB&B£25-£35 WB&B£84-£95 WBDi£105-£120 LDO 4.30pm
Lic ⊮ CTV 3P nc3yrs
£

GH 🇶🇶 **Carmel Private Hotel** 17 Craig-y-Don Pde,
Promenade LL30 1BG ☎(0492) 77643
Etr-Oct
Situated on the seafront, this large end terraced house is nicely
maintained throughout and provides well-equipped
accommodation with the advantage of its own small car park.
10rm(5🌙5hc)(4fb) CTV in all bedrooms ® ✱ sB&B£10.50
sB&B🌙£15 dB&B£21
dB&B🌙£26 WB&Bfr£73.50 WBDifr£105 LDO noon
⊮ CTV 6P nc4yrs

GH 🇶🇶 **Hotel Carmen** Carmen Sylva Rd, Craig-y-Don
LL30 1LZ ☎(0492) 76361
Situated approximately one hundred yards from the promenade,
this small family-run private hotel is convenient for the town centre
and other amenities. The bedrooms are well equipped and many
have en suite facilities.

15rm(10🛁🚿5hc)(5fb) CTV in all bedrooms ® ✻ sB&B£13.50 sB&B🛁🚿£16-£16.50 dB&B£25
dB&B🛁🚿£30 WB&B£85 WBDi£120 LDO 6pm
Lic ♨ CTV
£

GH QQ ***Cornerways Hotel*** 2 St Davids Place LL30 2UG
☎(0492) 77334
Etr-mid Oct
This well-furnished family-run hotel is situated in a quiet side road.
6rm(5🛁1🚿) CTV in all bedrooms ® LDO 4pm
Lic ♨ 5P nc15 yrs
Credit Cards [1] [3]

SELECTED

GH QQQQ Craiglands Private Hotel 7 Carmen Sylva Rd, Craig-y-Don LL30 1LZ ☎(0492) 75090
Mar-Nov
This detached, gabled house lies in a residential road close to the seafront, and within easy walking distance of shops. There are attractive bedrooms, a comfortable lounge and a pleasant dining room where a menu offering a choice of starters and desserts and good home cooking using fresh produce is served. Though unlicensed, guests may bring their own wine by prior arrangement. A warm welcome and friendly attentive service are assured.
6🚿 (1fb) CTV in all bedrooms ® ✻ WB&B£84-£91 WBDi£115-£125 LDO 4pm
♨ CTV nc4yrs

GH QQQ Cranberry House 12 Abbey Rd LL30 2EA
☎(0492) 879760
Apr-7 Oct
Good quality accommodation is offered at this charming Victorian house. Conveniently situated for access to the town centre and amenities, it has the advantage of its own car park. Cranberry house caters for non-smokers only.
5rm(2🛁🚿3hc)🚭in all bedrooms ® ✗ (ex guide dogs) ✻ dB&B£24-£26 dB&B🛁🚿£28-£30 LDO noon
♨ CTV 4P nc10yrs
Credit Cards [1] [3] £

GH QQ ***Cumberland Hotel*** North Promenade LL30 2LP
☎(0492) 76379
This tall seafront hotel has commanding views of the bay. The bedrooms are well equipped and there is a comfortable lounge. Family-owned and run, it offers good value for money.
18rm(4🚿14hc)(11fb) CTV in all bedrooms ®
✗ (ex guide dogs) LDO 6pm
Lic ♨ CTV Ᵽ
Credit Cards [1] [3]

GH QQQ Epperstone Hotel 15 Abbey Rd LL30 2EE
☎(0492) 78746
Mar-Dec
A high standard of accommodation and good home cooking are to be found at this elegant, detached Edwardian house, which is surrounded by well-tended gardens.
8rm(5🛁2🚿1hc)(5fb)🚭in 1 bedroom CTV in all bedrooms ® sB&B£14-£16
dB&B🛁🚿£33-£37 WB&B£95-£125 WBDi£135-£170 LDO 7.30pm
Lic ♨ 7P
£

GH QQ Granby Deganwy Av LL30 2DD ☎(0492) 76095
Apr-Oct
Bright, well-appointed guesthouse in quiet, residential area. ▶

7rm(5🚿2hc)(4fb) CTV in all bedrooms ® ✕ ✱ dB&B🚿fr£37 (incl dinner) WB&Bfr£105 WBDifr£129.50 LDO 4.30pm
Lic CTV 6P
Credit Cards 1 3 £

GH QQ Heath House Hotel Central Promenade LL30 1AT ☎(0492) 76538
Privately owned, this hotel has well-equipped bedrooms, several with en suite facilities. It enjoys a position on the promenade overlooking the bay.
22rm(12🛁10hc)(14fb) CTV in all bedrooms ® ✕ (ex guide dogs) ✱ sB&B£20.50-£22 sB&B🛁£25-£29 dB&B£27-£30
dB&B🛁£30.60-£38 WB&B£81-£170 WBDi£118.80-£212 LDO 4pm
Lic 🍽 CTV P̸ cabaret twice wkly in season (May-Sep)
£

GH QQQ Hên Dy Hotel 10 North Pde LL30 2LP ☎(0492) 76184
rs Nov-Mar
A well-appointed seaside hotel with friendly and helpful owners.
12rm(2🛁2🚿8hc)(3fb) CTV in all bedrooms ® ✱ sB&B£15.50-£20 dB&B£31-£35
dB&B🛁🚿fr£35 WB&B£100-£114 WBDi£146-£160 LDO 5.30pm
Lic 🍽 CTV nc3yrs
Credit Cards 1 3 £

GH QQQ Hilary Hotel 32 St Davids Rd LL30 2UL ☎(0492) 75623
Apr-Oct
A bright, modern hotel with well-equipped bedrooms and public rooms in a quiet position between the 2 seafronts.
8rm(1🛁3🚿4hc)(1fb)🚭in all bedrooms ® ✕ ✱ dB&Bfr£32 dB&B🛁🚿fr£38 WB&B£106-£125 WBDi£135-£155 LDO 6.30pm
🍽 CTV 3P nc5yrs
£

GH QQ Kinmel Private Hotel 12 Mostyn Crescent LL30 1AR ☎(0492) 76171
Etr-6 Oct
This privately owned, friendly hotel stands on the promenade overlooking the bay and beach. Many rooms have en suite facilities.
16rm(9🛁1🚿6hc)(1fb) CTV in all bedrooms ® ✱ sB&B£16-£17.50
dB&B£32-£34 WB&B£99.50 WBDi£131.50 LDO 5.30pm
Lic 🍽 P̸ snooker games room pool
Credit Cards 1 3 £

GH QQQ Mayfair Private Hotel 4 Abbey Rd LL30 2EA ☎(0492) 76170
Mar-Oct
Set in a residential area near the sea and shops, this family-run hotel offers comfortable accommodation.
12rm(9🛁🚿3hc)(7fb) CTV in all bedrooms ® sB&B£13.50-£16.50 dB&B£27-£33
dB&B🛁🚿£30-£32 WB&B£100-£140 WBDi£140-£160 LDO 6pm
Lic 🍽 CTV 3P
£

GH Q Mayfield 19 Curzon Rd, Craig-y-Don LL30 1TB ☎(0492) 77427
Etr-Sep
This small family-run guesthouse is situated in a quiet and peaceful side street on the east side of the town. It offers uncomplicated accommodation and is just a short walk from the sea front.
8hc (5fb) CTV in all bedrooms ® ✱ WB&Bfr£86.50 WBDifr£105 LDO 6pm
Lic CTV

GH QQ Minion Private Hotel 21-23 Carmen Sylva Rd LL30 1EQ ☎(0492) 77740
Etr-mid Oct
Detached Edwardian house in quiet residential area adjacent to the beach.
14rm(4🛁6🚿4hc)(4fb) ® ✱ sB&B£10-£11 sB&B🛁🚿£12-£13 dB&B£20-£22 dB&B🛁🚿£24-£26 WB&B£70-£77 LDO 4pm
Lic CTV 8P
£

GH QQ Montclare Hotel North Pde LL30 2LP ☎(0492) 77061
Mar-Oct
This tall, terraced hotel overlooks the bay, and offers a good all-round standard of food and service.
15rm(2🛁9🚿4hc)(6fb) CTV in all bedrooms ® LDO 3pm
Lic 🍽 4P
£

GH QQQ Orotava Private Hotel 105 Glan-Y-Mor Rd, Penrhyn Bay LL30 3PH ☎(0492) 49780
Mrs Hall provides home-cooked meals and offers bright accommodation of a high standard. Some rooms have en suite facilities, and many have sea views. The hotel has a small car park, and well-maintained gardens giving access to the seafront.
6rm(3🛁3hc)🚭in all bedrooms CTV in 1 bedroom ✕ ✱ sB&Bfr£16.50 dB&Bfr£25 dB&B🛁fr£30 LDO 8pm
Lic 🍽 CTV 8P nc15yrs
Credit Cards 1 3

↦**GH Q Rosaire Private Hotel** 2 St Seiriols Rd LL30 2YY ☎(0492) 77677
Mar-Oct
This is a small, family-run hotel, which is located in a quiet road. It provides convenient access to the town centre and to both shores.
10rm(4🚿6hc)(3fb) ® sB&B£11-£12.50 dB&B£21.50-£24 dB&B🚿£25.50-£29 WB&B£77-£101.50 WBDi£102-£144 LDO 4pm
Lic 🍽 CTV 6P nc3yrs

GH QQ St Hilary Hotel 16 Promenade, Craig-y-Don LL30 1BG ☎(0492) 75551
Jan-Nov rs Oct-Spring BH
Single-fronted Victorian terraced house three-quarters of a mile from main shopping area.
11rm(6🚿5hc)(6fb) CTV in all bedrooms ® ✕ (ex guide dogs) ✱ dB&B£21
dB&B🚿£25.50 WB&B£73.50-£89.25 WBDi£101.50-£117.25 LDO 5.30pm
Lic 🍽 CTV P̸
Credit Cards 1 3

GH QQ *Stratford Hotel* Promenade, Craig-y-Don LL30 1BG ☎(0492) 77962
This friendly hotel is family run and stands in the bay, giving good sea views. It provides well-furnished accommodation.
10rm(4🚿6hc)(6fb) CTV in all bedrooms ®
Lic 🍽 CTV P̸
Credit Cards 1 3

GH QQ Sunnyside Private Hotel Llewelyn Av LL30 2ER ☎(0492) 77150
Etr-Oct & Xmas
Set between Great Orme and the town centre, a few minutes from the seafront, this guesthouse offers well-kept bright rooms, some with en suite facilities. The bar and lounge areas are attractive and relaxing.
26rm(4🛁8🚿14hc)(4fb) CTV in 18 bedrooms TV in 1 bedroom ® sB&B£14-£16 dB&B£28-£32
dB&B🛁🚿£30-£34 WB&B£105-£115 WBDi£160-£165 LDO 7.30pm

Lic 🍴 CTV
£

⊷GH QQQ **Tan-y-Marian Private Hotel** 87 Abbey Rd,
West Shore LL30 2AS ☎(0492) 77727
Mar-Oct
*This well-furnished, comfortable detached hotel offers good value
for money. Standing on the west shore of the resort it is family
owned and run.*
8rm(3♠5hc)(2fb) ® ⊁ sB&B£13-£15 dB&B£24-£28
dB&B♠£28-£32 LDO 7pm
Lic 🍴 CTV 4P 2🚗 nc2yrs

GH QQ **Thorpe House** 3 St Davids Rd LL30 2UL
☎(0492) 77089
Closed Xmas
*Situated in an attractive residential area, this house is well
furnished and comfortable, and provides good, friendly hospitality.
It is very good value for money.*
10rm(1♠9hc)(4fb) ⊁
🍴 CTV ⸮

GH QQ **Warwick Hotel** 56 Church Walks LL30 2HL
☎(0492) 76823
*Standing on the lower slopes of the Great Orme, this large house is
a few minutes' walk from the promenade, pier and other amenities.
Many of the well-equipped rooms have en suite facilities. On-street
parking is available.*
17rm(8⇄2♠7hc)(9fb) CTV in all bedrooms ®
sB&B£14-£15.50 sB&B⇄♠£16-£17.50 dB&B£28-£31
dB&B⇄♠£32-£35 WB&B£95-£105 WBDi£125-£135 LDO
6.45pm
Lic 🍴 CTV ⸮
£

GH QQ **Wedgewood Hotel** 6 Deganwy Av LL30 2YB
☎(0492) 78016
Etr-Dec
*This is a friendly, family-run hotel which provides well-equipped
accommodation, many of the bedrooms having en suite facilities. It
is centrally situated, and has easy access to the town's amenities.*
12rm(2⇄4♠6hc)(1fb) CTV in all bedrooms ®
sB&B⇄♠fr£20 dB&B⇄♠fr£40 (incl dinner) LDO 3pm
Lic 🍴 CTV 7P

GH QQ **White Lodge Hotel** 9 Neville Crescent, Central
Promenade LL30 1At ☎(0492) 77713
Apr-Oct
*This seafront hotel is well furnished and comfortable and has
commanding views of the bay and offers good home comforts.*
12rm(8⇄4♠)(5fb) CTV in all bedrooms ® ✻
dB&B⇄♠fr£39 WB&Bfr£135 WBDi£340 LDO 5pm
Lic 🍴 12P nc5yrs
£

GH QQ **The Wilton Hotel** South Pde LL30 2LN
☎(0492) 76086 & 78343
Feb-Nov
*Well maintained and privately owned, this small hotel is close to
the shops, river and beach. The accommodation is well equipped,
most of the bedrooms having en suite facilities.*
14rm(7⇄5♠2hc)(7fb) CTV in all bedrooms ® ✻
sB&B£15-£17 sB&B⇄♠£17-£19 dB&B£30-£34
dB&B⇄♠£34-£38 WB&B£105-£115 WBDi£130-£140 LDO
4.30pm
Lic ⸮
£

Q is for quality. For a full explanation of this AA quality
award, consult the Contents page.

LLANEGRYN Gwynedd Map **06** SH50

FH QQQ Mrs Griffiths *Bryn Gwyn Country Farm House*
(SH610060) LL36 9UF ☎Tywyn(0654) 711771
Closed Jan-Feb
5rm(1⇄1♠2hc)(1fb)⊁in 3 bedrooms CTV in 1 bedroom TV
in 1 bedroom ® ⊁ (ex guide dogs) LDO 7.30am
🍴 CTV 7P 🐾 bicycles 4 acres non-working

LLANFACHRETH Gwynedd Map **06** SH72

SELECTED

GH QQQQ **Ty Isaf** LL40 2EA ☎Dolgellau(0341) 423261
*Situated in a small and peaceful village, and surrounded by
the splendid scenery of the Snowdonia National Park, this
traditional, stone-built Welsh longhouse dates back to 1624.
It has been modernised to provide present day comforts, yet
retains much of the building's original character. The personal
service and warm hospitality of proprietors Graham and
Diana Silverton make Ty Isaf a memorable place to visit.*
3⇄♠ ⊁in all bedrooms ® ✻ sB&B⇄♠£20-£30
dB&B⇄♠£40 WB&B£140 WBDi£196 LDO 7pm
CTV 3P 1🚗 nc13yrs
£

LLANFAIR CAEREINION Powys Map **06** SJ10

FH QQ Mrs J Cornes **Cwmllwynog** *(SJ071065)* SY21 0HF
☎(0938) 810791
Etr-Sep
*This 17th-century farmhouse with its exposed beams and
inglenook fireplace is just off the B4385. It offers a warm welcome
and traditional home cooking using local produce wherever
possible.*
▶

Welcome to the

WARWICK HOTEL

Church Walks, Llandudno Gwynedd
Telephone: (0492) 76823

Situated a few minutes
walk from the main
shopping centre, the
Pier and Promenade,
and ideally sited for
many of Llandudno's
attractions. Guests are
sure of comfortable
and relaxed surround-
ings to enable them to
enjoy their stay at the
Warwick Hotel. The
bedrooms are attrac-
tively styled, some
bedrooms have bath-
rooms en suite, all have an abundance of hot water,
shaver points, tea/coffee making facilities and colour
TV with central heating throughout. Restaurant and
residential licence.

3rm CTV in 2 bedrooms ® ✕ ✱ sB&Bfr£12
dB&Bfr£24 WB&Bfr£70 WBDifr£105 LDO 4pm
♨ CTV 3P 105 acres dairy

LLANFAIR CLYDOGAU Dyfed Map **02** SN65

SELECTED

FH QQQQ Mrs M Eleri-Davies ***Pentre*** *(SN625506)* SA48 8LE ☎Llangybi(057045) 313
Mar-Oct
Part of a working farm, this creeper-clad house lies north east of Lampeter, off an unclassified road east of the river Teifi. The bright bedrooms are well furnished and 2 have modern en suite facilities. There is a spacious, comfortable lounge with a welcoming woodburning stove in the inglenook fireplace. The hospitable Davies family are always to hand, and participation on the farm is welcomed.
3rm(1⇌1↱1hc)(2fb) ® ✕ LDO 6pm
♨ CTV ✓ 390 acres dairy sheep

LLANFAIR DYFFRYN CLWYD Clwyd Map **06** SJ15

SELECTED

GH QQQQ Eyarth Station LL15 2EE
☎Ruthin(08242) 3643
This former old railway station, on a disused line, has been cleverly and tastefully converted to provide good quality accommodation. The comfortable lounges are complemented by a bright and pleasant dining room which overlooks the Vale of Clwyd. These attributes, combined with the warm hospitality of Jen and Bert Spencer, ensure its understandable popularity.
4↱ Annexe 2↱ (2fb) CTV in 1 bedroom ® ✱
dB&B↱fr£35 WB&Bfr£112 WBDifr£195 LDO 6pm
♨ CTV 6P ⛆(heated)
Credit Cards [1] [3] £

FH QQ Mrs E Jones **Llanbenwch** *(SJ137533)* LL15 2SH
☎Ruthin(08242) 2340
Mar-Sep
Set in a 40-acre farm the accommodation here has been modernised yet retains its original character. A friendly atmosphere prevails and the meals are made from home-grown or local produce.
3hc (1fb) TV in all bedrooms ® ✕ ✱ sB&Bfr£10
dB&Bfr£18 WBDifr£90 LDO 5pm
♨ CTV 0P nc5yrs 40 acres mixed
£

LLANFIHANGEL-YNG-NGWYNFA Powys Map **06** SJ01

FH QQQ Mrs E Jenkins **Cyfie** *(SJ085147)* SY22 5JE (2m S on unclass road off B4382) ☎Llanfyllin(069184) 451
This 17th-century beamed farmhouse is situated in lovely countryside amid the Welsh hills. All of the bedrooms are very comfortable; one has its own lounge, and public rooms are of high quality with guests enjoying good Welsh food.
3rm(2⇌1↱)(1fb) CTV in 2 bedrooms ® ✕ ✱ sB&B⇌↱fr£26
dB&B⇌↱£42-£52 (incl dinner) WB&B£70-£100
WBDi£126-£156 LDO 7.30pm
♨ CTV 6P 2🚗 180 acres mixed
£

See the regional maps of popular holiday areas at the back of the book.

LLANFIHANGEL-Y-PENNANT Gwynedd Map **06** SH60

FH QQQ Mrs M Jones **Tynybryn** *(SH659080)* LL36 9TN
☎Abergynolwyn(065477) 277
Closed 25 Dec
Set amid mountains in a beautiful countryside yet close to Merseyside, delightful Tynybryn is a typical Welsh farmhouse.
3hc ⊬in all bedrooms ® ✱ sB&B£10-£15
dB&B£20-£30 WB&Bfr£69
♨ CTV 0P ✓ 300 acres mixed

LLANFYNYDD Dyfed Map **02** SN52

INN QQQ Penybont SA32 7TG ☎Dryslywn(05584) 292
This pleasant family-run inn is situated 5 miles north of the A40 road and provides modern and well-equipped bedrooms, all of which are en suite. À la carte meals are served in the attractive restaurant, and the carvery, available at weekends, is very popular locally.
8⇌↱ (2fb) CTV in all bedrooms ® ✱ sB&B⇌↱£18-£25
dB&B⇌↱£32.50-£40 WB&Bfr£136 WBDifr£178 Lunch £5.95&alc Dinner £6&alc LDO 9pm
♨ CTV 50P
Credit Cards [1] [3]
See advertisement under CARMARTHEN on page 105

LLANGATTOCK Powys Map **03** SO21

GH QQQ ***Ty-Croeso Hotel & Restaurant*** The Dardy NP8 1PU
☎Crickhowell(0873) 810573
8rm(6↱2hc)(1fb) CTV in all bedrooms ® ✕ (ex guide dogs)
LDO 9.45pm
Lic ♨ 35P
Credit Cards [1] [3]

LLANGOLLEN Clwyd Map **07** SJ24

FH QQ Mrs A Kenrick **Rhydonnen Ucha Rhewl** *(SJ174429)* Rhewl LL20 7AJ ☎(0978) 860153
Etr-Nov
Large, stone-built, 3-storeyed farmhouse, pleasantly situated with shooting on farm and trout fishing on River Dee (permit).
4hc (2fb) ✱ sB&Bfr£12 LDO 3pm
♨ CTV 0P 125 acres dairy

LLANGRANNOG Dyfed Map **02** SN35

FH QQ Mrs B Williams ***Hendre*** *(SN344538)* SA44 6AP (2m E B4321) ☎(023978) 342 due to change to (0239) 654342
Apr-Oct
Conveniently positioned 2 miles from the sandy beach; good home cooking.
3rm(1↱2hc)(1fb)⊬in 2 bedrooms CTV in 1 bedroom ® ✕
LDO noon
♨ CTV 6P 100 acres beef sheep

LLANGURIG Powys Map **06** SN98

⊢⊣**GH QQQ Old Vicarage** SY18 6RN ☎(05515) 280
Mar-Oct
Run by the very friendly Rollings family, this pleasant guesthouse lies in a cul-de-sac just off the main road. The modern bedrooms are well equipped and 2 comfortable lounges are available for guests' use.
5rm(2↱3hc)(2fb)⊬in 1 bedroom CTV in 2 bedrooms TV in 1 bedroom ® sB&B£13-£14 dB&B£26-£32
dB&B↱£32-£34 WB&B£91-£112 WBDi£140-£160 LDO 7pm
Lic ♨ CTV 8P
£

Visit your local AA Centre.

LLANRHAEADR Clwyd Map **06** SJ06

FH 🔲🔲 Mrs S Evans *Tan-yr-Accar (SJ078614)* LL16 4PH
☎Llanynys(074578) 232
Apr-Oct
This peacefully located farm stands on the outskirts of the village and is reached by following the signs to Wern Chapel off the main road, then to Bonttuchel.
2rm (1fb) ✘
🍴 TV 6P 80 acres dairy sheep

LLANRHYSTUD Dyfed Map **06** SN56

FH 🔲🔲🔲 Mrs T T Mizen **Pen-Y-Castell** *(SN539684)*
SY23 5BZ ☎Nebo(09746) 622
Just 2.5 miles from the A487 coast road and sign posted off the B4337, this delightful modernised farmhouse overlooks Cardigan Bay. The family-run accommodation is pretty and comfortable.
6rm(2⇌3🕯1hc)(1fb)🗲in all bedrooms CTV in 3 bedrooms ®
✘ (ex guide dogs) sB&B⇌🕯£20-£22
dB&B⇌🕯£40-£44 WBDi£215-£228 LDO 6pm
Lic 🍴 CTV 10P 2🚤 boating lake pitch & putt 35 acres beef sheep

LLANSANTFFRAID-YM-MECHAIN Powys Map **07** SJ22

FH 🔲🔲 Mrs M E Jones *Glanvyrnwy (SJ229202)* SY22 6SU
☎Llansantffraid(0691) 828258
This cosy farmhouse is set in very pretty lawns and gardens with an abundance of seasonal blossoms. It lies on the Llanymywech side of the village and provides bright and cheerful bedrooms.
2hc ® ✘ (ex guide dogs)
CTV 3P nc3yrs 42 acres beef

LLANSILIN Clwyd Map **07** SJ22

FH 🔲🔲🔲 Mrs B Jones & Mrs A Gallagher **Bwlch-Y-Rhiw** *(ST226298)* SY10 7PT ☎(069170) 261
Mar-Nov
Set in lovely border country with beautiful rural views, this early 19th-century farmhouse is very well furnished and offers spacious and comfortable accommodation.
3⇌🕯 (1fb) CTV in all bedrooms ® ✘ (ex guide dogs)
sB&B⇌🕯fr£22 dB&B⇌🕯fr£30
🍴 4P nc8yrs ⏋ 120 acres sheep
£

LLANTILIO CROSSENNY Gwent Map **03** SO31

FH 🔲🔲 Mrs B A Ford **Little Treadam** *(SO376159)* NP7 8TA
☎(060085) 326
This delightful 16th-century farmhouse is set amid beautiful open countryside overlooking the Black Mountains, 5 miles from Abergavenny on the B4233. Charming beamed interior with comfortable accommodation and good home cooking using fresh produce.
3rm(2🕯1hc)Annexe 1⇌ (1fb) ® ✘ ✱ sB&B⇌🕯£15-£17
dB&B⇌🕯£26-£28 WB&B£90-£95 WBDi£140-£145 LDO 6pm
Lic 🍴 CTV 12P 35 acres mixed
£

LLANTWIT MAJOR South Glamorgan Map **03** SS96

FH 🔲🔲🔲 Mrs Penny *Downs (SS952702)* Wick Rd CF6 9YU
☎(04465) 4252 Telex no 498627 FAX (04465) 6323
Dating back to the 1700s this light stone, listed building is peacefully situated off the B4265 and offers tasteful, modern accommodation with views towards the Somerset coastline.
3hc CTV in all bedrooms ® ✘ LDO 4pm
🍴 CTV 6P nc9yrs 4 acres small holding

Book as early as possible for busy holiday periods.

LLANUWCHLLYN Gwynedd Map **06** SH83

FH 🔲🔲 Mrs D Bugby *Bryncaled (SH866314)* Bryncaled
Farm LL23 7SU (6m from Bala) ☎(06784) 270
Closed Xmas Day
Small farmhouse with oak-beamed dining room, overlooking Aran mountains. A fishing river runs through the grounds.
3rm(2hc) ® ✘ (ex guide dogs) LDO am
Lic 🍴 CTV 6P ⏋ 500 acres mixed beef sheep

LLANVAIR DISCOED Gwent Map **03** ST49

FH 🔲🔲 Mr & Mrs Price *Great Llanmellyn (SO456923)*
NP6 6LU ☎Shirenewton(02917) 210
Apr-Oct
Family farmhouse full of character with flagstone floors and cosy accommodation.
2hc (2fb) ® ✘
🍴 CTV 3P 250 acres dairy mixed

LLANWDDYN Powys Map **06** SJ01

FH 🔲🔲 R B & H A Parry *Tynymaes (SJ048183)* SY10 0NN
☎(069173) 216
May-29 Sep
Situated just a few miles from Lake Vyrnwy this cosy farmhouse, run by the Parry family offers a warm welcome. The lounge is spacious and comfortable and the bedrooms are bright and cheerful.
3hc (1fb) ✘ LDO 5pm
🍴 CTV 4P 420 acres beef sheep

LLANWRIN Powys Map **06** SH70

FH 🔲🔲🔲 Mrs R J Hughes **Mathafarn** *(SN812055)*
Cemmaes Rd SY20 8QJ ☎Cemmaes Road(06502) 226
Set in the beautiful Dovey Valley, this ivy-clad house dates back to 1628. Henry VII is said to have stayed here en route to the Battle of Bosworth. Today's guests will find comfortable accommodation provided by the friendly Hughes family.
3rm(1⇌2hc) ® ✘ (ex guide dogs) ✱ sB&B£12.50 dB&B£25
dB&B⇌£28 WB&Bfr£175 WBDifr£140
🍴 CTV 3P 600 acres beef sheep
£

LLANWRTYD WELLS Powys Map **03** SN84

GH 🔲 *Carlton Court Hotel* Dolecoed Rd LD5 4SN
☎(05913) 248
9rm(1⇌8hc)(1fb) CTV in all bedrooms ® ✘ LDO 9pm
Lic 🍴 ⚊ nc10yrs sauna

LOCHINVER Highland *Sutherland* Map **14** NC02

GH 🔲🔲 **Ardglas** IV27 4LI ☎(05714) 257
Feb-Nov
Standing in an elevated position overlooking the bay, this friendly guesthouse offers comfortable, compact accommodation. There is a pleasant lounge and the neat dining room has particularly attractive views.
8hc (2fb)🗲in all bedrooms CTV in 1 bedroom ® ✱
sB&B£11-£12 dB&B£22-£24 WB&B£77-£84
🍴 CTV 12P

LOCHRANZA

See **ARRAN, ISLE OF**

LOCHWINNOCH Strathclyde *Renfrewshire* Map **10** NS35

FH 🔲🔲 Mrs A Mackie **High Belltrees** *(NS377584)* PA12 4JN
(situated 1m off the A737 to Largs road) ☎(0505) 842376
Overlooks Castle Semple Loch which has an RSPB Bird Sanctuary and yachting facilities.
▶

4rm(3hc)(2fb) CTV in all bedrooms ® ✹ (ex guide dogs) ✻
sB&B£14-£15.50 dB&B£24-£26 WB&B£78-£80
♨ CTV 6P 220 acres dairy mixed sheep

LOCKERBIE Dumfries & Galloway *Dumfriesshire*
Map **11** NY18

GH Q Q Q **Rosehill** Carlisle Rd DG11 2DR ☎(05762) 2378
*Bright, comfortable and tastefully appointed accommodation is
provided in this spacious, detached house on the outskirts of the
town. Public rooms are cosy and the proprietor hospitable.*
5hc (3fb) CTV in all bedrooms ® sB&B£15-£16 dB&B£24-£26
♨ CTV 5P

LODDISWELL Devon Map **03** SX74

GH Q Q Q **Woolston House** TQ7 4DU
☎Kingsbridge(0548) 550341
*This Georgian country house is non-smoking and caters especially
for children, with a a bright playroom packed with toys, and a
kitchen for mothers. Older members of the family will enjoy 30
acres of grounds with a heated pool, tennis court and adventure
playground. The wholesome food served here includes vegetarian
and low cholesterol meals.*
7⇨🛏 (5fb)✂in all bedrooms CTV in all bedrooms ✹
sB&B⇨�£49.50-£54.45
dB&B⇨�£74-£88 (incl dinner) WBDi£233-£291 LDO 10am
Lic ♨ 20P 2🚗 ⚕ ⚊(heated) ♙(hard)adventure playground
£

See advertisement under KINGSBRIDGE on page 205

London
Plan 1

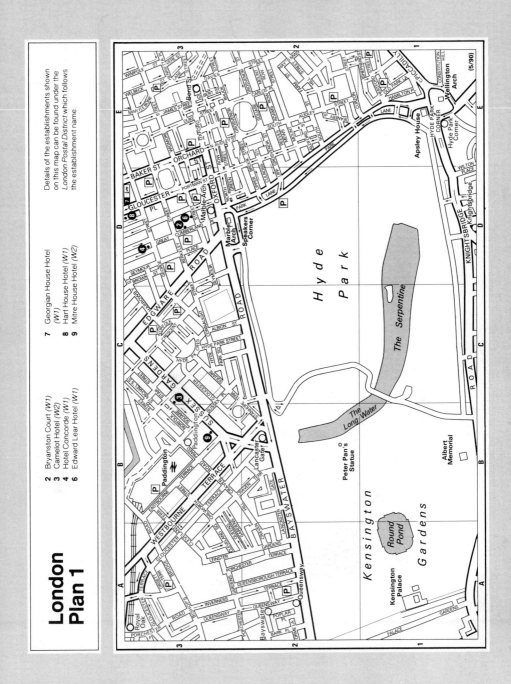

2 Bryanston Court (W1)
3 Camelot Hotel (W2)
4 Hotel Concorde (W1)
6 Edward Lear Hotel (W1)

7 Georgian House Hotel (W1)
8 Hart House Hotel (W1)
9 Mitre House Hotel (W2)

Details of the establishments shown on this map can be found under the *London Postal District* which follows the establishment name.

London
Plan 2

Details of the establishments shown on this map can be found under the *London Postal District* which follows the establishment name.

1 Atlas Hotel *(W8)*
2 Chesham House *(SW1)*
3 Number Eight Hotel *(SW7)*
5 Knightsbridge Hotel *(SW3)*
6 Claverley Hotel *(SW3)*

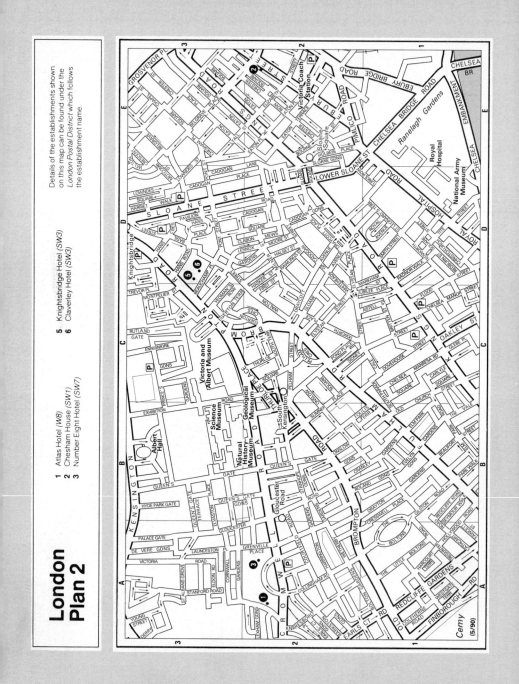

London
Plan 3

Details of the establishments shown on this map can be found under the *London Postal District* which follows the establishment name.

3 Winchester Hotel *(SW1)*

4 Windermere Hotel *(SW1)*

London Plan 4

The placenames highlighted by a **dot** are locations of AA listed establishments outside the Central London Plan area (Plans 1–3). Some of these fall within the London Postal District area and can therefore be found in the gazetteer under **London** in postal district order (see London Postal District map on following page). Others outside the London Postal District area can therefore be found under their respective placenames in the main gazetteer.

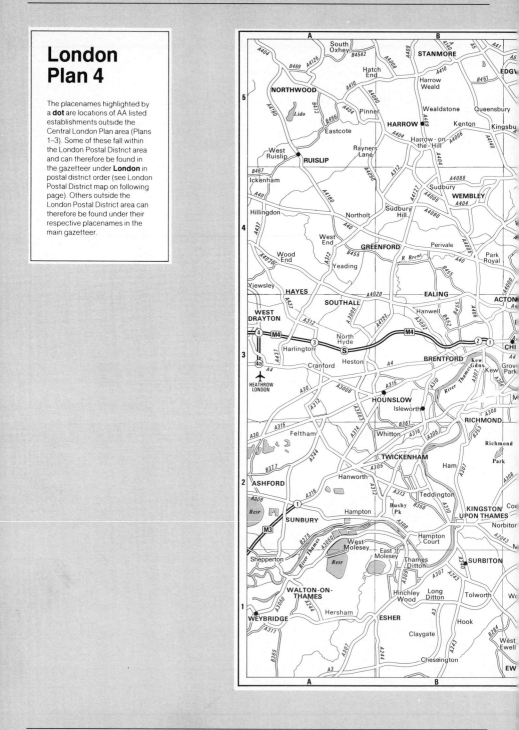

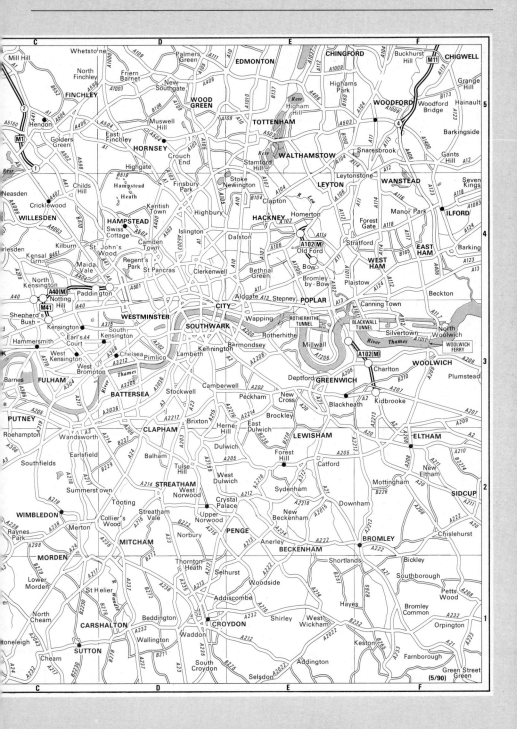

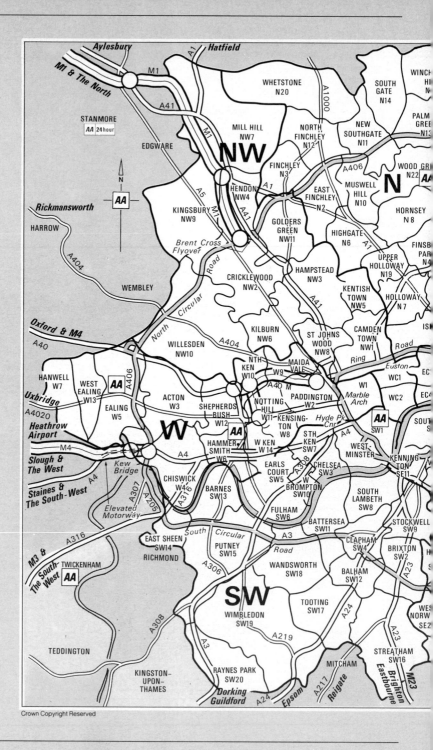

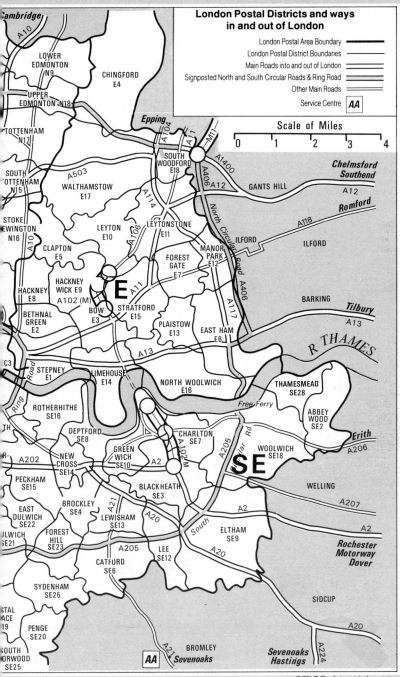

London Postal Districts and ways in and out of London

London Postal Area Boundary
London Postal District Boundaries
Main Roads into and out of London
Signposted North and South Circular Roads & Ring Road
Other Main Roads
Service Centre **AA**

Scale of Miles
0 1 2 3 4

LONDON Greater London Map **04**

See plans 1-4 pages 000-000. A map of the London postal area appears on pages 000-000.
Places within the London postal area are listed below in postal district order commencing East then North, South and West, with a brief indication of the area covered. Detailed plans **1-3** show the locations of AA-listed hotels within Central London postal districts which are indicated by a number. Plan **4** highlights the districts covered within the outer area keyed by a grid reference eg A5.
Other places within the county of London are listed under their respective placenames and are also keyed to this plan or the main map section.

E18 South Woodford

London plan **4** F5
GH Q Q **Grove Hill Hotel** 38 Grove Hill, South Woodford E18 2JG ☎081-989 3344 & 081-530 5286
This popular and well-managed small hotel has compact, well-maintained rooms, each with radio and TV. Generous breakfasts are inclusive and served daily.
21rm(10⇨2♠9hc)(2fb) CTV in all bedrooms ® ✱
sB&B£25-£34.20 sB&B⇨♠fr£34.20 dB&B£42.82-£49.15
dB&B⇨♠fr£49.15
Lic 泗 CTV 8P 4➔ (£2.25)
Credit Cards 1 2 3 £

N8 Hornsey

London plan **4** D5
GH Q Q **Aber Hotel** 89 Crouch Hill N8 9EG ☎081-340 2847
This small, family-run hotel offers warm and friendly service. It is situated in a busy residential area within easy reach of the city centre.
9hc (4fb) ✖ sB&B£16-£18 dB&B£30-£32 WB&B£95-£100
泗 CTV
Credit Cards 1 3 £

NW2 Cricklewood

London plan **4** C4
GH Q Q **Clearview House** 161 Fordwych Rd NW2 3NG ☎081-452 9773
This peaceful, family-run guesthouse is situated in a quiet residential area. The accommodation here is comfortable, and each bedroom is well equipped.
6hc (1fb) CTV in 1 bedroom TV in 5 bedrooms
✖ (ex guide dogs) ✱ sB&Bfr£12 dB&Bfr£24 WB&Bfr£80
泗 CTV ✗ nc5yrs
£

GH Q **The Garth Hotel** 64-76 Hendon Way NW2 2NL ☎081-455 4742 FAX 081-455 4744
Situated on the busy Hendon Way, this commercial hotel has nicely appointed bedrooms and functional public areas. It is at present being refurbished to provide additional bedrooms.
53rm(30⇨10♠13hc)(9fb) CTV in all bedrooms ®
sB&Bfr£39.95 sB&B⇨♠fr£56 dB&Bfr£58
dB&B⇨♠fr£76 LDO 11pm
Lic 泗 CTV 58P
Credit Cards 1 2 3 5

NW3 Hampstead

London plan **4** D4
GH Q Q **Seaford Lodge** 2 Fellows Rd, Hampstead NW3 3LP ☎071-722 5032
Close to Regents Park, this guesthouse has well equipped modern bedrooms with en suite facilities, some ideal for family use. The proprietors personally supervise the running of Seaford House.
15⇨♠ (1fb) CTV in all bedrooms ® ✱ sB&B⇨♠£50-£70
dB&B⇨♠£90 LDO noon

泗 3P 2➔
Credit Cards 1 3 5 £

NW4 Hendon

London plan **4** C5
GH Q Q Q **Peacehaven Hotel** 94 Audley Rd, Hendon Central NW4 3HB ☎081-202 9758 & 081-202 1225
Modern, bright bedrooms, all with colour TV and many with en suite facilities. A bright yellow breakfast room overlooking a landscaped garden, reflects the cheerful disposition of the proprietor.
13rm(7⇨2♠4hc) CTV in all bedrooms ® ✖ (ex guide dogs)
sB&B£38 sB&B⇨♠£45-£50 dB&B£55 dB&B⇨♠£65
泗 2P
Credit Cards 1 2 3 5 £

See advertisement on page 237

SE3 Blackheath

London plan **4** E3
GH Q Q **Stonehall House** 35-37 Westcombe Park Rd SE3 7RE ☎081-858 8706
Old fashioned and comfortable guesthouse with pleasant TV lounge and garden.
27rm(1⇨3♠23hc)(10fb) CTV in all bedrooms ✱ sB&Bfr£23
sB&B⇨♠fr£27 dB&B£32-£36 dB&B⇨♠fr£36
泗 CTV ✗
Credit Cards 1 3 £

See advertisement on page 237

GH Q Q Q **Vanbrugh Hotel** 21/23 St Johns Park SE3 7TD ☎081-853 5505
30rm(8⇨22♠) CTV in all bedrooms ® ✖ (ex guide dogs) ✱
sB&B⇨♠£58 dB&B⇨♠£78-£110
16P

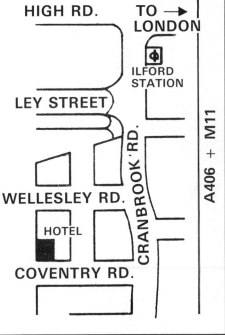

SE9 Eltham

London plan **4** F4

GH Q Q Q **Yardley Court Private Hotel** 18 Court Rd SE9
☎081-850 1850

This small privately managed hotel has comfortable bedrooms with showers and modern furnishings. The generous English breakfasts are freshly cooked.

9rm(6♠3hc)(1fb) CTV in all bedrooms ® ⅛ (ex guide dogs) ✱
sB&B£30 sB&B♠£36.50 dB&B£44.25 dB&B♠£49.50
🍴8P

Credit Cards ⌷1⌷ ⌷3⌷

SE19 Norwood

London plan **4** D2

GH Q Q **Crystal Palace Tower Hotel** 114 Church Rd SE19 2UB
☎081-653 0176

Large Victorian house, close to all amenities and with easy access to central London. Spacious, comfortable bedrooms, compact lounge and basement dining room. Car parking on hotel forecourt.

11rm(2⇔3♠6hc)(4fb) TV in all bedrooms ® ✱ sB&B£18-£21
sB&B⇔♠£21-£25 dB&B£28-£30 dB&B⇔♠£32-£35
🍴CTV 10P

Credit Cards ⌷1⌷ ⌷3⌷ £

SW1 Westminster

London plan **4** D3

GH Q Q **Belgrave House** 28-32 Belgrave Rd, Victoria
SW1V 1RG ☎071-828 1563 & 071-834 8620

This imposing 4-storeyed terraced house is ideally situated for Victoria. It offers reasonably priced accommodation, with the bedrooms having been recently refurbished.

46rm(2⇔4♠40hc)(8fb)⅌in 25 bedrooms ⅛ ✱ sB&B£20-£30
sB&B⇔♠£25-£30 dB&B£35-£40 dB&B⇔♠£40-£45
🍴CTV ⅌

GH Q Q **Chesham House** 64-66 Ebury St, Belgravia SW1N 9QD
☎071-730 8513 Telex no 946797

23hc (3fb) CTV in all bedrooms ⅛ ✱ sB&B£28-£30
dB&B£43-£45
🍴⅌

Credit Cards ⌷1⌷ ⌷2⌷ ⌷3⌷ ⌷5⌷

GH Q Q **Winchester Hotel** 12 Belgrave Rd SW1
☎071-828 2972 Telex no 269674 FAX 071-828 5191
Closed 23-29 Dec

A high standard of accommodation is offered here with nicely appointed rooms with en suite shower facilities. Breakfast is served in the pleasant lower ground floor dining.

18⇔♠ (2fb) CTV in all bedrooms ⅛ ✱ sB&B⇔♠£62
dB&B⇔♠£62
🍴⅌ nc10yrs

GH Q Q **Windermere Hotel** 142/144 Warwick Way, Victoria
SW1V 4JE ☎071-834 5163 & 071-834 5480 Telex no 94017182
FAX 071-630 8831

This friendly hotel offers pleasant accommodation in nicely equipped modern rooms. Windermere is within easy reach of central London.

24rm(20⇔♠4hc)(7fb) CTV in all bedrooms ⅛ (ex guide dogs)
✱ sB&B£30-£42 sB&B⇔♠£38-£46 dB&B£38-£48
dB&B⇔♠£54-£66
🍴⅌

Credit Cards ⌷1⌷ ⌷3⌷

See advertisement on page 239

Street plans of certain towns and cities
will be found in a separate section
at the back of the book.

SW3 Chelsea

London plan **4** D3

GH Q Q Q *Claverley House* 13-14 Beaufort Gardens,
Knightsbridge SW3 ☎071-589 8541

This delightful, elegant hotel has a warm atmosphere and comfortable rooms. Guests can relax in the leather Chesterfield sofas in the reading room. The pretty breakfast room is on the lower ground floor.

36rm(25⇔11hc)(2fb) CTV in all bedrooms ⅛
lift 🍴⅌

Credit Cards ⌷3⌷

GH Q Q Q **Knightsbridge Hotel** 10 Beaufort Gardens SW3 1PT
☎071-589 9271

The charm and elegance of the Victorian era shows in the architecture of this terraced hotel. Attractive and equipped with modern conveniences, and with a pleasant breakfast room on the lower ground floor, the hotel benefits from a convenient location.

20rm(4⇔5♠11hc)(4fb) CTV in all bedrooms ® ⅛
sB&B£38-£42 sB&B⇔♠£52.50-£57.50 dB&B£57.50-£60
dB&B⇔♠£60-£90 LDO 9.30pm
Lic 🍴⅌

Credit Cards ⌷1⌷ ⌷2⌷ ⌷3⌷ £

See advertisement on page 238

SW7 South Kensington

London plan **4** D3

GH Q Q *Number Eight Hotel* 8 Emperors Gate SW7 4HH
☎071-370 7516 Telex no 263849 FAX 071-373 3163

This small, friendly hotel offers pleasant bedrooms with limited public areas. Standing in a quiet terrace, it is conveniently placed for transport to the West End.

14rm(10⇔4♠)(2fb) CTV in all bedrooms ®

►

Lic 🍴 ⚓
Credit Cards ⓵ ⓶ ⓷ ⓹

SW19 Wimbledon

London plan **4** C2
GH ⓆⓆ **Kings Lodge** 5 Kings Rd, Wimbledon SW19 8PJ
☎081-545 0191 FAX 081-545 0381
Closed Xmas
7rm(2⇨5↑)(2fb) CTV in all bedrooms ® ✖ (ex guide dogs)
sB&B⇨↑£47-£53
dB&B⇨↑£60-£69 WB&Bfr£355 WBDifr£407 (wkly only 4th
wk Jun & 1st wk Jul) LDO 9pm
🍴 CTV 2P 2🚗
Credit Cards ⓵ ⓶ ⓷ ⓹ ⓔ

GH ⓆⓆ **Trochee Hotel** 21 Malcolm Rd SW19 4AS
☎081-946 1579 & 3924
A warm and comfortable atmosphere is found in this hotel.
Situated in a quiet residential area, it is ideally located for all local
amenities, and for easy access to both central London and the
countryside.
17hc (2fb) CTV in all bedrooms ® ✖ (ex guide dogs) ✳
sB&Bfr£32 dB&Bfr£45
🍴 CTV 3P
Credit Cards ⓵ ⓷ ⓔ

GH ⓆⓆⓆ **Wimbledon Hotel** 78 Worple Rd SW19 4HZ
☎081-946 9265
This small, family-run hotel offers a cosy and friendly atmosphere.
It is ideally situated, being only a ten minute walk from the main
street and the station.
14rm(4⇨4↑6hc)(6fb)⚲in 8 bedrooms CTV in all bedrooms
® ✖ ✳ sB&B£38 sB&B⇨↑£42 dB&B£48 dB&B⇨↑£54
🍴 CTV 10P
Credit Cards ⓵ ⓷

GH ⓆⓆⓆ **Worcester House** 38 Alwyne Rd SW19 7AE
☎081-946 1300
All the bedrooms at this hotel have en suite facilities and are
equipped with radio, colour TV, direct dial telephone, hairdryer
and beverage facilites. A pleasant atmosphere prevails, and
Worcester House is a few minutes' walk from the village centre.
9↑ (1fb) CTV in all bedrooms ® ✖ ✳ sB&B↑£46-£50
dB&B↑£58.50-£65
🍴 ⚓
Credit Cards ⓵ ⓷ ⓹ ⓔ

W1 West End

London plan **4** D3/4
GH ⓆⓆ **Bryanston Court** 60 Great Cumberland Place W1
(Best Western) ☎071-262 3141 Telex no 262076
The compact bedrooms at this hotel are attractively decorated and
have direct dial telephones (check the hotel unit charge, which is
not displayed), radio and TV. There is a comfortable bar, lounges
and a lift to all floors. The 'Brunswick' dining room is now only
open for breakfast and courteous staff are always pleased to help.
54rm(4⇨50↑)(3fb) CTV in all bedrooms ® ✖ ✳
sB&B⇨↑£65-£70 dB&B⇨↑£80-£88 LDO 10pm
Lic lift 🍴 ⚓
Credit Cards ⓵ ⓶ ⓷ ⓹

GH ⓆⓆ **Hotel Concorde** 50 Great Cumberland Place
W1H 7FD ☎071-402 6169 Telex no 262076
Tastefully decorated and comfortable accommodation with good
lounge. Well situated in the centre of London.
28rm(5⇨23↑)(1fb) CTV in all bedrooms ✖ ✳
sB&B⇨↑fr£62 dB&B⇨↑fr£72
Lic lift 🍴 ⚓
Credit Cards ⓵ ⓶ ⓷ ⓹

GH [Q] ***Edward Lear Hotel*** 28-30 Seymour St W1
☎071-402 5401
30rm(5🚿25hc)(3fb) CTV in all bedrooms [R] ✗
CTV P̸
Credit Cards [3]

GH [Q][Q][Q] Georgian House Hotel 87 Gloucester Place, Baker St W1H 3PG ☎071-935 2211 Telex no 266079
FAX 071-486 7535
Well-equipped, modern accommodation of a good standard is found at this pleasant central London hotel. The breakfast room is on the lower ground floor and there is a lift available to all floors.
19rm(14🛁5🚿)(3fb) CTV in all bedrooms [R] ✗ *
sB&B🛁🚿£40-£45 dB&B🛁🚿£55-£60 (wkly only Nov-Mar)
Lic lift ♨ P̸ nc5yrs
Credit Cards [1] [2] [3]

GH [Q] Hart House Hotel 51 Gloucester Place, Portman Sq W1H 3PE ☎071-935 2288
Imposing 5-storeyed terrace house with well-appointed bedrooms.
15rm(7🛁🚿8hc)(4fb) CTV in all bedrooms [R] ✗ sB&B£30-£35 dB&B£45-£50 dB&B🛁🚿£55-£65
♨ CTV P̸
Credit Cards [1] [2] [3] [£]

GH [Q] ***Montagu House*** 3 Montagu Place W1H 1RG
☎071-935 4632
With new ownership this year, this conveniently situated guesthouse near Marble Arch, is currently being upgraded.
18rm(1🚿17hc)(4fb) CTV in all bedrooms [R] ✗
♨ CTV P̸
Credit Cards [1] [3]

W2 Bayswater, Paddington

London plan **4** C/D3/4

SELECTED

GH [Q][Q][Q][Q] Byron Hotel 36-38 Queensborough Ter W2 3SH ☎071-243 0987 Telex no 263431
Setting the highest standards, the accommodation here recreates the style and elegance of the Victorian era, with reproduction furniture and yet with every modern facility and convenience, including air conditioning. The comfortable sitting room complements the attractive breakfast room. Helpful, friendly staff assist in creating a relaxing atmosphere. Business services and a small conference room are also available at this highly recommended and conveniently situated establishment.
43🛁 (2fb)🚭in 10 bedrooms CTV in all bedrooms [R]
✗ (ex guide dogs) * sB&B🛁fr£75
dB&B🛁fr£85 LDO 8pm
Lic lift ♨ CTV P̸
Credit Cards [1] [2] [3] [5] [£]

GH [Q][Q][Q] Camelot Hotel 45-47 Norfolk Square W2 1RX
☎071-723 9118 & 071-262 1980 Telex no 268312
FAX 071-402 3412
Friendly hotel providing modern facilities in a range of accommodation.
44rm(34🛁🚿6hc)(8fb) CTV in all bedrooms [R]
✗ (ex guide dogs) sB&B£35.50 sB&B🛁🚿£52 dB&B🛁🚿£70
lift ♨ CTV P̸
Credit Cards [1] [3] [£]

See advertisement on page 243

GH [Q][Q] Mitre House Hotel 178-184 Sussex Gardens, Hyde Park W2 1TU ☎071-723 8040 Telex no 914113
FAX 071-402 0990
This family-run licensed hotel is ideally situated in the heart of town. At the time of inspection, half of the house was closed due to the addition of full en suite facilities to all bedrooms, as well as the colour TVs, radios and direct dial telephones. There is a lift to all floors, a TV lounge and free parking on the forecourt.
70rm(64🛁🚿6hc)(3fb) CTV in all bedrooms ✗ * sB&Bfr£50
sB&B🛁🚿fr£50 dB&Bfr£60 dB&B🛁🚿fr£60
Lic lift ♨ CTV 25P jacuzzi
Credit Cards [1] [2] [3] [5]

GH [Q][Q][Q] Mornington Hotel 12 Lancaster Gate W2 3LG (Best Western) ☎071-262 7361 Telex no 24281
FAX 071-706 1028
One of the best bed and breakfast hotels in this part of London, the Mornington maintains high standards of management and customer care. Modern bedrooms are equipped to the highest degree and there is a library. The breakfast room provides an excellent continental buffet, or a cooked English breakfast is available on request. Light refreshments are available until 11.30pm in the bar lounge.
68🛁🚿 (6fb) CTV in all bedrooms sB&B🛁🚿£71
dB&B🛁🚿£82-£92
Lic lift ♨
Credit Cards [1] [2] [3] [5]

GH [Q][Q] ***Norfolk Towers Hotel*** 34 Norfolk Place W2 1QW
☎071-262 3123 Telex no 268583
Charming and tastefully restored, this Victorian house is well equipped to meet the needs of businessmen, travellers and tourists, with en suite accommodation. Hot and cold meals are served in the 'Cad's wine bar' and there is also a lounge bar.
85🛁🚿 (3fb) CTV in all bedrooms ✗ LDO 10pm
Lic lift ♨ P̸
Credit Cards [1] [2] [3] [5]

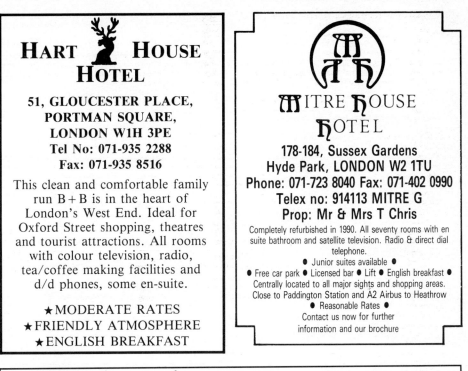

W2 Bayswater, Paddington - W8 Kensington

GH [Q][Q] Parkwood Hotel 4 Stanhope Place W2 2HB
☎071-402 2241
This elegant, 4-storeyed, terraced house has comfortable, well-appointed bedrooms and a friendly, informal atmosphere. It is conveniently close to the West End.
18rm(11🛁1🚿6hc)(5fb)🚭in 1 bedroom CTV in all bedrooms ® 🐕 (ex guide dogs) sB&B£39.50-£43 sB&B🛁🚿£55-£58 dB&B£53-£57 dB&B🛁🚿£63-£65
♨ CTV P̸
Credit Cards [1] [3]

GH [Q][Q][Q] Pembridge Court Hotel 34 Pembridge Gardens W2 4DX ☎071-229 9977 Telex no 298363
Very comfortable bedrooms with modern facilities. Separate restaurant 'Caps'.
17🛁🚿 Annexe 8🛁🚿 (4fb) CTV in all bedrooms ✱ sB&B🛁🚿£74-£97 dB&B🛁🚿£88.55-£135 LDO 11.15pm
Lic lift ♨ 2🚗
Credit Cards [1] [2] [3] [5]

GH [Q][Q] Slavia Hotel 2 Pembrudge Square W2 4EW
☎071-727 1316 & 071-229 0803 Telex no 917458
Hotel offering reasonably priced simple accommodation.
31🚿 (8fb) sB&B🚿£26-£42 dB&B🚿£40-£58
Lic lift ♨ CTV 1P (£6)
Credit Cards [1] [2] [3] [5] [£]

W4 Chiswick

London plan **4** C3
GH [Q][Q][Q] Chiswick Hotel 73 Chiswick High Rd W4 2LS
☎081-994 1712 FAX 081-742 2585
Ideally situated for central London and Heathrow Airport, this hotel offers attractive accommodation and good service. The restaurant has a residential bar and the standard of cooking is high.
30rm(8🛁22🚿)(7fb) CTV in all bedrooms ®
sB&B🛁🚿£45-£52
dB&B🛁🚿£60-£68 WB&B£180-£200 WBDi£250-£280 LDO 8.30pm
Lic ♨ CTV 15P sauna solarium jacuzzi
Credit Cards [1] [2] [3] [5]

W6 Hammersmith

London plan **4** C3
GH [Q][Q] Hotel West Six 99 Shepherd Bush Rd
☎071-603 0948 Telex no 929120
This imposing 3-storeyed terrace house has well-appointed en suite bedrooms and serves continental breakfasts.
12🚿 (2fb) CTV in all bedrooms ® 🐕 (ex guide dogs) ✱ sB&B🚿£23-£28 dB&B🚿£38-£40 WB&Bfr£140
♨ P̸
Credit Cards [1] [2] [3] [£]

W8 Kensington

London plan **4** C3
GH [Q][Q] Apollo Hotel 18-22 Lexham Gardens W8 5JE
☎071-835 1133 & 071-373 3236 Telex no 264189
FAX 071-370 4853
Closed 24 Dec-2 Jan
The proprietor of this well-managed hotel continues to offer friendly service and well-equipped accommodation. Many rooms have en suite facilities, and the public areas are to be upgraded this year.
59rm(40🛁10🚿9hc)(4fb) CTV in all bedrooms
🐕 (ex guide dogs) sB&B£30 sB&B🛁🚿£44 dB&B🛁🚿£54
Lic lift ♨ CTV P̸
Credit Cards [1] [2] [3] [5] [£]

GH [Q][Q] Atlas Hotel 24-30 Lexham Gardens W8 5JE
☎071-373 7873 & 071-835 1155 Telex no 264189
FAX 071-370 4853
Closed 24 Dec-2 Jan
Well situated and offering good value for money, this hotel has traditionally furnished rooms, many with en suite facilities, and all well equipped. There is also a small bar and separate lounge. The sister hotel, the Apollo, is next door.
64rm(15🛁30🚿19hc)(7fb) CTV in all bedrooms
🐕 (ex guide dogs) sB&B£30 sB&B🛁🚿£44 dB&B🛁🚿£54
Lic lift ♨ CTV P̸
Credit Cards [1] [2] [3] [5] [£]

GH [Q][Q] Observatory House Hotel 37 Hornton St W8 7NR
☎071-937-1577 & 071-937 6353 Telex no 914972
Delightfully situated in a quiet area a stroll away from Kensington High Street, this hotel offers bedrooms with private bath/shower, direct dial telephone, colour TV and other modern facilities. Tastefully designed, the rooms are to be refurbished this year.
24rm(7🛁17🚿)(5fb)🚭in 2 bedrooms CTV in all bedrooms ®
🐕 (ex guide dogs) sB&B🛁🚿£57.40-£62.90
dB&B🛁🚿£69.90-£79.90 WBDifr£360
♨ P̸
Credit Cards [1] [2] [3] [5] [£]

Street plans of certain towns and cities will be found in a separate section at the back of the book.

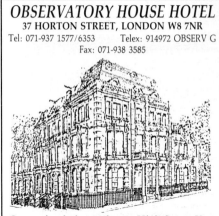

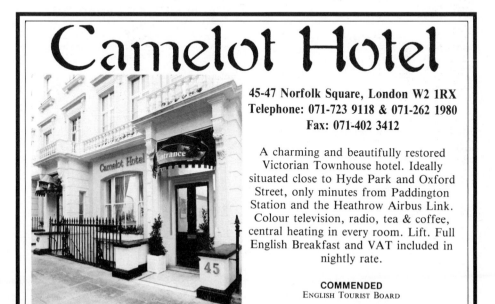

W14 West Kensington

SELECTED

GH [Q][Q][Q][Q] ***Aston Court Hotel*** 25/27 Matheson Rd W14 8SN ☎071-602 9954 Telex no 919208 FAX 071-371 1338

Recently refurbished to a high standard, the hotel is tastefully decorated and has a bar/lounge with a small conservatory. 24-hour room service and many thoughtful extras make this an excellent value-for-money hotel.

29rm(10🛁19🚿)(3fb) CTV in all bedrooms [R]
🚫🐕 (ex guide dogs)
Lic lift ♨ CTV 🚫P
Credit Cards [1] [2] [3] [5]

GH [Q] ***Centaur Hotel*** 21 Avonmore Rd W14 8RP
☎071-602 3857 & 071-603 5973

Small and family-run, this hotel has nicely equipped, simple accommodation with radio alarms and direct dial telephones. Ideally situated for Olympia and Earls Court, the Centaur Hotel is in a residential area with street parking.

12hc (4fb) CTV in all bedrooms 🚫🐕
♨

WC1 Bloomsbury, Holborn

London plan **4** D4

GH [Q][Q] Mentone Hotel 54-55 Cartwright Gardens WC1H 9EL
☎071-387 3927 & 071-388 4671

Comfortable family accommodation, with public shower facilities and friendly service.

27rm(11🚿16hc)(10fb) CTV in all bedrooms 🚫🐕 *
sB&B£25-£30 sB&B🚿£35-£38 dB&B£38-£42
dB&B🚿£48-£55 WB&B£175-£196 (wkly only Dec-Feb)
♨ 🚫P 🎾(hard)
[£]

LONGLEAT Wiltshire Map **03** ST84

FH [Q][Q][Q] Mrs J Crossman **Stalls** *(ST806439)* BA12 7NE
☎Maiden Bradley(09853) 323

Detached house built of Bath stone, originally the home farm for Longleat House. Sun terrace with trim lawns and garden to stream. Access off A362 at Corsley Lane End.

3hc 🚫🐕 * sB&Bfr£14 dB&Bfr£26
♨ CTV 6P table tennis table childrens play area 350 acres dairy

FH [Q][Q][Q] Mrs M A Cottle **Sturford Mead** *(ST834456)*
BA12 7QU ☎Chapmanslade(037388) 213 due to change to (0373) 832213

This 'no smoking' establishment overlooks the National Trust's Cley Hill and is a short distance from Longleat House. Comfortable, spacious and very well-kept accommodation is provided by the friendly Mr and Mrs Cottle.

3rm(1🚿2hc)(1fb) CTV in all bedrooms [R] 🚫🐕 (ex guide dogs)
sB&B£22 dB&B£29-£32 dB&B🚿£30-£33
♨ CTV 10P 5 acres pig

LONGRIDGE Lancashire Map **07** SD63

FH [Q][Q] Mr & Mrs Johnson ***Falicon*** *(SD629361)* Fleet St Ln, Hothersall PR3 3XE ☎Ribchester(0254) 878583

Delightful sandstone farmhouse over 200 years old in pleasant rural surroundings. Bedrooms are very comfortable and well equipped. Mrs Johnson enjoys cooking and offers freshly prepared food for the discerning palate. Situated off the B6245 Longridge to Ribchester road.

2🛁 (1fb)🚭in all bedrooms CTV in all bedrooms 🚫🐕 LDO 5pm
♨ 6P nc10yrs 13 acres beef sheep
Credit Cards [1] [3]

LONGSDON Staffordshire Map **07** SJ95

FH [Q][Q][Q] Mr & Mrs M M Robinson **Bank End** *(SJ953541)*
Old Leek Rd ST9 9QJ (0.5m SW off A53) ☎Leek(0538) 383638
Closed Xmas wk

The bedrooms of this busy and popular farm are above average in standard, all having been converted from stables or barns. Activities available include fishing, riding and swimming (in summer).

9rm(6🛁1🚿2hc)(3fb) CTV in all bedrooms [R]
sB&B🛁🚿£21.50-£24 dB&B£33-£36
dB&B🛁🚿£33-£36 WB&B£126 WBDi£196 LDO 8pm
Lic ♨ CTV 10P 🏊(heated) 🎣 62 acres beef

LONGTOWN Cumbria Map **11** NY36

FH [Q][Q] Mr & Mrs Elwen **New Pallyards** *(NY469713)*
Hethersgill CA6 6HZ (5.5 m E off the A6071 Brampton-Longtown road , take unclass road.)
☎Nicholforest(022877) 308 due to change to (0228) 577308

A modern farmhouse situated 5.5 miles east of Longtown on the Stapeleton road with pretty bedrooms, comfortable lounges and a friendly atmosphere.

5rm(2🛁1🚿2hc)(2fb) CTV in 2 bedrooms TV in 1 bedroom [R]
* sB&B£19-£21 sB&B🛁🚿£19-£21 dB&B£28-£32
dB&B🛁🚿£28-£32 WB&B£100 WBDi£150-£170 LDO 8pm
♨ CTV 8P 1🚗 🏡 🎣 🐎 bowls, putting 65 acres beef mixed sheep
[£]

LOOE Cornwall & Isles of Scilly Map **02** SX25

See also Widesgates

SELECTED

GH [Q][Q][Q][Q] Harescombe Lodge Watergate PL13 2NE
☎(05036) 3158

An outstanding location, on a tidal river surrounded by wooded countryside, is enjoyed by this former shooting lodge. Each bedroom has its own bath or shower room and the lounge and dining room are small and cosy. Jane and Barry Wynn are very hospitable and provide good fresh food including an excellent breakfast. Harescombe Lodge is 1.5 miles north west of Looe off the A387.

3rm(2🛁1🚿) [R] 🚫🐕 (ex guide dogs)
dB&B🛁🚿£27-£35 WB&B£94-£108 WBDi£160-£174 LDO 4pm
♨ CTV 4P nc12yrs
[£]

GH [Q] 'Kantara' 7 Trelawney Ter PL13 2AG ☎(05036) 2093

This pre-war mid-terrace house on the outskirts of the town provides simple family-run accommodation which is equally suitable for tourist or businessman ; guests enjoy a hearty breakfast, and a relaxed atmosphere is created by the friendly, caring proprietor.

6hc (3fb) CTV in all bedrooms * sB&B£9-£15
dB&B£20-£30 WB&B£63-£105 WBDi£105-£154 LDO 5pm
CTV 1P 2🚗
Credit Cards [1] [3] [£]

GH [Q][Q] Ogunquit Portuan Rd, Hannafore PL13 2DW
☎(05036) 3105
Feb-Nov

Personally-run guesthouse in an elevated position in Hannafore, West Looe. Superb views.

5rm(1🚿4hc)(2fb) * dB&Bfr£28 dB&B🚿fr£33
♨ CTV

GH Q Q Q **Panorama Hotel** Hannafore Rd PL13 2DE
☎(05036) 2123
Mar-Oct

Set in an elevated position on Hannafore Road, this establishment has beautiful views of the harbour and across the bay. The cosy rooms are decorated in cottage style and home-cooked food is served in the dining room. The service here is friendly.
10⇌♠ CTV in all bedrooms ® sB&B⇌♠£18-£28 dB&B⇌♠£36-£52 WB&B£108-£151 WBDi£150-£210 LDO 6.30pm
Lic CTV 7P
Credit Cards 1 3 £

GH Q Q Q **St Aubyns** Marine Dr, Hannafore, West Looe
PL13 2DH ☎(05036) 4351
Etr-end Oct

The Maher family offer bed and breakfast accommodation and a warm welcome at the Victorian house which has beautiful sea views. The bedrooms are spacious and the lounge elegantly furnished.
8rm(2⇌♠6hc)(5fb) CTV in 4 bedrooms ® ⊁ ✱ sB&B£16-£17 dB&B£32-£38 dB&B⇌♠£40-£44 WB&B£105-£147
CTV 4P
£

FH Q Q Mr & Mrs Hembrow **Tregoad Farm Hotel**
(SX272560) St Martins PL13 1PB ☎(05036) 2718
Etr-Oct

Georgian-style manor house on high ground with sea view.
6hc (4fb) CTV in all bedrooms ® ✱ sB&B£12.50-£17.50 dB&B£24-£36 WB&B£87.50-£122.50 WBDi£133-£150 LDO 4pm
Lic CTV 15P ✔ 60 acres dairy sheep

LOUGHBOROUGH Leicestershire Map **08** SK 51

GH Q **De Montfort Hotel** 88 Leicester Rd LE11 2AQ
☎(0509) 216061
9hc (1fb) CTV in all bedrooms ® sB&Bfr£17.50 dB&Bfr£30 WB&Bfr£119 WBDifr£143 LDO 4pm
Lic 🎪 CTV
Credit Cards 1 3 £

GH Q Q Q **Garendon Park Hotel** 92 Leicester Rd LE11 2AQ
☎(0509) 236557
The friendly proprietors of the Garendon Park Hotel offer a personal service and make every effort to meet the guests needs. The bedrooms are light and cheerful, as are the public rooms. The lounge is comfortable and provides books, games and satelite T.V.
8hc (2fb) CTV in all bedrooms ® sB&B£16-£20 dB&B£30 WB&B£112-£140 LDO 8pm
Lic 🎪 CTV
Credit Cards 1 3

GH Q *Sunnyside Hotel* 5 The Coneries LE11 1DZ
☎(0509) 216217
Ideally suited for business people and within walking distance of the town centre, this family-run hotel has well-equipped, compact bedrooms, with colour TV and tea and coffee making facilities.
11hc CTV in 10 bedrooms ® ⊁ LDO 4pm
🎪 CTV 8P 3🐾 nc5yrs
Credit Cards 1 3

LOW CATTON Humberside Map **08** SE75

GH Q Q Q **Derwent Lodge** YO4 1EA
☎Stamford Bridge(0759) 71468
Feb-Nov
Only 15 minutes drive from York, this period house retains its character with oak beams and York stone fireplaces. The bedrooms offer modern facilities and most have en suite shower rooms.
6rm(4♠2hc)(1fb)⊁in all bedrooms CTV in all bedrooms ® ✱ sB&B£20.25 sB&B♠£23.25 dB&B£27 dB&B♠£31 LDO 4pm

🎪 8P nc8yrs
See advertisement under YORK on page 409

LOWER BEEDING West Sussex Map **04** TQ22

FH Q Q Q Mr J Christian **Brookfield Farm Hotel**
(TQ214285) Winterpit Ln, Plummers Plain RH13 5LU
☎(0403) 891568
Enjoying attractive, peaceful surroundings, this hotel offers a wealth of activities an outdoor pool and play area for children and its own lake for boating and fishing. The accommodation is well equipped and there is a bar and a choice of restaurants.
20⇌♠ CTV in all bedrooms ⇌♠£28.75-£40.25 dB&B⇌♠£40.25-£51.75 LDO 9.30pm
Lic 🎪 CTV 100P ▶ 0 ✔ games room putting 300 acres mixed
Credit Cards 1 2 3
See advertisement under HORSHAM on page 187

LOWESTOFT Suffolk Map **05** TM59

GH Q Q Q **Albany Hotel** 400 London Rd South NR33 0BQ
☎(0502) 574394
Mr and Mrs Kelly provide a well-cared for house, situated just a few minutes' walk from both the shopping centre and the beach. The spacious rooms have some en suite facilities, and are complemented by attractive public areas.
7rm(3⇌♠4hc)(3fb) CTV in all bedrooms ® ⊁ (ex guide dogs) ✱ sB&Bfr£15 sB&B⇌♠fr£21 dB&Bfr£26 dB&B⇌♠fr£32 WB&Bfr£95 WBDifr£136 LDO 1pm
Lic 🎪 CTV 2P
Credit Cards 1 3 £

GH Q Q **Amity** 396 London Rd South NR33 0BQ
☎(0502) 572586
Closed Xmas & New Year
Easily distinguished by its red painted brickwork, this large detached Victorian house has well-equipped rooms and a pleasant lounge/bar and games room. The sea front is just a few minutes' walk away.
12rm(4♠8hc)(3fb) CTV in all bedrooms ® ✱ sB&Bfr£16 sB&B♠fr£22.50 dB&Bfr£30 dB&B♠fr£34 WB&Bfr£87.50 WBDifr£130 LDO 2pm
Lic 🎪 CTV ✗ solarium games room
Credit Cards 1 2 3

⊷–**GH** Q Q **Belmont** 270 London Rd South NR33 0BG
☎(0502) 573867
Situated south of the town centre, this guesthouse is just 100 yards from the shops and the beach. Mrs Manthorpe offers well-kept and comfortable accommodation, which has been recently redecorated to a high standard.
5rm(1♠4hc)(1fb) ® sB&B£13-£15.50 sB&B♠£17.50-£19.50 dB&B£25-£27 WB&B£85-£115 WBDi£120-£130 LDO 2pm
🎪 TV ✗ nc5yrs
£

GH Q Q **Cornerways** 12 Kensington Rd, London Rd South, Parefield NR33 0HY ☎(0502) 567821 FAX (0502) 585336
Less than a mile from the town centre, this hotel has well-equipped accommodation, mostly with en suite facilities, in spacious rooms. By October 1990, a 40-seater restaurant, bar and lounge will have been completed. Off-street parking is available.
10rm(7⇌♠2hc)(2fb)⊁in all bedrooms CTV in all bedrooms ® ⊁ (ex guide dogs) sB&B⇌♠£28-£32 dB&B£32-£36 dB&B⇌♠£38-£42 WB&Bfr£157 WBDifr£210 LDO 8.30pm
Lic 🎪 CTV 9P ♨
Credit Cards 1 2 3 £

GH Q Q **Fairways** 398 London Rd South NR33 0BQ
☎(0502) 572659
Mr and Mrs Shuard offer simple, well-maintained acoommodation at this guesthouse, and they ensure their visitors are provided with hospitality and comfort.

7rm(3⇆⬥4hc)(4fb) CTV in all bedrooms ® sB&Bfr£15 sB&B⇆⬥fr£20 dB&Bfr£30 dB&B⇆⬥fr£35 LDO 6pm
Lic 🍴 CTV 3P
Credit Cards 1 3 £

GH Q Q **Kingsleigh** 44 Marine Pde NR33 0QN
☎(0502) 572513
Closed Xmas
Close to the harbour and town centre, with car parking to the rear, this well- furnished, attractive guesthouse is family run and provides accommodation which is above average standards.
6hc (2fb) CTV in all bedrooms ® sB&B£15-£18 dB&B£25-£28
🍴 6P nc3yrs

GH Q Q Q *Lodge Private Hotel* London Rd South, Pakefield
NR33 7AA ☎(0502) 569805
Closed Xmas & New Year
Standing in secluded grounds, this creeper-clad Victorian house has well- furnished en suite rooms which are prettily decorated and well equipped. The lounge is particularly attractive and comfortable and retains some original features.
7rm(3⇆4⬥)(1fb)⚡in all bedrooms CTV in all bedrooms ®
✶ (ex guide dogs) LDO 7pm
Lic 🍴 15P
Credit Cards 1 2 3

GH Q Q Q **Rockville House** 6 Pakefield Rd NR33 0HS
☎(0502) 581011 or 574891
This quiet retreat, minutes from the seafront, offers quality accommodation. It is found off London Road South immediately after a no-entry sign on the right when approaching Lowestoft from Ipswich (A12).
8rm(2⇆1⬥5hc)(1fb) CTV in all bedrooms ®
✶ (ex guide dogs) sB&B£16.50-£18 sB&B⇆⬥£27-£29.50
dB&B£28.50-£31
▶

dB&B⇌⌐£34.50-£38.50 WB&B£98-£117 WBDi£147.50-£172 LDO 10am
Lic 🍴 beach hut
Credit Cards [1] [3] Ⓛ

GH QQ ***Seavilla Hotel*** 43 Kirkley Cliff Rd NR33 0DF
☎(0502) 574657
Situated on the southern side of Lowestoft, this hotel is in a mainly residential area and overlooks the sea. Mrs Stone maintains a good standard of comfort and accommodation, and offers a warm welcome.
9rm(2⌐7hc) CTV in all bedrooms Ⓡ ✗ (ex guide dogs) LDO 12.30am
Lic 🍴 CTV 3P nc7yrs
Credit Cards [1] [3]

GH QQ Somerton House 7 Kirkley Cliff NR33 0BY
☎(0502) 565665
Located south of Lowestoft, on the seafront, this guesthouse has commanding views to complement its brightly decorated and well-equipped comfortable rooms. There is a comfortable lounge with a well-stocked bar and a varied evening menu.
8rm(3⌐5hc)(4fb) CTV in all bedrooms Ⓡ ✱ sB&B£16.50-£17.50 sB&B⌐£22.50-£23.50 dB&B£28.50-£30.50 dB&B⌐£34.50-£36.50 WB&B£98-£105 WBDi£138-£147 LDO 5pm
Lic 🍴 CTV 1P
Credit Cards [1] [3] Ⓛ

LOW ROW North Yorkshire Map **07** SD99

GH QQQ Peat Gate Head DL11 6PP
☎Richmond(0748) 86388
This unique and friendly house enjoys superb views over the River Swale and surrounding countryside. The accommodation is charming, and the excellent meals are prepared by the proprietor with care and imagination.
6rm(3⌐3hc)⊘in all bedrooms Ⓡ ✗ sB&B£29.50-£32.50 dB&B£59-£65 dB&B⌐£65-£70 (incl dinner) LDO 5.30pm
Lic 🍴 CTV P̸
Ⓛ

LUDLOW Shropshire Map **07** SO57

GH QQ Cecil Sheet Rd SY8 1LR ☎(0584) 872442
This modern bungalow is in the suburbs of the town, reached via the Ludlow by-pass. The rooms are bright and warm and the comfortable lounge overlooks a mature rear garden. It is a friendly, family-run house.
10rm(2⌐8hc)(1fb) Ⓡ ✱ sB&Bfr£15.50 dB&B£31-£36 dB&B⌐£36 WB&B£105-£120 WBDi£156-£170 LDO 9am
Lic 🍴 CTV 10P 1🚗
Credit Cards [1] [3] Ⓛ

GH QQQ No. 28 Lower Broad St SY8 1PQ ☎(0584) 876996
Within walking distance from the Castle and town centre this half timbered town house is a small personal hotel which has much to offer its guests including a small courtyard garden.
2rm(1⇌1⌐) CTV in all bedrooms Ⓡ ✱
dB&B⇌⌐£32-£40 WB&B£105-£125 WBDi£190-£210 LDO 8.30pm
Lic 🍴 P̸

INN QQ ***The Church*** Church Street, Buttercross SY8 1AW
☎(0584) 872174
This old inn stands in the centre of the town, and is fully modernised. A popular tourist hotel, it has in the past been a smithy and a barber's shop, but now offers comfortable and well-equipped accommodation.
9rm(5⇌4⌐)(1fb) CTV in all bedrooms Ⓡ LDO 9.30pm
🍴 P̸
Credit Cards [1] [3]

LUTON Bedfordshire Map **04** TL02

GH QQ Ambassador Hotel 31 Lansdowne Rd LU8 1EE
☎(0582) 31411 or 451656
Closed Xmas
Friendly and comfortable house run by young proprietors.
14⌐ CTV in all bedrooms Ⓡ ✱ sB&B⌐£51.75 dB&B⌐£66.70 LDO 8.45pm
Lic 🍴 CTV 20P pool table
Credit Cards [1] [3]

GH QQ ***Arlington Hotel*** 137 New Bedford Rd LU3 1LF
☎(0582) 419614
Closed 25-26 Dec
Well-managed and comfortable commercial guesthouse.
19rm(1⇌11⌐7hc)(3fb) CTV in all bedrooms
✗ (ex guide dogs) LDO 8.30pm
Lic 🍴 25P
Credit Cards [2] [5]

GH QQ ***Humberstone Hotel*** 618 Dunstable Rd LU4 8RT
☎(0582) 574399
Very comfortable and clean hotel where the welcome is warm and friendly.
9hc Annexe 12rm(2⇌10⌐)(4fb) CTV in all bedrooms Ⓡ
✗ (ex guide dogs) LDO 5.30pm
Lic 🍴 35P
Credit Cards [1] [2] [3] [5]

LUTTERWORTH Leicestershire

See **Shearsby**

LYDFORD Devon Map **02** SX58

INN QQ Dartmoor EX20 4AY (on A386 between Tavistock & Okehampton) ☎(082282) 221
Closed Xmas Day
This friendly, family-run inn, much upgraded and improved since the recent change in ownership, provides welcoming bars, a cosy little restaurant and bright, comfortable bedrooms for guests. Its convenient position gives easy access to the National Park.
3⇌ CTV in all bedrooms Ⓡ sB&B⇌£25
dB&B⇌£40 Lunch £1.50-£5alc Dinner £1.50-£6.50alc LDO 9.55pm
🍴 50P nc
Credit Cards [1] [3] [5]

LYDNEY Gloucestershire Map **03** SO60

GH QQ Lower Viney Country Viney Hill GL15 4LT (2.5m from Lydney on A48 on unclassed road) ☎Dean(0594) 516000
The new owners of this pretty cottage-style guesthouse, which stands behind a neat lawn and garden off the A48, have renovated and refurbished the accommodation to modern standards of comfort.
6⌐ CTV in 4 bedrooms Ⓡ ✗ (ex guide dogs) sB&B⌐£17-£20 dB&B⌐£30-£40 LDO 1pm
🍴 CTV 10P
Credit Cards [1] [3] Ⓛ
See advertisement under BLAKENEY on page 73

LYME REGIS Dorset Map **03** SY39

⊢⊣**GH Q Coverdale** Woodmead Rd DT7 3AB ☎(02974) 2882 due to change to (0297) 442882
Mar-Oct
Situated in a residential area, this well-kept house has a cheerful dining room and comfortable television lounge.
8rm(2⌐6hc)(3fb) CTV in 2 bedrooms Ⓡ sB&B£13-£18
dB&B£23-£30
dB&B⌐£29-£36 WB&B£74-£99 WBDi£114-£146 LDO 4pm
🍴 CTV 12P nc3yrs
Ⓛ

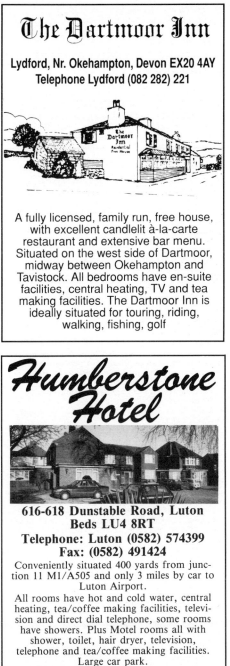

GH [Q][Q][Q] Kersbrook Hotel & Restaurant Pound Rd DT7 3HX ☎(02974) 2596 & 2576
rs Jan
Set in picturesque gardens with views over the town and sea, this thatched house has very well-equipped bedrooms and comfortable public areas. Jane and Eric Stephenson are excellent hosts, and the meals here have a strong local following.
11rm(5🛁6🚿)(1fb) CTV in 6 bedrooms TV in 1 bedroom [R] *
sB&B🛁🚿£24.50-£42
dB&B🛁🚿£45-£49 WB&B£145-£165 WBDi£230-£250 LDO 8.30pm
Lic 🛋 14P
Credit Cards [1] [3] [£]

GH [Q][Q] *Rotherfield* View Rd DT7 3AA ☎(02974) 2811
Closed Xmas
Situated close to the sea and town centre, this family-run hotel offers pleasant, comfortable accommodation and a warm, friendly atmosphere.
7rm(3🚿4hc)(2fb) CTV in all bedrooms [R] LDO 4pm
Lic 🛋 CTV 6P

GH [Q][Q][Q] White House 47 Silver St DT7 3HR ☎(02974) 3420
Apr-Oct
18th-century listed building close to beach, gardens and shops.
7rm(1🛁6🚿) CTV in all bedrooms [R]
dB&B🛁🚿£27-£34 WB&B£94.50-£108.50
Lic 🛋 7P nc10yrs
[£]

LYMINGTON Hampshire Map 04 SZ39

GH [Q][Q] Albany House Highfield SO41 9GB ☎(0590) 671900
This 3-storeyed Regency house is centrally situated and overlooks a municipal park. The delightful lounge is comfortable and restful and the dinner menus are imaginative.
5rm(1🛁4hc)(4fb)🚭in 2 bedrooms CTV in 4 bedrooms [R]
sB&Bfr£18.50 dB&B£32-£37
dB&B🛁£41-£48 WB&B£106-£162 WBDi£166-£212 LDO 7pm
🛋 CTV 4P
[£]

LYNDHURST Hampshire Map 04 SU30

GH [Q][Q][Q] Knightwood Lodge Southampton Rd SO4 7BU ☎(0703) 282502 FAX (0703) 283730
Closed Xmas Day
Run by an experienced, enthusiastic young couple, this hotel has a new lounge on the lower ground floor, adjacent to a steam room and sauna. The en suite bedrooms are well co-ordinated and equipped, and the meals provide value for money.
12🛁🚿 (2fb) CTV in all bedrooms [R] 🐕 (ex guide dogs) *
sB&B🛁🚿£26-£36 dB&B🛁🚿£40-£48 LDO 8pm
Lic 🛋 10P nc3yrs sauna turkish steam room exercise bicycle
Credit Cards [1] [2] [3] [5] [£]

GH [Q][Q][Q] Ormonde House Southampton Rd SO43 7BT ☎(0703) 282806 FAX (0703) 283775
Friendly, helpful service here is personally supervised by Paul and Lee Ames. Set back from the A35 towards Southampton, Ormonde House overlooks moorland and offers attractive, well-equipped rooms, a comfortable lounge and elegant breakfast room.
13rm(9🛁4🚿)(1fb) CTV in all bedrooms [R] *
sB&B🛁🚿£25-£33 dB&B🛁🚿£38-£50
🛋 15P
Credit Cards [1] [3] [£]

GH [Q][Q][Q] Whitemoor House Hotel Southampton Rd SO43 7BU ☎(0703) 282186
Closed Xmas
Beautifully maintained, this roadside guesthouse has spacious modern bedrooms with separate shower and bathroom facilities together with a lounge and breakfast room. Extensive service is provided throughout the day and there is ample parking space.
5hc (2fb) CTV in all bedrooms [R] sB&B£25-£30
dB&B£35-£40 WB&Bfr£160 WBDifr£230
Lic 🛋 CTV 8P
Credit Cards [1] [3] [£]

LYNMOUTH Devon Map 03 SS74

See **Town Plan Section**
See also Lynton

SELECTED

•**GH [Q][Q][Q][Q] *Countisbury Lodge Hotel*** Tors Park, Countisbury Hill EX35 6ND ☎Lynton(0598) 52388
Mr and Mrs Hollinshead take great pride in their small country house retreat, neatly tucked away in a wooded spot with spectacular views. Sympathetically restored, the former vicarage retains its original charm and offers richly furnished bedrooms which have modern facilities, and the cosy public rooms are nicely furnished. The tiny residents' bar is built into the rock face A degree of flair is evident in the home-cooked meals.
8rm(2🛁3🚿3hc)(3fb) [R] (wkly only Xmas) LDO 7.30pm
Lic 🛋 CTV 8P
Credit Cards [1] [3]

GH [Q][Q][Q] *East Lyn House* 17 Watersmeet Rd EX35 6EP ☎Lynton(0598) 52540
8rm(2🛁3🚿3hc)(2fb)🚭in 2 bedrooms CTV in all bedrooms [R] LDO 8.30pm
Lic 🛋 5P 8🚗 nc5yrs
Credit Cards [1] [3]

GH [Q][Q][Q] The Heatherville Tors Park EX35 6NB ☎Lynton(0598) 52327
Apr-Oct
Enjoying a secluded position overlooking the River Lyn, this south facing stone-built house has bright accommodation with comfortable bedrooms, lounge an residents' bar. The Heatheville is family run and offers good traditional English cooking.
8rm(4🚿4hc)(1fb) CTV in 1 bedroom [R] 🐕 sB&Bfr£17
dB&Bfr£34
dB&B🚿fr£37.50 WB&Bfr£119 WBDifr£162 LDO 5.30pm
Lic 🛋 CTV 8P nc7yrs

LYNTON Devon Map 03 SS74

See **Town Plan Section**
See also Lynmouth

GH [Q][Q][Q] Alford House Alford Ter EX35 6AT ☎(0598) 52359
A warm welcome awaits guests at this 1840s house which overlooks Lynton and the sea beyond. The cosy en suite rooms are brightly decorated and some have four-poster beds. Prompt informal service is offered in the well-stocked bar and public areas.
7rm(1🛁6🚿) CTV in all bedrooms [R] 🐕
dB&B🛁🚿£30-£40 WB&B£105-£120 WBDi£140-£165 LDO 4pm
Lic 🛋 CTV 🚫P nc8yrs
Credit Cards [1] [3] [£]

GH [Q][Q] *Gable Lodge Hotel* Lee Rd EX35 6BS ☎(0598) 52367
Mar-Nov
Still retaining much of its Victorian character, this lodge has been attractively modernised and provides cosy, well-equipped bedrooms.
9rm(2🛁4🚿3hc)(2fb) CTV in all bedrooms [R]
🐕 (ex guide dogs) LDO 4.45pm
Lic 🛋 CTV 8P nc12yrs

See advertisement on page 253

GH QQQ **Hazeldene** 27 Lee Rd EX35 6BP ☎(0598) 52364
Closed mid Nov-mid Dec rs mid Dec- Xmas
Standing on the edge of the town centre, this small hotel promotes a good standard throughout. The accommodation provides modern facilities and is an ideal base from which to tour Exmoor and the north Devon coast.
9⇔🐾 (2fb) CTV in all bedrooms ® sB&B⇔🐾£20-£25
dB&B⇔🐾£35-£40 WB&B£118-£128 WBDi£175-£190 LDO 5pm
Lic 🅿 CTV 8P nc5yrs
Credit Cards 1 2 3 £

GH QQQ **Ingleside Hotel** Lee Rd EX35 6HW ☎(0598) 52223
Mar-Oct
7rm(4⇔3🐾)(2fb) CTV in all bedrooms ® ✠
sB&B⇔🐾£21-£23
dB&B⇔🐾£38-£42 WB&B£126-£130 WBDi£210-£214 LDO 5.30pm
Lic 🅿 10P nc5yrs
Credit Cards 1 3 £

GH QQ **Kingford House Private Hotel** Longmead EX35 6DQ
☎(0598) 52361
Apr-Oct rs Nov-Mar
A friendly, relaxing atmosphere is maintained by the conscientious owners of this establishment. The bright bedrooms, cosy lounge and dining room are complemented by pretty gardens.
8rm(4🐾4hc)(1fb) ® ✠ (ex guide dogs) LDO 4.30pm
Lic CTV 8P nc5yrs

GH QQQ **Longmead House** 9 Longmead EX35 6DQ
☎(0598) 52523
rs Dec-Jan
Close to the town centre, yet within a quiet residential area, this beautifully restored, Victorian house provides attractive, personal bedrooms and well- furnished public rooms in small pretty grounds and gardens. The recent good work has seen the installation of 4 modern en suite facilities. The guesthouse offers friendly family service.
9hc (1fb) ® LDO 1pm
Lic 🅿 CTV 8P

GH QQ **Mayfair Hotel** Lynway EX35 6AY ☎(0598) 53227
Set on a hillside with commanding views of Exmoor and its coastline, this family-run establishment provides good home-cooked food and friendly service.
9rm(5⇔2🐾2hc)(1fb) CTV in all bedrooms ® sB&B£21-£23
dB&B£36-£40
dB&B⇔🐾£42-£46 WB&B£115-£136 WBDi£162-£183 LDO 5pm
Lic 🅿 10P
Credit Cards 1 2 3 £

GH Q **Retreat** 1 Park Gardens, Lydiate Ln EX35 6DF
☎(0598) 53526
This small, friendly guesthouse offers pleasant, spotlessly clean accommodation. While the public rooms are compact, the welcome by the caring owners is big. Good value for money.
6hc (2fb) ® ✻ sB&B£12-£14
dB&B£24-£28 WB&B£80-£93 WBDi£123-£140 LDO 5pm
🅿 CTV 3P
£

┝━·**GH** QQQ **St Vincent** Castle Hill EX35 6JA
☎(0598) 52244
Apr-Oct
This charming period house fronted with a pretty cottage garden, is conveniently close to the centre of Lynton, and next door to the Exmoor Museum. A Grade II listed building, with some parts dating back over 300 years, the hotel has many delightful features, including a splendid Regency spiral staircase, and a flagstone floor in the residents' bar. Bedrooms are bright and spotlessly clean, and

public rooms are cosy and have a cheerful atmosphere. The menu offers good home cooking.
6rm(1⇔1🐾4hc)(2fb) ® ✠ sB&B£11.50-£12.50 dB&B£23-£25
dB&B⇔🐾£28-£30 WB&B£77-£101 WBDi£125-£152 LDO 4.30pm
Lic CTV 3P
£

GH Q **Valley House Hotel** Lynbridge Rd EX35 6BD
☎(0598) 52285
Quietly secluded in an elevated position and commanding views over Lynton, the coast and woodland, this Victorian, chalet style property is personally owned and managed.
8rm(4🐾4hc)(2fb) CTV in 5 bedrooms ® LDO 6pm
Lic 🅿 CTV 8P
Credit Cards 1 2 3

SELECTED

GH QQQQ **Waterloo House Hotel** Lydiate Ln
EX35 6AJ ☎(0598) 53391
mid Mar-3 Jan
Combining the spirit of the 19th century with today's modern comforts, this is one of the oldest lodging houses in Lynton – now a gracious small hotel. Bright, with quality furnishings and decor, the bedrooms have modern en suites, colour TV and beverage facilities. There is a separate lounge for non-smokers, and wholesome cooking is served in the elegant restaurant. Mr and Mrs Mountie's house provides excellent value for money.
10rm(3⇔4🐾3hc)(1fb)⚹in 2 bedrooms CTV in all bedrooms ✠ sB&Bfr£16 sB&B⇔🐾fr£21.50
dB&Bfr£32
dB&B⇔🐾fr£43 WB&B£95-£129 WBDi£155-£199 LDO 5pm
Lic CTV 3P nc10yrs
£

LYTHAM ST ANNES Lancashire Map **07** SD32

GH Q **Beaumont Private Hotel** 11 All Saints Rd FY8 1PL
☎St Annes(0253) 723958
This small house offers a friendly atmosphere and home cooking of good value.
9hc (4fb) ® ✻ sB&B£12-£15
dB&B£20-£28 WB&B£70-£84 WBDi£98-£105 LDO 4pm
Lic CTV ✗ ⚶
£

GH QQ **Cullerne Hotel** 55 Lightburne Av, St Annes on Sea
FY8 1JE ☎St Annes(0253) 721753
This neat and well-maintained house, situated close to the sea front, in a quiet side street off the Inner Promenade, offers comfortable and well-kept accommodation.
6hc (2fb) CTV in all bedrooms ® ✠ ✻ sB&B£12
dB&B£24 WB&B£84 WBDi£102 LDO noon
Lic 🅿 CTV 4P
£

GH QQQ **Endsleigh Private Hotel** 315 Clifton Dr South
FY8 1HN ☎St Annes(0253) 725622
A comfortable house with attractive bedrooms and public rooms managed by friendly, resident proprietors, who provide home cooked meals.
16⇔🐾 (3fb) CTV in all bedrooms ® ✠
sB&B⇔🐾£16.75-£18.50
dB&B⇔🐾£33.50 WBDi£125-£135 LDO 4pm
Lic 🅿 8P

Visit your local AA Centre.

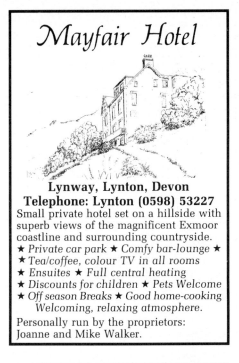

GH [Q][Q] Harcourt Hotel 21 Richmond Rd FY8 1PE
☎St Annes(0253) 722299
Closed Xmas & New Year
This pleasant, small guesthouse is situated just off the square. Family owned and run, it provides a good standard of home cooking, and offers good value for money.
10rm(5🛁🚿5hc)(4fb) CTV in 5 bedrooms Ⓡ * sB&Bfr£11.78 sB&B🛁🚿fr£12.98
dB&B🛁🚿fr£31.60 (wkly only Jul & Aug) LDO 6pm
Lic 🍴 CTV 6P
[£]

GH [Q] *Lyndhurst Private Hotel* 338 Clifton Dr North FY8 2PB
☎St Annes(0253) 724343
This is a family-run guesthouse which offers spacious accommodation. It is situated close to both the town centre and the sea.
12rm(1🛁3🚿8hc)(4fb) CTV in 4 bedrooms Ⓡ LDO noon
CTV 11P

GH [Q][Q][Q] Strathmore 305 Clifton Dr South FY8 1HN
☎St Annes(0253) 725478
The young proprietors continue to make improvements to this property which is a few minutes' walk from the shops and seafront. The bedrooms vary in size and are very well maintained.
10rm(2🛁3🚿5hc) CTV in all bedrooms Ⓡ 🐕 *
sB&B£15.75-£17.75 sB&B🛁🚿£17.75 dB&B£31.50
dB&B🛁🚿£35.50 WB&B£110.25-£117.25
WBDi£124.25-£138.25 LDO 5pm
Lic 🍴 10P nc9yrs

MACCLESFIELD Cheshire Map 07 SJ97

GH [Q][Q] Moorhayes House Hotel 27 Manchester Rd SK10 2JJ
☎(0625) 33228 due to change to 433228
Pleasingly furnished throughout, and personally run by resident owners, this attractive house stands in its own grounds in an elevated position close to the town centre.
9rm(4🚿5hc) CTV in all bedrooms Ⓡ sB&B£26 sB&B🚿£38
dB&B£46.50 dB&B🚿£50
🍴 15P
[£]

MACHRIHANISH Strathclyde *Argyllshire* Map 10 NR62

SELECTED

GH [Q][Q][Q][Q] Ardell House PA28 6PT ☎(058681) 235
Closed Xmas & New Year rs Nov-Feb
This fine detached Victorian house looks out to sea, to the distant islands of Islay and Jura. The accommodation varies in size and style, from the fine, spacious master bedrooms to the more functional, but equally well-equipped chalet rooms of the annexe, which are indeed very popular with guests. Hosts David and Jill Baxter make everyone feel at home, providing a self service honesty bar in the lounge.
7rm(1🛁5🚿1hc)Annexe 3🚿 (1fb) CTV in all bedrooms Ⓡ
dB&B🛁🚿£60-£70 (incl dinner) WB&B£140-£160
WBDi£250
Lic 🍴 CTV 12P
[£]

MACHYNLLETH Powys Map 06 SH70

GH [Q][Q] Maenllwyd Newtown Rd SY20 8EY ☎(0654) 702928
Built in the last century, this large detached manse stands opposite the cottage hospital. It provides comfortable accommodation with a friendly atmosphere.
7hc (2fb) CTV in all bedrooms Ⓡ * sB&Bfr£15
dB&Bfr£25 LDO 1pm
🍴 CTV 10P
Credit Cards [1][3] [£]

FH [Q] Mr & Mrs D Timms **Rhiwlwyfen** *(SH761983)* Forge SY20 8RP ☎(0654) 702683
Apr-Oct
This remote 17th-century farmhouse is comfortably furnished. Guests can enjoy a peaceful stay and beautiful surroundings.
3rm (2fb) Ⓡ 🐕 (ex guide dogs) * sB&B£11.50-£15
dB&B£23-£30 WB&Bfr£77 WBDifr£103 LDO 8pm
🍴 CTV 6P 100 acres beef sheep
[£]

INN [Q][Q][Q] The White Lion Hotel Heol Pentrerhedyn SY20 8ND ☎(0654) 703455
In the centre of the busy market town near the famous 'Clock' this former coaching inn provides attractive pine furnished bedrooms and a comfortable bar. A good range of food is available and all of the staff are friendly and helpful.
10rm(3🛁🚿7hc)(2fb) CTV in all bedrooms Ⓡ * sB&B£20
sB&B🛁🚿£30 dB&B£37 dB&B🛁🚿£52 LDO 9pm
🍴 45P
Credit Cards [1][2][3][5] [£]

MAIDSTONE Kent Map 05 TQ75

GH [Q][Q] *Carval Hotel* 56/58 London Rd ME16 8QL
☎(0622) 762100
Well equipped and maintained, this establishment has a comfortable lounge and a small bar where local tourist information may be found. The restaurant overlooks the rear garden and the hotel has its own car park.
9rm(4🚿5hc) CTV in all bedrooms Ⓡ 🐕
Lic 🍴 9P nc5yrs
Credit Cards [1][2][3][5]

GH [Q][Q][Q] Rock House Hotel 102 Tonbridge Rd ME16 8SL
☎(0622) 751616
Closed 24 Dec-1 Jan
This pleasant hotel offers good, modern accommodation, with an attractive dining room, recently redecorated in Victorian style, and a small cosy lounge.
12hc (2fb) CTV in all bedrooms Ⓡ 🐕 sB&B£27-£30
dB&B£38-£45 WB&B£126-£147
🍴 CTV 7P nc1yr
Credit Cards [1][3] [£]

MALDON Essex Map 05 TL80

INN [Q] Swan Hotel Maldon High St CM9 7EP ☎(0621) 53170
This small, lively and friendly inn has a limited breakfast room and lounge, but the simple accommodation is due to be refurbished to complement the cosy atmosphere.
6hc (2fb)🚭in 1 bedroom CTV in 1 bedroom TV in 5 bedrooms 🐕 sB&B£24
dB&B£34-£38 WB&Bfr£168 WBDifr£210 Lunch £5.75-£8.50&alc Dinner fr£5.75&alc LDO 9pm
🍴 CTV 30P 1🚗
Credit Cards [1][2][3][5] [£]

MALHAM North Yorkshire Map 07 SD96

GH [Q][Q][Q] Sparth House Hotel BD23 4DA
☎Airton(07293) 315
Set in this picturesque Dales village, Sparth House dates back to 1664, and retains many original features. Some bedrooms are spacious, while those in the new wing are more compact. The imaginative, traditional meals are the highlight of a stay here.
10rm(4🛁🚿6hc)🚭in all bedrooms CTV in 4 bedrooms Ⓡ 🐕 (ex guide dogs) sB&B£17.50 dB&B£31
dB&B🛁🚿£40 WBDifr£172 LDO 5pm
Lic 🍴 CTV 7P putting green table-tennis
[£]

MALMESBURY Wiltshire Map **03** ST98

FH Q Mrs E G Edwards **Stonehill** *(SU986894)* Charlton
SN16 9DY (1m E) ☎(0666) 823310
*Enjoying a peaceful setting surrounded by dairy cattle and sheep,
this farmhouse offers neat accommodation and a warm welcome.*
3rm(1♠)(1fb) ⓡ dB&B£26-£30 dB&B♠£34-£40
📺 CTV 4P 180 acres dairy sheep
ⓔ

MALVERN Hereford & Worcester Map **03** SO74

GH QQ Deacons Hotel & Restaurant 34 Worcester Rd
WR14 4AA ☎(0684) 566990 or 575323
Closed 25 Dec-1 Jan
*Georgian-style hotel near town centre. Relaxing lounge with good
views of Severn Valley.*
9rm(6⇆♠3hc)(2fb) CTV in all bedrooms ⓡ sB&B£20-£22
sB&B⇆♠£25-£30 dB&B£34-£36
dB&B⇆♠£38-£42 WBDifr£150 LDO 8pm
Lic 📺 CTV 10P
Credit Cards [1] [3] ⓔ

GH QQQ Sidney House Hotel 40 Worcester Rd WR14 4AA
☎(0684) 574994
rs Xmas & New Year
*This beautifully preserved house dates from the early 19th century
and stands on the A449 just west of the town centre. Well-
equipped accommodation is complemented by friendly hospitality
and personal service from Tom and Margaret Haggett, the
proprietors.*
8rm(4♠4hc)(2fb) CTV in all bedrooms ⓡ ✱ sB&B£17-£35
sB&B♠£30-£35 dB&B£36 dB&B♠£39-£46 LDO 2pm
Lic 📺 CTV 9P
Credit Cards [1] [2] [3] ⓔ

FH QQ Mrs S Stringer **Cowleigh Park** *(SO767475)* Cowleigh
Rd WR13 5HJ ☎(0684) 566750
*This charming family house is 1 mile from Malvern on the B4219,
and is part of a smallholding, complete with duck pond and
poultry. The rooms are well furnished, comfortable and simply
equipped.*
3rm(1♠2hc) CTV in all bedrooms sB&Bfr£20 sB&B♠fr£25
dB&Bfr£30
dB&B♠fr£35 WB&B£94.50-£157.50 WBDi£139.50-£202.50
LDO 11am
📺 6P nc5yrs 2 acres smallholding
ⓔ

MAN, ISLE OF Map **06**

DOUGLAS Map **06** SC37

GH Q Ainsdale Guest House 2 Empire Terrace, Central Prom
☎(0624) 676695
Mar-Oct
*Ainsdale is a personally-run guesthouse with basic facilities
situated just behind the seafront in a good central position.*
17hc (6fb) CTV in 1 bedroom TV in 4 bedrooms ⓡ
WB&B£80.50-£87.50 WBDi£94.50-£101.50 (winter) LDO 6pm
CTV ✗

GH QQ Edelweiss Queens Promenade ☎(0624) 675115
FAX (0624) 673194
*Situated just off the main promenade, with an attractive frontage,
this property has a comfortable lounge and all of the bedrooms
have en suite facilities.*
20rm(3⇆17♠)(3fb) CTV in all bedrooms ⓡ ✖ (ex guide dogs)
sB&B⇆♠fr£32.18
dB&B⇆♠fr£59.77 (incl dinner) WB&Bfr£160.91
WBDifr£209.21 LDO 9pm
Lic lift 📺 CTV ✗ solarium
Credit Cards [1] [3] [5]

GH Q Hydro Hotel Queen's Promenade ☎(0624) 676870
May-Sep rs Etr
*Under the personal supervision of the proprietors, with a reputation
for a friendly atmosphere, this large Edwardian hotel is situated in
a good position on the seafront.*
63rm(11⇆12♠40hc)(18fb) CTV in 23 bedrooms ⓡ
✖ (ex guide dogs) sB&B£18-£19 sB&B⇆♠£25.50-£26.50
dB&B£32-£34
dB&B⇆♠£38-£40 WB&B£112-£119 WBDi£140-£147 LDO
7pm
Lic lift 📺 CTV solarium pool table darts
Credit Cards [1] [3]

GH Q Rosslyn Guest House 3 Empire Ter, Central
Promenade ☎(0624) 676056
3 Jan-28 Nov
*This well-maintained terraced property is situated about 100 yards
from the seafront in a good central position. The guesthouse has a
cosy bar and small first floor television lounge.*
16rm(4⇆4♠8hc)(3fb) CTV in 5 bedrooms ⓡ
✖ (ex guide dogs) sB&Bfr£13.80 sB&B⇆♠fr£19.55
dB&B£27.60-£39.10
dB&B⇆♠£39.10 WB&B£96.60-£136.85 WBDi£120.75-£161
Lic 📺 CTV ✗
ⓔ

GH QQ Rutland Hotel Queen's Promenade ☎(0624) 621218
Etr-Oct
*This family-run, private hotel, which is situated on the seafront,
offers well-furnished bedrooms, most of which have en suite
facilities.*
86rm(55⇆25♠6hc)(20fb) CTV in all bedrooms ⓡ ✱
sB&Bfr£21 sB&B⇆♠fr£24 dB&Bfr£42
dB&B⇆♠fr£48 (incl dinner) LDO 7.30pm
Lic lift CTV ✗
Credit Cards [1] [3]

PORT ERIN Map **06** SC16

GH 🅠🅠 **Regent House** The Promenade ☎(0624) 833454
Well-appointed bedrooms, the majority of which have en suite facilities, are a feature of this guesthouse which commands fine views over the bay.
8rm(6⇨🏱2hc)✗in all bedrooms CTV in all bedrooms ® ✖
sB&B£17 dB&B⇨🏱£38 WB&B£126 WBDi£182 LDO 6.30pm
🕮 🅿

PORT ST MARY Map **06** SC16

GH 🅠 **Mallmore Private Hotel** The Promenade
☎(0624) 833179
19 May-6 Oct
This old established, private hotel is renowned for its warmth and hospitality, as well as its good home cooking. The bedrooms are basic and there are 5 lounges with splendid views over the bay.
43hc (10fb) ® ✖ ✳ sB&B£10-£10.50 dB&Bfr£20 LDO 6.45pm
CTV 🅿 snooker
Credit Cards 1️⃣ 2️⃣ 3️⃣ 5️⃣ £

MANCHESTER Greater Manchester Map **07** SJ89

GH 🅠🅠 **Ebor Hotel** 402 Wilbraham Rd, Chorlton Cum
Hardy M21 1UH ☎061-881 1911 & 061-881 4855
Closed Xmas
A very well-maintained, detached house dating from the late Victorian period is set in a busy suburb 3 miles from the city centre, offering easy access to both airport and motorway network.
16rm(1🏱15hc)(3fb) CTV in all bedrooms ® ✖ sB&B£20-£23
sB&B🏱fr£26 dB&B£31
dB&B🏱fr£36 WB&Bfr£126 WBDifr£164 LDO 5pm
Lic 🕮 CTV 20P 0🍴 nc4yrs darts
£

GH 🅠🅠 **Horizon Hotel** 69 Palatine Road, West Didsbury
M20 9LJ ☎061-445 4705
Good parking facilities and well-equipped bedrooms are provided by this semi detached Victorian house in a southern suburb of the city, only 10 minutes' journey from both centre and airport.
18rm(5⇨13🏱)(1fb) CTV in all bedrooms ® ✖ LDO 5pm
Lic 🕮 CTV 20P nc9yrs
Credit Cards 1️⃣ 2️⃣ 3️⃣

GH 🅠 **Kempton House Hotel** 400 Wilbraham Rd, Chorlton-
Cum-Hardy M21 1UH ☎061-881 8766
Closed 25 & 26 Dec
Family run and friendly, this late Victorian semi detached house stands on the A6010, well placed for airport, city centre and other business areas.
14rm(2🏱12hc) CTV in 11 bedrooms TV in 1 bedroom ®
✖ (ex guide dogs) ✳ sB&Bfr£20 sB&B🏱fr£24 dB&Bfr£29
dB&B🏱fr£34 LDO 5pm
Lic 🕮 CTV 9P
Credit Cards 1️⃣ 3️⃣ £

GH 🅠 **New Central Hotel** 144-146 Heywood St, Cheetham
M8 7PD ☎061-205 2169
Just off the A665, this house is located in a quiet residential street. The bedrooms are generally compact, but are very well maintained, some having shower cubicles. There is a pleasant lounge and also a welcoming bar.
10hc CTV in all bedrooms ® ✖ (ex guide dogs) ✳
sB&Bfr£21.50 dB&Bfr£34 LDO 7.30pm
Lic 🕮 CTV 10P
£

GH 🅠🅠🅠 **West Lynne Hotel** 16 Middleton Rd, Crumpsall
M8 6DS ☎061-721 4866 & 061-721 4922
Recently refurbished to offer a high standard of accommodation, this hotel has spacious, well-equipped bedrooms. It is conveniently situated on the A576 between Junction 18 of the M62 and Central Manchester.

12⇨ (2fb) CTV in all bedrooms ® ✖ (ex guide dogs)
sB&B⇨£34 dB&B⇨£40
Lic 🕮 15P
Credit Cards 1️⃣ 3️⃣

MAPPOWDER Dorset Map **03** ST70

FH 🅠 Mrs A K Williamson-Jones **Boywood** *(ST733078)*
Sturminster Newton DT10 2EQ (1.5m N unclass rd toward
Hazelbury Bryan) ☎Hazelbury Bryan(0258) 817416
This traditional farmhouse is part of a dairy farm set in peaceful, rural surroundings. The simple accommodation offered is comfortable.
3rm ✖ ✳ sB&B£14 dB&B£28
🕮 CTV 0P ⊡(heated) ♪(hard)17 acres beef poultry

MARGARET RODING (nr Gt Dunmow) Essex Map **05** TL51

FH 🅠🅠 Mr & Mrs J Matthews **Greys** *(TL604112)* Ongar Rd
CM6 1QR ☎Good Easter(024531) 509
Set away from the main farm buildings, this comfortable farmhouse of quality is cheerfully run by the proprietors. Open for most of the year, this farmhouse is totally 'no smoking'.
3rm(2hc)✗in all bedrooms ✖ dB&Bfr£26
🕮 3P nc10yrs 340 acres arable beef sheep

MARGATE Kent Map **05** TR37

GH 🅠🅠 **Beachcomber Hotel** 3-4 Royal Esplanade,
Westbrook CT9 5DL ☎Thanet(0843) 221616
This licensed hotel enjoys a good reputation for its cooking, which is complemented by the use of fresh ingredients and the involvement of proprietors Mr and Mrs Philip McGovern. Overlooking the sea, it offers well-maintained, simply furnished rooms and pleasant public areas.
15hc (3fb) ✖ ✳ sB&B£15-£16
dB&B£30-£32 WB&B£99.75 WBDi£126-£134 LDO 1pm
Lic 🕮 CTV 1P

GH 🅠🅠 **Charnwood Private Hotel** 20-22 Canterbury Rd
CT9 5BW ☎Thanet(0843) 224158
Old-fashioned, traditional accommodation under new and friendly management.
8hc (4fb) ® ✖ sB&B£15-£18
dB&B£28-£34 WB&B£85-£95 WBDi£110-£120 LDO 4pm
Lic 🕮 CTV 🅿
Credit Cards 1️⃣ 3️⃣ £

GH 🅠🅠🅠 **The Greswolde Hotel** 20 Surrey Road, Cliftonville
CT9 2LA ☎Thanet(0843) 223956
6rm(1⇨5🏱)(2fb) CTV in all bedrooms ® sB&B⇨🏱£18
dB&B⇨🏱£29
Lic 🕮
Credit Cards 1️⃣ 3️⃣ £

GH 🅠🅠 **Westbrook Bay House** 12 Royal Esplanade,
Westbrook CT9 5DW ☎Thanet(0843) 292700
The proprietors of this hotel offer a warm welcome. Bedrooms are well equipped and some have marvellous sea views. There is a comfortable, well-appointed lounge and an attractive dining room which incorporates a small bar.
11rm(3🏱8hc)(4fb) CTV in 10 bedrooms ® ✖ (ex guide dogs)
✳ sB&Bfr£14 dB&Bfr£28
dB&B🏱fr£30 WB&Bfr£86 WBDifr£99 LDO 4.30pm
Lic 🕮 CTV
£

Every effort is made to provide accurate
information, but details can change after we go to
print. It is advisable to check prices etc. before
you make a firm booking.

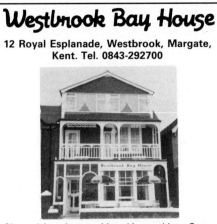

MARKET DRAYTON Shropshire Map 07 SJ63

FH 🅀🅀🅀 Mr J M Thomas **Stoke Manor** *(SH646279)* Stoke-on-Tern TF9 2DU ☎Hodnet(063084) 222
Closed Dec
This lovely old farmhouse is run by the Thomas family who provide a cellar bar and warm, comfortable bedrooms. A collection of vintage farm implements and a site of archaeological interest make this a memorable place to stay.
3⇨🜉 (1fb)⊬in all bedrooms CTV in all bedrooms ®
✠ (ex guide dogs) sB&B⇨🜉£20-£25 dB&B⇨🜉£38-£45
Lic 🍴 20P ✦ vintage tractor collection 250 acres arable
£

MARLBOROUGH Wiltshire Map 04 SU16

GH 🅀🅀 **Merlin Hotel** High St SN8 1LW ☎(0672) 512151
Set on the south side of Marlborough's main street, the Merlin Hotel caters for the bed and breakfaster. Bedrooms are simply decorated ; breakfast is served in the near dining room.
15rm(13⇨🜉2hc)Annexe 1🜉 (1fb) CTV in all bedrooms ®
sB&B£30-£35 sB&B⇨🜉£30-£35 dB&B£35-£40
dB&B⇨🜉£40-£45 LDO 9.30pm
Lic 🍴
Credit Cards 1 3 £

MARPLE Greater Manchester Map 07 SJ98

FH 🅀🅀🅀 Mrs M G Sidebottom **Shire Cottage Ernocroft** *(SJ982910)* Marple Bridge SK6 5NT ☎Glossop(0457) 866536
This modern bungalow is set a little way from the farm off the A626 between Marple and Glossop. The well-appointed accommodation has magnificent views over the surrounding countryside.
4rm(1🜉3hc)(1fb)⊬in 2 bedrooms CTV in all bedrooms ® ✲
sB&B£14-£18 dB&B£28-£36 dB&B🜉£30-£38 WB&B£91-£112
🍴 CTV 6P ♧ 180 acres mixed
£
See advertisement under STOCKPORT on page 341

MARSHFIELD Avon Map 03 ST77

INN 🅀🅀🅀 **Lord Nelson Inn & Carriages Restaurant** SN14 8LP ☎Bath(0225) 891820
This inn is 250 years' old, with many original features – look down the porthole in the bar to view the well – and specialises in fish dishes but also has an imaginative vegetarian menu. Meals are taken in the old stables, transformed into a lamplit, cobbled Victorian Street. The accommodation is well equipped and village memorabilia abound.
3⇨🜉 (1fb) CTV in all bedrooms ® ✠ (ex guide dogs) ✲
sB&B⇨🜉£42-£45
dB&B⇨🜉£55-£60 Lunch £5-£10 High tea £5-£10 Dinner
£5-£10&alc LDO 9.30pm
🍴
Credit Cards 1 3
See advertisement under BATH on page 56

MARTON Warwickshire Map 04 SP46

FH 🅀🅀🅀 Mrs P Dronfield *Marton Fields (SP402680)*
CV23 9RS ☎(0926) 632410
Closed Xmas
Tucked away behind the village (turn at the shop), this farmhouse enjoys a peaceful location and offers attractively appointed, comfortable public rooms. The bedrooms are of a good standard, and smoking is not permitted in them.
4hc ⊬in all bedrooms ® ✠ (ex guide dogs) LDO 6pm
🍴 CTV 10P ♧ ✦ croquet lawn painting holidays 240 acres
arable beef mixed sheep

MARY TAVY Devon Map 02 SX57

FH 🅀🅀🅀 Mrs B Anning **Wringworthy** *(SX500773)* PL19 9LT ☎(082281) 434
Apr-Oct
This delightful farmhouse has a dining room which is full of character with flagged floors and a traditional long table. The adjacent lounge is cosy. Bright bedrooms offer comfort and views over the countryside.
3rm (1fb)⊬in all bedrooms CTV in all bedrooms ®
✠ (ex guide dogs) dB&B£24-£26 LDO 10am
🍴 CTV 3P 80 acres beef sheep

MASHAM North Yorkshire Map 08 SE28

GH 🅀🅀🅀 Bank Villa HG4 4DB ☎Ripon(0765) 89605 due to change to 689605
Mar-Oct
Good home cooking in comfortable, personally-run guesthouse.
7hc ✲ sB&B£17
dB&B£29 WB&Bfr£95 WBDifr£175 LDO noon
Lic 🍴 CTV 7P nc5yrs

MATLOCK Derbyshire Map 08 SK36

FH 🅀🅀 Mrs M Brailsford **Farley** *(SK294622)* Farley Village DE4 5LR ☎(0629) 582533
Closed Xmas & New Year
This busy working farm, set high in the Derbyshire hills, has bright warm bedrooms, and a cheery welcome awaits guests from Mrs Brailsford and her dogs.
3hc (1fb) CTV in 1 bedroom ® sB&B£15
dB&B£24 WB&Bfr£84 WBDi£119 LDO 5pm
🍴 CTV 8P ☾ 245 acres arable beef dairy
£

FH 🅀🅀🅀 M Haynes **Packhorse** *(SK323617)* Tansley
DE4 5LF (2m NE of Matlock off A632 at Tansley)
☎(0629) 582781
Lovely countryside forms a backdrop to Mrs Haynes's lovingly maintained gardens, and the farmhouse accommodation has splendid views.
5hc (3fb) ✠ ✲ sB&Bfr£15 dB&Bfr£25 WB&Bfr£87.50
🍴 CTV 20P nc3yrs 40 acres mixed

FH 🅀🅀 Mrs Janet Hole **Wayside** *(SK324630)* Matlock Moor
DE4 5LF ☎(0629) 582967
Closed Xmas & New Year
At Matlock Moor, 2 miles from the town centre, this working farm offers fine views. Cattle byres stand next to the 17th-century farmhouse. A conservatory is soon to provide an attractive dining room to complement the comfortable, simple accommodation.
6hc (2fb) ✠ ✲ sB&B£14.50 dB&B£25-£27
🍴 CTV 8P 60 acres dairy
£

MAWGAN PORTH Cornwall & Isles of Scilly Map 02 SW86

GH 🅀🅀🅀 *White Lodge Hotel* TR8 4BN
☎St Mawgan(0637) 860512
Mar-Nov
Large detached building situated in a prominent position and enjoying sea views. Good bedrooms and friendly services.
15⇨🜉 (6fb) CTV in 13 bedrooms TV in 1 bedroom ® LDO 7.30pm
Lic 🍴 15P ♧ games room

MAYFIELD Staffordshire Map 07 SK14

INN 🅀 **Queen's Arms** DE6 2HH ☎Ashbourne(0335) 42271
Standing close to a busy junction, this lively house offers darts and pool, and live entertainment at weekends. Needless to say, it is well-supported by the locals.

4hc (2fb) CTV in all bedrooms ® ✍ (ex guide dogs) ✻
sB&B£19.50-£25
dB&B£25-£35 WB&B£70-£105 WBDi£105-£135 Bar Lunch
£3-£10 LDO 6.30pm
🍴 20P pool table
£

MELKSHAM Wiltshire Map **03** ST96

GH 🇶🇶 *Longhope* 9 Beanacre Rd SN12 7NS ☎(0225) 706737
*An ivy-clad detached Victorian house on the A350 north of the
town, Longhope offers a comfortable and friendly atmosphere.
Bedrooms are well equipped, and most are double-glazed. No
smoking is permitted in the dining room.*
7rm(1⇋5🐾1hc)(2fb) CTV in all bedrooms ® LDO 4pm
🍴 CTV 12P

GH 🇶🇶🇶 *Regency Hotel* 10-12 Spa Rd SN12 7NS
☎(0225) 702971 or 705772
*A terraced Regency house in town centre with attentive, friendly
owners.*
11rm(2⇋4🐾5hc)(1fb) CTV in all bedrooms ® LDO 8pm
Lic 🍴 🌶
Credit Cards [1] [3]

MELMERBY Cumbria Map **12** NY63

FH 🇶 Mrs M Morton *Meadow Bank* (*NY615375*) CA10 1HF
☎Langwathby(076881) 652
Feb-Nov
*This pleasantly furnished modern bungalow offers a good standard
of accommodation at a reasonable price. It is owned and run by
farmers, and guests are welcome to visit the nearby farm.*
2rm (1fb)⊁in all bedrooms ✍
🍴 CTV 3P 185 acres arable beef dairy sheep

MELROSE Borders *Roxburghshire* Map **12** NT53

GH 🇶🇶🇶 *Dunfermline House* Buccleuch St TD6 9LB
☎(089682) 2148
*Standing close to Melrose Abbey in this attractive border town,
this charming Victorian house has décor and furnishings of quality.
Scottish home cooking and hospitality are provided by the friendly
owners.*
2🐾 ⊁in all bedrooms CTV in all bedrooms ® ✍ ✻
dB&B🐾fr£34 LDO 5pm
🍴
£

MELTON MOWBRAY Leicestershire Map **08** SK71

GH 🇶 *Westbourne House Hotel* 11A-15 Nottingham Rd
LE13 0NP ☎(0664) 63556 & 69456
Closed Xmas
16hc (1fb) CTV in all bedrooms ✻ sB&B£16.50-£18
dB&B£29-£38 LDO 7.30
Lic 🍴 CTV 20P

MENDHAM Suffolk Map **05** TM28

FH 🇶🇶 Mrs J E Holden *Weston House* (*TM292828*) IP20 0PB
☎St Cross(098682) 206
Apr-Oct
*This white 16th-century farmhouse, with its Dutch roof, is easily
spotted when following signs to St Cross from Mendham. Mr and
Mrs Holden provide a friendly atmosphere along with simple,
comfortable accommodation with an attractive verandah and
conservatory.*
3hc (1fb) ® ✻ sB&Bfr£14
dB&Bfr£24 WB&Bfr£63 WBDifr£108.50 LDO 2pm
🍴 CTV 6P 300 acres arable beef mixed
£

MERE Wiltshire Map **03** ST83

GH Q Q Q **Chetcombe House Hotel** Chetcombe Rd BA12 6AZ
☎(0747) 860219
Closed 1-20 Feb
Set in an acre of lovely gardens, this country house hotel is run by charming proprietors. The main bedrooms have outstanding views, and all are nicely equipped. With comfortable public rooms, a traditional English atmosphere prevails here.
5⇌🛏 (1fb)⚌in all bedrooms CTV in all bedrooms ®
sB&B⇌🛏£25
dB&B⇌🛏£43-£45 WB&B£129.50-£154 WBDi£198-£222
LDO 7pm
Lic ♨ 10P
Credit Cards ①③

INN Q Q **Talbot Hotel** The Square BA12 6DR ☎(0747) 860427
Oak timbers abound both outside and inside this 16th-century village hostelry.
10rm(4⇌3🛏)(2fb) CTV in all bedrooms ® LDO 9pm
♨ 25P
Credit Cards ①

MERIDEN West Midlands Map **04** SP28

GH Q Q **Meriden Hotel** Main Rd CV7 7NH ☎(0676) 22005
FAX (0676) 23744
The past year has seen extensive redecoration of the rooms and public areas of this establishment, which provides good facilities, some single rooms being compact. The hotel is to be found on the main road through the village.
13rm(5⇌8🛏)(1fb) CTV in all bedrooms ® ✱
sB&B⇌🛏£34.50-£48.40
dB&B⇌🛏£57.50-£63.25 WB&B£189.75-£290.40 LDO 9pm
Lic ♨ CTV 15P
Credit Cards ①③

MERTON Devon Map **02** SS51

GH Q Q **Merton House** EX20 3DR ☎Beaford(08053) 364
Apr-Oct
This Georgian residence stands in its own grounds and has a grass tennis court.
5hc (1fb) ® ✱ sB&B£20-£24
dB&B£40-£48 (incl dinner) WB&Bfr£98 WBDi£140-£168
LDO 10am
Lic ♨ CTV 8P ⌅♪(grass)snooker putting green table tennis
£

MEVAGISSEY Cornwall & Isles of Scilly Map **02** SX04

GH Q Q Q **Headlands Hotel** Polkirt Hill PL26 6UX
☎(0726) 843453
Mar-Oct & Xmas
This small licensed hotel boasts one of the best sea views in Cornwall. The bedrooms are simply furnished and there is a welcoming bar lounge and dining room. Wholesome, homemade meals are provided, together with Mr and Mrs Patrick Grist's personal service.
14rm(8🛏6hc)(3fb) CTV in 8 bedrooms sB&B£14-£18
dB&B£28-£36
dB&B🛏£36-£44 WB&B£91-£147 WBDi£161-£217 LDO 7pm
Lic ♨ CTV 11P

GH Q Q Q **Mevagissey House** Vicarage Hill PL26 6SZ
☎(0726) 842427
Mar-Oct
This 18th-century vicarage is perched on a hillside in 4 acres of grounds. Well-equipped bedrooms, a sitting room with lovely views, and a candlelit dining room provide extensive service and wholesome English cooking to provide a relaxing place in which to stay.
6rm(1⇌3🛏2hc)(2fb) CTV in all bedrooms ®
✱ (ex guide dogs) sB&B£20-£23 sB&B⇌🛏£22-£25

dB&B£32-£38
dB&B⇌🛏£36-£42 WB&B£112-£147 WBDi£175-£213 LDO
5pm
Lic ♨ 12P nc7yrs
Credit Cards ①③

GH Q Q Q **Tremarne** Polkirt PL26 6UY ☎(0726) 842213
Mar-Nov
14rm(4⇌10🛏)(2fb) CTV in all bedrooms ® ✕ ✱
sB&B⇌🛏£28.50-£35.50
dB&B⇌🛏£50-£64 (incl dinner) WB&B£139.50-£154
WBDi£168-£196
Lic ♨ 14P nc3yrs ⌅(heated)
Credit Cards ①②③

FH Q Q Q Mrs L Hennah **Kerryanna** *(SX008453)* Treleaven
Farm PL26 6RZ ☎(0726) 843558
Mar-Oct
Linda Hennah's guesthouse is situated on a working farm overlooking the village. The bedrooms are well furnished, most with showers. It has a comfortable lounge, dining room and bar. No children under two years' old or pets.
6rm(5⇌🛏1hc)(2fb) CTV in all bedrooms ® ✕
dB&B⇌🛏fr£50 (incl dinner) WB&Bfr£126 WBDifr£160
(wkly only Jul & Aug) LDO 5pm
Lic ♨ 7P nc2yrs ⌅(heated) games room putting green 200
acres arable beef

FH Q Q Q Mrs A Hennah **Treleaven** *(SX008454)* PL26 6RZ
☎(0726) 842413
Closed 15 Dec-7 Jan
This modern farmhouse has bright, well-equipped bedrooms with en suite facilities, some having panoramic views. The lounge has a woodburning stove, adding to the comfortable and relaxing atmosphere. There is a swimming pool and ample car parking.
6🛏 (1fb) CTV in all bedrooms ® ✕ LDO 8pm
Lic ♨ CTV 6P ⌅(heated) games room, putting green 200
acres mixed
Credit Cards ①③

INN Q Q **The Ship** Fore St PL26 6UQ ☎(0726) 843324
A casual 'seafaring' atmosphere prevails at his popular inn, serving real ale, grills and local seafood in its lively bar. The bedrooms are modern and functional and there is a breakfast room on the first floor.
6hc (2fb) CTV in all bedrooms ® ✱ sB&B£15
dB&B£30 Lunch £2.80-£8 Dinner £2.80-£8 LDO 8.30pm
♨ ₽

MIDDLETON PRIORS Shropshire Map **07** SO69

GH Q Q Q **Middleton Lodge** WV16 6UR (1m NE on unclass rd)
☎Ditton Priors(074634) 228 or 675
Closed Xmas
This large, 17th-century house, which stands in 20 acres of grounds, was once the hunting-lodge of the Howard family. The bedrooms are large and comfortable, with modern amenities, while many original features have been retained.
3rm(2⇌1🛏) CTV in all bedrooms ® ✕ (ex guide dogs)
♨ CTV 4P nc5yrs

MIDDLETOWN Powys Map **07** SJ21

FH Q Q Mrs E J Bebb & Mrs G Corfield **Bank** *(SJ325137)*
SY21 8EJ (on the A458 Shrewsbury-Welshpool road)
☎Trewern(093874) 260 & 526
Etr-Oct
This cosy farmhouse with its own caravan site lies alongside the A458 between Shrewsbury and Welshpool at the foot of the Breidden Hills. It has bright, cheerful bedrooms and a cosy lounge.

2hc (1fb) ® ✕ ✱ dB&Bfr£22
♨ CTV 0P nc5yrs 30 acres sheep
£

MIDDLEWICH Cheshire Map **07** SJ76

FH 🇶🇶 Mrs S Moss **Forge Mill** *(SJ704624)* Warmingham CW10 0HQ ☎Warmingham(027077) 204
This attractive Victorian farmhouse stands in an acre of mature gardens. Both bedrooms have lovely views of the surrounding countryside and are comfortable and attractively decorated. There is a lounge and a cosy dining room for guests' use.
2hc ✖ (ex guide dogs) sB&B£13.50-£14
dB&B£27-£28 WB&B£94.50
♨ CTV 10P ♪(grass)150 acres mixed
£

MIDHURST West Sussex

See **Bepton and Rogate**

MILBORNE PORT Somerset Map **03** ST61

FH 🇶🇶 Mrs M J Tizzard **Venn** *(ST684183)* PT9 5RA ☎(0963) 250208
Attractive accommodation in a modern house, set back off main road on Shaftesbury side of village.
3rm(2hc)(2fb) CTV in all bedrooms ® ✖
♨ CTV 0P ♫ 375 acres dairy

MILFORD ON SEA Hampshire Map **04** SZ29

SELECTED

GH 🇶🇶🇶🇶 *Seaspray* 8 Hurst Rd SO41 0PY ☎Lymington(0590) 42627
This cosy chalet bungalow, run by the caring owners, Mr and Mrs Crates, enjoys superb views over to the Isle of Wight. The pretty bedrooms are light, airy and well equipped, 2 with en suite showers and lavatory on the ground floor. The cosy ▶

The Ship Inn

The Ship Inn, Mevagissey, Cornwalll
Tel: Mevagissey (0726) 843324

Following extensive renovations, The Ship Inn has now been restored to its original nautical character, complete with maritime decorations and the original open fireplace. We offer an excellent menu of good food and a fine selection of Beers, Wines and Spirits in these comfortable and relaxing surroundings.
- Extensively renovated
- 6 letting Bedrooms
- Colour T.V., Tea/Coffee facilities in all rooms
- Angling Parties catered for
- All rooms newly furnished
- 100 yards from Quay
- Children's room
- An excellent menu with 'Fresh Quayside Fish' our speciality

Park House

Bepton, Midhurst, West Sussex GU29 0JB
Tel: (073081) 2880 Fax: (073081) 5643

Park House is fully equipped to give maximum comfort with the atmosphere and amenities of an English Country House. Private bathrooms - television and telephone in all bedrooms. Large garden. Grass tennis courts, putting lawn. Croquet. Heated swimming pool.
Under the personal supervision of the resident owner. Licensed.
Barclay, Visa and Access accepted.

Llawnroc Inn

A family run hotel & village pub overlooking the picturesque harbour & fishing village of Gorran Haven. Enjoy the friendly atmosphere & breath taking views from our large terraced lawns.

★ Sample good beers including real ales
★ Delight in our varied home cooked meals & bar snacks

All rooms are en-suite, have colour TV, coffee/tea making & face the sea. Large private car park.

A warm welcome awaits you from licencees
John & Janet Gregory & Hilda Birch
Gorran Haven, St Austell, Cornwall PL26 6NU
Ring Mevagissey (0726) 843461

Send S.A.E. for brochure

lounge is complemented by the well-stocked bar, and in the dining room, every guest can appreciate Mrs Crates's cooking.
6rm(2↱4hc) CTV in all bedrooms LDO 10am
Lic ♨ 8P

MILNGAVIE Strathclyde *Dunbartonshire* Map **11** NS57

FH QQQ Mrs L Fisken ***The High Craigton*** *(NS525766)*
Craigton G62 7HA ☎041-956 1384
Off A809, 2-storeyed painted stone-built farmhouse on hill top with views over fields towards Glasgow.
2hc (1fb) ® ✗
♨ CTV 10P 1100 acres sheep

MILTON Derbyshire Map **08** SK32

INN QQQ The Coach House 1 Main St DE6 6EF
☎Burton-on-Trent(0283) 703531
3rm(1⇒2↱)(1fb)⊬in all bedrooms CTV in all bedrooms ®
sB&B⇒↱£22.50-£25
dB&B⇒↱£35-£37.50 Lunch £5.25-£11.50alc Dinner £5.25-£11.50alc LDO 9.30pm
♨ 50P
Credit Cards [1] [3]

MILTON COMMON Oxfordshire Map **04** SP60

INN QQ Three Pigeons OX9 2NS
☎Great Milton(0844) 279247
Located conveniently for the M40, this small country inn has a friendly and informal atmosphere. There are 3 comfortable, modern and well-equipped bedrooms and a small dining area where home-cooked meals are available.
3⇒↱ (1fb) CTV in all bedrooms ® ✗ ✱ sB&B⇒↱£25-£30
dB&B⇒↱£40-£45 Lunch £3-£12 High tea £4.90 Dinner £3-£12 LDO 10pm
♨ CTV 20P
Credit Cards [1] [2] [3] [5] £

MILTON KEYNES Buckinghamshire Map **04** SP83

See **Gayhurst, Newport Pagnell, Salford** and **Whaddon**

MILTON-UNDER-WYCHWOOD Oxfordshire Map **04** SP21

SELECTED

GH QQQQ Hillborough Hotel The Green OX7 6JH (off A424 Burton-Stow village centre)
☎Shipton-under-Wychwood(0993) 830501
Closed Jan
This delightful hotel faces the village green and has a peaceful and relaxing atmosphere. The charming conservatory, home to lovely plants, is furnished with comfortable sofas and chairs, and the restaurant has been extended to offer more space and comfort. There is also a friendly bar. The bedrooms have been tastefully decorated and furnished, and 3 new 'cottage' rooms are soon to be completed.
6rm(5⇒1↱)Annexe 4⇒ (3fb) CTV in all bedrooms ®
sB&B⇒↱£38-£40
dB&B⇒↱£48-£50 WB&B£151-£157 WBDi£224-£227.50 LDO 9.30pm
Lic ♨ 15P ⌂ croquet
Credit Cards [1] [2] [3] £
See advertisement under OXFORD on page 284

This guide is updated annually – make sure you use an up-to-date edition.

MINEHEAD Somerset Map **03** SS94

See **Town Plan Section**

GH QQQ Alcombe House Hotel Alcombe TA24 6BG
☎(0643) 705130
Mar-Oct rs Mar-Etr
This grade II listed Georgian house stands on the borders of Exmoor. The 6 comfortable double bedrooms are comfortable, mostly en suite and all with colour TV. The lounge has a small bar and the elegant dining room serves a simple table d'hôte menu. Mrs Stevens ensures guests of a pleasant stay.
6rm(5⇒1↱) CTV in all bedrooms ® ✱ sB&B⇒↱£33-£36
dB&B⇒↱£62-£70 (incl dinner) LDO 7.30pm
Lic 7P nc12yrs
Credit Cards [1] [3] £
See advertisement under DUNSTER on page 141

GH QQ Bactonleigh Private Hotel 20 Tregonwell Rd TA24 5DU ☎(0643) 702147
This small privately owned guesthouse is in a quiet residential area and provides adequately appointed, well-maintained accommodation. Nicely prepared simple English food is served.
8rm(1↱7hc)(1fb) ✱ sB&Bfr£12.50 dB&Bfr£25
dB&B↱fr£29 WB&Bfr£84 WBDifr£122.50 LDO 5pm
Lic ♨ CTV 8P
£

GH QQQ Gascony Hotel The Avenue TA24 5BB
☎(0643) 705939
Mar-Oct
Friendly and efficient Victorian house in a prime position, offering well-equipped bedrooms of a good size. Spacious dining room serves home-cooked meals.
13rm(7⇒6↱)(2fb) CTV in all bedrooms ®
sB&B⇒↱£18-£19.50
dB&B⇒↱£36-£39 WB&Bfr£116 WBDi£131-£148 LDO 5.30pm
Lic ♨ 14P nc5yrs
Credit Cards [1] [3] £

↤**GH QQ Marshfield Hotel** Tregonwell Rd TA24 5DU
☎(0643) 702517
Mar-Nov
Marshfield stands on level ground close to the shops and sea, and offers a smartly furnished dining room, TV lounge and sun lounge bar. The bedrooms are comfortable and well equipped.
12rm(8↱4hc)(1fb) ® sB&B£13-£15 sB&B↱£15-£17
dB&B£26-£30
dB&B↱£30-£34 WB&Bfr£84 WBDifr£119 LDO 6.30pm
Lic ♨ CTV 7P ⌂

GH QQQ Marston Lodge Hotel St Michaels Rd TA24 5JP
☎(0643) 702510
Standing high above the town with a terraced garden and enjoying splendid views, Marston Lodge has roomy bedrooms which are well equipped, a lounge, bar and a pretty dining room. Mr & Mrs Allen offer a warm welcome.
12rm(4⇒8↱)(3fb) CTV in all bedrooms ® ✗
sB&B⇒↱£23-£28
dB&B⇒↱£46-£56 (incl dinner) WB&B£115-£128
WBDi£161-£185 LDO 7pm
Lic ♨ 7P nc5yrs
Credit Cards [1] [3]

GH QQQ Mayfair Hotel 25 The Avenue TA24 5AY
☎(0643) 702719
Mar-Nov rs Feb
Enjoying a central location between the shops and the sea, Mayfair has cheerful accommodation and modern, well-equipped bedrooms. Some rooms are in a house across the road, equally well furnished, though all meals are served in the main building.

16rm(5⊃11♠)Annexe 9rm(4⊃5♠)(10fb) CTV in all
bedrooms ® ✠ (ex guide dogs) ✱ sB&B⊃♠£19-£22
dB&B⊃♠£40-£50 WB&B£100-£105 WBDi£140-£150 LDO
6pm
Lic ⊞ 23P nc5yrs
Credit Cards ①③ ⓔ

MINSTER LOVELL Oxfordshire Map **04** SP31

FH ⓆⓆⓆ Mrs K Brown **Hill Grove** *(SP314115)* OX8 5NA
☎Witney(0993) 703120
Closed Xmas
A modern Cotswold stone family farmhouse, Hill Grove is in a
quiet position with extensive views over the Windrush Valley. The
farmhouse stands off the B4047 1.5 miles east of the village,
towards Crawley, and is sheltered by mature trees.
2rm(1⊃♠)⧏in all bedrooms CTV in all bedrooms ®
✠ (ex guide dogs) ✱ dB&B£28-£30 dB&B⊃♠£32-£34
⊞ CTV 3P 300 acres arable beef mixed
ⓔ

MOFFAT Dumfries & Galloway *Dumfriesshire* Map **11** NT00

GH ⓆⓆ **Barnhill Springs Country** DG10 9QS ☎(0683) 20580
Quiet and friendly small country house offering plain but good
food.
6hc (1fb) ® ✱ sB&B£12.50-£13.50
dB&B£25-£27 WB&B£97.50-£104.50 WBDi£140-£147 LDO
6pm
Lic ⊞ CTV 10P
ⓔ

GH ⓆⓆⓆ **Bridge** Well Rd DG10 9JT ☎(0683) 20383
This early, Victorian, whinstone house stands on an elevated site in
well-maintained gardens and enjoys open country views. The
comfortable bedrooms are nicely decorated and the public rooms
evoke the Victorian era. The dining room features a collection of
teapots.
9rm(4♠5hc)(3fb)⧏in 4 bedrooms CTV in 7 bedrooms ®
sB&Bfr£15 dB&Bfr£28
dB&B♠fr£32 WB&B£98-£112 WBDi£145.50-£159.50 LDO
7pm
Lic ⊞ CTV 8P
ⓔ

GH ⓆⓆ *Buchan* 13 Beechgrove DG10 9HG ☎(0683) 20378
This white and stucco house is set in a quiet location on the
outskirts of the town. Though undergoing improvements, some
rooms with en suite facilities are available for the current season.
7hc (2fb) LDO 5pm
⊞ CTV 10P

SELECTED

⊷GH ⓆⓆⓆⓆ **Gilbert House** Beechgrove DG10 9RS
☎(0683) 20050
Dinner is especially recommended at this delightful house,
situated in a quiet area close to the town centre, and run by the
friendly and courteous resident proprietors. It also offers
comfortably appointed bedrooms, and a most attractive dining
room.
6rm(4♠2hc)(3fb) sB&B£12-£13.50 dB&B£24-£27
dB&B♠£26-£32 WB&B£76-£101 WBDi£128.50-£153.50
LDO 5pm
Lic ⊞ CTV 6P
Credit Cards ①③

GH ⓆⓆⓆ **Merkland House** Buccleuch Place DG10 9AN
☎(0683) 20957
Set within walled gardens in a quiet location close to the town
centre, this comfortable house offers spacious accommodation and
is run by friendly resident proprietors.

▶

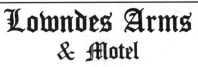

6rm(4⇄2♠)(2fb) CTV in 1 bedroom ® ✱ sB&B⇄♠fr£14
dB&B⇄♠fr£28 WB&Bfr£90
🍽 CTV 6P ► 18 ℘(hard)U

GH QQ St Olaf Eastgate, Off Dickson St DG10 9AE
☎(0683) 20001
Apr-Oct
*Tucked away in a side street just off the High Street, this
comfortable, well-maintained house offers tranquility and
convenience for the town centre. The bedrooms are bright and
cheerful, and the inviting first floor lounge is attractive and
comfortable.*
7rm(1♠6hc)(3fb) ® ✱ sB&B£15 dB&B£23
dB&B♠£25 WB&B£80.50 WBDi£126 LDO 6.30pm
🍽 CTV 4P 4🍴

INN QQ Black Bull Hotel Churchgate DG10 9EG
☎(0683) 20206
*A 16th-century inn situated close to the centre of this attractive
small town. The bars are cosy and full of character with a friendly
atmosphere. Bedrooms, though modest, are neat and modern.*
4rm(1⇄3hc) CTV in all bedrooms ® ✖ (ex guide dogs)
sB&B£24 sB&B⇄♠£35 dB&B£36
dB&B⇄♠£46 (wkly only 7 Jan-Mar) Lunch £4.70-£5.20 High
tea £3.85 Dinner £4.70-£15 LDO 9pm
🍽 6P ♪ solarium
Credit Cards [1][3] £

MOLD Clwyd Map **07** SJ26

See also Nannerch
FH QQ Mrs A Brown *Hill (SJ263265)* Llong CH7 4JP (on
A5118 between Chester and Mold) ☎Buckley(0244) 550415
*Standing in an elevated position above the A5118, this very well-
maintained Georgian farmhouse provides comfortable
accommodation and friendly hospitality.*
3hc (1fb)⤢in all bedrooms ® ✖ (ex guide dogs) sB&B£14-£16
dB&B£24-£28
🍽 CTV 5P 300 acres dairy mixed

MOLESWORTH Cambridgeshire Map **04** TL07

INN QQQ Cross Keys PE18 0QF ☎Bythorn(08014) 283
*A good range of bar meals and homemade dishes are prepared by
Mrs Bettsworth, the friendly proprietress of this archetypal village
inn, set just off the A604. It offers a high standard of
accommodation, all with good en suite facilities.*
4rm(1⇄3♠)Annexe 5rm(2⇄3♠)(1fb) CTV in all bedrooms
® sB&B⇄♠£17-£19
dB&B⇄♠£26-£28 Lunch £3.50-£5alc Dinner £3.50-£5alc
LDO 10.30pm
🍽 30P

MONEYDIE Tayside *Perthshire* Map **11** NO02

┠╌FH QQ Mrs S Walker **Moneydie** *Roger (NO054290)*
PH1 3JA (on unclass rd signed Methven, off B8063)
☎Almondbank(073883) 239
Apr-29 Sep
*In a secluded position overlooking picturesque countryside, this 2-
storeyed farmhouse is ideal for the tourist. Neatly furnished
bedrooms provide traditional comforts, and guests receive genuine
hospitality.*
3rm(2hc)⤢in all bedrooms ® ✖ sB&Bfr£12.50 dB&Bfr£23
3P nc12yrs 143 acres arable cattle sheep

MONTROSE Tayside *Angus* Map **15** NO75

GH QQ *Linksgate* 11 Dorward Rd DD10 8SB ☎(0674) 72273
*Close to the golf course and beach, this friendly, family-run
guesthouse stands in its own gardens and provides good value
holiday accommodation.*
9rm(2⇄7hc)(3fb) CTV in 2 bedrooms LDO 6pm
🍽 CTV 9P

FH QQ Mrs A Ruxton *Muirshade of Gallery (NO671634)*
DD10 9JU ☎Northwaterbridge(067484) 209
Apr-Oct
*Set amid pleasant scenery, 5 miles north west of the town, this
cottage style farmhouse provides traditional comforts and good
home cooking.*
2hc (1fb) ✖ LDO 4pm
CTV 3P 175 acres arable

MORCHARD BISHOP Devon Map **03** SS70

SELECTED

FH QQQQ Mr & Mrs S Chilcott **Wigham** *(SS757087)*
EX17 6RJ ☎(03637) 350
*Perched on a hillside overlooking the valley, this 16th-century
thatched longhouse is part of a 10-acre farm. Sympathetic
restoration has provided sylish accommodation with cosy en
suite bedrooms (one with a four poster). The public rooms are
equally comfortable and full of character. Fresh produce from
the farm is used in the imaginative, home-cooked meals which
are included in the quoted room rates.*
5⇄♠ (1fb)⤢in all bedrooms CTV in all bedrooms ® ✖
✱ dB&B⇄♠fr£72 (incl dinner)
Lic 🍽 9P nc10yrs ⩗(heated) U snooker table 31 acres
mixed

MORECAMBE Lancashire Map **07** SD46

GH QQQ Ashley Private Hotel 371 Marine Rd Promenade
East LA4 5AH ☎(0524) 412034
*Tastefully furnished, comfortable accommodation is offered at this
establishment. Its inviting bedrooms are very well appointed.*
13rm(3⇄8♠2hc)(3fb) CTV in all bedrooms ® ✖
sB&B£14-£16 sB&B⇄♠£18-£20
dB&B⇄♠£32-£36 WB&B£105-£120 WBDi£140-£160 LDO
3pm
Lic 🍽 5P 1🍴 (£2)
Credit Cards [1][3] £

GH QQ Beach Mount 395 Marine Rd East LA4 5AN
☎(0524) 420753
Mar-Nov
Modern, family-run hotel overlooking the bay.
26rm(22⇄4hc)(3fb) CTV in 22 bedrooms ® ✱
sB&B£14.75-£15.25 sB&B⇄♠£17.50-£18 dB&B£26.50-£27.50
dB&B⇄♠£32-£33 WB&B£83.50-£100 WBDi£119.50-£136 LDO
7pm
Lic 🍽 CTV 6P
Credit Cards [1][2][3][5]

GH QQ Craigwell Hotel 372 Promenade East LA4 5AH
☎(0524) 410095 & 418399
Closed 20 Dec-10 Jan
*This friendly, personally-run small hotel enjoys views over
Morecambe Bay's sands. The rooms are generally compact but
comfortably furnished, well equipped and all have modern en suite
facilities. Dinner features a choice of home-cooked dishes,
including vegetarian items.*
13rm(2⇄11♠)(2fb) CTV in all bedrooms ® ✱
sB&B⇄♠£18-£20
dB&B⇄♠£36-£40 WB&B£119-£133 WBDi£164-£194 LDO
9.30pm
Lic 🍽 4P
Credit Cards [1][3] £

GH Q Ellesmere Private Hotel 44 Westminster Rd LA4 4JD
☎(0524) 411881
*A friendly welcome is extended to guests at this small hotel.
Compact bedrooms are equipped with colour televisions and tea-
making facilities, and there is a comfortable lounge. The seafront
is within walking distance.*

►

6hc (2fb)🚭in 1 bedroom CTV in all bedrooms ®
🐕 (ex guide dogs) * sB&B£11-£12.50
dB&B£22-£25 WB&B£67-£78 WBDi£78-£91 LDO 3pm
♨ CTV
Credit Cards [1] [3] [£]

GH [Q][Q] New Hazelmere Hotel 391 Promenade East LA4 5AN
☎(0524) 417876
May-29 Nov
One of the larger seafront establishments, this hotel has comfortable bedrooms and attractive lounge areas featuring antique furnishings and bric-a-brac.
20rm(17🛁3🚿)(3fb) CTV in all bedrooms ® *
sB&B🛁🚿fr£15
dB&B🛁🚿fr£30 WB&Bfr£95 WBDifr£135 LDO 5.30pm
Lic CTV 3P
[£]

GH [Q][Q][Q] Hotel Prospect 363 Marine Rd East LA4 5AQ
☎(0524) 417819
Etr-Oct
This very comfortable seafront hotel offers friendly service and meals which are good value for money.
14🛁 (9fb) CTV in all bedrooms ® sB&Bfr£15 sB&B🛁fr£25
dB&B🛁fr£30 (incl dinner) WB&Bfr£90 WBDifr£115 LDO 3pm
Lic ♨ CTV 6P
Credit Cards [1] [3] [£]

GH [Q] *Stresa Private Hotel* 96 Sandylands Promenade LA3 1DP
☎(0524) 412867
Etr-Oct
This pleasantly furnished small hotel overlooks Morecambe Bay.
9hc (2fb) ® 🐕 LDO 4.30pm
♨ CTV P̸
Credit Cards [1]

GH [Q][Q] *Hotel Warwick* 394 Marine Rd East LA4 5AN
☎(0524) 418151
Comfortable accommodation, friendly service and home-cooked meals are features of this seafront hotel.
23rm(2🛁9🚿12hc)(4fb) CTV in 14 bedrooms TV in 2 bedrooms ® LDO 6pm
Lic lift ♨ CTV P̸
Credit Cards [1] [2] [3] [5]

GH [Q][Q] Wimslow Private Hotel 374 Marine Rd East LA4 5AH
☎(0524) 417804
Feb-Nov & Xmas
Managed by friendly resident proprietors, this comfortable hotel offers well-appointed bedrooms and inviting lounges.
14🚿 (2fb) CTV in all bedrooms ® 🐕 * sB&B🚿fr£23
dB&B🚿fr£46 WBDifr£140 LDO 4.30pm
Lic ♨ CTV 3P 6🚗
Credit Cards [1] [3] [£]

MORETONHAMPSTEAD Devon Map 03 SX78

GH [Q][Q][Q] Cookshayes 33 Court St TQ13 8LG ☎(0647) 40374
mid Mar-Oct
Standing on the edge of Dartmoor, this charming Victorian house is owned and run by Topsy and Doug Harding. Traditionally furnished, it offers a comfortable lounge, well-equipped bedrooms, and a bright dining room where Topsy's imaginative cooking is served.
8rm(6🚿2hc)(1fb) CTV in all bedrooms ® sB&B£18 dB&B£31
dB&B🚿£36-£39 WB&B£101.50-£129.50 WBDi£175-£203 LDO 5.30pm
Lic ♨ CTV 15P nc5yrs putting green
Credit Cards [1] [3] [£]

↔**GH [Q] Elmfield** Station Rd TQ13 8NQ ☎(0647) 40327
Etr-end Oct
Large, detached house at the foot of Dartmoor, with some lovely views.
6rm(3🚿3hc)(2fb) sB&B£12.50 dB&B£23
dB&B🚿£26 WB&B£80.50-£91 WBDi£120-£130 LDO 7pm
Lic ♨ CTV 8P

MORETON-IN-MARSH Gloucestershire Map 04 SP13

GH [Q][Q] Moreton House High St GL56 0LQ ☎(0608) 50747
Situated in the town centre, opposite the Market Square, this Cotswold stone house offers comfortable, well-equipped bedrooms with good en suite facilities. There is also an all day tea room, where the emphasis is on good home cooking.
12rm(5🛁🚿7hc) CTV in all bedrooms ® * sB&B£19.50
dB&B£34 dB&B🛁🚿£40-£44 LDO 8pm
Lic ♨ 5P
Credit Cards [1] [3] [£]

MORFA NEFYN Gwynedd Map 06 SH23

GH [Q] *Erw Goch Hotel* LL53 6BN ☎Nefyn(0758) 720539
Family owned and run, this detached Georgian house stands in its own grounds and provides good home comforts. The facilities provided include a three-quarter size snooker table.
15hc (5fb)
Lic ♨ CTV 25P
Credit Cards [1] [3]

MORTEHOE Devon Map 02 SS44

See also Woolacombe

SELECTED

GH [Q][Q][Q][Q] Sunnycliffe Hotel EX34 7EB
☎Woolacombe(0271) 870597
Feb-Nov
Mr and Mrs Bassett and their family put a lot of effort and enthusiasm into their charming hotel which offers comfortable, well-equipped and furnished bedrooms, all with commanding coastal views. The public rooms are equally comfortable with an elegant reading room, lounge bar and a spacious dining room with fine table appointments, serving traditional English cuisine. This quiet hotel enjoys a fine hillside position and is surrounded by open moorland and coastal walks.
8rm(4🛁4🚿)🚭in 4 bedrooms CTV in all bedrooms ® 🐕
sB&B🛁🚿£22-£26
dB&B🛁🚿£39-£50 WB&B£140-£155 WBDi£193-£208 LDO 6pm
Lic ♨ 10P nc
[£]

MOUNT Cornwall & Isles of Scilly Map 02 SX16

GH [Q][Q] Mount Pleasant Farm Hotel MOUNT PL30 4EX
☎Cardinham(020882) 342
Apr-Sep
Peaceful farmland surrounds this remote hotel which enjoys lovely views across the Glyn Valley. Accommodation comprises two lounges, a separate bar and dining room, plus a choice of bedrooms.
7rm(1🛁5🚿1hc)(1fb) ® 🐕 WBDi£140-£155 LDO 4pm
Lic ♨ CTV 10P
[£]

MOUSEHOLE Cornwall & Isles of Scilly Map 02 SW42

GH [Q][Q][Q] *Tavis Vor* TR19 6PR ☎Penzance(0736) 731306
mid Mar-Sep
Delightful country house style residence, in own grounds running to the edge of the sea.

7rm(3♪4hc)(1fb) ® LDO 5pm
Lic ₪ CTV 7P nc5yrs

MOYLEGROVE Dyfed Map **02** SN14

FH Q Q Q Mrs A D Fletcher *Penrallt Ceibwr (SN116454)*
SA43 3BX ☎(023986) 217
A warm Welsh welcome and good Welsh food are to be found at this family-run farm. Standing on the Newport coast road, it has view of the sea where seals are often seen. Table tennis and other games are available.
6rm(3♪3hc)(3fb) CTV in 1 bedroom LDO 7pm
Lic ₪ CTV 40P ⚓ ♪ pool table table tennis 280 acres arable dairy

---

MUDDIFORD Devon Map **02** SS53

FH Q Q Q Mrs M Lethaby **Home Park** *(SS553360)* Lower Blakewell EX31 4ET ☎Barnstaple(0271) 42955
Half a mile from the B3230, 3 miles from Barnstaple, this small farmhouse has marvellous views over rolling countryside. The 2 bright bedrooms offer a high standard of modern accommodation, and are fully en suite. The well-kept gardens have a play area and Wendy house.
2rm(1⇦1♪)(2fb) CTV in all bedrooms ® ✖ (ex guide dogs) (Jul-Aug)
₪ CTV 2P ⚓ 70 acres sheep
See advertisement under BARNSTAPLE on page 49

MUDFORD Somerset Map **03** ST51

INN Q Q Q *The Half Moon* Main St BA21 5TF
☎Marston Magna(0935) 850289
Conveniently situated on the A359 north east of Yeovil, this 17th-century inn has its bedrooms in a modern annexe. They are comfortable and well equipped and there is a lounge for non-smokers. The à la carte menu offers a variety of dishes. ▶

Annexe 11rm(1⇨10♠) CTV in all bedrooms ® LDO 9.30pm
🛏40P
Credit Cards ①②③
See advertisement under YEOVIL on page 403

MULL, ISLE OF Strathclyde *Argyllshire* Map **10**

BUNESSAN Map **10** NM32

GH Ⓠ**Ⓠ**Ⓠ *Ardachy* PA67 6DR ☎Fionnphort(06817) 505 &
506
The original farmhouse has been tastefully converted and extended
to provide accommodation which is modern and comfortable. Just
minutes from a fine sandy beach, Ardachy has panoramic views to
Jura and the mainland.
8rm(7♠1hc)(2fb) ® LDO 6pm
Lic 🛏CTV 8P ⏲ shooting
Credit Cards ①③

SALEN Map **10** NM54

GH Ⓠ**Ⓠ**Ⓠ **Craig Hotel** PA72 6JG ☎Aros(0680) 300347 &
300451
Etr-15 Oct
This cosy little hotel stands at the northern end of the village and
has a pleasant atmosphere. The comfortable lounge has lots of
books and a woodburning stove and the attractive dining room is
pine furnished.
6hc sB&Bfr£23 dB&Bfr£40 LDO 7.15pm
Lic CTV 7P
Credit Cards ①③

TOBERMORY Map **13** NM55

GH Ⓠ**Ⓠ**Ⓠ **Harbour House Hotel** 59 Main St PA75 6NT
☎(0688) 2209 FAX (0688) 2140
This small harbour front hotel offers views across the bay. The
tastefully furnished bedrooms vary in size and the attractive
restaurant is open to non-residents.
10rm(2⇨8hc)(2fb) CTV in 1 bedroom ® ✳ sB&B£15-£21
dB&B£30-£42 dB&B⇨£36-£48 WBDifr£267.80 LDO 7.45pm
Lic CTV 10P
Credit Cards ①③ Ⓔ

MUMBLES West Glamorgan Map **02** SS68

See also Bishopston& Langland Bay
GH Ⓠ**Ⓠ**Ⓠ **Harbour Winds Private Hotel** Overland Road,
Langland SA3 4LP ☎Swansea(0792) 369298
Apr-Sep
Situated in an elevated position with good garden and sea views,
this spacious hotel, with good comfortable bedrooms, has very
friendly and welcoming owners. Good food is served in an
attractive, panelled dining room, and the lounge is very relaxing.
8rm(1⇨2♠5hc)(3fb) ® ✳ sB&B£17-£18 dB&B£34-£36
dB&B⇨♠£38-£40 WB&B£105 WBDi£140-£150 LDO noon
Lic 🛏CTV 14P nc5yrs
Ⓔ
See advertisement under SWANSEA on page 353

GH Ⓠ *Mumbles Hotel* 650 Mumbles Rd, Mumbles SA3 4EA
☎Swansea(0792) 367147
Closed 23 Dec-3 Jan
Situated overlooking the harbour and Swansea Bay, this hotel
provides bedrooms that are bright and well kept. It has a first floor
lounge with good views and a popular restaurant providing all day
refreshment in the season.
8rm(4♠4hc)(1fb) CTV in all bedrooms ® ✖ LDO 9pm
Lic 🛏CTV ⏲ nc3 yrs
Credit Cards ①③

GH Ⓠ**Ⓠ**Ⓠ *The Shoreline Hotel* 648 Mumbles Road,
Southend SA3 4EA ☎Swansea(0792) 366322
This pretty guesthouse is situated opposite the harbour and has
good views of the bay. It provides modern and well-equipped
bedrooms, an attractive restaurant, and an open plan lounge and
bar.
14rm(5♠9hc)(3fb) CTV in all bedrooms ® ✖ LDO 6pm
Lic 🛏CTV ⏲ nc3yrs

MUNGRISDALE Cumbria Map **11** NY33

FH Ⓠ**Ⓠ**Ⓠ Mr G Weightman **Near Howe** *(NY286373)*
CA11 0SH (1.5m from the A66) ☎Threlkeld(059683) 678
Mar-Nov
This delightful farmhouse is set in beautiful countryside and
moorland. The house is very well appointed and a good standard of
food is provided.
7rm(5♠2hc)(3fb) ® ✖ ✳ sB&B£11.50-£14.50 dB&B£23
dB&B♠£29 WB&Bfr£119.50 WBDifr£140.50 LDO 5pm
Lic 🛏CTV 10P snooker 350 acres beef sheep
Ⓔ

FH Ⓠ Mrs J M Tiffin **Wham Head** *(NY373342)* Hutton-Roof
CA11 0XS ☎Skelton(08534) 289
Mar-Oct
Situated in a rural location, north of the village of Hutton Roof,
this farmhouse provides friendly service and simple
accommodation.
4rm(3hc)(2fb) ® ✳ sB&Bfr£10
dB&Bfr£20 WB&Bfr£70 WBDifr£105 LDO 4pm
CTV 8P 130 acres dairy mixed sheep
Ⓔ

INN Ⓠ**Ⓠ** **The Mill** CA11 0XR ☎Threlkeld(059683) 632 due to
change to (07687) 79632
This peaceful, 16th-century inn is on the banks of the River
Glendermakin. Full of character, the bar, with its lovely central
open fire, serves popular snacks cooked by Christine Seal, who also
provides the equally popular residents' meals.
7rm(2⇨1♠4hc) ® ✳ sB&B£15.50-£16.50 dB&B£31-£33
dB&B♠£37-£39 Bar Lunch 90p-£5.50 Dinner £9.75 LDO
8.30pm
🛏CTV 30P pool table
Credit Cards ③

NAILSWORTH Gloucestershire Map **03** ST89

GH Ⓠ**Ⓠ**Ⓠ **Apple Orchard House** Orchard Close, Springhill
GL6 0LX ☎(045383) 2503
Situated close to the town centre, this house offers very comfortable
and well- equipped bedrooms, all with en suite or private facilties,
and bright, attractive public areas that include an inviting garden.
3⇨♠ (1fb) CTV in all bedrooms ® ✳
sB&B⇨♠£15.50-£17.50
dB&B⇨♠£25-£29 WB&B£91-£98 WBDi£140-£147 LDO
10am
🛏3P
Ⓔ

NAIRN Highland *Nairnshire* Map **14** NH85

⊢⊷**GH** Ⓠ**Ⓠ** **Ardgour Hotel** Seafield St IV12 4HN
☎(0667) 54230
Mar-Oct
Not far from the seafront, this detached Victorian house has a
pleasant atmosphere and offers simple accommodation which is
good value for money.
10hc (2fb) ® sB&B£13
dB&B£22 WB&B£74 WBDi£107 LDO 5pm
🛏CTV 8P

GH QQQ **Greenlawns** 13 Seafield St IV12 4HG
☎(0667) 52738
This friendly guesthouse is close to the beaches and recreational facilities. It offers good value holiday accommodation with a comfortable, quiet lounge and an interesting gallery featuring local artists' work – including that of Isobel Caldwell, wife of the proprietor.
6rm(2⇨5♠4hc) CTV in all bedrooms ® ✱ sB&B£15-£19 dB&B£28-£30 dB&B⇨♠£34-£36
瞾 CTV 8P
Credit Cards ①£

NANNERCH Clwyd Map **07** SJ16

GH QQQ **Old Mill Guest Lodge** Melin-Y-Wern, Denbigh Rd CH7 5RH ☎Mold(0352) 741542
A tastefully restored stable block forms part of a mill complex. The bedrooms are equipped to a very high standard, the grounds include a pool and a mill stream, and nearby local hostelries are available for evening meals.
7rm(4⇨3♠)(3fb)⊬in all bedrooms CTV in all bedrooms ® ✱ sB&B⇨♠£19.75-£26.25 dB&B⇨♠£33 LDO 9am
瞾 12P
Credit Cards ①②③£

NANTGAREDIG Dyfed Map **02** SN42

FH QQQ Mrs J Willmott **Cwmtwrch Farm Hotel & Four Seasons Restaurant** *(SN497220)* SA32 7NY ☎(0267) 290238
Early 19th-century Welsh stone farmhouse, carefully modernised and furnished.
6rm(3⇨3♠)(2fb) CTV in 3 bedrooms ® sB&B⇨♠£28-£32 dB&B⇨♠£36-£40 WB&B£130-£200 WBDif£210-£280 LDO 9pm
Lic 瞾 CTV 20P 30 acres mixed
£

NANTWICH Cheshire Map **07** SJ65

FH QQQ Mrs S Allwood *Burland (SJ604534)* Wrexham Rd, Burland CW5 8ND (3m W A534) ☎Faddiley(027074) 210
Three miles west of the town on the A534 Wrexham Road, this attractive house in its mature grounds, has been in the proprietor's family since it was built 200 years' ago.
3rm(1⇨2♠) CTV in all bedrooms ® LDO 7pm
瞾 5P 205 acres dairy arable

NARBOROUGH Norfolk Map **09** TF71

INN Q *Ship* Swaffham Rd PE32 1TE ☎(0760) 337307
Set beside the main route through Narborough and next to a fast-running stream, this attractive country inn offers good quality meals in the bar and in the simple restaurant. The warmth of the host is enhanced by log fires in the wood- pannelled and beamed lounge bar.
6⇨♠ CTV in all bedrooms
50P 3☎ ♪

NEAR SAWREY Cumbria Map **07** SD38

SELECTED

GH QQQQ **Ees Wyke Country House** LA22 0JZ
☎Hawkshead(09666) 393
Ees Wyke means 'East of the Lake', and this striking Georgian house is, indeed, east of tranquil Esthwaite Water. It stands in its own grounds overlooking the water with unrivalled views of the nearby fells and distant Langdale Pike. Bedrooms are spacious, comfortable and individually furnished, and all look out onto the surrounding countryside. Five-course dinners are served each evening. Ees Wyke has associations with Beatrix Potter.

8⇨♠ CTV in all bedrooms ® ✖ (ex guide dogs)
sB&B⇨♠£34-£48 dB&B£34
dB&B⇨♠£48-£52 LDO 7.15pm
Lic 瞾 12P nc12yrs
See advertisement under HAWKSHEAD on page 179

SELECTED

GH QQQQ *The Garth* LA22 0JZ
☎Hawkshead(09666) 373
Feb-Nov Closed Dec & Jan
Set in its own grounds on the edge of the village, this delightful Victorian country house offers all modern comforts while retaining the charm of its period. With attractively furnished bedrooms and a charming, comfortable lounge with its log fire, The Garth is a warm, welcoming place to stay in. Dinner is home cooked using fresh produce and is eaten in the charming dining room.
7rm(2♠5hc)(1fb) CTV in 4 bedrooms ® LDO 4pm
Lic 瞾 CTV 10P nc6yrs ⚘
See advertisement under HAWKSHEAD on page 179

GH QQ **High Green Gate** LA22 0LF ☎Hawkshead(09666) 296
Mar-Oct rs Xmas & New Year
A small yet pleasant guesthouse with attractive gardens, in the heart of Beatrix Potter country.
6rm(1⇨2♠3hc)(4fb) dB&B£27.50
dB&B⇨♠£33 WB&B£96.25-£115.50 WBDif137.50-£148.50 LDO 6pm
瞾 CTV 7P
£

GH QQQ Sawrey House Country Hotel LA22 0LF
☎Hawkshead(09666) 387
Mar-Oct
Delightful house offering warm comfortable accommodation and good home cooking.
10rm(4⇆3↱3hc)(3fb) ® sB&B£17.75-£18.75 dB&B£35.50-£37.50
dB&B⇆↱£41.50-£43.50 WB&B£124-£145 WBDi£180-£200 LDO 4pm
Lic 🍽 CTV 15P

NEATH West Glamorgan Map **03** SS79

GH QQ Europa Hotel 32/34 Victoria Gardens SA11 3BH
☎(0639) 635094
Closed Xmas
Standing opposite the Victoria Gardens close to the town centre, this hotel offers bright bedrooms with modern facilities, and a relaxing lounge and bar.
12hc (2fb) CTV in all bedrooms ® ✗ (ex guide dogs) *
sB&B£15 dB&B£27 LDO 4pm
Lic 🍽 CTV 3P
Credit Cards [1] [3] (£)

NEATISHEAD Norfolk Map **09** TG32

GH QQ Regency Neatishead Post Office Stores NR12 8AD
☎Horning(0692) 630233
Mr and Mrs Wrigley offer very attractive accommodation in their 17th-century house, situated in the heart of the village. Each room is individually co-ordinated, and all are well equipped and comfortable, with en suite facilities available.
5rm(1⇆4hc)(2fb) CTV in all bedrooms ® sB&Bfr£18
dB&Bfr£28 dB&B⇆fr£37
CTV 6P
(£)

NEEDHAM MARKET Suffolk Map **05** TM05

SELECTED

GH QQQQ Pipps Ford Norwich Rd Rdbt IP6 8LJ (entrance off rdbt junct A45/A140)
☎Coddenham(044979) 208
Closed Xmas & New Year
This beautiful Tudor house has vine-covered walls, with well-maintained gardens down to the river. Bedrooms (all en suite) offer a unique style of comfort and décor, with handmade soft furnishings. In summer, supper is taken in the conservatory, while in winter, it is taken by the huge timbered recessed fireplace.
3⇆↱ Annexe 4⇆↱ 🚭in all bedrooms ®
✗ (ex guide dogs) * sB&B£15 sB&B⇆↱£25-£30
dB&B⇆↱£40-£50 LDO noon
Lic 🍽 CTV 12P nc5yrs ≋ 🎾(hard) 🎣

NESSCLIFF Shropshire Map **07** SJ31

INN Q *Nesscliff Hotel* SY4 1DB ☎(074381) 253
Standing on the A5 a few miles north west of Shrewsbury, this inn has pleasant, bright bedrooms which are simply furnished. The local atmosphere can be sampled in the bars together with a good range of bar meals.
5hc (2fb) ® LDO 10pm
CTV 30P 2🚗

This is one of many guidebooks pubished by the AA. The full range is available at any AA Centre or good bookshop.

NETLEY Hampshire Map **04** SU40

GH QQ La Casa Blanca SO3 5DQ
☎Southampton(0703) 453718
Closed Xmas & New Year
Three miles from the centre of Southampton, this friendly guesthouse has cosy accommodation with pretty, well-equipped bedrooms. It provides bed and breakfast only.
10rm(1↱9hc)(1fb) CTV in all bedrooms ® ✗ (ex guide dogs)
LDO 9.30pm
Lic 🍽 CTV 2P
(£)

NETTLECOMBE Dorset Map **03** SY59

INN QQ The Marquis of Lorne DT6 3SY
☎Powerstock(030885) 236
Closed Xmas Day
6rm(4↱2hc)(2fb) CTV in 1 bedroom ® ✗ (ex guide dogs) *
sB&B£19-£21 sB&B↱£20-£23 dB&B£38-£42
dB&B↱£40-£46 WB&B£112-£140 WBDi£157.50-£196 Lunch £8.95-£10.50&alc Dinner £8-£11&alc LDO 9.30pm
CTV 65P
(£)

NEWARK-ON-TRENT Nottinghamshire

See **Kirton and Laxton**

NEWBOLD ON STOUR Warwickshire Map **04** SP24

FH QQ Mrs J M Everett **Newbold Nurseries** *(SP253455)*
CV37 8DP ☎Alderminster(078987) 285 due to change to (0789) 450285
Mar-29 Oct
Modern farmhouse with large rooms and a quiet situation.
2rm(1hc)(1fb) CTV in all bedrooms ® dB&Bfr£25
🍽 CTV 2P 25 acres arable tomato nursery
(£)

NEWBY BRIDGE Cumbria Map **07** SD38

GH QQ Furness Fells LA12 8ND ☎(05395) 31260
Mar-Oct
Attractive house with annexe overlooking large well-tended garden.
4hc Annexe 2↱ ® ✗ dB&B£24-£28 dB&B↱£31-£35
Lic 🍽 CTV 8P nc3yrs
(£)

NEWCASTLE UPON TYNE Tyne & Wear Map **12** NZ26

GH QQQ Chirton House Hotel 46 Clifton Rd NE4 6XH
☎091-273 0407
This relaxing country house style hotel is in a quiet area of the city not far from the hospital and the A69. Comfortable, well-appointed bedrooms are complemented by equally comfortable lounges and a cosy cocktail bar.
11rm(2⇆3↱6hc)(3fb) CTV in all bedrooms ® sB&B£21-£23
sB&B⇆↱fr£32 dB&Bfr£36
dB&B⇆↱fr£44 WB&B£115-£135 WBDi£165-£200 LDO 5.30pm
Lic 🍽 CTV 12P
Credit Cards [1] [3] (£)

GH Q Clifton Cottage Dunholme Rd NE4 6XE ☎091-273 7347
Simple but comfortable accommodation and helpful proprietors.
6hc (2fb) CTV in all bedrooms ® sB&B£15 dB&B£26
🍽 CTV 6P
(£)

NEWDIGATE Surrey Map **04** TQ14

GH Ⓠ **Woods Hill Country** Village St RH5 5AD ☎(030677) 437
Compact, functional accommodation is offered here with a choice
of modern bedrooms and a breakfast room. Light refreshments are
served throughout the day, and car parking facilities can be
arranged.
4rm(1⇋1♠2hc)(2fb)✻in all bedrooms CTV in all bedrooms
Ⓡ ✖ ✳ dB&B£35 dB&B⇋♠£40
⑩ CTV 10P
Credit Cards ①③

NEWLYN EAST Cornwall & Isles of Scilly Map **02** SW85

FH ⓆⓆⓆ Mrs K Woodley *Degembris (SW852568)* TR8 5HY
☎Mitchell(0872) 510555
Etr-Oct
This 17th-century slate hung farmhouse has open country views.
Mrs Woodley uses home-grown vegetables in her traditional
farmhouse fare, and guests can enjoy the 'country trail' through a
beautiful wooded valley. The establishment is 'A Cream of
Cornwall' member.
5hc (2fb) CTV in 1 bedroom Ⓡ ✖ LDO 10am
CTV 8P 165 acres arable

NEWMARKET Suffolk

See **Kirtling**

NEWPORT Gwent Map **03** ST38

GH ⓆⓆ **Caerleon House Hotel** Caerau Rd NP9 4HJ
☎(0633) 264869
Run by the friendly Powell family this well-maintained guesthouse
is situated in a residential part of the town, close to the main
centre. The bedrooms have all recently been refurbished and
provide modern facilities.
8hc (1fb) CTV in all bedrooms Ⓡ sB&B£18-£22
dB&B£28-£32 LDO 9pm
Lic ⑩ 8P
£

GH ⓆⓆⓆ **Kepe Lodge** 46a Caerau Rd NP9 4HH
☎(0633) 262351
Closed 22-31 Dec
Set back from the road with a tree-lined private drive, this trim and
neat house is comfortably appointed. With cheerful and friendly
owners, it is ideally situated for the tourist and business person
alike.
8rm(1♠7hc) CTV in all bedrooms Ⓡ ✖ (ex guide dogs) ✳
sB&B£15 dB&Bfr£26 dB&B♠fr£30 WB&Bfr£105
⑩ 8P
£

See advertisement on page 273

GH ⓆⓆ *Knoll* 145 Stow Hill NP9 4FZ ☎(0633) 263557
Situated near the main shopping centre on Stow Hill, this large
Victorian house retains many of its original features. It offers
comfortable and well-equipped bedrooms and a spacious, relaxing
guest lounge.
7rm(4♠3hc)(1fb) CTV in all bedrooms Ⓡ
⑩ 6🛏

NEWPORT PAGNELL Buckinghamshire Map **04** SP84

GH ⓆⓆⓆ **Thurstons Private Hotel** 90 High St MK16 8EH
☎(0908) 611377
Originally a family house, this small hotel has been converted to
provide comfortable and bright accommodation. The bustle and
charm of a traditional English market town still remain in Newport
Pagnell.
8rm(2⇋6♠) CTV in all bedrooms Ⓡ ✖ (ex guide dogs) ✳
sB&B⇋♠£25-£38 dB&B⇋♠£35-£48
Lic ⑩ 14P
Credit Cards ①③

NEWQUAY Cornwall & Isles of Scilly Map **02** SW86

See **Town Plan Section**

See also **Newlyn East**

GH Q Arundell Hotel Mount Wise TR7 2BS ☎(0637) 872481

Large seasonal family hotel, comfortable and recently renovated.

36⇌🏠 (8fb) CTV in all bedrooms ® sB&B⇌🏠£15.50-£29
dB&B⇌🏠£31-£58 WB&B£93-£165 WBDi£113-£185 LDO
6pm
Lic lift 🍴 CTV 32P 8🚗 ⬛(heated) snooker sauna solarium
gymnasium
Credit Cards 1 2 3

GH QQQ Copper Beech Hotel 70 Edgcumbe Av TR7 2NN
☎(0637) 873376

mid May-mid Oct

*Mr & Mrs Lentern have run this hotel with care for the past 16
years. Quietly situated opposite Trenance Gardens, it provides
well-appointed accommodation with bright, airy bedrooms and a
very attractive bar lounge.*

14rm(3⇌8🏠3hc)(3fb) ® ✖ sB&B⇌🏠£17.25-£18.40
dB&B£34-£36
dB&B⇌🏠£34-£36 WBDi£123-£148 (wkly only Jun-Aug) LDO
6pm
Lic 🍴 CTV 14P

GH QQ Fistral Beach Hotel Esplanade Road, Pentire
TR7 1QA ☎(0637) 873993 due to change to (0637) 850626

Mar-Nov & Xmas

*This hotel has been fully modernised and has exceptional views
over Fistral Beach. Modern, well-equipped bedrooms and a
charming dining room make this an ideal holiday retreat.*

16rm(5⇌11🏠)(2fb) CTV in all bedrooms ®
sB&B⇌🏠£28-£39
dB&B⇌🏠£42-£57 (incl dinner) WB&B£114-£154
WBDi£142-£193 LDO 7.30pm
Lic 🍴 CTV 14P nc4yrs ⬛(heated)
Credit Cards 1 2 3 £

GH QQ Hepworth Hotel 27 Edgcumbe Av TR7 2NJ
☎(0637) 873686

Apr-Oct

*Centrally situated in a quiet area, this modern family hotel offers
comfortable and well-equipped accommodation.*

13rm(4🏠9hc)(4fb) CTV in all bedrooms ® ✖ ✳
WB&B£87.50-£101.50 WBDi£113-£146 (wkly only Jul & Aug)
LDO 6.30pm
Lic 🍴 CTV 12P
£

GH QQ Jonel 88-90 Crantock St TR7 1JW ☎(0637) 875084

*Within easy reach of the town centre and beaches, this family-run
property has bright bedrooms, a cosy bar and lounge and an
informal dining room which offers a table d'hôte menu.*

12hc (1fb) CTV in 11 bedrooms TV in 1 bedroom ® ✖ LDO
4.30pm
Lic CTV 7P

GH QQ Kellsboro Hotel 12 Henver Rd TR7 3BJ
☎(0637) 874620

Etr-Oct

Well-appointed family hotel, close to beaches.

14rm(10⇌3🏠1hc)(8fb)⤢in all bedrooms CTV in all bedrooms
® LDO 7pm
Lic 🍴 20P ⬛(heated)

GH QQ Links Hotel Headland Rd TR7 1HN ☎(0637) 873211

Apr-Oct

*Standing on the Towan Headland, withing easy reach of the town,
beaches and golf course, this hotel has simply furnished bedrooms,
some with en suite facilities. All have colour TV and there is a
lively bar and pool room.*

15rm(10⇌3🏠2hc)(3fb) CTV in all bedrooms ® (July & Aug)
LDO 4pm
Lic 🍴 CTV 🅿

GH QQQ Pendeen Hotel Alexandra Road, Porth TR7 3ND
☎(0637) 873521

Etr-Nov

*A modern private hotel only 200 yards from Porth Beach. Rooms
are pleasant, and equipped with metered TV.*

15rm(6⇌9🏠)(5fb)⤢in 3 bedrooms CTV in all bedrooms ® ✖
sB&B⇌🏠£17.25-£20
dB&B⇌🏠£28-£35 WB&B£70-£120 WBDi£112-£162 LDO
6pm
Lic 🍴 CTV 15P
Credit Cards 2 £

GH QQQ Porth Enodoc 4 Esplanade Road, Pentire TR7 1PY
☎(0637) 872372

Etr-Oct

*This elegant property stands in gardens overlooking Fistral Beach.
16 attractive en suite bedrooms are complemented by a quiet
lounge and cosy bar, and set meals are served every evening in the
relaxed atmosphere of the dining room.*

14🏠 Annexe 2rm(1⇌1🏠)(4fb) TV available ✖
sB&B⇌🏠£15.75-£18
dB&B⇌🏠£31.50-£36 WB&B£99.50-£126.50
WBDi£109.50-£149.50 (wkly only Jun-Sep) LDO 5.30pm
Lic 🍴 CTV 16P
£

GH QQQQ Priory Lodge Hotel Mount Wise TR7 2BH
☎(0637) 874111

Closed Jan-Feb

*Overlooking the town and the distant sea, this popular family-
run hotel has a friendly atmosphere. The bedrooms are
decorated and furnished to a high standard, all with direct
dial telephones and most with attractive en suite bath/shower
rooms. There are attractive surroundings in which to relax,
have a drink, enjoy the entertainment or to select a dish from
the table d'hôte menu. The outdoor heated pool and patio area
are popular with families.*

22rm(7⇌13🏠2hc)Annexe 4🏠 (17fb) CTV in all
bedrooms ® sB&B£29-£35 sB&B⇌🏠£33-£38
dB&B£58-£70
dB&B⇌🏠£66-£76 (incl dinner) WB&B£115-£170
WBDi£165-£210 LDO 7.30pm
Lic 🍴 CTV 30P ⚽ ⬛(heated) sauna solarium pool table
video machines
£

GH QQ Rolling Waves Alexandra Rd, Porth TR7 3NB
☎(0637) 873236

Etr-Oct Closed 2 days Xmas rs Nov-Dec

*Overlooking Porth Beach and the putting green, this bungalow
style house has comfortable accommodation and a convivial
atmosphere.*

10rm(6🏠4hc)(3fb) CTV in 4 bedrooms ® ✖ (ex guide dogs)
sB&B£17.08-£23.57 dB&B£39.86-£55
dB&B⇌🏠£43.20-£58.33 (incl dinner) WB&B£100-£145
WBDi£119.60-£165 (wkly only Jul & Aug) LDO 6.30pm
Lic CTV 10P
Credit Cards 1 3

GH QQQ Tir Chonaill Lodge 106 Mount Wise TR7 1QP
☎(0637) 876492

*This modern terraced hotel is close to the town centre and beaches
and offers bright bedrooms with en suite facilities and a relaxed
atmosphere in the public rooms and bar. Mr and Mrs Watts
provide friendly, personal serice.*

20rm(8⇄12♠)(9fb) CTV in all bedrooms ®
sB&B⇄♠£14.75-£16.75
dB&B⇄♠£27.50-£34 WB&B£82.50-£19 WBDi£95.50-£135
(wkly only end Jun-begining Sep) LDO 5pm
Lic ﾜ CTV 20P darts
£

GH **QQQ** **Wheal Treasure Hotel** 72 Edgcumbe Av TR7 2NN
☎(0637) 874136
May-mid Oct
*About 10 minutes' walk from the seafront, this detached house set
in its small garden offers comfortable bedrooms, and imaginative
food is served.*
12rm(3⇄8♠1hc)(3fb) ® ✖ ✱ WBDi£125-£150 (wkly only
Jun–Aug) LDO 5pm
Lic ﾜ CTV 10P nc5yrs

GH **QQQ** **Windward Hotel** Alexandra Road, Porth TR7 3NB
☎(0637) 873185
Etr-Oct & Xmas
*This small bungalow stands in an elevated position and enjoys
views of the distant coastline. Porth Beach is a short walk away.
The charming, outgoing owners provide compact, well-equipped
bedrooms.*
7rm(1⇄1♠5hc)(3fb) CTV in all bedrooms ®
✖ (ex guide dogs) sB&B⇄♠fr£15
dB&B⇄♠fr£30 WB&Bfr£100 WBDifr£123 (wkly only Jul-
Sep)
Lic ﾜ CTV 14P
£

⊢•⊣**FH** **QQQ** J C Wilson **Manuels** *(SW839601)* Lane
TR8 4NY ☎(0637) 873577
Closed 23 Dec-1 Jan ▶

This delightful 17th-century listed farmhouse stands in a wooded valley 2 miles from Newquay. Alan and Jean Wilson provide ample home-cooked meals using home-grown produce, and can provide packed lunches.
3hc (2fb)🚭in all bedrooms 🐕 (ex guide dogs) sB&B£11-£14 dB&B£22-£28 WB&B£77-£98 WBDi£120-£145 (wkly only Spring BH-Aug BH) LDO 4pm
CTV 6P 🏡 44 acres mixed
[£]

NEW QUAY Dyfed Map **02** SN35

SELECTED

GH [Q][Q][Q][Q] Park Hall Hotel Cwmtydu SA44 6LG ☎(0545) 560306
Superbly situated in the picturesque, wooded valley of Cwmtydu, with lovely views of the sea and countryside, this Victorian house has been carefully restored to provide excellent accommodation.
5🛁🚿 🚭in 1 bedroom CTV in all bedrooms [R] * dB&B🛁🚿£30-£35 (incl dinner) WB&B£120-£155 WBDi£210-£245 LDO 7.30pm
Lic ♨ CTV 20P
Credit Cards [1] [2] [3] [5] [£]

FH [Q][Q] Mr & Mrs White ***Nanternis*** *(SN374567)* Nanternis SA45 9RP (2m SW off A486) ☎(0545) 560181
Etr-Sep
Farmhouse of great character tucked away in a snug little village. Organic garden produce.
2hc (1fb)🚭in all bedrooms [R] 🐕 (wkly only mid Jul-Aug) LDO evening prior
♨ CTV 4P 8 acres sheep goats

FH [Q][Q][Q] Mr M Kelly **Ty Hen** *(SN365553)* Llwyndafydd SA44 6BZ (S of Cross Inn, A486) ☎(0545) 560346
This period farmhouse enjoys a quiet location. Accommodation is comfortable with en suite bedrooms. Good food, imaginatively prepared. Non-smoking establishment.
5🚿 Annexe 2🚿 (2fb)🚭in 5 bedrooms CTV in all bedrooms [R] * dB&B🚿£42-£56 WB&B£138-£184 WBDi£194-£240
Lic ♨ CTV 20P 🏊(heated) sauna solarium gymnasium bowls & skittles 40 acres sheep
Credit Cards [1] [3] [£]

NEW ROMNEY Kent Map **05** TR02

GH [Q][Q] ***Blue Dolphins Hotel & Restaurant*** Dymchurch Rd TN28 8BE ☎(0679) 63224
This pleasant roadside hotel has character and charm and its busy restaurant offers a choice of well-prepared dishes. Some of its bedrooms are in the older section of the building.
8rm(2🛁4🚿2hc)(1fb) CTV in 9 bedrooms [R] 🐕 (ex guide dogs) LDO 9.30pm
Lic ♨ CTV 15P
Credit Cards [1] [3]

NEWTON (nr Vowchurch) Hereford & Worcester Map **03** SO33

FH [Q][Q] Mrs J C Powell **Little Green** *(SO335337)* HR2 0QJ ☎Michaelchurch(098123) 205
Closed Xmas
Modernised farmhouse, once an inn, with friendly atmosphere.
3hc (2fb) dB&B£20 WB&B£70 WBDi£112
CTV 5P 50 acres beef sheep
[£]

NEWTON Northumberland Map **12** NZ06

FH [Q] Mrs C M Leech **Crookhill** *(NZ056654)* NE43 7UX ☎Stocksfield(0661) 843117
rs Nov-Mar
This comfortable stone-built farmhouse is set in an elevated situation, overlooking open countryside. It is conveniently sited, very close to the A69.
3rm(1hc)(1fb)🚭in all bedrooms [R] 🐕 * sB&B£12.50-£15 dB&B£25-£30 WB&Bfr£73.50
♨ CTV 4P 23 acres beef mixed sheep
[£]

NEWTON ABBOT Devon Map **03** SX87

GH [Q][Q] Lamorna Ideford Combe TQ13 0AR (3m N A380) ☎(0626) 65627
Conveniently situated adjacent to the A380 just outside Newton Abbot, this cosy modern guesthouse has pleasant views. Compact, well-equipped bedrooms are available here together with pleasant gardens.
7hc (1fb) CTV in 2 bedrooms TV in 5 bedrooms [R] 🐕 (ex guide dogs) sB&B£17-£19 dB&B£28-£30 WB&B£98-£105 LDO 6pm
Lic ♨ CTV 15P 1🚗 🏊(heated)

NEWTON STEWART Dumfries & Galloway *Wigtownshire* Map **10** NX46

GH [Q] ***Corsbie Villa*** Corsbie Rd DG8 6JB ☎(0671) 2124
This well-maintained guesthouse is situated in a residential area of the town, and has neat, compact bedrooms, a spacious lounge and a small bar. Home-cooked meals are served in the open plan dining room.
9hc (1fb)🚭in all bedrooms CTV in all bedrooms LDO 6pm
CTV 16P 🏡
Credit Cards [1]

GH [Q] Duncree House Hotel Girvan Rd DG8 6DP ☎(0671) 2001
This former house of the Earls of Galloway enjoys a secluded situation off the A714 on the town's north west outskirts. Popular with fishing and shooting parties, Duncree House offers simple accommodation and inexpensive meals.
6hc (5fb)🚭in 4 bedrooms CTV in 2 bedrooms [R] sB&B£16-£22 dB&B£32-£44 WB&B£106-£146 LDO 8.30pm
Lic CTV 25P nc3yrs
[£]

FH [Q][Q][Q] Mrs M Hewitson **Auchenleck** *(NX450709)* Minnigaff DG8 7AA ☎(0671) 2035
Etr-Oct
This turreted farm enjoys an isolated position within Glentrool National Park – ideal for naturalists and walkers. There are spacious, comfortable bedrooms and meals made from organically grown produce are taken around the large dining table.
3hc 🚭in all bedrooms [R] 🐕 dB&B£21-£23 WB&B£73.50
♨ CTV 6P 103 acres stock rearing sheep cattle

NEWTOWN Powys Map **06** SO19

FH [Q][Q][Q] L M & G T Whitticase ***Highgate*** *(SO111953)* SY16 3LF ☎(0686) 625981
Mar-Oct
15th-century, black and white-timbered farmhouse, in elevated position with commanding views over valley and hills. Rough shooting, fishing and ponies available.
3🚿 [R] 🐕 LDO 4.30pm
Lic ♨ CTV 0P 🎣 🐎 shooting 250 acres mixed sheep

[£] Remember to use the money-off vouchers.

NINFIELD East Sussex Map **05** TQ71

FH Q Q Q Mr & Mrs J B Ive **Moons Hill** *(TQ704120)* The Green TN33 9LH ☎(0424) 892645
Closed Dec
Extensive services are provided by the proprietors of this smallholding. The well-equipped bedrooms have generous bath and shower facilities and there is a pleasant lounge. Situated off Manchester Road, Moons Hill Farm has an excellent car park.
4rm(3⇌1hc)(1fb) CTV in 2 bedrooms TV in 2 bedrooms ® ✱
sB&B£14-£16 dB&B£28 dB&B⇌£32-£34
Ⓜ CTV 10P 2☎ ∪ 10 acres mixed smallholding
£

NITON

See **WIGHT, ISLE OF**

NORTHALLERTON North Yorkshire Map **08** SE39

GH Q Q Q *Porch House* 68 High St DL7 8EG ☎(0609) 779831
Peter and Shirley Thompson have sympathetically converted this 16th-century listed building to provide cosy accommodation with well-equipped en suite bedrooms. Wholesome meals are served around a communal table. Service is very informal and friendly.
5⁴ CTV in all bedrooms ®
Lic Ⓜ CTV 8P
Credit Cards [1] [3]

GH Q Q **Windsor** 56 South Pde DL7 8SL ☎(0609) 774100
Closed 24 Dec-2 Jan
A friendly, family-run hotel offering well-kept bedrooms with a comfortable lounge and dining room.
6hc (3fb) CTV in all bedrooms ® sB&B£17 dB&B£27
dB&B£35 LDO 3pm
Ⓜ CTV

NORTHAMPTON Northamptonshire Map **04** SP76

GH Q Q Q **Poplars Hotel** Cross Street, Moulton NN3 1RZ ☎(0604) 643983
Closed Xmas wk
21rm(2⇌13⁴6hc)(4fb) CTV in all bedrooms ® sB&B£15-£25
sB&B⇌⁴£20-£30 dB&B⇌⁴£40-£47.50 LDO 6pm
Lic Ⓜ CTV 22P
Credit Cards [1] [3] £

INN Q Q Q *The Fish* Fish St NN1 2AA (Berni/Chef & Brewer) ☎(0604) 234040
This city-centre pub, a popular lunchtime meeting place, serves good quality pub meals and restaurant grills. The rooms are well furnished and equipped, and there is a friendly team of staff.
12rm(1⇌1⁴10hc) CTV in all bedrooms ® ✗ LDO 10pm
✗
Credit Cards [1] [2] [3] [5]

NORTH BERWICK Lothian *East Lothian* Map **12** NT58

GH Q **Cragside** 16 Marine Pde EH39 4LD ☎(0620) 2879
Apr-Oct
Guests at this seafront guesthouse are sure to receive friendly service.
4hc ® ✗ sB&Bfr£14.50 dB&Bfr£29 WB&Bfr£94.50
Ⓜ CTV ✗
£

NORTH DUFFIELD North Yorkshire Map **08** SE63

FH Q Q Mrs A Arrand *Hall (SE692375)* YO8 7RY ☎Selby(0757) 288301
Etr-Sep
This charming and friendly working farm offers guests spacious and comfortable accommodation. It lies 12 miles south of historic York and a quarter of a mile north east of the village.
▶

3hc (2fb)🚭in all bedrooms 🐕
🍴 CTV 0P 170 acres arable sheep

NORTH NIBLEY Gloucestershire Map **03** ST79

GH [Q][Q][Q] Burrows Court Hotel Nibley Green, Dursley GL11 6AZ ☎Dursley(0453) 546230
Situated half a mile from the village centre, this former mill has been carefully modernised to provide a small hotel with modern facilities, whilst retaining many original features. Every bedroom is en suite, and the spacious public areas are comfortable.
8rm(6🛁2🚿) CTV in all bedrooms [R] 🐕 ✱ sB&B🛁🚿£26-£34 dB&B🛁🚿£36-£43 WBDi£189-£215 LDO 8pm
Lic 🍴 12P nc5yrs 🏊
Credit Cards [1] [2] [3]

NORTHOWRAM West Yorkshire Map **07** SE12

⊢⊣**FH [Q][Q]** Mrs P W Longbottom **Royd** *(SE107268)* Hall Ln HX3 7SN ☎Halifax(0422) 206718
Etr-Oct rs Oct-Mar
This simple farmhouse is found in a quiet lane close to the village, and is personally run by the resident owner. This establishment specialises in horse riding holidays.
2rm Annexe 2rm (3fb) TV in 1 bedroom [R] sB&B£10 dB&B£20 WB&B£65 WBDi£95 LDO noon
CTV 5P 🐎 22 acres Arab horse stud beef poultry
[£]

NORTH WALSHAM Norfolk Map **09** TG23

GH [Q][Q] Beechwood Private Hotel 20 Cromer Rd NR28 0HD ☎(0692) 403231
Closed 24 Dec-7 Jan
Well kept, attractive gardens surround this quiet guesthouse, which is located in a residential area close to the town centre. The rooms are generally spacious, many having their own bathrooms, and there are 2 lounges, one with a television.
11rm(3🛁4🚿4hc)(5fb) [R] sB&B£19 sB&B🛁🚿£22 dB&B£38 dB&B🛁🚿£44 WB&B£133 WBDi£150-£200 LDO 7pm
Lic 🍴 CTV 12P nc5yrs games room
[£]

NORTH WOOTTON Somerset Map **03** ST54

FH [Q][Q][Q] Mrs M White **Barrow** *(ST553416)* ☎Pilton(074989) 245
Feb-Nov
15th-century stone-built farmhouse on edge of village, situated between Wells, Glastonbury and Shepton Mallet.
3hc (1fb) [R] 🐕 ✱ sB&B£13-£15 dB&B£24-£28 WB&B£70-£85 WBDi£100-£140 LDO 9am
CTV 4P 150 acres working dairy
[£]

NORWICH Norfolk Map **05** TG20

GH [Q][Q][Q] Grange Hotel 230 Thorpe Rd NR1 1TJ ☎(0603) 34734
Closed Xmas wk
There is ample car parking space at this busy commercial establishment, which is on the main road.
36rm(4🛁32🚿)(1fb) CTV in all bedrooms [R] 🐕 ✱ sB&B🛁🚿£28-£34 dB&B🛁🚿£49 LDO 9.45pm
Lic 🍴 CTV 40P sauna solarium pool room
Credit Cards [1] [2] [3] [5] [£]

GH [Q][Q] Marlborough House Hotel 22 Stracey Road, Thorpe Rd NR1 1EZ ☎(0603) 628005
Situated close to the railway station and within easy walking distance from the town centre this guesthouse offers cheerful accommodation and although some rooms are a little compact they are well equipped and modestly furnished.
12🛁🚿 (2fb) CTV in all bedrooms [R] sB&B£15-£25 sB&B🛁🚿£15-£25 dB&B🛁🚿£35-£44 WB&B£110-£180 WBDi£154-£217 LDO 4.30pm
Lic 🍴 CTV 6P 2🚗

NOTTINGHAM Nottinghamshire Map **08** SK54

GH [Q][Q][Q] Balmoral Hotel 55-57 Loughborough, West Bridgford NG2 7LA ☎(0602) 455020 FAX (0602) 455683
Closed Xmas
This busy, family-run commercial hotel is situated on the outskirts of Nottingham, very near to the Nottingham Forest football ground, and to Trent Bridge cricket ground. The bedrooms are well equipped and there is a small conference room available.
33rm(2🛁23🚿8hc)(1fb) CTV in all bedrooms [R] 🐕 (ex guide dogs) ✱ sB&B£22-£26.50 sB&B🛁🚿£26.50-£34.50 dB&B🛁🚿£44-£53 LDO 7.45pm
Lic 🍴 CTV 35P three quarter size snooker table
Credit Cards [1] [3] [£]

GH [Q] Crantock Hotel 480 Mansfield Rd NG5 2EL ☎(0602) 623294
Conveniently set on the A60, 1.5 miles north of the city centre, this large detached house provides simple and comfortable accommodation, suitable for both tourists and commercial guests.
10rm(1🛁🚿9hc)(5fb)🚭in all bedrooms CTV in all bedrooms [R] ✱ sB&B£20-£35 sB&B🛁🚿£29-£35 dB&B£30-£38 dB&B🛁🚿£34-£45 WB&B£120-£175 WBDi£170-£225 LDO 9pm
Lic 🍴 70P pool table

GH [Q] Grantham Commercial Hotel 24-26 Radcliffe Rd, West Bridgford NG2 5FW ☎(0602) 811373
Simple and businesslike accommodation close to Trent Bridge.
24hc (2fb) CTV in all bedrooms ✱ sB&B£18-£20 dB&B£26-£30 WB&B£108-£120
🍴 CTV 8P 2🚗 nc3yrs
Credit Cards [1] [3] [£]

GH [Q][Q] Park Hotel 7 Waverley St NG7 4HF ☎(0602) 786299 & 420010
This period house is set close to the city centre, overlooking a park. Only street parking is available. The bedrooms are well equipped and the annexe rooms all have en suite facilities.
27rm(11🛁🚿16hc)(2fb) CTV in all bedrooms [R] 🐕 (ex guide dogs) LDO 9.30pm
Lic 🍴 CTV
Credit Cards [1] [2] [3] [£]

GH [Q] P & J Hotel 277-279 Derby Rd, Lenton NG7 2DP ☎(0602) 783996
Closed Xmas
Situated on one of the main roads into the town, this Victorian guesthouse caters mainly for bed and breakfast with bar snacks available in the evening.
20rm(6🚿14hc)(8fb) CTV in all bedrooms [R] ✱ sB&Bfr£20 sB&B🚿fr£30 dB&Bfr£35 dB&B🚿£40-£45 LDO 9.30pm
Lic 🍴 CTV 12P
Credit Cards [1] [3] [5]

GH [Q][Q][Q] Royston Hotel 326 Mansfield Rd NG6 2EF ☎(0602) 622947
The proprietor's care and attention is reflected in the comfortable, attractive accommodation of this detached Victorian house, some of the bedrooms having en suite facilities. The Royston is distinctive, with its ornate shutters and hanging baskets and has a terraced garden and off-street parking.
8rm(6🚿2hc)Annexe 4🚿 (2fb) CTV in all bedrooms [R] 🐕 (ex guide dogs) ✱ sB&B£28-£32 sB&B🚿£35-£36.50 dB&Bfr£40 dB&B🚿£46-£48
🍴 CTV 16P
Credit Cards [1] [2] [3] [5] [£]

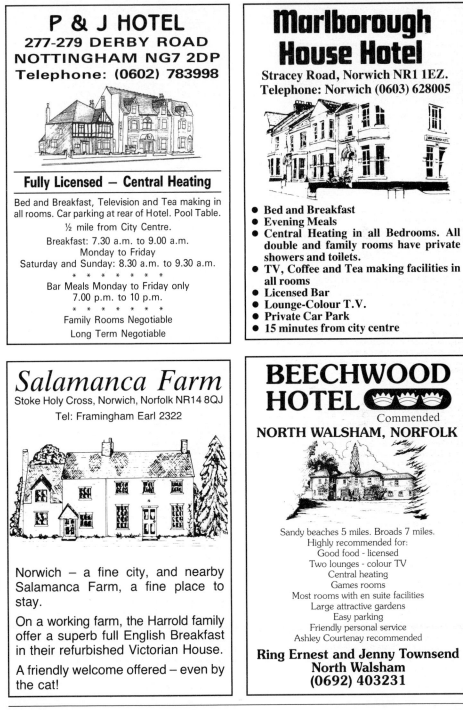
277

NUNEATON Warwickshire Map **04** SP39

GH QQQ **Drachenfels Hotel** 25 Attleborough Rd CV11 4HZ
☎(0203) 383030
Situated 10 minutes' walk from the town centre, this imposing
Edwardian house has been well modernised to provide comfortable,
well-equipped bedrooms and cosy public areas.
8rm(2👌6hc)(2fb) CTV in all bedrooms ® ✱
sB&B£18.50-£22.50 sB&B👌£21.50-£25.50 dB&B£27-£31
dB&B👌£30-£34 LDO 8pm
Lic ⬚ 8P
Credit Cards 1 3 £

NUNNEY Somerset Map **03** ST74

INN QQQ **George Inn & Restaurant** Church St BA11 4LW
☎(037384) 458 & 565
A large public house at the centre of the village, close to the castle,
provides accommodation in bedrooms of a good size which are very
well equipped with modern facilities; guests can relax in the first-
floor residents' lounge or in the cosy bar, and there is a separate
restaurant.
11rm(7👌4👌)(3fb) CTV in all bedrooms ® ✱
sB&B👌£38-£42
dB&B👌£47-£52 WB&B£160-£175 Lunch £6-£7.50&alc
High tea £3.50-£4.50 Dinner £10-£14&alc LDO 9.30pm
⬚ CTV 30P
Credit Cards 1 3 £

NUTHURST West Sussex Map **04** TQ12

FH QQQ Mrs S E Martin **Saxtons** *(TQ199274)* RH13 6LG
☎Lower Beeding(0403) 891231
Closed Xmas Day
This delightful Georgian farmhouse is situated in an unspoilt rural
area within easy reach of the coast. The generous bedrooms are
individually furnished and there is a combined lounge and dining
room. A friendly, welcoming atmosphere prevails.
4hc (1fb)✂in all bedrooms ® ✖ sB&B£20
dB&B£30 WB&B£105-£140
⬚ CTV 6P 2🐾 100 acres deer sheep goats
£

OAKAMOOR Staffordshire Map **07** SK04

FH QQQ Mrs M Wheeler **Old Furnace** *(SK043437)*
Greendale ST10 3AP ☎(0538) 702442
This extended brick house, standing in an elevated position
overlooking the Churnett Valley, has a warm, friendly atmosphere,
which is enhanced by the quality bedrooms, which are all
individually furnished. Self-catering accommodation is also
available here.
2rm(1👌1👌)(1fb) CTV in all bedrooms ✖ (ex guide dogs)
LDO 7pm
⬚ CTV 2P 2🐾 ✔ 42 acres beef sheep

INN QQ **Admiral Jervis Inn & Restaurant** Mill Rd ST10 3AG
☎(0538) 702187
Close to the river Churnett and surrounded by hilly woodland, this
fully modernised inn is conveniently situated for ALTON
TOWERS.
6👌👌 (4fb) CTV in all bedrooms ✖ sB&B👌fr£25
dB&B👌fr£39 LDO 9.30pm
⬚ 20P
Credit Cards 1 2 3 £

'Selected' establishments, which have the highest
quality award, are highlighted by a tinted panel.
For a full list of these establishments, consult the
Contents page.

OAKFORD Devon Map **03** SS92

FH QQQ Anne Boldry **Newhouse** *(SS892228)* EX16 9JE
☎(03985) 347
Closed Xmas
Set in 40 acres of peaceful valley and bordered by a trout stream,
this 17th-century farmhouse retains its character whilst providing
comfort. Homemade soups, patés, bread and preserves as well as
home-produced vegetables can be enjoyed here.
3👌 (1fb) ® ✖ sB&B👌£15-£16.50
dB&B👌£26-£29 WB&B£90 WBDi£135 LDO 4pm
⬚ CTV 3P nc10yrs ✔ 42 acres beef sheep
£

OBAN Strathclyde *Argyllshire* Map **10** NM83

⊢┉GH QQ **Ardblair** Dalriach Rd PA34 5JB ☎(0631) 62668
Apr-Sep rs Etr
This well-run family guesthouse overlooks the town and bay, and
the residents' lounge enjoys good views. The pleasant owners pay
every attention to their guests.
16rm(4👌7👌 5hc)(3fb) ® ✖ sB&B£12-£14 sB&B👌£15-£18
dB&B£24-£26
dB&B👌£30-£36 WB&B£86-£115 WBDi£120-£150 LDO
5.30pm
⬚ CTV 10P

GH QQQ **Glenburnie Private Hotel** The Esplanade PA34 5AQ
☎(0631) 62089
May-Sep
Friendly service is offered at this solid, stone-built house which
stands on the seafront overlooking the bay. Bedrooms are
comfortable and the public rooms are neatly appointed.
9👌👌 (1fb) CTV in all bedrooms ® ✖ (ex guide dogs) ✱
dB&B👌£35-£54
⬚ CTV 12P 1🏁 nc4yrs
Credit Cards 1 3

GH QQ **Roseneath** Dalriach Rd PA34 5EQ ☎(0631) 62929
Closed Xmas
Attractive sandstone house in terrace on hillside offering views
across bay to Kerrera.
10rm(2👌8hc)(1fb) CTV in 3 bedrooms ® ✖ ✱ sB&Bfr£13.50
dB&Bfr£27 dB&B👌fr£30
⬚ CTV 8P

⊢┉GH QQ **Sgeir Mhaol** Soroba Rd PA34 4JF ☎(0631) 62650
Small friendly guesthouse on the A816 just outside town centre.
7hc (3fb) ® ✖ (ex guide dogs) sB&B£12-£20
dB&B£24-£31 LDO 6pm
⬚ CTV 10P
£

GH QQQ **Wellpark Hotel** Esplanade PA34 5AQ
☎(0631) 62948
May-Oct rs Etr
Semi detached hotel built in granite and sandstone, offering good
standard of accommodation in a seafront location.
17👌 CTV in all bedrooms ® ✱ sB&B👌£22.50-£27
dB&B👌£37-£54 WB&B£233.10-£340.20
⬚ 12P nc3yrs

ODDINGTON Gloucestershire Map **04** SP22

INN QQQ **Horse & Groom** Upper Oddington GL56 0XH
☎Cotswold(0451) 30584
Closed 24-27 Dec
5rm(1👌4👌)Annexe 2hc (1fb) CTV in all bedrooms ®
✖ (ex guide dogs) ✱ sB&B👌£24.50-£28.50
dB&B👌£39-£42 LDO 9.30pm

🛆 40P
Credit Cards ①③ ⓔ

OKEHAMPTON Devon Map 02 SX59

FH Ⓠ Ⓠ Mrs K C Heard **Hughslade** *(SX561932)* EX20 4LR
☎(0837) 52883
Closed Xmas
This Devonshire farmhouse has commanding views of Dartmoor yet is conveniently close to the A30. The service here is friendly, and there is the additional feature of a full size snooker table in the games room.
5hc (3fb) ® sB&B£14-£15
dB&B£24-£30 WB&B£80-£85 WBDi£95-£110 LDO 6pm
CTV 10P Ʊ snooker games room horse riding 600 acres beef & sheep
ⓔ

See advertisement on page 281

OKEOVER Staffordshire Map 07 SK14

FH Ⓠ Ⓠ Mrs E J Harrison **Little Park** *(SK160490)* DE6 2BR
☎Thorpe Cloud(033529) 341
Apr-Oct
The long drive from the lane to this stone and brick built house nestling in the Dove Valley is rewarded by a warm welcome. Self-catering accommodation is also available in a cottage at Kniveton.
3hc ⊁in all bedrooms ✠ sB&B£14 dB&B£20-£24 LDO 10am
🛆 CTV 3P nc12yrs 123 acres dairy
ⓔ

Street plans of certain towns and cities
will be found in a separate section
at the back of the book.

Connel Village, Nr. Oban, Argyll PA37 1PH
Telephone: 0631-71-400

AA SELECTED   STB ♕♕♕   LES ROUTIERS
              COMMENDED

Set in its own grounds in the tranquil village of Connel, 5 miles from Oban. This small first-class hotel, with residential licence and private parking, has recently been fully modernised. All bedrooms are tastefully decorated and furnished, most have private facilities. All bedrooms have: ● Colour TV ● Radio Alarm ● Central Heating ● Tea-making Facilities. Emphasis is placed on food, cleanliness and comfort of guests.

SPECIAL TERMS: 3 or 7 day stays DBB.

Week Farm

Bridestowe, Okehampton, Devon EX20 4HZ
Telephone: Bridestowe (083 786) 221

Homely 17th century farmhouse accommodation with its friendly atmosphere set in peaceful surrounding ¾ mile from the main A30. Ideal touring centre for both the north and south coasts and Dartmoor with its beautiful walks and scenery. Close by are Lydford Gorge, Brentnor Church and Meldon Lake. Fishing, pony trekking, golf, tennis are nearby and a heated swimming pool at Okehampton. Good home cooking is assured, served at separate tables in the dining room. Lounge with log fire and colour television. All rooms have tea/coffee making facilities, heating and wash basins. Three bedrooms with colour TV, two bedrooms en-suite, one on the ground floor available. Many guests returning year after year. Fire certificate held.

Proprietress:
Mrs Margaret Hockridge.

ɑɱвıoɲ couɾɾ ɦoɾeʟ

The Green, Dadlington, Nuneaton CV13 6JB
Telephone: (0455) 212292
Fax: (0455) 213141

Charming, modernised Victorian farmhouse overlooking Dadlington's village green, 2 miles north of Hinckley, central for Leicester, Coventry and NEC and convenient for M1 and M6. Each room is comfortably furnished with en-suite bathroom, hospitality tray, colour TV, radio and telephone. There is a lounge, cocktail bar and restaurant and business facilities include a conference room and fax. Ambion Court offers comfort, hospitality and exceptional tranquillity for tourists and business people alike.

Personally managed by proprietor John Walliker

See gazetteer under Hinckley

OLD DALBY Leicestershire Map **08** SK62

FH Q Mrs V Anderson *Home* *(SK673236)* Church Ln
LE13 4LB ☎Melton Mowbray(0664) 822622
Closed Xmas
Although mostly Victorian, parts of this ivy and clematis-clad house date back to the 1700s. Set in a small and peaceful village, it provides modest and comfortable accommodation with a wealth of character.
3hc (1fb) ® ✠ (ex guide dogs) sB&Bfr£18 dB&B£24-£28
⊞ CTV 5P stables for guests horses 1 acres non-working
£

OLD SODBURY Avon Map **03** ST78

GH Q Q **Dornden** Church Ln BS17 6NB
☎Chipping Sodbury(0454) 313325
Closed Xmas & New Year & 3 wks in Oct
Situated east of the village, off the A432, this former Georgian rectory offers traditional comfort and hospitality. The building retains many original features, and the large gardens are very well maintained.
9rm(2⇄3🡑4hc)(4fb) CTV in all bedrooms sB&Bfr£23
sB&B⇄🡑£32 dB&Bfr£38 dB&B⇄🡑£45 LDO 3pm
⊞ CTV 15P ♫(grass)
£

ONICH Highland *Inverness-Shire* Map **14** NN06

GH Q *Tigh-A-Righ* PH33 6SE ☎(08553) 255
Closed 22 Dec-7 Jan
This single-storey, simple guesthouse is on the northern side of the village. Mrs MacCullum, the longstanding owner, is quite a character and looks after her guests very well, providing thoughtful extras in the compact bedrooms.
6rm(1⇄1🡑4hc)(3fb) ® LDO 9pm
Lic ⊞ CTV 15P

FH Q Q Q Mr & Mrs A Dewar *Cuilcheanna House*
(NN019617) PH33 6SD ☎(08553) 226
Etr-6 Oct
Large Victorian house with gardens set in sloping fields leading to Loch Linnhe. Excellent views over lochs and mountains.
8⇄ (2fb) ® LDO 7.30pm
Lic ⊞ 10P 120 acres beef

ORFORD Suffolk Map **05** TM44

INN Q Q **Kings Head** Front St IP12 2LW ☎(0394) 450271
This village centre inn dates from the 13th century and has simply furnished well-equipped accommodation. The cosy bar offers a good menu, and the restaurant serves imaginative dishes featuring locally caught fish.
6hc (1fb) CTV in all bedrooms ® sB&B£20
dB&B£34-£36 WB&B£45-£48 Lunch £5-£20alc Dinner
£10-£25alc LDO 9pm
⊞ 50P 1🐎
Credit Cards 5 £

OSWESTRY Shropshire Map **07** SJ22

See also Llansilin

GH Q Q Q *Ashfield Country House* Llwyn-y-Maen, Trefonen
Rd SY10 9DD ☎(0691) 655200
Set just 1 mile out of Oswestry, this is a friendly and personally run small hotel. It boasts well-equipped rooms and a large lounge that has extensive views over the hotel grounds and the Candy Valley.
12⇄🡑 (2fb) CTV in all bedrooms ® LDO 9pm
Lic ⊞ 50P

OTTERY ST MARY Devon Map **03** SY19

GH Q Q **Fluxton Farm Hotel** Fluxton EX11 1RJ
☎(0404) 812818
This 16th-century Devon longhouse enjoying a peaceful setting to the south of the town. Accommodation is neat and the proprietors give a pleasant welcome.
12rm(6⇄4🡑2hc)(2fb) ® ✱ sB&B£26-£30
dB&B⇄🡑£20-£60 (incl dinner) WB&B£125-£135
WBDi£170-£190 LDO 5.30pm
Lic ⊞ CTV 15P ✔ putting garden railway
£

OXFORD Oxfordshire Map **04** SP50

GH Q Q Q **Bravalla** 242 Iffley Rd OX4 1SE ☎(0865) 241326 &
250511
Small guesthouse offering cosy accommodation and a warm welcome.
6rm(4🡑2hc)(2fb) CTV in all bedrooms ® sB&B£18-£25
sB&B🡑£20-£35 dB&B£30-£35 dB&B🡑£30-£40
⊞ CTV 6P
Credit Cards 1 3 £

See advertisement on page 283

GH Q Q **Brown's** 281 Iffley Rd OX4 4AQ ☎(0865) 246822
Relaxing and full of character, this Victorian property has well-decorated, cosy bedrooms and a bright, pleasant breakfast room. It enjoys a convenient situation approximately one mile from the city.
6hc (1fb) CTV in all bedrooms ® ✱ sB&B£20-£25
dB&B£28-£36
⊞ CTV 4P
Credit Cards 1 3

See advertisement on page 283

GH QQQ **Chestnuts** 45 Davenant Rd, off Woodstock Rd
OX2 8BU ☎(0865) 53375

Ideally situated for exploring the city or Oxfordshire countryside, this comfortable establishment has modern facilities with a lot of personal touches from the attentive owners. The handsome breakfasts are taken in the conservatory which overlooks the garden.

4♪ CTV in all bedrooms ® ✠ (ex guide dogs) sB&B♪£24-£28 dB&B♪£44-£54

⁂ 5P nc12yrs

£

GH QQ **Combermere** 11 Polstead Rd OX2 6TW
☎(0865) 56971

Small and friendly, this Victorian-style property is in a residential area close to the city centre. All bedrooms have modern en suite facilities.

9♪ (2fb) CTV in 6 bedrooms TV in 3 bedrooms ®

⁂ 3P

Credit Cards 1 3

GH QQQ **Conifer** 116 The Slade, Headington OX3 7DX
☎(0865) 63055

This family-run, private hotel is well maintained, with compact and nicely appointed bedrooms. The lounge is complemented by an outdoor heated swimming pool. The proprietors offer a helpful and attentive service.

8rm(1⇨2♪5hc)(1fb) CTV in all bedrooms ® ✠ sB&B£20-£22 dB&B£30-£34 dB&B⇨♪£40-£44

⁂ 8P ⚬(heated)

Credit Cards 1 3

SELECTED

GH QQQQ **Cotswold House** 363 Banbury Rd OX2 7PL
☎(0865) 310558

Situated north of the city centre, this converted private home has been tastefully decorated and furnished to a high standard. The bedrooms are exceptionally good, being well equipped with modern facilities that cater for both the tourist and the businessman. The public rooms, including the bright breakfast room, offer similar standards of comfort, while Mr and Mrs O'Kane assure a warm welcome and a very attentive, helpful service.

6♪ (2fb)⅟in all bedrooms CTV in all bedrooms ® ✠ ❋ sB&B♪£24-£27 dB&B♪£44-£50

⁂ 6P nc6yrs

£

GH QQQ **Courtfield Private Hotel** 367 Iffley Rd OX4 4DP
☎(0865) 242991

Standing in a tree-lined road close to the Thames and with easy access to the city centre and colleges, this detached house has spacious, modern, en suite bedrooms. Furnished to a high standard, Courtfield is run by a conscientious family.

6rm(1⇨3♪2hc)(1fb) ✠ sB&B£20-£22 sB&B⇨♪£25-£28 dB&B£36-£38 dB&B⇨♪£40-£44

⁂ CTV 6P 2🚗 nc3yrs

Credit Cards 1 3 £

GH QQQ **Dial House** 25 London Rd, Headington OX3 7RE
☎(0865) 69944

Closed Xmas & New Year

This converted, half-timbered house has a small, well-kept garden and offers a high standard of accommodation. There are some well-appointed bedrooms and a bright breakfast room offering a freshly cooked breakfast.

8rm(4⇨4♪)(2fb)⅟in all bedrooms CTV in all bedrooms ® ❋ dB&B⇨♪£42-£46

⁂ 8P nc6yrs

£

GH QQ **Earlmont** 322-324 Cowley Rd OX4 2AF
☎(0865) 240236

Closed 24 Dec-1 Jan

Conveniently located within walking distance of the city centre, this personally-run small establishment has compact, well-equipped bedrooms and cosy, comfortable public areas.

6rm(2♪4hc)Annexe 7hc (2fb)⅟in 1 bedroom CTV in 11 bedrooms TV in 2 bedrooms ® ✠ sB&B£20-£25 dB&B£32-£36 dB&B♪£35-£40

⁂ CTV 10P 1🚗 nc5yrs

£

See advertisement on page 285

GH Q **Falcon** 88-90 Abingdon Rd OX1 4PX ☎(0865) 722995

Accommodation here is above average and the lounge is comfortable.

11hc (4fb) CTV in all bedrooms ® ✠ (ex guide dogs) sB&B£16-£18 dB&B£30-£34 dB&B£42-£54

⁂ CTV 10P

£

See advertisement on page 285

GH QQ **Galaxie Private Hotel** 180 Banbury Rd OX2 7BT
☎(0865) 515688

A popular, private, commercial hotel, this has been refurbished to provide well-decorated and equipped bedrooms. The atmosphere is informal and friendly, and the service attentive, under the supervision of the proprietor, Mrs Harris-Jones.

34rm(9⇨8♪17hc)(3fb) CTV in all bedrooms

lift ⁂ CTV 25P

See advertisement on page 285

GH [Q][Q] **Green Gables** 326 Abingdon Rd OX1 4TE
☎(0865) 725870
7 Jan-19 Dec
Situated just south of the city centre, this Edwardian house is set in a mature garden. The accommodation is comfortable, with some good sized bedrooms. The service is friendly and is under the owner's personal supervision.
8rm(3🚿5hc)(2fb) CTV in all bedrooms [R] 🚫🐕 (ex guide dogs) *
sB&B£15-£24 dB&B£30-£34 dB&B🚿£38-£40
🍴 CTV 8P
Credit Cards [1] [3]

GH [Q][Q] ***Micklewood*** 331 Cowley Rd OX4 2AQ
☎(0865) 247328
Visitors to this guesthouse receive a warm and friendly welcome. The modest-budget accommodation is simple with bright public rooms full of character.
6hc (2fb) CTV in all bedrooms 🚫🐕
🍴 CTV 6P

GH [Q][Q][Q] ***Pickwicks*** 17 London Rd, Headington OX3 7SP
☎(0865) 750487 FAX (0865) 742208
This family-run establishment is friendly and comfortable with bright, well-equipped and well-furnished bedrooms. It enjoys a corner site just outside the city centre.
9rm(3🛁4🚿2hc)Annexe 4rm(2🚿2hc)(2fb)🚭in 2 bedrooms CTV in all bedrooms [R] 🚫🐕 (ex guide dogs) (wkly only Nov-Feb) LDO 1pm
🍴 CTV 20P
Credit Cards [1] [3]

GH [Q][Q][Q] **Pine Castle** 290 Iffley Rd OX4 4AE
☎(0865) 241497 & 727230
Closed Xmas
Comfortable bedrooms and a warm welcome are offered at this small Edwardian house which has an attractive dining room and a well furnished lounge.
6hc (3fb) CTV in 5 bedrooms TV in 1 bedroom [R]
sB&B£18-£21 dB&B£35-£40
🍴 CTV 4P
Credit Cards [1] [3] [£]

SELECTED

GH [Q][Q][Q][Q] **Tilbury Lodge Private Hotel** 5 Tilbury Ln, Eynsham Rd, Botley OX2 9NB ☎(0865) 862138
Mr and Mrs Trafford ensure efficient and attentive service at this friendly hotel. The attractive bedrooms are well furnished and equipped and there is a quiet, well-appointed lounge. A relaxing jacuzzi is available to guests. Breakfast is freshly cooked.
9🛁🚿 (2fb) CTV in all bedrooms [R] 🚫🐕 sB&B🛁🚿£27-£30
dB&B🛁🚿£45-£60
🍴 7P 1🚗 nc6yrs jacuzzi
Credit Cards [1] [3] [£]

See advertisement on page 287

GH [Q][Q][Q] **Westwood Country Hotel** Hinksey Hill Top OX1 5BG ☎(0865) 735408 FAX (0865) 736536
Closed 17 Jun-1 Jul & 22 Dec-2 Jan
This small family-run hotel stands in 3 acres of lovely woodland on the outskirts of the city. Catering for tourists and business people alike, the accommodation is well equipped and there is a good range of on-site amenities including a jacuzzi and mini-gym.
26rm(14🛁12🚿)(5fb) CTV in all bedrooms [R]
🚫🐕 (ex guide dogs) * sB&B🛁🚿£45-£55
dB&B🛁🚿£60-£85 LDO 8pm
Lic 🍴 CTV 30P sauna jacuzzi mini gym
Credit Cards [1] [2] [3] [5] [£]

See advertisement on page 287

GH [Q][Q] **Willow Reaches Hotel** 1 Wytham St OX1 4SU
☎(0865) 721545 FAX (0865) 251139
In a quiet residential area south of the city, Willow Reaches has been completely refurbished to provide comfortable, well-equipped bedrooms. Public rooms are limited, but the dining room offers a choice of English and Indian cuisine.
9rm(2🛁7🚿)(1fb) CTV in all bedrooms Ⓡ ✗ *
sB&B🛁🚿£36-£39
dB&B🛁🚿£48-£80 WB&Bfr£252 WBDifr£336 (wkly only 27 Dec-Feb) LDO 6pm
Lic 🍺 CTV 6P 3🚗
Credit Cards [1] [2] [3] [5] [£]

See advertisement on page 289

OXHILL Warwickshire Map **04** SP34

FH [Q][Q][Q] Mrs S Hutsby **Nolands Farm & Country Restaurant** *(SP312470)* CV35 0RJ (1m E of Pillarton Priors on A422) ☎Kineton(0926) 640309
Closed 15-30 Dec
With the exception of 2 bedrooms and the lounge, all of the Nolands farm facilities are in carefully restored outbuildings which house comfortable bedrooms with en suite facilities, a pleasant dining room and a small comfortable bar area.
Annexe 9rm(1🛁7🚿1hc)(2fb) CTV in all bedrooms Ⓡ
✗ (ex guide dogs) sB&Bfr£20 sB&B🛁🚿fr£25 dB&Bfr£30 dB&B🛁🚿fr£30 LDO 8pm
Lic 🍺 25P 2🚗 nc7yrs 🎣 clay pigeon & rough shooting 300 acres arable
Credit Cards [1] [£]

OXWICH West Glamorgan Map **02** SS58

GH [Q][Q] **Oxwich Bay Hotel** Gower SA3 1LS
☎Swansea(0792) 390329 & 390491 FAX (0792) 391254
Closed 25 Dec
Family holiday hotel, close to the beach.
13🛁🚿 (4fb) CTV in all bedrooms Ⓡ ✗ sB&B🛁🚿£15-£40 dB&B🛁🚿£30-£60 WB&B£84-£224 WBDi£160.65-£300.65 LDO 10.45pm
Lic 🍺 70P
Credit Cards [1] [2] [3] [5]

OYNE Grampian *Aberdeenshire* Map **15** NJ62

GH [Q][Q][Q] ***Westhall House*** AB5 6RW ☎Old Rayne(04645) 225
Parts of this fine country mansion house date back to the 13th century. The bedrooms have private facilities, and guests can enjoy the other amemities which include a sauna, solarium and a tennis court.
12rm(4🛁3🚿5hc)(6fb) CTV in all bedrooms Ⓡ LDO 7.30pm
Lic 🍺 50P 🎾(hard)🎣 sauna solarium
Credit Cards [2]

PADSTOW Cornwall & Isles of Scilly Map **02** SW97

See also **Little Petherick, St Merryn** and **Trevone**

GH [Q][Q] **Alexandra** 30 Dennis Rd PL28 8DE ☎(0841) 532503
Etr-Oct
6hc (2fb) CTV in all bedrooms Ⓡ ✗ * sB&B£12-£13 dB&B£24-£26 WB&B£80-£87 WBDi£128-£135 LDO noon
5P nc5yrs

GH [Q][Q][Q] **Dower House** Fentonluna Ln PL28 8BA
☎(0841) 532317
Closed Xmas & New Year
A house of character with comfortable bedrooms and friendly service.
8rm(1🛁4🚿3hc)(3fb) TV available Ⓡ * sB&B£19.50 sB&B🛁🚿£25.50 dB&B£30-£36 dB&B🛁🚿£44 WB&B£94.50-£143.50 WBDi£150.50-£199.50 LDO 6.30pm
Lic 🍺 CTV 9P

GH [Q][Q][Q] ***Tregea Hotel*** High St PL28 8BB ☎(0841) 532455
8rm(1🛁7hc)(2fb) Ⓡ LDO 1pm
Lic 🍺 CTV 8P

PAIGNTON Devon Map **03** SX86

See **Town Plan Section**

GH [Q][Q][Q] **Beresford** 5 Adelphi Rd TQ4 6AW ☎(0803) 551560
Closed Oct, Xmas & New Year
Sound accommodation and personal service is provided by this small, friendly guesthouse. It is close to the town, beach and esplanade.
8rm(4🚿4hc)(1fb) Ⓡ ✗ * sB&Bfr£13 dB&Bfr£26 dB&B🚿fr£32 WBDi£95-£120 LDO 10am
Lic 🍺 CTV 3P
[£]

GH [Q][Q] **Channel View Hotel** 8 Marine Pde TQ3 2NU
☎(0803) 522432
Standing on the seafront with unrestricted views of the bay, this small, friendly hotel has bright, compact rooms with en suite facilities.
12🛁🚿 (3fb) CTV in all bedrooms Ⓡ ✗ (ex guide dogs) * dB&B🛁🚿£27.50-£30 WB&B£70-£150 WBDi£80-£190 LDO noon
Lic 🍺 CTV 10P
Credit Cards [1] [£]

See advertisement on page 289

[Q] is for quality. For a full explanation of this AA quality award, consult the Contents page.

Paignton

⊢⊶**GH** Q Q **Cherra Hotel** 15 Roundham Rd TQ4 6DN
☎(0803) 550723
Mar-Oct
*Standing in its own pleasant grounds with putting greens and
ample car parking space, this friendly hotel enjoys an elevated
position. The bedrooms are bright and compact and many have en
suite facilities. There is also a residents' bar.*
14rm(9🟃5hc)(7fb) CTV in all bedrooms ® sB&B£13-£16
sB&B🟃£16-£19 dB&B£26-£32
dB&B🟃£32-£38 (incl dinner) WBDi£110-£130 LDO 5.30pm
Lic 🍴 CTV 15P putting
£

GH Q Q Q *Clennon Valley Hotel* 1 Clennon Rise TQ4 5HG
☎(0803) 550304 & 557736
*Personally run by its owners who provide friendly, hospitable
service, this establishment has comfortable, well-equipped
bedrooms with satellite TV and video facilities. The small
restaurant proves popular and there is free access to Torbay
Leisure Centre.*
12rm(1🟃9🟃2hc)(2fb) CTV in all bedrooms ®
Lic 🍴 CTV 12P free access to Torbay leisure centre
Credit Cards 1 3

GH Q Q Q *Danethorpe Hotel* 23 St Andrews Rd TQ4 6HA
☎(0803) 551251
*There is friendly atmosphere and service at this comfortable small
hotel which stands in pretty gardens overlooking the town. Bright
and spotlessly clean, the cosy bedrooms are well decorated and
furnished with a good range of facilities and equipment. Three of
the bedrooms have excellent en suite bathrooms.*
10rm(3🟃7hc)(2fb) CTV in all bedrooms ® 🍴 (wkly only Jul &
Aug)
Lic 🍴 10P
Credit Cards 1

GH Q Q Q *Redcliffe Lodge Hotel* 1 Marine Dr TQ3 2NL
☎(0803) 551394
Apr-mid Nov
*Standing in its own grounds on the edge of the beach this hotel has
well-equipped en suite bedrooms and sunny public rooms
overlooking the sea. Conscientious owners and locaL staff provide
friendly service.*
17rm(10⇔7🟃)(2fb) CTV in all bedrooms ® 🍴 LDO 6.30pm
Lic 🍴 CTV 20P
Credit Cards 1 3

See advertisement on page 291

GH Q Q Q **Hotel Retreat** 43 Marine Dr TQ3 2NS
☎(0803) 550596
Etr-Sep
*This comfortable private hotel is family owned and set in pleasant
grounds in a secluded position on the seafront. The accommodation
is comfortable with cosy, bright and well-equipped bedrooms.*
13rm(5⇔8hc)(1fb) CTV in all bedrooms ® sB&B£16-£20
dB&B£32-£36
dB&B⇔£36-£40 WB&B£112-£140 WBDi£132-£145 LDO 6pm
Lic CTV 14P
Credit Cards 1 3 £

⊢⊶**GH** Q Q **St Weonard's Private Hotel** 12 Kernou Rd
TQ4 6BA ☎(0803) 558842
*One hundred yards from the seafront, this cosy hotel is run by a
friendly family and has bright, compact bedrooms plus a lounge
and dining room.*
8rm(4🟃4hc)(3fb) ® 🍴 sB&B£13-£15 sB&B🟃£15-£17
dB&B£26-£30
dB&B🟃£30-£34 WB&B£85-£102 WBDi£123.50-£140.50 LDO
3.30pm
Lic CTV 2P

GH Q Q **Sattva Hotel** 29 Esplanade TQ4 6BL ☎(0803) 557820
*Friendly, private hotel with comfortable modern bedrooms,
adjacent to the seafront.*
18rm(3⇔8🟃7hc)Annexe 2🟃 (6fb) CTV in all bedrooms ® 🍴
sB&B£15-£22 sB&B⇔🟃£18-£25 dB&B£30-£44
dB&B⇔🟃£36-£50 WBDi£125-£175 LDO 5pm
Lic lift 🍴 CTV 10P
Credit Cards 1 3

GH Q Q Q Q **The Sealawn Hotel** Sea Front, 20 Esplanade Rd
TQ4 6BE ☎(0803) 559031
*This Victorian seafront hotel has a friendly atmosphere and offers
well-equipped compact modern bedrooms. It is under conscientious
family ownership.*
13rm(6⇔7🟃)(3fb) CTV in all bedrooms ® 🍴
sB&B🟃£26-£37
dB&B⇔🟃£32-£44 WB&B£105-£147 WBDi£147-£189 LDO
6pm
Lic 🍴 CTV 13P 🐾 solarium
£

GH Q Q Q Q **Sea Verge Hotel** Marine Dr, Preston TQ3 2NJ
☎(0803) 557795
Closed Dec
*As its name suggests, this family-run hotel is close to the sea and
beaches. It has a cosy lounge and excellent bedroom
accommodation, and benefits from on-site parking.*
12rm(5🟃7hc)(1fb) CTV in all bedrooms ® 🍴 ✳ sB&B£16-£18
dB&B£28-£36 dB&B🟃£30-£40 WBDi£135-£170 LDO 5pm
Lic 🍴 CTV 14P nc9yrs
Credit Cards 1 3

Book as early as possible for busy holiday periods.

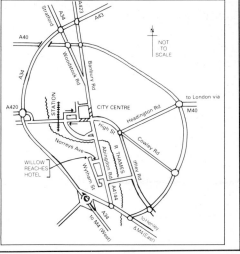

⊢━GH QQQ **Torbay Sands Hotel** 16 Marine Pde, Preston Sea Front TQ3 2NU ☎(0803) 525568

Bryan and Fiona Pearsons have created an hospitable atmosphere at their modern hotel which has panoramic views of the bay. The bright, cosy bedrooms are complemented by comfortable and tasteful public rooms.

14rm(9♠5hc)(4fb) CTV in all bedrooms ® sB&B£12-£15 sB&B♠£13.50-£16.50 dB&B£24-£30 dB&B♠£27-£33 WB&B£80-£100 WBDi£95-£120

Lic ♚ CTV 5P

Credit Cards ① ③ £

PAR Cornwall & Isles of Scilly Map **02** SX05

FH QQQ Mrs A Worne **Yondertown** *(SX066571)* Trethevy PL24 2SA ☎(072681) 7747

Feb-Oct

Surrounded by farmland and countryside, this delightful converted stone barn has comfortable bedrooms, and an elegant sitting room. A relaxing atmosphere prevails here.

2rm(1hc)(1fb)✠in all bedrooms CTV in all bedrooms ® ✗ dB&B£40-£44

♚ CTV 0P nc11yrs 7 acres non-working with livestock

PARKMILL (nr Swansea) West Glamorgan Map **02** SS58

FH Q Mrs D Edwards **Parc-le-Breos House** *(SS529896)* SA3 2HA ☎Swansea(0792) 371636

This farmhouse, situated in the heart of the Gower, is reached by a mile-long, tree-lined farm road, and offers spacious accommodation and the use of riding school facilities.

8rm(2♠5hc) ✗

♚ CTV ↻ snooker 55 acres mixed

PATELEY BRIDGE North Yorkshire Map **07** SE16

GH QQQ **Grassfields Country House Hotel** HG3 5HL ☎Harrogate(0423) 711412

Mar-Nov

Set in beautiful grounds in the Nidd Valley, this elegant Georgian country house has spacious and comfortable en suite bedrooms. Barbara Garforth provides a warm welcome and prepares enjoyable meals which are very good value.

9rm(5♠4♠)(3fb) ® ✳ sB&B♠£20-£22 dB&B♠£36-£40 WB&B£126-£133 WBDi£189-£196 LDO 7pm

Lic ♚ CTV 24P

£

GH QQQ **Roslyn House** 9 King St HG3 5AT ☎Harrogate(0423) 711374

Mr and Mrs Price are making continuous improvements to this pleasant little guesthouse, which is situated off the main street of Pateley Bridge. Bedrooms are comfortable and well equipped and there is a comfortable bar and attractive dining room.

6rm(1⇨5♠) CTV in all bedrooms ® ✗ (ex guide dogs) LDO 4pm

Lic ♚ 3P

FH Q Mrs C E Nelson **Nidderdale Lodge** *(SE183654)* Felbeck HG3 5DR ☎Harrogate(0423) 711677

Etr-Oct

This small stone bungalow is high up overlooking beautiful Nidderdale. The farm is mixed, and guests are welcome to explore. Bedrooms are simply furnished but clean, and there is a comfortable lounge.

3hc (1fb)✠in all bedrooms ® ✗ (ex guide dogs)

♚ CTV 3P 30 acres mixed

See the regional maps of popular holiday areas at the back of the book.

PATRICK BROMPTON North Yorkshire Map **08** SE29

GH QQQQ **Elmfield House** Arrathorne DL8 1NE (2m N unclass towards Catterick Camp) ☎Bedale(0677) 50558 & 50557

Conveniently situated close to Richmond and Leyburn with easy access to the A1, Elmfield house has uninterrupted views across countryside. Warm and welcoming, it has bedrooms which are very well equipped and comfortable. Fresh local produce is used for the freshly cooked meals which are the highlight of a stay here and are excellent value. A solarium and a games room are provided for guests' use.

9rm(4⇨5hc)(2fb) CTV in all bedrooms ® ✗ (ex guide dogs) ✳ sB&B⇨♠£25 dB&B⇨♠£34-£40 WB&B£112-£168 WBDi£175-£231 LDO before noon

Lic ♚ 12P solarium games room

£

See advertisement under BEDALE

PEEBLES Borders *Peeblesshire* Map **11** NT24

GH QQ **Lindores** Old Town EH45 8JE ☎(0721) 20441

Mar-Oct

Neat house with combined lounge and dining room.

5hc (1fb) ✗ (ex guide dogs) dB&B£24-£25

♚ CTV 3P

£

GH QQQ **Whitestone House** Innerleithen Rd EH45 8BD ☎(0721) 20337

This well-maintained guesthouse lies to the east of the town and in addition to accommodation offers a combined lounge and dining room.

5hc (2fb) ® ✗ (ex guide dogs) ✳ dB&B£23-£24

♚ CTV 5P

£

FH QQQ Mrs J M Haydock **Winkston** *(NT244433)* Edinburgh Rd EH45 8PH ☎(0721) 21264

Etr-Oct

Nicely decorated farmhouse 1.5 miles north of town off Edinburgh road. Shower room only, no bath.

3hc ✠in all bedrooms ® ✗ (ex guide dogs)

♚ CTV 4P 40 acres sheep

PELYNT Cornwall & Isles of Scilly Map **02** SX25

FH QQQ Mrs L Tuckett **Trenderway** *(SX214533)* PL13 2LY ☎Polperro(0503) 72214

Closed Xmas

Friendly accommodation and stylish bedrooms at this 16th-century farmhouse situated off the beaten track yet just 2 miles from Polperro and Looe.

3⇨♠ ✠in all bedrooms CTV in all bedrooms ® ✗ dB&B⇨♠£36-£40 WB&B£112-£126

♚ P 3🐎 nc9yrs 400 acres arable mixed sheep cattle

£

PEMBROKE Dyfed Map **02** SM90

GH QQ **High Noon** Lower Lamphey Rd SA71 4AB ☎(0646) 683736

Modern family-run guesthouse offering relaxed accommodation and attentive service.

9rm(3⇨♠4hc)(2fb) ✳ sB&B£11.50-£15 sB&B⇨♠£13.50-£15 dB&B£23-£30 dB&B⇨♠£27-£30 WB&B£80.50-£105 WBDi£116.50-£141 LDO 5pm

---

Lic ♉ CTV 9P
£

PENARTH South Glamorgan Map **03** ST17

GH **Q** **Q** **Albany Hotel** 14 Victoria Rd CF6 2EF
☎Cardiff(0222) 701598 & 701242
*Just a short walk away from the town centre and the railway
station, this friendly guesthouse provides a cosy bar, a large,
comfortable lounge and well-equipped bedrooms.*
14rm(1⇆5♦8hc)(4fb) CTV in all bedrooms ® ✴
sB&Bfr£21.50 sB&B⇆♦fr£27.50 dB&Bfr£36
dB&B⇆♦£41 LDO 8.30pm
Lic ♉ CTV 3P
Credit Cards ① ③ £
See advertisement under CARDIFF on page 103

PENLEY Clwyd Map **07** SJ44

GH **Q** **Q** **Q** **Bridge House** LL13 0LY
☎Overton-On-Dee(097873) 763
*Situated in a quiet rural area only 2 miles north of the village of
Penley is this much extended and considerably modernised former
farmhouse. The impeccably maintained accommodation is equally
suitable for tourists and business people.*
3rm(2hc)✂in all bedrooms CTV in all bedrooms ® ⋈ ✴
sB&B£13-£15 dB&B£24-£30 WB&B£80-£98 WBDi£140-£168
♉ CTV 6P 2🚗 nc10yrs
See advertisement under WREXHAM on page 403

PENNANT Dyfed Map **02** SN56

GH **Q** **Q** **Q** **Bikerehyd Farm** SY23 5PB ☎Nebo(09746) 365
*This pleasant family run guest house is situated just two miles off
of the A48 at Llanon and has been carefully converted to provide
very comfortable and well-equipped bedrooms. The popular*
▶

restaurant is also open to non-residents and a good selection of food is available.
Annexe 3🛏 (2fb) CTV in all bedrooms ® ✕ (ex guide dogs)
sB&B🛏£21 dB&B🛏£39 WB&B£115 LDO 10pm
Lic ⅏ 8P nc5yrs
Credit Cards [1]

PENRHYNDEUDRAETH Gwynedd Map 06 SH63

FH 🇶🇶 Mrs P Bayley **Y Wern** *(SH620421)* LLanfrothen
LL48 6LX (2m N off B4410) ☎(0766) 770556
Set at the foot of the Moelwyn mountains, this 17th-century farmhouse provides a good standard of accommodation with a friendly atmosphere.
5rm(1🛏4hc)(4fb) ® ✕ ✼ dB&B£23-£25
dB&B🛏£28-£30 WB&B£74.25-£78.75 WBDi£13-£116.50 LDO 6pm
⅏ CTV 6P 110 acres beef sheep
£

PENRITH Cumbria Map 12 NY53

⊢←GH 🇶🇶 **Brandelhow** 1 Portland Place CA11 7QN
☎(0768) 64470
Friendly, personal service is provided by the resident proprietors of this well- furnished, comfortable guesthouse. It is situated in a side road in the town centre.
6rm(5hc)(3fb)⤭in 2 bedrooms CTV in all bedrooms ®
sB&B£12-£16
dB&B£24-£28 WB&B£78-£90 WBDi£120-£132 LDO 5pm
⅏ CTV 1P
£

GH 🇶🇶 **The Grotto** Yanwath CA10 2LF ☎(0768) 63288
FAX (0768) 63432
Standing in its own secluded, tree-studded gardens next to the west coast railway line, this traditional, stone residence provides modernised accommodation with attractive public areas.
6rm(4🛏2hc)(2fb) CTV in all bedrooms ® ✕ sB&B£20
sB&B🛏£20 dB&B£40
dB&B🛏£40 WB&B£125 WBDi£200 LDO 6pm
Lic ⅏ 12P
£

GH 🇶 **Limes Country Hotel** Redhills, Stainton CA11 0DT (2m W A66) ☎(0768) 63343
Set in lovely countryside, yet conveniently situated for junction 40 of the M6, this Victorian country house provides friendly service.
6rm(1🛏4🛏1hc)(2fb) ® ✕ (ex guide dogs) sB&B£14-£17.50
sB&B🛏🛏£16.50-£20 dB&B£24-£30
dB&B🛏🛏£28-£35 WB&B£80-£120 WBDi£140-£180 LDO 3pm
Lic ⅏ CTV 8P
Credit Cards [3] £

GH 🇶 **Woodland House Hotel** Wordsworth St CA11 7QY
☎(0768) 64177
This elegant Victorian house is built of the local red sandstone, and is set in a quiet side street close to the town centre. Well furnished, it offers good all round comforts.
8rm(6🛏2hc)(2fb)⤭in all bedrooms CTV in all bedrooms ®
✕ sB&B£15 sB&B🛏🛏£18 dB&B£29
dB&B🛏🛏£33 WB&Bfr£119 WBDifr£168 LDO 4.30pm
Lic ⅏ CTV 10P 1🏕
£

PENRUDDOCK Cumbria Map 12 NY42

SELECTED

FH 🇶🇶🇶🇶 Mrs S M Smith **Highgate** *(NY444275)*
CA11 0SE ☎Greystoke(08533) 339
mid Feb-mid Nov
This delightful and attractive farmhouse is stone built and stands in a lovely garden beside the A66 Penrith to Keswick road. Tastefully decorated throughout, it provides a high standard of comfort and service. Two of the bedrooms boast king-size brass beds, and all have colour TV and beverage facilities. A hearty Cumbrian breakfast is provided.
3hc (1fb) CTV in all bedrooms ® ✕ ✼ sB&B£15-£16
dB&B£30-£32 WB&B£90-£95
⅏ 3P nc5yrs 400 acres mixed
£

PENRYN Cornwall & Isles of Scilly Map 02 SW73

SELECTED

GH 🇶🇶🇶🇶 **Prospect House** 1 Church Rd TR10 8DA
☎Falmouth(0326) 73198
Dinner and breakfast are taken around a large table in the flagstoned dining room at this 1830s house, and should not be missed. Most of the original distinctive features are retained by Prospect House and the attentive service and comfortable accommodation combine to make a memorable and enjoyable stay. Car access can be difficult, but a car space is available and every assistance is provided.
4rm(3🛏🛏1hc) TV available sB&B£15-£16
sB&B🛏🛏£20-£26
dB&B🛏🛏£36-£42 WB&B£94.50-£164.50
WBDi£182-£252 LDO noon
⅏ CTV 4P 1🏕 nc12yrs
£
See advertisement under FALMOUTH on page 155

PENYBONT Powys Map 03 SO16

SELECTED

GH 🇶🇶🇶🇶 **Ffaldau Country House & Restaurant**
LD1 5UD (2m E A44) ☎(059787) 421
This authentic cruck-framed longhouse lies in the beautiful Radnor Hills alongside the A44. There is an abundance of beamed ceilings and inglenook fireplaces, and a slate-fronted restaurant is a feature in its own right. Bedrooms are very pretty and well appointed, and there is a comfortable landing lounge with television and a good supply of books. The restaurant is very popular, with fresh local produce much in use. Sylvia Knott, together with her family and local staff, ensure that guests are well looked after. There is a cosy bar for a relaxing drink, and the house is surrounded by well-kept lawns and flower gardens.
3rm(1🛏2hc) ® ✕ (ex guide dogs) sB&B£22-£25
dB&B🛏£35-£37 LDO 9pm
Lic ⅏ CTV 25P nc10yrs
£

PEN-Y-CWM Dyfed Map 02 SM82

FH 🇶🇶🇶 Mrs M Jones **Lochmeyler** *(SM855275)* SA62 6LL
(4m N on unclass rd) ☎Croesgoch(0348) 837724 & 837705
This 16th-Century farmhouse has been carefully modernised and extended to provide a very high standard of accommodation. The bedrooms are spacious and well equipped. Two beamed lounges are available as well as attractive lawns and gardens.

6⇨ (5fb)✕in all bedrooms CTV in all bedrooms ®
dB&B⇨£25-£30 WB&B£91-£100 WBDi£140-£150 (wkly only Whitsun-early Sep) LDO 6pm
🍴 0P nc10yrs 220 acres dairy
£

PENZANCE Cornwall & Isles of Scilly Map **02** SW43

See **Town Plan Section**
GH 🆀🆀🆀 **Blue Seas Hotel** 13 Regent Ter TR18 4DW
☎(0736) 64744
This family-run establishment stands near the promenade and town centre. All of the comfortable bedrooms offer en suite facilities. Home-cooked meals are prepared with fresh local produce, and guests receive personal service and a warm welcome.
10rm(2⇨8🛏)(3fb) CTV in all bedrooms ® ✖ ✳
sB&B⇨🛏£15-£16.50
dB&B⇨🛏£27-£33 WB&B£90-£100 WBDi£142.50-£315 LDO 6.30pm
Lic 🍴 CTV 12P nc5yrs
Credit Cards ① ③ £

See advertisement on page 295

GH 🆀🆀 **Camilla Hotel** Regent Ter TR18 4DW ☎(0736) 63771
Character Regency residence overlooking seafront promenade with comfortable friendly family atmosphere, positioned close to parks and town centre amenities.
10rm(1⇨4🛏 5hc)(3fb) CTV in all bedrooms ® ✳
sB&B£13.50-£16 sB&B⇨🛏£25-£30 dB&B£27-£30
dB&B⇨🛏£31-£35 WB&B£90-£115 WBDi£142.50-£167.50
LDO noon
Lic 🍴 CTV 6P
£

See advertisement on page 295

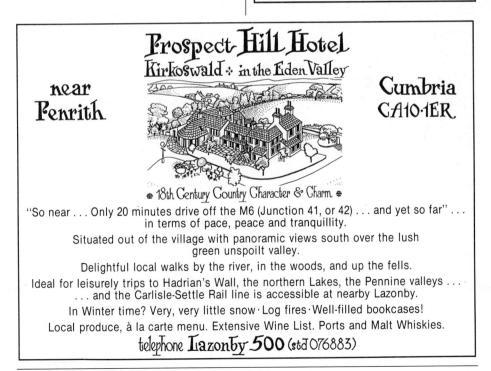

GH QQ Carlton Private Hotel Promenade TR18 4NN
☎(0736) 62081
Etr-19 Oct rs Mar
Small, modest family hotel, personally-run, and positioned on sea front offering commanding views.
10rm(8⇒2hc) CTV in all bedrooms ® ✗ (ex guide dogs) ✱
sB&Bfr£14 dB&Bfr£28 dB&B⇒fr£32 WB&B£98-£105
Lic CTV ✗P nc12yrs
£

⊷GH QQ **Dunedin** Alexandra Rd TR18 4LZ ☎(0736) 62652
Closed Xmas rs Jan-Etr
Very comfortable, small, personally-run guesthouse positioned close to seafront.
9rm(1⇌8⇒)(4fb) CTV in all bedrooms ®
sB&B⇌⇒£13-£14.50
dB&B⇌⇒£25-£28 WB&B£84-£94 WBDi£128-£138 LDO 5pm
Lic ⑪ CTV 1🚗 (£3) nc3yrs

GH QQ Georgian House 20 Chapel St TR18 4AW
☎(0736) 65664
rs Nov-Apr
Centrally situated opposite the famous Admiral Benbow Inn, this guesthouse is well presented and has well-furnished bedrooms.
12rm(4⇌2⇒6hc)(4fb) CTV in all bedrooms ®
✗ (ex guide dogs) ✱ sB&B£17.80 sB&B⇌⇒£20.70 dB&B£28
dB&B⇌⇒£40.60 LDO 8pm
Lic ⑪ CTV 11P
Credit Cards [1] [3] £

GH QQ *Kimberley House* 10 Morrab Rd TR18 4EZ
☎(0736) 62727
Jan-Oct
Small tastefully furnished residence offering warm and friendly welcome from resident proprietors.
9hc (2fb) CTV in 6 bedrooms ® ✗ (ex guide dogs) LDO 5pm
Lic ⑪ CTV 4P nc5yrs
Credit Cards [1] [3]

GH QQQ Hotel Minalto Alexandra Rd TR18 4LZ
☎(0736) 62923
Closed 18 Dec-3 Jan
11rm(2⇒9hc)(1fb) CTV in all bedrooms ® ✱ sB&B£11-£16
dB&B£22-£25
dB&B⇒£25-£32 WB&B£70-£90 WBDi£119-£139 LDO 5.30pm
Lic CTV 10P
Credit Cards [1] [3]

GH Q Mount Royal Hotel Chyandour Cliff TR14 3LQ
☎(0736) 62233
Mar-Oct
Small family hotel facing sea and harbour.
9rm(5⇌4hc)(3fb) CTV in 3 bedrooms ® sB&B£17
sB&B⇌£19 dB&B£34 dB&B⇌£38-£42 WB&B£112-£126
⑪ CTV 6P 4🚗 (£3 per night)
£

GH QQ *Penmorvah Hotel* Alexandra Rd TR18 4LZ
☎(0736) 63711
Closed Xmas
Personally-run private hotel with comfortable accommodation.
10rm(5⇌5⇒)(4fb) CTV in all bedrooms ® LDO 6pm
Lic ⑪ ✗P
Credit Cards [1] [2] [3]

GH QQ Trenant Private Hotel Alexandra Rd TR18 4LX
☎(0736) 62005
Closed Dec-Jan
A personally-run guesthouse, close to local amenities.
10rm(4⇌⇒6hc)(3fb) CTV in all bedrooms ® ✱ sB&Bfr£13
dB&Bfr£26
dB&B⇌⇒fr£32 WB&B£85-£105 WBDi£125-£150 LDO noon
Lic ⑪ CTV ✗P nc5yrs

GH Q *Trevelyan Hotel* 16 Chapel St TR18 4AW ☎(0736) 62494
Closed 25-26 Dec
17th-century property offering comfortable accommodation within town centre.
8rm(1⇌1⇒6hc)(4fb) CTV in all bedrooms ®
✗ (ex guide dogs) LDO am
Lic ⑪ CTV 8P

⊷GH QQ **Trewella** 18 Mennaye Rd TR18 4NG
☎(0736) 63818
Mar-Oct
Cosy little guesthouse with good home cooking about two minutes from seafront.
8rm(2⇒6hc)(2fb) ® sB&B£10.25-£11.25 dB&B£20.50-£22.50
dB&B⇒£23.50-£25.50 WB&B£68.25-£75.25
WBDi£106.75-£113.75 LDO noon
Lic ⑪ CTV ✗P nc5yrs
£

GH QQ The Willows Cornwall Ter TR18 4HL ☎(0736) 63744
Victorian corner house with attractive gardens.
6hc (2fb) CTV in all bedrooms ® ✗ (ex guide dogs) ✱
sB&B£13-£15
dB&B£26-£30 WB&B£85-£95 WBDi£130-£140 LDO 4.30pm
⑪ CTV 5P nc12yrs

INN Q The Yacht The Promenade TR18 4AU ☎(0736) 62787
This inn has uninterrupted views across Mount's Bay. The bar is decorated in Art Deco style, and the bedrooms have recently been refurbished.
6rm (1fb) CTV in all bedrooms ® ✗ (ex guide dogs) sB&B£15
dB&B£30 WB&Bfr£190 LDO 9pm
8P
Credit Cards [2] [3] £

PERELLE

See **GUERNSEY under CHANNEL ISLANDS**

PERRANPORTH Cornwall & Isles of Scilly Map **02** SW75

GH Q The Cellar Cove Hotel Droskyn Way TR6 0DS
☎Truro(0872) 572110
This hotel enjoys fine views over the bay and proves good value for family holidays, offering simply appointed accommodation and friendly service.
12rm(2⇒10hc)(7fb) CTV in all bedrooms ® sB&B£14-£16.50
dB&B£28-£33
dB&B⇒£34-£39 WB&B£95-£110 WBDi£130-£150 LDO noon
Lic CTV 20P ⩯table tennis pool table
Credit Cards [1] [3] £

GH Q Fairview Hotel Tywarnhayle Rd TR6 0DX
☎Truro(0872) 572278
Apr-Oct
Good views from this comfortable family hotel.
15rm(6⇒9hc)(6fb)⊬in 2 bedrooms ® ✗ (ex guide dogs) ✱
sB&B£11.50-£15
dB&B£23-£29 WB&B£80-£100 WBDi£110-£133 LDO 8pm
Lic ⑪ CTV 8P 3🚗
Credit Cards [1] [3]

GH QQ *Headland Hotel* Cliff Rd TR6 0DR
☎Truro(0872) 573222
Enjoying an elevated position overlooking Perranporth's sandy beach and rugged coastline, this family-run hotel is keen to please its guests.
25rm(1⇌8⇒16hc)(5fb) ® ✗ (ex guide dogs) LDO 7pm
Lic ⑪ CTV 7P 2🚗
Credit Cards [1] [3]

GH QQQ **Villa Margarita Country Hotel** Bolingey TR6 0AS
☎Truro(0872) 572063

Exceptionally well-appointed colonial style villa in an acre of well-tended gardens. Imaginative table d'hôte menus served by caring owners.

5rm(3♠2hc)Annexe 2♠ (1fb) TV in 1 bedroom ®
✖ (ex guide dogs) sB&B♠£19.50 dB&Bfr£36
dB&B♠fr£39 WB&B£108-£117 WBDi£180-£189 LDO 4pm
Lic CTV 8P nc8yrs ⌂solarium
£

PERTH Tayside *Perthshire* Map **11** NO12

GH QQQ **Clark Kimberley** 57-59 Dunkeld Rd PH1 5RP
☎(0738) 37406

A warm welcome awaits guests at this friendly guesthouse which has convenient access to the city bypass. Mr and Mrs Cattanach are to be congratulated on the high standard of accommodation they offer, most of the rooms having en suite facilities.

8rm(6♠2hc)(5fb) CTV in all bedrooms ® ✳ sB&B£13-£14
dB&B♠£26-£28 WB&B£91-£98
📺 CTV 12P
£

GH QQQ **Clunie** 12 Pitcullen Crescent PH2 7HT
☎(0738) 23625

A warm welcome is provided at Scott and Joan Miller's tastefully appointed guesthouse on the northern fringe of the city. It has a friendly atmosphere, and though compact, the comfortably furnished bedrooms are well equipped.

7⌂♠ (3fb) CTV in all bedrooms ® sB&B⌂♠fr£16
dB&B⌂♠fr£32 LDO noon
📺 CTV 8P

GH QQQ **The Darroch** 9 Pitcullen Crescent PH2 7HT
☎(0738) 36893

Comfortable accommodation and a friendly atmosphere are offered here, on the northern fringes of the city.

6rm(3♠3hc)(2fb) CTV in all bedrooms ® ✖ (ex guide dogs)
LDO 4pm
📺 CTV 10P
£

GH QQ **The Gables** 24-26 Dunkeld Rd PH1 5RW
☎(0738) 24717

Situated in the western end of the town, this family-run guesthouse has convenient access to the ring route and to the A9. It has a friendly atmosphere and offers well-maintained, practical accommodation.

8hc (3fb) CTV in all bedrooms ® ✳ sB&Bfr£12.50
dB&Bfr£23 WB&B£80.50-£87.50 WBDi£115-£122 LDO 4pm
Lic 📺 CTV 8P
Credit Cards 3 £

GH QQ **Kinnaird** 5 Marshall Place PH2 8AH
☎(0738) 28021

This tastefully appointed Georgian terrace house overlooks the South Inch, just a short walk from the city centre. Comfortably appointed, it has compact, well- equipped bedrooms, well maintained by the enthusiastic owner.

6rm(4♠2hc) CTV in all bedrooms ® ✖ (ex guide dogs)
sB&Bfr£15 sB&B♠fr£22 dB&Bfr£26 dB&B♠fr£29 LDO 4pm
📺 2P 3🚗

GH QQ **Pitcullen** 17 Pitcullen Crescent PH2 7HT
☎(0738) 26506

In a residential area beside the A94, this family-run guesthouse is a popular base for tourists, offering good value accommodation and an attractive first floor lounge.

6rm(2♠4hc)(1fb) CTV in all bedrooms ® ✖ ✳ sB&B£14-£20
dB&B£28-£32 dB&B♠£30-£40 LDO 6pm
📺 6P
£

PETERSFIELD Hampshire Map **04** SU72

See also Rogate

GH QQ **Concorde Hotel** Weston Rd GU31 4JF ☎(0730) 63442
10⌂♠ (5fb) CTV in all bedrooms ® ✳ sB&B£30.50-£37.50
sB&B⌂♠fr£37.50 dB&Bfr£41.50 dB&B⌂♠fr£48.50
Lic 📺 CTV 12P
Credit Cards 1 3

PEVENSEY East Sussex Map **05** TQ60

GH QQ **Napier** The Promenade BN24 6HD
☎Eastbourne(0323) 768875

Superbly situated on the beach, this well-maintained guesthouse is ideal for a relaxing holiday away from the crowds, yet convenient for Eastbourne. Modern functional bedrooms are complemented by a comfortable sun lounge, small bar, dining room, patio and friendly efficient service from the proprietors.

10rm(5♠5hc)(3fb) CTV in all bedrooms ® ✖
sB&B♠£16.25-£18.25 dB&B£27.50-£29.50
dB&B♠£30-£34 WB&B£93-£102 WBDi£120-£125 LDO 4pm
Lic 📺 CTV 7P ✆
£

See advertisement under EASTBOURNE on page 143

PICKERING North Yorkshire Map **08** SE88

⊢⊶**GH** QQQ **Bramwood** 19 Hallgarth YO18 7AW
☎(0751) 74066

Close to the town centre, but in a quiet location, this guesthouse has neat and comfortable accommodation. This establishment is especially recommended for its home-cooked dinners, and is for non-smokers only.

6rm(2♠4hc)(1fb)✂in all bedrooms ® ✖ (ex guide dogs)
sB&B£11-£13.50 dB&B£22-£27
dB&B♠£25-£30 WB&B£66-£90 WBDi£115-£139 LDO
2.30pm
CTV 6P nc3yrs
Credit Cards 1 2 3 5 £

PIDDLETRENTHIDE Dorset Map **03** SY79

INN QQ **The Poachers** DT2 7QX ☎(03004) 358

This attractive small inn can be found on the edge of the village. An annexe provides comfortable bedroom accommodation. Pretty garden by a stream.

2⌂♠ Annexe 9⌂♠ (2fb) CTV in all bedrooms ®
sB&B⌂♠£20
dB&B⌂♠£36 WBDi£164 Lunch £4-£12alc Dinner £6-£12alc
LDO 9pm
📺 40P ⌂(heated)
£

PITLOCHRY Tayside *Perthshire* Map **14** NN95

GH QQ **Adderley Private Hotel** 23 Toberargan Rd PH16 5HG
☎(0796) 2433
Etr-mid Oct

This small family-run guesthouse is situated beside the curling rink, not far from the town centre. It has a friendly atmosphere and offers good value holiday accommodation.

7rm(6⌂♠)(1fb) ® ✖ (ex guide dogs) sB&B⌂♠£16.85
dB&B⌂♠£32.70-£33.70 WB&B£108.85-£112 LDO 5pm
📺 CTV 9P nc6yrs
£

'Selected' establishments, which have the highest quality award, are highlighted by a tinted panel. For a full list of these establishments, consult the Contents page.

SELECTED

GH [Q][Q][Q][Q] Dundarave House Strathview Ter PH16 6AT ☎(0796) 3109
Apr-Oct
Mr and Mrs Shuttleworth's charming house stands in formal grounds in a quiet area above the town. Sympathetically refurbished to retain its original character, Dundarave has a relaxed atmosphere with a high standard of accommodation.
7rm(5🛁2hc)(1fb) CTV in all bedrooms Ⓡ
sB&B£21.75-£23.75
dB&B🛁£43.50-£47.50 WB&B£145.25-£159.25
♨ 7P
[£]

GH [Q][Q] *Duntrune* 22 East Moulin Rd PH16 5HY
☎(0796) 2172
Feb-Oct
Good value bed and breakfast accommodation with traditional comforts is offered at this substantial Victorian house. It stands in its own grounds in a quiet residential area, not far from the town centre.
7rm(5🚿2hc)(1fb) CTV in all bedrooms Ⓡ ✗
♨ 8P nc5yrs

GH [Q][Q] Fasganeoin Hotel Perth Rd PH16 5DJ ☎(0796) 2387
2 Apr-15 Oct
Set in its own grounds at the south entrance to the town, and convenient for the festival theatre, this family-run hotel offers a friendly atmosphere and provides good value traditional comforts.
9rm(4🛁🚿5hc)(3fb) ✗ (ex guide dogs) sB&B£17-£18.50
dB&B£35-£37
dB&B🛁🚿£47-£50 WB&B£115-£171 LDO 7.30pm
Lic ♨ CTV 20P
Credit Cards [1] [3] [£]

GH [Q][Q] Well House Private Hotel 11 Toberargan Rd PH16 5HG ☎(0796) 2239
Mar-Oct
In a residential area, not far from the centre of the town, this friendly family-run guesthouse has a relaxed atmosphere and provides well-equipped, comfortably furnished bedrooms and wholesome food.
6🚿 (1fb) CTV in all bedrooms Ⓡ
dB&B🚿£30-£32 WB&B£94.50-£100.80 LDO 5.30pm
Lic ♨ 8P
Credit Cards [1] [3]

PLUCKLEY Kent Map **05** TQ94

FH [Q][Q][Q] Mr & Mrs V.Harris **Elvey Farm Country Hotel** *(TQ916457)* TN27 0SU ☎(023384) 442
rs Nov-Mar
Friendly and welcoming, this charming farm has a wealth of atmosphere. The main house has 2 lovely bedrooms and well-appointed accommodation is available in the converted oast house and stables. Guests will enjoy the home-cooked meals here.
10rm(7🛁3🚿)(6fb) CTV in all bedrooms Ⓡ ✱
dB&B🛁🚿fr£49.50 LDO 4pm
Lic ♨ 40P 75 acres mixed
Credit Cards [1] [3] [£]

See advertisement on page 299

PLYMOUTH Devon Map **02** SX45

See **Town Plan Section**

GH [Q][Q][Q] Bowling Green Hotel 9-10 Osborne Place, Lockyer St, The Hoe PL1 2PU ☎(0752) 667485
Closed 25-30 Dec
Overlooking Drake's famous bowling green, this terraced Georgian property is close to the Hoe and the Barbican city centre. The ▶

attractive bedrooms offer all good facilities, and a full English breakfast is served in the lounge/dining room. A warm welcome is assured.

12rm(7⇨5hc)(3fb) CTV in all bedrooms ® sB&Bfr£20
sB&B⇨fr£27 dB&Bfr£28 dB&B⇨fr£38
♩ CTV 4⇔ (£2 per night)
Credit Cards 1 3 £

GH QQ Caraneal Hotel 12/14 Pier St, West Hoe PL1 3BS
☎(0752) 663589

Close to the seafront and within easy reach of The Hoe, Barbican and city centre, this Georgian terrace house offers en suite facilities, colour TV, direct dial telephones and tea-making facilities in all rooms. A set dinner is served in the informal dining room.

10rm(6⇨4)(1fb) CTV in all bedrooms ® ✕ (ex guide dogs)
✱ sB&B⇨£24-£27
dB&B⇨£32.50-£38 WB&B£113.75-£189
WBDi£162.75-£238
3P

GH QQQ Chester 54 Stuart Road, Pennycomequick PL3 4EE
☎(0752) 663706

Detached house in a large, walled garden, 1 mile from the city centre, and within walking distance of the shops and The Hoe.

11rm(2⚓9hc)(2fb) CTV in all bedrooms LDO 10am
Lic ♩ CTV 7P
£

GH QQ Cranbourne Hotel 282 Citadel Road, The Hoe
PL1 2PZ ☎(0752) 263858

Modern comforts provided in this end of terrace Georgian hotel.

12rm(5⚓7hc)(3fb) CTV in 11 bedrooms ® sB&Bfr£15-£20
sB&Bfr£25-£35 dB&B£30-£40 dB&Bfr£40-£45
Lic ♩ CTV 3⇔
Credit Cards 1 3 £

GH QQ Dudley 42 Sutherland Road, Mutley PL4 6BN
☎(0752) 668322
rs Xmas

This attractive, double-fronted Victorian house has cosy accommodation and stands in a quiet residential area convenient for the station.

6hc (3fb) CTV in all bedrooms ® sB&B£14
dB&B£24 WB&B£80 WBDi£122 LDO 9am
♩ CTV ✗
Credit Cards 1 3

GH QQQ Gables End Hotel 29 Sutherland Road, Mutley
PL4 6BW ☎(0752) 220803

This comfortable, family-run establishment is within easy reach of the city centre.

7hc (3fb) CTV in all bedrooms ® ✕ LDO 4pm
♩ CTV 3⇔ (charge)

GH QQQ Georgian House Hotel 51 Citadel Rd, The Hoe
PL1 3AU ☎(0752) 663237
Closed 23 Dec-5 Jan rs Sun

The bedrooms of this friendly Georgian house are equipped with en suite bathrooms, hairdryers, trouser presses, colour TVs and direct dial telephones. The attractive cocktail bar is an ideal place to pursue the imaginative à la carte menu offered in the 'Four Poster Restaurant'.

12rm(4⇨8)(1fb) CTV in all bedrooms ® ✕ (ex guide dogs)
✱ sB&B⇨£28-£30 dB&B⇨£38-£41 LDO 9.30pm
Lic ♩ CTV 2P
Credit Cards 1 2 3 5

GH QQQ Lockyer House Hotel 2 Alfred St, The Hoe
PL1 2RP ☎(0752) 665755
Closed Xmas

A family-run guesthouse, Lockyer House is within walking distance of the city centre and the famous Hoe and Barbican. It offers good home cooking and comfortable bedrooms.

6hc (1fb) CTV in all bedrooms ✕ sB&Bfr£14
dB&Bfr£28 WB&Bfr£98 WBDifr£164.50 LDO 10am
Lic ♩ CTV ✗ nc3yrs

GH Q Merville Hotel 73 Citadel Rd, The Hoe PL1 3AX
☎(0752) 667595

This terraced property, near the famous Hoe and Barbican is within easy reach of the city centre. The resident proprietor is on hand to welcome guests to the comfortable, compact lounge and dining room, and uncluttered bedrooms.

10hc (3fb) CTV in all bedrooms ® ✱ sB&Bfr£11
dB&Bfr£24 LDO 3pm
Lic ♩ CTV 2P

GH QQ Oliver's Hotel & Restaurant 33 Sutherland Rd
PL4 6BN ☎(0752) 663923

Mike and Joy Purser assure a warm welcome in this family-run hotel that is within walking distance of the city centre and the station. Interesting dishes are prepared from the best local produce and served in the attractive restaurant.

6rm(4⚓2hc)(1fb) CTV in all bedrooms ® ✕ LDO 9am
Lic ♩ 3P nc11yrs
Credit Cards 1 2 3 5

GH QQQ Riviera Hotel 8 Elliott Street, The Hoe PL1 2PP
☎(0752) 667379
Closed Xmas

Personally-run hotel on Plymouth Hoe with very well-equipped bedrooms.

11rm(6⇨5hc)(2fb) CTV in all bedrooms ® LDO 9.30pm
Lic ♩
Credit Cards 1 2 3 5

Visit your local AA Centre.

GH 🆀🆀 **Russell Lodge Hotel** 9 Holyrood Place, The Hoe PL1 2BQ ☎(0752) 667774

Part of a Georgian terrace right on the Hoe, close to the city centre, this personally run hotel provides bright, well-equipped accommodation and friendly service.

9rm(2🏶🏶7hc)(2fb) CTV in all bedrooms ® 🏋 (ex guide dogs) sB&B🏶£17-£18 dB&B🏶£35-£36 WB&B£110-£120
🍴 CTV 3P
Credit Cards 1 2 3 5

GH 🆀🆀 **Trillium** 4 Alfred Street, The Hoe PL1 2RP ☎(0752) 670452

This Georgian property has been modernised yet retains some original features. The bedrooms are soundly equipped and there is a comfortable lounge and dining room. Trillium stands in a quiet street close to the city centre and the famous Hoe.

7rm(5🏶2hc)(1fb) CTV in all bedrooms ® 🏋 sB&B£16 sB&B🏶£20.50 dB&B£32
dB&B🏶£41 WB&B£224-£287 WBDi£357-£432.50 LDO 4pm
Lic 🍴 CTV 3P
Credit Cards 1 2 3

POCKLINGTON Humberside Map **08** SE74

FH 🆀🆀 Mr & Mrs Pearson **Meltonby Hall** *(SE800524)* Meltonby YO4 2PW (2m N unclass) ☎(0759) 303214
Etr-Oct

Large 18th-century farmhouse on the edge of the Yorkshire Wolds. Situated 2.5 miles north of the town in attractive countryside.

2rm (1fb) 🏋 ✳ dB&B£20-£24 WB&B£70-£84 WBDi£110-£126
🍴 CTV 4P 118 acres mixed
£

PODIMORE Somerset Map **03** ST52

FH 🆀🆀 Mrs S Crang **Cary Fitzpaine** *(ST549270)* Cary Fitzpaine BA22 8JB 2m N, take A37 at junc. with A303 for 1 mile then t rt onto unclass rd
☎Charlton Mackrell(045822) 3250
Closed 23-26 Dec

One mile north of the A303 Podimore roundabout on the A37, this well kept Georgian farmhouse is surrounded by its own mixed farmland. The cosy dining room for breakfast and comfortable lounge complement the well-equipped bedrooms.

3rm(1🏶🏶2hc)(1fb) CTV in all bedrooms ® 🏋 (ex guide dogs) sB&B£15 dB&B£28 dB&B🏶🏶£34 WB&Bfr£90
🍴 CTV 3P nc2yrs ✒ 600 acres arable beef horses sheep
£

POLBATHIC Cornwall & Isles of Scilly Map **02** SX35

⊢⊶**GH** 🆀🆀 **The Old Mill** PL11 3HA ☎St Germans(0503) 30596

8hc (2fb) ® sB&B£10-£12
dB&B£20-£24 WB&B£65-£80 WBDi£110-£150 LDO 7.30pm
Lic CTV 12P 1🍴
£

POLMASSICK Cornwall & Isles of Scilly Map **02** SW94

GH 🆀🆀🆀 **Kilbol House Country Hotel** PL26 6HA ☎Mevagissey(0726) 842481

Set amid secluded grounds with a small stream, this 300-year-old cottage has functional bedrooms, 16th-century lounges, bar and an attractive dining room. There is also a peaceful cottage annexe. Early morning tea and home cooking are provided and the small farm is fun for all the family.

8rm(4🏶3hc)(2fb) ✳ sB&Bfr£16.50 dB&Bfr£33
dB&B🏶fr£33 WB&Bfr£109.25 WBDifr£157.55 LDO noon
Lic 🍴 CTV 12P ⌂
Credit Cards 1 2 3 5

POLPERRO Cornwall & Isles of Scilly Map **02** SX25

GH 🆀🆀🆀 **Landaviddy Manor** Landaviddy Ln PL13 2RT ☎(0503) 72210
Feb-19 Oct

Charming country house of Cornish stone, furnished in keeping with its style and character.

9rm(5🏶4hc) CTV in all bedrooms ®
dB&B🏶£40-£60 LDO 10am
Lic 🍴 CTV 12P nc5yrs
Credit Cards 1 3 5

GH 🆀🆀🆀 **Lanhael House** PL13 2PW ☎(0503) 72428
Mar-Oct

Dating back 300 years, this attractive Cornish cottage has pretty, well-kept gardens and an outdoor swimming pool. The bedroom have good decor and furnishings and the public areas have quality and character. Bed and breakfast are offered.

6rm(1⊶🏶4hc)🌙 in all bedrooms 🏋 ✳ dB&B£30
dB&B⊶🏶£33
🍴 CTV 6P nc14yrs ⌂
Credit Cards 1 3

POLZEATH Cornwall & Isles of Scilly Map **02** SW97

GH 🆀🆀🆀 **White Lodge Hotel** Old Polzeath PL27 6TJ ☎Trebetherick(020886) 2370

9rm(2⊶🏶7hc)(1fb) CTV in 2 bedrooms ® sB&B£15-£20
dB&B⊶🏶fr£55
Lic 🍴 CTV 12P

PONTRHYDFENDIGAID Dyfed Map **06** SN76

GH 🆀🆀 **Llysteg** SY25 6BB ☎(09745) 697

Set in a peaceful village, this friendly, family-run guesthouse is in the heart of Rural Wales. All the bedrooms have private bathrooms and the public rooms are comfortable.

6⊶🏶 (4fb)🌙 in all bedrooms sB&B⊶🏶£17.50
dB&B⊶🏶£35 WB&B£114 WBDi£173 LDO 10.30pm
Lic 🍴 CTV 6P

PONTYPRIDD Mid Glamorgan Map **03** ST09

INN 🆀 **White Hart Hotel** 1 High St CF37 1BD ☎(0443) 405922

This busy inn is close to the town centre and its disco bar is popular with the locals. There is also a small residents' bar on the first floor and a breakfast room and bright bedrooms.

5hc (5fb)🌙 in 1 bedroom CTV in all bedrooms ®
🏋 (ex guide dogs) sB&Bfr£20 dB&Bfr£30
🍴 CTV 15P snooker

POOLE Dorset Map **04** SZ09

See also Bournemouth

GH 🆀🆀 **Avoncourt Private Hotel** 245 Bournemouth Rd, Parkstone BH14 9HX ☎(0202) 732025

Neat and inexpensive accommodation is provided here, and the proprietors work hard to welcome their guests and make their stay comfortable. There is a small new bar and a cosy sitting room.

6hc (3fb) CTV in all bedrooms ® 🏋 sB&B£16-£22
dB&B£32-£44 LDO 8pm
Lic 🍴 CTV 5P 1🍴
Credit Cards 1 3

GH 🆀🆀🆀 **Seacourt** 249 Blandford Rd, Hamworthy BH15 4AZ ☎(0202) 674995

Situated on the A350 close to the ferry terminal, this recently renovated house has some long-stay parking. It offers well-equipped, modern bedrooms together with a fresh, light, breakfast room.

6rm(2⊶🌙3hc)(1fb) CTV in all bedrooms ®
🏋 (ex guide dogs) ✳ sB&B£13-£14 dB&B£26-£28
dB&B⊶🏶£32-£34 WB&B£105-£110
🍴 7P

GH QQ **Sheldon Lodge** 22 Forest Rd, Branksome Park
BH13 6DH ☎(0202) 761186
This detached house stands in a quiet area and has generous public rooms including a bar, sun lounge and snooker room. The bedrooms are neat and compact with modern facilities.
14rm(8⇆6♠)(1fb)✂in 4 bedrooms CTV in all bedrooms ®
sB&B⇆♠£20-£22
dB&B⇆♠£40-£44 WBDi£175-£185 LDO 7pm
Lic ⁽ᵐ⁾ 3P solarium
£

PORLOCK Somerset Map **03** SS84

GH QQ **The Gables Hotel** TA24 8LQ ☎(0643) 862552
Standing in a picturesque garden away from the main street of the village, this pretty thatched cottage has bedrooms with good views some which are furnished with antiques. There is also a comfortable TV lounge and an elegant dining room.
7rm(1⇆6hc) ® ✳ sB&Bfr£16 dB&Bfr£32
dB&B⇆fr£36 WB&Bfr£105
Lic ⁽ᵐ⁾ CTV ✗ nc8yrs
£

GH QQ **Lorna Doone Hotel** High St TA24 8PS
☎(0643) 862404
Set in the centre of the village, this house has cosy Victorian sitting rooms and a smart restaurant which is open to the public. The bathrooms are simple, and the bedrooms neat and comfortable.
10rm(3⇆4♠3hc) CTV in all bedrooms ® sB&B£16.50
dB&B£33 dB&B⇆♠£36 WB&B£108.50-£119 LDO 9.15pm
Lic ⁽ᵐ⁾ CTV 9P
Credit Cards 1 3 £

£ Remember to use the money-off vouchers.

LLYSTEG GUEST HOUSE

Pontrhydfendigaid, Ystrad Meurig,
Dyfed, SY25 6BB
Telephone: (09745) 697
Proprietors: Brian and Gillian Edwards

Our licensed guest house amidst magnificent scenery is a perfect location for all country pursuits and within easy reach of the coast. Spacious en-suite bedrooms, excellent food, friendly service, tea/coffee made on request. Car park adjacent. AA 2 Qs. Welsh Tourist Board 3-Crowns commended. Brochure available.

PORT ERIN

See **MAN, ISLE OF**

PORTESHAM Dorset Map **03** SY68

GH [Q][Q][Q] ***Millmead Country Hotel*** Goose Hill DT3 4HE ☎Abbotsbury(0305) 871432

Closed 24-26 Dec

The friendly proprietors offer good facilities, comfortable bedrooms and wholesome food. A non-smoking establishment.

8rm(3🛁2🚿3hc)🚭in all bedrooms CTV in all bedrooms 🐕 (ex guide dogs) LDO 6.30pm

Lic ♨ 16P nc10yrs

Credit Cards [1] [3]

PORTHCAWL Mid Glamorgan Map **03** SS87

GH [Q][Q] Collingwood Hotel 40 Mary St CF36 3YA ☎(065671) 2899

A short walk from the shops and seafront, this friendly family-run guesthouse has bright bedrooms, a small bar and a comfortable, modern lounge.

8hc (4fb)🚭in all bedrooms CTV in 1 bedroom [R] 🐕 (ex guide dogs) * sB&B£12-£15 dB&B£24-£30 WB&B£84-£105 LDO 5pm

Lic ♨ CTV P̸

GH [Q][Q][Q] ***Heritage*** 24 Mary St CF36 3YA ☎(0656) 771881

Only 200 yards from the seafront, close to the Grand Pavillion, this completely refurbished property has been recently acquired by Janet and John Smart, who provide attentive service. This is a non-smoking establishment.

7rm(1🛁5🚿1hc)(1fb)🚭in all bedrooms CTV in all bedrooms 🐕 LDO 6pm

Lic ♨ P̸

Credit Cards [1] [3]

🛏**GH [Q][Q] Minerva Hotel** 52 Esplanade Av CF36 3YU ☎(065671) 2428

Friendly and family run, this seafront guesthouse has cosy, well-equipped accommodation and a small cane-furnished bar. Minerva Hotel is conveniently placed for the town centre.

8rm(2🛁2🚿4hc)(3fb) CTV in all bedrooms [R] sB&B£13 sB&B🛁🚿£19 dB&B£26 dB&B🛁🚿£34 WB&B£80 WBDi£132.50 LDO 6pm

Lic ♨ CTV

[£]

PORTHCOTHAN BAY Cornwall & Isles of Scilly Map **02** SW87

GH [Q][Q] ***Bay House*** PL28 8LW ☎Padstow(0841) 520472

Apr-Oct

16hc (1fb) 🐕 (ex guide dogs) LDO 4.30pm

Lic CTV 17P

PORTHMADOG Gwynedd Map **06** SH53

🛏**GH [Q] Oakleys** The Harbour LL49 9AS ☎(0766) 512482

Apr-Oct

This town centre guesthouse is close to the Ffestiniog Railway terminus and offers very good value.

8rm(1🛁2🚿5hc)(3fb) 🐕 sB&B£13-£15 dB&B£24-£26 dB&B🛁🚿£26-£28 WBDi£115-£120 LDO 5pm

Lic CTV 18P nc5yrs

GH [Q][Q] Owen's Hotel 71 High St LL49 9EU ☎(0766) 512098

Mar-Oct

Situated in the centre of the town, this family-run hotel provides simple but well-appointed accommodation and friendly hospitality. Also contained in the premises are a coffee shop and a bakery/confectionery.

10rm(3🛁4🚿3hc)(3fb) CTV in 8 bedrooms [R] sB&B£15 sB&B🛁🚿£20 dB&B£28 dB&B🛁🚿£38 WB&B£99-£132

♨ CTV 4P 5🚗

Credit Cards [1] [3] [£]

PORTHTOWAN Cornwall & Isles of Scilly Map **02** SW64

GH [Q][Q] Beach Hotel TR4 8AE ☎(0209) 890228

Closed 19-30 Nov & 2-31 Jan

This family holiday hotel enjoys spectacular views from its elevated position.

14rm(7🚿7hc)(5fb) CTV in all bedrooms [R] * sB&B£14.50-£16.50 sB&B🚿£16.50-£18.50 dB&B£29-£33 dB&B🚿£33-£37 WB&B£98-£110 WBDi£154-£166 LDO 8pm

Lic ♨ 15P

Credit Cards [1] [2] [3] [5] [£]

PORT ISAAC Cornwall & Isles of Scilly Map **02** SW98

GH [Q] Bay Hotel 1 The Terrace PL29 3SG ☎Bodmin(0208) 880380

Etr-Oct

Double-fronted building in elevated position overlooking sea.

10rm(3🛁🚿7hc)(5fb) * sB&B£15.50-£19 dB&B£31-£38 dB&B🛁🚿£38-£47 WB&B£93-£146 WBDi£135-£190 LDO 7pm

Lic CTV 10P

GH [Q][Q] St Andrews Hotel The Terrace PL29 3SG ☎Bodmin(0208) 880240

With wonderful views from its clifftop setting, this house offers an attractive dining room, small bar, sun lounge and TV lounge. The en suite rooms have colour TVs while the other bedrooms are more modestly equipped.

13rm(2🛁4🚿7hc)(2fb)🚭in 5 bedrooms CTV in 6 bedrooms [R] 🐕 (ex guide dogs) sB&Bfr£19 dB&Bfr£38 dB&B🛁🚿fr£45 WB&B£114-£155.10 WBDi£180-£221.10 LDO 7.30pm

Lic ♨ CTV 14P

PORTNANCON Highland *Sutherland* Map **14** NC46

GH [Q][Q] Port-Na-Con House IV27 4UN ☎Durness(097181) 367

Apr-Sep

Standing on the water's edge with fine views across Loch Eriboll, this former Custom House offers comfortable, compact accommodation. Due to water restraints, only showers may be taken at busy periods. The small à la carte menu, an alternative to the inclusive set dinner, features local sea food.

4hc (2fb) [R] * dB&Bfr£46 (incl dinner) WBDifr£156

Lic ♨ 6P nc4yrs

Credit Cards [3]

PORT OF MENTEITH Central *Perthshire* Map **11** NN50

🛏**FH [Q][Q]** Mrs C Tough **Collymoon Pendicle** *(NN591961)* FK8 3JY ☎Buchlyvie(036085) 222

Apr-Oct

Close to the River Forth and Lake Monteith, this attractive modern bungalow enjoys a secluded location. The service is informal and friendly, and dinner is very good value.

3hc (1fb)🚭in all bedrooms [R] 🐕 (ex guide dogs) sB&B£11-£12 dB&B£22-£24 WB&B£77-£84 WBDi£119-£126 LDO 6pm

♨ CTV 3P 🚜 500 acres arable mixed

[£]

FH [Q][Q][Q] Mrs N Erskine **Inchie** *(NN592000)* FK8 3JZ ☎(08775) 233

Apr-Oct

Surrounded by 170 acres of pasture, this modernised stone farmhouse lies close to the shores of Lake Menteith. The bedrooms are modern and the public rooms are traditional in style.

2hc (1fb)🚭in all bedrooms 🐕 * sB&B£10-£12 dB&B£20-£24 WBDi£112-£126

♔ CTV 2P 170 acres beef sheep
£

PORTPATRICK Dumfries & Galloway *Wigtownshire*
Map **10** NX05

GH **Q Q Q** **Blinkbonnie** School Brae DG9 8LG ☎(077681) 282
Closed Nov–Dec
Set within attractive gardens overlooking the harbour, this small friendly guesthouse has comfortable accommodation (all on one level) and a friendly atmosphere. A choice of dishes is offered in the bright, well-maintained dining room.
6hc (1fb) ® ✱ sB&B£12-£14 dB&B£24-£28 LDO 5pm
♔ CTV 10P

PORTREE

See SKYE, ISLE OF

PORT ST MARY

See MAN, ISLE OF

PORTSMOUTH & SOUTHSEA Hampshire Map **04** SZ69

See **Town Plan Section**
GH **Q Q** *Abbey Lodge* 30 Waverley Rd PO5 2PW
☎(0705) 828285
9hc (2fb) ✈ (ex guide dogs)
♔ CTV ✗

GH **Q Q Q** **Beaufort Hotel** 71 Festing Rd PO4 0NQ
☎(0705) 823707 FAX (0705) 870270
Closed 24-31 Dec
Smart, comfortable hotel close to gardens and seafront. Modern, well-equipped bedrooms, separate lounge and basement dining room.
18rm(15⇪3♪)(9fb)⊁in 2 bedrooms CTV in all bedrooms ®
✈ sB&B⇪♪£24-£30
dB&B⇪♪£40-£48 WB&B£140-£168 WBDi£199-£210 LDO 4.30pm
Lic ♔ CTV 8P nc5yrs
Credit Cards 1 3 £

GH **Q Q** **Birchwood** 44 Waverley Rd PO5 2PP ☎(0705) 811337
This Victorian terraced house overlooks the grassy municipal garden. The seafront is a 5-minute walk away, and the accommodation is cosy and comfortable.
6rm(2♪4hc)(2fb)⊁in 2 bedrooms CTV in all bedrooms ®
✈ (ex guide dogs) ✱ sB&B£12-£16 dB&B£24-£32
dB&B♪£27-£35 WB&B£75-£90 WBDi£95-£120 LDO 3pm
Lic ♔ CTV ✗
Credit Cards 1 3 £
See advertisement on page 305

GH **Q Q Q** *Bristol Hotel* 55 Clarence Pde PO5 2HX
☎(0705) 821815
Closed Xmas
This small family-run hotel overlooks Southsea common. With well-equipped, comfortable bedrooms, it provides an ideal base from which to explore the area or an overnight stop for passengers using the ferry terminal.
13rm(9♪4hc)(7fb) CTV in 9 bedrooms TV in 4 bedrooms ®
✈ (ex guide dogs)
Lic ♔ CTV 7P
Credit Cards 1 3
See advertisement on page 305

GH **Q Q** **Collingham** 89 St Ronans Rd PO4 0PR
☎(0705) 821549
Closed 24-26 Dec
Compact, friendly establishment with comfortable modern bedrooms. Well-maintained accommodation with combined lounge and dining room.
6hc (3fb) CTV in 4 bedrooms ® ✱ sB&B£12.50-£13.50
dB&B£25-£27 WB&B£75-£81

►

♨ CTV P̸
[£]

⊢×⊣GH [Q] **The Elms Hotel** 48 Victoria Rd South PO5 2BT
☎(0705) 823924
6hc (3fb) CTV in all bedrooms ® 🚫🐕 (ex guide dogs)
sB&B£12-£13
dB&B£24-£26 WB&B£80-£88 WBDi£110-£120 LDO 9am
Lic ♨ CTV 2P
[£]

⊢×⊣GH [Q][Q] **Gainsborough House** 9 Malvern Rd PO5 2LZ
☎(0705) 822604
Set in a Victorian terrace minutes from the sea, this guesthouse has given visitors a warm, welcome for over twenty years. Bed and breakfast accommodation is provided, with pleasant bedrooms and a comfortable lounge.
7hc (2fb) CTV in all bedrooms ® 🚫🐕 sB&B£12.50-£13.50
dB&B£25-£27
♨ CTV P̸ nc3yrs

GH [Q][Q] **Glencoe** 64 Whitwell Rd PO4 0QS ☎(0705) 737413
This quietly situated terraced guesthouse is family run and has well-maintained comfortable bedrooms. Deceptively spacious, the lounge and attractive dining room are complemented by a colourful courtyard garden. An easy breakfast for those catching ferries or working locally.
7hc (1fb)🚭in 1 bedroom CTV in all bedrooms ® 🚫🐕 ✱
sB&B£13-£15 dB&B£25-£30
♨ CTV P̸
[£]

GH [Q][Q] ***Goodwood House*** 1 Taswell Rd PO5 2RG
☎(0705) 824734
Closed 24 Dec-2 Jan
Quietly situated close to all amenities, this guesthouse provides cosy old-fashioned accommodation that is comfortable and well maintained. The lounge/dinning room are combined.
8hc (1fb) TV in all bedrooms ® 🚫🐕 (ex guide dogs) LDO 5pm
Lic ♨ P̸

⊢×⊣GH [Q][Q][Q] **Hamilton House** 95 Victoria Rd North PO5 1PS
☎(0705) 823502
Deceptively spacious, this Victorian house is in a central residential area. The rooms are comfortable and well equipped, and 3 new bedrooms have en suite facilities. Handy for the ferry port and local attractions, it has a very happy atmosphere.
8rm(3🚿5hc)(3fb) CTV in all bedrooms ® 🚫🐕 sB&B£12.50-£14
sB&B🚿£16-£18 dB&B£25-£28
dB&B🚿£32-£36 WB&B£84-£95 WBDi£119-£130
♨ CTV P̸
[£]

GH [Q][Q] **Lyndhurst** 8 Festing Grove PO4 9QP ☎(0705) 735239
Cosy guesthouse with a friendly atmosphere and a good level of comfort. Compact dining room and separate TV lounge.
7hc ® ✱ sB&Bfr£13
dB&Bfr£25 WB&Bfr£84 WBDifr£108.50 LDO noon
♨ CTV P̸

GH [Q][Q][Q] **Rock Gardens Hotel** Clarence Rd PO5 2LQ
☎(0705) 833018
Closed Xmas
Quietly situated house with modern bedrooms and a large dining room. Bar and separate lounge. Friendly, personal service is offered at this family-run establishment.
15rm(8🛁🚿7hc)(3fb)🚭in 1 bedroom CTV in all bedrooms ®
🚫🐕 (ex guide dogs) ✱ sB&B£16-£25 sB&B🛁🚿fr£25
dB&Bfr£30
dB&B🛁🚿fr£36 WB&B£84-£115 WBDi£110-£150 LDO 7.00pm
Lic ♨ CTV 8P
Credit Cards [1][3]

GH [Q][Q] **Rydeview** 9 Western Pde PO5 3JF ☎(0705) 820865
Telex no 86626 FAX (0705) 291709
Part of a terrace overlooking the common and the distant sea views, this hotel has well-equipped, simply furnished bedrooms on 3 floors. Breakfast is served in the lower ground floor dining room and bar meals are served in the evening.
14rm(6🚿8hc)(6fb) CTV in all bedrooms ® 🚫🐕 (ex guide dogs)
✱ sB&B£20-£22 sB&B🚿£22-£26 dB&B£26-£30
dB&B🚿£36-£38 WB&B£120-£130
Lic ♨ CTV P̸
Credit Cards [1][3][5][£]

⊢×⊣GH [Q][Q] **St Andrews Lodge** 65 St Andrew's Rd PO5 1ER
☎(0705) 827079
Closed 21 Dce-3 Jan
Well situated for the shops, this guesthouse has well-equipped, modern bedrooms – some ideal for family use. The ground floor lounge is comfortable and the proprietors offer personal service.
8hc (2fb) CTV in all bedrooms ® 🚫🐕 (ex guide dogs)
sB&B£12.50-£18
dB&B£25-£30 WB&B£85-£126 WBDi£120-£161 LDO 5pm
♨ CTV P̸
[£]

See advertisement on page 307

GH [Q][Q][Q] **St David's** 19 St Davids Rd PO5 1QH
☎(0705) 826858
Conveniently located in a quiet tree-lined residential area, this semidetached Victorian house offers comfortable bedrooms (one 'no smoking'). There is a well-presented lounge and a friendly, relaxed atmosphere.
6hc (2fb)🚭in 4 bedrooms CTV in all bedrooms ® 🚫🐕 ✱
sB&B£13-£14 dB&B£25-£27 WBDi£91-£98
CTV P̸
[£]

See advertisement on page 307

305

GH **Q** ***Somerset Private Hotel*** 16 Western Pde PO5 3JF ☎(0705) 822495
Well maintained and efficiently managed with a friendly atmosphere. Some bedrooms on the top floors have extensive views of the harbour.
18rm(5↱13hc)(4fb) CTV in 19 bedrooms Ⓡ LDO 7.30pm
Lic ℍ CTV 0P
Credit Cards [1] [3]

GH **Q Q Q** **Upper Mount House Hotel** The Vale, Clarendon Rd PO5 2EQ ☎(0705) 820456
Listed 3-storeyed building set to the rear of a main road in a quiet lane.
11rm(3⇌7↱1hc)(3fb) CTV in all bedrooms Ⓡ sB&B£17-£22 sB&B⇌↱£24-£30
dB&B⇌↱£30-£46 WBDi£105-£170 LDO 6pm
Lic ℍ 7P
Credit Cards [1] [3] (£)

POUNDSGATE Devon Map **03** SX77

GH **Q Q** **Leusdon Lodge** TQ13 7PE ☎(03643) 304
Standing on the edge of Dartmoor, with panoramic views, this 150-year-old, granite-built house has well-equipped, bright bedrooms and comfortable and stylish public rooms. Friendly service and traditional fare make this the ideal etreat for walkers.
9rm(3⇌4↱2hc)(2fb) CTV in 8 bedrooms Ⓡ ✱ sB&Bfr£26
sB&B⇌↱fr£30 dB&Bfr£52
dB&B⇌↱fr£60 (incl dinner) WBDifr£200 LDO 6.30pm
Lic ℍ CTV 12P
Credit Cards [1] [2] [3] [5] (£)

PRESTATYN Clwyd Map **06** SJ08

INN **Q Q** **Bryn Gwalia** 17 Gronant Rd LL19 9DT ☎(07456) 2442 due to change to (0745) 852442
Closed 24 Dec-1 Jan
This small inn, close to the centre of the town, has pleasant and attractive bar and restaurant facilities. The bedrooms are simple but quite well equipped, and are equally suitable for both tourists and commercial guests.
8⇌↱ (2fb) CTV in all bedrooms Ⓡ ✗ (ex guide dogs)
sB&B⇌↱£30
dB&B⇌↱£40 WB&B£150 WBDi£220-£250 Lunch £5.50-£7&alc High tea fr£3.25&alc Dinner £6-£10&alc LDO 9pm
ℍ 24P
Credit Cards [1] [3] (£)

PRESTON Lancashire Map **07** SD52

GH **Q** ***Fulwood Park Hotel*** 49 Watling St Rd PR2 4EA ☎(0772) 718067
Closed Xmas & Boxing Day
A large rambling house, Fulwood Park has been converted to provide extensive modern facilities.
20rm(7⇌7↱6hc)(2fb) CTV in all bedrooms Ⓡ
✗ (ex guide dogs) LDO 7.15pm
Lic CTV 24P 1🚗 ⌂ pool
Credit Cards [1] [2] [3] [5]

GH **Q Q Q** **Tulketh Hotel** 209 Tulketh Road, Ashton PR2 1ES ☎(0772) 726250 & 728096
Closed Xmas-New Year
The bedrooms of this attractive house have very good facilities and the small restaurant serves home-cooked meals. Guests will find a friendly, relaxed atmosphere at Tulketh Hotel which stands in a side road off Preston's ring road.
12rm(4⇌7↱)(1fb) CTV in all bedrooms Ⓡ ✗ (ex guide dogs)
✱ sB&B⇌↱£30-£38
dB&B⇌↱£43-£50 WB&B£206-£250 LDO 7.30pm
Lic ℍ CTV 12P
Credit Cards [1] [3] (£)

GH **Q** **Withy Trees** 175 Garstang Road, Fulwood PR2 4LL (2m N on A6) ☎(0772) 717693
Situated beside the A6, to the north of the town centre, this mainly commercial bed and breakfast establishment offers modest accommodation in clean and freshly decorated surroundings.
11rm(2↱9hc)(2fb)⊘in 5 bedrooms CTV in 4 bedrooms ✱
sB&Bfr£17 sB&B↱fr£25 dB&Bfr£32 dB&B↱fr£41
ℍ CTV 20P
Credit Cards [1] [3]

PRESTWICK Strathclyde *Ayrshire* Map **10** NS32

GH **Q Q Q** **Fairways Hotel** 19 Links Rd KA9 1QG ☎(0292) 70396
Guests at this stone-built house will find comfortable bedrooms, an attractive first floor TV lounge, and substantial breakfasts. The house overlooks the golf course and is a short distance from the air terminal, although not on the flight path.
6hc (1fb) Ⓡ sB&B£15-£16 dB&B£30-£34 WB&B£100-£105
Lic ℍ CTV 8P
(£)

GH **Q Q Q** **Fernbank** 213 Main St KA9 1SU ☎(0292) 75027
Located in the centre of the town, convenient for the airport, Fernbank is a hospitable family-run guesthouse providing spotlessly clean and comfortable accommodation. Bedrooms are nicely designed and well equipped. There are 2 lounges for guests – 1 for non-smokers.
7rm(4↱3hc)(1fb) CTV in all bedrooms Ⓡ ✗ ✱ sB&B£12-£14
dB&B↱£28-£32
ℍ CTV 7P nc5yrs
(£)

Book as early as possible for busy holiday periods.

Leusdon Lodge

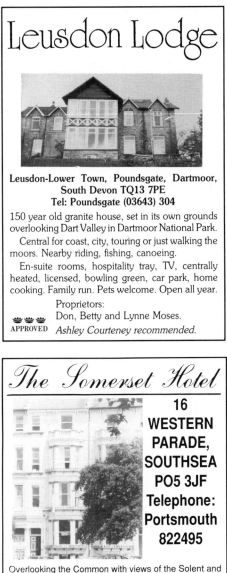

**Leusdon-Lower Town, Poundsgate, Dartmoor,
South Devon TQ13 7PE
Tel: Poundsgate (03643) 304**

150 year old granite house, set in its own grounds overlooking Dart Valley in Dartmoor National Park.

Central for coast, city, touring or just walking the moors. Nearby riding, fishing, canoeing.

En-suite rooms, hospitality tray, TV, centrally heated, licensed, bowling green, car park, home cooking. Family run. Pets welcome. Open all year.

Proprietors:
Don, Betty and Lynne Moses.

APPROVED *Ashley Courteney recommended.*

St David's Guest House

**19 St David's Road, Southsea,
Portsmouth PO5 1QH
Telephone: Portsmouth (0705) 826858**

English Tourist Board

COMMENDED

A beautiful large Victorian house situated in a quiet tree lined road which is very convenient for the King's Theatre, the shopping centres and the attractions of this maritime town such as the Mary Rose and HMS Victory. Centrally heated and all rooms with colour TV and tea/coffee making facilities. A large TV lounge with video recorder is available for relaxation. Should your destination be France the continental ferry port is just five minutes away.

Write, enclosing s.a.e, or telephone for further details to Keith and Jackie Newton.

The Somerset Hotel

16 WESTERN PARADE, SOUTHSEA PO5 3JF Telephone: Portsmouth 822495

Overlooking the Common with views of the Solent and Isle of Wight. Within easy reach of the beach, shopping centres, amusements, HMS Victory, Mary Rose and D-Day Museum. Few minutes to continental & Isle of Wight Ferry Terminals(early breakfast served). Open all year including Christmas. All rooms H&C, centrally heated, radio, colour TV & tea/coffee making facilities. Most of the rooms have en-suite showers & toilet with sea view. Free car parking facilities opposite the hotel. Keys provided for access to rooms at all times. Attractive new licensed residents' bar. SAE for colour brochure & terms.

St. Andrews Lodge

**65 St. Andrews Road
Southsea, Portsmouth PO5 1ER
Tel: (0705) 827079**

ST ANDREWS LODGE is a first class Guest House modernised to the highest standard with your comfort in mind. Rapidly establishing a reputation for standards of cleanliness and friendly service second to none. Situated in central location, 5 minutes to Ferry Ports, Naval Base etc; St Andrews Lodge will appeal to almost any discerning person looking for Hotel standard accommodation at Guest House prices, albeit for one night, weekend or longer. St Andrews Lodge offers 9 well appointed centrally heated bedrooms each with H&C, razor points and CTV together with tea/coffee making facilities. Olde Worlde style dining room, comfortable colour TV lounge. Bed and Breakfast from £13.50 per person per night. **Resident Proprietors: Deborah Rowling & Brenda Watson.**

GH Q Q **Kincraig Private Hotel** 39 Ayr Rd KA9 1SY
☎(0292) 79480
Situated on the main road, this charming detached house has a
comfortable and relaxing lounge. It also has a period dining room
and some well-appointed bedrooms.
6rm(3♥3hc)(1fb) CTV in all bedrooms ® ✻ sB&B£13
dB&B£28 dB&B♥£32 LDO 5pm
Lic 卿 CTV 8P nc3yrs

PWLLHELI Gwynedd Map **06** SH33

GH Q Q Q **The Old Rectory** Bodaun LL53 6DT
☎Nefyn(0758) 720923 & 721363
Situated on the A497, midway between Pwllheli and Nefyn this
family-run hotel has been extensively refurbished to provide good
quality, modern and well-equipped accommodation.
4⇥ (1fb) CTV in all bedrooms ® ✻ sB&B⇥£18
dB&B⇥£32 LDO 9pm
Lic 卿 0P
Credit Cards ① ③

RAMSGATE Kent Map **05** TR36

⊷GH Q Q **St Hilary Private Hotel** 21 Crescent Rd CT11 9QU
☎Thanet(0843) 591427
rs 25-26 Dec
Cheerful compact bedrooms, basement dining room, situated in
residential area.
7hc (4fb) TV available ✗ sB&B£12-£16
dB&B£20-£28 WB&B£60-£70 WBDi£70-£80 (wkly only Jul &
Aug) LDO 3.30pm
Lic CTV ⅌ nc4yrs
Credit Cards ① ③ ⓕ

RASKELF North Yorkshire Map **08** SE47

SELECTED

GH Q Q Q Q **Old Farmhouse Country Hotel** YO6 3LF
☎Easingwold(0347) 21971
28 Jan-21 Dec
Comfort and friendly service are assured at this charming
converted farmhouse which is set in a sleepy village. The
public rooms have exposed beams and are warmed by log fires,
and the attractive bedrooms have many thoughtful extras.
The dinner menu offers a choice of interesting dishes, all
freshly prepared. Guests will enjoy the homemade breads and
preserves.
10rm(6⇥4♥)(2fb) sB&B⇥♥£34-£37
dB&B⇥♥£62-£68 (incl dinner) WBDifr£217 LDO 4pm
Lic 卿 CTV 12P

RAVENSCAR North Yorkshire Map **08** NZ90

GH Q Q Q **The Smugglers Rock Country** YO13 0ER
☎Scarborough(0723) 870044
Converted and restored farmhouse, close to moors and sea.
10rm(2⇥8♥)(2fb) CTV in all bedrooms ®
sB&B⇥♥£16-£16.50
dB&B⇥♥£32-£33 WB&B£99-£99.50 WBDi£137-£138 LDO
4.30pm
Lic 卿 CTV 12P nc3yrs snooker
ⓕ

RAVENSTONEDALE Cumbria Map **12** NY70

FH Q Mrs M Wildman **Ellergill** *(NY737015)* CA17 4LL
☎Newbiggin-on-Lune(05873) 240
Mar-Nov
This tranquil farm house overlooks beautiful countryside yet is a
short drive from junction 38 of the M6. The friendly, informal
household assures guests of a warm welcome.
3hc (1fb)⊭in all bedrooms ® ✗ (ex guide dogs)

CTV 6P 300 acres dairy sheep
ⓕ

READING Berkshire Map **04** SU77

GH Q Q **Aeron Private Hotel** 191 Kentwood Hill, Tilehurst
RG3 6JE (3m W off A329) ☎(0734) 424119 FAX (0734) 451953
Mrs Berry supervises this well-run 3-storeyed house, which is close
to the town centre. The simply appointed bedrooms all have colour
TV, direct dial 'phones and tea and coffee facilities.
13rm(4♥9hc)Annexe 10hc (1fb) CTV in all bedrooms ® ✻
sB&Bfr£26 sB&B♥fr£38.50 dB&Bfr£42
dB&B♥£50.50-£55 LDO 8.15pm
Lic 卿 CTV 20P
Credit Cards ① ③ ⓕ

GH Q Q **Thames House Hotel** 18/19 Thameside, Brigham Rd
RG1 8DR ☎(0734) 507951
This hotel comprises 2 adjoining houses with bedrooms overlooking
the River Thames. It has been under new ownership since last year,
and the bedrooms will be upgraded in the near future.
10rm(6♥4hc)(2fb) CTV in all bedrooms ® ✗ ✻ sB&B£18-£20
sB&B♥fr£20 dB&B♥fr£40 WB&Bfr£120 LDO 8pm
Lic 卿 CTV 20P 4☂ (£1 per night)
Credit Cards ① ③

REDCAR Cleveland Map **08** NZ62

GH Q *Claxton House* Private Hotel, 196 High St TS10 3AW
☎(0642) 486745
Closed 24 Dec-2 Jan
Accommodation here is clean and comfortable and there is an
interesting lounge/dining room.
17rm(6♥11hc)(2fb) CTV in 15 bedrooms ®
Lic 卿 CTV 10P snooker

REDDITCH Hereford & Worcester Map **07** SP06

SELECTED

GH Q Q Q Q **The Old Rectory** Ipsley Ln, Ipsley B98 0AP
☎(0527) 23000 & 26739
Set in 2.5 acres of grounds, this very hospitable hotel offers
guests a peaceful and comfortable stay. Bedroom facilities are
of an extremely high standard and this part Elizabethan
house has been converted to a hotel of character and warmth.
10⇥♥ CTV in 1 bedroom ✗ (ex guide dogs) ✻
sB&B⇥♥£30-£45 dB&B⇥♥£48-£59 LDO noon
Lic 卿 CTV 16P 2☂
Credit Cards ① ③

REDHILL (nr Bristol) Avon Map **03** ST46

FH Q Q Q Mrs M J Hawkings **Hailstones** *(ST502638)*
BS18 7TG ☎Wrington(0934) 862209
Feb-Dec
Set in a peaceful location yet only 1.5 miles from Bristol airport,
this charming farmhouse offers comfortable, well-furnished rooms.
Mrs Hawkings looks after her guests personally and extends a
warm welcome.
4rm(1♥3hc)(2fb)⊭in all bedrooms CTV in 1 bedroom TV in 2
bedrooms ® ✗ ✻ sB&B£20 sB&B♥£20-£25 dB&B£30
dB&B♥£30-£35
卿 CTV 4P croquet 150 acres dairy mixed sheep
ⓕ

This guide is updated annually – make sure you
use an up-to-date edition.

REDHILL **Surrey** Map **04** TQ25

GH [Q][Q] Ashleigh House Hotel 39 Redstone Hill RH1 4BG
☎(0737) 764763
Closed Xmas
Very comfortable homely accommodation with outstanding hospitality. The swimming pool is available some mornings and after 5pm.
9rm(1🚿8hc)(1fb) 🚫🐕 (ex guide dogs) * sB&B£24-£25 dB&B£36-£40 dB&B🚿£42-£44
♨ CTV 9P 🏊(heated)

REDMILE Leicestershire Map **08** SK73

GH [Q][Q] ***Peacock Farm Guest House & Restaurant*** NG13 NGQ
☎Bottesford(0949) 42475
4hc Annexe 5🛁🚿 CTV in 3 bedrooms TV in 2 bedrooms [R] 🚫🐕
LDO 8.30pm
Lic ♨ CTV 30P 🏠 🏊snooker solarium
Credit Cards [1]

REETH North Yorkshire Map **07** SE09

GH [Q][Q][Q] ***Arkleside Hotel*** DL11 6SG
☎Richmond(0748) 84200
Closed 3–31 Jan
Set behind the village green with superb views of the Dales, this 17th-century row of cottages is now a small, quality hotel with comfortable, pretty bedrooms and an elegant restaurant and lounge. Good home cooking is served.
8rm(5🚿3hc) CTV in all bedrooms [R] LDO 7pm
Lic ♨ 7P 3🚗 nc 🎾(hard)
Credit Cards [1] [3]

REIGATE Surrey Map **04** TQ25

GH [Q][Q][Q] Cranleigh Hotel 41 West St RH2 9BL
☎(0737) 223417 FAX (0737) 223734
An efficient, well-managed hotel, with well-equipped modern bedrooms, an outdoor heated swimming pool and rear garden.
10rm(6🛁1🚿3hc)(2fb) CTV in all bedrooms [R]
🚫🐕 (ex guide dogs) sB&B£30-£40 sB&B🛁🚿£45-£55 dB&B£45-£55 dB&B🛁🚿£55-£65 LDO 9pm
Lic ♨ CTV 6P 🏊(heated)
Credit Cards [1] [2] [3] [5] [£]

See advertisement on page 311

RHANDIRMWYN Dyfed Map **03** SN74

INN [Q][Q] Royal Oak SA20 0NY ☎(05506) 201
Reached by a picturesque drive through a wooded valley along the A48 north of Llandovey, this secluded inn has pretty, well-equipped bedrooms and a warm, welcoming bar.
5rm(2🛁1🚿)(1fb) CTV in 3 bedrooms [R] * sB&B£12-£15 dB&B🛁🚿£32.50-£36.50 LDO 10.30pm
20P pool table clay pigeon wknds
Credit Cards [1] [3] [£]

RHOSCOLYN Gwynedd Map **06** SH27

SELECTED

GH [Q][Q][Q][Q] The Old Rectory LL65 2DQ (left off A5 at Valley) ☎Trearddur Bay(0407) 860214
Feb-Nov
This well-preserved and maintained Georgian country house is situated in attractive gardens in a peaceful location, from where excellent views of the surrounding countryside and of the sea may be enjoyed. The bedrooms are well-equipped and all have modern en suite facilities, while a choice of lounges accommodates both smoking and non-smoking guests. The house contains many antique pieces of furniture and has a restful atmosphere. ▶

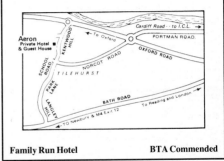

5rm(3🛁2🚿)(2fb) CTV in all bedrooms Ⓡ 🚫 (ex guide dogs) sB&B🛁🚿£21.50 dB&B🛁🚿£41 WB&B£125-£131 WBDi£195-£205 LDO 5pm
Lic 🍴 CTV 6P
Credit Cards [1] [3] [£]

RHOS-ON-SEA Clwyd

See **Colwyn Bay**

RHYL Clwyd Map **06** SJ08

GH [Q][Q] **Pier Hotel** 23 East Pde LL18 3AL ☎(0745) 350280
Closed Xmas
This private hotel is personally run and stands on the promenade, within easy reach of all the town's amenities. The bedrooms are well equipped, most having en suite facilities.
9rm(3🛁3🚿3hc)(3fb) CTV in all bedrooms Ⓡ ✱ sB&B£11-£13 dB&B£22-£26
dB&B🛁🚿£28-£34 WB&B£70-£90 WBDi£85-£125 LDO 3pm
Lic 🍴 CTV 2P
Credit Cards [1] [3] [£]

RICHMOND North Yorkshire Map **07** NZ10

See also Low Row, Reeth and **Thwaite**
GH [Q][Q][Q] **Pottergate** 4 Pottergate DL10 4AB ☎(0748) 3826
Closed 23 Dec-2 Jan
Standing on the A6108 on its eastern approach to the town, this guesthouse has comfortable well-appointed bedrooms with double glazing, and is very well maintained.
6hc (2fb)🚭in 3 bedrooms CTV in all bedrooms Ⓡ 🚫
sB&B£15-£16 dB&B£24-£26
Lic 🍴 CTV 3P nc2yrs

SELECTED

FH [Q][Q][Q][Q] Mrs M F Turnbull **Whashton Springs** *(NZ149046)* DL11 7JS (3m W on unclass rd) ☎(0748) 2884
Closed Xmas & New Year
Attractive and unusual, this stone farmhouse enjoys lovely views over the rolling countryside. 3 miles from the historic town of Richmond, deep in 'Herriot country', visitors will enjoy the tranquility yet find plenty of persuits to fill their time. The house offers 3 spacious bedrooms and converted outbuildings provide charming rustic style rooms. All are well appointed with many thoughtful extras. Mrs Turnbull prepares mouthwatering farmhouse meals with substantial Yorkshire breakfasts, while Mr Turnbull is the ideal host. A worthy winner of 'Farmhouse of the Year 1988' for the north.
3🛁 Annexe 5rm(2🛁3🚿)(2fb)🚭in 1 bedroom CTV in all bedrooms Ⓡ 🚫 (ex guide dogs) sB&B🛁🚿fr£25
dB&B🛁🚿£34-£40 WB&B£115-£135 LDO am
Lic 🍴 10P nc5yrs 600 acres arable beef mixed sheep

RIEVAULX North Yorkshire Map **08** SE58

FH [Q][Q] Mrs M E Skilbeck **Middle Heads** *(SE584869)* YO6 5LU ☎Bilsdale(04396) 251
Mar-Nov
This stone farmhouse, set in a fairly remote location one mile east of the B1257 and 3 miles north west of Helmsley, is ideally situated for walkers and visitors to the moors. Warm and friendly, it offers 3 bedrooms (sharing a modern bathroom) and a comfortable lounge.
3rm (1fb)🚭in all bedrooms 🚫 ✱ dB&Bfr£22
🍴 CTV 6P nc2yrs 170 acres arable beef mixed sheep

Visit your local AA Centre.

RINGMER East Sussex Map **05** TQ41

INN [Q][Q] ***Ringmer*** Lewes Rd BN8 5QB ☎(0273) 812348
8🛁🚿 (2fb) CTV in all bedrooms Ⓡ LDO 9.30pm
🍴 50P
Credit Cards [1] [2] [3] [5]

RINGWOOD Hampshire Map **04** SU10

SELECTED

GH [Q][Q][Q][Q] **Little Forest Lodge Hotel** Poulner Hill BH24 3HS ☎(0425) 478848
Three acres of landscaped gardens surround this attractive country house which is set back from the A31 eastbound carriageway from Ringwood. The charming rooms are equipped with colour TV and beverage making facilities. A 4-course dinner is served in the candlelit, oak-panelled dining room. A choice is available at each course, including vegetarian dishes. Mr and Mrs Martin provide attentive service and fishing, sailing and horse-riding can be arranged. Little Forest Lodge provides an excellent base for touring the area.
5rm(2🛁1🚿2hc)(2fb) CTV in all bedrooms Ⓡ
sB&B£27.50-£29.50 dB&B£40-£43
dB&B🛁🚿£44-£55 WB&B£120-£165 WBDi£189-£234 LDO 4pm
Lic 🍴 CTV 10P 2🚗 solarium
Credit Cards [1] [3] [£]

RIPON North Yorkshire Map **08** SE37

GH [Q][Q] **Crescent Lodge** 42 North St HG4 1EN ☎(0765) 2331
This attractive guesthouse is run by Christine Bunce who is a competent and friendly host. The bedrooms vary in shape and size and there is a cosy dining room and an attractive lounge.
10rm(3🚿7hc)(4fb) CTV in all bedrooms Ⓡ 🚫 sB&B£14 dB&B£24-£28 dB&B🚿£34 WB&B£91
Lic 🍴 CTV 🚫P

ROADWATER Somerset Map **03** ST03

FH [Q][Q] Mr & Mrs Brewer **Wood Advent** *(ST037374)* TA23 0RR ☎Washford(0984) 40920
Set in 340 acres at the foot of the Brendon Hills in Exmoor National Park, this delightful farmhouse has spacious bedrooms some with en suite facilities and relaxing public rooms. Mrs. Brewer uses home produce whenever possible for the set menu.
5rm(1🛁2🚿1hc)(3fb) Ⓡ 🚫 ✱ sB&B£23
sB&B🛁🚿£25 (incl dinner) WB&B£120-£130
Lic 🍴 CTV 10P 2🚗 🎱 🏊(heated) 🎾(grass)350 acres arable beef sheep
See advertisement under DUNSTER on page 141

ROBIN HOOD'S BAY North Yorkshire Map **08** NZ90

FH [Q][Q] Mrs P Featherstone **Croft** *(NZ941051)* Fylingthorpe YO22 4PW ☎Whitby(0947) 880231
Apr-Sep
A 40-acre dairy farm, Croft Farm is on the outskirts of Fylingthorpe on the unclassified Hawksey road. Accommodation is traditional and well-furnished and overlooks the cliffs, while the well-tended gardens are reached via the farmyard.
3rm(1hc)(1fb)🚭in all bedrooms 🚫 ✱ sB&B£10-£12 dB&B£20-£24 WB&B£70
CTV 4P nc5yrs 40 acres dairy

[Q] is for quality. For a full explanation of this AA quality award, consult the Contents page.

ROCHDALE Greater Manchester Map **07** SD81

FH [Q][Q] Mrs J Neave **Leaches** *(SD835838)* Ashworth Valley OL11 5UN ☎(0706) 41116 & 41117
Closed 24 Dec-1 Jan
Guests will feel at home at this friendly hill farmhouse which dates from 1675 and has fine panoramic views over the Manchester plain – particularly impressive at night. Leaches Farm is signposted from the B6222 and A680.
3hc (2fb)🚭in all bedrooms CTV in 1 bedroom TV in 1 bedroom 🐕✗ (ex guide dogs) sB&B£17-£20 dB&B£30
🛋 CTV 6P 🎣 coarse fishing 140 acres beef sheep
[£]

ROCHE Cornwall & Isles of Scilly Map **02** SW96

GH [Q][Q][Q] ***Asterisk*** Mount Pleasant PL26 8LH
☎St Austell(0726) 890863
Charming and personally run, this family guesthouse has good views of the countryside yet is close to the A30. The cosy bedrooms are furnished in cottage style. Three acres of grounds contain poultry, goats and ponies.
7rm(2🚿5hc)(2fb) [R]
Lic 🛋 CTV 10P 2🚗

ROCHESTER Northumberland Map **12** NY89

FH [Q][Q] Mrs J H Chapman **Woolaw** *(NY821984)* NE19 1TB
☎Otterburn(0830) 20686
Comfortable farmhouse in a tranquil setting with lovely views over surrounding countryside.
3rm(2🚿)(1fb) CTV in 1 bedroom 🐕✗ (ex guide dogs) *
sB&B🚿£10-£12 dB&B£20-£24
dB&B🚿£24 WB&B£70-£84 LDO 7.30pm
🛋 CTV 10P 🎣 740 acres beef sheep

INN [Q][Q] **Redesdale Arms** NE19 1TA
☎Otterburn(0830) 20668 & 20530
This cosy stone-built inn on the A68 offers a neat bedrooms and a good range of bar meals.
12rm(7🛁🚿5hc)(1fb) CTV in all bedrooms [R] *
sB&B£16-£17.50 dB&B£32 dB&B🛁🚿£40-£45 LDO 9pm
🛋 30P 2🚗
Credit Cards [1] [3] [5] [£]

ROCK Cornwall & Isles of Scilly Map **02** SW97

GH [Q] **Roskarnon House Hotel** PL27 6LD
☎Trebethrick(0208) 862329
Mar-Nov
Standing within an acre of lawns in an elevated position with beautiful views across the Camel Estuary, this detached house has simply appointed bedrooms and an attractive dining room with a table d'hôte menu.
15rm(4🛁2🚿9hc)(5fb) CTV in 4 bedrooms TV in 1 bedroom
🐕✗ sB&B🛁🚿fr£25 dB&Bfr£35
dB&B🛁🚿fr£40 WB&Bfr£120 WBDifr£180 LDO 8pm
Lic CTV 14P 2🚗 (£1 per night) [£]

ROEWEN Gwynedd Map **06** SH77

↔**GH** [Q][Q][Q] **Gwern Borter Country Manor** Barkers Ln LL32 8YL ☎Tyn-y-Groes(0492) 650360
Closed 23 Dec-2 Jan
Gwern Baxter Manor is set in nine acres of grounds at the foot of Talytan Mountain, north of the village. Short breaks are the main business at the manor house which can be enhanced by supervised horse rides. For complete freedom, self-catering units are available.
4rm(2🚿)(1fb) TV available [R] sB&B£12-£17 sB&B🚿£14-£19
dB&B£24-£30
dB&B🚿£28-£34 WB&B£75-£119 WBDi£110-£150 (wkly only Jul-mid Sep) LDO 4pm
Lic 🛋 CTV 10P nc3yrs 🐎 cycle hire

ROGART Highland *Sutherland* Map **14** NC70

SELECTED

FH QQQQ Mrs J S R Moodie **Rovie** *(NC716023)* IV28 3TZ ☎(04084) 209
Apr-Oct
Set in sheltered gardens in the picturesque valley of Strath Fleet, this farmhouse belongs to Stan and Christine Moodie who have welcomed guests for over 30 years, many returning regularly, and the farmhouse is often fully booked. Bedrooms are spacious and comfortable, and the public rooms include a sun lounge with TV. All food is home cooked, with baking a speciality, and the reasonable charge includes morning and evening tea.
6hc (1fb) ✱
dB&B£28 WB&B£118 WBDi£196 LDO 6.30pm
CTV 8P ⚑9 ✓ 120 acres beef sheep
£

ROGATE West Sussex Map **04** SU82

SELECTED

FH QQQQ Mrs J C Francis **Mizzards** *(SU803228)* GU31 5HS ☎(0730) 821656
Closed Xmas
Situated in a tranquil rural setting, the house is full of character with attractive, comfortable and well-equipped accommodation. The house is elegant, spacious and has a very comfortable lounge.
3⇔⋒ ⊁in all bedrooms CTV in all bedrooms ® ✗
dB&B⇔⋒£36-£41 WB&B£252-£287
⊞ 10P 2⌂ nc6yrs ⌒(heated) 13 acres sheep non-working
£

FH QQQ Mrs J Baigent **Trotton** *(SU835225)* GU31 5EN ☎Midhurst(0730) 813618
This modern farmhouse is set on a 200-acre working farm, situated 2 miles from Rogate in a tranquil and rural area. The accommodation is well equipped and maintained with a lounge/ games room and family-style breakfast room.
3rm(2⋒1hc)⊁in all bedrooms CTV in 1 bedroom ®
✗ (ex guide dogs) sB&B£15-£25 dB&B⋒£35-£40
⊞ CTV 0P ✓ table tennis darts 230 acres arable, beef, horticulture

ROMFORD Greater London Map **05** TQ58

GH QQ ***Repton Private Hotel*** 18 Repton Dr, Gidea Park RM2 5LP ☎(0708) 45253
Closed 23 Dec-1 Jan
9hc CTV in all bedrooms
⊞ CTV ⊁

ROSLIN Lothian *Midlothian* Map **11** NT26

INN QQ Olde Original Rosslyn 4 Main St EH25 9LD ☎031-440 2384
Early 18th-century inn, full of character, providing a good standard of modern accommodation. Pleasant, popular bars.
6⇔⋒ CTV in all bedrooms ® ✱ sB&B⇔⋒fr£30 dB&B⇔⋒fr£36 Bar Lunch £1.75-£7.50&alc Dinner £10-£12&alc LDO 10pm
⊞ 14P
Credit Cards [1] [2] [3]

See the regional maps of popular holiday areas at the back of the book.

ROSS-ON-WYE Hereford & Worcester Map **03** SO52

For details of farmhouse accommodation in the vicinity, see **St Owen's Cross**

GH QQ The Arches Country House Walford Rd HR9 5PT ☎(0989) 63348
This small guesthouse is located on the southern side of the town. The rooms here are modest but well kept. There is a comfortable lounge in addition to the pleasant dining room, and a friendly informal atmosphere prevails.
6rm(1⇔5hc)(2fb)⊁in 1 bedroom CTV in all bedrooms ® ✱ sB&B£16 sB&B⇔£17.50 dB&B£29 dB&B⇔£36 WB&B£90-£100 WBDi£144-£166 LDO 5pm
Lic ⊞ CTV 9P
£

GH QQ Brookfield House Ledbury Rd HR9 7AT ☎(0989) 62188
rs Nov-Jan
This guesthouse is situated within walking distance of the town centre and has its own car park. Brookfield House is run by Mr and Mrs Baker who are friendly and helpful.
8rm(1⇔2⋒5hc) CTV in all bedrooms ® sB&B£15 dB&B£27 dB&B⇔⋒£30 WB&B£90-£100
Lic ⊞ 10P
Credit Cards [1] [3]

GH QQQ Edde Cross House Edde Cross St HR9 7BZ ☎(0989) 65088
Feb-Nov
Edde Cross House is a Georgian grade II listed building, once the summer palace of the Bishops of Hereford, it was also the home of Sibyl Hathaway, Dame of Sark. Accommodation is comfortable, attractive and well equipped with some thoughtful extras. Some rooms have good views across the horseshoe bend of the River Wye, and there is an attractive small garden from which guests can also enjoy the view. The proprietors are friendly and welcoming and work hard to ensure that guests are comfortable. This is a 'no smoking' house.
5rm(2⋒3hc)⊁in all bedrooms CTV in all bedrooms ®
✗ (ex guide dogs) sB&B£17-£18 dB&B£32-£34 dB&B⋒£40-£42 WB&Bfr£101
⊞ 1⌂ (£1 per day) nc10yrs
£

GH QQQ ***Ryefield House Hotel*** Gloucester Rd HR9 5NA ☎(0989) 63030
mid Feb-Xmas
Situated on the outskirts of the town, approximately half a mile from its centre, this large Victorian house offers comfortable accommodation. The bedrooms are well equipped and maintained, and many have en suite facilities. The proprietors' warm and friendly hospitality contributes much to its popularity.
7rm(2⇔1⋒4hc)(4fb) CTV in all bedrooms ® LDO 5pm
Lic ⊞ CTV 10P 1⌂

GH QQ Sunnymount Hotel Ryefield Rd HR9 5LU ☎(0989) 63880
Closed Xmas
Sunnymount is situated in a quiet residential area close to the town. The accommodation is comfortable and spacious and Mr and Mrs Williams are welcoming hosts.
9rm(6⇔⋒3hc) ® ✗ (ex guide dogs) sB&B£16-£18 sB&B⇔⋒£29 dB&B£33 dB&B⇔⋒£44 WB&Bfr£110 WBDi£195 LDO 6.30pm
Lic ⊞ CTV 7P
Credit Cards [1] [3] £

See advertisement on page 315

Book as early as possible for busy holiday periods.

313

ROTHBURY Northumberland Map **12** NU00

GH Q Q Q **Orchard** High St NE65 7TL ☎(0669) 20684
Mar-Nov
The interesting meals provided by the friendly proprietors of this delightful house are especially recommended. It is set back from the high street and offers a very good standard of accommodation with many thoughtful extras.
6rm(4🌂2hc)(1fb) CTV in all bedrooms ® 🅍
sB&B£16.50-£18.50 dB&B£33-£35
dB&B🌂£37-£39 WB&B£115.50-£129.50
WBD£178.50-£185.50 LDO 7pm
Lic ⁹⁹⁹ 4P
£

ROTHLEY Leicestershire Map **08** SK51

GH Q Q Q **The Limes Hotel** 35 Mountsorrel Ln LE7 7PS
☎Leicester(0533) 302531
Closed Xmas
Friendly, efficiently run hotel with comfortable bedrooms and pleasant bars.
12⇌🌂 CTV in all bedrooms ® 🅍 (ex guide dogs) ✳
sB&B⇌🌂fr£37.50 dB&B⇌🌂£40-£50 LDO 9pm
Lic ⁹⁹⁹ 15P nc12yrs
Credit Cards 1 3

ROTTINGDEAN East Sussex Map **05** TQ30

GH Q Q **Braemar House** Steyning Rd BN2 7GA
☎Brighton(0273) 304263
This pleasant family-run hotel combines traditional accommodation, which is very well maintained, with a comfortable television lounge and a cosy dining room. The hotel is adjacent to the village green and is within easy walking distance of the seafront.
16hc (2fb) ✳ sB&B£12-£13 dB&B£24-£26
⁹⁹⁹ CTV 🗶
£

GH Q Q **Corner House** Steyning Rd BN2 7GA
☎Brighton(0273) 304533
This is a rather cosy establishment that is personally run. The accommodation offered is functional and well kept, and breakfast here is taken in a relaxing atmosphere.
6hc (1fb) CTV in 5 bedrooms TV in 1 bedroom ® ✳
sB&B£14-£14.50 dB&B£28-£29
⁹⁹⁹ 🗶
£

ROWLEY REGIS West Midlands Map **07** SO98

GH Q Q **Highfield House Hotel** Holly Rd B65 0BH
☎021-559 1066
Closed Xmas
Mr and Mrs Pedlar make guests welcome at this predominantly commercial guesthouse, which has easy access to motorways and Black Country business centres. The rooms are modestly furnished but well kept, and light snacks are always available.
14rm(1⇌1🌂12hc) CTV in all bedrooms ® 🅍 (ex guide dogs)
sB&B£24-£28 sB&B⇌🌂£35 dB&B£38-£46 dB&B⇌🌂£43-£57
Lic ⁹⁹⁹ CTV 12P nc5yrs
£

ROWTON Shropshire Map **07** SJ61

FH Q **Mr & Mrs Evans** *Church* *(SJ614198)* TF6 6QY (1m along unclass road, off the A442 Whitchurch to Telford road)
☎High Ercall(0952) 770381
Part of a working farm, this 300-year-old house is 6 miles north of Wellington in a small, peaceful village. The bedrooms are simply furnished and the lounge features an unusual wood panelled inglenook fireplace.

4rm(2🌂2hc)(1fb)🗶in all bedrooms ® sB&B£15-£18
sB&B🌂£30 dB&B£24-£30
dB&B🌂£30-£35 WB&B£85-£105 LDO 5pm
⁹⁹⁹ CTV 6P 2🐾 ∞ ✈ 35 acres dairy pigs sheep
£

ROXTON Bedfordshire Map **04** TL15

FH Q Q Q **Mrs J Must** *Church (TL153545)* 41 High St
MK44 3EB ☎Bedford(0234) 870234
This attractive, tastefully appointed farmhouse with its well-kept gardens and peaceful village setting offers spacious bedrooms and comfortable public rooms. A warm, friendly atmosphere prevails here.
2rm(1hc)(1fb) ®
⁹⁹⁹ CTV 6P 66 acres arable

RUCKHALL Hereford & Worcester Map **03** SO44

SELECTED

INN Q Q Q Q **The Ancient Camp** HR2 9QX
☎Golden Valley(0981) 250449
Standing high above the River Wye, this inn seems isolated, but it is only 10 minutes from Hereford town centre. David and Nova Hague are popular and competant hosts and provide comfortable accommodation and a varied and interesting menu. Flagged floors and stone walls are warmed by open fires and a choice of traditional local ales is available.
5rm(2⇌3🌂) CTV in all bedrooms ® 🅍 (ex guide dogs) ✳
sB&B⇌🌂£30-£40
dB&B⇌🌂£42-£52 Bar Lunch £2.50-£5.75alc Dinner £10-£15alc LDO 9.30pm
⁹⁹⁹ 30P nc10yrs ✈
Credit Cards 1 3 £

RUFFORTH North Yorkshire Map **08** SE55

GH Q Q **Wellgarth House** Wetherby Rd YO2 3QB
☎(090483) 592 & 595
Closed 25-26 Dec
A large well-appointed modern house on the edge of the village.
8rm(3🌂5hc)(1fb) CTV in all bedrooms ® 🅍 sB&Bfr£15
dB&B£26-£30 dB&B🌂£28-£34 LDO 5pm
⁹⁹⁹ CTV 8P nc6yrs

RUGBY Warwickshire Map **04** SP57

GH Q Q **Avondale** 16 Elsee Rd CV21 3BA ☎(0788) 578639
Quietly situated in a residential area close to the town centre and the famous Rugby School, this guesthouse has the benefit of private parking. The friendly proprietors provide comfortable surroundings.
4rm(1🌂3hc)(1fb) CTV in 2 bedrooms ® 🅍 ✳ sB&B£18-£22
sB&B🌂£25 dB&B£32 dB&B🌂£36 LDO 3pm
⁹⁹⁹ CTV 6P 2🐾
£

GH Q Q *Mound Hotel* 17-19 Lawford Rd CV21 2EB
☎(0788) 543486
Closed Xmas
Formerly 3 late-Victorian houses, this hotel, situated on the A428 close to the town centre, retains some original features. Although only room and breakfast are provided, there is a good lounge for guests' use.
17rm(6🌂11hc)(4fb) CTV in 6 bedrooms TV in 11 bedrooms
🅍 (ex guide dogs) LDO 3pm
Lic ⁹⁹⁹ CTV 14P
Credit Cards 1

FH Q Mrs S Moses *Lawford Hill* *(SP466746)* Lawford Heath Ln CV23 9HG ☎(0788) 542001
Closed Xmas
This friendly farmhouse is a hub of activity offering bed and breakfast accommodation which is simple and comfortable. Popular with business travellers and tourists alike, the farm has open days and a small museum.
4rm(1⇆3hc)(1fb) ®
CTV 12P 200 acres arable stock mixed

RUISLIP Greater London

London plan **4** A5 (pages 230-231)
GH QQQ **Barn Hotel** West End Rd HA4 6JB
☎(0895) 636057 Telex no 892514 FAX (0895) 638379
Two acres of landscaped gardens surround this charming building which dates back to 1628. The bedrooms, all in an annexe which is set in the grounds, vary in style and are well equipped.
Annexe 66rm(64⇆🏠2hc)(1fb)⚥in 4 bedrooms CTV in all bedrooms ® 🏃 (ex guide dogs) ✱ sB&B£50-£60 sB&B⇆🏠£69.50 dB&B⇆🏠£85 LDO 9.30pm
Lic ᵐ CTV 60P
Credit Cards [1][2][3][5]

RUSHTON SPENCER Staffordshire Map **07** SJ96

FH Q Mrs J Brown **Barnswood** *(SJ945606)* SK11 0RA
☎(0260) 226261
Closed 24 Dec-5 Jan
Smoking is discouraged in the good-sized bedrooms of a comfortable farmhouse which overlooks Rudyard Lake from its position on the A523 Macclesfield road, approximately five miles from Leek.
4rm(2hc)(2fb) ® 🏃 ✱ sB&Bfr£13 dB&Bfr£23
ᵐ CTV 4P 100 acres dairy

RUSTINGTON West Sussex Map **04** TQ00

GH QQ **Kenmore** Claigmar Rd BN16 2NL ☎(0903) 784634
rs Xmas
Close to shops and seafront with modern well-appointed rooms.
5rm(1⇆2🏠)(2fb) CTV in all bedrooms ® sB&B£15-£20 sB&B⇆🏠£15-£20 dB&B⇆🏠£40-£45 WB&B£95-£125
ᵐ CTV 5P
Credit Cards [1][3] £

RUTHIN Clwyd Map **06** SJ15

⊢↔FH Q Margaret E Jones **Pencoed** *(SJ107538)* Pwllglas LL15 2LT ☎Clawdd Newydd(08245) 251
Closed Xmas
A steep, narrow lane leads to this isolated farm where a friendly welcome is given by Mr Jones, who with his dog Spot won the 1988 Supreme Champion Sheepdog Trials. The house is adorned with his trophies.
2hc (2fb) sB&B£11-£11.50 dB&B£21-£22 WB&Bfr£75
ᵐ CTV 0P 160 acres mixed
£

RYDAL Cumbria

See **Ambleside**

RYDE

See **WIGHT, ISLE OF**

RYE East Sussex Map **05** TQ92

GH QQQ **Holloway House** High St TN31 7JF
☎(0797) 224748
This beautiful ivy-clad Tudor house with its medieval vaulted cellar has some bedrooms with four-poster or brass beds and an oak-panelled Elizabethan room which has an antique French bed. All of the rooms have modern facilities.
7rm(5⇆2🏠)(2fb) CTV in all bedrooms ® 🏃 (ex guide dogs)
sB&B⇆🏠£30-£50 dB&B⇆🏠£70

Lic ᵐ 🅟
Credit Cards [1][3]

See advertisement on page 317

GH QQQ *Little Saltcote* 22 Military Rd TN31 7NY
☎(0797) 223210
Situated in an elevated position with its own cottage garden, this cosy establishment has well-furnished and maintained bedrooms. Parking is available and the town centre is only 5 minutes' walk away.
6rm(2🏠4hc)(2fb) TV in all bedrooms ® 🏃
ᵐ 0P

GH QQQ **Old Borough Arms** The Strand TN31 7DB
☎(0797) 222128
Built into the medieval town walls, this pleasant guesthouse enjoys an elevated position. The comfortable modern accommodation includes a charming 18th-century dining room and bedrooms with en suite shower rooms.
▶

9🚿 (3fb) CTV in all bedrooms [R] sB&B🚿£20-£25 dB&B🚿£40-£50 LDO 8pm
Lic ♨ CTV 2P
Credit Cards [1] [3] [£]

SELECTED

GH [Q][Q][Q][Q] The Old Vicarage Hotel & Restaurant 15 East St TN31 7JY ☎(0797) 225131
Set in the centre of this charming port, this listed building has been sympathetically converted into a comfortable and elegant small hotel. Individually decorated and furnished in period style, the bedrooms are all en suite and very well equipped. The attractive dining room offers an à la carte menu and reasonably-priced wines are available. The hotel maintains a relaxed, informal atmosphere.
4🛁 (2fb) CTV in all bedrooms [R] sB&B🛁£42-£47 dB&B🛁£62-£70 WB&B£189-£203 WBDi£294-£308 LDO 9pm
Lic ♨ 🚫🅿
Credit Cards [1] [3] [5] [£]

FH [Q][Q][Q] Mrs P Sullivin **Cliff** *(TQ933237)* Iden Lock TN31 7QE ☎Iden(07978) 331
Mar-Oct
Quietly situated with views over Romney Marsh, this typical Sussex peg tile farmhouse is over 150 years' old and offers cosy accommodation. Wholesome breakfasts are served in the pretty breakfast room. The general shower room is located on the ground floor.
3hc (1fb) [R] ✱ dB&B£24-£28
♨ CTV 6P 6 acres smallholding
[£]

ST AGNES Cornwall & Isles of Scilly Map 02 SW75

GH [Q] Penkerris Penwinnick Rd TR5 0PA ☎(087255) 2262
Attractive, detached house in lovely garden on the edge of the village.
5rm(1🚿4hc)(3fb) CTV in 3 bedrooms TV in 2 bedrooms [R] ✱ sB&B£12-£20 dB&B£20-£30 dB&B🚿£25-£35 WB&B£70-£100 WBDi£105-£140 LDO 10am
Lic CTV 8P badminton court childrens swings
Credit Cards [1] [3] [£]

GH [Q][Q][Q] *Porthvean Hotel* Churchtown TR5 0QP ☎(087255) 2581
Closed Dec & Mar
Comfortable village centre guesthouse with friendly owners, also Frin's Restaurant with some vegetarian dishes.
6rm(5🚿1hc)(3fb) CTV in all bedrooms [R] 🚫🐕 (ex guide dogs) LDO 9pm
Lic ♨ 8P
Credit Cards [1] [3]

GH [Q][Q] St Agnes Hotel Churchtown TR5 0QP ☎(087255) 2307
Centrally situated in this attractive Cornish village endearingly known as 'the Aggie', 2 character bars here serve traditional bar meals. A separate restaurant operates during the suumer season. Bedrooms have colour televisions and tea-making facilities.
5rm(1🛁2🚿2hc)(5fb) CTV in 3 bedrooms [R] ✱ sB&B£16.50-£22.50 sB&B🛁🚿£22.50-£27.50 dB&B£33-£37 dB&B🛁🚿£40-£45 LDO 9pm
Lic CTV 50P
Credit Cards [1] [3] [£]

[Q] is for quality. For a full explanation of this AA quality award, consult the Contents page.

ST ALBANS Hertfordshire Map 04 TL10

GH [Q][Q][Q] Ardmore House 54 Lemsford Rd AL1 3PR ☎(0727) 59313 & 69313
This appealing hotel offers modern accommodation of a good standard, the rooms being well equipped and pleasantly decorated. The attractive dining rooms overlooks the garden.
26rm(23🛁🚿3hc)(2fb) CTV in all bedrooms [R] sB&B£28.75 sB&B🛁🚿£41.40 dB&B£39.10 dB&B🛁🚿£49.45
Lic ♨ 20P
Credit Cards [1]

GH [Q][Q] Melford 24 Woodstock Rd North AL1 4QQ ☎(0727) 53642
This attractive house occupies a peaceful site in a residential area. Neat and well maintained, the accommodation includes a dining room and comfortable lounge which overlooks the rear garden.
12rm(4🚿8hc)(3fb) [R] ✱ sB&B£24.15 sB&B🚿£43.70 dB&B£36.80 dB&B🚿£46
Lic ♨ CTV 12P

ST ANDREWS Fife Map 12 NO51

GH [Q][Q] Albany 56 North St KY16 9AH ☎(0334) 77737
Neat and compact terraced house with functional, well-equipped bedrooms.
12rm(5🚿7hc)(2fb)🚭in 2 bedrooms CTV in all bedrooms [R] sB&B£15-£24 dB&B£28-£36 dB&B🚿£38-£48 WBDi£130-£210 LDO 6pm
Lic ♨ 🚫🅿
Credit Cards [1] [3]

GH [Q][Q] Amberside 4 Murray Pk KY16 9AW ☎(0334) 74644
Closed Nov
This compact, modern and well-equipped house is part of a tenement row between the town centre and the sea. The dining room is combined with the residents' lounge.
5rm(4🚿1hc)(1fb) CTV in all bedrooms [R] sB&B£14-£18 dB&B🚿£30-£38 WB&B£92-£120
♨ CTV 🚫🅿

GH [Q][Q] Argyle Hotel 127 North St KY16 9AG ☎(0334) 73387
Apr-Oct
Large private hotel on prominent corner site, with spacious bedrooms and good lounge accommodation.
19🚿 (5fb) CTV in all bedrooms [R] ✱ sB&B🚿£20-£24 dB&B🚿£40-£50 WB&B£150
Lic ♨ CTV 🚫🅿 nc2yrs
Credit Cards [1] [3]

GH [Q][Q] Arran House 5 Murray Park KY16 9AW ☎(0334) 74724 FAX (0334) 72072
Compact and nicely decorated house with some attractive bedrooms and a combined residents' lounge and dining room.
6rm(3🚿3hc)(4fb) CTV in all bedrooms [R] 🚫🐕 ✱ sB&B£15-£20 dB&B£25-£40 dB&B🚿£32-£40
♨ CTV 🚫🅿
[£]

GH [Q][Q] *Beachway House* 6 Murray Park KY16 9AW ☎(0334) 73319
Conversion of 2 adjoining houses in between town centre and sea.
6rm(5🚿1hc)(2fb) CTV in all bedrooms [R]
♨ 🚫🅿

GH [Q][Q] *Bell Craig* 8 Murray Park KY16 9AW ☎(0334) 72962
A neat house with combined lounge/dining room.
5rm(3🚿2hc)(3fb) CTV in all bedrooms [R]
♨ CTV 🚫🅿

[£] Remember to use the money-off vouchers.

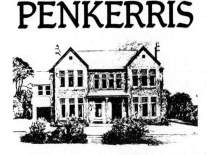

317

GH QQ *Burness House* Murray Park KY16 9AW
☎(0334) 74314
Standing on a corner site, this compact, modernised house has a combined lounge and dining-room and well-equipped bedrooms.
5♠ (1fb) CTV in all bedrooms ®
⁂ CTV ⚥

GH QQ **Cleveden House** 3 Murray Place KY16 9AP
☎(0334) 74212
Nicely decorated house in side street between town centre and sea.
6rm(3♠3hc)(2fb) ✱ (ex guide dogs) ✲ sB&B£13-£18
dB&B♠£30-£40
⁂ CTV ⚥
£

GH QQ **Craigmore** 3 Murray Park KY16 9AW
☎(0334) 72142 & 77963
Smartly decorated, comfortable guesthouse conveniently situated for town centre and the Old Course.
5rm(1⇨4♠)(4fb) CTV in all bedrooms ® ✱ sB&B£16-£30
sB&B⇨♠£18-£35 dB&B£24-£36
dB&B⇨♠£26-£40 WB&B£105-£195
⁂ CTV ⚥
£

GH QQ **Hazlebank Private Hotel** 28 The Scores KY16 9AS
☎(0334) 72466
Close to the front and with superb views of the coast, Hazelbank has modern bedrooms and a friendly atmosphere
10⇨♠ (6fb) CTV in all bedrooms ® sB&B⇨♠£25-£50
dB&B♠£40-£60
Lic ⁂ ⚥
£

GH QQ *Number Ten* 10 Hope St KY16 9HJ ☎(0334) 74601
Apr-Oct
Attractively decorated hotel in terraced row off town centre.
10rm(2⇨4♠4hc)(4fb) ® ✱ (ex guide dogs)
⁂ CTV ⚥ nc2yrs

GH QQ **West Park House** 5 St Mary's Place KY16 9UY
☎(0334) 75933
Mar-Nov
Small but stylish detached Georgian house close to town centre. Attractive dining room also open to non-residents, including á la carte dinners.
5rm(3♠2hc)(1fb) CTV in all bedrooms ® ✱ (ex guide dogs)
dB&B£29-£40
⁂ ⚥
£

GH QQ **Yorkston Hotel** 68 & 70 Argyle St KY16 9BU
☎(0334) 72019
rs Xmas & New Year
Neatly appointed house on roadside leading into town from west.
10rm(1⇨4♠5hc)(3fb) ® ✱ (ex guide dogs) sB&B£17-£19.50
sB&B⇨♠£32-£40 dB&B£32-£36
dB&B⇨♠£37-£50 WB&B£112-£175 WBDi£175-£240 LDO
6.30pm
Lic ⁂ CTV ⚥

FH QQ Mrs A E Duncan **Spinks Town** *(NO541144)*
KY16 8PN ☎(0334) 73475
Just 2 miles east of the popular golfing resort, this modern house is on the picturesque A917 coast road. The bright, spacious accommodation is of a very high standard.
3rm(2⇨♠1hc)⚥in all bedrooms ✱ ✲ dB&B£22-£25
dB&B⇨♠£26-£30
⁂ CTV 3P 250 acres arable cattle

ST ASAPH Clwyd Map **06** SJ07

FH QQQ Mrs A Roberts **Bach-Y-Craig** *(SJ075713)*
Tremeirchion LL17 0UH ☎Trefnant(074574) 627 due to change to (0745) 730627
Closed Dec
This delightful and unusual old house is in a fairly remote position 4 miles south east of St Asaph. Warm hospitality and good wholesome cooking feature along with well-equipped bedrooms. The farm's 200 acres include 40 acres of ancient woodland with a nature trail.
3⇨♠ (1fb)⚥in all bedrooms CTV in all bedrooms ® ✱
✲ dB&B⇨♠fr£90 WB&Bfr£105
⁂ CTV 3P ⚓ 200 acres dairy
£

ST AUBIN

See **JERSEY** under **CHANNEL ISLANDS**

ST AUSTELL Cornwall & Isles of Scilly Map **02** SX05

GH Q **Alexandra Hotel** 52-54 Alexandra Rd PL25 4QN
☎(0726) 74242
Closed Xmas
This comfortable, modestly appointed house is both close to the town centre and ideally situated for touring the south coast. It has the benefit of its own car park.
14rm(4♠10hc)(6fb) CTV in all bedrooms ® sB&B£15-£21
sB&B♠fr£24 dB&B£30
dB&B♠£36 WB&B£100-£119 WBDi£140-£159 LDO 5pm
Lic ⁂ CTV 16P
Credit Cards ①②③ £

GH Q **Cornerways** Penwinnick Rd PL25 5DS ☎(0726) 61579
This detached, pebbledashed house stands in a sunny corner position set back from the Truro road, and offers simple accommodation.
6hc (2fb) CTV in 1 bedroom ® LDO 4pm
Lic ⁂ CTV 15P

INN QQQ **Rashleigh Arms** Quay Rd, Charlestown PL25 3NJ
☎(0726) 73635
Standing on the A3061 to Charlestown, this popular inn sells real ale. Modern bedrooms are offered along with spacious bars, a restaurant and a children's room. With friendly service and good car parking facilities, this inn offers good value for money.
5♠ CTV in all bedrooms ® ✱ sB&B♠£20-£24
dB&B♠£40-£44 WB&B£130-£155 WBDi£180-£205 Lunch
£3.95-£7 High tea £2.50-£3.50 Dinner £7.25-£8.95&alc LDO
10pm
⁂ 60P
Credit Cards ①③

ST BRIDES-SUPER-ELY South Glamorgan Map **03** ST17

GH QQQ **Sant-y-Nyll** CF5 6EZ
☎Peterston-Super-Ely(0446) 760209
A beautifully proportioned country house set in the Vale of Glamorgan, under the personal supervision of the resident proprietors Mr and Mrs Renwick.
6rm(1⇨5hc)(1fb) CTV in all bedrooms ® sB&B£20
dB&B£30-£35 WB&B£120-£140 LDO 6pm
Lic ⁂ 20P croquet
Credit Cards ②£
See advertisement under **CARDIFF** on page 102

ST BURYAN Cornwall & Isles of Scilly Map **02** SW42

GH 🅠🅠 *Higher Trevorian Hotel & Restaurant* TR19 6EA
☎(0736) 810348
Closed 24 Dec-2Jan rs Nov-Etr
Friendly family hotel offering relaxed happy atmosphere and home cooking.
6rm(2⇔2♠2hc)(1fb) CTV in all bedrooms ® LDO 8pm
Lic ♈ 10P
Credit Cards ① ③

ST CATHERINE'S Strathclyde *Argyllshire* Map **10** NN10

GH 🅠🅠🅠 *Thistle House* PA25 8AZ ☎Inveraray(0499) 2209
May-mid Oct
This large, detached Victorian house is set in its own gardens beside the A815 and boasts fine views over Loch Fyne and Inveraray. It provides an ideal base from which to tour the beauties of Argyll, being comfortable and well maintained throughout.
6rm(3♠3hc)(1fb) ® ✲ (ex guide dogs) sB&Bfr£14
sB&B♠fr£16.50 dB&Bfr£28 dB&B♠fr£33 WB&Bfr£98
♈ 10P nc5yrs
£

ST CLEARS Dyfed Map **02** SN21

INN 🅠🅠 *Black Lion Hotel* SA33 4AA ☎(0994) 230700
Neat and well-kept bedrooms are provided in this friendly inn, which stands in the centre of the village. A good choice of food is available in the pretty restaurant, or in the bar.
13rm(1⇔3♠9hc) CTV in all bedrooms ® ✲
sB&B£16-£18 sB&B⇔♠£22-£24 dB&B£30-£35
dB&B⇔♠£40-£45 WB&B£140-£160 LDO 9pm
♈ 25P snooker
Credit Cards ③

ST DAVID'S Dyfed Map **02** SM72

GH 🅠🅠 *The Ramsey* Lower Moor SA62 6RP ☎(0437) 720321
Run by the friendly Thompson family, this bright, cosy guesthouse lies just outside the town with easy access to the cathedral. It has neat bedrooms and comfortable open-plan lounge and bar areas.
7rm(2♠5hc) ® sB&B£15.95-£18.40 dB&B£27.60-£32.20
dB&B♠£31.60-£36.20 WB&B£96.60-£112.70
WBDi£136.20-£156 LDO 7pm
Lic CTV 9P nc12yrs
£

GH 🅠🅠 *Redcliffe House* 17 New St SA62 6SW ☎(0437) 720389
Apr-Oct
This small family-run guesthouse provides comfortable accommodation close to the town centre and cathedral.
6hc (2fb) CTV in all bedrooms ® ✲
♈ CTV 2P nc6yrs

GH 🅠🅠 *Y Glennydd* 51 Nun St SA62 6NU ☎(0437) 720576
Closed Jan-Feb
This bright and cheerful guesthouse lies within easy walking distance of the shops and cathedral. The bedrooms and lounges are comfortable and the restaurant serves good food which is also popular with the locals.
10rm(3⇔♠7hc)(4fb) CTV in all bedrooms ®
✲ (ex guide dogs) sB&B£13.50-£25 sB&B⇔♠£30 dB&B£27
dB&B⇔♠£32 WB&B£94.50-£112 WBDi£154-£171.50 LDO 9pm
Lic ♈ CTV 🅟
Credit Cards ① ③

See the regional maps of popular holiday areas at the back of the book.

ST ERME Cornwall & Isles of Scilly Map **02** SW84

FH 🅠🅠🅠 Mr & Mrs E Dymond *Trevispian Vean* *(SW850502)* TR4 9bl ☎Truro(0872) 79514
Mar-Oct
Recently extended, this Cornish farmhouse is 4 miles from Truro, and provides some en suite bedrooms and a choice of lounges. Home-cooked dinners are served in the evening and children are made very welcome.
12rm(2⇔7♠3hc)(7fb) ✲ (ex guide dogs) LDO 4.30pm
Lic ♈ CTV 20P ⏚ ⏁ games room 300 acres arable beef pigs sheep
See advertisement under TRURO on page 369

ST HELIER

See **JERSEY** under **CHANNEL ISLANDS**

ST IVES Cornwall & Isles of Scilly Map **02** SW54

GH 🅠🅠 *Bay View* Headland Road, Carbis Bay TR26 2nx ☎Penzance(0736) 796469
Extended chalet bungalow in quiet residential area. Friendly owners provide good home cooking.
9rm(2♠7hc)(3fb)✂in all bedrooms ✲ LDO 6pm
Lic CTV 9P 2🍴

GH 🅠🅠🅠 *Blue Mist* The Warren TR26 2EA ☎Penzance(0736) 795209
Etr-Oct
Set in the heart of St Ives, this personally-run guesthouse offers well-appointed bedrooms, many with sea views. Good standards of cooking are complemented by hospitable and friendly service.
9rm(8♠1hc)(1fb) CTV in all bedrooms ® ✲ (ex guide dogs)
sB&B£14-£16.50 sB&B♠£16.45-£18.95
dB&B♠£32.90-£40.50 WB&B£98-£141.75
WBDi£125.50-£169.55 LDO 5pm
▶

🛏 4P (£14.50 per wk) nc4yrs
Credit Cards ① ③ £

GH Q Q **Channings Hotel** 3 Talland Rd TR26 2DF
☎Penzance(0736) 795681
Informally run by Mr and Mrs Juggins, this small hotel has a pleasant, friendly atmosphere. With commanding views over the town and bay, Channings has brightly decorated bedrooms with modern en suite facilities, a comfortable bar and dining room
12rm(2⇨9♠1hc)(5fb) ® ⊁ ✳ sB&B⇨♠£15-£19
dB&B£26-£34
dB&B⇨♠£30-£38 WB&B£105-£133 WBDi£119-£161 LDO
4pm
Lic 🛏 CTV 12P
Credit Cards ① ③

⊷⊷**GH** Q Q **Chy-an-Creet Private Hotel** Higher Stennack
TR26 2HA ☎Penzance(0736) 796559
mid Mar-mid Oct rs mid Nov-mid Mar
Close to the renowned Leach Pottery, this small hotel is run by jovial proprietors who pride themselves in its friendly atmosphere. A choice of traditional home-cooked meals is offered and there is a cosy, well-stocked bar for guests.
10⇨♠ (4fb) ® sB&B⇨♠£12.50-£25
dB&B⇨♠£25-£50 WB&B£110-£165.75 WBDi£125-£190
(wkly only Jul-Sep) LDO 4pm
Lic 🛏 CTV 16P ॐ
Credit Cards ① ③ £

GH Q Q **Cottage Hotel** Carbis Bay TR26 2NQ
☎Penzance(0736) 796351 & 795252 FAX (0736) 798636
Apr-Nov
Set in a wooded location overlooking St Ives Bay, and only 300 yards from the beach, by private footpaths, this large family hotel has well-equipped bedrooms and functional public rooms.
64⇨ (51fb) CTV in all bedrooms ® sB&B⇨£18-£23
dB&B⇨£36-£46 WB&B£150-£200 WBDi£170-£220 LDO
7.30pm
Lic lift 🛏 CTV 100P ⇌(heated) squash snooker sauna table
tennis & pool tables
Credit Cards ① ③

GH Q Q Q **Dean Court Hotel** Trelyon Av TR26 2AD
☎Penzance(0736) 796023
Mar-Oct
The 2 comfortable, well-furnished lounges of this charming establishment overlook the bay, as does the dining room where Roger and Mary Dean present well-cooked, traditional fare. Bedrooms are well decorated.
12⇨♠ (2fb) CTV in all bedrooms ® ⊁ sB&B⇨♠£24-£30
dB&B⇨♠£48-£60 WB&B£140-£170 WBDi£180-£210 LDO
5pm
Lic 🛏 12P nc14yrs

GH Q Q Q **The Hollies Hotel** 4 Talland Rd TR26 2DF
☎Penzance(0736) 796605
The jovial and friendly owner of this well-furnished guesthouse provides good, home-cooked meals. It is the ideal spot for a relaxed holiday in Cornwall.
10⇨♠ (4fb) CTV in all bedrooms ® ⊁ sB&B⇨♠£17-£20.50
dB&B⇨♠£34-£41 WB&B£119-£143.50 WBDi£135-£180
LDO 9am
Lic 🛏 CTV 12P
£

GH Q Q *Island View* 2 Park Av TR26 2DN
☎Penzance(0736) 795111
Mar-Oct
Perched above St Ives and enjoying fine views across the town and harbour, this personally-run Victorian house provides a bright and friendly atmosphere and tasty traditional fare.
10hc (4fb) CTV in all bedrooms ® LDO 6.30pm
🛏 ⊁

GH Q Q **Kandahar** 11 The Warren TR26 2EA
☎Penzance(0736) 796183
Closed Xmas, New Year & owners hols
Kandahar comprises two separate premises: one which provides bed and breakfast accommodation at the sea's edge with superb views, while the other has more modest accommodation over a popular tea shop.
5rm(2♠3hc)(1fb) CTV in all bedrooms ® ⊁ sB&Bfr£15
dB&B£26-£32 dB&B♠£30-£36
🛏 CTV 6P (wkly only Apr-Oct)
£

GH Q Q **Kynance** The Warren TR26 2EA
☎Penzance(0736) 796636
Feb-Nov
In the heart of the town, yet within sight and sound of the ocean, May and Tony Smith's cosy fishermen's cottage now provides accommodation which is full of character and charm. The garden won an award for 'Best Guesthouse Garden' in St Ives in 1988.
8rm(1♠7hc)(1fb) TV in all bedrooms ® ⊁ ✳ sB&B£12-£18
dB&B£24-£36 dB&B♠£28-£40 WB&B£84-£140
🛏 CTV P
£

GH Q Q **Longships Hotel** Talland Rd TR26 2DF
☎Penzance(0736) 798180
This holiday hotel enjoys a good position and views over the bay. The bedrooms are well equipped and there is a good choice of meals at dinner.
24rm(5⇨19♠)(7fb) CTV in all bedrooms ®
sB&B♠£15-£22
dB&B⇨♠£30-£44 WB&B£105-£155 WBDi£136-£187 LDO
7pm
Lic 🛏 CTV 17P
Credit Cards ① ③ £

GH Q Q *Lyonesse Hotel* 5 Talland Rd TR26 2DF
☎Penzance(0736) 796315
Mar-Oct
Comfortable family hotel in good position with views of bay.
15♠ (6fb) CTV in all bedrooms ® ⊁ LDO 6.30pm
Lic 🛏 CTV 10P pool table

GH Q Q Q **Monowai Private Hotel** Headland Road, Carbis
Bay TR26 2NR ☎Penzance(0736) 795733
Beautifully located in a quiet area, with glorious views of the bay, this cosy family hotel provides comfortable accommodation and a friendly atmosphere. A small, outdoor swimming-pool stands in the secluded, mature gardens.
10rm(6♠4hc)(3fb) ® sB&B£14.50-£18.50 dB&B£29-£37
dB&B♠£34.50-£42 WB&B£95-£129 WBDi£118-£189 LDO
6.30pm
Lic 🛏 CTV 7P nc5yrs ⇌(heated)
£

GH Q Q Q **The Old Vicarage Hotel** Parc-An-Creet TR26 2ET
☎Penzance(0736) 796124
Mar-Oct
Retaining its Victorian character yet with every modern convenience, this spacious house provides comfortable accommodation and imaginatively prepared food. Tucked away from the hurly-burly of the town, its grounds offer a safe play area for children.
8rm(3⇨1♠4hc)(3fb) CTV in all bedrooms ®
sB&B£16.50-£17.50 sB&B⇨♠£18.50-£19.50 dB&B£29-£31
dB&B⇨♠£35-£37 WB&B£90-£96 LDO 6.45pm
Lic 🛏 CTV 12P
Credit Cards ① ③

GH Q Q Q **Pondarosa Hotel** 10 Porthminster Ter TR26 2DQ
☎Penzance(0736) 795875
Standing in a convenient position close to the town and beaches, this guesthouse has a friendly, relaxed atmosphere. Good home cooking is provided by friendly and welcoming Welsh owners.

9rm(1⇌1↱7hc)(4fb) CTV in all bedrooms ® ✕ (ex guide dogs) * sB&B£12-£13 dB&B£26-£28 dB&B⇌↱£30-£32 WB&B£84-£112 WBDi£124-£145 LDO 4pm
Lic 🍽 CTV 12P nc3yrs
£

GH QQ Primrose Valley Hotel Primrose Valley TR26 2ED
☎Penzance(0736) 794939
Closed Jan-Feb
Pleasant, small family hotel ideally positioned about 100 yards from Porthminster beach.
11rm(6⇌↱5hc)(6fb) CTV in all bedrooms ® ✕ * sB&B£16-£21 dB&B£32-£42 dB&B⇌↱£36-£52 WB&B£112-£180 WBDi£137.50-£210 (wkly only Jun, Jul & Aug)
Lic CTV 12P

GH QQ Hotel Rotorua Trencrom Ln, Carbis Bay TR26 2TD
☎Penzance(0736) 795419
Purpose-built, in quiet lane just off St Ives Rd, close to Carbis Bay.
13⇌↱ (10fb)⊬in 2 bedrooms ® sB&B⇌↱£15-£21 dB&B⇌↱£30-£42 WB&B£161-£196 LDO 5pm
Lic 🍽 CTV 10P ⛆

GH Q St Margaret's 3 Parc Av TR26 2DN
☎Penzance(0736) 795785
Mar-Sep
Friendly owners create a warm atmosphere at this comfortable hotel. It enjoys a commanding position overlooking the town and harbour.
7hc (2fb) CTV in all bedrooms ® ✕ * sB&B£12-£13 dB&B£24-£26 WB&B£84-£91 WBDi£129.50-£136.50 LDO previous day
Lic 🍽 ⅊
Credit Cards [1] [3]

GH QQ *St Merryn Hotel* Trelyon TR26 2PF
☎Penzance(0736) 795767 & 797248
Mar-Nov
Set back off the main road, behind a large garden, this large, detached family hotel is just outside St Ives. It has spacious public rooms and comfortable bedrooms.
19rm(11⇌8hc)(8fb) CTV in all bedrooms ® ✕ LDO 6pm
Lic 🍽 CTV 20P nc4yrs
Credit Cards [1] [3]

GH QQ *Sunrise* 22 The Warren TR26 2AT
☎Penzance(0736) 795407
Feb-Oct
This welcoming cottage has the distinction of being owned by Mrs Mason, chosen by the AA as one of the top 5 seaside landladies in 1988. Cosy accommodation and outstanding traditional breakfasts (which also cater for vegetarians) await guests.
7rm(3⇌1↱3hc)(2fb) CTV in all bedrooms ®
🍽 CTV 4P (charged)

See advertisement on page 323

⊢GH QQ **Thurlestone Private Hotel** St Ives Road, Carbis Bay TR26 2RT ☎Penzance(0736) 796369
Mar-Sep
Attractive detached granite house with friendly service and public rooms of character.
9rm(1⇌4↱4hc)(3fb) ® ✕ sB&B£10-£15 dB&B£20-£30 dB&B⇌↱£22-£32 WB&B£70-£87 WBDi£98-£120 (wkly only Jul-Aug) LDO 5pm
Lic 🍽 CTV 6P nc3yrs

GH QQ *Tregorran Hotel* Headland Bay, Carbis Bay TR26 2NU ☎Penzance(0736) 795889
Apr-Oct & Xmas
An attractive outdoor swimming pool and small gym are features of this small, well-appointed hotel which enjoys a scenic location overlooking Carbis Bay.

▶

15rm(8🚿7hc)(3fb) Ⓡ LDO 6pm
Lic 🍴 CTV 25P 🏠 🏊(heated) solarium gymnasium pool table

GH [Q][Q] White House Hotel The Valley, Carbis Bay TR26 2QY
☎Penzance(0736) 797405
Closed Nov rs Dec-Mar
This detached house stands in its own gardens at the foot of a wooded valley, 150 yards from safe, sandy beaches and 1 mile from St Ives. Comfortable bedrooms and cosy public areas are complemented by home-cooked food.
8🛁🚿 Annexe 2🛁🚿 (2fb) Ⓡ 🐕 sB&B🛁🚿£18-£25
dB&B🛁🚿£30-£40 LDO 8pm
Lic 🍴 CTV 10P
Credit Cards [1]

ST JUST (near Land's End) Cornwall & Isles of Scilly
Map **02** SW33

GH [Q][Q][Q] Boscean Country Hotel TR19 7QP
☎Penzance(0736) 788748
Mar-Nov
This interesting house has been tastefully converted to provide comfortable, en suite accommodation. The wood panelled public rooms contain unique fitments. Three acres of walled grounds surround this building, and guests will receive a warm welcome.
9🛁🚿 Annexe 2🛁 (3fb) Ⓡ ✱
dB&B🛁🚿£28-£30 WB&B£93-£100 WBDi£148-£155 LDO 7pm
Lic 🍴 CTV 12P 🏠

GH [Q][Q][Q] Boswedden House Cape Cornwall TR19 7NJ
☎Penzance(0736) 788733
Feb-Nov
Comfortable Georgian family house in peaceful surrounding.
8rm(7🚿1hc)(1fb) sB&Bfr£15 sB&B🚿fr£15 dB&Bfr£30
dB&B🚿fr£30 WB&Bfr£100 WBDifr£155 LDO noon
Lic 🍴 CTV 6P 🏊(heated)

⟼**GH [Q][Q] Kenython** Kenython Ln TR19 7PT
☎Penzance(0736) 788607
Etr-Oct
This large, comfortable house stands in 3 acres of grounds on the Land's End peninsula, approached by an unmade track. Beautiful views to the Scilly Isles are complemented by home cooking and a warm, friendly atmosphere.
4rm(2🛁2hc)(2fb) TV in 1 bedroom sB&B£13-£14
dB&B£26-£28
dB&B🛁£28-£30 WB&B£87.50-£101.50 WBDi£143-£157 LDO 10am
🍴 CTV 4P 🏊

ST JUST-IN-ROSELAND Cornwall & Isles of Scilly
Map **02** SW83

SELECTED

GH [Q][Q][Q][Q] Rose-Da-Mar Hotel TR2 5JB
☎St Mawes(0326) 270450
Apr-Oct
In a sheltered site overlooking the creeks of Carrick Roads Fal Estuary, this elegant and tastefully furnished house has been thoughtfully appointed. All bedrooms have splendid views across the water and the spacious drawing room is complemented by a small bar and attractive dining room. Mrs Marilyn Brown serves a wholesome 5-course dinner, after which guests can relax on the sheltered sun terrace and in the gardens. Early reservations are advised.
8rm(4🛁1🚿3hc)(1fb) Ⓡ sB&B£34.50 dB&B£31.50-£32.50
dB&B🛁🚿£34.50-£37 (incl dinner) WB&B£129.50-£168
WBDi£220.50-£259 LDO 6.30pm
Lic 🍴 CTV 9P nc11yrs

FH [Q] Mrs W Symons *Commerrans (SW842375)* TR2 5JJ
☎Portscatho(087258) 270
Etr-Oct
Pleasant modernised farmhouse, attractively decorated throughout, and situated in a large garden.
4rm(3hc)(1fb) Ⓡ LDO 9am
CTV 6P nc1yr 61 acres arable sheep

ST KEYNE Cornwall & Isles of Scilly Map **02** SX26

GH [Q][Q][Q] *Old Rectory Country House Hotel* PL14 4RL
☎Liskeard(0579) 42617
This secluded former Rectory dating from the 16th century, is peacefully situated in over 3 acres of gardens and woodland, 3 miles from Liskeard. Mr and Mrs Wolfe provide a short à la carte menu, served between 7pm and 8pm, and pre-dinner drinks are available from the bar on an 'honesty' system. No smoking in the dining room. After dinner, coffee is provided in the elegantly furnished lounge. Bedrooms are comfortable; each is individually furnished and decorated and some have four-poster beds.
8rm(4🛁3🚿1hc) CTV in all bedrooms Ⓡ LDO 7pm
Lic 🍴 20P
Credit Cards [1] [3]

ST MARY'S
See **SCILLY, ISLES OF**

ST MARY'S LOCH Borders *Selkirkshire* Map **11** NT22

INN [Q][Q][Q] Tibbie Shiels TD7 5NE
☎Capercleuch(0750) 42231
rs Mon Nov-Feb
Standing on the edge of the loch, this historic inn, named after one of the first inhabitants, offers good accommodation in most attractive surroundings. It offers a variety of bar meals as well as an à-la-carte menu in the evening.
5hc (1fb) Ⓡ 🐕 (ex guide dogs)
dB&B£29 Lunch fr£2.80alc High tea fr£6alc Dinner fr£6alc LDO 8.30pm
🍴 CTV 30P 🎣
Credit Cards [1] [3]

ST MERRYN Cornwall & Isles of Scilly Map **02** SW87

INN [Q][Q][Q] Farmers Arms PL28 8NP ☎Padstow(0841) 520303
Recently renovated, this village pub offers well-equipped bedrooms which are prettily decorated and have limed oak furniture. An extensive bar menu is available and the separate restaurant has a carvery. A salad counter is open through the summer.
4🚿 CTV in all bedrooms Ⓡ ✱ sB&B🚿fr£25
dB&B🚿fr£40 WB&Bfr£240 LDO 9.30pm
🍴 100P
Credit Cards [1] [2] [3]

ST NEOTS Cambridgeshire Map **04** TL16

INN [Q][Q] The Old Falcon Hotel Market Square, Huntingdon PE1 2AW ☎Huntindon(0480) 72749
This inn, facing the market place and backing on to the River Great Ouse, provides comfortable and very well-equipped accommodation. There is also a popular, convivial bar, and a coffee shop where hot and cold meals are available all day.
8rm(4🛁3🚿1hc) CTV in all bedrooms Ⓡ 🐕 (ex guide dogs) ✱
sB&B🛁🚿fr£40
dB&B🛁🚿fr£50 Bar Lunch fr£1alc Dinner fr£5alc LDO 9.30pm
10P
Credit Cards [1] [2] [3] [5]

Visit your local AA Centre.

ST OWEN'S CROSS Hereford & Worcester Map **03** SO52

FH Ⓠ Ⓠ Ⓠ Mrs F Davies **Aberhall** *(SO529242)* HR2 8LL
☎Harewood End(098987) 256
Feb-Nov
Set in the beautiful Wye Valley with some superb views, this 17th century farmhouse is 5 miles from Ross-on-Wye. Energetic visitors can use the hard tennis court or enjoy tabletennis, darts and pool in the basement games room.
3rm(1♠2hc)✗in all bedrooms ® ✘ (ex guide dogs)
dB&B£24-£26 dB&B♠£28-£30 LDO 5pm
🍴 CTV 3P nc9yrs ♪(hard)pool & table tennis 132 acres arable beef
£

ST PETER PORT

See **GUERNSEY under CHANNEL ISLANDS**

ST SAMPSON

See **GUERNSEY under CHANNEL ISLANDS**

ST TEATH Cornwall & Isles of Scilly Map **02** SX08

FH Ⓠ Mrs S M Mewton **Hillcrest** *(SX056809)* PL30 3LH
☎Bodmin(0208) 850258
Closed Xmas
A detached farmhouse situated on the edge of the village.
3rm(2hc)(1fb) ® ✱ sB&B£12-£13
dB&B£20-£22 WBDi£112-£115
🍴 CTV 3P 19 acres mixed
See advertisement under PORT ISAAC on page 303

SALCOMBE Devon Map **03** SX73

GH Ⓠ Ⓠ Ⓠ **Bay View Hotel** Bennett Rd TQ8 8JJ
☎(054884) 2238
Mar-Sep
Small private hotel in a commanding position with unrestricted views of estuary and coastline.
5rm(2⇔3hc)(2fb) ® ✘ ✱ dB&B£34-£44 dB&B⇔♠£44-£48
Lic 🍴 CTV 6P
Credit Cards 1 3 £

GH Ⓠ Ⓠ Ⓠ **Lyndhurst Hotel** Bonaventure Rd TQ8 8BG
☎(054884) 2481
Closed Dec
This charming establishment enjoys views of the bay, and new accommodation to a fine standard. The bedrooms are well equipped and there is a neat dining room and cosy lounge. Smoking is not permitted here.
8♠ (1fb)✗in all bedrooms CTV in all bedrooms ® ✘
sB&B♠£18.50-£22
dB&B♠£37-£44 WB&B£126-£150.50 WBDi£196-£217 LDO 4.30pm
Lic 🍴 4P nc7yrs

GH Ⓠ Ⓠ Ⓠ **Torre View Hotel** Devon Rd TQ8 8HJ
☎(054884) 2633
Feb-Oct
Arthur and Julie Bouttle have upgraded this hotel, all bedrooms now having en suite or designated private facilities. The public areas are bright and comfortable and guests can enjoy the well tended garden.
8⇔♠ (2fb) CTV in 2 bedrooms ® ✘ sB&B⇔♠£23-£29
dB&B⇔♠£39-£46 WBDi£179-£199 LDO 6pm
Lic 🍴 CTV 4P
Credit Cards 1 3 £

GH Ⓠ Ⓠ **Trennels Private Hotel** Herbert Rd TQ8 8HR
☎(054884) 2500
Good views of Salcombe, the estuary and the countryside from this friendly, personally-run hotel.

7rm(1⇔4♠2hc)(1fb)✗in all bedrooms CTV in 5 bedrooms ®
✘ ✱ sB&B£14-£18 dB&B£28-£36
dB&B⇔♠£31-£39 WB&B£98-£112 WBDi£154-£168 LDO 10am
Lic 🍴 CTV 8P nc4yrs
£

SALEN

See **MULL, ISLE OF**

SALFORD Bedfordshire Map **04** SP93

INN Ⓠ Ⓠ *Red Lion Country Hotel* Wavendon Rd MK17 8AZ
☎Milton Keynes(0908) 583117
A small village inn with lots of character, the Red Lion has comfortable accommodation with modern facilities. The small restaurant has an à la carte menu and bar snacks are also available.
10rm(6⇔4hc) CTV in all bedrooms ® ✘ LDO 9.30pm
🍴 40P nc3yrs putting course petanque
Credit Cards 1 2 3 5

SALFORD Greater Manchester Map **07** SJ89

GH Ⓠ Ⓠ **Hazeldean Hotel** 467 Bury New Rd M7 0NX
☎061-792 6667
Closed 4 days Xmas
Large and well-equipped family-run house with good restaurant.
21rm(17⇔♠4hc)Annexe 3rm(1⇔♠2hc)(2fb) CTV in all bedrooms ® sB&Bfr£40.25 sB&B⇔♠fr£47.15 dB&Bfr£52.90
dB&B⇔♠fr£59.80 LDO 9pm
Lic 🍴 CTV 21P
Credit Cards 1 2 3 5

SALHOUSE Norfolk Map **09** TG31

GH [Q][Q][Q] Brooksbank Hotel Lower St NR13 6RW
☎Norwich(0603) 720420
Five miles east of Norwich, 1 mile from Salhouse Broad, Mr & Mrs Coe's 18th- century cottage is now a quality guesthouse. The rooms are comfortable and well equipped with private facilities.
3rm(2🛁1🚿)(1fb) CTV in all bedrooms [R] ✱
sB&B🛁🚿£16-£19 dB&B🛁🚿£25-£30 WB&B£85-£100
♨ CTV 3P
[£]

SALISBURY Wiltshire Map **04** SU12

See also Downton (6.5m S off A338)

GH [Q][Q] Byways House 31 Fowlers Rd SP1 2QP
☎(0722) 28364 due to change to 328364 FAX (0722) 322146
This bed and breakfast establishment is a Victorian house with adjoining coachouse which has been fully modernised. Family run, it enjoys a central location with views of the distant cathedral.
17rm(11🚿6hc)(5fb) CTV in all bedrooms [R] sB&Bfr£17
sB&B🚿fr£19 dB&Bfr£30
dB&B🚿fr£35 WB&Bfr£100 WBDifr£160 LDO 6.30pm
Lic ♨ 15P 🏠
Credit Cards [1] [3] [£]

GH [Q][Q][Q] Cricket Field Cottage Skew Bridge, Wilton Rd SP2 7NS ☎(0722) 22595 due to change to 322595
5rm(1🛁4🚿)(2fb) CTV in all bedrooms [R] 🐕 (ex guide dogs) ✱ sB&B🛁🚿£18.50-£20 dB&B🛁🚿£34-£36
♨ 8P
[£]

GH [Q][Q] Glen Lyn 6 Bellamy Lane, Milford Hill SP1 2SP
☎(0722) 27880 due to change to 327880
Glen Lyn is a converted and comfortably furnished Victorian house situated on a peaceful lane close to the city centre. A husband and wife team run this hotel with charm.
9rm(2🛁2🚿3hc)(1fb)🚭in 4 bedrooms CTV in all bedrooms [R] 🐕 (ex guide dogs) sB&B£14-£16 dB&B£28-£30
dB&B🛁🚿£34-£36
♨ 7P nc12yrs
[£]

GH [Q][Q] Hayburn Wyke 72 Castle Rd SP1 3RL
☎(0722) 412627
This small, personally-run family house has the advantage of standing next to a public park. The rooms are airy and tastefully appointed.
6rm(2🚿4hc)(2fb) CTV in all bedrooms [R] 🐕 (ex guide dogs)
sB&B£19-£23 dB&Bfr£30 dB&B🚿fr£36
♨ CTV 5P 1🚗 🏠
[£]

GH [Q] Holmhurst Downton Rd SP2 8AR ☎(0722) 23164 due to change to 323164
Mar-Oct
Detached brick-built villa situated on main A338 adjacent to Cathedral.
8rm(5🚿3hc)(2fb)🚭in 1 bedroom 🐕 sB&B£16-£26
sB&B🚿£20-£32 dB&B£28 dB&B🚿£32
♨ CTV 8P nc5yrs

GH [Q][Q] Leena's 50 Castle Rd SP1 3RL ☎(0722) 335419
6rm(3🚿3hc)(1fb) CTV in all bedrooms [R] 🐕 (ex guide dogs)
sB&B£17-£19 dB&B£27.50-£30 dB&B🚿£32-£35
♨ CTV 6P
[£]

GH [Q] Roman House 49 Roman Rd SP2 9BJ ☎(0722) 414633
Set in a quiet residential area, this detached Edwardian house is simply furnished, comfortable and well equipped. The bedrooms and breakfast room are of a good size and the house has a relaxed, friendly atmosphere.
5rm(1🛁1🚿3hc)(1fb) CTV in all bedrooms [R]
🐕 (ex guide dogs) ✱ sB&B£16-£18 dB&Bfr£30
dB&B🛁🚿fr£34
♨ 5P
Credit Cards [1]

INN [Q][Q] Old Bell 2 Saint Ann St SP1 2DN ☎(0722) 27958
FAX (0722) 477019
Ideally situated opposite St Ann's Gate, close to the cathedral, this small 14th-century inn combines well kept, en suite accommodation with an abundance of charm.
7rm(1🛁6🚿) [R] 🐕 ✱ sB&B🛁🚿£55-£60
dB&B🛁🚿£55-£60 Bar Lunch £1.50-£6.50
♨ CTV 🚫 nc9yrs solarium
Credit Cards [1] [2] [3] [5]

SANDOWN

See **WIGHT, ISLE OF**

SANDPLACE Cornwall & Isles of Scilly Map **02** SX25

GH [Q][Q][Q] Polraen Country House Hotel PL13 1PJ
☎Looe(05036) 3956
Two acres of grounds surround this attractive granite house. Its spacious bedrooms have quality beds and many extras, and the lounge and bar are well furnished and comfortable.
5rm(1🛁4🚿)(2fb) CTV in all bedrooms [R] sB&B🛁🚿£25-£28
dB&B🛁🚿£44-£48 WB&B£144-£151 WBDi£210-£225 LDO 8pm
Lic ♨ 21P
Credit Cards [1] [3] [£]

SANDWICH Kent Map **05** TR35

INN [Q][Q][Q] St Crispin The Street CT14 0DF
☎Dover(0304) 612081
A charming inn dating back to 1426, refurbished, yet retaining its original character, Crispin's Inn is set in a picturesque village and offers a good selection of cask conditioned beers, and a fine choice of food. The bedrooms are well equipped.
4rm(2🛁2🚿)Annexe 3🛁 (2fb) CTV in all bedrooms [R]
sB&B🛁🚿£28
dB&B🛁🚿£40 Lunch £4.50-£8.55alc LDO 9.30pm
♨ 30P
Credit Cards [1] [3]

SANQUHAR Dumfries & Galloway *Dumfriesshire*
Map **11** NS71

↦**GH [Q][Q] Drumbringan** 53 Castle St DG4 6AB
☎(0659) 50409
Guests can be sure of a warm welcome at this well-maintained town house which stands on the main road to the south of the town. The accommodation is comfortable and pleasantly decorated.
5hc (2fb) sB&B£12
dB&B£24 WB&B£80 WBDi£110 LDO 6pm
Lic ♨ CTV 6P
[£]

INN [Q][Q][Q] *Blackaddie House Hotel* Blackaddie Rd DG4 6JJ
☎(0659) 50270
The home-cooked dishes on the menu at this riverside hotel are very good value, and to be especially recommended. The public areas are elegant, and the bedrooms comfortable and well appointed. Service here is friendly and courteous.
8rm(1🛁7🚿)(1fb) CTV in all bedrooms [R] 🐕 (ex guide dogs)
LDO 9pm
♨ 20P 4🚗 ⛳9
Credit Cards [1] [3]

[£] Remember to use the money-off vouchers.

SARISBURY GREEN Hampshire Map **04** SU50

GH Q Q Q **The Dormy** SO3 6DA ☎Locks Heath(0489) 572626
Mollie and Eddie Rees provide friendly caring service at their
quietly situated guesthouse which has well-equipped, very
comfortable bedrooms. Home-prepared food is served from the
open plan kitchen. Dormy is convenient for Southampton,
Portsmouth and Hamble.
10rm(6♠4hc)(1fb) CTV in all bedrooms ® ✖ (ex guide dogs)
sB&Bfr£20 sB&B♠£32 dB&B£40 dB&B♠£46 LDO noon
♀ CTV 18P

SAUNDERSFOOT Dyfed Map **02** SN10

GH Q Q **Jalna Hotel** Stammers Rd SA69 9HH ☎(0834) 812282
Mar-Oct
This is a well-maintained and family-run hotel that is situated just
above the harbour. It provides modern and well-equipped
bedrooms, a cosy bar and a comfortable lounge.
14rm(8⇨6♠)(8fb) CTV in all bedrooms ® ✱
sB&B⇨♠£18-£20
dB&B⇨♠£32-£36 WBDi£142-£167 LDO 6.30pm
Lic ♀ CTV 14P solarium
Credit Cards 1 3 £

GH Q Q Q *Merlewood Hotel* St Brides Hill SA69 9NP
☎(0834) 812421
Etr-Nov
This large family hotel, with its own heated swimming pool, lies in
an elevated position over the harbour. The bedrooms are modern
and well equipped while the public rooms are spacious and
comfortable.
30rm(15⇨13♠2hc)(15fb) CTV in all bedrooms ® ✖ (wkly
only Jul-Aug) LDO 7.30pm
Lic ♀ CTV 30P ⚓ ⇌(heated) ▶ 9 putting green
Credit Cards 1 3

⊢⊶**GH** Q Q Q **The Sandy Hill** Sandy Hill Road/Tenby Rd
SA69 9DR ☎(0834) 813165
Mar-Sep
Once a farm, this friendly, family-run guesthouse lies alongside the
A478 on the approach to the town. The bedrooms are pretty and
cosy, while good value home cooking and a comfortable lounge and
bar are also offered.
5hc (3fb) CTV in all bedrooms ® sB&B£12.50
dB&B£25 WB&B£87.50 WBDi£119 (wkly only Jul-Aug)
Lic ♀ 7P nc3yrs ⇌
£

GH Q Q Q *Springfield* St Brides Hill SA69 9NP
☎(0834) 813518
This small guesthouse is family run, and offers warm hospitality.
The bedrooms are cosy and very well kept, while a comfortable
lounge is available for guests' use.
5rm(2♠2hc)(1fb) ®
Lic ♀ CTV 6P ⚓

GH Q Q Q **Vine Farm** The Ridgeway SA69 9LA
☎(0834) 813543
Apr-Oct
A spacious lounge, with a cheerful open fire, and good value,
enjoyable food are offered at this old farmhouse, part of which
dates back to the early 19th century. The bedrooms here are
comfortable and well equipped.
5⇨♠ (1fb) CTV in all bedrooms ® ✱ sB&B⇨♠fr£15
dB&B⇨♠£30-£33 WB&B£105-£115.50 WBDi£130-£155.55
LDO 6pm
Lic ♀ 10P nc2yrs

This guide is updated annually – make sure you
use an up-to-date edition.

SAWLEY Lancashire Map **07** SD74

GH Q Q Q *Spread Eagle Hotel* BB7 4NH
☎Clitheroe(0200) 41202
The restaurant of this hotel overlooks the pituresque river Ribble
and is open for lunch and dinner. Breakfast is served in guests'
rooms which are comfortable and well equipped and located in a
converted barn.
10rm(7⇨3♠)(2fb) CTV in all bedrooms ® ✖ (ex guide dogs)
LDO 9pm
Lic ♀ 80P
Credit Cards 1 2 3 5

SAXELBY Leicestershire Map **08** SK62

FH Q Q Mrs M A Morris **Manor House** *(SK701208)*
LE14 3PA ☎Melton Mowbray(0664) 812269
Etr-Oct
The manor house, parts of which date back to the 12th and 15th
centuries, is situated on the edge of the village, 5 miles from
Merton Mowbray.
3hc (2fb) CTV in all bedrooms ® ✖ (ex guide dogs)
sB&Bfr£18 dB&Bfr£26 WB&Bfr£90 WBDifr£138 LDO noon
♀ CTV 6P 125 acres dairy sheep

SCARBOROUGH North Yorkshire Map **08** TA08

See **Town Plan Section**
GH Q Q **Avoncroft Hotel** 5-7 Crown Ter YO11 2BL
☎(0723) 372737
Part of an attractive Georgian terrace overlooking Crown
Gardens, Avoncroft is a friendly guesthouse, simply furnished.
34rm(1⇨20♠)(13fb) CTV in all bedrooms ®
sB&B£16-£18 sB&B⇨♠£19.50-£21.50 dB&B£32-£36
dB&B⇨♠£39-£43 WBDi£139-£152 LDO 6pm
Lic ♀ CTV ✗ games room pool table
£

GH QQQ *Bay Hotel* 67 Esplanade, South Cliff YO11 2UZ
☎(0723) 373926
Mar-Nov
Enjoying a commanding position overlooking the South Bay, this hotel is very well furnished and offers a warm, friendly welcome and a high standard of cooking.
18rm(2⇺16↑)(2fb) CTV in all bedrooms ® LDO 6pm
Lic lift 鬥 10P

GH QQ **Burghcliffe Hotel** 28 Esplanade, South Cliff YO11 2AQ
☎(0723) 361524
The friendly proprietor of this seafront hotel, attends to the menus which offer freshly cooked dishes. The bedrooms are bright and comfortable, and all are well equipped.
12rm(4⇺8↑)(6fb) CTV in all bedrooms ® ✱
dB&B⇺↑£42-£46 WB&B£140-£154 WBDi£203-£217 LDO 4pm
Lic 鬥 CTV ⅌
Credit Cards ①③ ⓔ

GH Q **Dolphin Hotel** 151 Columbus Ravine YO12 7QZ
☎(0723) 374217
A mid-terrace house close to North Bay, offering good accommodation and home-cooked dinners served by the friendly resident owners.
6⇺↑ (2fb) CTV in all bedrooms ® ✱ sB&B⇺↑fr£19.50
dB&B⇺↑fr£39 WB&Bfr£136.50 WBDi£199.50-£220.50 LDO 8.30pm
Lic 鬥 CTV ⅌ nc5yrs
Credit Cards ①③ ⓔ

GH QQ **Geldenhuis Hotel** 145-147 Queens Pde YO12 7HU
☎(0723) 361677
Etr-end Oct
Terraced houses on sea front overlooking North Bay with comfortable lounge and separate bar lounge.
30rm(3⇺6↑21hc)(6fb) ® ✱ (ex guide dogs) ✱
sB&B£18.40-£23 dB&B£36.80
dB&B⇺↑£42.55 (incl dinner) LDO 6pm
Lic 鬥 CTV 24P nc5yrs
ⓔ

GH QQ **Manor Heath Hotel** 67 Northstead Manor Dr
YO12 6AF ☎(0723) 365720
An attractive residence with gardens to the front and parking to the rear. The accommodation is tasteful and modern and a home-cooked 5-course dinner is served.
17rm(2⇺9↑6hc)(5fb) CTV in 16 bedrooms ® ✱
sB&B£14-£16 sB&B⇺↑£16-£18 dB&B£28-£32
dB&B⇺↑£32-£36 WB&B£98-£126 WBDi£120-£154 LDO 4.30pm
Lic 鬥 CTV 16P
ⓔ

GH QQQ **Paragon Hotel** 123 Queens Pde YO12 7HU
☎(0723) 372676
This very well-furnished and comfortable small hotel occupies one of the best positions overlooking the north bay. Personally owned and run, the hotel offers excellent value for money.
15rm(4⇺9↑2hc)(5fb) CTV in all bedrooms ® sB&B£18-£19
sB&B⇺↑£22-£24 dB&B£30-£32
dB&B⇺↑£32-£36 WB&B£132-£168 WBDi£177.50-£213.50 LDO 6.30pm
Lic 鬥
Credit Cards ①③

GH QQ **Parmelia Hotel** 17 West St YO11 2QN
☎(0723) 361914
Apr-1 Nov
A comfortable, family-run house, offering dinners of very good value.
15rm(1⇺10↑4hc)(4fb) CTV in 8 bedrooms ®
✱ (ex guide dogs) sB&B£15.50-£16 sB&B⇺↑£18-£18.50
dB&B£31-£32 dB&B⇺↑£36-£37 LDO 4pm

Lic 鬥 CTV
ⓔ

GH QQQ *Premier Hotel* 66 Esplanade YO11 2UZ
☎(0723) 361484
Mar-Nov
A good standard of service, accommodation and food is offered at this well-furnished hotel which occupies a beautiful situation overlooking the South Bay.
20rm(17⇺3↑)(5fb) CTV in all bedrooms ® LDO 6pm
Lic lift 鬥 8P

GH QQQ **Riveria Hotel** St Nicholas Cliff YO11 2ES
☎(0723) 372277
Closed Xmas & New Year
20rm(15⇺5↑)(6fb) CTV in all bedrooms ® ✱ (ex guide dogs)
✱ sB&B⇺↑£20-£23
dB&B⇺↑£40-£46 WB&B£140-£150 WBDi£196-£206 LDO 7pm
Lic lift 鬥 ⅌
Credit Cards ①③

GH Q **Sefton Hotel** 18 Prince of Wales Ter YO11 2AL
☎(0723) 372310
Mar-Oct
Victorian town house with spacious public rooms and some charming bedrooms.
16rm(3⇺13hc)(2fb)⅋in 6 bedrooms ✱ (ex guide dogs)
sB&B£16-£16.50 dB&B£32-£33
dB&B⇺↑£36-£37 (incl dinner) WB&B£98-£101.50
WBDi£112-£119 LDO 6pm
Lic lift 鬥 CTV nc12yrs
ⓔ

⊩⊸**GH** QQ **West Lodge Private Hotel** 38 West St YO11 2QP
☎(0723) 500754
Close to the South Cliff and town centre, this comfortable hotel has modestly furnished and equipped bedrooms, and serves home-cooked evening meals. A small bar offers a choice of drinks.
7rm(1↑6hc) TV available ® ✱ sB&Bfr£10 sB&B↑fr£12.50
dB&B↑fr£25 LDO 10am
Lic 鬥 CTV 0P

SCILLY, ISLES OF

ST MARY'S

GH QQQQ **Brantwood Hotel** Rocky Hill TR21 0NW
☎Scillonia(0720) 22531 Telex no 45117
Jun-Aug
Just 20 minutes' walk from the town and harbour this single storeyed guesthouse offers well-equipped bedrooms of individual style. Cosy lounge and attractive dining room. Run by restaurant proprietors, David and Dorothy Oxford, who are responsible for the excellent cuisine and fine hospitality.
4↑ CTV in all bedrooms ® ✱ (ex guide dogs)
dB&B↑£110 (incl dinner) WBDi£385 LDO 6.30pm
Lic 鬥 ⅌ nc10yrs croquet
Credit Cards ①②③ ⓔ

GH QQQQ **Carnwethers Country House** Carnwethers,
Pelistry Bay TR21 0NX ☎Scillonia(0720) 22415
23 Mar-5 Oct
Situated in a quiet, rural retreat near Pelistry Bay, this delightful guesthouse has been tastefully refurbished to provide a well-appointed, comfortable lounge, bright bedrooms

and a cheerful dining room where Roy and Joyce Graham offer a good standard of cuisine. Outside, the neat lawns and gardens contain the added attraction of a heated swimming pool.
9rm(8⇨♠1hc)Annexe 1♠ (2fb) CTV in all bedrooms ®
✻ (ex guide dogs) sB&B£24-£30 sB&B⇨♠£32-£38
dB&B£54-£66
dB&B⇨♠£54-£78 (incl dinner) LDO 6.30pm
Lic ∰ CTV 4P nc7yrs ⇌(heated) sauna pool table croquet lawn library

---

SCOTCH CORNER North Yorkshire Map **08** NZ20

SELECTED

INN Q Q Q Q *Vintage Hotel* DL10 6NP
☎Richmond(0748) 4424 due to change to 824424
rs Jan & Feb
A popular hotel situated on the A66 just minutes from the A1. A warm welcome is assured by the charming proprietors and their friendly staff. Bedrooms are small but cosy and the rustic style lounge and bar feature a wealth of chunky stone and wood. The extensive menus in both bar and restaurant are good value, with generous portions of well-presented food.
8rm(5⇨♠3hc) CTV in all bedrooms ® ✻ (ex guide dogs)
✷ sB&B£25 sB&B⇨♠£32.50 dB&B£39.50
dB&B⇨♠£45 LDO 9.15pm
∰ 50P
Credit Cards 1 3 ⓔ

SEAFORD East Sussex Map **05** TV49

GH Q Q Q *Avondale Hotel* 4-5 Avondale Rd BN25 1RJ
☎(0323) 890008
Extensively modernised, this conveniently situated and well-run hotel has bedrooms with generous facilities and a combined lounge and dining room. The extensive service is personally supervised by Mr and Mrs Jenkins.
16rm(4♠12hc)(8fb)⊁in 6 bedrooms CTV in all bedrooms ®
✻ (ex guide dogs) ✷ sB&B£14-£16 dB&B£28-£32
dB&B♠£35 WB&B£98-£105 WBDi£143.50-£150.50 LDO 2pm
lift ∰ CTV

SEASCALE Cumbria Map **06** NY00

GH Q Q Q *Cottage* Black How CA20 1LQ ☎(0940) 28416 due to change to (09467) 28416
Delightful guesthouse at edge of Seascale with high standard of accommodation and lovely fells views.
8rm(7⇨♠1♠)(1fb) CTV in all bedrooms ® ✻
∰ CTV 10P

SEATON (nr Looe; 7m) Cornwall & Isles of Scilly
Map **02** SX35

├──**GH** Q Q Q *Blue Haven Hotel* PL11 3JQ
☎Downderry(05035) 310
6rm(5♠1hc)(3fb) CTV in 2 bedrooms TV in 2 bedrooms ®
sB&B£12-£14 sB&B♠£14-£16 dB&B£24-£28
dB&B♠£26-£30 WB&B£77-£92 WBDi£119.50-£134 LDO 8pm
Lic CTV 6P
Credit Cards 1 3 ⓔ

This is one of many guidebooks published by
the AA. The full range is available at any
AA Centre or good bookshop.

SEATON Devon Map **03** SY29

├──**GH** Q Q *Harbourside* 2 Trevelyan Rd EX12 2NL
☎(0297) 20085
Jan-Sep
Close to the town centre and overlooking the harbour, this small family-run guesthouse has comfortable bedrooms and a compact lounge/dining room. Set, home-cooked dishes are served.
4rm(1♠3hc)(2fb) CTV in all bedrooms ® sB&B£12.50-£14
dB&B£21-£23 WB&B£75 WBDi£120 LDO 9pm
Lic ∰ CTV 8P

GH Q Q Q *Mariners Hotel* Esplanade EX12 2NP
☎(0297) 20560
Mar-Dec
Neat, clean accommodation on seafront offering good, well-prepared English and Continental dishes.
10rm(3⇨7♠)(1fb) CTV in all bedrooms ®
Lic ∰ CTV 10P
Credit Cards 1

SEAVIEW

See **WIGHT, ISLE OF**

SEDBERGH Cumbria Map **07** SD69

GH Q Q *Cross Keys Hotel* LA10 5NE ☎(05396) 20284
Etr, Apr-Dec & New Year
Built of stone in 1732, this house is full of character with low ceilings, beams, flagged floors and open fires. There is a very pleasant lounge and a good standard of home cooking is provided. Special diets are catered for by arrangement. The hotel is 'no smoking' throughout.
5rm(1⇨♠4hc)⊁in all bedrooms ® ✻ (ex guide dogs) ✷
sB&B£20 dB&B£40
dB&B⇨♠£46 WB&B£140-£161 WBDi£225.25-£246.25 LDO 24hr notice 9P ⓔ

Cober Hill

Cloughton, Scarborough, North Yorks YO13 0AR
Telephone: (0723) 870310

A family Guest House north of Scarborough in the National Park. Set in six acres of gardens. Ideal position from which to explore North Yorkshire or in which to spend a relaxing holiday.

Full social programme with resident Hosts during the Summer plus safe children's play area.

Reductions for children, under fives free.

Activity holidays plus bargain breaks.

Write or telephone for brochure.

SEDGEFIELD Co Durham Map **08** NZ32

INN [Q][Q] ***Dun Cow*** High St TS21 3AT ☎(0740) 20894
This inn prides itself on its good food and warm hospitality. Substantial meals are served in the attractive bars and the restaurant offers an appetising à la carte menu. The bedrooms are spacious and functional, and provide a good base for racegoers.
6hc CTV in all bedrooms [R] LDO 10pm
♨ 25P
Credit Cards [1] [2] [3] [5]

SELBY North Yorkshire Map **08** SE63

GH [Q] Hazeldene 32-34 Brook St, Doncaster Rd YO8 0AR (A19) ☎(0757) 704809
Closed Xmas wk
Friendly guesthouse near the town centre with comfortable accommodation. There is a TV lounge and a separate breakfast room.
7hc (2fb) TV in all bedrooms [R] 🐕̸ ✽ sB&B£13-£15 dB&B£25-£30
CTV 5P

SELKIRK Borders *Selkirkshire* Map **12** NT42

GH [Q][Q][Q] ***Hillholm*** 36 Hillside Ter TD7 4ND ☎(0750) 21293
Mar-Sep
This immaculate semidetached Victorian villa has a small front garden and stands on the A7, south of the town. A very hospitable house, it is tastefully and attractively decorated throughout.
3hc [R] 🐕̸
♨ CTV P̸ nc10yrs

GH [Q][Q][Q] 34 Hillside Terrace TD7 4ND ☎(0750) 20792
Closed Dec-Jan rs Nov & Feb-Mar
This semidetached Victorian villa stands on the A7 on the southern approaches to Selkirk.
3hc [R] 🐕̸ ✽ sB&B£15-£17
dB&B£23-£25 WB&B£75-£80 LDO 3pm
♨ CTV P̸

SEMLEY Wiltshire Map **03** ST82

INN [Q] Benett Arms SP7 9AS ☎East Knoyle(074783) 221 due to change to (0747) 830221 Telex no 41671
Closed 25 & 26 Dec
This small personally-run inn continues to offer interesting meals and bar snacks. Some of the simply appointed accommodation is situated in an annexe, and all rooms have en suite facilities.
2rm(1🛁1🚿)Annexe 3🚿 CTV in all bedrooms [R]
sB&B🛁🚿£27.50
dB&B🛁🚿£43 WB&Bfr£192.50 WBDifr£280 Lunch £8.80&alc Dinner £10.50-£18alc LDO 9.45pm
♨ 30P
Credit Cards [1] [2] [3] [5] [£]

SENNEN Cornwall & Isles of Scilly Map **02** SW32

GH [Q] The Old Manor TR19 7AD ☎(0736) 871280
Closed 23-28 Dec
8rm(5🚿3hc)(3fb) CTV in 7 bedrooms [R] 🐕̸ LDO 6.30pm
Lic ♨ CTV 50P putting green
Credit Cards [1] [2] [3] [£]

⊢⊣**GH [Q][Q] Sunny Bank Hotel** Sea View Hill TR19 7AR ☎(0736) 871278
Closed Dec
This attractive, stone-built detached house has enthusiastic owners who provide friendly service. Enjoying a rural position just outside the village, it provides family accommodation with commanding views over the sea and countryside.
11hc (2fb) [R] sB&B£12-£16
dB&B£24-£32 WB&B£84-£112 WBDi£120-£144 LDO 7.30pm
Lic ♨ CTV 12P

SENNYBRIDGE Powys Map **03** SN92

See also Trecastle

SELECTED

FH [Q][Q][Q][Q] Mrs M C Adams **Brynfedwen** *(SN963297)* Trallong Common LD3 8HW ☎(0874) 82505
Closed Feb & Mar
Situated 2 miles east of Sennybridge, this stone-built farmhouse occupies one of the finest locations in the principality with fine views over the Brecon Beacons. There are 2 bedrooms in the main house and 1 in the former granary which has been adapted to accommodate disabled visitors. Public areas are comfortable and relaxing. A friendly welcome and good home-cooked food is provided by Mary Adams.
2🛁🚿 Annexe 1🚿 (2fb) CTV in 1 bedroom [R]
🐕̸ (ex guide dogs) ✽ sB&B🛁🚿fr£14
dB&B🛁🚿fr£28 WB&Bfr£98 WBDifr£140 LDO 6.30pm
♨ CTV 6P 118 acres sheep cattle horses
[£]

SETTLE North Yorkshire Map **07** SD86

GH [Q][Q] Liverpool House Chapel Square BD24 9HR ☎(07292) 2247
Closed 21 Dec-Jan
Charming 200-year-old house of great character, in quiet part of town.
7hc [R] 🐕̸ sB&B£15-£18
dB&B£30-£36 WB&B£105 WBDi£182 LDO 10am
Lic CTV 8P
[£]

SEVENOAKS Kent

See **Wrotham**

SHALDON Devon

See **Teignmouth**

SHANKLIN

See **WIGHT, ISLE OF**

SHAP Cumbria Map **12** NY51

GH [Q][Q][Q] ***Brookfield*** CA10 3PZ ☎(09316) 397
Closed Jan
Set on the southern approach to the village and flanked by a charming garden, this welcoming, comfortable establishment specialises in the provision of enjoyable home-cooked meals which are served in an attractive dining room. Housekeeping and maintenance are of a high standard throughout.
6hc (3fb) 🐕̸ LDO 8.15pm
Lic ♨ CTV 30P 6🚗

⊢⊣**FH [Q]** E & S Hodgson **Green Farm** *(NY551121)* CA10 3PW ☎(09316) 619
Etr-Sep
This typical Cumbrian farmhouse offers warm, friendly hospitality. It stands on the A6, on the south side of the village.
3rm(2hc)(2fb) [R] 🐕̸ sB&Bfr£11 dB&Bfr£21
CTV 4P 167 acres mixed

This guide is updated annually – make sure you use an up-to-date edition.

SHAWBURY Shropshire Map **07** SJ52

FH Ⓠ Mrs S J Clarkson **Longley** *(SJ602228)* Stanton Heath
SY4 4HE ☎(0939) 250289
Closed Xmas
A long drive leads to this extended cottage-style farmhouse, surrounded by 15 acres. The house is some 250 years'old, and has a friendly family atmosphere.
2hc Annexe 1⇨ ® ✱
dB&B£24-£30 WB&B£90-£120 WBDi£120-£130
⑪ CTV 4P 15 acres arable sheep

FH ⒬⒬⒬ G C Evans **New** *(SJ586215)* TF6 6RJ
☎(0939) 250358
This extended and modernised farmhouse is situated to the north east of Shrewsbury, and is reached via the A53. It is well maintained throughout, many of the well-equipped bedrooms having en suite facilities.
4rm(3⋔1hc) CTV in all bedrooms ® ⊁ sB&B£15-£18
dB&B⋔£30-£35 WB&B£100-£110
⑪ CTV 10P nc3yrs 70 acres arable sheep
Ⓕ

FH ⒬⒬⒬ Mr & Mrs Grundey **The Sett** *(SY571239)* Village
Farm SY4 4LR ☎(0939) 250391
Closed 21 Dec-4 Jan
Standing in the centre of the village, this fully modernised converted barn makes use of a farm trail to encourage guests to stroll around the area. Non-smoking guests are preferred.
6rm(1⇨5⋔)(1fb)⊁in all bedrooms ® LDO 4pm
Lic ⑪ CTV 14P ♪ farm trail & conservation area 130 acres
arable

SHEARSBY Leicestershire Map **04** SP69

FH ⒬⒬⒬ Mrs A T Hutchinson **Knaptoft House Farm & The
Greenway** *(SP619894)* Bruntingthorpe Rd LE17 6PR
☎Leicester(0533) 478388
Closed Xmas
Situated 1 mile from the village of Shearsby towards Bruntingthorpe, this family farm offers accommodation and separate public areas in adjoining houses. Surrounded by beautiful open countryside and well-tended gardens with well- stocked carp ponds, the accommodation is thoughtfully furnished with guests' comfort foremost in mind, the majority of bedrooms having en suite shower rooms. A high standard is maintained throughout.
3hc Annexe 3hc ® sB&Bfr£14 dB&Bfr£27
⑪ CTV 10P nc3yrs ♪ stabling 145 acres mixed
Ⓕ

FH ⒬⒬ Mrs S E Timms **Wheathill** *(SP622911)* Church Ln
LE17 6PG ☎Leicester(0533) 478663
Closed Xmas
Old brick-built farmhouse retaining original beams and inglenook fireplaces.
4rm(3hc)(1fb)⊁in all bedrooms ® ⊁ (ex guide dogs) ✱
sB&Bfr£14 LDO am
⑪ CTV 3P 133 acres dairy
Ⓕ

SHEFFIELD South Yorkshire Map **08** SK38

GH ⒬⒬ **Lindum Hotel** 91 Montgomery Rd S7 1LP
☎(0742) 552356
Closed Xmas
Used mainly by commercial travellers, this 2-storeyed hotel is located in a leafy residential suburb of Sheffield. Attractive, co-ordinated and well- equipped rooms with good standards of housekeeping are provided within this stone faced, semidetached house.
12rm(1⇨11hc)(1fb) CTV in 11 bedrooms TV in 1 bedroom ®
sB&B£15.50-£25 sB&B⇨£25 dB&B£31-£38
dB&B⇨£39 LDO 6pm

▶

Lic ⊞ CTV 6P
£

GH Q Q Q **Millingtons** 70 Broomgrove Rd S10 2NA (off A625 Eccleshall Rd) ☎(0742) 669549
This large terraced house stands in a quiet leafy avenue in Sheffield, overlooking the Polytecnic. With parking in front and an enclosed garden to the rear, it provides thoughtfully furnished and very pleasing accommodation.
6rm(2♠4hc) CTV in all bedrooms ® ✻ (ex guide dogs) ✳
sB&Bfr£20 sB&B♠£25 dB&Bfr£35 dB&B♠£38
⊞ CTV 4P nc12yrs
£

SHEPTON MALLET Somerset Map **03** ST64

INN Q Q **Kings Arms** Leg Square BA4 5LN ☎(0749) 343781
Closed Xmas rs Sun evenings
An attractive 17th-century inn in the older part of the town offers 2 warm and cosy bars with a small dining room. Bedrooms are fresh and bright, with some modern facilities, and there is a clean, well-kept bathroom.
3♠ CTV in all bedrooms ® ✻ (ex guide dogs) ✳
sB&B♠£25-£29 dB&B♠£33-£38 LDO 9.30pm
⊞ 6P nc10yrs games room
Credit Cards ① £

SHEPTON MONTAGUE Somerset Map **03** ST63

INN Q **Montague** BA9 8JW ☎Bruton(0749) 813213
Just 3 miles from Wincanton, this small roadside inn has ample space for cars. The bedrooms all have en suite facilities and the bar/lounge has an informal atmosphere in which to enjoy home-cooked food and speciality real ales.
3♠ TV in all bedrooms ® sB&B♠£20
dB&B♠£38 Lunch £2.20-£4alc Dinner £6-£9.50 LDO 8pm
⊞ 24P nc14yrs
Credit Cards ① ③

SHERBOURNE Warwickshire

See **Warwick**

SHERIFF HUTTON North Yorkshire Map **08** SE66

GH Q Q Q **Rangers House** Sheriff Hutton Park YO6 1RH ☎(03477) 397
This interesting and unusual house is peacefully located within attractive gardens. The oak-beamed bedrooms are cosy and the lounge features a minstrels' gallery. Guests will enjoy a high standard of cooking.
6rm(2⇨2♠2hc)(1fb) ® ✻ ✳ sB&B⇨♠£29 dB&B£52
dB&B⇨♠£56 WB&B£182 LDO 9.30pm
Lic ⊞ CTV 30P
£
See advertisement under YORK on page 412

SHERINGHAM Norfolk Map **09** TG14

GH Q Q Q **Beacon Hotel** Nelson Rd NR26 8BT ☎(0263) 822019
May-Sep
This attractive residence, on Beeston Hill, is only minutes from the beach and town centre. All rooms enjoy good views, are very well maintained and are thoughtfully furnished. The restaurant includes a small bar, and there is a comfortable lounge.
7rm(1⇨3♠3hc) ® ✻ WBDi£165
Lic ⊞ CTV 6P nc14yrs
Credit Cards ① ③

GH Q Q Q **Fairlawns** 26 Hooks Hill Rd NR26 8NL ☎(0263) 824717
Etr-Oct
Situated in a quiet residential area away from the town centre, this guesthouse provides a relaxing and quiet retreat. Comfortable

---

rooms, thoughtfully designed with good quality en suite facilities, all having bath and shower. Evening meals are freshly prepared and show skill and imagination. This licensed hotel benefits from pleasant, well-tended gardens and car parking.
5⇨♠® ✻ (ex guide dogs)
dB&B⇨♠£37 WB&B£105 WBDi£158
Lic ⊞ CTV 6P nc12yrs
£

GH Q Q Q **Melrose Hotel** 9 Holway Rd NR26 8HN ☎(0263) 823299
rs Xmas
The new restaurant offers a choice of freshly prepared dishes at this hotel, situated in a mainly residential area a few minutes' walk from the town centre. Peter and Sandra Foster are caring hosts, who provide some en suite accommodation.
10rm(5♠5hc)(1fb) CTV in 5 bedrooms ® sB&B£14.50-£15.50 sB&B♠£19-£20 dB&B£29-£31
dB&B♠£38-£40 WB&B£95-£112 WBDi£130-£150 LDO 9am
Lic ⊞ CTV 10P cycle hire dinghy hire & tuition
Credit Cards ① ③ £

SHETLAND Map **16**

LERWICK Map **16** HU44

GH Q Q Q *Glen Orchy* 20 Knab Rd ZE1 0AX ☎Shetland(0595) 2031
Sitting high above the town centre, this guesthouse has bright, airy bedrooms together with a combined lounge/dining room.
6rm(1♠5hc)(1fb) CTV in all bedrooms ®
⊞ CTV ▶9

SHOTTLE Derbyshire Map **08** SK34

GH Q Q **Shottle Hall Farm** DE5 2EB ☎Cowers Lane(077389) 276 & 203
Closed Xmas
Guests are assured of a warm welcome at this large family home. Surrounded by 3 acres of grounds and a large farm, this is the ideal spot for a relaxing holiday.
9rm(1⇨8hc)(3fb)✕in all bedrooms ® sB&B£20.50-£22.50 dB&B£36-£38
dB&B⇨♠£50-£55 WB&Bfr£140 WBDifr£210 LDO 6pm
Lic ⊞ CTV 30P
£
See advertisement under DERBY on page 133

Every effort is made to provide accurate information, but details can change after we go to print. It is advisable to check prices etc. before you make a firm booking.

SHREWLEY Warwickshire Map **04** SP26

SELECTED

GH Ⓠ Ⓠ Ⓠ Ⓠ **Shrewley House** CV35 7AT
☎Claverdon(092684) 2549
*This grade II listed Georgian farmhouse has an elegant
drawing room opening on to 1.5 acres of well-tended gardens,
and the dining room serves traditional English food. The
delightful bedrooms are very well equipped with en suite
bathrooms and the deluxe rooms have king-size, draped four-
poster beds.*
3⇌♠ Annexe 4⇌♠ (1fb) CTV in 5 bedrooms ®
sB&B⇌♠£30-£40 dB&B⇌♠£40-£52 LDO 7.30pm
🎵 CTV 15P 2🐾 ፚ
Credit Cards ① ③ ⓔ
See advertisement under WARWICK on page 372

SHREWSBURY Shropshire Map **07** SJ41

GH Ⓠ **Cannock House Private Hotel** 182 Abbey Foregate
SY2 6AH ☎(0743) 56043 due to change to 356043
Closed Xmas
*This small guesthouse stands on the main road, opposite
Shrewsbury's famous abbey. The owners provide a friendly and
informal service to complement the modest but well-maintained
accommodation.*
7hc (1fb)
🎵 CTV 5P

GH Ⓠ Ⓠ Ⓠ **Fieldside Hotel** 38 London Rd SY2 5NX
☎(0743) 53143 due to change to 353143
*Easily accessible from both the A49 and the A5, this large,
beautifully maintained Victorian house stands on the A5112, east
of the town centre. The well-equipped accommodation is of good
quality and suitable for business guests and tourists.*
9rm(1⇌5♠3hc) CTV in all bedrooms ® ✖ ✱ sB&B£18
sB&B⇌♠£28-£30 dB&B⇌♠£38-£40
Lic 🎵 10P 2🐾 nc9yrs
Credit Cards ① ② ③

GH Ⓠ Ⓠ Ⓠ **Sandford House Hotel** St Julians Friars SY1 1XL
☎(0743) 3829 due to change to 343829
*A charming, small hotel, close to English Bridge and river walks,
yet minutes from the town. The elegant lounge overlooks a well-
tended rear garden. A warm welcome is assured.*
10rm(1⇌4♠5hc)(2fb) CTV in all bedrooms ® sB&Bfr£18
sB&B⇌♠fr£22 dB&Bfr£32 dB&B⇌♠fr£37
Lic 🎵 CTV 3P ⓔ

GH Ⓠ Ⓠ **Sydney House Hotel** Coton Crescent, Coton Hill
SY1 2LJ ☎(0743) 54681 due to change to 354681
Closed 24-30 Dec
*This Victorian house stands on the northern edge of the town.
Family run, it offers fully modernised rooms.*
7rm(3♠4hc)(4fb) CTV in all bedrooms ® ✖ (ex guide dogs)
sB&B£24.50-£30 sB&B♠£37 dB&B£36
dB&B♠£48 WB&B£115-£235 WBDi£169-£289 LDO 8.30pm
Lic 🎵 7P 1🐾 (£2.50 per night)
Credit Cards ① ③ ⓔ
See advertisement on page 333

FH Ⓠ Ⓠ Mrs P A Roberts *The Day House* (SJ465104)
Nobold SY5 8NL (2.5m SW between A488 & A49)
☎(0743) 860212
Closed Xmas & New Year
*Mostly built in the 1840s, this rambling farmhouse is surrounded
by attractive gardens in a peaceful area 2.5 miles south south west
of the town centre and provides spacious accommodation.*
3rm(1⇌1♠1hc)(3fb) CTV in all bedrooms ®
✖ (ex guide dogs)
🎵 CTV 10P 1🐾 ✔ rough & game shooting 400 acres arable
dairy

FH 🇶🇶 Mrs J M Jones **Grove** *(SJ537249)* Preston Brockhurst SY4 5QA ☎Clive(093928) 223
Closed Xmas & New Year
This 17th-century farmhouse with Victorian modifications provides well- maintained, traditional accommodation. Situated in the village of Preston Brockhurst it is just 8.5 miles north of the historic county town of Shrewsbury.
3hc (1fb)⊁in all bedrooms ® ✖ (ex guide dogs) ✱
sB&B£12.50-£13.50 dB&B£28-£30
🛏 CTV 4P nc5yrs 320 acres arable mixed

SIDMOUTH Devon Map **03** SY18

GH 🇶🇶🇶 **Canterbury** Salcombe Rd EX10 8PR
☎(0395) 513373
Mar-Nov
Close to the river and park, yet convenient for the town centre, this period house has well-equipped bedrooms, many with good en suite facilities – some of the many improvements carried out by Mr and Mrs Lever.
8rm(7⇨3♠1hc)(4fb) CTV in all bedrooms ®
sB&B£15.50-£18.50 sB&B⇨♠£18.50-£21.50 dB&B£30-£33
dB&B⇨♠£36-£38 WB&B£105-£125 WBDi£140-£165 LDO 4.30pm
Lic CTV 6P
£

⊢⊣**GH** 🇶 **Ryton House** 52-54 Winslade Rd EX10 9EX
☎(0395) 513981
This semidetached property has its own garden and is located away from the town centre, but still within easy reach of all local amenities. The recently refurbished lounge complements the bright bedrooms and the informal dining room.
9rm(1♠8hc)(3fb) ® sB&B£12-£15 dB&B£22-£28
dB&B♠£26-£32 WB&B£82-£102 WBDi£115-£135 (wkly only 1-19 Aug) LDO 4.30pm
Lic 🛏 CTV 9P
£

SILLOTH Cumbria Map **11** NY15

GH 🇶🇶 **Nith View** 1 Pine Ter CA5 4DT ☎(06973) 31542
Well run with a friendly atmosphere, this guesthouse is in a delightful location overlooking the Solway Firth. Well furnished, comfortable accommodation is offered.
8rm(4♠4hc)(4fb) CTV in 2 bedrooms TV in 1 bedroom ®
LDO 4pm
Lic 🛏 CTV 8P 1🍴

SIMONSBATH Somerset Map **03** SS73

FH 🇶🇶 Mrs A R Brown **Emmett Grange** *(SS753369)*
TA24 7LD (2.5m SW unclass towards Brayford)
☎Exford(064383) 282
Mar-Oct
This large farmhouse is approached by an attractive drive, and stands in unspoilt moorland within Exmoor National Park. Fine views are to be had, and comfortable accommodation is coupled with good food, freshly prepared by the owner.
4rm(2⇨2hc) CTV in all bedrooms ® sB&Bfr£29
sB&B⇨fr£32 dB&Bfr£58
dB&B⇨fr£64 (incl dinner) WB&B£105-£125 WBDi£180-£195
LDO 8pm
Lic 🛏 6P 1200 acres hill stock £

SKEGNESS Lincolnshire Map **09** TF56

GH 🇶🇶 **Chatsworth Hotel** North Pde PE25 2UB ☎(0754) 4177
May-Sep rs Mar-Apr & Oct-Nov
This is a popular seafront hotel, close to amenities at the north end of the town. The sound, well-kept accommodation includes en suite facilities, and is supplemented by a television lounge, a lounge bar and a steak restaurant.

22⇨3♠ (7fb) CTV in all bedrooms ® LDO 7.30pm
Lic 🛏 CTV 8P 4🍴
Credit Cards 1 3

GH 🇶🇶 **Crawford Hotel** South Pde PE25 3HR ☎(0754) 4215
Situated in a quiet area at the bottom of the South Parade, this establishment offers peaceful surroundings along with its own excellent range of public rooms and leisure facilities. These include a good indoor swimming pool, and a games room.
20rm(10⇨7♠3hc)(8fb) CTV in all bedrooms ® LDO 5pm
Lic lift 🛏 CTV 8P ▨(heated) jacuzzi games room
Credit Cards 1 3

GH 🇶🇶 **Northdale** 12 Firbeck Av PE25 3JY ☎(0754) 610554
The seafront is just a few minutes walk away from this friendly, family-run hotel. Some bedrooms have en suite facilities and all are bright and comfortable. There is a TV lounge and a bar lounge.
11rm(2⇨1♠8hc)(3fb) CTV in 1 bedroom TV in 4 bedrooms ® LDO 5.30pm
Lic CTV 8P 🍴

SKIPTON North Yorkshire Map **07** SD95

GH 🇶🇶 **Craven House** 56 Keighley Rd BD23 2NB
☎(0756) 794657
Closed Xmas Day & New Years Day
The Rushtons provide a welcome at their guesthouse, situated on the main Keighley road and a short walk from the town centre. The comfortable accommodation gives good value, and there is a pleasant dining room and a relaxing lounge.
7rm(2⇨1♠4hc) CTV in all bedrooms ® sB&B£14 dB&B£28
dB&B⇨♠£34
🛏 CTV 3P

GH 🇶🇶 **Highfield Hotel** 58 Keighley Rd BD23 2NB
☎(0756) 793182
Closed 6-20 Jan rs 24 Dec-5 Jan
A cosy bar, lounge and dining room are available at this comfortable guesthouse, which has easy access to the town centre. The rooms have excellent facilities including hairdryers and trouser presses.
11rm(3⇨5♠3hc)(2fb) CTV in all bedrooms ® sB&B£17-£18
sB&B⇨♠£27-£28 dB&B£34-£36
dB&B⇨♠£34-£36 LDO 5pm
Lic 🛏 CTV ✗
Credit Cards 1 3

INN 🇶🇶 **Red Lion Hotel** High St BD23 1DT ☎(0756) 790718
Cosy, well-furnished inn (the oldest building in Skipton).
3⇨♠ (1fb) CTV in all bedrooms ® ✖ sB&B⇨♠fr£25
dB&B⇨♠fr£35
🛏 4P
Credit Cards 1 3 £

SKYE, ISLE OF Highland *Inverness-Shire* Map **13**

DUNVEGAN Map **13** NG24

GH 🇶 **Roskhill** Roskhill IV55 8ZD (3m S A863) ☎(047022) 317
Mar-Nov
A friendly comfortable guesthouse with an attractive stone walled dining room.
5hc (2fb) ® LDO 6pm
Lic 🛏 CTV 6P

See advertisement on page 335

ISLE ORNSAY Map **13** NG71

GH 🇶🇶 **Old Post Office House** IV43 8QR ☎(04713) 201
Apr-Oct
Tidy garden with pleasant hill and sea views.
2hc Annexe 2hc
CTV 10P nc10yrs

PORTREE Map 13 NG44

GH Q Bosville Hotel Bosville Ter IV51 9DG ☎(0478) 2846
May-Sep
This town centre hotel has a combined restaurant and tea-room which is open to the public, with compact and functional bedrooms above.
16rm(9🌂7hc) CTV in 13 bedrooms ® ✱ sB&Bfr£20
sB&B🌂fr£25 dB&Bfr£30 dB&B🌂fr£40 LDO 8pm
Lic ⊞ CTV 10P
Credit Cards [1] ⓔ

GH QQQ Craiglockhart Beaumont Crescent IV51 9DF
☎(0478) 2233
Closed Dec
Two comfortable, adjoining houses looking out onto the harbour with fine views of the bay and Isle of Raasay. The accommodation is pleasant and guests share tables in the dining room.
10rm(3🌂7hc)(1fb) CTV in 9 bedrooms ® ✱ sB&B£14-£16
dB&B£28-£32 dB&B🌂£32-£36
⊞ CTV 4P

GH QQQ Quiraing Viewfield Rd IV51 9ES ☎(0478) 2870
Nicely appointed, this modern bungalow stands on the main road entering the town from the south and is 3 minutes' walk from the town centre. All bedrooms have colour television and a comprehensive Scottish breakfast menu is offered. Each bedroom has its own dining table allocated.
6rm(2🌂4hc)(3fb)✎in all bedrooms CTV in all bedrooms ® ✱
sB&Bfr£15 dB&Bfr£28 dB&B🌂£30-£32
⊞ CTV 8P

FH QQ Mrs M Bruce *Cruachanlea* *(NG513373)* Braes
IV51 9LJ ☎Sligachan(047852) 233
Closed 20 Dec-10 Jan
This detached, modern house is part of a smallholding in a small coastal hamlet, with outstanding views across to the Isle of Raasay. The lounge and dining room are combined and guests may expect to share table.
4hc (2fb) ®
⊞ CTV 6P 15 acres sheep

SLAIDBURN Lancashire Map 07 SD75

SELECTED

GH QQQQ Parrock Head Farm House Hotel
Woodhouse Ln BB7 3AH ☎(02006) 614
mid Feb-mid Dec
Peacefully situated in rolling countryside, this 17th-century long house has been carefully converted to provide a most comfortable and relaxing place in which to stay. The bedrooms are appointed to a very high standard and a delightful first floor lounge enjoys lovely views of the surrounding countryside. The neighbouring library is full of information on the locality. The attractive and well-appointed restaurant serves freshly cooked local produce complemented by a well chosen wine list – a particular interest of Richard Umbers.
3⇨ Annexe 6⇨ (1fb) CTV in all bedrooms ® LDO
8.15pm
Lic ⊞ 20P
Credit Cards [1] [2]

SLEAFORD Lincolnshire Map 08 TF04

INN QQ Carre Arms Hotel Mareham Ln NG34 7JP
☎(0529) 303156
This is a small, friendly, family-managed hotel on the outskirts of Sleaford, and is convenient for the railway station. The covered Vinery Courtyard is suitable for parents with children wishing to take bar food and drinks.

14rm(3⇨11hc) CTV in all bedrooms ® sB&Bfr£24
sB&B⇨fr£29
dB&Bfr£45 Bar Lunch £3.50-£5.55alc Dinner £7.95-£16.20alc
LDO 9pm
⊞ CTV 50P
Credit Cards [1] [3]

SLEDMERE Humberside Map 08 SE96

INN Q Triton YO25 0XQ ☎Driffield(0377) 86644
Good value accommodation in a period inn in this attractive estate village.
6rm(2⇨2🌂2hc)(1fb) CTV in all bedrooms ® ✱ sB&B£15-£21
dB&B£30-£42
dB&B⇨🌂£42 WBDi£140-£175 Lunch fr£5.95&alc Dinner
fr£7&alc LDO 9pm
⊞ CTV 30P
Credit Cards [1] [3] [5] ⓔ

SLOUGH Berkshire Map 04 SU97

GH QQ Colnbrook Lodge Bath Rd, Colnbrook SL3 0NZ (3m
E A4) ☎(0753) 685958
Closed 24-25 Dec
A cosy house with a friendly, informal atmosphere within easy reach of Heathrow Airport.
8rm(1⇨1🌂6hc)(2fb) CTV in 3 bedrooms ® ✖ (ex guide dogs)
sB&B£25-£30 sB&B⇨🌂£33-£36 dB&B£38-£40
dB&B⇨🌂£45-£50 WB&B£181-£200
Lic ⊞ CTV 12P
Credit Cards [1] [3] ⓔ

SMEATON, GREAT North Yorkshire Map 08 NZ30

FH QQQ Mrs N Hall **Smeaton East** *(NZ349044)* DL6 2ET
☎Great Smeaton(060981) 336
Jun-Oct
In a village location, set between Yorkshire's beautiful moors and dales, this 17th-century working farm is an ideal base for exploring both the countryside and the attractions of York and Durham. Attractive bedrooms, equipped with all modern facilities, and the superbly furnished dining room and comfortable lounge all add to its period character. A substantial breakfast is served, with great emphasis on quality and variety.
2hc CTV in 1 bedroom ® ✖ ✱ sB&B£15-£16 dB&B£26-£28
⊞ CTV 4P nc7yrs 120 acres dairy mixed
ⓔ

SOLVA Dyfed

See Llandeloy & Pen-y-Cwm

SOMERTON Somerset Map 03 ST42

GH QQQ Church Farm School Lane, Compton Dandon
TA11 6PE ☎(0458) 72927
Jan-3 wk Dec Closed Xmas & New Year
Most of the comfortable, thoughtfully equipped accommodation is in the annexe of this charming cottage. A warm welcome is assured and the new owners personally supervise the running of Church Farm.
2rm(1⇨1🌂)Annexe 5rm(2⇨2🌂1hc)(1fb) CTV in 6 bedrooms
® LDO 5.30pm
Lic ⊞ 6P nc4yrs

SOPWORTH Wiltshire Map 03 ST88

FH Q Mrs D M Barker **Manor** *(ST826865)* SN14 6PR
☎Didmarton(045423) 676
Etr-Oct
3rm (1fb) ✖ (ex guide dogs) ✱ sB&Bfr£12
dB&Bfr£22 WB&Bfr£70
⊞ TV 5P 300 acres arable beef horses sheep

SOUTHAMPTON Hampshire Map **04** SU41

See **Town Plan Section**

GH 🇶🇶 **Banister House Hotel** Banister Rd SO9 2JJ
☎(0703) 221279

Closed 25-27 Dec

Private hotel with warm and friendly atmosphere. Popular bar meals and dining room.

23rm(1⇔4ℕ18hc)(3fb) CTV in all bedrooms ®
sB&B£21-£27.50 sB&B⇔ℕ£23.50-£27.50 dB&B£29.50-£35
dB&B⇔ℕ£34.50-£35 LDO 7.45pm

Lic ⁴⁴⁴ 14P

Credit Cards 1 3 £

GH 🇶 **Hill Lodge Hotel** 126-128 Hill Ln, Shirley SO1 5DD
☎(0703) 223071

This simple guesthouse enjoys a quiet position yet is within easy reach of all amenities. Guests here receive friendly family service and have the advantage of a large car park.

19rm(16⇔3hc)(3fb)⚓in 3 bedrooms CTV in all bedrooms
® ✠ (ex guide dogs) ✳ sB&B£14-£25 sB&B⇔ℕ£21-£25
dB&B£25-£30
dB&B⇔ℕ£35-£40 WB&B£98-£175 WBDi£140-£217 LDO
6pm

⁴⁴⁴ CTV 20P

£

GH 🇶🇶🇶 **Hunters Lodge Hotel** 25 Landguard Road, Shirley
SO1 5DL ☎(0703) 227919 FAX (0703) 230913

Closed 17 Dec-7 Jan

With a good bar, well-maintained and equipped rooms and a small lounge, this friendly, family-managed hotel enjoys a quiet situation with parking and garaging facilities.

18rm(8⇔4ℕ6hc)(2fb)⚓in 1 bedroom CTV in all bedrooms ®
✳ sB&B£23-£25.88 sB&B⇔ℕ£32.78-£35 dB&Bfr£43.13
dB&B⇔ℕfr£51.18 WB&Bfr£115 WBDifr£149.50 LDO 6pm

Lic ⁴⁴⁴ CTV 16P 4🚗 (75p per night)

Credit Cards 1 3

GH 🇶🇶 **Landguard Lodge** 21 Landguard Rd SO1 5DL
☎(0703) 636904

Landguard Lodge is a quietly located semidetached property in a residential area. The accommodation has recently been refurbished throughout. This bed and breakfast establishment offers simple yet well-equipped bedrooms and an attractive pine furnished breakfast room.

13rm(1ℕ12hc)(1fb) CTV in all bedrooms ® ✠ (ex guide dogs)
✳ sB&B£12.50-£15 sB&Bℕ£15 dB&B£25 dB&Bℕ£30

CTV 4P nc5yrs

⊢—GH 🇶🇶 **Linden** 51-53 The Polygon SO1 2BP
☎(0703) 225653

Closed Xmas

This double-fronted house stands in the city centre and provides neat, bright and comfortable accommodation. Mr and Mrs Hutchins have run this guesthouse for many years and provide pleasant, efficient service and a well cooked breakfast.

12hc (4fb) CTV in all bedrooms ® ✠ sB&B£13-£14
dB&B£26-£28

⁴⁴⁴ CTV 7P

£

GH 🇶🇶🇶 **Lodge** 1 Winn Rd, The Avenue SO2 1EH
☎(0703) 557537

Closed Xmas wk

Quietly situated Tudor-style hotel close to the city centre. Well-equipped bedrooms are complemented by good lounge and bar amenities. Extensive services are available.

14rm(2⇔4ℕ8hc)(2fb) CTV in all bedrooms ® ✳
sB&B£19-£20.50 sB&B⇔ℕ£27.50-£29.50 dB&B£32-£33
dB&B⇔ℕ£37.50-£39.50 WBDi£160-£250 LDO 9pm

Lic ⁴⁴⁴ CTV 10P

Credit Cards 1 3 £

GH 🇶 **Madison House** 137 Hill Ln SO1 5AF ☎(0703) 333374
rs 23 Dec-2 Jan

A cosy, simple and well-maintained guesthouse, this is set in a residential area giving easy access to the city centre and the docks. There are facilities for guests to make tea and coffee at any time.

9rm(1ℕ8hc)(2fb) CTV in all bedrooms ® ✠ ✳
sB&B£14.95-£16.70 dB&B£27.60-£31.50
dB&Bℕ£33.60-£37.50

⁴⁴⁴ CTV 7P

£

GH 🇶🇶 **Villa Capri** 52 Archers Rd SO1 2LU ☎(0703) 632800

Centrally positioned for all of Southampton's amenities, this detached Victorian property has recently been refurbished. The bedrooms vary in size, and the dining room is compact but is understood to be extended. Good car parking space is available around landscaped gardens. Room 15 has a water bed.

14rm(9ℕ5hc) CTV in all bedrooms ® ✳ sB&B£12.10-£15.50
sB&Bℕ£12.10-£15.50 dB&B£24.20-£31
dB&Bℕ£24.20-£31 LDO 1pm

CTV 14P nc2yrs steam room

Credit Cards 1 3 £

See advertisement on page 337

SOUTH BRENT Devon Map **03** SX66

FH 🇶🇶 M E Slade **Great Aish** *(SX689603)* TQ10 9JG
☎(0364) 72238

Closed Dec

Home-cooked produce from the extensive kitchen garden features on the menu at this spacious Victorian farmhouse. It is close to Dartmoor National Park and enjoys fine views of the countryside.

5hc (3fb) ® ✠ (ex guide dogs) ✳ WB&Bfr£91

CTV 8P 60 acres beef dairy mixed

£

SOUTHEND-ON-SEA Essex Map **05** TQ88

GH [Q][Q] Argyle Hotel 12 Clifftown Pde SS1 1DP
☎(0702) 339483
Closed Xmas
Small, comfortable hotel overlooking sea and public gardens.
11hc (3fb) CTV in all bedrooms Ⓡ 🚫🐕 ✱ sB&Bfr£14
dB&Bfr£28 dB&Bfr£30
Lic ♨ CTV 🚫🅿 nc5yrs

GH [Q][Q] Bay 187 Eastern Esplanade, Thorpe Bay SS1 3AA
☎(0702) 588415
Closed Xmas
This small, family-run, seafront hotel is within walking distance of the town centre. The accommodation includes 2 annexe bedrooms with private facilities.
7hc Annexe 2rm(1🛁1🚿)(1fb) CTV in all bedrooms Ⓡ
sB&B£15-£18 dB&B🛁🚿£25-£30 WB&B£78-£90
♨ CTV 3P

GH [Q][Q][Q] *Cobham Lodge Hotel* 2 Cobham Rd, Westcliff On Sea SS0 8EA ☎(0702) 346438
This hotel stands in a peaceful residential area, and has much to commend it. The modern bedrooms are attractive and there are 2 tastefully appointed lounges and a full-size snooker table.
30rm(9🛁13🚿8hc)(3fb) CTV in all bedrooms Ⓡ 🚫🐕 LDO 7pm
Lic ♨ CTV 🚫🅿 snooker
Credit Cards [1] [3] [5]

SELECTED

GH [Q][Q][Q][Q] Ilfracombe House Hotel 11-13 Wilson Rd SS1 1HG ☎(0702) 351000
Two early Victorian town houses have been tastefully refurbished to create an elegant and comfortable atmosphere. Sympathetically designed, and offering modern facilities, the accommodation is tastefully furnished. Home-cooked traditional English fare can be enjoyed in the dining room.
14🛁🚿 (2fb) CTV in all bedrooms Ⓡ 🚫🐕
sB&B🛁🚿£28.75-£35.65
dB&B🛁🚿£42.55-£49.45 WB&B£228.85-£266.80
WBDi£297.10-£335.05 LDO 6pm
Lic ♨ CTV 🚫🅿 ⌂
Credit Cards [1] [2] [3] [5] [£]

GH [Q][Q] Marine View 4 Trinity Av, Westcliff on Sea SS0 7PU
☎(0702) 344104
Marine View is run with ease by its capable proprietress, and provides simply appointed accommodation in pleasant surroundings.
6hc (1fb) CTV in all bedrooms Ⓡ 🚫🐕 (ex guide dogs) ✱
sB&B£15-£17.50 dB&B£28-£35 WB&B£96
♨ CTV 🚫🅿

GH [Q][Q] Mayflower Hotel 5-6 Royal Ter SS1 1DY
☎(0702) 340489
Closed Xmas
The flowers in front of this grade II Regency building enliven the street. The modest accommodation is neat and well equipped, the front rooms overlooking the sea. The proprietors are charming.
23rm(4🚿19hc)(3fb) CTV in all bedrooms Ⓡ ✱ sB&B£17-£20
sB&B🚿£25-£30 dB&B£32-£35 dB&B🚿£38-£40
♨ CTV 2P pool table

GH [Q][Q] *Terrace Hotel* 8 Royal Ter SS1 1DY ☎(0702) 348143
Closed mid Dec-mid Jan
This small, nicely kept guesthouse is well managed by the proprietor and has a cosy atmosphere. Some bedrooms have excellent sea views.
9hc (3fb) Ⓡ
Lic ♨ CTV 🚫🅿 nc5yrs

GH [Q][Q][Q] Tower Hotel 146 Alexandra Rd SS1 1HE
☎(0702) 348635
First used as a hotel in 1923, this fully modernised house lies in a quiet residential area a few yards from the cliff. While some rooms are compact, all are well equipped.
16rm(1🛁13🚿2hc)Annexe 16rm(3🛁13🚿)(6fb) CTV in all bedrooms Ⓡ ✱ sB&Bfr£28 sB&B🛁🚿£35-£39.50
dB&B🛁🚿£40-£55 LDO 9pm
Lic ♨ CTV 2P residents membership of near by sports club
Credit Cards [1] [2] [3] [5] [£]

GH [Q][Q][Q] West Park Private Hotel 11 Park Road, Westcliff-on-Sea SS0 7PQ ☎(0702) 330729 & 334252 FAX (0702) 338162
This large, well-managed guesthouse has been nicely upgraded over the years and now offers well-equipped, modern bedrooms and welcoming service.
21rm(13🛁3🚿5hc) CTV in all bedrooms Ⓡ sB&B£31-£33
sB&B🛁🚿£33-£35 dB&B£51-£55
dB&B🛁🚿£51-£55 LDO 6.30pm
Lic ♨ CTV 16P
Credit Cards [1] [3] [£]

SOUTHPORT Merseyside Map **07** SD31

See **Town Plan Section**

GH [Q][Q][Q] Ambassador Private Hotel 13 Bath St PR9 0DP
☎(0704) 543998 & 530459
Closed 1-7 Jan
Situated between fashionable Lord Street and the Promenade, this small hotel offers comfort with well-appointed bedrooms. Fresh, seasonal produce is used for the dishes offered at dinner.
8🚿 (4fb)🚭in 1 bedroom CTV in all bedrooms Ⓡ ✱
sB&B🚿£26
dB&B🚿£40 WB&Bfr£120 WBDifr£150 LDO 6pm
Lic ♨ 6P nc5yrs
Credit Cards [1] [3]

GH [Q] Brentwood 16 Duke St PR8 1LW ☎(0704) 541185
Closed Xmas & New Year
Pleasant well-furnished guesthouse, family owned and run, offering a warm welcome. Close to the famous Lord Street.
9rm(4🚿5hc)(3fb) CTV in all bedrooms Ⓡ ✱ sB&B£13-£16
dB&B£26-£32
dB&B🚿£30-£36 WB&B£84-£94 WBDi£105-£115 LDO 3pm
♨ CTV 5P
[£]

GH [Q][Q] Crimond Hotel 28 Knowsley Rd PR9 0HN
☎(0704) 536456 FAX (0704) 548643
With its own conference and leisure facilities, this family-run hotel, situated in a quiet residential area, is popular with businessmen. The bedrooms vary in size and style, and all are well equipped.
10rm(5🛁5🚿)(2fb) CTV in all bedrooms Ⓡ ✱
sB&B🛁🚿£38-£40 dB&B🛁🚿£58-£60 LDO 8.30pm
Lic ♨ 12P 🏊(heated) sauna
Credit Cards [1] [2] [3] [5] [£]

GH [Q][Q] Fairway Private Hotel 106 Leyland Rd PR9 0JQ
☎(0704) 542069
Mar-Nov
Midway between Hesketh Park and the town centre, this small hotel offers traditionally furnished bedrooms and pleasant public areas with a small lounge bar.
9rm(4🚿5hc)(4fb) CTV in 8 bedrooms Ⓡ 🚫🐕 (ex guide dogs) ✱
dB&B£38-£40
dB&B🚿£42-£46 (incl dinner) WB&B£112-£114
WBDi£133-£140 LDO 6pm
Lic CTV 10P

GH [Q][Q][Q] The Gables Private Hotel 110 Leyland Rd PR9 0JE
☎(0704) 535554
Apr-Oct

Quietly situated off the northern end of the promenade, this neat establishment has well-furnished bedrooms and a charming dining room where good home-cooked meals are served.
9rm(2⇔6♠1hc) CTV in all bedrooms ® ✘
dB&B£36-£40 WBDi£158-£170 LDO 3pm
Lic ♛ CTV 9P nc12yrs

GH Q Q Lake Hotel 55-56 The Promenade PR9 0DY
☎(0704) 530996
Close to the theatre on the Promenade, Lake Hotel provides comfortable accommodation and a friendly atmosphere. The bedrooms vary in size, but all are equipped to the same standard, with en suite showers.
20♠ (5fb) CTV in all bedrooms ® sB&B♠£17.80-£18.86
dB&B♠£32.40-£34.40 WB&B£115.70-£124.10
WBDi£147.20-£155 LDO 4.30pm
Lic ♛ CTV 14P
Credit Cards 3 £

↦GH Q Q **Lyndhurst** 101 King St PR8 1LQ ☎(0704) 537520
Neat, compact accommodation is offered at this friendly guesthouse, which is conveniently situated in a side street close to the town centre.
7hc CTV in all bedrooms ® ✘ (ex guide dogs) sB&B£13
dB&B£26 WB&B£84 WBDi£120 LDO 12pm
Lic ♛ CTV 2P nc5yrs

GH Q Q Q Oakwood Private Hotel 7 Portland St PR8 1LJ
☎(0704) 531858
Etr-Nov
Close to the centre of town, this detached Victorian villa offers well-maintained, comfortable accommodation with character.
7rm(4♠3hc)✗in all bedrooms CTV in all bedrooms ® ✘
Lic ♛ CTV 8P nc5yrs

GH Q Q Rosedale Hotel 11 Talbot St PR8 1HP
☎(0704) 530604
Guests can be sure of a warm welcome at this small guesthouse which is close to the town centre. The bedrooms vary in size, and there is a comfortable quiet lounge and pleasant bar in which to relax.
10rm(1⇔4♠5hc)(3fb)✗in all bedrooms CTV in all bedrooms
® ✘ (ex guide dogs) sB&B£14-£18 sB&B⇔♠£17-£21
dB&B£28-£36
dB&B⇔♠£33-£41 WB&B£90-£116 WBDi£110-£140 LDO
4pm
Lic ♛ 8P
£

GH Q Q Q Sunningdale Hotel 85 Leyland Rd PR9 0NJ
☎(0704) 538673
The bedrooms are well equipped at this personally-run hotel, situated in a quiet road, near the golf course and Hesketh Park. There is a comfortable television lounge, a spacious lounge bar, a pool table and a dartboard.
14rm(1⇔11♠2hc)(4fb) CTV in all bedrooms ® sB&B£19
sB&B⇔♠£21
dB&B⇔♠£40 WB&B£126-£133 WBDi£175-£182 LDO
4.30pm
Lic ♛ CTV 10P half size snooker table dart board
Credit Cards 1 3

↦GH Q Q **The White Lodge Private Hotel** 12 Talbot St
PR8 1HP ☎(0704) 536320
Pleasant, well-maintained accommodation is offered at this family-run guesthouse, which is convenient for the town centre. The public areas include an attractive basement lounge bar.
9rm(4♠5hc)(3fb) ® ✘ (ex guide dogs) sB&B£13-£16
sB&B♠£15-£18 dB&B£26-£32
dB&B♠£30-£36 WB&B£85-£110 WBDi£100-£140 LDO 6pm
Lic CTV 6P ⌀
£

GH [Q][Q] ***Windsor Lodge Hotel*** 37 Saunders St PR9 0HJ
☎(0704) 530070
This friendly and appealing small hotel is near the promenade and the marine lake. It is well decorated throughout and, in addition to a comfortable lounge, offers a pleasant basement bar and games room.
12rm(1🛁11hc)(1fb) CTV in all bedrooms [R] 🐕 (ex guide dogs) LDO 4pm
Lic 🍽 CTV 6P pool table games room

SOUTHSEA Hampshire

See **Portsmouth & Southsea**

SOUTHWELL Nottinghamshire Map **08** SK75

SELECTED

GH [Q][Q][Q][Q] Upton Fields House NG25 0QA
☎(0636) 812303
This large detached house is located midway between Southwell and Upton. High quality bedrooms and a unique staircase are only some of the features offered here to the discerning visitor to the area.
5rm(1🛁4🚿)🚭in 4 bedrooms CTV in all bedrooms [R] ✱ sB&B🛁🚿£25-£30 dB&B🛁🚿£40-£42.50
🍽 CTV 6P 1🚗 nc3yrs
[£]

See advertisement on page 339

SOUTHWOLD Suffolk Map **05** TM57

INN [Q][Q][Q] Kings Head Hotel 23/25 High St IP18 6AD
☎(0502) 723829
Ideally situated in the centre of Southwold, this sympathetically modernised inn is comfortable, charming and friendly. The rooms are excellent and a collection of brass blow torches and lamps are a talking point. The varied menu includes fresh, local fish.
Annexe 3rm(1🛁2hc) CTV in all bedrooms [R] ✱ dB&B£42 dB&B🛁£45 Bar Lunch £2.65-£9.25alc Dinner £2.65-£9.25alc LDO 9.30pm
🍽 nc5yrs
Credit Cards [3] [£]

SOUTH ZEAL Devon Map **03** SX69

GH [Q][Q][Q] Poltimore EX20 2PD ☎Okehampton(0837) 840209
This pretty thatched cottage stands in its gardens on the fringe of Dartmoor. The bedrooms are simply furnished and comfortable, and there are 2 lounges. Home-produced vegetables are used whenever possible in the home-cooked meals.
7rm(2🛁2🚿3hc) [R] ✱ sB&B£14-£19 dB&B£28-£38 dB&B🛁🚿£38-£44 WB&B£88-£140 WBDi£141-£190 LDO 5pm
Lic 🍽 CTV 25P nc12yrs
Credit Cards [1] [3]

SPEAN BRIDGE Highland *Inverness-Shire* Map **14** NN28

GH [Q][Q] Coire Glas PH34 4EU ☎(039781) 272
Closed Nov–Dec
Well-appointed modern bungalow with private garden situated 50 yards back from the A86.
12rm(10🚿2hc)(2fb) [R] sB&Bfr£15 dB&Bfr£25 dB&B🚿fr£30 WB&Bfr£87.50 WBDifr£150 LDO 8pm
Lic CTV 20P
[£]

GH [Q][Q][Q] Inverour PH34 4EU ☎(039781) 218
Apr-Oct
An attractive roadside house in a central position with a pleasant lounge featuring an open fire.
7rm(3🚿4hc) TV in all bedrooms [R] ✱ sB&Bfr£13 dB&Bfr£26 dB&B🚿fr£30 WB&Bfr£86.50 LDO 6pm
🍽 7P
[£]

STAFFORD Staffordshire Map **07** SJ92

GH [Q][Q] Leonards Croft Hotel 80 Lichfield Rd ST17 4LP
☎(0785) 223676
Closed Xmas
Friendly hosts ensure that guests feel at home here in a large detached house with extensive and well-tended rear gardens which stands on the edge of the town.
12hc (2fb) [R] sB&B£16 dB&B£32 LDO 9pm
Lic 🍽 CTV 10P

STAMFORD BRIDGE Humberside

See **Low Catton & High Catton**

STARBOTTON North Yorkshire Map **07** SD97

SELECTED

GH [Q][Q][Q][Q] Hilltop Country BD23 5HY
☎Kettlewell(075676) 321
Mar-mid Nov
The family home of the Rathmells since the 17th century, Hilltop has been lovingly converted to an excellent guesthouse by Tim and Marie Louise Rathmell. Standing at the foot of Buckden Pike, the house retains its character. The dining room features an original 'beef loft' and there is a cosy lounge with an open fire and a tiny bar. Dinner is a very enjoyable experience.
4rm(1🛁3🚿)Annexe 1🚿 (1fb)🚭in 4 bedrooms CTV in all bedrooms [R] 🐕 (ex guide dogs)
dB&B🛁🚿fr£36 (incl dinner) LDO 6pm
Lic 🍽 6P
[£]

STEEPLE ASTON Oxfordshire Map **04** SP42

GH [Q][Q] Westfield Farm Motel The Fenway OX5 3SS
☎(0869) 40591
Westfield Farm, with converted farm buildings of motel style, is set in peaceful rural surroundings on the fringe of the village. The comfortable bedrooms are compact but well equipped.
7🚿 (1fb) CTV in all bedrooms [R] ✱ sB&B🚿£28-£32 dB&B🚿£38-£43
Lic 🍽 CTV 12P U
Credit Cards [1] [3] [£]

STEPASIDE Dyfed Map **02** SN10

GH [Q][Q] Bay View Hotel Pleasant Valley SA67 8LR
☎Saundersfoot(0834) 813417
Apr-Oct
Modern proprietor-run hotel catering for family holidays.
12rm(7🚿5hc)(4fb) [R] 🐕 (ex guide dogs) ✱ sB&B£15-£17.85 dB&B£30-£35.70
dB&B🚿£32.90-£38.60 (incl dinner) WB&B£80.50-£98 WBDi£105-£125 (wkly only mid Jun-Aug) LDO 5pm
Lic 🍽 CTV 14P 🏠 🏊(heated)

STEVENAGE Hertfordshire Map **04** TL22

GH [Q][Q][Q] ***Archways Hotel and Restaurant*** 11 Hitchin Rd SG1 3BJ ☎(0438) 316640
This spacious Victorian hotel comprises 3 houses close to the old town. The middle house contains an elegant reception, dining room and bar. The large bedrooms are comfortable and well equipped.
15🛁 Annexe 22🛁 (8fb) CTV in all bedrooms [R] 🐕 LDO 9pm
🍽 CTV 60P 🏠
Credit Cards [1] [2] [3] [5]

STEVENTON Oxfordshire Map **04** SU49

GH [Q][Q][Q] **Steventon House Hotel** Milton Hill OX13 6AB
☎Abingdon(0235) 831223
A warm, friendly atmosphere prevails at his individual house which stands in mature gardens. Bright, modern bedrooms are available in the house and also in the adjacent converted coach house. An outdoor, heated pool is tucked away in the grounds.
8rm(3🛁5🚿)Annexe 15🛁🚿 (2fb) CTV in all bedrooms Ⓡ
🐕 (ex guide dogs) sB&B🛁🚿£35-£55
dB&B🛁🚿£45-£65 LDO 8.30pm
Lic ♨ 50P 🏊(heated)
Credit Cards [1] [2] [3] [5]

STEWARTON Strathclyde *Ayrshire*

See **Dunlop**

STEYNING West Sussex Map **04** TQ11

GH [Q][Q][Q] **Nash Hotel** Horsham Rd BN4 3AA
☎(0903) 814988
This peaceful country house has its own vineyard and wine tasting room. Tastefully furnished and well-equipped bedrooms are found here together with an elegant lounge and small dining room. The shared driveway can be difficult to negotiate.
4rm(1🛁3hc)(2fb) CTV in all bedrooms Ⓡ sB&B£25-£30
dB&B🛁£45 WB&B£175-£210 LDO 7pm
Lic ♨ CTV 18P 🏊🎾(hard)wildfowl lake vineyard
[£]

GH [Q][Q][Q] **Springwells Hotel** 9 High St BN4 3GG
☎(0903) 812446 & 812043
Two of the bedrooms at this friendly hotel have four-poster beds. The comfortable accommodation includes a pleasant lounge, pretty dining room and an appealing conservatory-style bar/lounge. Springwells enjoys a central location and has an outdoor swimming pool.

10rm(6⇔4hc)(1fb) CTV in all bedrooms ® ✱ sB&B£28-£43
sB&B⇔£34 dB&Bfr£48 dB&B⇔£55-£72
Lic ⌘ CTV 6P ⌒(heated)
Credit Cards 1 2 3 5 £

STIPERSTONES Shropshire Map **07** SJ30

⊢⊶GH QQ **Tankerville Lodge** SY5 0NB
☎Shrewsbury(0743) 791401
*Set in a lovely area this hotel is found off the A488 near Minsterley
from the north, and from the south you should follow signs via
Shelve and Pennerley. Guests will be well rewarded with
comfortable and relaxing accommodation.*
4hc ® sB&B£12-£14
dB&B£24 WB&B£75.60-£88.20 WBDi£119.70-£132.30 LDO
4pm
Lic ⌘ CTV 4P
£

STIRLING Central *Stirlingshire*

See **Denny**

STOCKBRIDGE Hampshire Map **04** SU33

GH QQQ **Carbery** Salisbury Hill SO20 6EZ
☎Andover(0264) 810771
Closed 2 wks Xmas
*This long-established family run guesthouse is very close to the
River Test, and offers very pleasant views. Guests can enjoy the
swimming pool and terraced, walled garden, and the service is
personally provided by the resident proprietors.*
11rm(2⇔6↑3hc)(2fb) CTV in all bedrooms ® ✈ sB&B£17.25
sB&B⇔£25 dB&B£34.50
dB&B⇔↑£40.25 WB&B£177.34 WBDi£230.77 LDO 6pm
Lic ⌘ 14P ⌒(heated) badminton pool table

GH QQQ **Old Three Cups Private Hotel** SO20 6HB
☎Andover(0264) 810527
Feb-Xmas Eve rs Sun eve & Mon
*15th-century coaching inn with comfortable bedrooms and popular
well-managed restaurant.*
8rm(3⇔5hc)(2fb) CTV in 7 bedrooms TV in 1 bedroom
✈ (ex guide dogs) ✱ sB&B£22 sB&B⇔£32 dB&B£32
dB&B⇔£42 LDO 9.30pm
Lic ⌘ 12P
Credit Cards 1 3 £

STOCKPORT Greater Manchester Map **07** SJ98

GH QQQ **Ascot House Hotel** 195 Wellington Rd North,
Heaton Norris SK4 2PB ☎061-432 2380 Telex no 666514
FAX 061-443 1936
Closed 2 wks Xmas
*One mile north of the town centre on the A6, this detached
Victorian hotel has well-appointed rooms, most with en suite
facilities. All have radio, TV and tea-making facilities.*
18rm(10⇔2↑6hc)(1fb) CTV in all bedrooms ®
✈ (ex guide dogs) ✱ sB&B£25-£33 sB&B⇔↑£33 dB&B£38
dB&B⇔↑£40-£45 LDO 7.15pm
Lic ⌘ CTV 20P 1⌣ sauna
Credit Cards 1 2 3

STOCKTON-ON-TEES Cleveland Map **08** NZ41

GH QQ **The Court Private Hotel** 49 Yarm Rd TS18 3PE
☎(0642) 604483
*Three-storeyed, mid-terrace property near the town centre with
small dining room and comfortable dining room.*
9hc (3fb) CTV in all bedrooms ® ✈ (ex guide dogs)
sB&B£17-£19 dB&B£30-£32 LDO 6pm
Lic ⌘ CTV ✗ nc2yrs

STOFORD Wiltshire Map **04** SU03

INN QQ **The Swan** SP2 0PR ☎Salisbury(0722) 790236
*This 300-year-old inn, alongside the A36 and the River Wylye, has
well-appointed, comfortable bedrooms and a popular skittle alley.
The bar and restaurant serve a good range of food, including home
made specials and vegetarian dishes.*
6rm(3↑3hc)(3fb) CTV in all bedrooms ® ✈ (ex guide dogs) ✱
sB&B£15-£20 dB&B£30-£40
dB&B↑£30-£40 WB&B£105-£140 Lunch £8-£20alc Dinner
£8-£20alc LDO 10.30pm
⌘ CTV 100P skittle alley

STOKE FLEMING Devon Map **03** SX84

GH QQ *Endsleigh Hotel* TQ6 0NR ☎(0803) 770381
*With a good car park and a well-tended garden, standing on the
edge of this pretty village, Endsleigh Hotel offers bright attractive
bedrooms and well-furnished open-plan public areas.*
8rm(2↑6hc)(2fb) ® LDO 8.00pm
Lic CTV 20P

STOKE HOLY CROSS Norfolk Map **05** TG20

FH QQ Mr & Mrs Harrold **Salamanca** *(TG235022)* NR14 8QJ
☎Framlingham Earl(05086) 2322
Closed 15 Dec-15 Jan & Etr
*This large farmhouse stands in the village centre and dates back to
the 16th century. Surrounded by well tended-gardens, it offers
simple, comfortably furnished accommodation and an attractive
relaxing lounge.*
3hc Annexe 1⇔3 ✈ sB&Bfr£15 dB&Bfr£26 dB&B⇔fr£30
⌘ CTV 7P nc6yrs 175 acres dairy mixed
£

See advertisement under NORWICH on page 277

STOKE-ON-TRENT Staffordshire Map **07** SJ84

GH QQQ **White Gables Hotel** Trentham Rd, Blurton
ST3 3DT ☎(0782) 324882
Closed 2 wks Xmas & New Year
*Set on the outskirts of the town and enjoying a rural outlook,
White Gables has well-equipped bedrooms with pretty furnishings.
Guests are ensured of a pleasant visit and may take advantage of
the basement games room.*
8rm(3⇔3↑2hc)(2fb) CTV in all bedrooms ®
✈ (ex guide dogs) ✱ sB&B£25-£30 sB&B⇔↑£38-£44
dB&B£36-£40 dB&B⇔↑£44-£52 LDO 7.30pm
Lic ⌘ CTV 12P 2⌣ ♪(hard)games room
Credit Cards 1 3 £

GH QQ **The White House** Stone Rd, Trent Vale ST4 6SP
☎(0782) 642460 or 657189
Closed Xmas & New Year
*Extended and modernised, this Victorian house is run by friendly
hosts who ensure their guests of an enjoyable stay and maintain the
good reputation of The White House.*
8hc Annexe 2↑ (2fb) CTV in 5 bedrooms ® ✈ (ex guide dogs)
✱ sB&B£20-£22 sB&B↑£34-£35 dB&B£36-£38
dB&B↑£44-£48 WB&B£120-£210 WBDi£176-£250 LDO 6pm
Lic ⌘ CTV 10P
Credit Cards 1 2 3 £

STOKE ST GREGORY Somerset Map **03** ST32

GH QQ **Jays Nest** TA3 6HZ ☎North Curry(0823) 490250
*Conference facilities are available at this cottage style property
which has its own sunny garden. Some of the bright and
comfortable bedrooms have en suite facilities and the recently
extended public areas are tastefully furnished and decorated.*

Visit your local AA Centre.

6rm(1⇌2↱3hc)(2fb)⊁in 2 bedrooms ® sB&B£16.50-£18 sB&B⇌↱£18-£22.50 dB&B£32-£36 dB&B⇌↱£36-£40 WB&B£110-£140 WBDi£170-£200 LDO 9pm
Lic ꟷ CTV 15P 2🚗
Credit Cards 2 ⓔ

STONE (in Oxney) Kent Map **05** TQ92

FH QQQ Mrs E I Hodson ***Tighe*** *(TQ937268)* TN30 7JU
☏Appledore(023383) 251
Mar-Nov
This captivating 17th-century farmhouse is owned by Jimmy and Elsie Hodson who offer warm hospitality and comfortable, peaceful accommodation. A concealed iron winch, possibly used by smugglers, is one of the interesting features here.
3hc (1fb) ✗
ꟷ CTV 3P nc8yrs ✓ 100 acres sheep

STONEHOUSE Gloucestershire Map **03** SO80

FH Q Mrs D A Hodge **Welches** *(SO813065)* Standish GL10 3BX ☏(0453) 822018
Closed Xmas
On the edge of Standish, 1 mile north of the town, this large Cotswold stone farmhouse dates back to 1600. Local legend has it that Oliver Cromwell once visited here. Mrs Hodge provides bed and breakfast in a traditional atmosphere.
3rm(1hc)(2fb) CTV in 1 bedroom ✗ (ex guide dogs) ✱
sB&B£12 dB&B£24
ꟷ CTV 10P 101 acres beef
ⓔ

See the regional maps of popular holiday areas at the back of the book.

SHIRE COTTAGE

Benches Lane, Chisworth, Hyde, Cheshire
Telephone: 061-427 2377 (daytime)
0457 866536 (after 4pm)

(Off A626 Marple-Glossop opposite Woodheys Restaurant)

Real home from home accommodation in peaceful location. Magnificent views overlooking Etherow Country Park. Convenient for Manchester Airport, City Centre, exploring the Peak District, Kinder Scout, Derwent Dams, stately homes and many places of interest. Family room en-suite and ground floor rooms. Early breakfasts can be arranged

The Topps

Fintry Road, Denny,
Stirlingshire FK6 5JF
Telephone: 0324 822471

Eight bedroomed, modern bungalow with tastefully appointed rooms. Situated in beautiful countryside, 4 miles west of Denny on the B818.

See gazetteer under Denny.

Springwells Hotel

STEYNING, WEST SUSSEX (Nr. Brighton)
Telephone: 0903-812446
Once a Georgian merchant's town house now an elegant ten-bedroomed bed & breakfast hotel. All rooms have telephones & colour TV and most have private facilties.
Tea/coffee making facilities if required. Some four-poster beds. Lovely walled gardens, outdoor swimming pool. Victorian style conservatory. Half hour from Gatwick/Newhaven. £28-£72 per room.

STORNOWAY

See **LEWIS, ISLE OF**

STOURBRIDGE West Midlands Map **07** SO98

GH Q Q **Limes** 260 Hagley Rd, Pedmore DY9 0RW
☎Hagley(0562) 882689
This guesthouse is situated 1.5 miles from Stourbridge in a pleasant residential area. The rooms are well kept although some are quite compact. This is a friendly household which is particularly popular with commercial travellers.
11hc (1fb) CTV in 7 bedrooms ® ✱ sB&B£24.50-£31
dB&B£34.50-£47.50 (incl dinner) WB&Bfr£171.50 WBDi£217
LDO 7.30pm
♨ CTV 12P
Credit Cards [1] [3]

STOW-ON-THE-WOLD Gloucestershire Map **04** SP12

GH Q Q **Cotstone House** Union St GL54 1BU
☎Cotswold(0451) 32210
Opposite the fire station close to the town centre, this Cotswold stone house has cosy public rooms and comfortable, pretty bedrooms. Jan Wegerdt is a trained chef and takes pride in her breakfasts. This is a 'no-smoking' house.
3hc ⌇in all bedrooms ® ⨳ ✱ sB&Bfr£20 dB&Bfr£30
♨ CTV 4P nc

GH Q Q **Limes** Evesham Rd GL54 1EJ
☎Cotswold(0451) 30034
Closed Dec-1 Jan
Large gabled house within walking distance from town centre offering friendly family service.
3rm(2↟1hc)Annexe 1↟ (1fb) CTV in all bedrooms
dB&B£25-£27 dB&Bↄ↟£30-£32
♨ CTV 6P 1🐾

FH Q Q Mr R Smith **Corsham Field** *(SP217249)* Bledington
Rd GL54 1JH ☎Cotswold(0451) 31750
Closed 25-26 Dec
Newly constructed, Cotswold stone farmhouse incorporating many traditional features.
3rm(1ↄ2hc)(1fb) CTV in all bedrooms ® ✱ sB&B£12.50-£18
dB&B£24-£30 dB&Bↄ£25-£32 WB&B£84-£112 LDO 6pm
♨ CTV 10P 100 acres arable beef sheep

STRATFORD-UPON-AVON Warwickshire Map **04** SP25

See **Town Plan Section**

GH Q Q **Ambleside** 41 Grove Rd CV37 6PB ☎(0789) 297239 &
295670
Closed Xmas
On the Evesham road close to the town centre, this hotel has the benefit of a spacious car park. Facilities are constantly being improved, and Ambleside offers good value for money.
7rm(3↟4hc)(3fb)⌇in 3 bedrooms CTV in all bedrooms ®
sB&B£14-£16 dB&B£28-£32 dB&Bↄ↟£30-£38
♨ CTV 15P 1🐾 (50p per night)
Credit Cards [1] [3] £

GH Q Q **Avon View Hotel** 121 Shipston Rd CV37 7LW
☎(0789) 297542
This small private hotel has the benefit of its own car park and is a short walk from the town centre. Recent improvements have given all the bedrooms en suite facilities. Light meals and snacks can be served in the evening upon request.
9ↄ↟ ⌇in 3 bedrooms CTV in all bedrooms ® ⨳
sB&Bↄ↟£28-£32
dB&Bↄ↟£49-£54 WB&B£343-£378 LDO 4pm
Lic ♨ CTV 12P nc12yrs
Credit Cards [1] [2] [3] [5] £

GH Q Q Q **Brook Lodge** 192 Alcester Rd CV37 9DR
☎(0789) 295988
Closed Xmas
Close to Anne Hathaway's cottage on the Alcester Road, this recently modernised hotel has comfortable, well-equipped bedrooms and good public area facilities.
7rm(5↟2hc)(2fb) CTV in all bedrooms ® dB&B£32-£34
dB&Bↄ↟£34-£36 WB&B£100-£115
♨ CTV 10P
Credit Cards [1] [3] £

GH Q Q **Courtland Hotel** 12 Guild St CV37 6RE
☎(0789) 292401
The Courtland Hotel is a comfortable Georgian grade II listed building situated in the town centre behind Shakespears birthplace. Mrs Johnson's friendly manner helps to create a relaxed and informal atmosphere.
7rm(1ↄ1↟5hc)(1fb) CTV in all bedrooms ® ✱ sB&B£13-£14
dB&B£26-£28 dB&Bↄ↟£36-£40 WB&B£80-£110
♨ CTV 2P 1🐾

GH Q Q Q **Craig Cleeve House** 67-69 Shipston Rd CV37 7LW
☎(0789) 296573
Situated 100 yards from Clopton Bride, this large Edwardian house has been totally refurbished to provide very comfortable accommodation. Terry and Margarita Palmer are charming hosts and Margarita's Spanish origin is very much in evidence with lots of ornaments and attractive ceramic tiling.
15rm(9↟6hc) CTV in all bedrooms ® ✱ sB&B£15.50-£33
sB&B↟£33 dB&B£33 dB&B↟£41 WB&B£108.50-£143.50
Lic ♨ 15P
Credit Cards [1] [3] [5]

See advertisement on page 345

GH Q Q Q **Eastnor House Hotel** Shipston Rd CV37 7LN
☎(0789) 268115
Closed Xmas
Attentive, friendly service at this comfortable Victorian house close to centre.
9⇌♠ (3fb) CTV in all bedrooms ® sB&B⇌♠£30-£47
dB&B⇌♠£43-£50 WB&B£129-£150
Lic ⅏ 9P
Credit Cards ① ③ £

GH Q Q **Eversley Bears** 37 Grove Rd CV37 6PB
☎(0789) 292334
Close to the town centre, this well-appointed family-run guesthouse has a friendly atmosphere. Mrs. Thomas has a large collection of teddy bears for guests to admire.
6hc (2fb) ⊁ (ex guide dogs) sB&B£16-£18
dB&B£32-£36 WB&B£105-£119
⅏ CTV 3🚘 (.50p) nc14yrs
£

GH Q Q Q **Hardwick House** 1 Av Rd CV37 6UY ☎(0789) 204307
Closed Xmas
14rm(7⇌♠7hc)(3fb) CTV in all bedrooms ®
⊁ (ex guide dogs) sB&B£15-£19.50 dB&B£32-£40
dB&B⇌♠£42-£50
⅏ 12P
Credit Cards ① ② ③ £

GH Q Q Q **Hollies** 16 Evesham Place CV37 6HQ
☎(0789) 266857
Closed Xmas
Mrs Morgan is a very amiable host and is anxious for guest to feel at home in this pleasant guesthouse. Hollies stands close to the town centre and has its own car park.
6rm(1♠5hc)(2fb) CTV in all bedrooms ® ✱ dB&B£27
dB&B♠£35
⅏ CTV 6P

GH Q Q **Hunters Moon** 150 Alcester Rd CV37 9DR
☎(0789) 292888
Standing on the Alcester Road, this hotel offers simple public areas and comfortable bedrooms, most of which have private facilities.
7rm(5♠2hc)(5fb) CTV in all bedrooms ® sB&B£16-£21
dB&B♠£32-£49
⅏ CTV 6P
Credit Cards ① ② ③ £

GH Q Q Q *Kawartha House* 39 Grove Rd CV37 6PB
☎(0789) 204469
Semidetached house not far from the town centre, pleasantly situated opposite a small park and with family atmosphere.
6rm(3♠3hc)(2fb) CTV in 4 bedrooms ®
⅏ CTV 4🚘

GH Q Q **Marlyn** 3 Chestnut Walk CV37 6HG ☎(0789) 293752
Closed Xmas
Situated in a Chestnut tree lined, town centre lane, this spacious terraced house offers comfortable bed and breakfast accommodation, with well-equipped traditional style bedrooms.
8hc ® ⊁ (ex guide dogs) ✱ sB&B£15-£16 dB&B£28-£30
⅏ CTV

GH Q Q **Melita Private Hotel** 37 Shipston Rd CV37 7LN
☎(0789) 292432
Closed Xmas
This attractive Victorian house stands on the A34 close to the town centre and its major attractions. En suite bedrooms are comfortably furnished providing up-to-date facilities in this friendly, family-run guesthouse.
12⇌♠ (3fb)⊁in 6 bedrooms CTV in all bedrooms ®
sB&B⇌♠£27-£43 dB&B⇌♠£45-£52
Lic ⅏ CTV 12P
Credit Cards ① ② ③ £

GH Q Q Q **Moonraker House** 40 Alcester Rd CV37 9DB
☎(0789) 299346 FAX (0789) 295504
Situated half a mile from the town centre this establishment offers good bed and breakfast accommodation which is spread over 4 buildings. Bedrooms vary in size and all have en suite facilities, modern fitted furniture and tasteful colour schemes.
6♠ Annexe 9rm(2⇌7♠)(1fb)⊁in 4 bedrooms CTV in all
bedrooms ® ✱ sB&B⇌♠£25-£32
dB&B⇌♠£33-£52 WB&B£99-£156
⅏ 12P 3🚘
Credit Cards ① ③

See advertisement on page 347

GH Q Q *Nando's* 18-19 Evesham Place CV37 6HT
☎(0789) 204907
21rm(1⇌6♠14hc)(10fb) CTV in all bedrooms
⅏ CTV 8P
Credit Cards ① ③

GH Q Q **Parkfield** 3 Broad Walk CV37 6HS ☎(0789) 293313
Friendly, attentive services and excellent breakfasts have earned proprietress Pauline Rush a good reputation at this spacious corner house situated just 5 minutes' walk from the town centre. It also offers well-equipped, comfortable bedrooms and a good private car park.
7rm(3♠4hc)(1fb) CTV in all bedrooms ® sB&B£15-£17
dB&B£29-£32 dB&B♠£34-£40
⅏ 9P nc7yrs
Credit Cards ① ③

See advertisement on page 347

GH Q Q **Penryn House** 126 Alcester Rd CV37 9DP
☎(0789) 293718
This semidetached house on Alcester Road, 1 mile from the town centre, has small but attractive public areas, well-equipped bedrooms, including one in a former garden chalet, and offers good private car parking facilities.

▶

Kawartha House is a well appointed town house with a friendly atmosphere overlooking the 'old town' park. It is located just a few minutes walk from the town centre and ideal for visiting the places of historic interest. Private parking is available as are evening meals by arrangement. With pretty en suite bedrooms and quality food these are the ingredients for a memorable stay.

39 Grove Rd, Stratford-Upon-Avon CV37 6PB Tel: (0789) 204469

RAVENHURST

2 Broad Walk, Stratford-upon-Avon
Tel: (0789) 292515

Ravenhurst, a family run guest house, is ideally situated for your visit to Stratford-upon-Avon. Quiet central location just a few minutes walk from town centre, Royal Shakespeare Theatre and places of historical interest.

A Victorian town house with a friendly restful atmosphere. Comfortable bedrooms all with tea and coffee making facilities, colour TV, central heating and some 'en-suite'.

PARKFIELD GUEST HOUSE

Proprietor:
Pauline Rush

3 Broad Walk,
Stratford-upon-Avon,
Warwickshire.

Tel:
Stratford-upon-Avon
(0789) 293313

A most attractive Victorian house in a quiet but central location, only 6 minutes' walk to the Town, Royal Shakespeare Theatre and places of interest. Spacious accommodation. Excellent full English breakfast. Central heating throughout. Colour TV and tea and coffee making facilities in all rooms. Full en suite facilities available. Unrestricted access. Fire Certificate. Large private car park. Tourist and Theatre information available. Member of Hotel & Caterers' Association. Highly recommended by Arthur Frommer. ETB rating: 2 crowns.

MOONRAKER HOUSE

MORE THAN 50%

OF OUR GUESTS ARE ON THEIR 2ND, 3RD, 4TH . . . VISIT. COME AND SEE WHY THEY RETURN.

* **ALL** rooms are elegantly decorated and designed with your comfort in mind.

* 5 minutes walk from town centre.

* CAR PARK (open and garage).

* Ideal centre for exploring the Cotswolds, Shakespeare's countryside, Warwick Castle and Shakespeare Theatres.

* **ALL** rooms have en-suite bathrooms, tea & coffee making facilities, colour TV, clock radios and fitted hairdryers.

* There are also extra special rooms with **four poster beds,** lounge area and garden patio (non-smoking).

* Enjoy an excellent English breakfast prepared with care by the resident proprietors, Mauveen and Mike Spencer.

AA   **40 Alcester Road, Stratford-upon-Avon CV37 9DB**
Tel: (0789) 299346 or 267115 Fax: (0789) 295504

MinOtels
Les Routiers

6rm(1⇨5♪)Annexe 1♪ (4fb) CTV in all bedrooms ® ✳
sB&B⇨♪£20-£30 dB&B⇨♪£30-£40 WB&B£90-£120
卿 9P
Credit Cards 1 3

See advertisement on page 346

GH Q Q **Penshurst** 34 Evesham Place CV37 6HT
☎(0789) 205259
This guesthouse is personally run by the friendly proprietors who
provide sound accommodation. A good breakfast is served in the
pleasant, Victorian-decorated dining room.
7rm(2♪ 5hc) CTV in all bedrooms ® ✕ (ex guide dogs)
LDO 6pm
Lic 卿 2P ⚲

GH Q Q **Ravenhurst** 2 Broad Walk CV37 6HS ☎(0789) 292515
Closed Xmas
Situated in a quiet road, just 5 minutes' walk from the centre of the
town, this spacious Victorian house offers well-equipped,
comfortable bedroom accommodation and an attractive dining
room.
7rm(1⇨2♪4hc)(2fb) CTV in all bedrooms ® ✕ sB&Bfr£16
sB&B⇨♪fr£25 dB&Bfr£28 dB&B⇨♪fr£35 WB&Bfr£95
卿
Credit Cards 1 2 3 5

GH Q **Salamander** 40 Grove Rd CV37 6PB ☎(0789) 205728
This Victorian terraced house stands on the Evesham Road and
provides simply appointed public areas and good public areas.
7rm(2♪ 5hc)(3fb) ® sB&B£13.50-£15 dB&B£26-£30
dB&B♪£30-£34 WB&B£87.50-£105 WBDi£133-£150 LDO
6.30pm
卿 CTV 4P 2⚲

GH Q Q Q **Sequoia House Private Hotel** 51-53 Shipston Rd
CV37 7LN ☎(0789) 268852 FAX (0789) 414559
Closed 24-25 Dec
This warm and spacious Victorian house is run by friendly
proprietors who pride themselves in offering high quality
breakfasts, which prove popular with guests. The bedrooms here
are well appointed.
16rm(2⇨10♪4hc)Annexe 5♪ (4fb) CTV in all bedrooms ®
✕ sB&Bfr£27.50 sB&B⇨♪£32-£45 dB&Bfr£33
dB&B⇨♪fr£59 LDO 4pm
Lic 卿 CTV 26P nc5yrs
Credit Cards 1 2 3 5 £

See advertisement on page 346

GH Q **Stretton House Hotel** 38 Grove Rd CV37 6PB
☎(0789) 68647
This small, family-run guesthouse is close to the town centre and
its amenities. Rooms are simply furnished and equipped and are
comfortable. Mr and Mrs Machin are pleased to help guests plan
their tour of 'Shakespeare Country'.
7hc (2fb) CTV in all bedrooms ® ✳ sB&B£14-£24
dB&B£24-£36 LDO 4pm
卿 3P

GH Q Q Q **Twelfth Night** Evesham Place CV37 6HT
☎Stratford(0789) 414595
Friendly proprietors John and Margaret Harvard offer a warm
welcome to guests and provide a good standard of accommodation.
All bedrooms (no-smoking) are individually decorated, and are
very clean and well maintained. The public rooms have been
tastefully refurbished to offer quality and comfort.
7rm(6♪ 1hc)(1fb)✍in all bedrooms CTV in all bedrooms ® ✕
sB&Bfr£18 dB&B♪fr£36
卿 3P 2⚲ nc5yrs

Q is for quality. For a full explanation of this AA quality
award, consult the Contents page.

GH Q Q Q **Victoria Spa Lodge** Bishopton Ln CV37 9QY
☎(0789) 267985 & 204728
Once a popular 'spa' hotel (there are still 17 springs in the area)
this house is beautifully situated and affords a high standard of
accommodation with well- equipped bedrooms with a Victorian air.
Substantial breakfasts are served.
7rm(1⇨3♪3hc) CTV in all bedrooms ® ✕ ✳ sB&Bfr£30
sB&B⇨♪fr£35 dB&Bfr£35 dB&B⇨♪fr£43 LDO 4pm
卿 12P
Credit Cards 1 3

GH Q Q Q **Virginia Lodge** 12 Evesham Place CV37 6HT
☎(0789) 292157
The friendly proprietor takes great pride in the garden and
hanging baskets surrounding this guesthouse. The well-appointed
bedrooms are equally pleasing, with lovely soft furnishings
matching the individual decor.
7rm(4♪ 3hc)(1fb) CTV in all bedrooms ® ✳ sB&B£12-£15
dB&B£26-£30 dB&B♪£28-£36
Lic 卿 CTV 7P 2⚲

⊢→FH Q Q **Mrs R M Meadows Monk's Barn** *(SP206516)*
Shipston Rd CV37 8NA ☎(0789) 293714
Closed 25-26 Dec
The farm is on the A34, just 2 miles from Stratford towards
Shipton on Stour. A warm welcome is offered by Mr and Mrs
Meadows, who make every effort to meet guests' needs, making a
comfortable and friendly stay.
4rm(2♪2hc)(1fb)✍in all bedrooms ® ✕ (ex guide dogs)
sB&Bfr£13 dB&Bfr£22 dB&B♪fr£24 WB&Bfr£77
卿 CTV 5P 75 acres mixed

FH Q Q Q **Mr & Mrs R Evans Oxstalls** *(SP217566)*
Warwick Rd CV37 4NR ☎(0789) 205277
5hc Annexe 13rm(3⇨8♪2hc)(5fb)✍in all bedrooms CTV in 2
bedrooms TV in 1 bedroom ® ✕ (ex guide dogs) ✳
sB&B£13-£20 dB&Bfr£26 dB&B⇨♪fr£40
卿 CTV P ▶ 18 ✈ 70 acres stud farm

STRATHAVEN Strathclyde *Lanarkshire* Map 11 NS74

GH Q Q Q **Springvale Hotel** 18 Letham Rd ML10 6AD
☎(0357) 21131
Closed 26-27 Dec & 1-2 Jan
Grey stone detached house with painted annexe on opposite side of
road. A friendly and comfortable family-run establishment in a
residential area not far from the central shopping area.
14rm(1⇨10♪3hc)(1fb) CTV in all bedrooms ® ✳ sB&Bfr£20
sB&B⇨♪fr£20 dB&B⇨♪fr£30 LDO 6.45pm
Lic 卿 CTV 8P

STRATHYRE Central *Perthshire* Map 11 NN51

GH Q Q Q **Auchtubmor House** Balquidder FK19 8NZ
☎(08774) 632
This delightful country house is an ideal base for the holidaymaker
seeking relaxation. Comfortably appointed, each of the bedrooms
has magnificent views across countryside. Prime Scottish produce
is used in the imaginative dinner menu.
5rm(3⇨2hc)(1fb) ® ✳ sB&B£14.50-£20 sB&B⇨£16.50-£25
dB&B£25-£29 dB&B⇨£29-£33 LDO 6pm
卿 CTV 6P

STRETTON Leicestershire Map 08 SK91

INN Q Q *The Shires Hotel* LE15 7QT
☎Castle Bytham(078081) 332
Situated on the A1 Great North Road north of Stratford, this
stone-built Georgian inn has pleasant public areas and
comfortable, simple bedrooms.
5rm(4hc)(3fb) CTV in all bedrooms ® LDO 10.30pm

▶

〒 100P
Credit Cards 1 3

STRETTON GRANDISON Hereford & Worcester
Map **03** SO64

FH QQ Mrs E Godsall *Moor Court (SO638448)* HR8 2TR
〒Trumpet(053183) 408
Feb-Nov
This beautifully preserved timber-framed farmhouse dates back to the 14th century and has a wealth of charm and character. It is set in a pleasant area, midway between Ledbury and Hereford. The accommodation is comfortable and very well maintained.
3hc ® LDO 10am
CTV 0P 2🐾 ♪ 200 acres mixed

STROUD Gloucestershire Map **03** SO80

GH QQ **Downfield Hotel** 134 Cainscross Rd GL5 4HN
〒(0453) 764496
Closed 2 wks from 25 Dec
Pleasant, personally-run hotel situated on the A419 on the western edge of town.
21rm(5⇄8🛏8hc)(4fb) CTV in 15 bedrooms ® sB&B£21-£23 sB&B⇄🛏fr£30 dB&B£33-£36 dB&B⇄🛏fr£41 LDO 8pm
Lic 〒 CTV 25P
Credit Cards 1 3 £

STUDLAND Dorset Map **04** SZ08

GH QQ **Studholme Hotel** Ferry Rd BH19 3AQ 〒(092944) 271
mid Mar-mid Oct
A pleasant detached hotel situated close to Studland Beach in its own gardens, offering good home cooking and an informal atmosphere.

6rm(4⇨3🌂2hc)(2fb) CTV in 4 bedrooms ® ✠ ✳ sB&B£17-£25 dB&B£34-£50
dB&B⇨3🌂£38-£54 WB&B£119-£175 WBDi£168-£200 LDO 6pm
Lic CTV 6P nc3yrs

STURMINSTER NEWTON Dorset Map **03** ST71

FH QQ Mrs S Wingate-Saul **Holebrook** *(ST743117)*
Lydlinch DT10 2JB ☎Hazelbury Bryan(0258) 817348
Closed Xmas Day & New Years Day rs Nov-Mar
Attractive 'stable' bedroom suites at this farm which also offers simply fly fishing, clay-pigeon shoot and a small outdoor swimming pool. The farm is 3 miles west of the A357 Stalbridge Road.
2rm(1hc)Annexe 4rm(3🌂) CTV in 4 bedrooms ®
✠ (ex guide dogs) sB&B🌂£14-£17 dB&B🌂£28-£34 LDO 4pm
🍴CTV 12P ⌓clay pigeon shooting games room 126 acres beef
£

STURTON BY STOW Lincolnshire Map **08** SK88

SELECTED

FH QQQQ Mrs S Bradshaw **The Village** *(SK889807)*
LN1 2AE ☎Gainsborough(0427) 788309
Apr-Oct
This attractive 19th-century farmhouse enjoys a central position in the village. Bedrooms have been tastefully furnished by the proprietor, Mrs Bradshaw, whose embroidery is featured throughout on samplers and cushions. The rooms also benefit from her other hobby of collecting and selling antiques.
3rm(1⇨3🌂2hc)✂in all bedrooms ® ✠ ✳ sB&B£12-£15 dB&B£24-£30
dB&B⇨3🌂£28-£34 WB&B£77-£90 LDO day before
🍴CTV 6P nc9yrs ♟(hard)🏌 400 acres arable beef sheep
£

SUMMERCOURT Cornwall & Isles of Scilly Map **02** SW85

FH QQQ Mrs R J B Richards *Goonhoskyn (SW871573)*
TR8 4PP ☎Truro(0872) 510226
Mar-Oct
Set back from the Summercourt – Newquay road, this farmhouse has well-equipped rooms with comfortable beds. Many thoughtful touches are provided by Mrs Richards who serves traditional home cooking taken at an oval dining table. Children over the age of 6 are welcome.
3hc (1fb) CTV in all bedrooms ® ✠
🍴CTV 3P nc6yrs 50 acres arable sheep

SURBITON Greater London

London plan **4** B1 (pages 230-231)
GH QQ **Warwick** 321 Ewell Rd KT6 7BX ☎081-399 5837
Small centrally located guesthouse run by cheerful and friendly proprietors. Comfortable bedrooms but limited public areas.
9rm(1⇨5 8hc)(2fb) CTV in all bedrooms ✠ sB&B£26-£28 sB&B⇨3£32 dB&B£34-£36
dB&B⇨3£42 WB&B£120-£150 WBDi£155-£185 LDO 2pm
🍴CTV 8P
Credit Cards 1 3 £

See the regional maps of popular holiday areas at the back of the book.

SUTTON Greater London

London plan **4** C1 (pages 230-231)
GH QQQ **Ashling Tara Hotel** 50 Rosehill SM1 3EU
☎081-641 6142
Closed Xmas Day
This pleasant detached house has neat, well-maintained accommodation, some of which is in an annexe. The rooms are quite well equipped and there is a small, nicely appointed breakfast room.
10rm(2⇨5🌂3hc)Annexe 5rm(3🌂2hc)(2fb) CTV in 14 bedrooms TV in 1 bedroom ® ✠ ✳ sB&B£25-£31
sB&B⇨3🌂£47 dB&B£38-£41 dB&B⇨3🌂£48-£52 LDO 8pm
Lic 🍴CTV 10P nc6yrs
Credit Cards 1 3 £

GH QQ **Dene Hotel** 39 Cheam Rd SM1 2AT ☎081-642 3170
With a choice of well-equipped bedrooms and an attractive breakfast room, this hotel offers particular value for money. The rooms are individually furnished according to size, and generally meet all requirements.
28rm(8⇨4🌂16hc)(3fb) CTV in all bedrooms ®
✠ (ex guide dogs)
🍴18P

GH QQ **Eaton Court Hotel** 49 Eaton Rd SM2 5ED
☎081-643 6766
Closed Xmas
Located in a quiet residential area, this friendly hotel offers functional accommodation together with a spacious lounge/bar in which guests can relax.
14rm(2🌂12hc)Annexe 7rm(1⇨6🌂)(3fb) CTV in all bedrooms ® ✳ sB&Bfr£31 sB&B⇨3🌂fr£41 dB&Bfr£42 dB&B⇨3🌂fr£51
Lic 🍴CTV 10P
Credit Cards 1 2 3 £

GH QQQ **Thatched House Hotel** 135 Cheam Rd SM1 2BN
☎081-642 3131
This charming thatched hotel offers well-appointed and pretty bedrooms, some of which overlook the rear garden. There is a nicely appointed dining room in addition to the cosy lounge bar.
29rm(1⇨18🌂10hc) CTV in all bedrooms ® LDO 8.45pm
Lic 🍴CTV 24P
Credit Cards 1 3

SUTTON COLDFIELD West Midlands Map **07** SP19

GH Q **Standbridge Hotel** 138 Birmingham Rd B72 1LY
☎021-354 3007
Conveniently situated for access to the Midlands motorway network, Birmingham and Sutton Coldfield, this hotel has some compact, but well-kept rooms. There is a comfortable lounge and an attractive rear garden.
8hc Annexe 1hc CTV in all bedrooms ® ✳ sB&Bfr£19.75 dB&Bfr£39.50 WB&B£138.25-£182 WBDi£182.70-£226.45 LDO 6pm
Lic 🍴CTV 11P nc5yrs jacuzzi
See advertisement under BIRMINGHAM on page 67

SWAFFHAM Norfolk Map **05** TF80

GH QQQ **Corfield House** PE32 2EA ☎(0760) 23636
mid Mar-mid Dec
This small family-run guest house in the village of Sporle is close to Swaffham and well situated for touring north west Norfolk. The accommodationa is attractively decorated and furnished offering a good range of modern facilities. There is a comfortable, no smoking lounge and a cosy dining room where a set 4-course dinner is served. Mr and Mrs Hickey are very hospitable hosts.
5rm(2⇨3🌂) CTV in all bedrooms ® sB&B⇨3🌂£17 dB&B⇨3🌂£30-£34 WB&B£105-£119 WBDi£155-£170 LDO 6pm

---

Lic 卌 5P
Credit Cards [1] [3]

SWANAGE Dorset Map **04** SZ07

GH QQQ Bella Vista Hotel 14 Burlington Rd BH19 1LS
☎(0929) 422873
Mar-Oct
Neat, pleasant accommodation in a cottage style property within easy reach of beach and town centre.
6rm(5↱1hc)(4fb) ® ✗
dB&B£30-£36 WB&B£95-£115 (wkly only Jul & Aug)
Lic 卌 CTV 6P nc4yrs
(£)

⊢×⊣**GH QQ Burlington House Hotel** 7 Highcliffe Rd BH19 1LW ☎(0929) 422422
16 Mar-4 Nov
Enjoying excellent sea views, this small, comfortably appointed hotel has good lounge facilities and compact bedrooms. Personally supervised by owners, Mr and Mrs Bishop, a warm welcome is assured.
9rm(6⇌↱3hc)(5fb) CTV in 5 bedrooms TV in 3 bedrooms ®
✗ sB&B£12-£15 dB&B£27-£33
dB&B⇌↱£29.50-£35.50 WB&B£90-£110
WBDi£127.50-£147.50 (wkly only mid Jun-mid Sep) LDO 5pm
Lic 卌 CTV 9P musical evenings
(£)

GH QQQ Chines Hotel 9 Burlington Rd BH19 1LR
☎(0929) 422457
24 Apr-Sep rs Mar-Oct
Neat 2-storeyed house in quiet road near beach and town.
13rm(6↱7hc)(3fb)⊬in all bedrooms CTV in all bedrooms ®
✗ ✱ sB&Bfr£16.10 dB&Bfr£32.20
dB&B↱fr£36.80 WB&Bfr£96.60 WBDifr£151.80 (wkly only Jul-Aug) LDO 4pm
Lic 卌 CTV 9P ⌂
(£)

GH QQ *Eversden Private Hotel* Victoria Rd BH19 1LY
☎(0929) 423276
Mar-Nov
Private hotel with good views, a few minutes' walk from the beach.
12rm(2⇌3↱7hc)(3fb)⊬in 2 bedrooms CTV in 1 bedroom TV in 1 bedroom ® ✗ LDO 6pm
Lic 卌 CTV 12P

GH QQ *Firswood Hotel* 29 Kings Rd BH19 1HF
☎(0929) 422306
Closed Xmas
This small guesthouse is family run and provides comfortable accommodation in this pleasant seaside town.
7rm(1↱6hc)(4fb) CTV in 5 bedrooms ® ✗
卌 CTV 7P nc5yrs

GH QQ *Glenlee Hotel* 6 Cauldon Av BH19 1PQ
☎(0929) 425794
Closed Nov & Dec
This small and friendly private hotel has modern, well-equipped bedrooms. It is conveniently situated, close to the seafront and shops, overlooking tennis courts.
7rm(5⇌2↱)(2fb) ® LDO 6.30pm
Lic CTV 5P 2🚗

GH QQQ Havenhurst Hotel 3 Cranbourne Rd BH19 1EA
☎(0929) 424224
Pleasant guesthouse in quiet area with neat bedrooms.
▶

See the regional maps of popular holiday areas at the back of the book.

17rm(6⇨11🌂)(4fb) ® ✖ (ex guide dogs)
sB&B⇨🌂£17-£23.50
dB&B⇨🌂£34-£47 WBDi£150-£186 (wkly only Jun-Aug) LDO 7pm
Lic ⬛ CTV 17P

GH 🆀🆀🆀 **Oxford Hotel** 3 & 5 Park Rd BH19 2AA
☎(0929) 422247
Mar-Oct
Located on the rise of hill leading from town centre and seafront.
14rm(6⇨🌂8hc)(4fb) CTV in 12 bedrooms ® ✖ sB&B£18-£19
sB&B⇨🌂£21-£22 dB&B£36-£38
dB&B⇨🌂£42-£44 WB&B£121-£128 WBDi£175-£182 LDO 4.30pm
Lic ⬛ CTV nc3yrs
Ⓔ

GH 🆀🆀🆀 **St Michael Hotel** 31 Kings Rd BH19 1HF
☎(0929) 422064
Feb-Nov
Neat town centre guesthouse with attractive bedrooms and attentive service.
6rm(3🌂3hc)(4fb) CTV in all bedrooms ® ✳ dB&B£29-£40
dB&B🌂£32-£42 WB&B£90-£115 LDO 2pm
Lic ⬛ 5P nc5yrs
Ⓔ

GH 🆀🆀🆀 **Sandringham Hotel** 20 Durlston Rd BH19 2HX
☎(0929) 423076
Mar-Nov rs Dec-Mar
Comfortable, well-maintained accommodation is offered at this small, private hotel. Situated in a quiet residential area close to the sea, Sandringham Hotel is personally supervised by owners Mr & Mrs Ward, and has a warm, friendly atmosphere.
11rm(9🌂2hc)(5fb) ® ✖ (ex guide dogs)
sB&B£19-£22 WB&B£118-£140 WBDi£165-£187 LDO 6.30pm
Lic ⬛ CTV 8P

GH 🆀🆀🆀 **Seychelles Private Hotel** 7 Burlington Rd
BH19 1LR ☎(0929) 422794
May-Oct
Personally supervised by the proprietors, Mr and Mrs Fisher, this small hotel which has its own private beach has been tastefully refurbished to provide comfortable accommodation.
9rm(2⇨6🌂1hc)(4fb) CTV in all bedrooms ® ✖✳ sB&Bfr£16
sB&B⇨🌂fr£18 dB&Bfr£32
dB&B⇨🌂fr£36 WB&Bfr£100 WBDifr£150
Lic ⬛ 10P
Ⓔ

SWANSEA West Glamorgan Map 03 SS69

See also Bishopston, Langland Bay and **Mumbles**
GH 🆀🆀 **Alexander Hotel** 3 Sketty Road, Uplands, Sketty
SA2 0EU ☎(0792) 470045 & 476012
Closed Xmas
Close to the busy Uplands Shopping Centre, this friendly hotel provides a comfortable lounge and bar, and modern, well-equipped bedrooms. There is also a basement games room.
7rm(4⇨3🌂1hc)(3fb) CTV in all bedrooms ® ✖ ✳
sB&B⇨🌂£30-£31 dB&B⇨🌂£44 WB&Bfr£175
Lic ⬛ nc2yrs games room
Credit Cards 1 2 3 5 Ⓔ

GH 🆀🆀🆀 **Cefn Bryn** 6 Uplands Crescent SA2 0PB
☎(0792) 466687
Closed Xmas
Close to the Uplands shopping area and convenient for the city centre, this comfortable, well-furnished hotel has a relaxing lounge containing an interesting collection of photographs of old Swansea and other bric-a-brac.

6rm(5🌂1hc)(2fb) CTV in all bedrooms ® ✖ sB&B🌂£20
dB&B🌂£40 WB&Bfr£90 WBDifr£140 LDO noon
CTV ✗

GH 🆀 **Channel View** 17 Bryn Rd, Brynmill SA2 0AR
☎(0792) 466834
The rear bedrooms of this friendly, family-run guesthouse provide a grandstand view of the St Helens Rugby and cricket grounds, and all accommodation is bright and clean, though modestly furnished.
6hc (1fb)✂in all bedrooms CTV in all bedrooms ® ✳
sB&B£12-£14 dB&B£24-£28 LDO 10am
⬛ CTV
Ⓔ

GH 🆀🆀 **Crescent** 132 Eaton Crescent, Uplands SA1 4QR
☎(0792) 466814
Closed Xmas & New Year
Convenient for the Uplands Shopping Centre and not too far from the town and the Gower, this friendly, family-run hotel is in a quiet residential area and provides bright, comfortable accommodation.
7rm(1🌂6hc)(1fb) TV in all bedrooms ® ✳ sB&Bfr£15
dB&B🌂fr£26 WB&Bfr£98
⬛ CTV 4P
Ⓔ

GH 🆀🆀 *The Guest House* 4 Bryn Rd SA2 0AR
☎(0792) 466947
This cosy guesthouse lies opposite the Swansea Cricket and Rugby Ground. The bedrooms are comfortable and pretty, and 7 additional en suite bedrooms are being added by the friendly owners.
7hc (1fb) ✖ (ex guide dogs) LDO 1pm
Lic ⬛ CTV ✗ nc9yrs

GH 🆀🆀🆀 *Tredilion House Hotel* 26 Uplands Crescent,
Uplands SA2 0PB ☎(0792) 470766
rs Xmas
A short distance from the town centre and convenient for the Gower, this Victorian town house has been tastefully refurbished to provide excellent accommodation. Bedrooms are pine furnished with every modern comfort and facility, and a very comfortable lounge is available.
7⇨5🌂 (1fb) CTV in all bedrooms ® ✖ (ex guide dogs)
sB&B⇨🌂£31-£35
dB&B⇨🌂£45-£48 WB&B£142-£220 WBDi£212-£290 LDO noon
Lic ⬛ CTV 8P 1🐾
Credit Cards 1 3 Ⓔ

GH 🆀 *Tregare Hotel* 9 Sketty Rd, Uplands SA2 0EU
☎(0792) 470608 & 456612
Conveniently situated for the shops, this family-run guesthouse has comfortable, well-equipped bedrooms.
10rm(3⇨6🌂1hc)(3fb) CTV in all bedrooms ® LDO 4pm
Lic ⬛ CTV 5P snooker
Credit Cards 1 3

SWINDERBY Lincolnshire Map 08 SK86

GH 🆀🆀 **Halfway Farm Motel & Guest House** A46 LN6 9HN
(8m N of Newark on A46, 8m SW Lincoln) ☎(052286) 749
Visitors can choose cosy lodgings in the old farmhouse, or modern en suite accommodation in a separate building. The emphasis is on a comfortable, friendly and relaxing stay.
8rm(1🌂7hc)Annexe 7🌂 (5fb) CTV in all bedrooms ®
✖ (ex guide dogs) ✳ sB&B£15-£17 sB&B🌂£25-£27
dB&B£26-£32 dB&B🌂£36-£44
⬛ CTV 20P nc2yrs
Credit Cards 1 2 3
See advertisement under LINCOLN on page 215

GH Ⓠ **The Lodge** Sheep Walk, Newark Rd LN6 9PU
☎(052286) 651
The resident proprietors give a friendly welcome to this small hotel, which despite its location on the A46 near RAF Swinderby, offers a quiet stay in compact but warm, double glazed bedrooms. There is a television lounge and residential licence.
6rm(5hc)(2fb) Ⓡ sB&B£16 dB&B£32 WB&B£100-£112
Lic CTV 10P

SWINDON Wiltshire Map **04** SU18

GH ⓆⓆ **Grove Lodge** 108 Swindon Rd SN3 4PT
☎(0793) 825343
North of Swindon, this prominently positioned terraced guesthouse offers well- equipped, simple bedrooms, each with an easy chair, and caters mainly for the commercial sector.
8⇨↑ (1fb) CTV in all bedrooms Ⓡ ✳ sB&B⇨↑£25
dB&B⇨↑£40 LDO 6pm
🍽12P
£

SYMONDS YAT (EAST) Hereford & Worcester
Map **03** SO51

GH ⓆⓆⓆ **Garth Cottage Hotel** HR9 6JL ☎(0600) 890364
Comfortable, cosy and well maintained, this small hotel stands on the river's edge in one of the most popular spots of the Wye Valley. The Eden family are friendly hosts and provide well-equipped accommodation.
4↑ Ⓡ ✖ (ex guide dogs)
dB&B↑£44 WB&B£140 WBDi£224 LDO 3pm
Lic 🍽 CTV 9P nc12yrs ✔
Credit Cards ①③

INN [Q][Q] **Saracens Head** HR9 6JL ☎(0600) 890435
Standing on the bank of the River Wye in this popular and picturesque tourist area, this half-timbered inn provides modern, well-maintained accommodation.
10rm(7🚿3hc)(1fb) Ⓡ 🐕 ✱ sB&B🚿£17.50-£21.50 dB&B🚿£35-£43 LDO 9.30pm
♨ CTV 60P 🎣
Credit Cards [1][2][3][5]

SYMONDS YAT (WEST) (near Ross-on-Wye) Hereford & Worcester Map **03** SO51

GH [Q][Q] **Woodlea Hotel** HR9 6BL ☎(0600) 890206
22 Feb-Nov
With lovely views across the valley to wooded hills, this pleasant and cosy house is quietly situated at the end of a narrow lane above the Wye rapids. Many of the bedrooms have en suite facilities and the amenities include a pleasant bar.
9rm(6🛁🚿3hc)(1fb) Ⓡ sB&Bfr£19.75 dB&Bfr£58 dB&B🛁🚿fr£64 WBDifr£179 LDO 7pm
Lic ♨ CTV 9P 🏊
Credit Cards [1][3] [£]

TADCASTER North Yorkshire Map **08** SE44

GH [Q][Q][Q] **Shann House** 47 Kirkgate LS24 9AQ
☎(0937) 833931
This 3-storeyed Georgian house, situated in the town centre, offers consistently high standards. The well-equipped, spacious accommodation is complemented by a warm dining room and an elegant lounge, with marble fireplace and Chesterfield sofa.
8🛁🚿 (1fb) CTV in all bedrooms Ⓡ ✱ sB&B🛁🚿fr£18.50 dB&B🛁🚿fr£28
Lic ♨ 8P
Credit Cards [1][3]

TALGARTH Powys Map **03** SO13

FH [Q][Q] Mrs B Prosser ***Upper Genffordd*** *(SO171304)* LD3 0EN ☎(0874) 711360
Just off the A479 and 3 miles south of Talgarth, these 16th-century farm buildings have been converted to provide farmhouse accommodation. Mr and Mrs Powell provide pretty bedrooms and a lounge with character. A cheerful welcome awaits guests.
2rm(1🛁1🚿)(1fb) CTV in all bedrooms Ⓡ LDO 5pm
♨ CTV 4P 200 acres dairy mixed

TAL-Y-LLYN Gwynedd Map **06** SH60

GH [Q][Q][Q] **Dolffanog Fawr** LL36 9AJ ☎Corris(065473) 247
Originally a 17th-century farmhouse rebuilt in 1907, this charming house stands beside the Tal-y-Llyn lake and has been furnished with great care.
3hc 🚭in all bedrooms Ⓡ 🐕
dB&B£27 WB&B£94.50 WBDi£154 LDO 6pm
♨ CTV 8P nc

TAUNTON Somerset Map **03** ST22

⊢⊣**GH** [Q][Q] **Brookfield** 16 Wellington Rd TA1 4EQ
☎(0823) 272786
A friendly, family-run hotel standing beside the A38 near the town centre provides accommodation in bedrooms with some modern facilities.
8hc (2fb) CTV in all bedrooms Ⓡ sB&B£13-£18 dB&B£24-£28 WB&B£91-£126 WBDi£126-£175 LDO 2.30pm
Lic ♨ 8P
[£]

This guide is updated annually – make sure you use an up-to-date edition.

SELECTED

GH [Q][Q][Q][Q] **Meryan House Hotel** Bishop's Hull TA1 5EG ☎(0823) 337445
In a quiet village, 1 mile from the centre of Taunton, this informal family-run establishment has been carefully extended to provide 12 well-equipped en suite bedrooms of a very high standard. The comfortable lounge has access to the lawned garden. A 3-course set meal is served nightly in the attractive dining room with its inglenook fireplace. Mrs Clarke welcomes her guests and assures them of friendly serice.
12🛁🚿 (3fb)🚭in 4 bedrooms CTV in all bedrooms Ⓡ ✱ sB&B🛁🚿£32-£35 dB&B🛁🚿£45-£50 WB&B£200-£220 WBDi£270-£300 LDO 6.30pm
Lic ♨ CTV 17P solarium tennis net croquet
Credit Cards [1][3] [£]

TEIGNMOUTH Devon Map **03** SX97

GH [Q][Q] **Glen Devon Hotel** 3 Carlton Place TQ14 8AB
☎(0626) 772895
Compact, brightly decorated bedrooms and comfortable public areas are offered at this simply appointed, family-run hotel, which is in a road just off the seafront, close to the town centre.
7rm(2🛁2🚿3hc)(4fb) Ⓡ 🐕 ✱ sB&B£11-£12 sB&B🛁🚿£12.50-£13.50 dB&B£22-£24 dB&B🛁🚿£25-£27 WB&B£77-£84 WBDi£90-£112 LDO 5pm
Lic ♨ CTV 6P
[£]

GH [Q][Q] **Hill Rise Hotel** Winterbourne Rd TQ14 8JT
☎(0626) 773108
Bright, well-equipped bedrooms and good, comfortable public areas are provided by a large detached Edwardian house located in a residential area.
8rm(2🚿6hc)(3fb)🚭in all bedrooms CTV in 2 bedrooms Ⓡ 🐕 (ex guide dogs) ✱ sB&B£13.50-£14.50 dB&B£27-£29 dB&B🚿£27-£29 WB&B£90-£95
Lic ♨ CTV 4P 1🚗 ⌂
[£]

GH [Q][Q][Q] ***Lyme Bay House Hotel*** Den Promenade TQ14 8SZ
☎(0626) 772953
Apr-Oct
A large Victorian house, standing on the Promenade close to the town centre, provides spaciously comfortable public rooms and well-equipped, individually styled bedrooms.
9rm(3🚿6hc)(1fb) Ⓡ
Lic lift ♨ CTV P̸
See advertisement under EXETER on page 153

GH [Q][Q] **Rathlin House Hotel** Upper Hermosa Rd TQ14 9JW
☎(0626) 774473
Mar-19 Oct
10rm(3🚿7hc)(5fb) Ⓡ ✱ sB&B£11-£13.50 dB&B£22-£27 dB&B🚿£26.50-£31.50 WB&B£70-£87.50 WBDi£90-£110 LDO 6.15pm
Lic CTV 12P
[£]

SELECTED

GH [Q][Q][Q][Q] **Thomas Luny House** Teign St TQ14 8EG
☎(0626) 772976
Closed mid Dec-mid Jan
Built in the 1800s by marine artist Thomas Luny, this quietly situated house retains the elegance of its past and is a worthy winner of the Best Newcomer award for 1991 for the western region. The 4 spacious bedrooms are equipped with every facility and guests may browse through the many books in the

comfortable lounge. John and Alison Allan join guests for
drinks before serving excellent meals, which are taken around
the table in the attractive dining room.
4rm(3⇉1♠) CTV in all bedrooms ✗ (ex guide dogs) ✱
sB&B⇉♠£27.50 dB&B⇉♠£55 LDO 8pm
Lic 8P nc12yrs

TELFORD Shropshire Map **07** SJ60

See also Rowton

GH Q Q Q **Church Farm** Wrockwardine, Wellington TF6 5DG
☎(0952) 244917
Adjacent to the church in the heart of the village, this 200-year-old
listed farmhouse has charming gardens and buildings with some
animals roaming freely. The hospitable hosts are keen to make
their guests welcome.
5rm(2⇉3hc)Annexe 1♠ (1fb) CTV in all bedrooms ® ✱
sB&Bfr£20 sB&B⇉♠fr£25 dB&Bfr£32 dB&B⇉♠fr£40
🍴 CTV 10P ₰

INN Q Q **Cock Hotel** 148 Holyhead Rd, Wellington TF1 2ED
☎(0952) 244954
This roadside inn stands on the outskirts of Wellington. The
bedrooms are well equipped, though without en suite facilities, and
breakfast is taken in an oak panelled room. All meals are prepared
by the host, Mr Miles.
7hc (1fb) CTV in all bedrooms ® ✗ LDO 9pm
🍴 30P 4🐾

INN Q Q **Swan Hotel** Watling St, Wellington TF1 2NH
☎(0952) 223781
This red brick hotel has comfortable modern bars and a restaurant
serving a good range of food. The bedrooms are pleasant and
bright. The Swan stands alongside historic Watling Street (now
the A5) at Wellington.
▶

12hc (5fb) CTV in all bedrooms ® ✶ sB&B£25
dB&B£32 Bar Lunch £2.25-£7.25 Dinner £2.25-£7.95 LDO
10pm
🛏150P ▶ 18
Credit Cards 1 2 3 5 £

TEMPLE CLOUD Avon Map 03 ST65

FH Q Q Mr & Mrs Wyatt **Temple Bridge** *(ST627575)*
BS18 5AA ☎(0761) 52377
Mar-Oct
*This 17th-century white farmhouse with mullion windows and oak
beams also has a large garden available to guests. The house is
situated south of the village and set back from the A37 road. It is
within easy distance of Bath, Wells and Bristol. Simple
accommodation is provided in comfortable rooms.*
2hc (2fb) ® ✹ ✶ sB&B£13-£15 dB&B£23-£28
🛏 CTV 2P 1🐾 nc2yrs 250 acres beef arable
£

TENBURY WELLS Hereford & Worcester

See **Frith Common**

TENBY Dyfed Map 02 SN10

GH Q Q **Castle View Private Hotel** The Norton SA70 8AA
☎(0834) 2666
Mar-Oct
*This friendly, family-run hotel is situated near the town centre and
is adjacent to the town's north beach. The first floor lounge, and
many bedrooms, have excellent views over the harbour and the
beach.*
10rm(7⇨3♠)(4fb) CTV in all bedrooms ® sB&B⇨♠£16-£20
dB&B⇨♠£32-£40 WB&B£112-£140 WBDi£161-£180 LDO
6.30pm
Lic CTV 7P
Credit Cards 3 £

GH Q Q *Clareston House Hotel* Warren St SA70 7AL
☎(0834) 4148
rs Nov-Feb
*Claresdon House is a bright and cosy guesthouse situated near the
railway station and just a short walk from the sandy beaches and
town centre. There is a comfortable lounge and cosy basement bar.*
6hc (5fb) CTV in all bedrooms ® ✹ ✶ sB&B£12-£14
dB&B£22-£28 WB&B£80-£90 WBDi£100-£120 (wkly only Jun-
Aug) LDO 11am
Lic 🛏 CTV 4P
£

GH Q Q *Gumfreston Private Hotel* Culver Park SA70 7ED
☎(0834) 2871
Closed Nov
*Bright and friendly, this small hotel is a few yards from the south
beach and close to the shops. It has modern bedrooms and
comfortable public rooms and features excellent displays of flowers
and hanging baskets.*
11rm(1⇨10♠)(5fb) ® ✹ LDO 4pm
Lic 🛏 CTV ℐ
Credit Cards 3

GH Q Q *Heywood Lodge* Heywood Ln SA70 8BN
☎(0834) 2684
rs Xmas & New Year
*This 18th-century stone house is situated among pleasant lawns
and gardens on the outskirts of the town, just a short drive from the
sandy beaches. The bedrooms are bright, and there is a
comfortable lounge and cosy foyer bar.*
13rm(4⇨2♠7hc)(4fb) ® LDO 8pm
Lic 🛏 CTV 20P 🐾
Credit Cards 1 3

GH Q Q **Hildebrand Hotel** Victoria St SA70 7DY
☎(0834) 2403
Apr-Oct rs Jan-Mar & Nov
*Just off the seafront and a short walk from the town centre, this
holiday guesthouse is decorated with an abundance of floral
baskets and displays. The bedrooms are all well equipped and
there is a cosy basement bar.*
11rm(3⇨5♠3hc)(6fb) CTV in all bedrooms ® sB&B£16-£20
sB&B⇨♠£20-£24 dB&B£25-£32
dB&B⇨♠£33-£40 WB&B£105-£124 WBDi£160-£180 LDO
4pm
Lic 🛏 ℐ
Credit Cards 1 2 3 5 £

GH Q Q Q **Myrtle House Hotel** St Mary's St SA70 7HW
☎(0834) 2508
Mar-Nov
*A well-maintained and enthusiastically run small hotel with bright,
airy bedrooms and restaurant of character.*
8rm(1⇨6♠1hc)(3fb)✂in all bedrooms CTV in all bedrooms
® ✹ (ex guide dogs) sB&B£15 sB&B⇨♠£18 dB&B£30
dB&B⇨♠£36 WB&B£95-£105 WBDi£130-£145 LDO 4pm
Lic 🛏 ℐ
Credit Cards 1 3

GH Q Q **Ripley St Marys Hotel** St Mary's St SA70 7HN
☎(0834) 2837
Apr-Oct rs Feb-Mar & Nov
*Set within Tenby's historic walls, this town house is run by the
friendly Mace family and is 100 yards from the seafront.*
14rm(8⇨6hc)(6fb) CTV in all bedrooms ® sB&B£17-£25
dB&B£32-£40
dB&B⇨♠£36-£50 WB&B£110-£130 WBDi£145-£200 LDO
6pm
Lic CTV ℐ
Credit Cards 1 3 £

GH Q Q **Sea Breezes Hotel** 18 The Norton SA70 8AA
☎(0834) 2753
Jun-Sep rs Mar-May & Oct-Nov
*Guesthouse with popular residents' bar, near harbour town and
North Beach. Friendly, hospitable, family service.*
11rm(5⇨1♠5hc)(3fb)✂in 6 bedrooms CTV in 6 bedrooms
TV in 5 bedrooms ® ✹ (ex guide dogs) ✶ sB&B£15-£20
sB&B⇨♠£18-£23 dB&B£30-£40
dB&B⇨♠£36-£46 WBDi£110-£130 LDO 4.30pm
Lic 🛏 CTV ℐ
£

GH Q Q Q **Tall Ships Hotel** 34 Victoria St SA70 7DY
☎(0834) 2055
Mar-Oct
*Run by the friendly Richards family, this guesthouse is located just
off the town's south beach, and is a short walk from the town
centre. It provides bright, well-equipped bedrooms, a large lounge
and a cosy basement bar.*
9rm(5♠4hc)(6fb) CTV in all bedrooms ® ✹ (ex guide dogs) ✶
sB&B£12-£15 sB&B♠£14.50-£17.50 dB&B£24-£30
dB&B♠£29-£35 WB&B£80-£115 WBDi£115-£155 LDO 5pm
Lic CTV ℐ
Credit Cards 1 3 £

TETBURY Gloucestershire Map 03 ST89

INN Q Q Q **Priory** London Rd GL8 8JJ ☎(0666) 502251
*Friendly and attentive services are provided by hosts Pat and Paul
Gregory and their staff at this inn, located on the edge of the
village. The well-equipped bedrooms complement the imaginative
food served in the bar and formal restaurant.*
3hc (1fb) CTV in all bedrooms ® ✶ sB&Bfr£20
dB&B£36-£40 LDO 10pm

♨ 100P
Credit Cards 1 3 £

TEWKESBURY Gloucestershire Map **03** SO83

GH Q Q *The Abbey Hotel* 67 Church St GL20 5RX
☎(0684) 294247
Comfortable town house with walled garden to the rear.
16rm(7⇌7♠2hc)(3fb) CTV in all bedrooms ® LDO 8.30pm
Lic ♨ 11P
Credit Cards 1 2 3

FH Q Q Q Mick & Anne Meadows **Home** *(SO933390)*
Bredons Norton GL20 7HA ☎Bredon(0684) 72322
Closed Dec
Situated 100 yards up the lane beside the village school, this 300-year-old farmhouse is set in 150 acres of land with mixed sheep, cattle and poultry. Home Farm has been tastefully improved to provide pretty and comfortable bedrooms with en suite or private facilities.
3rm(2⇌1hc)(1fb) ® ✱ sB&B⇌£15-£16
dB&B⇌£28-£30 WB&B£98-£112 WBDi£161-£175
6P 🐾

THAME Oxfordshire Map **04** SP70

GH Q Q Q **Essex House** Chinnor Rd OX9 3LS
☎(084421) 7567
Originally a station hotel, Essex House is personally run by friendly owners and offers well-equipped bedrooms and cosy public rooms. The addition of a new annexe provides bright, modern bedrooms and there is on-site parking.
10rm(1⇌6♠3hc)Annexe 6rm(3⇌3♠)(2fb)⊬in 5 bedrooms
CTV in all bedrooms ® ✖ (ex guide dogs) LDO 7pm
Lic ♨ CTV 20P
Credit Cards 1 3

SELECTED

FH Q Q Q Q Mrs M Aitken **Upper Green** *(SP736053)*
Manor Rd, Towersey OX9 3QR (1.5m E unclass rd)
☎(084421) 2496
Closed Xmas & New Year
This 15th-century, thatched farmhouse stands in 7 acres of lovely countryside, and is carefully restored to retain many original features, while providing comfortable and thoughtfully equipped accommodation. One bedroom contains a priests's hole There is a no-smoking rule.
3rm(1♠1hc)Annexe 6⇌♠ ⊬in all bedrooms CTV in 6
bedrooms TV in 3 bedrooms ® ✖ sB&B£15
sB&B⇌♠£27.50 dB&Bfr£30 dB&B⇌♠£42-£48
♨ CTV 11P nc16yrs 7 acres poultry sheep

THAXTED Essex Map **05** TL63

INN Q Q Q **Farmhouse** Monk St CM6 2NR ☎(0371) 830864
FAX (0371) 831196
Situated in picturesque Monk Street, 1 mile south of Thaxted off the B184, this 15th-century building now provides quality en suite accommodation and a 50- seater restaurant where a selection of freshly prepared meals is served.
11⇌♠ ⊬in 4 bedrooms CTV in all bedrooms
✖ (ex guide dogs) sB&B£42 sB&B⇌♠£42
dB&B⇌♠£55 WB&B£230 WBDi£295 Lunch £7.95 Dinner
£7.95&alc LDO 9.30pm
♨ 48P
Credit Cards 1 2 3 £

Q is for quality. For a full explanation of this AA quality
award, consult the Contents page.

THE ABBEY HOTEL

Centrally situated in a conservation area.

This warm family run hotel offers private and
business accommodation at reasonable cost.

The hotel has a residents car park and all rooms
have a colour TV and Telephone.

There is a Residents' Bar and meals are available
Monday to Friday.

67 Church Street, Tewkesbury, Glos GL20 5RX
Telephone: (0684) 294247 & 294097

SEE
BRITAIN
BY
TRAIN

L et BR do the driving while you
and your family enjoy a relaxing
and different view of some of Britain's
best scenery. 50 railway routes
through England, Wales and Scotland
are described and illustrated,
identifying landmarks to see from the
train and places of interest to stop off
and visit.

PLUS Route maps • Standard
and narrow gauge preserved
railways • Suggested walks,
cycling routes, etc • All the
practical information you need to
make your journey easy.

A joint AA/British Rail publication **AA**

THEYDON BOIS Essex Map **05** TQ49

FH [Q][Q][Q] S & M Dale **Parsonage** *(TQ459989)* Abridge Rd CM16 7NN ☎(037881) 4242

This 15th-century farmhouse stands on the edge of Theydon Bois and has been carefully restored by the owners. Some of the well-appointed bedrooms look out over the 2 acres of gardens and surrounding countryside.

6rm(1🛁1🚿4hc)(4fb)🚭in all bedrooms CTV in 2 bedrooms [R] 🐕 (ex guide dogs) * sB&Bfr£25 sB&B🛁🚿fr£28 dB&B£35-£45 dB&B🛁🚿fr£45 WB&Bfr£125

♨ 10P 6 acres non working

THIRLMERE Cumbria Map **11** NY31

FH [Q][Q] Mr & Mrs J Hodgson **Stybeck** *(NY319188)* CA12 4TN ☎Keswick(07687) 73232

Closed 25 Dec

This typical lakeland farmhouse is well furnished with bedrooms of a good standard and friendly, welcoming service.

3hc (1fb) [R] 🐕 * sB&B£14-£15 dB&B£28-£30

♨ CTV 4P nc5yrs 200 acres dairy mixed sheep working

THORGANBY North Yorkshire Map **08** SE64

INN [Q][Q][Q] ***Jefferson Arms*** Main St YO4 6DB ☎Wheldrake(090489) 316

300-year-old inn fitted and furnished in 'cottage'-style with beamed bars and comfortable bedrooms. Local fresh produce used in restaurant.

3🛁 Annexe 3rm(2🛁)(1fb)🚭in 3 bedrooms CTV in 5 bedrooms [R] LDO 9.30pm

♨ 60P

Credit Cards [1] [2] [3] [5]

See advertisement under YORK on page 414

THORNEY Cambridgeshire Map **04** TF20

FH [Q][Q] Mrs Y G Baker **Oversley Lodge** *(TF269041)* The Causeway PE6 0QH ☎Peterborough(0733) 270321

Three quarters of a mile from the village of Thorney, Oversley Lodge is a modern detached house set on an arable farm. Surrounded by an acre of well-tended, landscaped and walled gardens, the guesthouse has large comfortable rooms thoughtfully set out by cheerful hosts Mr and Mrs Baker.

3hc (1fb)🚭in all bedrooms CTV in all bedrooms [R] * sB&B£15-£18 dB&B£25-£30 LDO 7pm

♨ CTV 0P 0🚗 260 acres arable

THORNTON Lancashire Map **07** SD34

SELECTED

GH [Q][Q][Q][Q] **The Victorian House** Trunnah Rd FY5 4HF ☎Blackpool(0253) 860619

The charming hosts, Louise and Didier Guerin, have decorated and furnished this delightful house with care. It stands in an attractive walled garden close to the B5268. The authentic Victorian parlour is crammed with objects d'art, and comfortable easy chairs enable guests to relax. Apéritifs can be taken in the snug bar prior to sampling Mr Guerin's French cuisine which is served by waitresses wearing Victorian costume. The spacious bedrooms are furnished and equipped to a very high standard.

3🛁🚿 CTV in all bedrooms [R] * sB&B🛁🚿£37.50 dB&B🛁🚿£57.50-£65 WB&B£262.50 WBDi£381.50 LDO 9.30pm

Lic ♨ 20P nc6yrs

Credit Cards [1] [3]

THORNTON DALE North Yorkshire Map **08** SE88

GH [Q][Q] **Easthill** Wilton Rd YO18 7QP ☎Pickering(0751) 74561

8rm(3🛁5🚿)(2fb) TV in 1 bedroom 🐕 sB&B🛁🚿£18 dB&B🛁🚿£31-£35 WB&B£101.50-£115.50 WBDi£150.50-£164.50 LDO noon

Lic ♨ CTV 12P 🎾(grass)crazy golf games room

[£]

THORPE BAY Essex

See **Southend-on-Sea**

THRAPSTON Northamptonshire Map **04** SP97

INN [Q] **Court House Hotel** NN14 4NF ☎(08012) 3618

Built in 1858 as a courthouse, police station and lock-up, this building was converted to an inn in 1976. The restaurant is the original courtroom with a remarkable hammerbeam roof. The simple bedrooms are comfortable and have beverage facilities.

7rm(2🛁1🚿4hc) TV in all bedrooms [R] 🐕 (ex guide dogs) sB&B£18-£25 sB&B🛁🚿fr£25 dB&Bfr£30 dB&B🛁🚿fr£36 Lunch fr£7.50&alc Dinner fr£5&alc LDO 9.30pm

♨ 5P

Credit Cards [1] [3] [£]

THREE COCKS Powys Map **03** SO13

GH [Q][Q][Q] **Old Gwernyfed Country Manor** Felindre LD3 0SU ☎Glasbury(04974) 376

mid Mar-mid Nov

Set in beautiful countryside, this Elizabethan manor house, where Charles I once stayed, has a minstrel's gallery, an oak panelled banquetting hall that is now a lounge and many other interesting features. Most of the bedrooms are en suite.

11rm(7🛁2🚿2hc)(4fb) sB&Bfr£32 sB&B🛁🚿fr£35 dB&B£42-£70 dB&B🛁🚿£57-£70 LDO 7.30pm

Lic 15P croquet

THREE LEGGED CROSS Dorset Map **04** SU00

FH [Q][Q] Mr & Mrs B Gent **Homeacres** *(SU096054)* Homelands Farm BH21 6QZ ☎Verwood(0202) 822422

This modern style farmhouse stands peacefully in 270 acres of farmland. It is comfortably appointed with some spacious bedrooms.

5rm(2🚿3hc)(3fb) [R] * sB&B🚿£15 dB&B£24 dB&B🚿£30 WB&B£77-£98

♨ CTV 5P 3🚗 🏇 games room 270 acres beef

[£]

THRESHFIELD North Yorkshire Map **07** SD96

GH [Q][Q][Q] **Greenways** Wharfeside Av BD23 5BS ☎Skipton(0756) 752598

Apr-Oct

Delightfully furnished house in own grounds with superb views across the River Wharfe.

5hc (1fb) [R] * sB&B£18-£22 dB&Bfr£36 WB&B£115-£140 WBDi£176-£200 LDO 5pm

Lic ♨ CTV 8P nc7yrs

See advertisement under GRASSINGTON on page 167

THRINGSTONE Leicestershire Map **08** SK41

FH [Q] Miss F E White **Talbot House** *(SK423173)* LE6 4NQ ☎Coalville(0530) 222233

Mostly built in Victorian times, around a much earlier building, this large, rambling farmhouse provides simple, old-fashioned and comfortable accommodation. It stands on the B587, 4.5 miles west of M1 junction 23.

4rm (2fb) CTV in 1 bedroom TV in 1 bedroom 🐕 (ex guide dogs) * sB&Bfr£13 dB&Bfr£25 WB&Bfr£86 WBDifr£138 LDO noon

🏵 CTV 6P croquet 150 acres dairy
£

THURNING Norfolk Map **09** TG02

FH 🇶🇶 Mrs A M Fisher **Rookery** *(TG078307)* NR24 2JP
☎Melton Constable(0263) 860357
Feb-Nov
*Good, comfortable accommodation is provided at this 17th-century
detached farmhouse, set in a secluded location among well-tended
gardens. Guests are strongly advised to obtain detailed directions
from the caring host, Mrs Fisher.*
3rm(1🛇)(1fb) ℝ ✱ sB&B£11-£12 dB&B🛇£22-£24
CTV 0P 400 acres arable

THURSBY Cumbria Map **11** NY35

FH 🇶🇶 Mrs M G Swainson **How End** *(NY316497)* CA5 6PX
☎Wigton(06973) 42487
*This neat farmhouse offers good accommodation at a reasonable
price along with friendly service provided by the resident owner. It
stands on the A595 between Carlisle and Wigton.*
3rm (2fb)⊁in all bedrooms 🛪 (ex guide dogs) ✱ sB&B£11-£13
dB&B£22-£26 WB&B£77-£91 WBDi£119-£140 LDO noon
🏵 CTV 4P 200 acres dairy mixed

THWAITE North Yorkshire Map **07** SD89

GH 🇶🇶 **Kearton** DL11 5DR
☎Richmond (North Yorks)(0748) 86277
Mar-Dec
*Set in the heart of this pretty village, this comfortable guesthouse
has a delightful, spacious restaurant, which provides quality
morning coffee, lunch, afternoon tea and dinner.*
13hc (2fb) ℝ 🛪 (ex guide dogs) ✱ sB&B£19.50-£21
dB&B£39-£42 (incl dinner) WB&B£105 WBDi£136.50 LDO
6.30pm
Lic 🏵 50P
£

TIDEFORD Cornwall & Isles of Scilly Map **02** SX35

FH 🇶🇶 Mrs B A Turner **Kilna House** *(SX353600)* PL12 5AD
☎Landrake(0752) 851236
Closed Xmas & New Year
*Stone-built house set in a large pleasant garden on A38, quarter of
a mile outside village. It overlooks the River Tiddy Valley.*
5hc (2fb) CTV in all bedrooms ℝ sB&B£14-£16
dB&B£24-£28 WB&B£84-£112
🏵 CTV 6P 12 acres arable pasture
£

TIMSBURY Avon Map **03** ST65

GH 🇶🇶 **Old Malt House Hotel & Licensed Restaurant**
Radford BA3 1QF ☎(0761) 70106
Closed Xmas
*On the outskirts of the village. This former malting house has been
renovated to provide spacious public areas and well-equipped
bedrooms which all have en suite facilities. The Holder family also
operate a shire horse stud adjacent to the house.*
10rm(5⇩5🛇)(2fb) CTV in all bedrooms ℝ 🛪
sB&B⇩🛇£29.50-£30.50
dB&B⇩🛇£48-£51 WB&B£150.50-£196 WBDi£234.50-£287
LDO 8.30pm
Lic 🏵 40P nc3yrs
Credit Cards 1️⃣ 2️⃣ 3️⃣ 5️⃣ £

TINTAGEL Cornwall & Isles of Scilly Map **02** SX08

GH Q Q **Belvoir** Tregatta PL34 0DY
☎Camelford(0840) 770265
Closed Xmas
Mrs Martin provides a warm welcome here. The house is cottage-like in style, with a sun lounge in addition to another cosy lounge. The bedrooms are comfortable, and most contain en suite facilities.
7rm(1⇔4♠2hc)(1fb) TV in 1 bedroom ® ✳ sB&B£11-£12
dB&B£22-£24
dB&B⇔♠£24-£26 WB&B£75-£89 WBDi£108.75-£122.75
LDO 5.30pm
Lic CTV 12P nc1yr
£

GH Q Q Q **Castle Villa** Molesworth St PL34 0BZ
☎Camelford(0840) 770373
This small cottage of Cornish stone provides neat bedrooms, equipped with tea and coffee-making facilities. There is a cosy lounge with stone fireplaces, and a conservatory dining room. Fresh homemade food and home brewed beer are on offer.
5hc (1fb)⅍in 3 bedrooms CTV in 2 bedrooms ® ✳
sB&B£10.50-£13.50
dB&B£21-£27 WB&B£73.50-£94.50 WBDi£119.70-£141.75
LDO 10am
Lic ℳ CTV 6P
Credit Cards [1][3] £

GH Q Q Q *Trebrea Lodge* Trenale PL34 0HR
☎Camelford(0840) 770410
Closed 21-28 Dec & 5-30 Jan
This interesting 14th-century stone-built house has views over the village, the sea and open country. Mr and Mrs Radford provide a relaxed atmosphere and good home cooking. The bedrooms are comfortable and there is an elegant drawing room.
7rm(2⇔3♠2hc)Annexe 2♠ (3fb) CTV in all bedrooms ®
LDO 8.45pm
Lic ℳ 15P ♒ badminton lawn
Credit Cards [1][3]

⌕⌕**GH** Q Q **The Trevervan Hotel** Trewarmett PL34 0ES
☎Camelford(0840) 770486
In the village of Trewarmett, this is a detached house with fine sea views. It is personally run by the resident proprietors and offers a warm welcome, together with neat and well-kept accommodation.
6hc (3fb)⅍in 2 bedrooms ® sB&B£13-£14
dB&B£26-£28 WB&B£86-£93 WBDi£127-£135 LDO 7pm
Lic ℳ CTV 6P ♒
Credit Cards [1][3] £

GH Q Q Q **Trewarmett Lodge** PL34 0ET
☎Camelford(0840) 770460
Closed Nov rs Dec-Etr
Standing in a small hamlet, 1 mile from Tintagel, with distant coastal views, this small, stone-built hotel has a popular and busy restaurant.
6rm(1♠5hc)(2fb)⅍in all bedrooms ® LDO 9pm
Lic ℳ CTV 10P ♒
Credit Cards [1][3] £

INN Q Q Q **Tintagel Arms Hotel** Fore St PL34 0BD
☎Camelford(0840) 770780
Standing in the centre of the village (reputed home of King Arthur), this inn has well-equipped, attractive bedrooms. An extensive range of bar meals is available and the restaurant has a wide choice of English, Continental and vegetarian dishes.
7⇔♠ (1fb) CTV in all bedrooms ® ✖ (ex guide dogs) ✳
sB&B⇔♠£20-£26
dB&B⇔♠£40-£60 Bar Lunch £1-£6 Dinner £9-£16alc LDO
9.30pm
ℳ 8P nc6yrs
Credit Cards [1][3] £

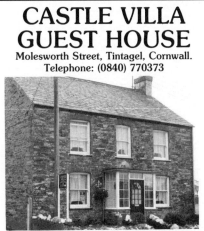

TINTERN Gwent Map **03** SO50

GH 🅠🅠 **Valley House** Raglan Rd NP6 6TH ☎(0291) 689652
Set in a tranquil valley, this Georgian house has en suite, well-
equipped bedrooms and a comfortable residents' lounge. Valley
House is half a mile from the A466.
3⇌🎨 ⅍in 2 bedrooms CTV in all bedrooms ®
✖ (ex guide dogs) ✳ sB&B⇌🎨£18
dB&B⇌🎨£28-£30 WB&Bfr£94.50 WBDifr£149.50 LDO 8pm
🎏 7P pool table table tennis
£

⊢⊷INN 🅠 **Fountain** Trellech Grange NP6 6QW
☎(0291) 689303
Just 2 miles west of the village, (turn at the Royal George Hotel),
this 17th-century inn is full of character and has a cosy bar and an
à la carte restaurant offering a good choice of meals.
5hc (2fb) CTV in 4 bedrooms TV in 1 bedroom ®
sB&B£12-£17
dB&B£27 WB&B£78-£93 WBDi£138 Lunch £6-£10 Dinner
£12-£16 LDO 10.30pm
🎏 40P
Credit Cards ①③£

TISSINGTON Derbyshire Map **07** SK15

FH 🅠🅠🅠 Mrs B Herridge **Bent** *(SK187523)* DE6 1RD
☎Parwich(033525) 214
Etr-Oct
Part of a country estate within the Peak District National Park,
this stone-built house is part of a working farm. Guests will enjoy
comfortable accommodation and a charming country garden.
4rm(2⇌2hc)(1fb) ® ✖ (ex guide dogs) dB&B£23-£25
dB&B⇌£30-£32 WB&B£78-£103 WBDi£120-£145 LDO 5pm
🎏 CTV 6P nc5yrs 280 acres beef dairy mixed sheep

TIVERTON Devon Map **03** SS91

GH 🅠🅠🅠 *Bridge* 23 Angel Hill EX16 6PE ☎(0884) 252804
This large Victorian house stands on the river-bank close to the
town centre. The house retains many original features and is
traditionally furnished. Guests can enjoy private fishing from the
river garden.
10rm(2🎨8hc)(2fb) TV in all bedrooms ® LDO 6.30pm
Lic 🎏 CTV 6P 1🏖 ⌗ ⌗ riverside tea garden

⊢⊷**FH** 🅠🅠 Mr & Mrs Fullilove **Lodge Hill** *(SS945112)*
Ashley EX16 5PA ☎(0884) 252907
This large rendered farmhouse on a hillside in the Exe Valley is
situated 1 mile south of the town, off the A396.
9rm(7🎨2hc)(1fb) CTV in 4 bedrooms ® sB&Bfr£13
sB&B🎨fr£15 dB&Bfr£26 dB&B🎨fr£30 WB&B£80-£90
Lic 🎏 CTV 10P 1🏖 (£1 per night) 10 acres poultry sheep
£

SELECTED

FH 🅠🅠🅠🅠 Mrs R Olive **Lower Collipriest** *(SS953117)*
EX16 4PT ☎(0884) 252321
Etr-Oct
This thatched farmhouse with its cobbled courtyard, lies
beside the River Exe, and has lovely views across meadows.
The 2 bedrooms are en suite and the evening meal is served
around one large table. Mrs Olive looks after her guests well.
2⇌ ⅍in all bedrooms ® ✖ (ex guide dogs)
sB&B⇌£25-£27
dB&B⇌£50-£55 (incl dinner) WBDi£165 LDO noon
🎏 CTV 2P 2🏖 nc16yrs ⌗ 220 acres beef dairy

TOBERMORY

See **MULL, ISLE OF**

TORBAY Devon

See **Brixham, Paignton and Torquay**

TORQUAY Devon Map **03** SX96

See **Town Plan Section**
GH 🅠 **Allandene Seapoint Hotel** 5 Clifton Grove, Old
Torwood Rd TQ1 1PE ☎(0803) 211808
Etr-Nov
10hc (3fb) ® ✖ LDO 4pm
Lic 🎏 CTV 4P 1🏖

GH 🅠🅠 **Avron Hotel** 70 Windsor Rd TQ1 1SZ
☎(0803) 294182
May-Sep
14rm(6🎨8hc)(1fb) TV in all bedrooms ® WBDi£98-£122
(wkly only Jun-Aug)
CTV 8P

GH 🅠🅠🅠 **Barn Hayes Country Hotel** Brim Hill,
Maidencombe TQ1 4TR ☎(0803) 327980
rs Nov-Feb
Set in a peaceful valley 2 miles from the centre of Torquay, this
most attractive property stands in its own well-tended gardens with
a swimming pool and some lovely sea views. Some of the bedrooms
offer en suite facilities, and the lounges and dining room are
tastefully decorated. A simple menu offers home-cooked dishes.
10rm(5🎨5hc)Annexe 3rm(2⇌1🎨)(2fb) CTV in 3 bedrooms ®
✳ sB&B£13-£16 sB&B⇌🎨£17-£20 dB&B£26-£32
dB&B⇌🎨£30-£36 WB&B£85-£133 WBDi£123-£182
16P ⌂
Credit Cards ①③

GH 🅠🅠🅠 **Braddon Hall Hotel** Braddons Hill Rd East
TQ1 1HF ☎(0803) 293908
Within easy reach of the harbour and beaches, this quietly set hotel
has en suite facilities and public areas of a high standard. The
resident proprietors provide a choice of menu and a warm welcome.
11⇌🎨 (3fb) CTV in all bedrooms ® ✳ sB&B⇌🎨£18-£20
dB&B⇌🎨£36-£40 LDO 5pm
Lic 🎏 8P

GH 🅠🅠🅠 **Burley Court Hotel** Wheatridge Lane, Livermead
TQ2 6RA ☎(0803) 607879
mid Mar-Oct
Situated in an elevated position overlooking Livermead Beach,
Burley Court has well-equipped bedrooms with en suite facilities.
An indoor leisure complex has a plunge pool, solarium, mini gym
and games room. There is a heated swimming pool outside as well.
21rm(1⇌20🎨)(7fb) CTV in all bedrooms ® ✖ (ex guide dogs)
sB&B⇌🎨£24-£28
dB&B⇌🎨£48-£56 (incl dinner) WB&B£118-£138
WBDi£148-£168 (wkly only Jul-Aug) LDO 6.30pm
Lic 🎏 25P ▣(heated) ⌂(heated) solarium gymnasium
£

⊢⊷**GH** 🅠🅠🅠 **Chesterfield Hotel** 62 Belgrave Rd TQ2 5HY
☎(0803) 292318
This charming Victorian house is part of a terrace close to the
seafront. The bedrooms are tastefully furnished and the public
rooms still have their original carved ceilings.
11rm(5🎨6hc)(4fb) CTV in all bedrooms ® sB&B£12-£15
sB&B🎨£15-£18 dB&B£22-£28
dB&B🎨£28-£36 WB&B£74-£95 WBDi£99-£130 LDO 4pm
Lic 🎏 CTV 3P
Credit Cards ①③£

Book as early as possible for busy holiday periods.

GH QQQ **Hotel Concorde** 26 Newton Rd TQ2 5BZ
☎(0803) 292330
Standing on the outskirts of town, this guesthouse has been well modernised and offers spacious public rooms, well-equipped bedrooms and a sheltered swimming pool.
22rm(14⇌🛏8hc)(7fb) CTV in all bedrooms ® ✱
sB&B£12-£14 sB&B⇌🛏£14-£18 dB&B£24-£28
dB&B⇌🛏£28-£36 WBDi£96-£146 LDO 6pm
Lic ㎜ CTV 18P ⌁(heated)
Credit Cards ① ③

GH QQQ **Craig Court Hotel** 10 Ash Hill Rd, Castle Circus
TQ1 3HZ ☎(0803) 294400
Etr-Oct
Spacious and detached, an early Victorian house in a quiet road close to the shopping centre offers large, comfortable bedrooms and a choice of 2 lounges.
10rm(4🛏6hc)(2fb) ® ✖ (ex guide dogs) sB&B£15-£18
dB&B£30-£36
dB&B🛏£35-£41 WB&B£105-£126 WBDi£140-£161 LDO noon
Lic CTV 8P model railway in garden
£

⊢⊶**GH** QQQ **Cranborne Hotel** 58 Belgrave Rd TQ2 5HY
☎(0803) 298046
Closed Dec
This fine Victorian house has been carefully modernised by Mr and Mrs Dawkins, and has very well-equipped bedrooms, most of which have en suite facilities, and good public areas. The small front garden is a past winner of the 'Devon in Bloom' competition.
12rm(9⇌🛏3hc)(6fb) CTV in all bedrooms ® ✖ sB&B£13-£15
sB&B⇌🛏£16-£18 dB&B£26-£30
dB&B⇌🛏£32-£36 WB&B£79-£107 WBDi£99-£132 LDO 3pm
Lic CTV 3P
Credit Cards ① ③ £

⊢⊶**GH** QQQ **Cranmore** 89 Av Rd TQ2 5LH ☎(0803) 298488
Ken and Margaret Silver have totally refurbished their attractive semi detached house. The open plan public areas have a Tudor theme and the bedrooms are well equipped with orthopaedic beds. Little personal touches make guests feel at home.
8rm(4⇌🛏4hc)(2fb) CTV in all bedrooms ® ✖ (ex guide dogs)
sB&B£10-£12 dB&B£20-£24
dB&B⇌🛏£24-£28 WB&B£70-£98 WBDi£108.50-£136.50
LDO 5pm
㎜ CTV 4P
Credit Cards ① ③

GH QQQ *Daphne Court Hotel* Lower Warberry Rd TQ1 1QS
☎(0803) 212011
Apr-Oct
This Victorian villa has a heated swimming pool in its gardens. All bedrooms have colour TV and are tastefully furnished. Simple dishes are served in the relaxed dining room and Geoff and Jenny Langley create a welcoming atmosphere.
15rm(2⇌🛏12🛏1hc)(8fb) CTV in all bedrooms ®
✖ (ex guide dogs) LDO 7.30pm
Lic ㎜ CTV 15P ⌁(heated) games room
Credit Cards ③

GH QQ **Devon Court Hotel** Croft Rd TQ2 5UE
☎(0803) 293603
Etr-Oct
The public rooms of a large Victorian house close to the Riviera Centre retain many original features, and some of its comfortable bedrooms have good en suite facilities.
13rm(8🛏5hc)(3fb) CTV in all bedrooms ® ✖ ✱ sB&B£11-£21
dB&B£22-£42
dB&B🛏£26-£46 WB&B£77-£133 WBDi£98-£154 LDO 4.30pm
Lic ㎜ CTV 14P ⌁(heated)
Credit Cards ① ③ £

⊢⊶**GH** Q **Durlstone** 156 Av Rd TQ2 5LQ ☎(0803) 212307
This semidetached guesthouse, with its own car park, is a short walk from the town centre and beaches. The lounge and dining room are warm and comfortable and the bedrooms are simply furnished. A relaxed atmosphere prevails.
6hc (1fb) CTV in all bedrooms ® sB&B£10-£12
dB&B£20-£24 WB&B£67-£80 WBDi£97-£110 LDO 5pm
㎜ CTV 7P
£

GH QQQ **Elmdene** Rathmore Rd TQ2 6NZ ☎(0803) 294940
rs Oct-Mar
Situated near the cricket field and convenient for the station, this spacious detached Victorian house retains many original features in the public areas and in the modern and comfortable bedrooms.
12rm(3⇌🛏2fb) CTV in all bedrooms ® ✱
sB&B£15-£20 sB&B⇌🛏£18-£23 dB&B£30-£40
dB&B⇌🛏£36-£46 WB&B£95-£120 WBDi£135-£170 LDO 6pm
Lic ㎜ CTV 12P nc3yrs
Credit Cards ① ③ £

⊢⊶**GH** QQ **Exmouth View Hotel** St Albans Rd, Babbacombe Down TQ1 3LG ☎(0803) 327307
This large family hotel has a commanding view overlooking Barracombe. Extensive improvements have increased the comfort in the public rooms and provided modern en suite facilities.
32rm(19⇌🛏13hc)(9fb) CTV in all bedrooms ®
sB&B£12.95-£23.75 sB&B⇌🛏£14.95-£25.75
dB&B£25.90-£47.50
dB&B⇌🛏£29.90-£51.50 (incl dinner) WB&B£75-£151.50
WBDi£88.50-£179 LDO 6.30pm
Lic ㎜ CTV 25P
Credit Cards ① ③ £

Craig Court Hotel

**10 Ash Hill Road, Castle Circus,
Torquay TQ1 3HZ
Telephone: Torquay (0803) 294400**

A detached, listed building, quiet, facing south and only 200 yards from the town centre. Craig Court has a lovely garden, ample car parking and offers every comfort for an enjoyable and relaxed holiday. Ensuite, ground floor and family bedrooms.

Superb food with a choice of menu, a large comfortable lounge with colour TV and a cosy licensed bar overlooking the garden.

Resident Proprietors: Joyce & David Anning

SELECTED

GH Q Q Q Q **Glenorleigh Hotel** 26 Cleveland Rd
TQ2 5BE ☎(0803) 292135
6 Jan-14 Oct & Xmas

*A regular award winner, this friendly family hotel offers a
flower filled garden with an inviting swimming pool. Inside,
the cosy dining room is complemented by a comfortable bar
that has live entertainment and a dance floor. The bedrooms
are freshly decorated and beautifully kept, while some of the
general bathrooms have wirlpool baths. Michael and Maureen
Rhodes take great care of their guests, who enjoy the sociable
atmosphere.*

16rm(9♪7hc)(5fb) ® ✕ (ex guide dogs) sB&B£17-£20
sB&B♪£19-£22 dB&B£34-£40
dB&B♪£38-£44 WBDi£121-£184 (wkly only Jul-Aug &
Xmas) LDO 6pm
Lic ⊕ CTV 10P ⇌(heated) solarium pool table

GH Q Q *Ingoldsby Hotel* 1 Chelston Rd TQ2 6PT
☎(0803) 607497

*Standing in its own grounds away from the town centre, this hotel
is run by friendly, welcoming proprietors. Most of the bedrooms
have en suite facilities and there are comfortable, simple public
areas. A table d'hôte menu is offered.*

15rm(2⇌6♪7hc)(5fb) ® ✕ (ex guide dogs) LDO 7pm
Lic ⊕ CTV 15P
Credit Cards ①③

⊢▸◂GH Q **Jesmond Dene Private Hotel** 85 Abbey Rd TQ2 5NN
☎(0803) 293062
rs Oct-Apr

*Located within walking distance of the town centre, this pleasant
guesthouse offers comfortable accommodation that is ideal for the
family. During the summer months, evening dinners are available
for guests.*

11hc (3fb) ® sB&B£11-£14
dB&B£22-£28 WB&B£66-£77 WBDi£82-£95 LDO noon
⊕ CTV 3P
£

GH Q *Lindum Hotel* Abbey Rd TQ2 5NP ☎(0803) 292795
Mar-Nov

*Close to the promenade and town centre, this spacious Victorian
house has well-furnished bedrooms and public rooms plus a cosy
bar.*

20rm(1⇌10♪9hc)(3fb) CTV in all bedrooms ® LDO 7.15pm
Lic ⊕ CTV 14P

GH Q Q Q **Mapleton Hotel** St Lukes Rd North TQ2 5PD
☎(0803) 292389

*Surrounded by its own grounds, with glorious views across the bay,
this hotel extends a warm welcome to its guests and provides
attractive and comfortable rooms. A choice of home-cooked dishes
is available from the table d'hôte menu.*

10rm(1⇌6♪3hc)(3fb) CTV in all bedrooms ®
✕ (ex guide dogs) sB&B£18.50-£22 dB&B£37-£44
dB&B⇌♪£41-£49.50 (incl dinner) WB&B£110-£130
WBDi£125-£160 LDO 6.30pm
Lic ⊕ 10P nc5yrs
Credit Cards ①③

GH Q *Marlow Hotel* 23 Belgrave Rd TQ2 5HU
☎(0803) 292833

*This attractive, Victorian terraced house stands on the main road
leading to the seafront, close to the Riviera Centre. The bedrooms
are compact and well equipped.*

12rm(2♪10hc)(4fb) LDO 4pm
Lic ⊕ CTV 2P nc5yrs

GH Q Q Q **Olivia Court** Upper Braddons Hill Rd TQ1 1HD
☎(0803) 292595

*This picturesque property is in a quiet residential area close to the
town centre. The bedrooms are tastefully decorated, while the
lounge and bar offer a warm, relaxed atmosphere. Meals are
served in the elegant dining room.*

16rm(4⇌5♪7hc)(2fb)⊬in 4 bedrooms CTV in all bedrooms
® sB&Bfr£15 dB&Bfr£30
dB&B⇌♪fr£34 WB&Bfr£104.50 WBDifr£147.50 LDO 7pm
Lic ⊕ CTV 4P
Credit Cards ①③ £

GH Q Q Q **Pencarrow Hotel** 64 Windsor Rd TQ1 1SZ
☎(0803) 293080

13rm(8♪5hc)(2fb) CTV in all bedrooms ® sB&Bfr£14
sB&B♪fr£16 dB&Bfr£28
dB&B♪fr£32 WB&Bfr£88 WBDifr£105 (wkly only Jul & Aug)
LDO 6pm
Lic CTV 8P games room
£

GH Q Q **The Porthcressa Hotel** 28 Perinville Road,
Babbacombe TQ1 3NZ ☎(0803) 327268

12hc (3fb) TV in all bedrooms ® ✕ (ex guide dogs) ✳
sB&B£12.50-£13.50
dB&B£25-£27 WB&B£70-£85 WBDi£90-£120 (wkly only Jul-
Aug) LDO 8pm
Lic ⊕ CTV 6P

GH Q Q Q **Rawlyn House Hotel** Rawlyn Road, Chelston
TQ2 6PL ☎(0803) 605208
Mar-Oct & Xmas

17rm(2⇌10♪5hc)(3fb) CTV in all bedrooms ® ✕
sB&B£21-£25 sB&B⇌♪£24-£28 dB&B£42-£50
dB&B⇌♪£48-£56 (incl dinner) WB&B£133-£182
WBDi£144-£195 LDO 7.15pm
Lic ⊕ 15P ⇌(heated) games room badminton
£

GH Q Q Q **Richwood Hotel** 20 Newton Rd TQ2 5BZ
☎(0803) 293729

*Open all year round, this hotel is ideal for families, with cosy
bedrooms that are brightly decorated and furnished. It has an
attractive bar and an elegant lounge, with meals available in the
relaxed dining room.*

21rm(3⇌11♪7hc)(9fb) CTV in all bedrooms ® ✳
sB&B£13-£21 sB&B⇌♪£15-£23 dB&B£26-£42
dB&B⇌♪£30-£46 WB&B£78-£147 WBDi£92-£159 (wkly only
mid summer) LDO 6.30pm
Lic ⊕ CTV 12P ⇌(heated) pool table games room
Credit Cards ①③ £

GH Q Q **Riva Lodge** 26 Croft Rd TQ2 5UE ☎(0803) 292614

25rm(15⇌♪10hc)(11fb) CTV in all bedrooms ® ✳
sB&B£12.65-£18.50
dB&B£25.30-£37 WB&B£68.50-£114.50 LDO 4pm
Lic ⊕ 14P ⇌(heated) snooker pool table darts
Credit Cards ①③

GH Q Q Q *Seaway Hotel* Chelston Rd TQ2 6PU
☎(0803) 605320

*This spacious, Edwardian semidetached house, with its attractive
garden and sun terrace, is close to the railway station and beach.
The bedrooms are compact and well equipped, and the public
rooms are pleasant.*

14rm(1⇌7♪6hc)(3fb) ✕ LDO 7pm
Lic ⊕ CTV 14P ♨
Credit Cards ③

⊢▸◂GH Q Q Q **Sevens Hotel** 27 Morgan Av TQ2 5RR
☎(0803) 293523

*Supervised by resident proprietors, this small hotel is in a quiet
avenue within walking distance of the town and seafront. The
simply appointed bedrooms are comfortable, and there is a
spacious bar where guests can play pool and darts.*

12rm(3♠9hc)(3fb) ✗ sB&B£11-£14 dB&B£22-£28
dB&B♠£27-£33 WB&B£77-£98 WBDi£101-£126 LDO
4.30pm
Lic ♐ CTV 10P
£

▸◂GH Ⓠ **Skerries Private Hotel** 25 Morgan Av TQ2 5RR
☎(0803) 293618
*Family run, this cosy private hotel has comfortable public rooms
and well-maintained, compact bedrooms. It is conveniently close
to the town centre and has parking facilities.*
12hc (3fb) CTV in 9 bedrooms Ⓡ sB&B£10.50-£15
dB&B£21-£30 WB&B£70-£100 WBDi£101.50-£126 LDO 2pm
Lic ♐ CTV 7P
£

GH ⓆⓆ *Southbank Hotel* 15/17 Belgrave Rd TQ2 5HU
☎(0803) 296701
Closed Xmas
*Convenient for shops, beaches and entertainment, Southbank has
simple bedrooms with some good en suite facilities. There is a lively
bar and a quiet lounge on the lower ground floor where 3 dining
rooms serving table d'hôte menus are situated.*
20rm(7⇆4♠9hc)(3fb) CTV in 18 bedrooms TV in 1 bedroom
Ⓡ LDO 5pm
Lic ♐ TV 14P
Credit Cards ①③

GH Ⓠ **Torbay Rise** Old Mill Rd TQ2 6HL ☎(0803) 605541
Apr-Oct
15rm(9⇆5♠1hc)(2fb) CTV in all bedrooms Ⓡ (wkly only Jul
& Aug) LDO 11am
Lic 8P ⇌(heated)
Credit Cards ①③£

GH Ⓠ *Torcroft Hotel* Croft Rd TQ2 5UE ☎(0803) 298292
*Friendly private hotel conveniently positioned for sea and town
centre. Compact modern accommodation.*
21rm(6♠15hc)(6fb) Ⓡ ✗ LDO 4pm
Lic CTV 15P

GH ⓆⓆⓆ **Tregantle Hotel** 64 Bampfylde Rd TQ2 5AY
☎(0803) 297494
Closed 3 wks during Dec-Jan
*Close to the Riviera Centre, this spacious detached house has
comfortable public areas and bright, modern bedrooms – some with
en suite facilities. Owners Bernard and Rosemary Sellick provide
friendly and attentive service, and their background as
restaurateurs ensures good quality, imaginative food.*
10⇆♠ (3fb) CTV in all bedrooms Ⓡ ✗ ✳ sB&B⇆♠£18-£23
dB&B⇆♠£36-£46 WB&B£122-£154 WBDi£162-£188 LDO
5pm
Lic ♐ CTV 10P nc7yrs
Credit Cards ①③£

GH ⓆⓆⓆ *Villa Marina Hotel* Cockington Ln, Livermead
TQ2 6QU ☎(0803) 605440
Apr-Oct
*In Cockington Lane close to Livermead Beach, this modern hotel
offers well-equipped bedrooms and open plan public areas. Ideally
suited to the lively holidaymaker, there is also a good outdoor
heated swimming pool with a sunbathing area.*
26rm(20⇆4♠2hc)(6fb) CTV in all bedrooms Ⓡ LDO 6.45pm
Lic ♐ CTV 20P
Credit Cards ①③

GH ⓆⓆ **Westgate Hotel** Falkland Rd TQ2 5JP
☎(0803) 295350
11♠ (2fb) CTV in all bedrooms Ⓡ ✗ ✳ sB&B♠£15.50-£18.50
dB&B♠£31-£37 WB&B£102-£123 WBDi£150-£170 LDO
10pm ▶

Lic CTV 12P nc5yrs
Credit Cards 1 3 £

TORRINGTON, GREAT Devon Map 02 SS42

GH QQ **Smytham Manor** EX38 8PU (2m S A386)
☎Torrington(0805) 22110
Mar-Oct
A campsite and self-catering cabins stand in the 15 acres surrounding this manor house. The bedrooms are simply appointed and public areas, which are also enjoyed by those using the campsite, include a TV lounge and bar lounge.
6rm(3⇨1♠2hc) ® ✱ sB&B£11-£13 sB&B⇨♠£15-£17 dB&B£22-£26
dB&B⇨♠£30-£34 WB&B£70-£110 WBDi£85-£160 LDO 9pm
Lic ⴱ CTV 14P ⌿(heated) croquet mini golf table tennis games room
Credit Cards 1 3

FH Q Mrs E J Watkins **Lower Hollam** *(SS501161)* Little Torrington EX38 8QS (on unclass rd 3m S of Torrington off A386) ☎(0805) 23253
Mar-Oct
Historic house situated in a peaceful, picturesque position, offering good play facilities for children.
3hc (2fb)⊬in all bedrooms ® ✖ (ex guide dogs) ✱
WB&B£60-£72 WBDi£84-£96 LDO 5pm
CTV 3P 220 acres beef cereal sheep
£

TOTLAND BAY

See **WIGHT, ISLE OF**

TOTNES Devon Map 03 SX86

See also Harberton

> ### SELECTED
>
> GH QQQQ **The Old Forge** Seymour Place TQ9 5AY
> ☎(0803) 862174
> rs Xmas wk
> *An attractive licensed property standing in a walled garden, The Old Forge is over 600 years' old and of great historic interest. Peter Allnutt runs the smithy/workshop and many of his creations are for sale. His wife Jeannie runs the bed and breakfast establishment which has comfortable and well-equipped bedrooms, some with en suite facilities. Special diets are catered for in the Tudor-style dining room, and cream teas are served on summer afternoons.*
> 10rm(6⇨♠4hc)(4fb)⊬in all bedrooms CTV in all bedrooms ® ✖ (ex guide dogs) sB&B£27-£30
> sB&B⇨♠£35-£40 dB&Bfr£35
> dB&B⇨♠£40-£45 WB&B£108-£143
> Lic ⴱ CTV 8P ♣ badminton putting
> Credit Cards 1 3 £

FH QQQ Mrs G J Veale **Broomborough House** *(SX793601)* Broomsborough Dr TQ9 5LU ☎(0803) 863134
Mar-Nov
Spacious, manor house building in hilly parkland with views of Dartmoor and the surrounding countryside. Games room and local game fishing.
3hc (1fb) CTV in all bedrooms ® ✖ ✱ sB&Bfr£16
dB&Bfr£32 WB&Bfr£108
Lic ⴱ CTV 0P ⌿ games room small lake 600 acres arable beef dairy

---

Visit your local AA Centre.

TOTTENHILL Norfolk Map 09 TF61

GH QQ **Oakwood House Private Hotel** PE33 0RH
☎Kings Lynn(0553) 810256
Just 5 miles south of King's Lynn, this family-run hotel is set in very attractive lawns, woodland and gardens. Bedrooms are very comfortable and well equipped.
7rm(5⇨♠2hc)Annexe 3⇨♠ CTV in all bedrooms ®
sB&Bfr£23 sB&B⇨♠fr£33
dB&B⇨♠fr£44 WB&B£154-£231 WBDi£190-£270 LDO 8.30pm
Lic ⴱ 20P
Credit Cards 1 3

TREARDDUR BAY Gwynedd Map 06 SH27

GH QQ **Highground Hotel** Off Ravenspoint Rd LL65 2YY
☎(0407) 860078
Closed 19 Dec-4 Jan
Enjoying a superb location overlooking the sea, this hotel is privately owned and offers comfortable accommodation and value for money.
7rm(2⇨1♠4hc)(1fb) CTV in all bedrooms ® ✖
sB&B£14.50-£16 dB&B£29-£32
dB&B⇨♠£35-£38 WB&B£101.50-£122.50 WBDi£168-£189 LDO noon
Lic ⴱ 7P
Credit Cards 1 3 £

⊢⊣GH QQ **Moranedd Guest House** Trearddur Rd LL65 2UE
☎(0407) 860324
This well-furnished house is family run and stands in its own delightful gardens. The bedrooms are friendly and there is a comfortable lounge. Good home cooking is provided.
6hc (1fb) ® sB&Bfr£12 dB&Bfr£24 LDO 5pm
Lic ⴱ CTV 10P
£

TRECASTLE Powys Map 03 SN82

INN QQQ *Castle Hotel* LD3 8UH
☎Sennybridge(087482) 354 & 669
Charming and thoughtfully furnished Georgian building offering good food and excellent modern bedrooms.
9rm(3⇨1♠3hc)(2fb) CTV in all bedrooms ® LDO 9.30pm
ⴱ 30P
Credit Cards 1 3

TREGARON Dyfed Map 03 SN65

FH QQ Mrs M J Cutter **Neuadd Las Farm Country Guest House** *(SN663620)* SY25 6LG ☎(0974) 298905
Set in its own grounds, with panoramic views of the Cambrian Mountains, this cosy guesthouse is just 1 mile from the town, off the Aberystwyth road. Private fishing is available, and the Cors Caron Nature Reserve is nearby.
4rm(2⇨1♠1hc)(2fb) CTV in 1 bedroom ®
dB&B£32-£36 WB&B£112-£126 WBDi£161-£175 LDO 9pm
ⴱ CTV 10P ⌿ 25 acres mixed

TRENEAR (nr Helston) Cornwall & Isles of Scilly Map 02 SW63

FH Q Mrs G Lawrance **Longstone** *(SW662319)* TR13 0HG
☎Helston(0326) 572483
Mar-Nov
Well-appointed farmhouse set in beautiful countryside. Facilities include a playroom and sun lounge.
5hc (2fb) ✱ sB&B£11-£12
dB&B£22-£24 WB&B£70-£80 WBDi£100-£115 LDO 4pm
ⴱ CTV 6P 62 acres dairy
£

TRESAITH Dyfed Map **02** SN25

GH Q Q Q *Bryn Berwyn* SA43 2JG ☎Aberporth(0239) 811126
Feb-23 Dec
*Just 7 minutes' walk from the beach, this country guesthouse has
lovely sea views. There is a comfortable lounge and all of the
bedrooms have been completely refurbished to provide very good
accommodation. The Chamberlain family are very hospitable and
make guests feel very much at home.*
5hc (2fb) CTV in 6 bedrooms ® ✗ (ex guide dogs) LDO 6pm
Lic ⬜ CTV 9P pitch & putt

TREVONE Cornwall & Isles of Scilly Map **02** SW87

GH Q Q *Coimbatore Hotel* West View PL28 8RD
☎Padstow(0841) 520390
*Set in its own gardens at the end of a cul-de-sac, this comfortable
hotel is just 150 yards from Trevone beach.*
8rm(5➤3hc)(2fb) ® LDO 4.30pm
Lic CTV 4P 6🛶
Credit Cards ⬜1⬜ ⬜3⬜

SELECTED

GH Q Q Q Q **Green Waves Private Hotel** PL28 8RD
☎Padstow(0841) 520114
Etr-Oct
*In a quiet residential area, only a few minutes from 2 beaches,
one of which has a natural bathing pool, this hotel has well-
equipped, comfortable rooms, some with lovely coastal views.
There is a small bar for residents, a very comfortable lounge
and a billiard room. Mrs Chellew supervises the kitchen, and
has a good reputation for her meals and homemade bread. A
selective wine list complements her cooking skills.*
▶

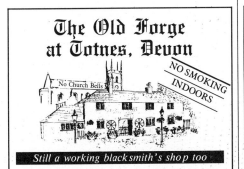

20rm(15🚿5hc)(4fb) CTV in all bedrooms [R] ✱ sB&Bfr£15 dB&Bfr£30
dB&B🚿fr£34 WB&Bfr£105 WBDifr£125 LDO 7pm
Lic ♨ 17P nc4yrs half size snooker table
See advertisement under PADSTOW on page 287

TRINITY

See **JERSEY under CHANNEL ISLANDS**

TROON Cornwall & Isles of Scilly Map **02** SW63

⊢⊣**GH [Q] Sea View** TR14 9JH ☎Praze(0209) 831260
Closed Dec
7hc (3fb)🚭in all bedrooms [R] sB&B£10-£14
dB&B£20-£28 WB&B£62-£90 WBDi£97-£125 LDO 6pm
♨ CTV 8P 🏊(heated)
[£]

TROTTON West Sussex Map **04** SU82

FH [Q][Q] Mrs J R Field **Mill** *(SU832224)* GU31 5EL
☎Midhurst(0730) 813080
This 1930s farmhouse, situated on a working farm in a slightly elevated position, overlooks attractive open countryside. The house has a comfortable family atmosphere, with open fires and an elegant lounge. The bedrooms are cosy and well equipped.
2hc (1fb)🚭in all bedrooms CTV in all bedrooms [R]
🚫 (ex guide dogs) ✱ sB&B£15 dB&B£25-£30
♨ CTV 8P 🎾(grass)15 acres sheep beef
[£]

TROUTBECK (near Keswick) Cumbria Map **11** NY32

⊢⊣**FH [Q][Q]** Mrs A Bird **Askew Rigg** *(NY371280)* CA11 0SZ
☎Threlkeld(07687) 79638
A good standard of comfort and hospitality is offered at this typical lakeland farmhouse. It is to be found just off the A66 after taking the signs for Mungrisdale.
3rm(2hc)(2fb) [R] sB&B£12-£15 dB&B£24-£30 WB&B£84-£105
♨ CTV 4P 200 acres beef sheep

FH [Q][Q] Mr & Mrs A F Bew **Lane Head** *(NY375271)*
CA11 0SY ☎Threlkeld(07687) 79220
Mar-Oct
Situated on the A66 between Penrith and Keswick, this farmhouse offers a good all round standard of accommodation. Set in open countryside, it features original beams, good lounges and friendly services.
7rm(3🛁1🚿3hc)(1fb) CTV in 6 bedrooms [R] 🚫 (ex guide dogs)
sB&Bfr£17 sB&B🛁🚿fr£21 dB&Bfr£30
dB&B🛁🚿£37-£38 WB&B£114-£142 WBDi£170-£198 LDO 10.30am
Lic ♨ CTV 10P 🏇 110 acres non-working
[£]

TRURO Cornwall & Isles of Scilly Map **02** SW84

⊢⊣**GH [Q][Q][Q] Lands Vue** Three Burrows TR4 8JA
☎(0872) 560242
Closed Xmas & New Year
Mr and Mrs Hutchings take pride in their comfortable accommodation, warm relaxed atmosphere and good home cooking. To find Lands Vue from the A30, take the A390 then the first left turn (signposted Tregevethan). The house is surrounded by lovely gardens and beautiful countryside.
3hc Annexe 1🚿 TV in 1 bedroom [R] 🚫 (ex guide dogs)
sB&B£11-£14 sB&B🚿£12-£15 dB&B£22-£28
dB&B🚿£24-£30 WB&B£77-£105 WBDi£129.50-£157.50 LDO 5pm
♨ CTV 6P nc8 yrs 🏊croquet
[£]

TUNBRIDGE WELLS (ROYAL) Kent Map **05** TQ53

GH [Q][Q][Q] Firwood 89 Frant Rd TN2 5LP ☎(0892) 511624
FAX (0892) 25596
10🛁 (2fb) CTV in all bedrooms 🚫 ✱ sB&B🛁£48 dB&B🛁£60
♨ CTV 16P
Credit Cards [1] [2] [3] [5] [£]

TWEEDSMUIR Borders *Peebleshire* Map **11** NT02

SELECTED

GH [Q][Q][Q][Q] Menzion Farmhouse ML12 6QR
☎(08997) 247
Traditional comfort and tranquility are offered at this tastefully converted farmhouse which nestles among hills just off the A701 – a remote setting but with easy access to the A74, Edinburgh, Glasgow and Carlisle. Guests here are made very welcome and comfortable, and an interesting 5-course menu changes daily. Although there is no licence, guests are welcome to supply their own wines.
4hc [R] 🚫 sB&Bfr£17 dB&Bfr£30 LDO 24hrs prior
♨ CTV 12P nc12yrs croquet
[£]

TWO BRIDGES Devon Map **02** SX67

GH [Q][Q][Q] Cherrybrook Hotel PL20 6SP
☎Tavistock(0822) 88260
Closed 20 Dec-4 Jan
With panoramic views across the moors, this secluded house has an attractive, comfortable bar lounge. A television is available in the bedrooms on request. There is a good choice of well-cooked dishes and a fine selection of local cheeses.
7rm(6🚿1hc)(2fb) CTV in all bedrooms [R]
sB&B🚿£20.70-£22.50
dB&B🚿£41.40-£45 WB&B£145 WBDi£207 LDO 7.15pm
Lic ♨ 12P
[£]

TWYNHOLM Dumfries & Galloway *Kirkcudbrightshire*
Map **11** NX65

SELECTED

GH [Q][Q][Q][Q] Fresh Fields DG6 4PB ☎(05576) 221
Closed mid Nov-Dec
This charming house stands within its own gardens amid attractive countryside. The accommodation is tastefully appointed with many thoughtful extras. The home cooked meals can be especially recommended, and guests are assured of a warm welcome.
5🚿 🚭in 2 bedrooms [R] sB&B🚿£32-£34
dB&B🚿£64-£68 (incl dinner) WB&B£140 WBDi£224
LDO 5.30pm
Lic ♨ CTV 10P

TYWARDREATH Cornwall & Isles of Scilly Map **02** SX05

GH [Q][Q][Q] ***Elmswood*** Tehidy Rd, Tywardreath Park
PL24 2QD ☎Par(072681) 4221
Home cooking and friendly service are provided by the proprietor of this comfortable guesthouse, which is an easy car ride from secluded Cornish beaches. Tastefully appointed public areas complement the bedrooms, some of which have en suite facilities.
6rm(2🚿4hc)(2fb) CTV in 4 bedrooms LDO noon
Lic ♨ CTV 8P

[£] Remember to use the money-off vouchers.

UCKFIELD East Sussex Map **05** TQ41

SELECTED

GH [Q][Q][Q][Q] Hooke Hall 250 High St TN22 1EN
☎(0825) 761578 Telex no 95228 FAX (0825) 768025
Closed Xmas
Delightfully furnished and decorated, using Mrs Percy's skill as an interior designer, this appealing Queen Anne house has an atmosphere of warmth and elegance. Each room, named after a famous mistress or lover, has its own individuality and charm, while being as well appointed as the lounge and attractive restaurant. Although the restaurant is usually only open on Friday and Saturday evenings, private dinners or other meals may be arranged.
6rm(5🛁1hc) CTV in all bedrooms [R] ✗ sB&B🛁£40-£80 dB&B🛁£55-£90 LDO 8.30pm
Lic ♨ 6P nc10yrs
Credit Cards [1] [3]

UFFCULME Devon Map **03** ST01

FH [Q][Q] Mrs M D Farley ***Houndaller*** *(ST058138)* EX15 3ET
☎Craddock(0884) 40246
The Farley family's farmhouse stands on the A38, a few hundred yards from Junction 27 of the M5. Comfortable bedrooms are complemented by spacious public areas, and guests are treated as part of the family.
3hc (2fb) [R] LDO 6pm
CTV 3P 1🚗 176 acres arable beef dairy sheep
Credit Cards [1] [2] [3] [5]

ULLINGSWICK Hereford & Worcester Map **03** SO54

SELECTED

GH [Q][Q][Q][Q] The Steppes HR1 3JG
☎Hereford(0432) 820424
Closed 2 wks before Xmas & 2 wks after New Year
The Steppes is a charming small hotel situated in a tiny hamlet, yet close to the A417, and is ideal for touring this beautiful area. The rooms in the main house are more compact than the 2 courtyard cottage rooms which are excellent. The house has a wealth of character from the well-appointed dining room to the fascinating cellar bar which has been converted from the former cider cellar and dairy. An appetising gourmet menu which changes daily in addition to an à la carte menu are on offer as well as traditional breakfast items, the more unusual, such as devilled kidneys, will set you up for the day.
3🚿 Annexe 2🛁🚿 (1fb) CTV in all bedrooms [R] ✻
dB&B🛁🚿£80-£90 (incl dinner) WBDi£259-£273 LDO 6.30pm
Lic ♨ 8P nc10yrs
[£]

UNDERBARROW Cumbria Map **07** SD49

FH [Q][Q][Q] Mrs D M Swindlehurst **Tranthwaite Hall** *(SD469930)* LA8 8HG ☎Crosthwaite(04488) 285
Approached by a long farm track, this pleasant house dates back to the 15th century and is part of a working farm. The accommodation is attractive and well maintained and the comfortable lounge features oak beams and an original stove.
2hc (1fb) [R] ✗ (ex guide dogs) dB&B£25-£27 WB&B£70-£85
♨ CTV 2P 200 acres dairy sheep

Book as early as possible for busy holiday periods.

CHERRYBROOK HOTEL
TWO BRIDGES
YELVERTON
DEVON PL20 6SP

Telephone: (0822) 88260

Set in the heart of the National Park, this early 19th century, family run hotel has a splendidly central position for a Dartmoor holiday. All bedrooms have own private facilities and the views from the front are magnificent.
There is good quality home cooked food, where possible using fresh local produce, including fresh herbs from the garden. There is always a choice on the menu.

Trevispian-Vean Farm
St. Erme, Truro, Cornwall TR4 9BL
Telephone: Truro 79514

English Tourist Board
AA RECOMMENDED

Trevispian-Vean is an attractive old Farmhouse nestling in the Cornish countryside. It has recently been extended to give increased lounge facilities and most bedrooms now have en suite accommodation. Other facilities include a fishing lake, games room and of course the day to day feeding of the animals on this 300 acre farm. The meals are prepared with great care by Bridget. The premises are licensed and drinks are served with meals.

UPPER HULME Staffordshire Map **07** SK06

FH |Q||Q| Mrs J Lomas *Keekorok Lodge (SK005616)* ST13 8UA
☎Blackshaw(053834) 218
Etr-Oct
*Modernised stone-built house with views over Titlesworth
Reservoir, well known locally for fishing. It is situated 1 mile north
west of the village, towards the local landmark of The Roaches.*
3rm(2hc) ✷ LDO 10am
🍴 CTV 8P nc2yrs 15 acres arable

UPTON PYNE Devon Map **03** SX99

⊢←**FH** |Q||Q| Mrs Y M Taverner *Pierce's (SK910977)* EX5 5JA
☎Exeter(0392) 841252
25 May-Aug
*Set in the centre of the village between Exeter and Crediton,
Pierce's Farm has 2 bedrooms which have wash basins and share a
bathroom. The attractive lounge and dining room are tastefully
furnished, and Mrs Taverner is a very friendly host.*
2hc (2fb) ® ✷ sB&B£12 WB&B£78
🍴 CTV 2P 300 acres mixed
£

UPTON UPON SEVERN Hereford & Worcester
Map **03** SO84

GH |Q||Q||Q| **Pool House** WR8 0PA ☎(06846) 2151
Closed Dec
*Pool House is a lovely Queen Anne residence situated close to
Upton-upon- Severn. The gardens area delightful and lead down to
the River Severn. Accommodation is attractive, well furnished and
spacious.*
9rm(3⇆3♠3hc)(2fb)⅍in all bedrooms CTV in 1 bedroom ✷
sB&B£19-£23 sB&B⇆♠£28-£32 dB&B£32-£37
dB&B⇆♠£42-£48 LDO 6.30pm
Lic CTV 20P ✔
Credit Cards |1||3|

UTTOXETER Staffordshire Map **07** SK03

GH |Q||Q||Q| **Hillcrest** 3 Leighton Rd ST14 8BL ☎(0889) 564627
Closed Xmas Day
*Perched on a hill on the edge of town, this friendly family-run hotel
has well- equipped accommodation, some rooms having en suite
facilities.*
7♠ (7fb) CTV in all bedrooms ® ✷ sB&B♠£24-£26
dB&B♠£32-£34 LDO 4pm
Lic 🍴 CTV 10P 2🐾
Credit Cards |1||2||3| £

VENN OTTERY Devon Map **03** SY09

GH |Q||Q||Q| *Venn Ottery Barton Country Hotel* EX11 1RZ
☎Ottery St Mary(040481) 2733
*Situated in the centre of this charming village, this hotel, parts of
which date back to 1530, retains some original features while
providing modernised, well- equipped bedrooms.*
16rm(5⇆6♠5hc)(3fb) ® LDO 7.30pm
Lic 🍴 CTV 20P large games room
Credit Cards |1||3|
See advertisement under OTTERY ST MARY on page 280

VENTNOR

See **WIGHT, ISLE OF**

VOWCHURCH Hereford & Worcester Map **03** SO33

SELECTED

GH |Q||Q||Q||Q| **The Croft Country House** HR2 0QE
☎Peterchurch(0981) 550226
*The Croft is a delightful small country house situated in the
centre of the beautiful Golden Valley on the B4348 between
Ross on Wye and Hay on Wye. The house dates back from
the 18th century and has been furnished with comfort in mind.
Rooms are all en suite and have good modern facilities. There
is a charming lounge area and a dining room and conservatory
in which to enjoy meals prepared by the proprietor. The lounge
looks out towards the Black Mountains, with excellent views
at sunset. Lovely gardens are a feature of The Croft, complete
with summerhouse and lily pond. The proprietors ensure that
guests are given a warm welcome.*
5⇆♠ Annexe 3⇆♠ (1fb)⅍in 3 bedrooms CTV in all
bedrooms ® ✷ (ex guide dogs) sB&B⇆♠£20
dB&B⇆♠£40 WB&B£119 WBDi£199.50 LDO 9pm
Lic 🍴 15P 2🐾 nc10yrs croquet lawn
Credit Cards |3| £

WADEBRIDGE Cornwall & Isles of Scilly Map **02** SW97

INN |Q||Q||Q| **Swan Hotel** PL27 7DD ☎(0208) 812526
*Situated in the town centre, the inn has recently been renovated
and offers a spacious and comfortable bar with bar snacks in
addition to the daily special dish. A choice of table d'hôte and à la
carte manus are available. The well-decorated bedrooms are of a
very high standard with good quality furniture. All bedrooms are
en suite and have modern facilities.*
6⇆ (1fb) CTV in all bedrooms ® ✷ (ex guide dogs) ✷
sB&B⇆£20-£30
dB&B⇆£32-£42 WB&B£120-£140 WBDi£150-£170
6P
Credit Cards |1||2||3|

WANSFORD Cambridgeshire Map **04** TL09

INN |Q| **Cross Keys** PE8 6JD ☎Stamford(0780) 782266
2hc Annexe 5hc (2fb) CTV in all bedrooms ® ✷ ✷
sB&B£18-£22
dB&B£36-£40 Bar Lunch £3.75-£8.25alc LDO 9.30pm
🍴 pool table

WARE Hertfordshire Map **05** TL31

INN |Q||Q||Q| **Feathers Hotel** Wadesmill SG1 2TN (Berni/Chef
& Brewer) ☎(0920) 462606
*The Feathers has a busy and very popular bar and 'Berni' carvery.
The bedrooms are all new, compact and attractive with co-
ordinated décor and many extras.*
Annexe 22rm(11⇆4♠7hc) CTV in all bedrooms ®
✷ (ex guide dogs) ✷ sB&B£44.50 sB&B⇆♠£48.50
dB&B£55.50
dB&B⇆♠£59.50 Lunch £8-£15 Dinner £8-£15 LDO 10.30pm
🍴 100P
Credit Cards |1||2||3||5|

WAREHAM Dorset Map **03** SY98

FH |Q||Q| L S Barnes **Luckford Wood** *(SY873865)* East Stoke
BH20 6AW ☎Bindon Abbey(0929) 463098
5rm(1♠2hc)(3fb)⅍in 1 bedroom CTV in 2 bedrooms TV in 2
bedrooms ® sB&B£16-£18 sB&B♠£17-£19 dB&B£26-£30
dB&B♠£28-£34 WB&B£84-£105

Ⅷ CTV 5P 167 acres dairy
Ⓔ

SELECTED

FH 🅠🅠🅠🅠 Mrs J Barnes **Redcliffe** *(SY932866)*
BH20 5BE ☎(0929) 552225
Closed Xmas
To reach this modern farmhouse, that has wonderful views of the River Frome, take the B3075 from Wareham towards Stoborough, and after crossing the river bridge take 3 successive left turns. Three very comfortable bedrooms share a modern bathroom, while downstairs, a sun lounge overlooking the garden complements a family lounge with a television. Breakfast is generally served in the dining room, but is sometimes served on the garden terrace.
4rm(1⇄3hc)↙in 3 bedrooms ✖ (ex guide dogs)
Ⅷ CTV 4P 250 acres dairy mixed

WARLEY West Midlands Map 07 SP08

GH 🅠🅠 **Bearwood Court Hotel** 360-366 Bearwood Rd,
Bearwood B66 4ET ☎021-429 9731
The Doyle family are friendly hosts and are sure to make guests welcome at their hotel, situated on a busy road within easy reach of the city centre. The accommodation varies in size and furnishings, but is well maintained throughout.
24rm(20⇄🅵4hc)(2fb) CTV in all bedrooms Ⓡ
✖ (ex guide dogs) ✳ sB&Bfr£18 sB&B⇄🅵fr£25 dB&Bfr£30
dB&B⇄🅵fr£39 LDO 6pm
Lic Ⅷ CTV 24P
Credit Cards ①③

WARREN STREET (nr Lenham) Kent Map 05 TQ95

INN 🅠🅠🅠 **Harrow** ME17 2ED ☎Maidstone(0622) 858727
Enjoying a good local reputation for its homemade food in the well-appointed restaurant and spacious bar, this establishment also has very well-equipped accommodation, which is furnished in a modern style.
7rm(2⇄4🅵1hc)(1fb) Ⓡ ✖ ✳ sB&B£35-£45 sB&B⇄🅵£45
dB&Bfr£45
dB&B⇄🅵fr£58 Lunch £7-£13&alc Dinner £7-£13&alc LDO 10pm
Ⅷ CTV 40P
Credit Cards ①③

WARRINGTON Cheshire Map 07 SJ68

GH 🅠🅠 **The Kenilworth Hotel** 2 Victoria Rd, Grappenhall
WA4 2EN ☎(0925) 62323
Situated in a pleasant residential area, this detached Victorian house stands on the A50, 2.75 miles from junction 20 of the M6 motorway.
17rm(16🅵1hc)(2fb) CTV in all bedrooms Ⓡ ✳ sB&B£18-£30
sB&B🅵£18-£30 dB&B£30-£42 dB&B🅵£30-£42
Ⅷ CTV 18P
Credit Cards ①③ Ⓔ

WARSASH Hampshire Map 04 SU40

GH 🅠🅠🅠 **Solent View Private Hotel** 33-35 Newtown Rd
SO3 6FY ☎Locks Heath(0489) 572300
Ideally situated for leisure and commercial guests, a friendly and relaxed atmosphere is generated by the owners Anne and Roy Mills. Solent View is situated in the village centre, within short walking distance of the River Hamble. The bedrooms are comfortable and well equipped. A lounge is available for guests, and good freshly cooked breakfasts are served in the dining room cum bar.
6rm(1⇄5🅵) CTV in all bedrooms Ⓡ ✳ sB&B⇄🅵fr£25
dB&B⇄🅵fr£38 LDO noon

Lic Ⅷ CTV 8P
Ⓔ

WARWICK Warwickshire Map 04 SP26

See also **Lighthorne**

GH 🅠🅠 **Austin House** 96 Emscote Rd CV34 5QJ
☎(0926) 493583
Derick and Daphne Edwards offer a modest but well-maintained establishment. Most bedrooms have en suite showers and all have colour televisions. The comfortable ground floor lounge also offers the use of a large colour television.
6rm(4🅵2hc)(3fb) CTV in all bedrooms Ⓡ dB&B£26-£33
dB&B🅵£26-£33 WB&B£91-£115.50
Ⅷ CTV 8P 2🚗

GH 🅠🅠 **Avon** 7 Emscote Rd CV34 4PH ☎(0926) 491367
Small, well-run private hotel on Warwick-Leamington Road. Close to tourist amenities.
7hc (4fb) Ⓡ ✖ ✳ sB&B£12.50-£13 dB&B£25-£26 LDO 8.00pm
Lic Ⅷ CTV 6P 1🚗
Credit Cards ③ Ⓔ

GH 🅠🅠🅠 *Cambridge Villa Private Hotel* 20A Emscote Rd
CV34 4PL ☎(0926) 491169
Closed Xmas
16rm(4🅵12hc)(2fb) CTV in all bedrooms Ⓡ ✖ (ex guide dogs)
LDO 7pm
Lic Ⅷ CTV 16P solarium
Credit Cards ①③

GH 🅠🅠🅠 **The Old Rectory** Sherbourne CV35 8AB (off A46
2m SW) ☎Barford (Warwicks)(0926) 624562
Jan-23 Dec
Tastefully restored house offering very comfortable accommodation and home-cooked food.

▶

7 Emscote Road, Warwick
Tel: (0926) 491367

Lyn & Nobby offer you a warm welcome at their licensed family run guest house. All rooms have tea/coffee making facilities and central heating, some rooms have showers. Other facilities are a cosy bar, guests' TV lounge and a large car park. Interesting menus available at breakfast and dinner. The Avon is a Victorian building and situated within 5 minutes walk to Warwick Castle and the many attractions that the county town has to offer.

7rm(1🛁6🚿)Annexe 7🛁🚿 (2fb) CTV in all bedrooms [R]
sB&B🛁🚿£20-£34 dB&B🛁🚿£32-£50 LDO 3pm
Lic ♨ CTV 10P
[£]

INN [Q][Q] Tudor House West St CV34 6AW ☎(0926) 495447
FAX (0926) 492948

This scheduled Tudor house, still retaining much wattle and daub and timbers, was built in 1472. The bedrooms are of a cosy nature, being equipped with good en suite facilities. Its attractive public rooms are complemented by traditional wholesome food.

11rm(8🛁🚿3hc)(1fb) CTV in all bedrooms [R]
🚫🐕 (ex guide dogs) sB&B£23-£26 sB&B🛁🚿£35-£39
dB&B£48-£54
dB&B🛁🚿£48-£54 Lunch £9.95-£15&alc High tea £3-£4
Dinner £9.95-£15 LDO 10.30pm
♨ 5P ⌂
Credit Cards [1] [2] [3] [5]

See advertisement on page 375

WASHFORD Somerset Map **03** ST04

INN [Q][Q][Q] *Washford* TA23 0PP ☎(0984) 40256

The Quantock and Brendon Hills are easily reached from this roadside inn which is just 6 miles from Minehead. The tastefully modernised bedrooms offer good facilities and a bar menu is available in the busy, attractive public bar.

8🚿 CTV in all bedrooms [R] 🚫🐕 (ex guide dogs) LDO 9pm
♨ 30P nc12yrs
Credit Cards [1] [2] [3] [5]

See advertisement on page 375

WATERHOUSES Staffordshire Map **07** SK05

GH [Q][Q] Croft House Farm Waterfall ST10 3HZ (1m NW unclass) ☎(0538) 308553

THE OLD RECTORY

VICARAGE LANE
SHERBOURNE
NR. WARWICK
CV35 8AB
Tel: (0926) 624562

The Old Rectory is a licensed Georgian country house with a wealth of beams, flagstone floors and Inglenook fireplaces, situated in a gem of an English village yet only one third of a mile from M40, junction 15.

The 14 elegantly appointed ensuite bedrooms provide comfortable easy chairs, colour t.v.'s, and most have antique brass or brass and iron beds. A 17th Century barn conversion provides several suites whilst the detached coach house is ideal for honeymooners.

Hearty English breakfasts are served in a traditional oak dining room with cosy fires in the winter months.

The Coach House

The 17th Century barn conversion

The compact, but well-equipped, cheerful bedrooms enhance the warm and friendly atmosphere at this stone-built house, which lies, surrounded by farmland, in the moorland village of Waterfall.
6hc (2fb) CTV in all bedrooms ® ✠ sB&Bfr£17
dB&Bfr£31 WB&Bfr£108.50 WBDifr£161 LDO 8pm
Lic ꝒꝒ CTV 15P

FH Q Mrs K Watson *Weaver (SK102467)* ST10 3HE
☎Oakamoor(0538) 702271
Solid stone-built 19th-century farm in a hollow of the Weaver Hills.
5rm (3fb) ® ✠ LDO 9am
ꝒꝒ CTV 4P solarium 350 acres beef dairy mixed sheep

INN Q Ye Olde Crown ST10 3HL ☎(0538) 308204
A warm and friendly atmosphere awaits you at this 17th-century village inn on the A523.
7rm(5⇨₃¶2hc)(1fb) CTV in all bedrooms ® ✠ (ex guide dogs)
✻ sB&B£14-£16.50 sB&B⇨₃¶£16.50 dB&B£33
dB&B⇨₃¶£33 Lunch £4.75-£16alc Dinner £4.75-£16alc LDO 10pm
ꝒꝒ 50P
See advertisement under ASHBOURNE

WATERPERRY Oxfordshire Map **04** SP60

FH QQQ Mrs S Fonge **Manor** *(SP628064)* OX9 1LB
☎Ickford(08447) 263
Stone farmhouse standing in large garden, in centre of village. Coarse fishing available.
3hc ✻ sB&B£13.50-£15.50
dB&B£25-£31 WB&B£91-£105 WBDi£147-£168 LDO 10am
ꝒꝒ CTV 4P 160 acres beef sheep poultry
£

WATERROW Somerset Map **03** ST02

INN QQ The Rock TA4 2AX ☎Wiveliscombe(0984) 23293
A 400-year-old inn offering a character bar and modern bedrooms. Situated on the A361 approximately two miles from Wiveliscombe.
6rm(4⇨₃1hc)(1fb) CTV in all bedrooms LDO 10pm
ꝒꝒ CTV 20P
Credit Cards ①③
See advertisement under TAUNTON on page 355

WATFORD Hertfordshire Map **04** TQ19

GH QQQ White House Hotel 26-31 Upton Rd WD1 7EL
☎(0923) 37316 Telex no 8955439 FAX (0923) 33109
Close to town centre, offers well-equipped bedrooms. Ideal for business people.
62⇨₃¶ Annexe 27⇨₃¶ (1fb)⅙in 6 bedrooms CTV in all bedrooms ® ✠ (ex guide dogs) ✻ sB&B⇨₃¶£60-£100
dB&B⇨₃¶£80-£110 WB&B£360-£600 WBDi£465-£705 LDO 9.45pm
Lic lift ꝒꝒ 35P
Credit Cards ①②③£

WEETON Lancashire Map **07** SD33

FH QQ Mr & Mrs J Colligan **High Moor** *(SD388365)*
PR4 3JJ ☎(039136) 273 Due to change to (0253) 836273
Closed Xmas & New Year
A charming and neat farmhouse, where the cooking is largely prepared from farm produce.
2rm (1fb) CTV in all bedrooms ® ✠ ✻
dB&Bfr£20 WB&Bfr£60
ꝒꝒ CTV 10P 7 acres non-working

WELCOMBE Devon Map **02** SS21

FH QQQ Mrs P Tonnicliffe **Henaford Manor** *(SS249187)*
EX39 6HE ☎Morwenstow(028883) 252
Built in the 17th century, this farmhouse has an elegant dining room and comfortable lounge. One of the nicely appointed bedrooms has en suite facilities and all are equipped to modern standards. There is also a self-catering cottage next to the house.
3rm(1⇨₃¶2hc)(1fb) CTV in all bedrooms ® ✠ ✻ dB&Bfr£28
dB&B⇨₃¶fr£30 WBDi£115-£135 LDO 6pm
ꝒꝒ CTV 6P 226 acres dairy mixed
See advertisement under BIDEFORD

WELLINGBOROUGH Northamptonshire Map **04** SP86

GH QQQ Oak House Private Hotel 9 Broad Green NN8 4LE
☎(0933) 71133
Closed Xmas
This substantial guesthouse has en suite shower facilities in its neat, well-equipped rooms. Standing on the former village green, close to the town centre, Oak House is run by caring, professional proprietors.
13rm(12¶1hc)(1fb) CTV in 10 bedrooms ® ✻ sB&B£28
sB&B¶£28 dB&B£38
dB&B¶£38 WB&B£133-£196 WBDi£185.50-£255.50 LDO noon
Lic ꝒꝒ CTV 8P
Credit Cards ①③£

WELLINGTON Shropshire

See **Telford**

WELLINGTON Somerset Map **03** ST12

GH Q *Blue Mantle Hotel* 2 Mantle St TA21 8AW
☎(0823) 662000
Located in the town centre, this is a small and privately owned guesthouse. The accommodation is comfortable and well maintained. There is a small cosy dining room which offers sound English cuisine.
8hc (1fb) CTV in all bedrooms ® LDO 7pm
Lic ꝒꝒ CTV ✗ ⌀ ⌂
Credit Cards ①②③

FH QQQ Mrs N Ash **Pinksmoor Mill House** *(ST109198)*
Pinksmoor TA21 0HO (3m W off A38 'at Beam Bridge Hotel)
☎Greenham(0823) 672361
Closed 23-29 Dec
Part 13th-century property, 3 miles west of Wellington, with neat comfortable accommodation. Original mill house on site.
3rm(2⇨₃¶1hc)(1fb)⅙in all bedrooms CTV in all bedrooms ®
sB&B£17-£17.50 sB&B⇨₃¶£17-£17.50 dB&B£29-£30
dB&B⇨₃¶£29-£30 WB&B£98-£115.50 WBDi£171.50-£189
LDO 4pm
ꝒꝒ CTV 6P 98 acres dairy sheep
£

WELLS Somerset Map **03** ST54

GH QQQ Bekynton House 7 St Thomas St BA5 2UU
☎(0749) 72222
Closed Xmas & New Year
Comfortable, well-appointed accommodation is provided at this well-maintained guesthouse which stands on the fringe of the city centre.

Street plans of certain towns and cities
will be found in a separate section
at the back of the book.

9rm(3🔥6hc)(2fb)⌿in all bedrooms CTV in all bedrooms ® ✗
sB&B£17.50-£19.50 dB&B£31-£33
dB&B🔥£34-£39 WB&B£100-£126
💷 6P nc5yrs
Credit Cards ①③ ⓐ

SELECTED

GH ⓠⓠⓠⓠ **Coach House** Stoberry Park BA5 3AA
☎(0749) 76535
Closed 24-31Dec
Standing in 6 acres of parkland, The Coach House has
splendid views of the city across to Gastonbury Tor. The
spacious bedrooms offer comfortable accommodation and en
suite facilities, and there is a vast open lounge and dining
room. The proprietors are most hospitable.
3⇨⌿in all bedrooms ® ✳ sB&B⇨£23.50
dB&B⇨£29-£32 WB&B£101.50-£164.50
Lic 💷 CTV 6P nc3yrs
ⓐ

GH ⓠⓠ **Tor** 20 Tor St BA5 2US ☎(0749) 72322
This charming 17th-century house, close to the cathedral, is being
thoughtfully restored to provide comfortable accommodation and
yet maintain the house's character. The owners offer a warm
welcome to their guests.
7rm(2🔥5hc)(2fb) ® sB&B£16-£20 dB&B£32-£36
dB&B🔥£36-£42 WB&B£110-£130 WBDi£164-£196 LDO
10am
💷 CTV 11P 1🛏
ⓐ

FH ⓠⓠ Mrs P Higgs **Home** *(ST538442)* Stoppers Ln, Upper
Coxley BA5 1QS (2m SW off A39) ☎(0749) 72434
Closed 2wks Xmas
Situated off the A39, 1.5 miles south west from the city, this
farmhouse offers a friendly welcome from the proprietor, Mrs
Higgs. The comfortable, attractively decorated bedrooms are
adequately equipped and furnished.
7hc (1fb) ✳ sB&B£13.50-£15.50
dB&B£27-£31 WB&B£90-£105
Lic 💷 CTV 12P 15 acres pigs

FH ⓠⓠⓠ Mr & Mrs Gnoyke **Littlewell** *(ST536445)* Coxley
BA5 1QP (2 miles SW on A39) ☎(0749) 77914
Closed Jan
4rm(1⇨3🔥) CTV in 5 bedrooms ® ✗ (ex guide dogs)
sB&B⇨🔥£19.50-£24.50 dB&B⇨🔥£33-£36 LDO 4pm
Lic 💷 4P 4🛏 nc10 yrs 2 acres non-working

⊢⋯**FH** ⓠⓠ Mrs J Gould **Manor** *(ST546474)* Old Bristol Rd,
Upper Milton BA5 3AH (1m W A39 towards Bristol, 200 yds
beyond rdbt) ☎(0749) 73394
Closed Xmas
Part of a large beef farm, this charming house offers traditional
informal hospitality and a relaxing atmosphere together with
comfortable accommodation.
3hc (1fb) ® ✗ (ex guide dogs) sB&B£13-£16
dB&B£24-£30 WB&B£84-£100
💷 CTV 6P 130 acres beef

FH ⓠⓠⓠ Mr & Mrs Frost **Southway** *(ST516423)* Polsham
BA5 1RW (3m SW off A39) ☎(0749) 73396
A warm and cosy atmosphere is found at this charming Georgian
farmhouse. The bedrooms are attractively decorated and well
furnished, and the public rooms are comfortably appointed.
Further upgrading is in progress.
3hc ✗ (ex guide dogs) ✳ sB&B£16-£17 dB&B£26-£27
💷 CTV 5P 170 acres dairy

WELLS-NEXT-THE-SEA Norfolk Map **09** TF94

GH ⓠⓠⓠ **Scarborough House** Clubbs Ln NR23 1DP
☎Fakenham(0328) 710309 & 711661
This Victorian detached house is situated in a quiet lane a few
minutes' walk from the centre, and a mile from the beach. The
accommodation is well equipped and comfortable, the flintstone
restaurant being housed in the former stable block.
7rm(2⇨5hc)(3fb) CTV in all bedrooms ® sB&B£23-£26
sB&B⇨frf£26 dB&B£36
dB&B⇨£42 WB&B£115-£136 WBDi£190-£211
Lic 💷 CTV 8P ⓐ
Credit Cards ③ ⓐ

WELSHPOOL Powys Map **07** SJ20

FH ⓠⓠⓠ Mrs E Jones **Gungrog House** *(SJ235089)* Rhallt
SY21 9HS (1m NE off A458) ☎(0938) 553381
Apr-Oct
Providing good quality bedrooms and public rooms this guesthouse
has superb views from its elevated position over the Severn Valley.
It is reached via a country lane opposite to the junction of the A483
and A458.
3rm(2🔥1hc) ✗ LDO 5pm
💷 CTV 6P 21 acres mixed

FH ⓠⓠ Mr & Mrs M C Payne **Heath Cottage** *(SJ239023)*
Kingswood, Forden SY21 8LX (3m S off A490)
☎Forden(093876) 453
Etr-Oct
This former country pub, just yards away from Offa's Dyke, is run
by the friendly Payne family. There is a comfortable lounge
available for guests, and the bedrooms have recently been improved
with all rooms now having en suite facilities.
3⇨🔥 (1fb) ® ✗ sB&B⇨🔥£14
dB&B⇨🔥£28 WB&B£90 WBDi£139
💷 CTV 4P 6 acres poultry sheep
ⓐ

FH ⓠⓠⓠ Mr & Mrs W Jones **Moat** *(SJ214042)* SY21 8SE
☎(0938) 553179
Apr-Oct
One mile south of Welshpool, this working farm dates back to the
16th century and provides comfortable accommodation. The Jones
family are welcoming and a tennis court and pool table are
available. The River Severn runs through the grounds.
3rm(2🔥1hc)(1fb) CTV in all bedrooms ® ✗ ✳ LDO 2pm
💷 3P ♪(grass)pool table 260 acres dairy
ⓐ

FH ⓠⓠⓠ Mrs F Emberton **Tynllwyn** *(SJ215085)* SY21 9BW
☎(0938) 553175
Providing good comfortable bedrooms and spacious lounge this
large 18th-century farmhouse is situated off the A490 north of
Welshpool with good rural views.
6hc (3fb) CTV in all bedrooms ® ✗ sB&Bfr£14
dB&Bfr£24 WB&Bfr£80 WBDifr£110 LDO 6.30pm
Lic 💷 CTV 150 acres mixed
ⓐ

See advertisement on page 379

WEM Shropshire Map **07** SJ53

FH ⓠⓠⓠ Mrs A P Ashton **Soulton Hall** *(SJ543303)* Soulton
SY4 5RS ☎(0939) 32786
Steeped in history and standing on a site mentioned in the
Domesday Book, this 16th-century manor house features a
pillared courtyard, walled garden and 50 acres of woodland
together with 2 miles of fishing. All bedrooms are spacious and
comfortable with interesting features.
3rm(2⇨1hc)(1fb) CTV in all bedrooms ® LDO 9pm
Lic 💷 4P 2🛏 ⓐ ♪ ∪ 560 acres mixed
See advertisement under SHREWSBURY on page 331

WEST BAGBOROUGH Somerset Map **03** ST13

GH [Q][Q][Q] Higher House TA4 3EF
☎Bishops Lydeard(0823) 432996
Closed Xmas rs Dec-Mar
Nestling on the slopes of the Quantocks, this 17th-century farmhouse has been converted by William and Jo Beaumont to offer 6 attractive bedrooms with good facilities. A three-quarter sized snooker table is provided, as well as an outdoor pool. A set meal is served around a large antique table.
6rm(3🛁1🚿2hc)(1fb) CTV in all bedrooms Ⓡ sB&B£26-£30 sB&B🛁🚿£30-£34 dB&B£35-£37
dB&B🛁🚿£44-£48 LDO 4.30pm
Lic 🍴 CTV 13P 🏊(heated) three quarter snooker table
Credit Cards [1] [3]

INN [Q][Q][Q] Rising Sun TA 4 3EF
☎Bishops Lydeard(0823) 432575 Telex no 94013345
In a peaceful village at the foot of the Quantocks, this inn is within easy reach of motorway routes. The tasteful bedrooms are en suite and provide modern amenities. There is also a bar lounge with log fire and a relaxed atmosphere.
Annexe 4🚿 (1fb) CTV in all bedrooms Ⓡ 🐕 sB&B🚿£30-£35
dB&B🚿£45-£50 WB&B£141.75-£157.50 WBDi£211-£227
Lunch £5-£8 Dinner £6-£12alc LDO 9.30pm
🍴 6P
[£]

WEST BUCKLAND Devon Map **03** SS73

FH [Q][Q] Mrs B J Payne **Huxtable** *(SS666308)* EX32 0SR
☎Filleigh(05986) 254
Closed 25 Dec
The present house was built in 1520 and retains much of its original character and charm. Bedrooms are comfortable and well equipped, and there is a choice of quiet and television lounges. Early children's suppers are served in a separate dining room.
3hc Annexe 3rm(2🛁1hc)(2fb) CTV in 2 bedrooms Ⓡ
🐕 (ex guide dogs) * sB&B🛁£16-£20
dB&B🛁£30-£34 WB&B£94.50-£119 WBDi£164.50-£189 LDO 6pm
🍴 CTV 8P sauna games room 80 acres mixed sheep
[£]

WEST CHILTINGTON West Sussex Map **04** TQ01

FH [Q][Q][Q] Mrs A M Steele **New House** *(TQ091185)*
Broadford Bridge Rd RH20 2LA ☎(0798) 812215
Closed Dec
The standards throughout this 15th-century listed farmhouse are very high. The accommodation comprises traditionally furnished bedrooms, complemented by a cottage-style annexe, and a beamed lounge and breakfast room.
3🛁🚿 (2fb) CTV in all bedrooms Ⓡ 🐕 *
dB&B🛁🚿£36-£44 WB&B£126-£140
CTV 4P 2🚗 nc9yrs 50 acres mixed
[£]

WESTCLIFF-ON-SEA Essex

See **Southend-on-Sea**

WEST DOWN Devon Map **02** SS54

SELECTED

GH [Q][Q][Q][Q] The Long House EX34 8NF
☎Ilfracombe(0271) 863242
mid Mar-mid Nov
The former forge and post office of this sleepy North Devon village have been converted by Pauline and Rob Hart to provide 4 individually furnished bedrooms. The dining room serves a choice of starters and sweets with a set main course – eg poached salmon with asparagus sauce – and in the day it is a tea shop offering a selection of teas, homemade cakes and light meals. There is also a bar lounge and tranquil sitting room.
4rm(3🛁1🚿)🚭in 1 bedroom CTV in all bedrooms Ⓡ
🐕 (ex guide dogs)
dB&B🛁🚿£62 (incl dinner) WBDi£199.50 LDO 8.15pm
Lic 🍴 CTV
Credit Cards [1] [£]

GH [Q][Q][Q] Sunnymeade Country House Hotel Dean Cross EX34 8NT (1m W on A361) ☎Ilfracombe(0271) 863668
Feb-Nov
Half a mile south of the Ilfracombe/Woolacombe junction on the B3230, this modern guesthouse offers bright, attractive en suite bedrooms which are well equipped. The public areas are spacious and comfortable.
10rm(8🚿2hc)(2fb) CTV in all bedrooms Ⓡ 🐕 sB&B£14-£16
dB&B£28-£32 dB&B🚿£32-£36 WBDi£130-£149 LDO 6pm
Lic 🍴 CTV 14P
Credit Cards [1] [2] [3] [5]

WESTGATE Co Durham Map **12** NY93

FH [Q][Q] Mrs B Reed **Lands** *(NY913379)* DL13 1SN
☎Weardale(0388) 517210
Two hundred and eighty acres of sheep and cattle pasture surround this family farmhouse which offers well-appointed accommodation with private bath or shower rooms. It is to be found just off the A689 – turn south at the village pub.
2🛁🚿 (1fb) CTV in all bedrooms Ⓡ sB&B🛁🚿£14
dB&B🛁🚿£28
4P 280 acres hill farm cattle & sheep

WEST LINTON Borders *Peebleshire* Map **11** NT15

SELECTED

GH [Q][Q][Q][Q] ***Medwyn House*** Medwyn Rd EH46 7HB
☎(0968) 60542
An outstanding country house set in 30 acres of grounds on the southern outskirts of town. Spacious and thoughtfully equipped bedrooms and delightfully appointed public rooms, including a wood-panelled baronial hall and an elegant drawing room. The hospitality extended by Mrs Waterson, cannot be bettered, and includes a complimentary sherry before the beautifully cooked set dinner.
3🛁 🚭in all bedrooms TV available Ⓡ LDO noon
🍴 CTV 12P 2🚗 nc12yrs sauna

WESTON-SUPER-MARE Avon Map **03** ST36

See **Town Plan Section**

GH [Q][Q] Almond Lodge 42 Clevedon Rd BS23 1DQ
☎(0934) 625113
In a road opposite the Tropicana Centre, this Edwardian house offers good accommodation with simply appointed, well-equipped rooms. Kathleen and Dennis Hall provide friendly service.
4hc (2fb) CTV in all bedrooms Ⓡ 🐕 * sB&B£13-£14
dB&B£26-£28 WB&B£80-£88 WBDi£115-£120
CTV

GH [Q][Q][Q] Ashcombe Court 2 Elmhyrst Rd BS23 2SJ
☎(0934) 625104
A short drive from the seafront and town, this attractive property offers good accommodation with some thoughtful extras. Guests will find a hospitable atmosphere here.
7rm(4🚿3hc)(1fb)🚭in all bedrooms CTV in all bedrooms Ⓡ
🐕 (ex guide dogs) sB&B£14 dB&B£28
dB&B🚿£34 WB&B£84-£102 WBDi£120-£138 LDO 6pm
🍴 CTV 9P
[£]

GH Q Q **Baymead Hotel** Longton Grove Rd BS23 1LS
☎(0934) 622951
This large, family-run hotel is close to the amenities and has a popular bar and upgraded bedrooms with modern facilities.
33rm(26⇌↑7hc)(3fb) CTV in all bedrooms ® sB&B£15-£17
sB&B⇌↑£20-£23 dB&B£34-£36
dB&B⇌↑£37-£40 LDO 6.30pm
Lic lift ₪ CTV 4P
£

GH Q **Kara** Hewish BS24 6RQ (1m E of junc 21 M5 on A370)
☎Yatton(0934) 834442
Close to the M5 and 3 miles from Weston-super-Mare, this house has an attractive garden which the friendly proprietors are happy for guests to enjoy. The accommodation is simple and public areas are full of character.
6rm(2⇌↑4hc)(3fb) CTV in all bedrooms ® LDO 3pm
Lic ₪ CTV 5P small putting green swing seesaw
See advertisement on page 381

GH Q Q Q **Milton Lodge** 15 Milton Rd BS23 2SH
☎(0934) 623161
Apr-Sep
Adrienne and Les Cox have totally refurbished this charming Victorian house to provide comfortable public rooms and spacious, well-equipped bedrooms with modern en suite facilities. It stands on the town's outskirts, yet is close to the amenities.
6rm(3⇌3↑) CTV in all bedrooms ® ✗ ✳ sB&B⇌↑£21
dB&B⇌↑£32 WB&B£91-£96 WBDi£126-£137 (wkly only 25
May-14 Sep) LDO 10am
₪ CTV 6P nc9yrs

GH Q Q **Newton House** 79 Locking Rd BS23 3DW
☎(0934) 629331
Closed Dec 23-Jan2

▶

Rising Sun Inn
West Bagborough, Nr Taunton,
Somerset TA4 3EF
Telephone: (0823) 432575

Situated in a peaceful village but within easy reach of motorway routes. Four tasteful bedrooms all en suite and with modern facilities. Home cooked food served in the bar lounge with log fire and a relaxed atmosphere.

Almond Lodge
42 Clevedon Road,
Weston-super-Mare

You are assured of a warm welcome at our small family run guest house for your holidays or business stopovers.

Very near to beach and tropicana shop and bus/train station.

Ring Kath or Dennis Hall
ON 0934 625113
For Brochure and Price List

TYNLLWYN FARM
WELSHPOOL
POWYS SY21 9BW
Tel: Welshpool (0938) 553175

Tynllwyn Farm stands on a hillside with beautiful views of the Severn Valley and Long Mountain, 1 mile from the market town of Welshpool, on the A490 north.

All bedrooms have colour TV, hot & cold wash units and tea/coffee making facilities. Modernised bathroom & shower room.

High standard home cooking and friendly service. Licensed bar.

2-day short bargain breaks available October-March.

Ideal touring centre for Mid and North Wales.

East of the seafront and town centre, this friendly guesthouse has comfortable, well-maintained rooms. The public rooms include a cosy lounge, separate bar and dining room.
8rm(5⇔♠3hc)(4fb) CTV in all bedrooms ® sB&B£15
sB&B⇔♠£17.50 dB&B£30
dB&B⇔♠£35 WB&B£98-£115.50 WBDi£144-£161.50 LDO
2pm
Lic ♔ CTV 9P
Credit Cards ①②③④

GH QQQ Wychwood Hotel 148 Milton Rd BS23 2UZ
☎(0934) 627793
Located on the outskirts of the town, this recently renovated Victorian house offers an outside heated swimming pool, in addition to the well-equipped, modern bedrooms, many of which have en suite facilities.
11rm(1⇔7♠3hc)(1fb) CTV in all bedrooms ®
✠ (ex guide dogs) sB&B£19-£20 sB&B⇔♠£21-£22
dB&B⇔♠£40-£42 WB&B£133-£154 WBDi£175-£182 LDO
6.30pm
Lic ♔ 14P ⇌(heated)
Credit Cards ①③④

WEST PENNARD Somerset Map 03 ST53

INN QQQ *Red Lion* Newton BA6 8NN
☎Glastonbury(0458) 32941
Standing on the A361 between Glastonbury and Shepton Mallet this inn has its bedrooms in a converted barn, all equipped to a high, modern standard, yet retaining character. The main building houses the bar and several eating areas.
Annexe 7⇔ CTV in all bedrooms ® ✠ (ex guide dogs) LDO
9.45pm
♔ 50P 2🐾
Credit Cards ①②③

WEST RUDHAM Norfolk Map 09 TF82

GH QQQ White House Farm Lynn Rd PE31 8RW
☎East Rudham(048522) 327
The outbuildings of this 16th century farm now provide en suite accommodation as well as an antique restoration and upholstery business. Courses are run by the proprietor, and his love of furniture is reflected by the quality pieces furnishing the rooms.
3hc Annexe 2⇔ (1fb) ® ✱ sB&B£22-£27.50 sB&B⇔frf27.50
dB&Bfrf39 dB&B⇔frf49 WBDi£207-£387.60 LDO 12noon
Lic ♔ CTV 12P
④

WEST SCRAFTON North Yorkshire Map 07 SE08

GH QQQ Coverdale Country Hotel Great Swineside
DL8 4RX ☎Wensleydale(0969) 40601
Closed 2 wks Jan
A converted farmhouse situated in an unspoilt, rural area of the dales. Friendly atmosphere.
11rm(4⇔7♠)(2fb) CTV in all bedrooms ® ✱ sB&B⇔♠frf27
dB&B⇔♠£46-£54 LDO 8.30pm
Lic ♔ 15P
Credit Cards ①③

WEST STOUR Dorset Map 03 ST72

INN QQ *The Ship* SP8 5RP ☎East Stour(074785) 640
Just 3.5 miles from the city centre, this 17th-century coaching house is in a lovely setting on the banks of the River Ouse. Paul and Elaine Eckart have refurbished the quaint bedrooms in pine and pretty prints. The cosy bars and restaurants provide a delightful setting for the substantial meals.
6⇔♠ (1fb) CTV in all bedrooms ® ✠ (ex guide dogs) LDO
10pm
♔ 40P
Credit Cards ①③

WESTWARD HO Devon Map 02 SS42

GH QQQ The Buckleigh Lodge 135 Bayview Rd EX39 1BJ
☎Bideford(0237) 475988
Standing on the edge of the village, this spacious Victorian house has tastefully furnished bedrooms and good public areas, retaining original features.
6rm(1⇔1♠4hc)(2fb) CTV in all bedrooms ®
✠ (ex guide dogs) sB&B£14-£16 dB&B£24-£32
dB&B⇔♠£32 WB&B£95-£108 WBDi£140-£165 LDO 4pm
Lic ♔ CTV 8P

WETHERBY West Yorkshire Map 08 SE44

⊢●⊣GH Q Prospect House 8 Caxton St LS22 4RU
☎(0937) 62428
This house is set on a corner in a side road, and is close to the town centre. The resident owners provide a friendly service, providing honest accommodation and value for money.
6hc (1fb) CTV in 1 bedroom sB&B£13-£13.50
dB&B£26-£27 WB&B£91-£94.50
♔ CTV 6P
④

WEYBRIDGE Surrey

London plan 4 A1 (pages 000-000)

GH QQQ Warbeck House Hotel 46 Queens Rd KT13 0AR
☎(0932) 848764
Fine Edwardian house with comfortable, modernised bedrooms and relaxing atmosphere.
10rm(1⇔9hc)(1fb) CTV in all bedrooms ® ✠ ✱
sB&B£32.20-£39.10 sB&B⇔£39.10 dB&B£44.85
dB&B⇔£48.30
Lic ♔ CTV 20P

WEYMOUTH Dorset Map 03 SY67

GH Q Beechcroft Private Hotel 128-129 Esplanade DT4 7EU
☎(0305) 786608
Apr-Sep
Located on seafront with continental awnings.
28rm(22⇔♠6hc)(11fb) CTV in all bedrooms ® ✱
sB&B£13.28-£13.99 sB&B⇔♠£15.41-£16.10
dB&B⇔♠£30.82-£32.20 WB&B£92-£109.25
WBDi£120.75-£138 LDO 4.00pm
Lic 🖉
Credit Cards ①③

⊢●⊣GH QQ Hazeldene 16 Abbotsbury Rd, Westham DT4 0AE
☎(0305) 782579
Comfortably furnished guesthouse, a short distance from the town centre and harbour, situated on the Bridport road.
7hc (4fb) ® ✠ sB&B£13-£16
dB&B£26-£32 WB&B£75-£90 WBDi£85-£120 LDO noon
Lic ♔ CTV 7P 1🐾 nc5yrs
④

GH QQQ Kenora 5 Stavordale Rd DT4 0AB ☎(0305) 771215
Etr & 7 May-1 Oct
In quiet cul-de-sac a short distance from the harbour.
15rm(4⇔9♠2hc)(5fb) ® ✠ (ex guide dogs) sB&B£15-£25.50
sB&B⇔♠£18-£25.50
dB&B⇔♠£32-£41 WB&B£100-£123 WBDi£123-£146 (wkly
only Jun-Aug) LDO 4.30pm
Lic ♔ CTV 20P

GH QQ Kings Acre Hotel 140 The Esplanade DT4 7NH
☎(0305) 782534
13 Jan-Sep rs Oct
Terraced Georgian hotel on seafront.

13rm(5🚿7hc)(4fb) CTV in all bedrooms [R] 🐕 * sB&B£15-£19 sB&B🚿£34-£36 dB&B£28-£32 dB&B🚿£36-£43 WB&B£98-£131 WBDi£121.50-£159 LDO 4.30pm
Lic 🛋 CTV 9P
Credit Cards [1] [3]

GH [Q][Q] Sou'west Lodge Hotel Rodwell Rd DT4 8QT
☎(0305) 783749
Closed 21 Dec-1 Jan
Family-run guesthouse, a short distance from seafront and town centre. Good bedrooms and friendly service.
9rm(2🛁4🚿3hc)(2fb) CTV in all bedrooms [R] sB&B£16-£18 sB&B🛁🚿£18-£20 dB&B£32-£36 dB&B🛁🚿£36-£40 WB&Bfr£90 WBDifr£128.50 LDO 3pm
Lic 🛋 CTV 14P
[£]

GH [Q][Q][Q] Sunningdale Private Hotel 52 Preston Rd, Overcombe DT3 6QD ☎(0305) 832179
Mar-Oct
Hotel set back off main Preston road enjoying elevated position.
20rm(5🛁2🚿13hc)(8fb) CTV in 12 bedrooms TV in 2 bedrooms [R] sB&B£18-£22.50 sB&B🛁🚿£22.60-£27.15 dB&B£36-£45 dB&B🛁🚿£40.60-£49.60 WB&B£113.50-£144 WBDi£142-£180 LDO 6.30pm
Lic CTV 20P 🏊(heated) putting green table tennis pool table games room
[£]

GH [Q][Q][Q] Tamarisk Hotel 12 Stavordale Rd, Westham DT4 0AB ☎(0305) 786514
Mar-Oct
Situated in a quiet cul-de-sac a short walk from the town centre and harbour.
16rm(4🛁8🚿4hc)(7fb) CTV in 6 bedrooms [R] 🐕 * sB&B£15-£19 sB&B🛁🚿£17-£21 dB&B£30-£36 dB&B🛁🚿£34-£42 (incl dinner) WB&Bfr£100 WBDi£128-£138 (wkly only Jul-Aug) LDO 2pm
Lic 🛋 CTV 19P

GH [Q][Q] The Westwey 62 Abbotsbury Rd DT4 0BJ
☎(0305) 784564
This small family-run hotel offers comfortable accommodation and good English cooking in a warm and friendly atmosphere.
11rm(1🛁8🚿2hc)(2fb) CTV in all bedrooms [R] 🐕 sB&B£15-£16 dB&B£30-£32 dB&B🛁🚿£36-£38 WB&B£94-£143 WBDi£114-£168 (wkly only Jul-Aug) LDO 6.30pm
Lic 🛋 CTV 10P nc6yrs

WHADDON Buckinghamshire Map **04** SP83

INN [Q][Q][Q] Lowndes Arms & Motel 4 High St MK17 0NA
☎Milton Keynes(0908) 501706 FAX (0908) 504185
Enjoying a quiet rural setting, this country inn with its modern annexe offers comfortable, well-equipped accommodation in a friendly and relaxing atmosphere.
Annexe 11🚿 CTV in all bedrooms [R] 🐕 (ex guide dogs) LDO 9.30pm
🛋 30P nc14yrs
Credit Cards [1] [3] [5]
See advertisement under MILTON KEYNES on page 263

WHAPLODE Lincolnshire Map **08** TF32

FH [Q][Q][Q] Mrs A Thompson **Guy Wells** *(TF337241)* Eastgate PE12 6TZ ☎Holbeach(0406) 22239
Closed 20-31 Dec
Beautifully preserved Queen Anne farmhouse with a wealth of charm and character.
3hc (1fb)🚭in all bedrooms CTV in 1 bedroom [R] 🐕 (ex guide dogs) * sB&B£19 dB&B£27 WB&B£84
🛋 CTV 4P nc10yrs 85 acres arable flowers

WHEDDON CROSS Somerset Map **03** SS93

GH [Q][Q][Q] The Higherley TA24 7EB
☎Timberscombe(0643) 841582
Higherley is an attractive modern detached building standing in pleasant gardens alongside 6 acres of smallholding. Well-appointed rooms enjoy superb country views.
6hc (1fb) CTV in 2 bedrooms * WB&Bfr£117.25 WBDifr£185.50 LDO 9pm
Lic 🛋 CTV 25P 6🚗 nc3mths

WHIMPLE Devon Map **03** SY09

GH [Q][Q][Q] Down House EX5 2QR ☎(0404) 822860
rs Nov-Feb & Mon evenings
A fine, spacious Edwardian house, set in its own landscaped gardens and commanding good views over the surrounding countryside, offers large, comfortable public rooms and well-equipped bedrooms. Friendly hosts create a house party atmosphere, guests gathering round the large dining table to share an enjoyable evening meal which includes many home-grown items.
7rm(2🚿5hc)(2fb) CTV in 5 bedrooms TV in 2 bedrooms [R] 🐕 (ex guide dogs) sB&Bfr£14 dB&Bfr£28 dB&B🚿fr£34 WB&B£87-£108 WBDi£132-£153 LDO 4.30pm
🛋 CTV 8P games lounge
[£]

See the regional maps of popular holiday areas at the back of the book.

WHITBY North Yorkshire Map **08** NZ81

SELECTED

GH ⓠⓠⓠⓠ **Dunsley Hall** Dunsley YO21 3TL
☎(0947) 83437

Built at the turn of the century, this magnificent wood-panelled hall stands high above Whitby and Sandsend and provides fine views over landscaped grounds to the sea. Mr and Mrs Buckle create a restful atmosphere where guests can relax in the lounge or play snooker on the match-play standard carved oak table. More energetic guests can play tennis, swim in the heated indoor swimming pool or work out in the gymnasium. Excellent food is provided by Mrs Buckle, and she and her staff make all their guests feel completely at home. Dunsley Hall was the North of England winner of the AA's Best Newcomer Award for 1989/90.

7⇨🛏 (2fb) CTV in all bedrooms ®
dB&B⇨🛏£54-£62 WB&B£175-£202 WBDi£273-£300
LDO 6pm
Lic 🅿 10P ⬛(heated) ℘(hard)snooker gymnasium
croquet putting green
Credit Cards ⓵ ⓷ ⓔ

⤙⤙**GH** ⓠⓠⓠ **Europa Private Hotel** 20 Hudson St YO21 3EP
☎(0947) 602251

Feb-Nov

Pleasant small guesthouse near harbour, well-furnished and with good, comfortable accommodation.

9rm(1🛏8hc)(1fb) CTV in all bedrooms ® ✖ sB&B£11-£12
dB&B£22-£24 dB&B🛏£26-£28 LDO 4.30pm
🅿 CTV nc2yrs

GH ⓠ *Glendale* 16 Crescent Av YO21 3ED ☎(0947) 604242
Apr-Oct

Glendale is a very comfortable and friendly guesthouse with neat bedrooms. It offers very good value for money.

6hc (3fb) CTV in all bedrooms ® LDO 4.15pm
Lic CTV 6P

GH ⓠ **Haven** 4 East Crescent YO21 3HD ☎(0947) 603842
Feb-Oct

An attractive guesthouse nicely furnished. Front-facing rooms overlook the sea.

8rm(4⇨🛏4hc)(1fb) CTV in all bedrooms ® ✖ sB&B£15-£17
dB&B£28-£32
dB&B⇨🛏£35-£39 WB&B£95-£133 WBDi£147-£182 LDO
4pm
Lic 🅿 CTV nc2yrs
ⓔ

GH ⓠ **Prospect Villa** 13 Prospect Hill YO21 1QE
☎(0947) 603118

Feb-Nov

This pleasant, friendly guesthouse offers good-value accommodation.

6rm(1🛏5hc)(2fb) CTV in 2 bedrooms ® ✖ ✱ sB&Bfr£12.50
dB&Bfr£25 dB&B🛏fr£40 WB&Bfr£80
Lic 🅿 CTV 4P sauna
ⓔ

GH ⓠⓠⓠ **Seacliffe Hotel** North Promenade, West Cliff
YO21 3JX ☎(0947) 603139

A charming small hotel, Seacliffe overlooks the sea and offers guests a warm welcome. All bedrooms are en suite and have telephones and colour TV. A cosy bar and comfortable lounge complement the 'Candlelight' restaurant where an extensive à la carte menu is served.

19⇨🛏 (4fb) CTV in all bedrooms ® ✱ sB&B⇨🛏£25-£41.50
dB&B⇨🛏£45-£47 WB&B£157.50-£164.50 LDO 8.45pm

Lic 🅿 CTV 8P
Credit Cards ⓵ ⓶ ⓷ ⓹ ⓔ

⤙⤙**GH** ⓠⓠ **Waverley Private Hotel** 17 Crescent Av YO21 3ED
☎(0947) 604389

Mar-Oct

Warm, friendly service and value for money are assured at this pleasant, comfortable house, which has the benefit of a spacious lounge and cosy bar.

6rm(4🛏2hc)(4fb) CTV in all bedrooms ® ✖ sB&B£12.50
dB&B£25-£26
dB&B🛏£29-£31 WB&B£80-£94 WBDi£112.50-£126.50 LDO
5.45pm
Lic 🅿 CTV nc3yrs
ⓔ

WHITCHURCH Hereford & Worcester Map **03** SO51

GH ⓠⓠ **Portland** HR9 6DB ☎Symonds Yat(0600) 890757
Closed Jan rs Nov-Mar

The Portland guest house is ideal for touring as it is close to Ross-on-Wye, Goodrich, and Symonds Yat situated in the village centre. The rooms are well equipped and modestly furnished.

8hc (2fb) CTV in all bedrooms ® ✱ sB&B£14.50-£16.50
dB&B£29-£33 WB&B£100-£115 WBDi£145-£160 LDO 6pm
Lic 🅿 CTV 7P
ⓔ

INN ⓠ **Crown Hotel** HR9 6DB ☎Symonds Yat(0600) 890234
Closed Xmas Day & Boxing Day

Situated in the centre of the village, and close to the A40, this large inn offers character, and modest but well-equipped bedrooms. A range of bar meals is available, both at lunchtime and in the evening.

5rm(1⇨4🛏)(3fb) CTV in all bedrooms ® sB&B⇨🛏£25-£30
dB&B⇨🛏£40-£45 WB&B£140-£150 WBDi£160-£180 Lunch
£6-£8&alc Dinner £6-£12&alc LDO 10pm
🅿 CTV 40P skittle alley pool room
Credit Cards ⓵ ⓶ ⓷ ⓹ ⓔ
See advertisement under ROSS-ON-WYE on page 313

WHITCHURCH Shropshire Map **07** SJ54

FH ⓠⓠ Mrs M H Mulliner **Bradeley Green** *(SJ537449)*
Waterfowl Sanctuary, Tarporley Rd SY13 4HD ☎(0948) 3442
Closed Xmas

This is an interesting place to stay in, the farm being surrounded by a wildfowl sanctuary. In addition to the well-equipped bedrooms in the house, there is a self-catering cottage available to let.

3rm(1⇨2🛏)(1fb)⥱in all bedrooms ® ✖ (ex guide dogs) ✱
sB&B⇨🛏£15-£18
dB&B⇨🛏£28-£30 WB&Bfr£90 WBDi£135-£150 LDO 9am
🅿 CTV 6P ⤳ water gardens 180 acres dairy waterfowl fish
farming
ⓔ

WHITESTONE Devon Map **03** SX89

⤙⤙**FH** ⓠⓠ Mrs S K Lee **Rowhorne House** *(SX880948)*
EX4 2LQ ☎Exeter(0392) 74675

Farmhouse set in attractive gardens and lawns.

3hc (2fb) CTV in 1 bedroom TV in 1 bedroom ✖ sB&B£11
dB&B£22 WB&B£77 WBDi£112
CTV 6P 103 acres dairy
Credit Cards ⓵ ⓶ ⓷ ⓹ ⓔ

WHITEWELL Lancashire Map **07** SD64

INN ⓠⓠⓠ *The Inn at Whitewell* BB7 3AT
☎Dunsop Bridge(02008) 222

Full of traditional atmosphere and character, this old inn provides friendly service and fresh food. The bedrooms are generally spacious and are of a very high standard, with fine furniture,

paintings and sophisticated hi-fi, as well as some original Victorian baths and showers.
11rm(6⇄5hc)(4fb) CTV in 6 bedrooms LDO 9.30pm
〽 CTV 60P ✔ clay pigeon shooting by arrangement
Credit Cards 1 2 3 5

WHITHORN Dumfries & Galloway *Wigtownshire*
Map **10** NX44

FH QQ Mrs E C Forsyth *Baltier (NX466429)* DG8 8HA
☎Garlieston(09886) 241
Mar-Nov
With fine views of the surrounding countryside, this stone-built farmhouse has modern extensions and offers comfortable accommodation. Meals are taken around the traditional farmhouse table.
2hc (1fb) ® ✻
〽 CTV 4P 220 acres dairy sheep

WHITLAND Dyfed Map **02** SN21

FH QQ C M & I A Lewis *Cilpost (SN191184)* SA34 0RP
☎(0994) 240280
Apr-Sep
Pleasant accommodation is provided on this working farm by the Lewis family. The spacious dining room offers imaginative and enjoyable food, and the comfortable public areas include an excellent snooker room and an indoor swimming pool.
7rm(3⇄3♠1hc)(3fb) ✻
Lic 〽 12P ◱(heated) ✔ snooker 160 acres dairy

WHITLEY BAY Tyne & Wear Map **12** NZ37

GH QQ **Lindisfarne Hotel** 11 Holly Av NE26 1EB
☎091-251 3954 & 091-297 0579
The attractive little front garden distinguishes this small guesthouse from the other houses in the terrace. Within easy reach of the sea and town centre, Lindisfarne has an attractive dining room and offers friendly service.
9rm(2♠7hc)(1fb) CTV in all bedrooms ® ✻ ✽ sB&B£14-£15
sB&B♠£18-£20 dB&Bfr£26
dB&B♠fr£30 WB&B£85-£99.50 WBDi£130.50-£144.50 LDO 9am
Lic 〽 CTV ₽
Credit Cards 1 3

GH QQQ **Marlborough Hotel** 20-21 East Pde, Central Promenade NE26 1AP ☎091-251 3628
Spacious and comfortable, this family-run hotel occupies a position on the seafront overlooking the bay. With well-equipped bedrooms it is ideal for business or pleasure.
17rm(8⇄8♠9hc)(2fb) CTV in all bedrooms ® ✽ sB&B£20
sB&B⇄♠£24 dB&B£30
dB&B⇄♠fr£36 WB&B£125-£150 WBDi£177-£202 LDO 5pm
Lic CTV 7P
Credit Cards 1 3

See advertisement on page 385

GH QQ **White Surf** 8 South Pde NE26 2RG ☎091-253 0103
This friendly establishment is between the town and the sea, and has a comfy lounge and attractive dining room. The bedrooms have modern furnishings and are bright and fresh.
8hc (2fb)⚲in all bedrooms CTV in all bedrooms ®
✻ (ex guide dogs) ✽ sB&B£12.50-£14.50
dB&B£25-£29 WBDi£125.50-£140.50 LDO 7.30pm
〽 CTV 7P 2🐾 nc2yrs
£

GH QQQ **York House Hotel** 30 Park Pde NE26 1DX
☎091-252 8313 & 091-251 3953
Part of an attractive terrace, this family-run guesthouse has well-appointed bedrooms and features a ground floor room with special facilities for disabled guests.

▶

8rm(7♠1hc)(2fb) CTV in all bedrooms ® sB&Bfr£18
dB&B♠fr£31 WB&Bfr£101.50 WBDifr£147 LDO 7pm
Lic ᵐ CTV 2P
Credit Cards ①③

WHITNEY-ON-WYE Hereford & Worcester Map **03** SO24

SELECTED

INN QQQQ **The Rhydspence** HR3 6EU (2m W A438)
☎Clifford(04973) 262
*Set in a lovely location exactly on the border between England
and Wales this lovely 14th-century inn provides
accommodation which has been totally modernised with
attractive furnishings. The congenial, busy bars are popular
with locals and tourists alike who spill out onto the patio in
summer, overlooking a stream. There is a very attractive
restaurant which makes full use of local produce and bar
snacks are also very enjoyable. Peter and Pam Glover are
good hosts who are sure to make guests very welcome.*
5rm(4⇄1♠) CTV in all bedrooms ® ✕
sB&B⇄♠£23-£25
dB&B⇄♠£46-£50 Lunch £10-£20alc Dinner £10-£20alc
LDO 9.30pm
ᵐ 60P
Credit Cards ①②③

WHITTINGTON Shropshire Map **07** SJ33

FH QQQ Mrs H M Ward **Perry** *(SJ348303)* SY11 4PF
☎Oswestry(0691) 662330
Mar-Oct
*Comfortable accommodation in a large, early 19th-century
farmhouse 1 mile east of the A5, approximately two miles from the
village.*
2hc ✕in all bedrooms ® ✕
dB&B£25-£30 WB&B£87-£95 WBDi£143-£151 LDO am
ᵐ CTV 0P ⚲ cycle hire 750 acres arable beef dairy mixed

WIDDINGTON Essex Map **05** TL53

FH QQQ Mrs L Vernon **Thistley Hall** *(TL556311)* CB11 3ST
☎Saffron Walden(0799) 40388
Jun-Sep
*Approached by a tree-lined drive, this historic farmhouse is
pleasantly surrounded by lovely gardens and pasture. The
atmosphere here is warm and the proprietors are charming.*
2hc ✕in all bedrooms ® ✕ (ex guide dogs) ✳ dB&B£28-£30
ᵐ CTV 4P nc5yrs 30 acres mixed working

WIDEGATES Cornwall & Isles of Scilly Map **02** SX25

GH QQQ **Coombe Farm** PL13 1QN ☎(05034) 223
Mar-Oct
*This attractive 1920s house has superb views and offers large,
comfortable family bedrooms. There is a cosy lounge and the
dining room is furnished with antiques.*
8hc (4fb) CTV in 6 bedrooms ® ✕ (ex guide dogs) ✳
sB&B£14.50-£18.50
dB&B£29-£37 WB&B£101.50-£129.50 WBDi£160-£186 LDO
7pm
Lic ᵐ CTV 12P nc5yrs ⌂(heated)
See advertisement under LOOE on page 245

WIDEMOUTH BAY Cornwall & Isles of Scilly Map **02** SS20

GH Q **Beach House Hotel** EX23 0AW ☎(0288) 361256
Etr-Sep
13rm(8♠5hc)(5fb) ® ✕ sB&Bfr£18 dB&Bfr£34
dB&B♠fr£38 WBDifr£139 LDO 7pm
Lic CTV 20P games room childrens play area

£
See advertisement under BUDE on page 93

GH QQ *Trelawney Hotel* Marine Dr EX23 0AH
☎(0288) 361328
Etr-Oct
9rm(7♠2hc)(3fb) CTV in all bedrooms ® LDO 7.30pm
Lic 12P

WIGAN Greater Manchester Map **07** SD50

GH QQ **Aalton Court** 23 Upper Dicconson St WN1 2AG
☎(0942) 322220
*This terraced property is close to the town centre and has compact,
well- equipped bedrooms, all with en suite facilities. There is a
small car park to the rear.*
6rm(2⇄4♠)(1fb) CTV in all bedrooms ® ✕
sB&B⇄♠£30
dB&B⇄♠£39-£45 WB&B£171-£183 WBDi£255-£267 LDO
2pm
Lic ᵐ CTV 11P

WIGHT, ISLE OF Map **04**

FRESHWATER Map **04** SZ38

GH QQQ **Blenheim House** Gate Ln PO40 9QD
☎(0983) 752858
May-Sep
*Built in 1870, this fine family-run Victorian house is beautifully
situated, within 300 yards of the beach and caves at Freshwater
Bay. Tastefully furnished and equipped, it provides personal
service and good home cooked food.*
8♠ (4fb) CTV in all bedrooms ® ✕ sB&B♠fr£17.50
dB&B♠fr£33 WB&Bfr£122.50 WBDifr£175 LDO noon
Lic ᵐ 6P nc10yrs ⌂(heated) table tennis billards darts

NITON Map **04** SZ57

GH QQQ **Pine Ridge Country House** Niton Undercliff
PO38 2LY ☎(0983) 730802
*Occupying a prime location overlooking the sea, this fine hotel is
comfortably furnished and is set in spacious grounds directly off
the main road. Mrs Rita Healy personally supervises the friendly,
informal service.*
9rm(6⇄♠1hc)(2fb) CTV in all bedrooms ® sB&B£23
dB&B⇄♠£52 WBDi£230 LDO 9pm
Lic ᵐ CTV 10P ♨
Credit Cards ①③£

RYDE Map **04** SZ59

GH Q *Dorset Hotel* 31 Dover St PO33 2BW ☎(0983) 64327
*A small privately owned hotel, the Dorset has a warm and friendly
atmosphere and on some evenings provides entertainment. The
bedrooms are nicely appointed.*
25rm(1⇄6♠18hc)(4fb) CTV in all bedrooms ®
Lic CTV 25P ⇄▶

GH QQ **Teneriffe Hotel** 36 The Strand PO33 1JF
☎(0983) 63841
Closed Jan-Feb
*This long established holiday hotel is well managed and provides
modern en suite rooms, now serviced by a lift. There are generous
public rooms, a licensed function room and an attractive dining
room, and the service is friendly and helpful.*
50⇄♠ (7fb) CTV in all bedrooms ® ✕ (ex guide dogs) ✳
sB&B⇄♠£20 dB&B⇄♠£40 WB&B£130 LDO 7pm
Lic lift ᵐ CTV 9P
Credit Cards ①③£

Visit your local AA Centre.

SANDOWN Map **04** SZ58

GH [Q][Q][Q] Braemar Hotel 5 Broadway PO36 9DG
☎(0983) 403358 & 407913
Completely refurbished and upgraded, the accommodation at this hotel has been skilfully extended. The individually decorated, modern bedrooms are all equipped to the same high standards, and there is an elegant and very comfortable lounge, plus a separate bar. The dining room features a menu which is changed daily.
14rm(5🛁9🚿)(5fb) CTV in all bedrooms Ⓡ 🐕 (ex guide dogs)
sB&B🛁🚿fr£25
dB&B🛁🚿£50-£64 (incl dinner) WB&B£125-£148
WBDi£150-£185 LDO 8.30pm
Lic ♨ 12P
Credit Cards [1] [2] [3] [5] [£]

GH [Q][Q] *Chester Lodge Hotel* Beachfield Rd PO36 8NA
☎(0983) 402773
mid Jan-mid Dec rs Oct
Conveniently situated within easy reach of the shops and Cliff Walk, this guesthouse has modernised, well-equipped bedrooms, some of which are on the ground floor. A bar-lounge and separate dining room complete the accommodation.
19rm(2🛁8🚿9hc)(4fb) CTV in all bedrooms Ⓡ (wkly only Jul-Aug)
Lic ♨ CTV 19P

GH [Q][Q][Q] Culver Lodge Hotel Albert Rd PO36 8AW
☎(0983) 403819 & 402902
This hotel has the benefit of a first floor laundry room and a games room on the ground floor. The public areas are pleasant and the bedrooms modern and well equipped. The staff are friendly and helpful.
21rm(20🛁🚿1hc)(2fb) CTV in all bedrooms Ⓡ 🐕
sB&Bfr£13.50 sB&B🛁🚿£16-£19.50
dB&B🛁🚿£39-£51 WB&B£107-£130 WBDi£146-£170 LDO 10pm
Lic ♨ CTV 20P pool room
Credit Cards [1] [£]

GH [Q] *Meadway House Hotel* 12 Beachfield Rd PO36 8ND
☎(0983) 402137
Closed Jan-Feb
Some of the bedrooms at this family-run guesthouse are on the ground floor, and all are equipped with satellite TV. The popular bar has a snack menu and guests will find ample car parking space.
13rm(11🚿2hc)(11fb) CTV in all bedrooms Ⓡ
🐕 (ex guide dogs) LDO 9am
Lic ♨ CTV 13P 🏡

GH [Q][Q] Rose Bank Hotel 6 High St PO36 3DA
☎(0983) 403854
6rm(1🛁5hc)Annexe 2🛁 (2fb) Ⓡ * sB&B£12-£13
sB&B🛁£15-£16 dB&B£24-£26
dB&B🛁£30-£32 WB&B£96-£98 WBDi£100-£102 LDO 7pm
Lic ♨ CTV 🅿̸ nc6yrs

SELECTED

GH [Q][Q][Q][Q] St Catherine's Hotel 1 Winchester Park Rd PO36 8HT ☎(0983) 402392
A few minutes' walk from the pier and sandy beaches, this Purbeck stone house is run by the Barker family who are very friendly hosts. Television, telephone and tea facilities equip the restful and comfortable bedrooms, and the tastefully furnished lounge has a small bar. A choice of dishes is offered at each of the 4 courses at dinner – try the ice cream speciality
18rm(11🛁7🚿)(3fb) CTV in all bedrooms Ⓡ 🐕
sB&B🛁🚿£18.50-£20
dB&B🛁🚿£37-£40 (incl dinner) WB&B£120.25-£130
WBDi£165.75-£191.75 LDO 7pm
Lic ♨ CTV 8P
Credit Cards [1] [3] [£]

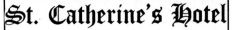

GH Ⓠ *Seacourt* Cliff Path PO36 9PN ☎(0983) 403759
This small family-run hotel is in a secluded area. The bedrooms are of a good standard and there are good leisure facilities.
13rm(10⇆1♠2hc)Annexe 9rm(8⇆1♠) CTV in all bedrooms Ⓡ LDO 7pm
Lic 20P
Credit Cards ⅠⅢ

SEAVIEW Map 04 SZ69

GH ⓆⓆⓆ *Northbank Hotel* Circular Rd PO34 5ET
☎(0983) 612227
Etr-Sep
This traditional, family-run hotel occupies a prime position overlooking the sea and has its own access to the beach. The comfortable accommodation includes a library, bar and a small dining room, where the home cooking includes local seafood.
18hc (6fb) CTV in 3 bedrooms Ⓡ LDO 8pm
Lic 🏵 CTV 8P 4🏖 ◑ ♪ snooker

SHANKLIN Map 04 SZ58

See Town Plan Section

GH ⓆⓆⓆ **Apse Manor Country House** Apse Manor Rd
PO37 7PN ☎(0983) 866651
Set in countryside 1.5 miles from the town, this 15th-century manor stands in 2 acres of grounds. A choice of dishes is offered in the dining room and the bedrooms are comfortable.
7⇆ (2fb) CTV in all bedrooms Ⓡ ✳
dB&B⇆£56-£62 (incl dinner) WBDi£195-£215 LDO 7.30pm
Lic 🏵 10P nc6yrs
Ⓔ

GH ⓆⓆⓆ **Aqua Hotel** The Esplanade PO37 6BN
☎(0983) 863024
Etr-5 Nov
Enjoying a superb elevated position facing the sea, this modern, well-run, friendly hotel offers well-equipped, compact bedrooms, 6 with balconies overlooking the sea. Facilities include a bar featuring live entertainment, a restaurant, sun terrace and a patio.
22⇆♠ (4fb) CTV in all bedrooms Ⓡ ✖ sB&B⇆♠£15-£20
dB&B⇆♠£30-£40 WB&B£100-£150 WBDi£125-£175 (wkly only Jul & Aug) LDO 4.30pm
Lic 🏵 2P
Credit Cards Ⅰ③Ⓔ

GH ⓆⓆⓆ **Carlton Hotel** 9 Park Rd PO37 6AY
☎(0983) 862517 & 864513
The spacious lounge takes full advantage of the hotel's cliff top situation. All except 2 single rooms are en suite and the well-equipped accommodation is complemented by good home cooking.
12rm(9⇆1♠2hc)Annexe 1♠ (1fb) CTV in all bedrooms Ⓡ
✖ (ex guide dogs) sB&B£22-£27 dB&B£44-£54
dB&B⇆♠£44-£54 (incl dinner) WB&B£140-£154
WBDi£160-£190 LDO 6.30pm
Lic 🏵 CTV 10P
Credit Cards Ⅰ③Ⓔ

SELECTED

GH ⓆⓆⓆⓆ **Chine Lodge** East Cliff Rd PO37 6AA
☎(0983) 862358
Closed Xmas & New Year
The spacious, tastefully appointed bedrooms are a feature of this charming early Victorian house. Comfortably appointed throughout and with an attractive garden, the house has a warm and friendly atmosphere and is personally supervised by Mrs. May, the proprietress. It is said that the Duke of Hamilton was born here, and there are 2 tunnels used in the past by smugglers.
7⇆ CTV in all bedrooms Ⓡ ✖ sB&B⇆£18-£21
dB&B⇆£36-£42 WBDi£178-£198 LDO 7.15pm

Lic 🏵 7P nc
Ⓔ

⊢•GH ⓆⓆ **Culham Lodge** 31 Landguard Manor Rd
PO37 7HZ ☎(0983) 862880
Apr-Oct
Attractive small hotel in tree-lined road with heated swimming pool in secluded garden.
10rm(1⇆7♠2hc) Ⓡ ✖ (ex guide dogs) sB&Bfr£13 dB&Bfr£26
dB&B⇆♠fr£30 WB&B£85-£107 WBDi£110-£134 LDO 4pm
🏵 CTV 8P nc12yrs ⏳(heated) solarium
Ⓔ

GH ⓆⓆⓆ **Curraghmore Hotel** 22 Hope Rd PO37 6EA
☎(0983) 862605
Mar-Oct
A varied menu is always available at this modern, well-equipped hotel. Several bedrooms have sea views, and the restaurant and ballroom are complemented by a roof-top sun lounge and a lively bar lounge, all well maintained throughout.
24rm(10⇆6♠8hc)(9fb) CTV in all bedrooms Ⓡ LDO 6pm
Lic CTV 20P putting

GH ⓆⓆ **Edgecliffe Hotel** Clarence Garden PO37 6HA
☎(0983) 866199 Telex no 89441
Closed Nov-Dec
Quietly situated away from the town centre, this hotel can arrange Red Funnel bookings for guests at advantageous rates. Accommodation here comprises a resident bar, dining room, cosy lounge and well-equipped bedrooms together with home cooking and friendly service.
10rm(2⇆4♠4hc)(2fb) CTV in all bedrooms CTV in all bedrooms Ⓡ ✖ sB&B£17-£25 sB&B⇆♠£20-£28 dB&B£34-£50
dB&B⇆♠£40-£56 WB&Bfr£102 WBDi£120-£185 LDO 6.30pm
Lic 🏵 3P nc5yrs cycles for hire
Credit Cards Ⅰ②③Ⓔ

GH ⓆⓆⓆ **Hambledon Hotel** Queens Rd PO37 6AW
☎(0983) 862403 & 863651
Children are especially catered for at this hotel which provides a baby listening service. The bedrooms are comfortable and well equipped and there is a licensed bar and a comfortable lounge. The Hambledon provides easy access to local amenities.
11♠ (4fb) CTV in all bedrooms Ⓡ sB&B♠£17-£21
dB&B♠£34-£42 WB&B£105-£126 WBDi£118-£159 LDO 6pm
Lic 🏵 CTV 8P ◑
Credit Cards Ⅰ③Ⓔ

GH ⓆⓆ **Harrow Lodge** Eastcliff Promenade PO37 6BJ
☎(0983) 862800
22rm(12⇆10♠)(7fb) CTV in all bedrooms Ⓡ ✳
sB&B⇆♠£18-£22
dB&B⇆♠£36-£44 WB&B£120-£145 WBDi£140-£190 LDO 6pm
Lic 🏵 16P
Credit Cards Ⅰ③Ⓔ

GH ⓆⓆ **Kenbury Private Hotel** Clarence Rd PO37 7BN
☎(0983) 862085
Etr-Oct
Comfortable accommodation in a small family hotel.
19rm(4⇆11♠4hc)(3fb)⅟4in 4 bedrooms CTV in all bedrooms Ⓡ ✖ (ex guide dogs) ✳ sB&B£15.50-£17 sB&B⇆♠£17.50-£19
dB&B£31-£34
dB&B⇆♠£35-£38 WB&B£112.50-£119 WBDi£125-£150
LDO 6.30pm
Lic 🏵 CTV 8P nc3yrs
Credit Cards Ⅰ③Ⓔ

GH 🇶🇶🇶 **Luccombe Chine House Country House** PO37 6RH
☎(0983) 862037
Closed Dec-Jan
Enjoying a peaceful location with its own access to the beach, this Tudor manor house has a four-poster bed in each well-equipped bedroom. There is also a spacious lounge, bar and dining room together with a terrace and sun lounge.
6⇄ Annexe 2⇄ CTV in all bedrooms ® ✠ (ex guide dogs)
sB&B⇄£47-£51
dB&B⇄£52-£72 (incl dinner) WB&B£182-£210
WBDi£212.80-£239.40 LDO 8pm
Lic ♨ 20P nc15yrs
Credit Cards 1 3

SELECTED

GH 🇶🇶🇶🇶 **Osborne House** Esplanade PO37 6BN
☎(0983) 862501
Jan-24 Oct
Liz and Mike Hogarth have a natural aptitude for making guests comfortable and relaxed, and provide excellent food as well as well-equipped bedrooms with many thoughtful extras. The house is colourful all year with plants and floral displays.
12⇄🏱 CTV in all bedrooms ® ✠ ✳ sB&B⇄🏱fr£26
dB&B⇄🏱fr£52 LDO 8pm
Lic ♨ ⅌ nc13yrs
Credit Cards 1 3

⊢⊷GH 🇶🇶🇶 **Soraba Private Hotel** 2 Paddock Rd PO37 6NZ
☎(0983) 862367
Closed Dec
Within easy reach of the beach, shops and amenities, this Victorian house has simply furnished bedrooms and offers excellent value for money. Mr and Mrs Wynn Davies provide wholesome evening meals and friendly service.
6rm(3🏱3hc)(1fb) TV in 3 bedrooms sB&B£12-£14.50
dB&B£24-£29
dB&B🏱£29.50-£34.50 WB&B£77-£91 WBDi£95-£115 LDO 3pm
Lic ♨ CTV 4P nc3yrs
£

GH 🇶🇶🇶 *Swiss Cottage Hotel* 10 St Georges Rd PO37 6BA
☎(0983) 862333
Situated in a quiet area, yet conveniently close to the town and its amenities, this licensed guesthouse has bright and comfortable bedrooms all equipped to a high standard and with private facilities. Home cooking is complemented by personal service.
12rm(3⇄4🏱5hc)(2fb) CTV in 1 bedroom TV in 1 bedroom ®
✠ LDO 4pm
Lic CTV 10P nc5yrs

TOTLAND BAY Map **04** SZ38

GH 🇶🇶 *Hermitage Hotel* Cliff Rd PO39 0EW ☎(0983) 752518
Mar-Nov
Standing in sheltered gardens overlooking the sea and with a separate children's play area, this hotel has well preserved traditional bedrooms. The comfy lounge boasts a piano and organ and Debbie and David Blake provide friendly service and good English cooking.
12rm(2⇄4🏱6hc)(3fb) LDO 7pm
Lic ♨ CTV 12P 1🏊 🅙 ⌂
Credit Cards 1 3

See advertisement on page 389

GH 🇶🇶 *Lismore Private Hotel* 23 The Avenue PO39 0DH
☎(0983) 752025
Closed Nov-Dec
This lovely villa dates from 1896 and has been lovingly maintained and modernised by resident proprietors, who provide good food and traditional hospitality.

▶

7rm(5♪2hc)(3fb) CTV in all bedrooms ® ✕ (ex guide dogs)
sB&B£19.50-£22.50
dB&B♪£43-£49 (incl dinner) WB&B£108.50-£129.50
WBDi£136.50-£157.50 LDO 3pm
Lic ♔ 8P nc5yrs
£

GH Q Q **The Nodes Country Hotel** Alum Bay Old Rd
PO39 0HZ ☎Freshwater(0983) 752859 FAX (0705) 201621
*Backing on to Tennyson Down, this country house stands in 2.5
acres of grounds. The courtyard bar is the hub of the hotel which is
ideal for young families, providing highchairs, cots and a baby
listening service. The traditional country cooking uses fresh local
produce.*
11rm(3⇔6♪2hc)(5fb) CTV in all bedrooms ® sB&B£25-£28
sB&B⇔♪£28-£31.50 dB&B£46-£52
dB&B⇔♪£52-£59 (incl dinner) WB&B£112-£148
WBDi£150-£189 LDO 3pm
Lic ♔ CTV 15P badminton table tennis
£

GH Q Q Q **Sandford Lodge Hotel** 61 The Avenue PO39 0DN
☎(0983) 753478
*A well-appointed house with comfortable bedrooms and a relaxing
atmosphere.*
6rm(3⇔2♪1hc)(1fb)⅟in all bedrooms ® ✕ (ex guide dogs) ✱
sB&B£12-£15 sB&B⇔♪£13-£18
dB&B⇔♪£25-£34 WB&B£80-£119 WBDi£115-£158 LDO
4pm
Lic ♔ CTV 6P
£

GH Q Q Q **Westgrange Country Hotel** Alum Bay Old Rd
PO39 0HZ ☎(0983) 752227
Mar-Oct
*Small, friendly country hotel with comfortable bedrooms and good
cooking.*
13rm(2⇔7♪4hc)(11fb) TV available ® ✱ sB&Bfr£16
dB&Bfr£32 WBDifr£147 LDO 7.30pm
Lic ♔ CTV 30P

VENTNOR Map 04 SZ57

GH Q Q *Channel View Hotel* Hambrough Rd PO38 1SQ
☎(0983) 852230
Apr-19 Oct rs Mar
*Enjoying a prominent position overlooking the seam this family-
run hotel has bright, well-maintained bedrooms and a lovely first
floor lounge and balcony, together with a popular bar and
restaurant.*
14rm(2♪12hc)(6fb) ® ✕ (ex guide dogs) LDO 8pm
Lic CTV ⅃
Credit Cards 1 3

GH Q Q Q *Glen Islay Hotel* St Boniface Rd PO38 1NP
☎(0983) 854095
*This late Victorian house stands in a rural location with a secluded
garden yet close to the town. The modern bedrooms are of good
size and well furnished. Good lounge and bar facilities complement
the good service and friendly atmosphere.*
10rm(1⇔7♪2hc)(8fb) CTV in all bedrooms ®
Lic ♔ CTV 5P

GH Q Q Q *Hillside Private Hotel* Mitchell Av PO38 1DR
☎(0983) 852271
*Two acres of wooded grounds surround this hotel, which has
literary connections and affords excellent sea views. The bedrooms
are modern and the generous, comfortable lounges are
complemented by a small bar. The service is particularly friendly
and helpful.*
11rm(4⇔7♪)(2fb) CTV in all bedrooms ® LDO 4.30pm
Lic ♔ 16P nc5yrs
Credit Cards 1 3

⊢⇥**GH** Q Q Q **Lake Hotel** Shore Rd, Bonchurch PO38 1RF
☎(0983) 852613
Mar-Oct
*Quietly set in 2.5 acres of lovely terraced gardens, this hotel offers
a choice of accommodation, including a new wing and coachman's
cottage, complemented by good cooking and friendly service.
There are several public rooms and a games room.*
11rm(9⇔7♪2hc)Annexe 10⇔7♪ (7fb) ® sB&B£12-£15
sB&B⇔♪£15-£17 dB&B£24-£30
dB&B⇔♪£30-£34 WB&B£105-£119 WBDi£120-£157.50
LDO 6.30pm
Lic ♔ CTV 20P nc3yrs
£

GH Q Q Q **Llynfi Hotel** 23 Spring Hill PO38 1PF
☎(0983) 852202
28 Mar-Oct
*Full of character and atmosphere, this guesthouse offers
modernised bedrooms, lounges for non-smokers, a dining-room and
separate bar. The cooking is of a good standard and the service is
friendly and helpful.*
10rm(7♪3hc)(2fb) CTV in all bedrooms ® ✕ (ex guide dogs)
sB&B£14.50-£19.50 sB&B♪£14.50-£19.50 dB&B£29-£39
dB&B♪£29-£39 WB&B£101.50-£136.50 WBDi£136-£170
LDO 6.30pm
Lic CTV 7P
Credit Cards 1 3 £

GH Q Q **Macrocarpa Hotel** Mitchell Av PO38 1DP
☎(0983) 852428
3 Mar-2 Jan
*Standing in an acre of gardens, this Victorian house overlooks the
Channel and Ventnor, and is next to the bowling green. The
majority of the simply furnished, well-equipped bedrooms are en
suite, and the young owners and staff give friendly service.*
21rm(7⇔12♪2hc)(6fb)⅟in 1 bedroom CTV in all bedrooms
® ✕ (ex guide dogs) ✱ dB&B£12.50-£20.50
dB&B⇔♪£15.50-£22.60 WB&B£105-£145.50
WBDi£126.50-£166.75 LDO 7.30pm
Lic CTV 25P ⏍ snooker pool table
Credit Cards 1 3 £

GH Q Q Q **Picardie Hotel** Esplanade PO38 1JX
☎(0983) 852647
Mar-Oct
*Picardie Hotel faces the sea and offers tastefully modernised
accommodation. The cosy, comfortable lounge is complemented by
a separate bar and dining room. The cooking is of a good standard
and the resident proprietors provide friendly service.*
10⇔♪ (3fb)⅟in all bedrooms CTV in all bedrooms ®
sB&B⇔♪£15 dB&B£30 WB&B£100 WBDi£135 LDO 4.30pm
Lic CTV
Credit Cards 1 3 £

GH Q Q Q **St Maur Hotel** Castle Rd PO38 1LG
☎(0983) 852570
Feb-Nov
*This peaceful hillside hotel overlooks the park and offers cheerful
modern bedrooms and generous public rooms. The traditional,
well-managed service is personally supervised by the proprietor.*
14rm(13⇔♪1hc)(4fb) ® sB&B⇔♪fr£23
dB&B⇔♪fr£46 (incl dinner) WBDifr£168 LDO 7pm
Lic CTV 12P nc3yrs
Credit Cards 1 3

WIGMORE Hereford & Worcester Map 07 SO46

INN Q *Compasses Hotel* HR6 9UN ☎(056886) 203
*Set in a pleasant village close to the Herefordshire/Shropshire
border, this ivy-clad hotel is popular with walkers exploring the
beautiful countryside of this area, and provides simple
accommodation.*
3hc (1fb) CTV in all bedrooms ® LDO 9.30pm

🍴 70P
Credit Cards [1] [2] [3] [5]

WILBERFOSS Humberside Map **08** SE75

FH [Q] Mrs J M Liversidge **Cuckoo Nest** *(SE717510)*
☎(07595) 365
Closed Xmas
Traditional Yorkshire farmhouse with bright, comfortable rooms. situated 1 mile west of the village on the south side of the A1079.
2hc (1fb)🚭in all bedrooms 🐕 sB&B£15-£16 dB&B£26-£28
🍴 CTV 0P nc2yrs 150 acres arable beef dairy mixed sheep
[£]

WILLAND Devon Map **03** ST01

FH [Q][Q] Mrs J M Granger ***Doctors*** *(ST015117)* Halberton Rd EX15 2QQ ☎Tiverton(0884) 820525
Mar-Oct
Parts of this farmhouse date back to the 15th century. Peacefully set in 90 acres and with well-kept gardens, it has 2 comfortable bedrooms which share a bathroom, and the public rooms are full of character. This is a bed and breakfast establishment only.
2rm (1fb)🚭in all bedrooms [R] 🐕
CTV 6P 🎣 95 acres dairy

This is one of many guidebooks pubished by the AA. The full range is available at any AA Centre or good bookshop.

WILLERSEY Gloucestershire Map **04** SP13

SELECTED
GH ⓆⓆradoxically Ⓠ **Old Rectory** WR12 7PN
☎Broadway(0386) 853729
Closed Xmas
The old rectory is a haven of peace and tranquility, tucked away alongside the church in this village on the outskirts of Broadway. The accommodation is exceptional and furnished with comfort in mind with lots of thoughtful extras provided by Mr and Mrs Jones. Guests will always be made very welcome and even chauffer driven tours of the Cotswoslds are available. Well thought-out room information is provided to show guests where to eat as the Old Rectory does not provide dinner, Mrs. Jones will happily drive guests to restaurants. However, the breakfasts served here have been highly praised by our inspectors, making this a delightful place to stay which wholly deserves our highest award.
6rm(4⇔2♠)⊁in all bedrooms CTV in all bedrooms Ⓡ ✠
sB&B⇔♠£49-£59 dB&B⇔♠£59-£95
🍴 CTV 10P 2�car nc9yrs
Credit Cards ① ③ ⓔ
See advertisement under BROADWAY on page 91

WILMSLOW Cheshire Map **07** SJ88

GH ⓆⓆⓆ **Fernbank** 188 Wilmslow Rd, Handforth SK9 3JX
☎(0625) 523729 or 539515
This large Victorian house, situated near to the airport, has been tastefully restored to provide comfortable bedrooms and warm hospitality. Residential weekend ceramics courses are a feature of this guesthouse.
3⇔♠ (1fb) CTV in all bedrooms Ⓡ sB&B⇔♠£28-£30
dB&B⇔♠£38-£42 LDO 4pm
🍴 CTV 3P china restoration and weekend leisure courses

WIMBORNE MINSTER Dorset Map **04** SZ09

SELECTED
GH ⓆⓆⓆⓆ **Beechleas** 17 Poole Rd BH21 1QA
☎(0202) 841684
This elegant Georgian house, close to the town centre and with its own car park, has recently been renovated to provide luxurious bedrooms with very good quality bathrooms. The pretty bedrooms have co-ordinated soft furnishings and are equipped to modern standards. There is a small, smartly furnished lounge, where drinks are served, and a spacious dining room which extends into the conservatory.
5⇔♠ Annexe 2⇔♠ CTV in all bedrooms ✠
sB&B⇔♠£39.50-£59.50
dB&B⇔♠£49.50-£69.50 WB&B£222.25-£465.50
WBDi£327.25-£570.50 LDO 9pm
Lic 🍴 9P
Credit Cards ① ③

GH Ⓠ **Riversdale** 33 Poole Rd BH21 1QB ☎(0202) 884528
Closed Xmas rs Nov-Feb
Detached guesthouse with sound, neat accommodation on the edge of town centre.
8rm(1♠7hc)(3fb) CTV in all bedrooms Ⓡ ✱ sB&B£12-£24
dB&B£24-£48 dB&B♠£30-£50 LDO 10am
🍴 CTV 5P nc3yrs
Credit Cards ①

GH ⓆⓆ **Stour Lodge** 21 Julian's Rd BH21 1EF
☎(0202) 888003
Closed 20 Dec-5 Jan
Small, comfortable well-appointed house with sufficient parking, a pleasant garden and friendly hosts. On A31 Dorchester Road.

3rm(1⇔2hc)(2fb) CTV in all bedrooms Ⓡ sB&B£25-£30
sB&B⇔£25-£30 dB&B£50-£60
dB&B⇔£50-£60 WB&B£150-£170 WBDi£200-£220 LDO 9pm
Lic 🍴 CTV 4P croquet
ⓔ

WIMPSTONE Warwickshire Map **04** SP24

FH ⓆⓆ Mrs J F James **Whitchurch** *(SP222485)* CV37 8NS
☎Alderminster(078987) 275 due to change to (0789) 450275
Lovely Georgian farmhouse built 1750, set in park-like surroundings on edge of Cotswold, 4.5 miles from Stratford-upon-Avon.
3hc (2fb) Ⓡ ✠ sB&B£15-£16 dB&B£24-£26 LDO 6.30pm
🍴 CTV 6P 220 acres arable beef sheep
ⓔ

WINCANTON Somerset Map **03** ST72

FH ⓆⓆⓆ Mrs A Teague **Lower Church** *(ST721302)* Rectory Ln, Charlton Musgrove BA9 8ES ☎(0963) 32307
Closed Xmas & New Year
18th-century, brick built farmhouse with inglenook fireplace and beams.
3rm(1♠2hc)⊁in all bedrooms Ⓡ dB&B£22-£24
dB&B♠£24-£28 WB&B£70-£80
🍴 CTV 3P nc6yrs 60 acres dairy sheep

WINCHELSEA East Sussex Map **05** TQ91

SELECTED
GH ⓆⓆⓆⓆ **The Country House at Winchelsea** Hastings Rd TN36 4AD ☎Rye(0797) 226669
Closed Xmas
This delightful 17th-century former Sussex farmhouse stands in its own well-kept grounds of 2 acres, which are a haven for many species of birds and butterflies, and which is the home of 2 glorious peacocks. The well-equipped bedrooms offer guests comfort and lovely garden views. The Carmichaels' hospitality and good home-cooked food makes this hotel a place to remember.
4rm(2♠2hc) CTV in all bedrooms Ⓡ ✠ ✱
sB&B♠£23-£26
dB&B♠£33-£36 WB&B£161-£182 WBDi£231-£252 LDO 7.30pm
Lic 🍴 3P 3🚗 nc9yrs

GH ⓆⓆⓆ **The Strand House** TN36 4JT ☎Rye(0797) 226276
Reputed to be one of the oldest houses in the area, The Strand House is set in well-kept gardens and overlooks meadowland. Full of character with some very low beams, is offers well-equipped accommodation.
10rm(2⇔6♠2hc)(1fb) CTV in 3 bedrooms TV in 7 bedrooms
Ⓡ sB&B£20-£24 sB&B⇔♠£20-£24 dB&B£28-£30
dB&B⇔♠£36-£40
Lic 🍴 12P nc2yrs

WINCHESTER Hampshire Map **04** SU52

GH ⓆⓆⓆ **Aerie** 142 Teg Down Meads, (off Dean Lane)
SO22 5NS ☎(0962) 62519 due to change to 862519
Situated in a quiet residential area, this detached property, with far reaching views, offers immaculate rooms which are light, airy and well equipped, and is popular with tourists and commercial guests. Parking is available on the premises, and there is a 'no smoking' policy throughout.
4hc ⊁in all bedrooms CTV in all bedrooms Ⓡ ✠ ✱ sB&B£15
dB&B£29 WB&Bfr£105
🍴 6P nc10yrs
ⓔ

GH ![Q][Q] *Harestock Lodge Hotel* Harestock Rd SO22 6NX
(situated 2m N of the city on the B3420) ☎(0962) 881870
Closed 24 Dec-3 Jan
A commercial hotel with functional modern accommodation.
Public rooms are spacious and popular.
20rm(9🅵11hc)(5fb) CTV in all bedrooms ® ✖ (ex guide dogs)
LDO 9.15pm
Lic 🎠 CTV 20P ⌇spa pool
Credit Cards ①②③

SELECTED

INN ![Q][Q][Q][Q] *The Wykeham Arms* 73 Kingsgate St
SO23 9PE ☎(0962) 53834
This historic coaching inn located close to the Cathedral,
features a popular choice of bars, with real ales and
blackboard menus. The standard of cooking is good, with
attentive service. The interior is tastefully furnished, and
bedrooms are particulary well equipped.
7rm(5🅵2hc)(1fb) CTV in all bedrooms ® LDO 8.45pm
🎠 14P nc14yrs sauna

WINCLE Cheshire Map **07** SJ96

GH ![Q][Q] **Four Ways Diner Motel** Cleulow Cross SK11 0QL (1m
N of A45) ☎(0260) 227228
rs Oct-Mar
Situated in the Peak National Park, with many places of interest
nearby, this establishment has well-equipped accommodation with
en suite facilities. There are fine views over the Dane valley.
6rm(1⌐5🅵)Annexe 5🅵 (2fb) CTV in all bedrooms ®
sB&B⌐5🅵£25-£30 dB&B⌐5🅵£35-£40 LDO 8pm
Lic 🎠 50P
Credit Cards ①③£

THE COUNTRY HOUSE
AT WINCHELSEA
'Your comfort is our pleasure'

Hastings Rd, Winchelsea, E. Sussex, TN36 4AD.
Tel: Rye (0797) 226669
Mary Carmichael

A delightful setting and wonderful country views
make our 17th Century Listed country house an
ideal choice for that 'Special Break'. Comfortable
pretty bedrooms with en-suite or private facilities,
colour TV and complimentary hot drinks trays.
A cozy sitting room with log fire for those chillier
evenings, and in our licenced dining room only
the finest local produce is served. Ample parking.
Tariff: Bed and Full English Breakfast £16.50-
£18pp. Pre-booked three course Table d'hôte
dinner £10.00pp. Brochure available.

ETB 👑👑👑   AA "Selected"
commended   MEMBER   Country House

The Strand House

Winchelsea, East Sussex TN36 4JT
Telephone: Rye (0797) 226276

Beautiful 14th century house, overlooking National Trust land.
En-suite facilities, full English breakfast,
residents' sitting room and licensed.
Open all year.

NORTHILL HOUSE
Horton · Wimborne · Dorset · BH21 7HL
Telephone Witchampton (0258) 840407

Six miles north of Wimborne. Peaceful rural
situation, mid-19th century farmhouse providing
spacious reception rooms and all bedrooms en-
suite with TV and tea/coffee making facilities.
Within easy reach of Kingston Lacy, Cranborne
Chase, Blackmore Vale, New Forest and Salisbury. Traditional English breakfasts with homemade bread and preserves. Excellent evening
meals from local produce. One room equipped
for disabled guests.

WINDERMERE Cumbria Map **07** SD49

See **Town Plan Section**

GH Q Q Q **Applegarth Hotel** College Rd LA23 3AE
☎(09662) 3206

Close to the railway station, this hotel retains the elegance of the Victorian era. Some of the comfortable bedrooms have four-poster beds and all have en suite facilities. Many have views towards the lake and fells.

15♠ (4fb) CTV in all bedrooms ® ✱ sB&B♠£25-£30
dB&B♠£36-£60 WB&B£126-£210
Lic ♔ CTV 20P
Credit Cards 1 2 3

GH Q Q **Archway Country** College Rd LA23 1BY
☎(09662) 5613

This delightful Victorian guesthouse has a unique atmosphere, and excellent home cooking. Friendly personal service is provided at dinner and breakfast. The bedrooms have a Victorian theme and modern comfort.

6rm(5♠1hc)✄in all bedrooms CTV in all bedrooms ® ✖
sB&Bfr£16 sB&B♠£18-£22 dB&B♠£38-£44 LDO 3pm
Lic ♔ 3P nc12yrs
Credit Cards 2 £

See advertisement on page 395

GH Q Q Q **Belsfield House** 4 Belsfield Ter LA23 3EQ
☎(09662) 5823

An attractive Victorian house in the centre of Bowness, this establishment has very well-appointed bedrooms and a comfortable lounge for guests.

9♠ (4fb) CTV in all bedrooms ✖ (ex guide dogs) ✱
sB&B♠£20-£22.50 dB&B♠£38-£43
♔ ⅌ £

GH Q Q Q **Blenheim Lodge** Brantfell Rd, Bowness on
Windermere LA23 3AE ☎(09662) 3440

Situated in a quiet area, yet close to the village of Bowness, this picturesque house enjoys an elevated position with a panoramic view. It is well furnished and comfortable, and fine home cooking is provided.

11rm(1⇨8♠2hc)(1fb)✄in all bedrooms CTV in all bedrooms
® ✖ sB&Bfr£17.50 sB&B⇨♠fr£21
dB&B⇨♠£37-£50 WB&B£126-£172 WBDi£189-£234 LDO
4pm
Lic ♔ 12P 2🐾 nc6yrs
£

GH Q Q **Brendan Chase** 1&3 College Rd LA23 1BU
☎(09662) 5638

Family owned and run, this guesthouse offers good all-round comforts and service. Brendan Chase is situated in a quiet side road close to the town centre.

8rm(4♠4fb)(4fb)✄in 1 bedroom CTV in all bedrooms ® ✱
sB&B£12.50-£20 sB&B♠£20-£25 dB&B£25-£30
dB&B♠£30-£40 WB&B£170-£250
♔ CTV 8P
£

GH Q Q Q **Brooklands** Ferry View, Bowness LA23 3JB
☎(09662) 2344

This is a delightful small guesthouse, which is family owned and run. It is located in a rural setting, near to Bowness, and a good standard of accommodation is offered.

6rm(3♠3hc)(3fb) ® sB&B£15 sB&B♠£17 dB&B£30
dB&B♠£34 WB&B£119-£133 WBDi£189-£203 LDO 5.30pm
Lic ♔ CTV 6P
£

This guide is updated annually – make sure you
use an up-to-date edition.

GH Q Q **Clifton House** 28 Ellerthwaite Rd LA23 2AH
☎(09662) 4968

This neat little terraced house, run by a friendly proprietress, has attractive and well-equipped bedrooms. It is conveniently situated a short distance from the centre of Windermere, in a quiet road off New Road.

5rm(1⇨4hc)(1fb) CTV in 4 bedrooms ® ✖ ✱ sB&B£11-£12
dB&B£24-£26 dB&B⇨♠fr£30
♔ CTV 5P nc5yrs

GH Q Q Q **Cranleigh Hotel** Kendal Road, Bowness LA23 3EW
☎(09662) 3293

Mar-Oct

Just a short distance from Bowness and Lake Windermere, this charming Victorian house is furnished to a high standard. The bedrooms are well equipped and there are 2 comfortable lounges, one of which is for non-smokers.

9⇨♠ Annexe 6♠ (1fb) CTV in all bedrooms ® ✖ ✱
sB&B⇨♠£23-£35
dB&B⇨♠£42-£50 WB&B£140-£175 WBDi£175-£240 LDO
7pm
Lic ♔ CTV 15P nc5yrs
Credit Cards 1 3 £

GH Q Q Q **Fir Trees** Lake Rd LA23 2EQ ☎(09662) 2272

This charming Victorian house stands between Windermere and Browness, and displays an interesting collection of clocks. The comfortable en suite rooms have colour televisions, and Mr and Mrs Fishman offer friendly, relaxed service with a hearty breakfast. Coffee is freely available in the lounge from 3pm to 7pm.

7⇨♠ (2fb) CTV in all bedrooms ✖ sB&B⇨♠£22.50-£26.50
dB&B⇨♠£35-£43 WB&B£115-£145
♔ 8P
Credit Cards 1 2 3 £

See advertisement on page 395

GH 🅠🅠🅠 **Glenburn** New Rd LA23 2EE ☎(09662) 2649
*This delightful guesthouse offers a high standard of comfort and
service. The bedrooms are very well appointed and home-cooked
meals are served in the pleasant dining room.*
14rm(3⇆9↑2hc)(3fb)⚊in 4 bedrooms CTV in all bedrooms
® ✕ (ex guide dogs)
dB&B⇆↑£34-£54 WB&B£109-£169 WBDi£179-£245 LDO
4.30pm
Lic ⏰ CTV 15P nc5yrs
Credit Cards ①③ £

GH 🅠🅠🅠 **Glencree Private Hotel** Lake Rd LA23 2EQ
☎(09662) 5822
Mar-Dec rs Feb
*A cheerful Lakeland stone building, Glencree, lies between
Windermere and Bowness. It is very well furnished with well-
equipped bedrooms and a charming lounge, and provides friendly,
helpful service.*
5rm(3⇆2↑) CTV in all bedrooms ® ✕ ✳ dB&B⇆↑£39-£55
Lic ⏰ 8P nc9yrs
Credit Cards ①③

GH 🅠🅠 **Glenville Hotel** Lake Rd LA23 2EQ ☎(09662) 3371
Feb-Nov
*Midway between Bowness and Windermere, this pleasant family-
run guesthouse offers good standards of accommodation and
service.*
9rm(1⇆7↑1hc)(1fb)⚊in 2 bedrooms CTV in all bedrooms ®
✕ sB&B⇆↑£16.50-£21
dB&B⇆↑£33-£42 WB&B£140-£147 LDO 2pm
Lic ⏰ 12P
£

GH 🅠🅠🅠 **Green Gables** 37 Broad St LA23 2AB
☎(09662) 3886
Closed Xmas & New Year
*This is an attractive house which is furnished and equipped to a
high standard. It is family owned and run, and offers a comfortable
and relaxed atmosphere and good personal service.*
6rm(2↑4hc)(2fb)⚊in 3 bedrooms CTV in all bedrooms ®
✕ (ex guide dogs) ✳ sB&B£12-£14 dB&B£22-£26
dB&B↑£27-£34 WB&B£77-£112
⏰ CTV 2P£
See advertisement on page 397

GH 🅠🅠🅠 *Greenriggs* 8 Upper Oak St LA23 2LB
☎(09662) 2265
*Set in a quiet and peaceful side road close to the town centre, this is
a family-run guesthouse. It has recently been thoroughly
refurbished and is a delightful place in which to stay.*
7rm(4↑3hc)(1fb) CTV in all bedrooms ® LDO noon
⏰ CTV 3P nc5yrs

GH 🅠🅠 *Haisthorpe* Holly Rd LA23 2AF ☎(09662) 3445
Mar-Oct
*This pleasant and comfortable house stands in a quiet side road
close to the town and lake, and provides friendly family service.*
6rm(1↑5hc)(3fb)⚊in all bedrooms ® ✕ (ex guide dogs)
⏰ CTV ₽

SELECTED

GH 🅠🅠🅠🅠 **The Hawksmoor** Lake Rd LA23 2EQ
☎(09662) 2110
Feb-Nov
*A warm and friendly welcome is provided by Barbara and Bob
Tyson at this delightful small hotel, situated midway between
Bowness and Windermere. The bedrooms are very
comfortable, and are attractively furnished to a high standard.
The lounge is comfortable and relaxing, and the elegant
dining room provides well-produced dishes.*

10⇆↑ (3fb)⚊in 3 bedrooms CTV in all bedrooms ®
✕ (ex guide dogs) sB&B⇆↑£22.50-£25.50
dB&B⇆↑£34-£50 WB&B£117-£150 WBDi£175-£205
LDO 5pm
Lic ⏰ 12P nc6yrs
£
See advertisement on page 397

GH 🅠 **Holly Lodge** 6 College Rd LA23 1BX ☎(09662) 3873
*This Victorian house is situated off the main road, close to the
village centre. Personally owned and run, it offers a good standard
of accommodation together with friendly service from the
proprietors.*
10hc (5fb) CTV in 11 bedrooms ® ✕ (ex guide dogs)
sB&Bfr£14 dB&Bfr£28 WB&Bfr£98 WBDifr£154 LDO 10am
Lic 6P
£

GH 🅠🅠🅠 **Holly Park House** 1 Park Rd LA23 2AW
☎(09662) 2107
Mar-Oct
*Built of lakeland stone, this attractive house stands on the corner
of a quiet side road. Resident owners provide well-furnished
bedrooms and friendly service.*
6rm(1⇆5↑)(4fb) CTV in all bedrooms ® ✕
sB&B⇆↑£22-£25 dB&B⇆↑£28-£35 WB&B£92.50-£115
Lic ⏰ 4P
£

GH 🅠🅠🅠 **Kenilworth** Holly Rd LA23 2AF ☎(09662) 4004
Mar-Oct
*Well furnished and pleasing, this guesthouse offers good
accommodation and service. It stands in a quiet side road and is a
short walk from the village centre.*
6rm(3↑3hc)(2fb)⚊in 3 bedrooms ® ✕ (ex guide dogs) ✳
sB&B£11.50-£13.50 dB&B£23-£27
dB&B↑£28-£32 WB&B£76-£93
⏰ CTV ₽
£

GH 🅠🅠🅠 *Kirkwood* Prince's Rd LA23 2DD ☎(09662) 3907
*This hotel is situated in a quiet residential area, located between
Bowness and Windemere. The house, which is both personally
owned and run, is a friendly and a comfortable one.*
8rm(3↑5hc)(6fb) CTV in all bedrooms ® LDO breakfast
⏰ 1P

GH 🅠🅠 **Lynwood** Broad St LA23 2AB ☎(09662) 2550
*Close to the town centre in a quiet side road, this well furnished,
comfortable guesthouse is family owned and run, and offers a
friendly welcome.*
11rm(4↑7hc)(4fb)⚊in all bedrooms CTV in all bedrooms ®
✕ ✳ sB&B↑£15-£20 dB&B£20-£27
dB&B↑£30-£40 WB&B£70-£135
⏰ 2P 2🐾 nc5yrs
£ *See advertisement on page 397*

GH 🅠🅠🅠 *Meadfoot* New Rd LA23 2LA ☎(09662) 2610
Feb-Nov
*This is a well-furnished and comfortable modern house with an
attractive garden. The bedrooms are very pleasant and have a
lounge with a relaxed atmosphere. The owners offer a warm,
friendly welcome to all.*
8rm(4↑4hc)(1fb) CTV in all bedrooms ® ✕ (ex guide dogs)
⏰ 9P nc3yrs

GH 🅠🅠🅠 **Mylne Bridge House** Brookside, Lake Rd LA23 2BX
☎(09662) 3314
Mar-Oct
*Situated in a quiet side road, this comfortable family-run
guesthouse has well- furnished bedrooms with good facilities.*

▶

GLENVILLE

Lake Road, Windermere.
Tel (09662) 3371

A comfortable small family run hotel with friendly service and a good hearty breakfast to start the day. Pleasant gardens & woodland views. Large car park, situated midway between Windermere & Bowness. H&C, central heating, complimentary tea or coffee, colour TV in all bedrooms en-suite rooms available. Comfortable lounge & licensed bar. Short stays & midweek bookings welcome. Access to hotel all day.
Proprietors: Joseph & Vera Crawford, Brochures on request, S.A.E. please or telephone for room availability.

Fir Trees

LAKE ROAD
WINDERMERE
CUMBRIA
LA23 2EQ
Telephone:
WINDERMERE
(09662) 2272

Charming Victorian guest house of considerable character and furnished with antiques throughout. Within easy walking distance to Windermere, Bowness, or the lake. Luxurious accommodation with spacious and lovely bedrooms, all with private bath/shower rooms en suite and colour televisions. Simply scrumptious breakfasts. Most of all, old-fashioned hospitality. Recommended by major prestige guides.

GLENBURN

New Road, Windermere, Cumbria, LA23 2EE
Telephone: 09662 2649

Please telephone for Brochure and Reservations

* Licensed Bar * Large private car park

OPEN ALL YEAR

Glenburn is a luxuriously appointed house offering the highest standards of comfort, cleanliness and service. 16 delightful en-suite bedrooms all with colour TV, radio and telephone. Charming dining room. Good home cooking. Optional evening meal. Leisure facilities including swimming pool available to our guests only at the nearby Windermere Marina village.
We are situated between Windermere and the Lake.

THE ARCHWAY

College Road, Windermere, Cumbria LA23 1BY
Telephone: 09662 5613
Mr & Mrs Anthony Greenhalgh

An impeccable Victorian stone-built house, beautifully furnished, and in an ideal quiet location with magnificent open mountain views yet close to Windermere village centre. There are six comfortable bedrooms, mostly en suite. A delightful lounge and dining room with period furnishings throughout; antiques, interesting paintings and prints. Fresh flowers, good books, colour TV. Renowned for gourmet home cooking. Interesting wine list. NO SMOKING. A British Tourist Authority Commended Country Guest House.

10rm(7♠3hc)(1fb) CTV in all bedrooms ® ✱
sB&B£15.50-£17.50 sB&B♠£17.50-£19.50 dB&B£27-£32
dB&B♠£31-£36 WB&B£90-£100
Lic ♔10P £

GH Ⓠ *Oakthorpe Hotel* High St LA23 1HF ☎(09662) 3547
Closed 25 Dec-24 Jan
*Family owned and run, this hotel stands in the centre of
Windermere.*
18rm(4⇌3♠11hc)(4fb) ® LDO 8.15pm
Lic ♔ CTV 18P
Credit Cards ① ③

⊢⊷**GH** ⒶⒶⒶ **Oldfield House** Oldfield Rd LA23 2BY
☎(09662) 88445
*Well furnished and comfortable, this house offers friendly, personal
service. It stands on a quiet side road convenient for the village
centre.*
7rm(1⇌3♠3hc)(2fb) CTV in all bedrooms ®
✗ (ex guide dogs) sB&B£13-£15.50 sB&B⇌♠£16-£18.50
dB&B£26-£32 dB&B⇌♠£29-£35 WB&B£82-£117
♔ CTV 7P nc2yrs free membership to leisure club
Credit Cards ① ③ £

GH ⒶⒶⒶ **Rosemount** Lake Rd LA23 2EQ ☎(09662) 3739
*Well furnished and comfortable, this is a small hotel located
midway between Windemere and Bowness, in the south of the
appealing Lake District. It is a friendly and relaxing place in
which to stay and is totally 'no smoking'.*
8rm(5♠3hc)✗in all bedrooms CTV in all bedrooms ® ✗
sB&B♠£17.50-£22 dB&B♠£35-£44 WB&B£120-£146
Lic ♔ 6P 2🛏
Credit Cards ① ③ £

GH ⒶⒶⒶ **St Johns Lodge** Lake Rd LA23 2EQ ☎(09662) 3078
Closed Dec
A charming private hotel with comfortable accommodation.
14rm(1⇌13♠)(3fb) CTV in all bedrooms ® LDO 6pm
Lic ♔ 11P nc2yrs

GH Ⓠ *Thornleigh* Thornbarrow Road, Bowness LA23 2EW
☎(09662) 4203
Mar-Oct
*This friendly and comfortable guesthouse stands in a quiet side
road between Bowness and Windermere.*
6hc (4fb) CTV in 5 bedrooms ® ✗ (ex guide dogs)
sB&B£14-£17 dB&B£28-£34 WB&B£93-£114
♔ CTV 5P
Credit Cards ① ③ £

See advertisement on page 399

GH ⒶⒶⒶ **Westlake** Lake Rd LA23 2EQ ☎(09662) 3020
*This small, friendly family-run guesthouse offers a very high
standard of comfort and helpfulness.*
8rm(2⇌6♠)(2fb) CTV in all bedrooms ® ✗
dB&B⇌♠£32-£42 WB&B£112-£147 WBDi£180-£205 LDO
3.30am
Lic ♔ CTV 8P

See advertisement on page 399

GH ⒶⒶⒶ **White Lodge Hotel** Lake Rd LA23 2JJ
☎(09662) 3624
Mar-Nov
*Attractively furnished and comfortable, this guesthouse offers
good, all round service and a friendly atmosphere. It is close to all
amenities in Bowness.*
12⇌♠ (3fb) CTV in all bedrooms ® ✗ (ex guide dogs)
sB&B⇌♠£21-£26
dB&B⇌♠£42-£46 WB&B£145-£170 WBDi£200-£220 LDO
6.30pm
Lic ♔ CTV 14P
Credit Cards ① ③

See advertisement on page 393

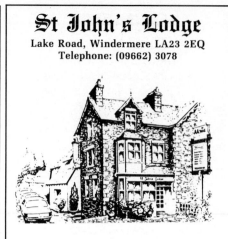

⊘ldfield ⊦ouse

B E D & B R E A K F A S T

We would like to welcome you to Oldfield House, which has a friendly, informal atmosphere within a traditionally-built Lakeland residence.
7 Bedrooms, some en-suite, four poster room, all with Colour TV · Quiet central location · Leisure Club facilities · Car Park
Bob & Maureen Theobald, Oldfield House, Oldfield Road, Windermere, Cumbria LA23 2BY
Telephone (09662) 88445 ☙☙
COMMENDED

HAWKSMOOR

Lake Road, Windermere, Cumbria LA23 2EQ
Telephone: (09662) 2110

Large ivy-clad house with every modern facility and superb private car park. Ideally situated between Windermere and Bowness. All rooms en-suite, some ground floor rooms. All rooms have colour TV and tea/coffee facilities.

See colour advertisement in colour section.

LYNWOOD

Broad Street, Windermere, Cumbria LA23 2AB
Telephone: Windermere (096 62) 2550

Gateway to the Lake District

Frances and Brian Holcroft welcome you to their lovely Victorian house, quiet setting near car park. Superb bedrooms most en suite. 5 minutes bus and rail. All rooms have colour TV, central heating, hair dryer and tea & coffee makers. Your host is a Lakeland tour guide. B&B from £10.00 to £20.00.

Green Gables
Guest House

37 Broad Street, Windermere, Cumbria LA23 2AB
Telephone: Windermere (09662) 3886

Family run guest house situated in a pleasant position. Shops, restaurants, bus and railway stations are all nearby. TV lounge, separate dining room, central heating, first class bathrooms, toilets and showers. All our cosy bedrooms have colour TV, hair dryers and tea/coffee making facilities. Some rooms en-suite. Family rooms available.
Cleanliness, friendliness and a good hearty breakfast is the key to our success

A warm welcome awaits you from Sheila and Joe Lawless.

GH ⓆⓆⓆ **Winbrook** 30 Ellerthwaite Rd LA23 2AH
☎(09662) 4932
Mar-Nov & Xmas
This cosy well-furnished guesthouse is in a quiet road close to the village. The bedrooms are well equipped and there is a comfortable lounge for guests.
6rm(1⇌2♠3hc)⊁in all bedrooms CTV in all bedrooms Ⓡ ✳
sB&B£14-£20 dB&B£22-£28
dB&B⇌♠£24-£34 WB&B£73.50-£115.50
Ⅷ CTV 7P nc6yrs
£

GH ⓆⓆⓆ **Woodlands** New Rd LA23 2EE ☎(09662) 3915
Very comfortable and well furnished, this guesthouse offers friendly service and attention from the resident owners. It stands half way between Windermere and Bowness.
11rm(9♠2hc)(2fb)⊁in 2 bedrooms CTV in all bedrooms Ⓡ
✖ (ex guide dogs) sB&B♠£16-£25 dB&B♠£30-£44 LDO 3pm
Lic Ⅷ 11P nc5yrs
Credit Cards ① ③

WINDSOR Berkshire Map **04** SU97

GH ⓆⓆⓆ **Melrose House** 53 Frances Rd SL4 3AQ
☎(0753) 865328
This elegant detached Victorian house is located just 5 minutes' walking distance from the castle and town centre. The accommodation is comfortable, well maintained and offers good modern facilities. There is a pleasantly appointed breakfast room and cosy television lounge.
9⇌♠ (2fb)⊁in 2 bedrooms CTV in all bedrooms Ⓡ
sB&B⇌♠£28-£34 dB&B⇌♠£38-£44
Ⅷ CTV 10P

WINSTER Derbyshire Map **08** SK26

GH ⓆⓆⓆ **The Dower House** Main St DE4 2DH
☎(062988) 213
Mar-Oct
This Elizabethan country house with its walled garden stands in the heart of the Peak District village. It has spacious bedrooms and a lounge with a log fire. Breakfast is served 'en famille'.
3hc CTV in all bedrooms Ⓡ sB&B£15-£30
dB&B£30 WB&B£105 LDO 10am
Lic Ⅷ 4P nc10yrs

WINTERBOURNE ABBAS Dorset Map **03** SY69

GH ⓆⓆ **Churchview** DT2 9LS ☎Martinstown(0305) 889296
rs Nov-Feb
This attractive Dutch-style listed house provides an ideal base for touring the area, and has a warm, friendly atmosphere. The bedrooms are compact and nicely appointed and 1 of the 2 lounges is reserved for non-smokers.
10rm(2⇌2♠6hc)(1fb) Ⓡ dB&B£26-£32
dB&B⇌♠£32-£38 WB&B£90-£130 WBDi£140-£180 LDO
7pm
Lic Ⅷ CTV 9P 1🏠 nc3yrs
£
See advertisement under DORCHESTER on page 135

WISBECH Cambridgeshire Map **09** TF40

FH ⓆⓆⓆ Mrs S M King **Stratton** *(TF495140)* West Drove
North, Walton Highway PE14 7DP ☎(0945) 880162
All the bedrooms in this bungalow-style farmhouse have en suite facilities, one being suitable for wheelchair users. A covered heated swimming pool is available, as is a small lake for carp fishing.
3⇌♠ ⊁in all bedrooms CTV in all bedrooms Ⓡ
✖ (ex guide dogs) sB&B⇌♠£16 dB&B⇌♠£32 WB&B£112
Ⅷ CTV 6P nc5yrs ⇘(heated) ♪ 22 acres beef dairy

WIVELISCOMBE Somerset Map **03** ST02

GH ⓆⓆ **Deepleigh Country Hotel** Langley Marsh TA4 2UU
☎(0984) 23379
6⇌♠ (2fb) CTV in all bedrooms Ⓡ ✖ (ex guide dogs) ✳
dB&B⇌♠£48 WB&B£168 WBDi£210 LDO noon
Lic Ⅷ 5P ⚤ ♫(hard)◡
£

GH ⓆⓆ **The Mount Country** Ford TA4 2RL ☎(0984) 23992
A detached country cottage of character, offering pleasant accommodation in a rural setting.
5hc sB&B£13.50
dB&B£27-£29 WB&B£84-£90 WBDi£140-£147 LDO previous day
Ⅷ CTV 10P
£

WIX Essex Map **05** TM12

FH ⓆⓆⓆ Mrs H P Mitchell **New Farm House** *(TM165289)*
CO11 2UJ (0.5m N off Wix-Bradfield road) ☎(0255) 870365
Some rooms of this farmhouse are suitable for disabled guests. All are well equipped and have individually controlled central heating. Smoking is permitted in one of the spacious lounges and a kitchenette offers a microwave and facilities for making drinks.
6rm(1♠5hc)Annexe 6♠ (5fb)⊁in 10 bedrooms CTV in all
bedrooms Ⓡ sB&Bfr£15.50 sB&B♠fr£18.50 dB&Bfr£29
dB&B♠fr£35 WB&B£97.65-£116.55 WBDi£138.15-£157.05
LDO 6pm
Ⅷ CTV 12P ⚤ 52 acres arable
Credit Cards ① ③ £

WOKING Surrey Map **04** TQ05

GH ⓆⓆⓆ **Glencourt** St Johsn Hill Rd GU21 1RQ
☎(04862) 64154
One-and-a-half acres of secluded gardens and woodland surround this attractive house. The traditionally furnished accommodation is particularly well equipped and à la carte meals are served in the adjoining Fountain Restaurant which specialises in flambé cookery. Service is very friendly and supervised by the proprietor Zelda Lewis.
9rm(6⇌3♠)Annexe 2⇌ (1fb) CTV in all bedrooms Ⓡ ✳
sB&B⇌♠£40.25-£45 dB&B⇌♠£57.50-£65 LDO 10pm
Lic Ⅷ 29P table tennis
Credit Cards ① ③ £

WOODBRIDGE Suffolk Map **05** TM24

GH ⓆⓆ **Grove House** 39 Grove Rd IP12 4LG ☎(03943) 2202
Mr and Mrs Kelly are friendly hosts at this hotel which is set back from the A12 with car parking to the front. The well-kept and equipped accommodation has some en suite facilities, and a small menu is offered.
9rm(5♠4hc)(1fb) CTV in all bedrooms Ⓡ ✳ sB&B£16-£17.50
dB&B£30-£35
dB&B♠£35-£40 WB&B£98-£140 WBDi£139-£185.50 LDO
7.30pm
Lic Ⅷ CTV 12P
Credit Cards ① ③

WOODHALL SPA Lincolnshire Map **08** TF16

GH ⓆⓆ **Duns** The Broadway LN10 6SQ ☎(0526) 52969
Set on the eastern edge of the town, near the championship golf course and popular with golfers, tourists and commercial users alike, the hotel provides a noteworthy standard of friendly service.
7rm(1♠6hc)(2fb) Ⓡ ✳ sB&Bfr£15 sB&B♠fr£25 dB&Bfr£28
dB&B♠fr£40 WB&Bfr£98 WBDifr£147 LDO noon
Ⅷ CTV 10P

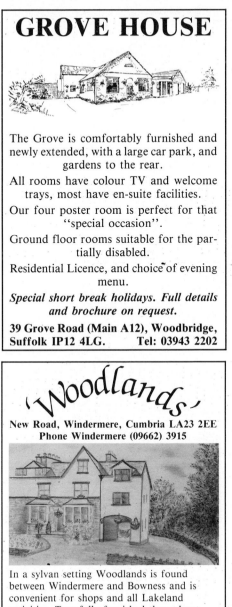

WOODY BAY Devon Map 03 SS64

GH Q Q **The Red House** EX31 4QX ☎Parracombe(05983) 255
Apr-Oct
Detached house in lovely elevated position, set in a wooded valley, offering friendly, personal services, comfort, and good home cooking.
6rm(3⇋1🐾2hc)(1fb) CTV in all bedrooms ® ✱ dB&B£33
dB&B⇋🐾£37 WB&B£116-£126 WBDi£175-£190 LDO
6.30pm
Lic ⫞ CTV 8P nc4yrs

WOOKEY HOLE Somerset Map 03 ST54

GH Q Q Q **Glencot House** Glencot Ln BA5 1BH
☎Wells(0749) 77160
Closed 25-28 Dec
This splendid Grade II listed mansion stands in 18 acres of parkland, including river frontage with trout fishing. Two bedrooms have four-poster beds and in addition to the comfortable public rooms there are hairdressing facilities, a sauna, jet stream pool and a snooker table.
10rm(3⇋7🐾)(3fb) CTV in all bedrooms ® ✱
sB&B⇋🐾£30-£35
dB&B⇋🐾£45-£55 WB&B£210-£258 WBDi£280-£308 LDO
8.30pm
Lic ⫞ CTV 21P ⊡(heated) ✔ snooker sauna solarium
Credit Cards [1][3] ⓔ

WOOLACOMBE Devon Map 02 SS44

See also Mortehoe
⊢←GH Q Q Q **Camberley Hotel** Beach Rd EX34 7AA
☎(0271) 870231
This family-run guesthouse enjoys panoramic countryside views. Guests can use an outdoor heated swimming pool, sauna, solarium and squash courts at the large hotel next door.
6⇋🐾 (3fb) CTV in all bedrooms ® sB&B⇋🐾£10-£17.50
dB&B⇋🐾£20-£35 LDO 6.30pm
Lic CTV 6P
ⓔ

GH Q Q Q **The Castle** The Esplanade EX34 7DJ
☎(0271) 870788
Apr-Oct
Built as a private house by a retired Indian Army colonel in 1890, this superbly situated hotel has many original features, including a fine, hand-carved, cedarwood ceiling.
8🐾 (2fb) ® ✈ (ex guide dogs) ✱
dB&B🐾£44-£49 (incl dinner) WB&B£105-£122
WBDi£143-£164 LDO 6pm
Lic ⫞ CTV 8P nc5yrs
ⓔ

GH Q Q *Combe Ridge Hotel* The Esplanade EX34 7DJ
☎(0271) 870321
Mar-Oct
8rm(4🐾4hc)(4fb) CTV in 7 bedrooms ® (wkly only Jul-Aug)
LDO 5pm
Lic ⫞ CTV 7P

GH Q Q **Holmesdale Hotel** Bay View Rd EX34 7DQ
☎(0271) 870335
Closed Jan
Many guests return regularly to this well-equipped holiday hotel with its friendly and outgoing Spanish proprietors. The Gema restaurant offers an extensive menu and features interesting Basque dishes.
15🐾 (10fb) CTV in all bedrooms ® (wkly only high season)
LDO 8.30pm
Lic ⫞ CTV 14P
Credit Cards [1][3]

GH Q Q Q **Pebbles Hotel & Restaurant** Combesgate Beach,
Mortehoe EX34 7EA ☎(0271) 870426
Closed Jan
A stone's throw away from sandy Combesgate beach, this elevated terrace property has superb views of the Devon coastline. A carvery and separate restaurant offer a comprehensive choice of meals with seafood a spaciality. The bedrooms are well equipped.
12rm(11⇋1hc)(5fb) CTV in all bedrooms ® sB&B£18-£22
sB&B⇋£18-£22 dB&B£36-£44
dB&B⇋£36-£44 WB&B£119-£147 WBDi£182-£210 LDO
9.30pm
Lic 25P 1🐾
Credit Cards [1][3]

WOOLHOPE Hereford & Worcester Map 03 SO63

INN Q Q **Butchers Arms** HR1 4RF ☎Fownhope(043277) 281
due to change to (0432) 860281
Located just outside the rural village, and close to Hereford, this inn has extensive bar and restaurant menus, with some unusual choices. The bar areas are 'olde worlde' in style, with beamed ceilings and traditional country inn hospitality.
3hc TV in all bedrooms ® ✈ (ex guide dogs) ✱ sB&Bfr£20.50
dB&Bfr£33 LDO 8.30pm
⫞ 80P nc14yrs
ⓔ

WOOLSTONE Oxfordshire Map 04 SU28

SELECTED

INN Q Q Q Q **The White Horse** SN7 7QL
☎Uffington(036782) 566 & 726
Part of Tom Brown's Schooldays *is said to have been written in this 16th-century inn. Six modern, en suite, well-equipped bedrooms surround a courtyard and the public rooms retain the original character of the building. Ray and Maureen Batty offer an extensive à la carte menu accompanied by a wide selection of wines.*
Annexe 6⇋🐾 CTV in all bedrooms ® ✈ (ex guide dogs)
✱ sB&B⇋🐾£37.50-£41
dB&B⇋🐾£46.50-£57.50 Lunch fr£8.50&alc Dinner
£10-£20alc LDO 10pm
⫞ 60P
Credit Cards [1][2][3][5] ⓔ

WORCESTER Hereford & Worcester Map 03 SO85

See also Leigh
GH Q *The Barbourne* 42 Barbourne Rd WR1 1HU
☎(0905) 27507
Closed Xmas
Just north of the city centre on the A449, this small family-run guesthouse provides simple, well-maintained accommodation which is popular with commercial visitors.
7rm(6hc)(3fb) CTV in all bedrooms LDO noon
Lic ⫞ CTV ⊬
Credit Cards [1][2][3]

WORKINGTON Cumbria Map 11 NX92

GH Q Q **Morven Hotel** Siddick Rd CA14 1LE
☎(0900) 602118 & 602002
On the Maryport road north of the town, this pleasantly furnished hotel, offers good value for money and is personally supervised by resident owners.
6rm(4⇋2hc)(1fb) CTV in all bedrooms ® LDO 4pm
Lic ⫞ CTV 20P

ⓔ Remember to use the money-off vouchers.

WORTHING West Sussex Map **04** TQ10

GH [Q][Q][Q] Blair House 11 St Georges Rd BN11 2DS
☎(0903) 34071
Close to the seafront, Beach House Park and bowling greens, this hotel offers a warm, friendly welcome. A comfortable, well-appointed lounge complements the modern bedrooms. The proprietors offer personal service and good home-cooked meals.
7rm(2🛁4🚿1hc)(1fb) CTV in all bedrooms Ⓡ
✖ (ex guide dogs) * sB&B🛁🚿£17-£19.50
dB&B🛁🚿£34-£39 WB&B£119-£136 WBDi£167-£185 (wkly only Xmas) LDO 6.30pm
Lic ♨ 3P 1🚗 (£5 per day)
Credit Cards [1] [3] [£]

GH [Q][Q] Camelot House 20 Gannon Rd BN11 2DT
☎(0903) 204334
Closed 21 Dec-6 Jan
This is a small, privately owned guesthouse, located close to the seafront. The accommodation here is basic but comfortable. The guesthouse has an atmosphere that is both pleasant and relaxing, under the owners' supervision.
5rm(1🛁1🚿3hc)(1fb) CTV in all bedrooms Ⓡ
✖ (ex guide dogs) * sB&B£13-£14 dB&B£26-£28
dB&B🛁🚿£30-£32 WB&Bfr£87.50 LDO noon
Lic ♨ 1P
[£]

GH [Q][Q][Q] Delmar Hotel 1-2 New Pde BN11 2BQ
☎(0903) 211834
This family-run licensed hotel overlooks the sea and offers friendly helpful service. Four of the well-equipped bedrooms have sea views, and there is a comfortable lounge, a large dining room and a roof garden.
13rm(10🛁🚿3hc)(2fb)🚭in all bedrooms CTV in all bedrooms Ⓡ ✖ (ex guide dogs) sB&Bfr£20.70 sB&B🛁🚿fr£22.43 dB&Bfr£41.40
dB&B🛁🚿fr£44.86 WB&Bfr£144.90 WBDifr£228.83 LDO 6.30pm
Lic ♨ CTV 5P 1🚗
Credit Cards [1] [3]

GH [Q][Q][Q] Heene House 140 Heene Rd BN11 4PJ
☎(0903) 33213 & 210804
This charming detached house, in Victorian style, offers comfortable, well- equipped bedroom accommodation. There is a delightful conservatory which overlooks the garden, a comfortable lounge with a small bar and a nicely appointed dining room.
15rm(3🛁8🚿4hc)(3fb) CTV in all bedrooms Ⓡ sB&B£28
sB&B🛁🚿£33-£38 dB&B£40
dB&B🛁🚿£45-£50 WB&B£180-£220 WBDi£230-£270 LDO 8pm
Lic ♨ 7P
Credit Cards [1] [2] [3] [5] [£]

GH [Q][Q][Q] Moorings 4 Selden Rd BN11 2LL ☎(0903) 208882
This is a comfortable and welcoming guesthouse, with well-appointed bedrooms. There is a very pleasing lounge and attractive dining room where a good selection of home cooking is offered. The restaurant is open to non-residents by prior arrangement.
8rm(2🛁6🚿)(2fb) CTV in all bedrooms Ⓡ ✖
sB&B🛁🚿£19-£20
dB&B🛁🚿£33-£35 WB&Bfr£104 WBDifr£152 LDO noon
Lic ♨ 5P
Credit Cards [1] [3] [£]

GH [Q][Q] Osborne 175 Brighton Rd BN11 2EX ☎(0903) 35771
A friendly and welcoming establishment, this has a good seafront location and extensive views. The bedrooms vary in size, and are neat and well equipped. There is a pleasant breakfast room.
8rm(2🚿6hc)(4fb) CTV in all bedrooms Ⓡ * sB&B£15.50-£17 dB&B£31-£34 dB&B🚿£34
Lic ♨ CTV 🚫 nc9yrs
Credit Cards [1] [2] [3]

GH [Q][Q][Q] *South Dene* 41 Warwick Gardens BN11 1PF
☎(0903) 32909
This bright and cheerful, end-of-terrace house is set in a quiet cul-de-sac away from the seafront. It has been tastefully modernised and furnished, creating a warm and friendly atmosphere.
6rm(1🚿5hc)(1fb) CTV in 3 bedrooms Ⓡ ✖ LDO 3pm
Lic ♨ CTV 🚫 nc9yrs

GH [Q][Q] Wolsey Hotel 179-181 Brighton Rd BN11 2EX
☎(0903) 36149
Closed mid Dec
This establishment commands a good seafront location with some exceptional sea views. The accommodation is traditional, with neat, simply decorated bedrooms. There is a lounge with adjoining bar, in addition to the dining room.
13rm(3🚿10hc)(2fb) CTV in all bedrooms Ⓡ
sB&B£18.50-£19.50 sB&B🚿£27.50-£28.50 dB&B£37-£39
dB&B🚿£55-£57 WB&B£127.50-£195 WBDi£182.50-£250 LDO 6.30pm
Lic ♨ CTV 🚫
Credit Cards [1] [3] [£]

WREXHAM Clwyd

See **Hanmer & Penley** **Also advertisement on page 403**

WROTHAM Kent Map **05** TQ65

INN [Q][Q] The Bull Hotel Bull Ln, Wrotham Heath TN15 7RF
☎Borough Green(0732) 885522
This 14th-century inn first accommodated pilgrims to Canterbury and retains much of its early character while providing well-equipped rooms. Freshly prepared meals are offered in the restaurant and an extensive bar menu is available. Mrs Elaine Dunnell provides helpful service.
9rm(5🛁4hc)(1fb) CTV in all bedrooms Ⓡ sB&B£38
sB&B🛁£52 dB&B£46
dB&B🛁£56 Lunch fr£2.50&alc LDO 10pm
▶

卿 50P
Credit Cards [1] [2] [3] [5]
See advertisement under SEVENOAKS on page 329

WYBUNBURY Cheshire Map **07** SJ64

FH **QQ** Mrs Jean E Callwood **Lea** *(SJ717489)* Wrinehill Rd
CW5 7NS ☎Crewe(0270) 841429
*Lea Farm is a modern house with country views from all rooms
and peacocks meandering around the charming gardens. The
comfortable lounge has a small snooker table for guests use.*
2hc (1fb) CTV in all bedrooms ® ✳ sB&B£12-£13
dB&B£22-£24 WB&B£77-£84 WBDi£110-£133 LDO 5pm
CTV 22P ✔ 150 acres dairy
£

WYE Kent Map **05** TR04

INN **QQ** *New Flying Horse* Upper Bridge St TN25 5AN
☎(0233) 812297
*Comfortable and well-managed inn with well-equipped bedrooms,
an á la carte dining room and a rear patio garden.*
6hc Annexe 4⇨ (1fb) CTV in all bedrooms ® LDO 9.50pm
卿 100P
Credit Cards [1] [2] [3] [5]

YARMOUTH, GREAT Norfolk Map **05** TG50

GH **QQ** **Balmoral Private Hotel** 65 Avondale Rd NR31 6DJ
☎(0493) 662538
*Situated on a quiet street adjacent to the seafront this modest
accommodation is cheerfully decorated and furnished and some
bedrooms have en suite facilities.*
7rm(2♠5hc)(3fb) CTV in all bedrooms ® ✳ sB&B£15-£19
sB&B♠£18-£22 dB&B£30-£38
dB&B♠£36-£44 WB&B£80-£120 WBDi£95-£140 LDO 4pm
Lic 卿 CTV ✗
£

GH **QQQ** *Bradgate Hotel* NR30 1DY ☎(0493) 842578
*With easy access to the town centre and seafront, this quality
guesthouse has large, airy bedrooms, all with modern en suite
facilities.*
5⇨ (4fb) CTV in all bedrooms ®
Lic 卿 5P
Credit Cards [1] [3]

GH **Q** **Frandor** 120 Lowertoft Rd NR31 6ND (2m S off A12)
☎(0493) 662112
*Situated on a busy road close to the town centre and with off street
parking. This accommodation is spacious, simply furnished and
has a homely atmosphere. The evening meal is freshly prepared
with a choice of main courses.*
6rm(2♠4hc)(3fb)✗in 4 bedrooms CTV in all bedrooms ® ✳
sB&B£12-£15 sB&B♠£15-£18 dB&B£24-£30
dB&B♠£30-£34 WB&B£75-£95 WBDi£95-£120 (wkly only
mid May-Sep) LDO 6.30pm
Lic 卿 CTV 12P
Credit Cards [1] [3]

GH **QQ** **Georgian House Private Hotel** NR30 4EW
☎(0493) 842623
Closed Xmas-Feb rs Nov-Etr
*Situated on the seafront on the quieter north side of the town
centre. This family-run hotel has modestly furnished rooms with
some en suite facilities and sea views. The hotel offers good value
for money.*
25rm(10⇨5♠10hc)(1fb) CTV in all bedrooms ® ✖
sB&B£20-£25 sB&B⇨♠£25-£30 dB&B£30-£35
dB&B⇨♠£35-£45 WB&B£90-£120 (wkly only end Jun-Sep)
Lic 卿 24P nc5yrs

GH **Q** **Gladstone House** NR30 3AU ☎(0493) 843181
Closed Xmas
A neat, modern guesthouse offering fresh home cooking.
11hc (1fb) CTV in all bedrooms ✳ sB&B£13-£16
dB&B£24-£28 WB&B£76-£98 WBDi£87-£106 LDO 6pm
Lic CTV 4P
Credit Cards [1] [3] £

GH **QQ** **Helm House** 2 Trafalgar Rd NR30 2LD
☎(0493) 843385
*Situated between the sea front and the town centre Helm House
has quite compact rooms which are attractively furnished and
decorated in bright fresh shades and have good facilities.*
11hc (5fb) CTV in all bedrooms ® ✖ (ex guide dogs) LDO
5pm
卿 CTV ✗

↤↦**GH** **Q** **Jennis Lodge** 63 Avondale Rd NR31 6DJ (2m S off
A12) ☎(0493) 662840
*Adjacent to the seafront and within easy walking from the shops
this establishment is modestly furnished with cheerful, tidy rooms.
The evening meal is freshly prepared and there is a small bar next
to the dining room.*
11hc (4fb) CTV in all bedrooms ® sB&B£13-£17
dB&B£26-£34 WB&B£84-£110 WBDi£95-£115 LDO 4pm
Lic 卿 CTV ✗
£

GH **QQ** **Palm Court Hotel** NR30 1EF ☎(0493) 844568
Closed Jan
47rm(35⇨12hc)(6fb) CTV in all bedrooms ® sB&B£25-£30
sB&B⇨♠£42-£50 dB&B£38-£42
dB&B⇨♠£50-£60 WB&B£99-£189 WBDi£122-£220 LDO
8pm
Lic lift 卿 CTV 47P ▨(heated) sauna solarium gymnasium
pool table
Credit Cards [1] [3]

GH **QQ** **Squirrels Nest** 71 Avondale Rd NR31 6DJ
☎(0493) 662746
9rm(1⇨8♠)(1fb) CTV in all bedrooms ® sB&B⇨♠£25-£30
dB&B⇨♠£50-£60 WB&B£160-£190 WBDi£195-£250 LDO
9.30pm
Lic 卿 CTV 5P
Credit Cards [1] [2] [3] £

YEALAND CONYERS Lancashire Map **07** SD57

GH **QQQ** **Holmere Hall Hotel** LA5 9SN
☎Carnforth(0524) 735353 FAX (0524) 734860
*A small comfortable country hotel in a garden setting. The
building is 17th century.*
8rm(2⇨6hc)(2fb) CTV in all bedrooms ® ✳ sB&Bfr£19.50
dB&Bfr£39 dB&B⇨♠fr£54 LDO 10pm
Lic 卿 20P
Credit Cards [1] [3] [5]

YEALMPTON Devon Map **02** SX55

FH **QQQ** Mrs A German **Broadmoor** *(SX574498)* PL8 2NE
☎Plymouth(0752) 880407
*This attractive 16th-century stone-built house is to be found on the
Yealmpton to Newton Ferrers road. Retaining many original
features, the farmhouse offers comfortable open plan public areas
and spacious bedrooms.*
3hc CTV in 2 bedrooms TV in 1 bedroom ® ✖ ✳ sB&Bfr£11
dB&Bfr£22
P nc7yrs 200 acres mixed

Q is for quality. For a full explanation of this AA quality
award, consult the Contents page.

YELVERTON Devon Map **02** SX56

GH [Q][Q][Q] ***Harrabeer Country House Hotel*** Harrowbeer Ln PL20 6EA ☎(0822) 853302

Closed Xmas

This friendly family-run hotel stands in attractive gardens with an outdoor pool. The comfortable rooms have good facilities and there is an attractive bar and lounge. Home-cooked dishes are served in the dining room.

7rm(2🛁3🚿2hc)(1fb) CTV in all bedrooms [R] 🐕 LDO 7.30pm Lic ♨ CTV 10P 🏊

Credit Cards [1] [2] [3] [5]

See advertisement under PLYMOUTH on page 299

GH [Q][Q] **Waverley** 5 Greenbank Ter PL20 6DR ☎(0822) 854617

This imposing Victorian terraced house overlooks the village common and has comfortable public areas and spacious, well-equipped bedrooms, each with a private shower.

5hc (2fb) CTV in all bedrooms [R] sB&Bfr£15 dB&Bfr£30 WB&Bfr£105 WBDifr£164 LDO 10am ♨ CTV 2P [£]

YEOVIL Somerset Map **03** ST51

FH [Q][Q][Q] Mrs M Tucker **Carents** *(ST546188)* Yeovil Marsh BA21 3QE (2m N of Yeovil off A37) ☎(0935) 76622

Feb-Nov

Charm and character abound in this mellow 16th-century stone farmhouse, which is set in a quiet location. A hearty cooked breakfast is served in the attractive dining room, while the large, comfortable lounge has an open fireplace.

3hc 🚭in all bedrooms [R] 🐕 ✱ sB&B£14-£15 dB&B£27-£28 CTV 6P 350 acres arable beef

YORK North Yorkshire Map **08** SE65

See also **Acaster Malbis, Copmanthorpe** & **Rufforth**

GH QQ Abbingdon 60 Bootham Crescent YO3 7AH
☎(0904) 621761

This is an attractive guesthouse standing to the north of the city walls and it provides value for money. Comfortable, well-equipped bedrooms are complemented by a lovely lounge and cosy dining room.

7rm(5♠2hc)(2fb) CTV in all bedrooms ® ✖ (ex guide dogs) ✳
sB&B£16-£17 dB&B£32-£34 dB&B♠£36-£38
⏣CTV 4P 2🏐

GH QQ Aberford Hotel 35 East Mount Rd YO2 2BD
☎(0904) 622694

Aberford House is a pleasantly appointed, family-run establishment situated close to the city centre, with comfortable, well-equipped bedrooms. There is a cosy cellar bar for guests' use, and breakfast is served in the pretty dining room.

12rm(2➘♠10hc)(1fb)✂in 2 bedrooms CTV in all bedrooms
® ✖ (ex guide dogs) sB&B£17-£19 sB&B➘♠£23-£26
dB&B£32-£36 dB&B➘♠£38-£50 WB&Bfr£100
Lic ⏣7P 1🏐
Credit Cards ①②③ⓔ

GH QQ Acer Hotel 52 Scarcroft Hill, The Mount YO2 1DE
☎(0904) 653839 & 628046

The city centre and railway station are within walking distance of this quietly located establishment. The recently refurbished bedrooms are attractive and well equipped, and are complemented by a lounge and small dining room.

6rm(1➘4♠1hc)(1fb) CTV in all bedrooms ® sB&B£30-£40
sB&B➘♠£30-£40 dB&B£40-£50
dB&B➘♠£40-£50 WB&B£140-£175 WBDi£200-£220 LDO
6.30pm
Lic ⏣CTV 4P 1🏐
Credit Cards ①③ⓔ

GH Q Acomb Road 128 Acomb Rd YO2 4HA ☎(0904) 792321
The simple accommodation at this guesthouse is good value for money. It is about one mile from the city centre.
12rm(6♠6hc)(3fb) CTV in all bedrooms ® ✳ sB&B£12-£14
dB&B£24-£28
dB&B♠£28-£32 WB&B£84-£112 WBDi£119-£147 LDO
7.30pm
Lic CTV 20P

GH QQ Adams House Hotel 5 Main Street, Fulford YO1 4HJ
☎(0904) 655413

Closed Xmas

Mr and Mrs McCloud run this friendly, welcoming guesthouse which is set in a pleasant district south of the city centre on the A19. The accommodation is attractive and comfortable, and there is a car park for guests' use.
7rm(2➘4♠1hc)(2fb) CTV in all bedrooms ®
Lic ⏣8P

GH Q Alcuin Lodge 15 Sycamore Place, Bootham YO3 7DW
☎(0904) 632222

Feb-Nov

Three-storeyed, brick built Edwardian mid-terraced property in quiet residential area a short distance from the city centre.
6rm(2♠4hc)(1fb) CTV in all bedrooms ® ✖ (ex guide dogs) ✳
sB&B£15-£17 dB&B£24-£27 dB&B♠£30-£34 WB&B£84-£119
⏣2P nc5yrs

GH QQQ Alfreda 61 Heslington Ln, Fulford YO1 4HN
☎(0904) 631698

Pair of Edwardian houses in Regency style with lawns and trees. Small cosy public rooms with style and character and bedrooms are spacious with modern fittings.
10rm(4♠6hc)(4fb) CTV in all bedrooms ® dB&B£25-£36
dB&B♠£30-£40 WB&B£85-£125

⏣CTV 20P 2🏐 (£2 per night)
Credit Cards ①③ⓔ

GH QQ Ambleside 62 Bootham Crescent YO3 7AH
☎(0904) 637165

This comfortable house has a congenial atmosphere enhanced by the beamed dining room and the relaxing lounge.
7rm(4♠3hc) CTV in all bedrooms ® ✖
⏣CTV ✗ nc9yrs

GH QQQ Arndale Hotel 290 Tadcaster Rd YO2 2ET
☎(0904) 702424

Closed Xmas & New Year

This elegant Victorian house overlooks the racecourse and has spacious bedrooms with en suite facilites. Several rooms have half-tester or four-poster beds. Every modern facility is provided by David and Gillian Reynard, together with ample parking space and splendid gardens.
10➘♠ (1fb) CTV in all bedrooms ® ✖ (ex guide dogs)
dB&B➘♠£43-£57 LDO noon
Lic ⏣15P nc5yrs
ⓔ

⌐►**GH Q Arnot House** 17 Grosvenor Ter, Bootham YO3 7AG
☎(0904) 641966

Closed Dec-Jan

This spacious house has a great deal of character. The bedrooms are large, and imaginative home-cooked meals are served. A warm, friendly welcome is assured.
6hc (2fb) CTV in all bedrooms ® ✖ sB&B£11-£14
dB&B£22-£28 WB&B£77-£98 WBDi£143.50-£164.50 LDO
1pm
Lic ⏣2P nc5yrs
ⓔ

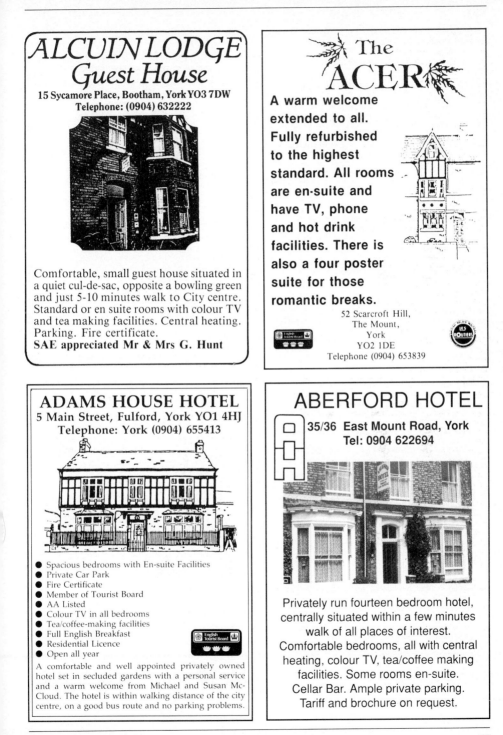

GH Q Q *Ascot House* 80 East Pde YO3 7YH ☎(0904) 426826
Attractive Victorian house with unusual oriel staircase window.
Bedrooms have modern fittings.
9rm(2⇔7↖)(2fb) CTV in all bedrooms ® LDO 6pm
♨ CTV 10P 1☂ sauna solarium

GH Q Q Q Ashbourne House 139 Fulford Rd YO1 4HG
☎(0904) 639912
High standards are maintained at this guesthouse, which is 1 mile
from the city centre on the A19, and has off-street parking. The
rooms are well furnished and equipped, and some have en suite
facilities.
6rm(2↖4hc)(1fb) CTV in all bedrooms ® ✱ dB&B£28-£36
dB&B↖£30-£39 LDO 7.30pm
Lic ♨ CTV 5P 1☂
Credit Cards 1 3 £

GH Q Q Avenue 6 The Avenue, Clifton YO3 6AS
☎(0904) 620575
Feb-Oct
Three-storeyed, late Victorian house with attractive small
forecourt garden, in quiet tree-lined street, near city centre.
6rm(2↖4hc)(2fb) CTV in 2 bedrooms TV in 4 bedrooms ✱
sB&Bfr£13 sB&B↖fr£15 dB&Bfr£26 dB&B↖fr£30
♨ CTV 𝄞 nc4yrs

GH Q Q Q The Beckett 58 Bootham Crescent YO3 7AH
☎(0904) 644728
Closed 15 Dec-13 Jan
Comfortable and well maintained, this attractively decorated
Victorian house has well-appointed bedrooms. Personally
supervised by the owners, The Beckett stands off the A19 within
easy reach of the city centre.
7rm(5↖2hc)(2fb) CTV in all bedrooms ® ✕ (ex guide dogs) ✱
sB&B£14-£15 dB&B£28-£30 dB&B↖£30-£34 WB&B£98-£119
♨ CTV 3P
£

GH Q Q Bedford 108/110 Bootham YO3 7DG ☎(0904) 624412
A short distance from the cathedral and historic town centre, this
turn of the century building has outstanding architectural
decoration. The bedrooms are well equipped, and the public rooms
cosy.
14rm(3⇔11↖)(3fb) CTV in all bedrooms ® ✕ (ex guide dogs)
sB&B⇔↖£24-£32
dB&B⇔↖£34-£44 WB&B£119-£224 WBDi£175-£280 LDO
1pm
Lic ♨ CTV 14P
Credit Cards 1 3

GH Q Q Beech House 6-7 Longfield Terrace, Bootham
YO3 7DJ ☎(0904) 634581 & 630951
Closed Xmas & New Year
A pair of Victorian terraced houses converted into very smart and
comfortable accommodation.
9↖ CTV in all bedrooms ® ✕ ✱ sB&B↖£18-£24
dB&B↖£30-£42 LDO breakfast
Lic ♨ 5P nc10yrs
£

GH Q Q Q Bootham Bar Hotel 4 High Petergate YO1 2EH
☎(0904) 658516
Closed 7-13 Jan
This delightful 18th-century house is just inside one of the fortified
gateways to the city. It is well furnished with good facilities and a
Victorian Parlour tea room which is open all day.
9rm(1⇔8↖)(2fb) CTV in all bedrooms ® ✕ (ex guide dogs)
dB&B⇔↖£44-£58 LDO 7.30pm
Lic ♨ 𝄞
Credit Cards 1 3 £

GH [Q][Q] ***Brönte House*** 22 Grosvenor Terrace, Bootham YO3 7AG ☎(0904) 621066
Closed 5 days Xmas
Just 5 minutes' walk from the city, this Victorian town house provides simple and comfortable accommodation. The bedrooms are rather compact, but nicely decorated. Providing friendly family-run accommodation, the guesthouse has a pleasant dining room and combined lounge.
5rm(3🚿2hc)(1fb) [R] 🚫🐕
♨ CTV 3P nc2yrs

GH [Q][Q][Q] Byron House Hotel The Mount YO2 2DD ☎(0904) 632525 FAX (0904) 613174
Closed 25 Dec-4 Jan
Close to the city centre on the A1036, this attractive building features elegant rooms with high ceilings. The bedrooms are mostly en suite and of generous proportions, well equipped and very comfortable. There is also an attractive lounge and dining room.
10rm(7🛁🚿3hc)(4fb) CTV in all bedrooms [R] 🚫🐕 (ex guide dogs) sB&B£26-£32 sB&B🛁🚿£39-£45 dB&B🛁🚿£58-£68 WB&B£180-£270 WBDi£260-£324 LDO noon
Lic ♨ 7P
Credit Cards [1] [2] [3] [5]

GH [Q][Q] City 68 Monkgate YO3 7PF ☎(0904) 622483
Centrally situated, this small guesthouse is just a few minutes from the Minster and City Walls. A totally non-smoking establishment it provides compact, nicely decorated bedrooms, a small lounge and well-appointed dining room.
6rm(3🚿3hc)(3fb)🚭in all bedrooms CTV in all bedrooms [R] 🚫🐕 sB&B£20-£22 sB&B🚿£25-£27 dB&B£28-£30 dB&B🚿£32-£36 WB&B£75-£90
♨ 6P nc5yrs
Credit Cards [1] [3] [£]

GH [Q][Q] Clifton Green Hotel 8 Clifton Green, Clifton YO3 6LH ☎(0904) 623597
On the A19 opposite the green, this attractive little guesthouse is light and airy, with a comfy lounge bar and cosy dining room. Ideal bed and breakfast accommodation is provided with attractive, compact bedrooms.
8rm(2🚿6hc) CTV in all bedrooms [R] 🚫🐕 (ex guide dogs) dB&Bfr£32 dB&B🚿fr£44
Lic ♨ CTV 0P 5🚗

GH [Q][Q][Q] ***Coach House Hotel*** Marygate YO3 7BH ☎(0904) 652780
The interior of this hotel, with its exposed beams and brickwork, is most attractive and complements the accommodation which includes an appealing restaurant. Situated in Marygate off the A19, it is a short walk from the Minster.
13rm(5🛁6🚿2hc) [R] 🚫🐕 (ex guide dogs) LDO 9.30pm
Lic ♨ CTV 13P
Credit Cards [1] [3]

GH [Q][Q][Q] Collingwood Hotel 163 Holgate Rd YO2 4DF ☎(0904) 783333
This 200-year-old Georgian house has been sympathetically restored to retain many period features. Comfortable well-equipped bedrooms, lounge bar, separate television room and a small attractive dining room.
10🛁🚿 (2fb) CTV in all bedrooms [R] 🚫🐕 (ex guide dogs) dB&B🛁🚿£36-£42 WB&B£126-£147 LDO 10am
Lic ♨ CTV 10P
Credit Cards [1] [2] [3] [5] [£]

GH [Q] Coppers Lodge 15 Alma Terrace, Fulford Rd YO1 4DQ ☎(0904) 639871
Simple, good value accommodation in a former police HQ (and gaol) 1 mile from the town centre.
8rm(1🛁🚿7hc)(5fb) CTV in all bedrooms [R] ✱ sB&B£12-£15 dB&B£24-£30 dB&B🛁🚿£30-£35 WB&B£84-£105 WBDi£126-£147 (wkly only Nov-Feb) LDO 2pm
♨ CTV 2P
[£]

GH [Q][Q] Crescent 77 Bootham YO3 7DQ ☎(0904) 623216
This attractive 18th-century house is close to Bootham Bar and the Minster, and has been carefully converted to offer well-appointed accommodation. All rooms are prettily decorated and there is also a cosy lounge.
10rm(6🛁🚿4hc)(5fb) CTV in all bedrooms [R] 🚫🐕 ✱ sB&B£14.50-£17.50 dB&B£27-£40 dB&B🛁🚿£30-£40 WB&B£101.50-£140 WBDi£164.50-£203 LDO noon
Lic ♨ CTV 3P 1🚗
Credit Cards [1] [2] [3] [5] [£]

GH [Q][Q][Q] Curzon Lodge and Stable Cottages 23 Tadcaster Rd, Dringhouses YO2 2QG ☎(0904) 703157
Closed 23 Dec-1 Jan
Many original features remain in this listed building which stands close to the racecourse on the main route into the city. The bedrooms, some of which are in a converted stable block, are comfortable and well equipped.
5rm(3🛁2🚿)Annexe 5rm(3🛁2🚿)(1fb) CTV in all bedrooms [R] 🚫🐕 sB&B🛁🚿£27-£32 dB&B🛁🚿£42-£52 WB&B£133-£168
♨ 15P nc7yrs
[£]

GH [Q][Q] Dray Lodge Hotel Moor Ln, Murton YO1 3UH (3m E off A166) ☎(0904) 489591 FAX (0904) 488587
Converted from a 19th-century carriage works, Dray Lodge is in a small village on the eastern edge of the city. The Mortimer family create a cosy, welcoming atmosphere. All of the well-equipped bedrooms are en suite.
10🛁🚿 (1fb) CTV in all bedrooms [R] 🚫🐕 (ex guide dogs) ✱ sB&B🛁🚿£26.45-£32.50 dB&B🛁🚿£42.40-£46 WB&B£141-£153 WBDi£196 LDO 8pm
Lic ♨ CTV 15P fitness training room
Credit Cards [1] [2] [3] [£]

See advertisement on page 411

GH [Q][Q][Q] ***Field House Hotel*** 2 St George's Place YO2 2DR ☎(0904) 639572
Closed Xmas
Beautiful gardens surround this carefully refurbished late 19th-century building situated close to the racecourse. The fine Victorian exterior combines a superb mix of modern styles and comfort inside, including a tasteful spacious ground floor lounge and separate lounge bar. On the lower ground floor there is an elegant and charming dining room.
17rm(1🛁10🚿6hc) CTV in all bedrooms [R] 🚫🐕 (ex guide dogs) LDO 7pm
Lic ♨ 20P
Credit Cards [1] [2] [3]

See advertisement on page 411

GH [Q][Q][Q] Four Poster Lodge 68-70 Heslington Rd YO1 5AU ☎(0904) 651170
Closed 24 Dec-7 Jan
Attractive and very well appointed, this guesthouse stands by the city walls. Judith Jones and her family offer a warm welcome and provide cosy, well-equipped bedrooms, mostly en suite and with four-poster beds. Dinner is available.
10rm(6🚿4hc)(2fb) CTV in all bedrooms [R] ✱ sB&B🚿£20-£22 dB&Bfr£31 dB&B🚿£38-£40 WB&B£273 LDO 6pm
Lic ♨ 4P 3🚗
[£]

GH Q *Georgian* 35 Bootham YO3 7BT ☎(0904) 622874
Closed Xmas
This Georgian town house is close to the historic city centre. The rear of the hotel is of greater age, and features interesting oak beams. The dining room and lounge are on the first floor.
12rm(2⇨1↑9hc)(1fb) CTV in 5 bedrooms ®
♨ CTV 26P

SELECTED

GH QQQQ **Grasmead House Hotel** 1 Scarcroft Hill, The Mount YO2 1DF ☎(0904) 629996
Situated a short walk from the city centre, this guesthouse is full of character, and Len and Eileen Spray enjoy welcoming guests to their home. They will provide details of a comprehensive tour of the city. Four-poster beds grace each bedroom, promising a restful night. A cosy bar provides relaxation and there are many restaurants to visit nearby.
6⇨↑ (2fb)✁in 3 bedrooms CTV in all bedrooms ® ✖
dB&B⇨↑£45-£48 WB&B£141-£150
Lic ♨ CTV 1P
Credit Cards ① ③ ⓔ

GH QQ **Greenside** 124 Clifton YO3 6BQ ☎(0904) 623631
Charming detached house in centre of Clifton Hamlet, about a mile from city centre.
6rm(3↑3hc)(2fb) CTV in all bedrooms ✳ sB&Bfr£13
sB&B↑fr£28 dB&Bfr£25 dB&B↑fr£28
Lic ♨ CTV 5P 1🐾 ⚙
ⓔ

GH Q **Heworth** 126 East Pde YO3 7YG ☎(0904) 426384
Neat and tidy guesthouse convenient for town facilities.
6hc CTV in all bedrooms ® ✳ sB&B£11.50-£14.50
dB&B£23-£29 WB&B£74.50-£94
Lic ♨ 1P 1🐾

GH QQQ **Hobbits Hotel** 9 St Peters Grove, Clifton YO3 6AQ ☎(0904) 624538
Closed 24-26 Dec
Set amidst a garden of trees and shrubs this large Victorian house offers comfortable accommodation with interesting well-equipped bedrooms.
5⇨↑ (2fb)✁in 1 bedroom CTV in all bedrooms ®
sB&B⇨↑£20-£25 dB&B⇨↑£40-£45
Lic ♨ CTV 6P
Credit Cards ① ③ ⓔ

GH QQ **The Hollies** 141 Fulford Rd YO1 4HG ☎(0904) 634279
Closed Xmas & New Year
The Hollies is a comfortable family-run guesthouse, a mile or so from the city centre, providing a warm and friendly atmosphere. The comfortable bedrooms are attractively decorated. A lounge is available for guests, and breakfast is served in a small dining room.
5rm(2↑3hc)(2fb) CTV in all bedrooms ® sB&B£17-£20
sB&B↑£20-£25 dB&B£26-£34 dB&B↑£30-£38
♨ CTV 5P

GH QQQ **Holmwood House Hotel** 112-114 Holgate Rd YO2 4BB ☎(0904) 626183
Closed 24 Dec-1 Jan
Two large terrace houses now provide attractive, well-appointed and elegant accommodation. Some of the bedrooms are reserved for non-smokers. Christina and Roberto Gramellini run this guesthouse in an informal manner, and provide guests with a substantial breakfast.
10⇨↑in 3 bedrooms CTV in all bedrooms ®
sB&B⇨↑£35-£38 dB&B⇨↑£45-£48 LDO 10am
Lic ♨ 10P 1🐾 (£2 per night) nc8yrs
Credit Cards ① ③

GH QQQ **Inglewood** 7 Clifton Green YO3 6LH ☎(0904) 653523
Commendable hotel with delightful fittings and furnishings in bustling suburb of Clifton.
7rm(3↑4hc)(2fb) CTV in all bedrooms ✖ sB&Bfr£18
dB&Bfr£32 dB&B↑fr£42
♨ CTV 1🐾
ⓔ

GH QQ *Limes* 135 Fulford Rd YO1 4HE ☎(0904) 624548
Set in attractive gardens to the south of the city, this large guesthouse has spacious bedrooms and a well-appointed dining room and lounge bar.
9rm(6↑3hc)(4fb) CTV in all bedrooms ® LDO 6.30pm
Lic ♨ CTV 14P
Credit Cards ① ② ③ ⑤

See advertisement on page 413

GH QQ **Linden Lodge Hotel** Nunthorpe Avenue, Scarcroft Rd YO2 1PF ☎(0904) 620107
Closed mid Dec-mid Jan
This attractive, detached Victorian house is located within walking distance of the city centre. Mr and Mrs Wharton provide comfortable accommodation that is well equipped. There are 2 comfortable lounges available for guests' use.
12rm(2↑10hc)(3fb) CTV in 2 bedrooms ® ✖ ✖ sB&Bfr£13.50
dB&B£27-£30
dB&B↑£36-£40 WB&B£87.50-£91.50 LDO noon
Lic ♨ CTV ✗
Credit Cards ① ③

See advertisement on page 413

Visit your local AA Centre.

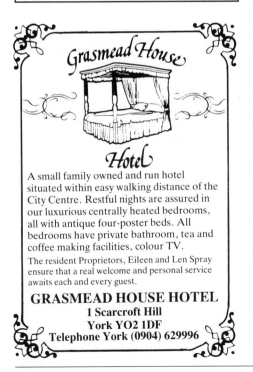

GH QQQ *Midway House Hotel* 145 Fulford Rd YO1 4HG
☎(0904) 659272
This detached Victorian house has been sympathetically modernised to offer well- appointed and comfortable accommodation with an attractive dining room and pleasant, relaxing lounge.
9rm(8🟘1hc)(2fb) CTV in all bedrooms ® ✕ (ex guide dogs) LDO 5pm
Lic ♛ 12P
Credit Cards 1 3

GH QQ *Minster View* 2 Grosvenor Ter YO3 7AG
☎(0904) 655034
Tall Victorian terraced house, comfortably converted, situated about half a mile from the town centre.
8rm(3⇄1🟘4hc)(4fb) CTV in all bedrooms ® LDO 5.30pm
Lic ♛ CTV 6P

GH Q *Moat Hotel* Nunnery Ln YO2 1AA ☎(0904) 652926
Benefiting from its own car park, this well-furnished hotel is close to the city walls, and is an ideal base from which to tour the city.
9rm(6🟘3hc)(1fb) CTV in all bedrooms ® ✕ (ex guide dogs) ✱
sB&Bfr£25 sB&B🟘fr£30 dB&Bfr£36 dB&B🟘fr£40
Lic ♛ CTV 10P ✔
Credit Cards 1 2 3 5 £

GH QQQ *Orchard Court Hotel* 4 St Peters Grove YO3 6AQ
☎(0904) 653964
An elegant Victorian house in quiet cul-de-sac, close to city centre. The lofty public rooms are tastefully decorated.
11rm(8⇄🟘3hc)(4fb) CTV in all bedrooms ®
✕ (ex guide dogs) ✱ sB&B£19-£29
dB&B⇄🟘£40-£56 LDO 7.30pm
Lic ♛ CTV 12P
Credit Cards 1 3 £

GH Q *Le Petit Hotel & Reataurant Francais* 103 Mount Rd
YO2 2AX ☎(0904) 647339
Conveniently situated between the town centre and racecourse, this small guesthouse has neat accommodation and the resident proprietor gives guests a warm welcome.
10rm(2🟘8hc)(1fb) CTV in all bedrooms ® LDO 4pm
Lic ♛ CTV 1🛏
Credit Cards 3

GH QQ *Priory Hotel* 126 Fulford Rd YO1 4BE
☎(0904) 625280
Closed Xmas
A pair of large double-fronted Victorian town houses with rear gardens, near city centre.
20rm(2⇄18🟘)(5fb) CTV in all bedrooms ® ✕ (ex guide dogs)
✱ sB&B⇄🟘£20-£25
dB&B⇄🟘£40-£50 (wkly only Nov-Mar) LDO 9.15pm
Lic ♛ CTV 25P
Credit Cards 1 2 3 5 £

See advertisement on page 415

GH QQQ *St Denys Hotel* St Denys Rd YO1 1DQ
☎(0904) 622207
Closed 2wks Xmas
Former vicarage offers comfortable spacious accommodation and cosy lounge.
11rm(7⇄4🟘)(4fb) CTV in all bedrooms ® sB&B⇄🟘£27-£42
dB&B⇄🟘£42 LDO noon
Lic ♛ CTV 9P
£

GH QQ *St Raphael* 44 Queen Anne's Rd, Bootham YO3 7AF
☎(0904) 645028
This 3-storeyed mock Tudor town house is set in a residential area only a short walk away from the Minster and provides comfortable accommodation.

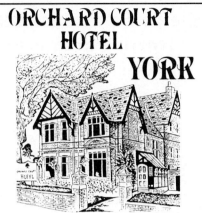

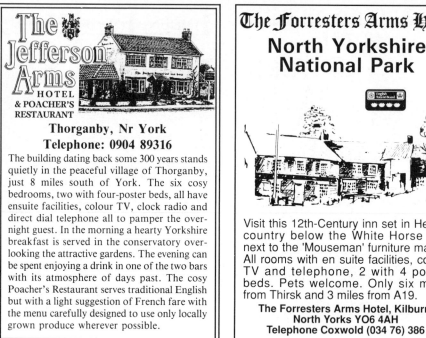

The Priory Hotel, York

The Priory offers comfortable accommodation with full English breakfast, and is situated 600 yards south of York's medieval city walls, within easy direct reach of the nearby inner and outer ring roads. The city centre can be reached by a pleasant riverside walk.

The 20 bedrooms, all equipped with colour TV and tea/coffee making facilities, include single, double and family accommodation, all with en suite shower and toilet facilities.

The Hotel is AA listed, and has full central heating, a licensed bar and restaurant. The pleasant garden leads to the large private car-park.

Reductions are available for children sharing accommodation with their parents. Please send for brochure and tariff.

Proprietors:
George and Barbara Jackson
The Priory Hotel
Fulford Road
York YO1 4BE
Telephone York (0904) 625280

8rm(2🌂6hc)(2fb) CTV in all bedrooms ® ✱ sB&B£11-£14
dB&B£22-£28
dB&B🌂£26-£35 WB&B£77-£108 WBDi£119-£150 (wkly only
Nov-Mar) LDO 4pm
🍴 CTV ⅌
Credit Cards ①③

GH ◙◙◙ *Skeldergate House Hotel* 56 Skeldergate YO1 1DS
☎(0904) 635521
*Built in 1760 by a prominent architect, this riverside house is in the
town centre and retains several original features. The
accommodation is charming and the resident proprietors provide
natural hospitality.*
8rm(1⇔7🌂)(2fb) CTV in all bedrooms ® ✂ LDO 6pm
Lic 🍴 CTV 6P
Credit Cards ①③

GH ◙◙ *Sycamore* 19 Sycamore Place YO3 7DW
☎(0904) 624712
Closed Dec
*This small family-operated guesthouse is set in a quiet corner of
town, about a mile north of the centre.*

6rm(3🌂3hc)(1fb) CTV in all bedrooms ® ✂ ✱ dB&B£22-£26
dB&B🌂£26-£32 WB&B£85-£95
🍴 3P nc5yrs
£

See advertisement on page 414

YOULGREAVE Derbyshire Map **08** SK26

INN ◙◙ **The Bulls Head** Church St DE4 1UR
☎(0629) 636307
4hc (2fb) CTV in all bedrooms ® ✂ ✱ dB&B£24 LDO 8.30pm
8P nc5yrs
Credit Cards ③ £

Reader's Report

Please use this form to record your comments on any guesthouse, farmhouse or inn at which you stay. We shall be most interested to hear about any recommendations of establishments not included in our Guide, or about any criticisms or complaints. All complaints will be treated seriously and passed on to our Inspectorate, but we do urge you to take up any complaint in the first instance with the owner or manager of the establishment to give them the chance to put things right.

Please post to: Editorial Department
Automobile Association
Fanum House,
Basingstoke
Hants RG21 2EA

Your name (block capitals): _____

Your address (block capitals): _____

_____

AA Membership Number: _____

Reader's Report

Please use this form to record your comments on any guesthouse, farmhouse or inn at which you stay. We shall be most interested to hear about any recommendations of establishments not included in our Guide, or about any criticisms or complaints. All complaints will be treated seriously and passed on to our Inspectorate, but we do urge you to take up any complaint in the first instance with the owner or manager of the establishment to give them the chance to put things right.

Please post to: Editorial Department
Automobile Association
Fanum House,
Basingstoke
Hants RG21 2EA

Your name (block capitals): _____

Your address (block capitals): _____

_____

AA Membership Number: _____

_____

_____

_____

_____

_____

_____

_____

_____

_____

_____

_____

_____

_____

_____

Reader's Report

Please use this form to record your comments on any guesthouse, farmhouse or inn at which you stay. We shall be most interested to hear about any recommendations of establishments not included in our Guide, or about any criticisms or complaints. All complaints will be treated seriously and passed on to our Inspectorate, but we do urge you to take up any complaint in the first instance with the owner or manager of the establishment to give them the chance to put things right.

Please post to: Editorial Department
Automobile Association
Fanum House,
Basingstoke
Hants RG21 2EA

Your name (block capitals): _____

Your address (block capitals): _____

AA Membership Number: _____

Index of Town Plans

Key to Town Plans

Recommended Route	*i* Tourist Information Centre	❻ Guesthouse, inn, etc.
Other Routes		**◀ ½m** Distance to guesthouses, etc, from edge of plan
Restricted Roads	**AA** AA Centre	
✝ Churches	**P** Car Parking	**ASHFORD 16m** Mileage to town from edge of plan

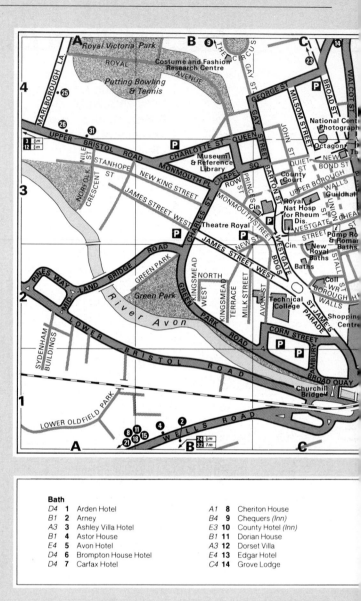

Bath

D4	**1**	Arden Hotel
B1	**2**	Arney
A3	**3**	Ashley Villa Hotel
B1	**4**	Astor House
E4	**5**	Avon Hotel
D4	**6**	Brompton House Hotel
D4	**7**	Carfax Hotel
A1	**8**	Cheriton House
B4	**9**	Chequers *(Inn)*
E3	**10**	County Hotel *(Inn)*
B1	**11**	Dorian House
A3	**12**	Dorset Villa
E4	**13**	Edgar Hotel
C4	**14**	Grove Lodge

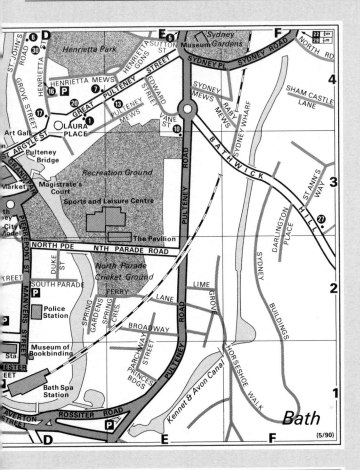

B1 **15**	Highways House	B1 **24**	Paradise House Hotel
D4 **16**	Kennard Hotel	A4 **25**	Parkside
D4 **17**	Laura Place Hotel	A4 **26**	Hotel St Clair
B1 **18**	Leighton House	F3 **27**	Somerset House
D4 **20**	Millers Hotel	F4 **29**	The Tasburgh Bath
A1 **21**	Oldfields	D4 **30**	Villa Magdala Private Hotel
F4 **22**	Orchard House Hotel	A4 **31**	Waltons
C4 **23**	Oxford Private Hotel	B1 **32**	Wentworth House Hotel

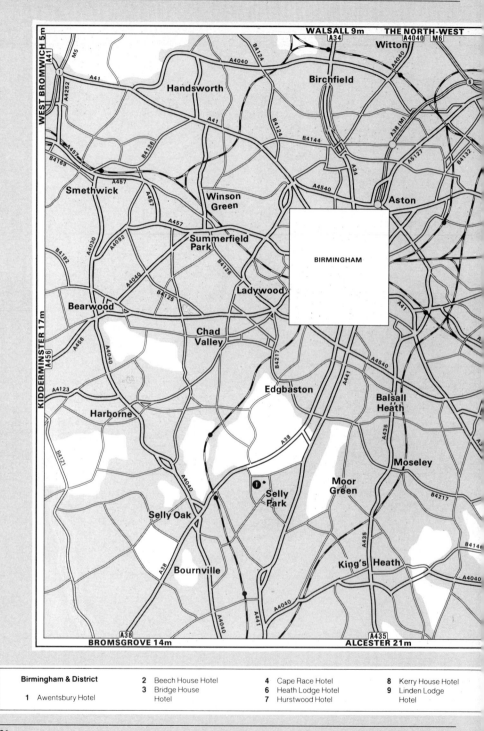

Birmingham & District

1 Awentsbury Hotel

2 Beech House Hotel
3 Bridge House
   Hotel

4 Cape Race Hotel
6 Heath Lodge Hotel
7 Hurstwood Hotel

8 Kerry House Hotel
9 Linden Lodge
   Hotel

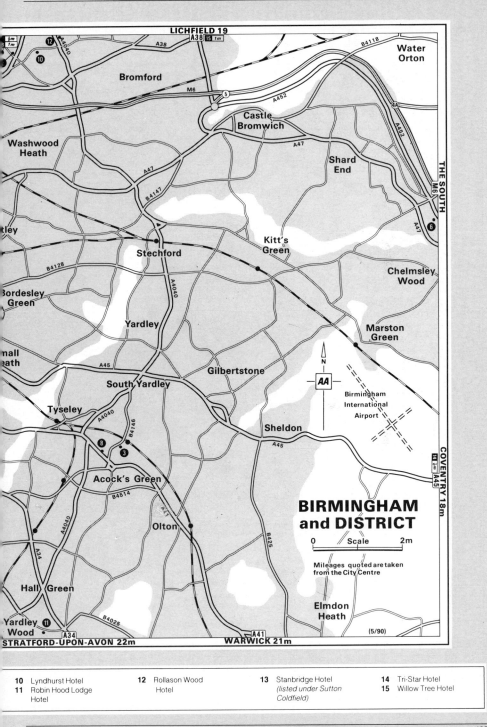

BIRMINGHAM and DISTRICT

Scale 0 — 2m

Mileages quoted are taken from the City Centre

(5/90)

10	Lyndhurst Hotel	12	Rollason Wood Hotel	13	Stanbridge Hotel *(listed under Sutton Coldfield)*	14	Tri-Star Hotel
11	Robin Hood Lodge Hotel					15	Willow Tree Hotel

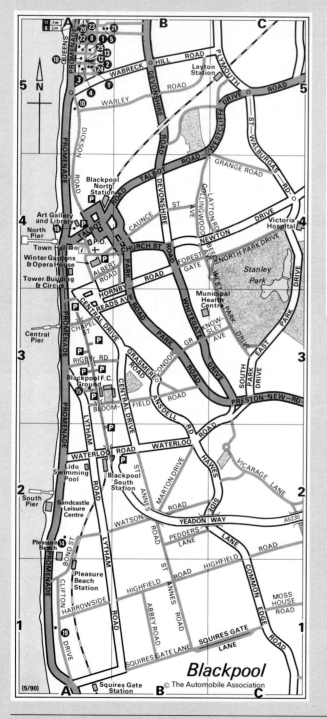

Blackpool

A5	1	Arosa Hotel
A5	2	Ashcroft Private Hotel
A5	3	Berwick Private Hotel
A5	4	Brooklands Hotel
A5	5	Burlees Hotel
A5	6	Cliff Head Hotel
A5	8	Cliftonville Hotel
A5	9	Denely Private Hotel
A5	10	Derwent Private Hotel
A5	11	The Garville Hotel
A5	12	Hartshead Hotel
A5	13	Lynstead Private Hotel
A2	14	Lynwood
A3	15	Hotel Mimosa
A4	16	New Austin
A5	18	North Mount Private Hotel
A1	19	Rewa Private Hotel
A5	20	Sunny Cliff
A5	21	Sunray Private Hotel
A5	22	Surrey House Hotel
A5	23	Westmorland Hotel
A5	24	Windsor Hotel
A5	25	Woodleigh Private Hotel

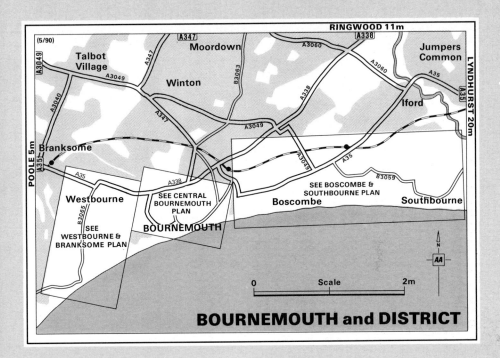

BOURNEMOUTH and DISTRICT

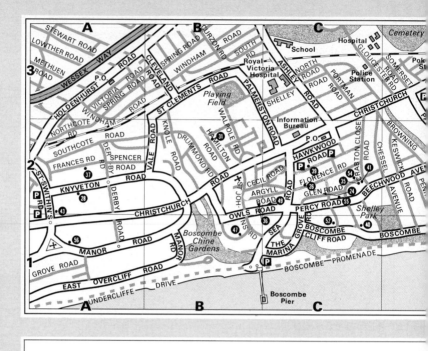

Boscombe & Southbourne

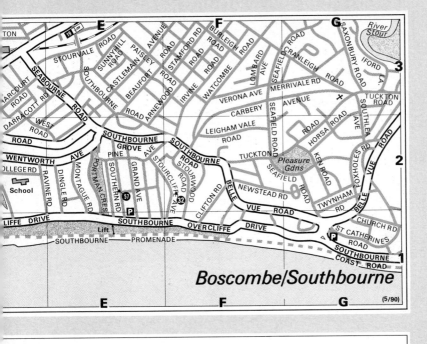

Boscombe/Southbourne

(5/90)

C1 **40**	Norland Private Hotel	C1 **52**	Valberg Hotel
C2 **41**	Oak Hall Private Hotel	C2 **54**	Weavers Hotel
A2 **43**	St John's Lodge Hotel	C2 **55**	Woodlands Hotel
B1 **47**	Sea View Court Hotel	A1 **56**	Wood Lodge Hotel
C2 **49**	Hotel Sorrento	E2 **57**	Woodside Private Hotel

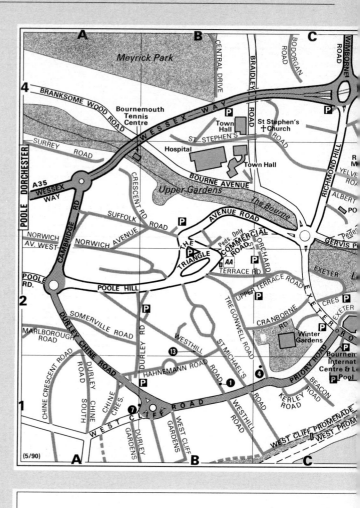

Central Bournemouth

B1 **1** Albemarle Private Hotel

C1 **4** Carisbrooke Hotel
B1 **7** Croham Hurst Hotel

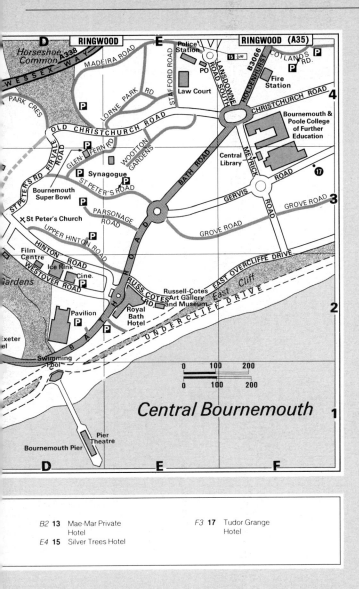

Central Bournemouth

| 0 | 100 | 200 |
| 0 | 100 | 200 |

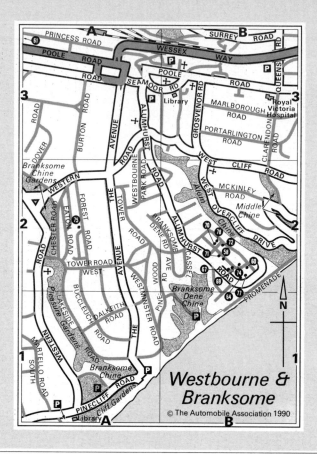

Westbourne & Branksome

B2 **58**	Alum Bay Hotel	
B2 **60**	Alum Grange Hotel	
A3 **61**	Avoncourt Private Hotel *(listed under Poole)*	
B2 **64**	Cliff House Hotel	
B2 **67**	Golden Sands Hotel	
B2 **69**	Highclere Hotel	
B2 **70**	Holmcroft Hotel	
B2 **71**	Newfield Private Hotel	
B2 **72**	Northover Private Hotel	
B2 **74**	Sea-Dene Hotel	
A2 **75**	Sheldon Lodge *(listed under Poole)*	
B2 **77**	West Dene Private Hotel	
B2 **78**	Woodford Court Hotel	

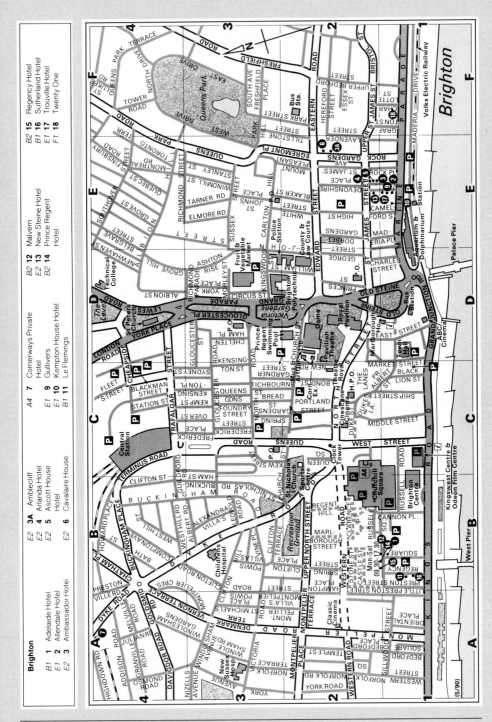

Brighton

B1	**1**	Adelaide Hotel
E1	**2**	Allendale Hotel
E2	**3**	Ambassador Hotel
E2	**3A**	Amblecliff
E2	**4**	Arlanda Hotel
E2	**5**	Ascott House Hotel
E2	**6**	Cavalaire House
A4	**7**	Cornerways Private Hotel
E1	**9**	Gullivers
E1	**10**	Kempton House Hotel
B1	**11**	Le Flemings
B2	**12**	Malvern
E2	**13**	New Steine Hotel
B2	**14**	Prince Regent Hotel
B2	**15**	Regency Hotel
B1	**16**	Sutherland Hotel
E1	**17**	Trouville Hotel
F1	**18**	Twenty One

Brighton

(5/90)

435

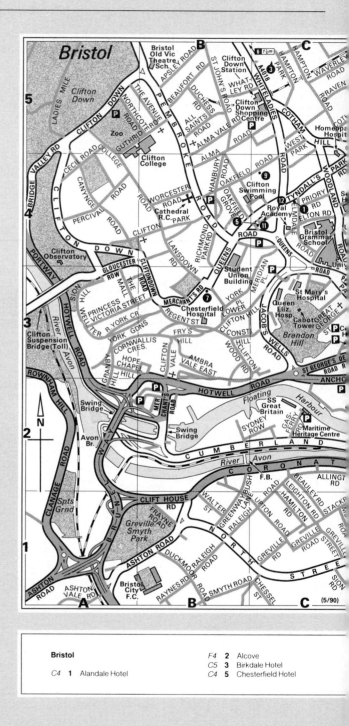

Bristol

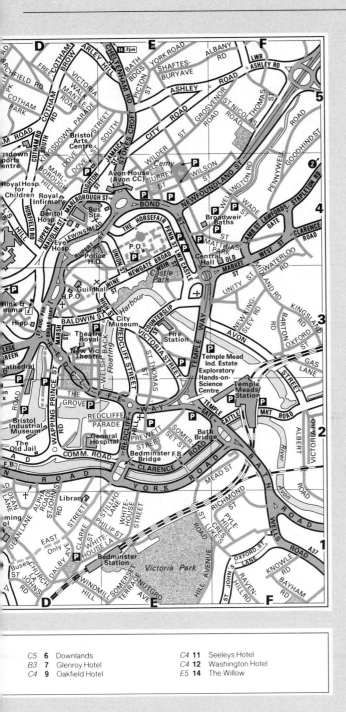

C5	**6**	Downlands
B3	**7**	Glenroy Hotel
C4	**9**	Oakfield Hotel
C4	**11**	Seeleys Hotel
C4	**12**	Washington Hotel
E5	**14**	The Willow

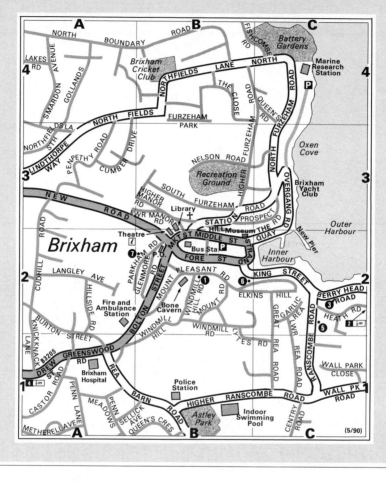

Brixham

B2	**1**	Cottage Hotel
C2	**2**	Greenbrier Hotel
C2	**3**	Harbour Side

A1	**4**	Raddicombe Lodge
C2	**5**	Ranscombe House Hotel
B2	**6**	Sampford House
B2	**7**	Woodlands

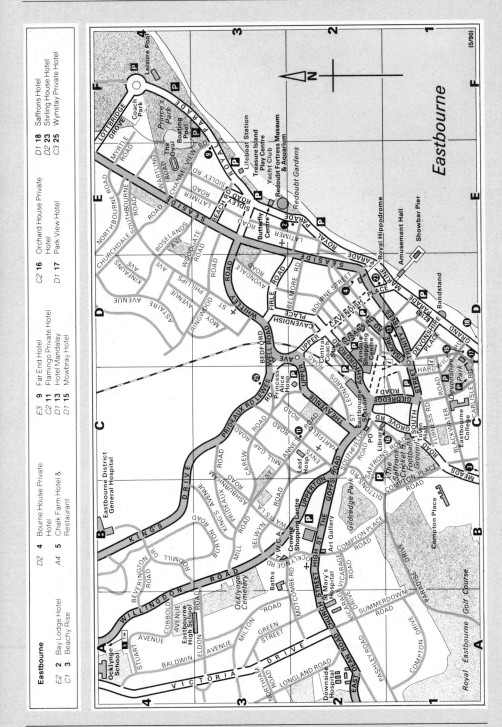

Eastbourne

Eastbourne		Bourne House Private	*D2* **4**
Bay Lodge Hotel	*E2* **2**	Hotel	
Beachy Rise	*C1* **3**	Chalk Farm Hotel &	*A4* **5**
		Restaurant	

Far End Hotel	*E3* **9**	
Flamingo Private Hotel	*C2* **11**	
Hotel Mandalay	*D1* **13**	
Mowbray Hotel	*D1* **15**	

Orchard House Private	*C2* **16**	
Hotel		
Park View Hotel	*D1* **17**	

Saffrons Hotel	*D1* **18**	
Stirling House Hotel	*D2* **23**	
Wynstay Private Hotel	*C3* **25**	

(5/90)

439

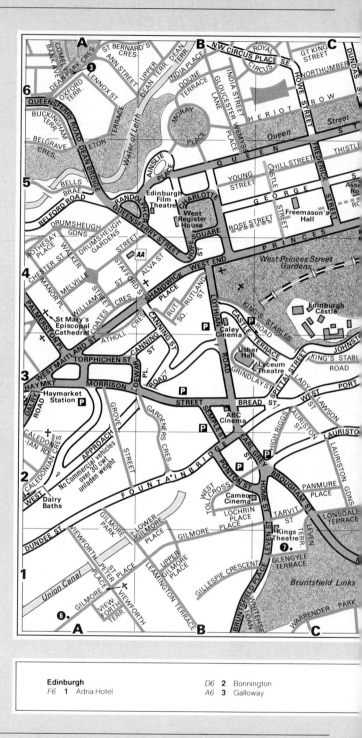

Edinburgh

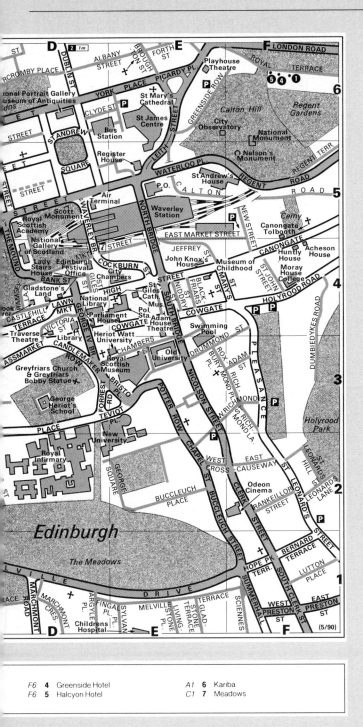

F6 **4** Greenside Hotel   *A1* **6** Kariba
F6 **5** Halcyon Hotel   *C1* **7** Meadows

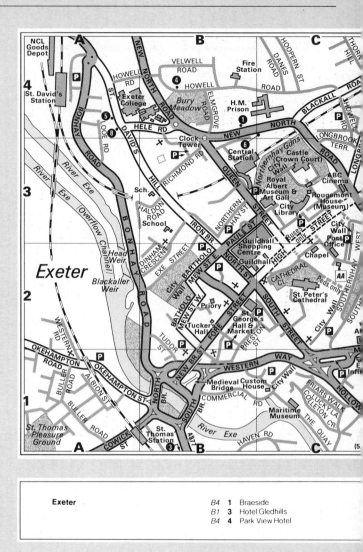

Exeter

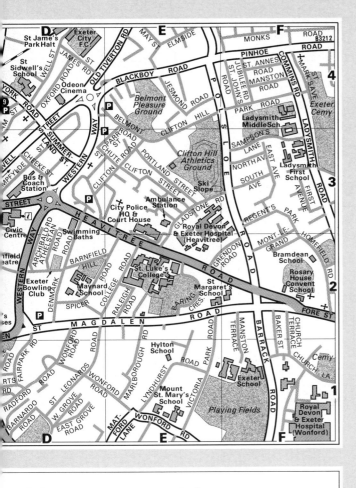

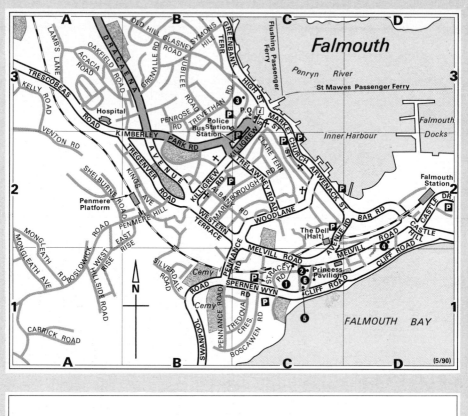

Falmouth

C1	**1**	Cotswold House Private Hotel	*C1*	**2**	Gyllyngvase House Hotel	*D2*	**4**	Penty Bryn Hotel
			C3	**3**	Harbour Hotel	*C1*	**5**	Rathgowry Hotel
						C1	**6**	Westcott Hotel

B2 **1** Belmonte Private Hotel

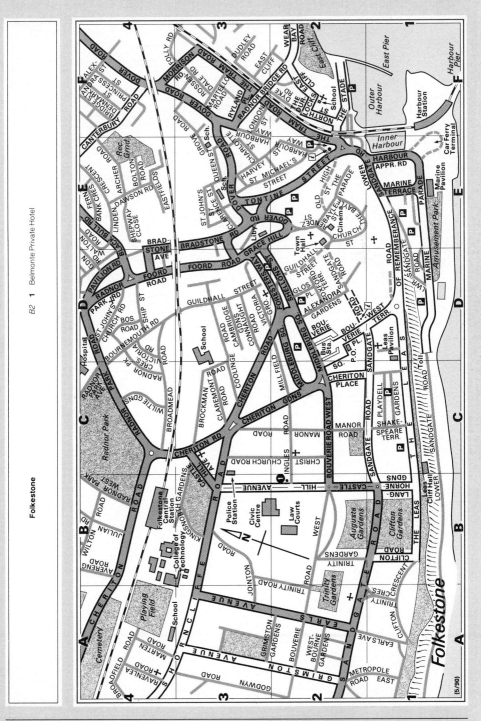

Folkestone

(5/90)

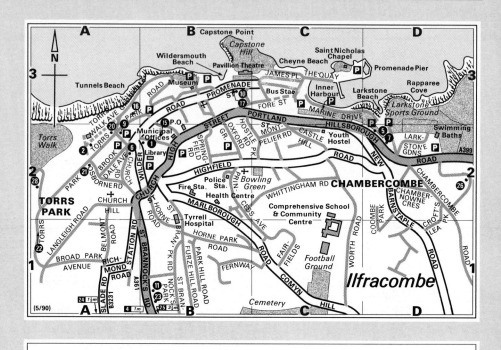

Ilfracombe

			A2	**9**	Cresta Private Hotel		*A1*	**22**	South Tor Hotel
			B3	**10**	Dèdès Hotel		*B1*	**23**	Strathmore Private Hotel
B2	**1**	Avenue Private Hotel	*B1*	**11**	Earlsdale Hotel		*A1*	**24**	Sunny Hill
A2	**2**	Avoncourt Hotel	*B2*	**15**	Lympstone Private Hotel		*B1*	**25**	Sunnymeade County House
A1	**4**	Cairngorm Hotel	*A3*	**16**	Merlin Court Hotel				Hotel *(listed under West Down)*
D2	**5**	Cavendish Hotel	*B3*	**17**	Queens Court Hotel		*D2*	**26**	Varley House
A2	**6**	Chalfont Private Hotel	*A2*	**20**	Seven Hills Hotel		*A2*	**28**	Westwell Hall Hotel
D2	**7**	Collingdale Hotel	*A2*	**21**	Southcliffe Hotel				

Inverness

C2	**1**	Aberfeldy Lodge
B1	**2**	Ardmuir House
D1	**3**	Ardnacoille House
B1	**5**	Brae Ness Hotel
C2	**6**	Craigside House
C1	**7**	Culduthel Lodge
C1	**8**	Four Winds
C1	**9**	Leinster Lodge
C2	**10**	The Old Rectory
B1	**11**	Riverside House Hotel
A3	**12**	St Ann's Hotel

(5/90)

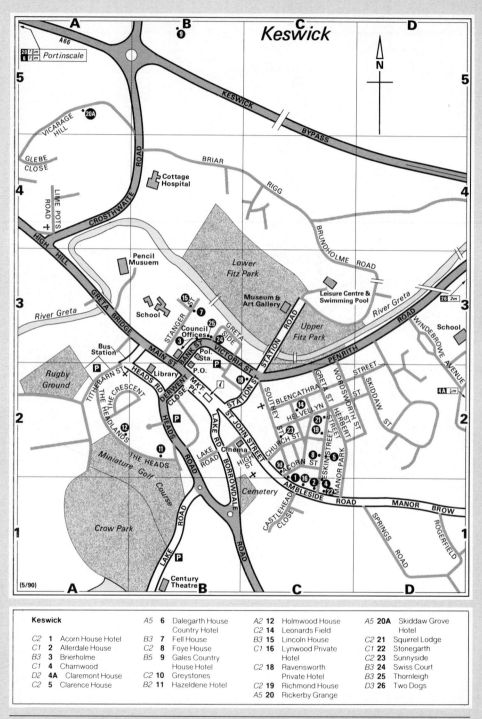

Keswick

C2	1	Acorn House Hotel
C1	2	Allerdale House
B3	3	Brierholme
C1	4	Charnwood
D2	4A	Claremont House
C2	5	Clarence House
A5	6	Dalegarth House Country Hotel
B3	7	Fell House
C2	8	Foye House
B5	9	Gales Country House Hotel
C2	10	Greystones
B2	11	Hazeldene Hotel
A2	12	Holmwood House
C2	14	Leonards Field
B3	15	Lincoln House
C1	16	Lynwood Private Hotel
C2	18	Ravensworth Private Hotel
C2	19	Richmond House
A5	20	Rickerby Grange
A5	20A	Skiddaw Grove Hotel
C2	21	Squirrel Lodge
C1	22	Stonegarth
C2	23	Sunnyside
B3	24	Swiss Court
B3	25	Thornleigh
D3	26	Two Dogs

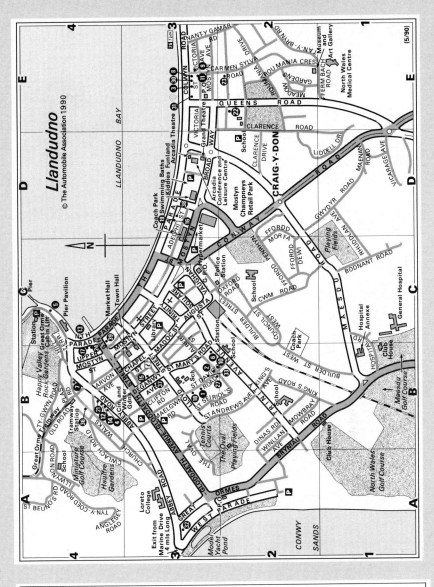

Llandudno

© The Automobile Association 1990

(5/90)

449

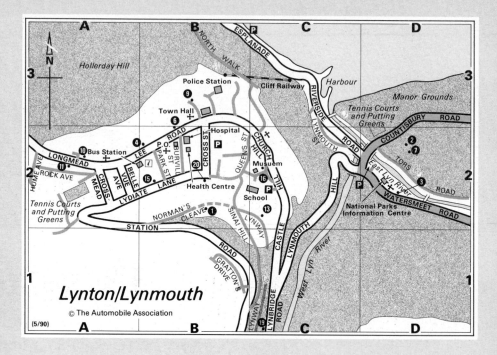

Lynton/Lynmouth

© The Automobile Association

(5/90)

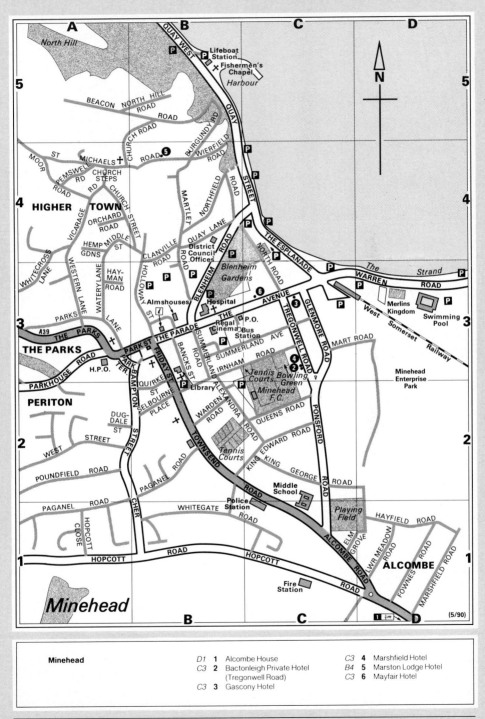

Minehead				
	D1	**1** Alcombe House	C3	**4** Marshfield Hotel
	C3	**2** Bactonleigh Private Hotel	B4	**5** Marston Lodge Hotel
		(Tregonwell Road)	C3	**6** Mayfair Hotel
	C3	**3** Gascony Hotel		

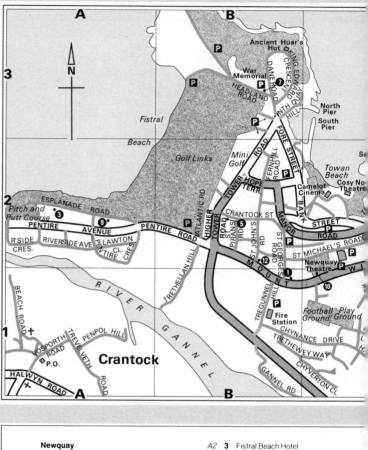

Newquay

B1	**1**	Arundell Hotel	A2	**3**	Fistral Beach Hotel
D2	**2**	Copper Beach Hotel	D2	**4**	Hepworth Hotel
			B2	**5**	Jonel
			E3	**6**	Kellsboro Hotel

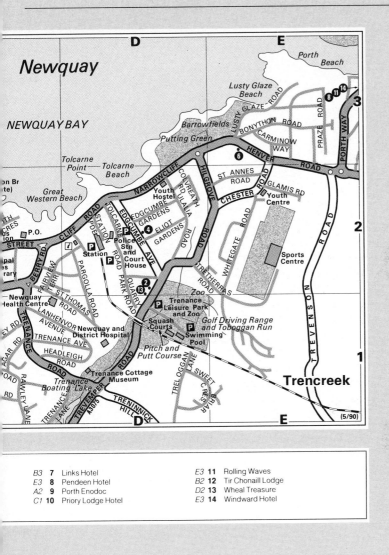

B3	**7**	Links Hotel		
E3	**8**	Pendeen Hotel		
A2	**9**	Porth Enodoc		
C1	**10**	Priory Lodge Hotel		
E3	**11**	Rolling Waves		
B2	**12**	Tir Chonaill Lodge		
D2	**13**	Wheal Treasure		
E3	**14**	Windward Hotel		

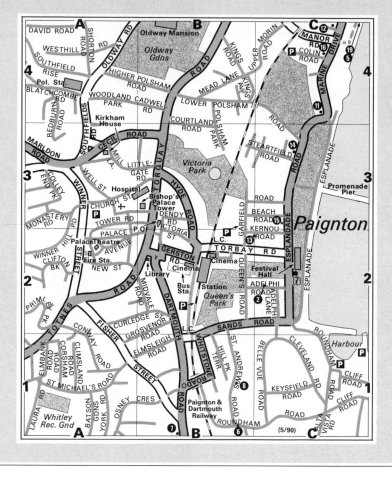

Penzance				C3	**7**	Georgian House		B2	**14**	Trenant Private Hotel
D2	**3**	Blue Seas Hotel		C2	**8**	Kimberley House		C3	**15**	Trevelyan Hotel
C2	**4**	Camilla Hotel		B2	**9**	Hotel Minalto		B2	**16**	Trewella
B1	**5**	Carlton Private Hotel		D4	**10**	Mount Royal Hotel		C2	**17**	The Willows
A2	**6**	Dunedin		A2	**11**	Penmorvah Hotel		D2	**18**	The Yacht *(Inn)*

Paignton				B1	**7**	Clennon Valley Hotel		C3	**14**	Sattva Hotel
				B1	**8**	Danethorpe Hotel		C3	**15**	The Sealawn Hotel
C2	**2**	Beresford		C4	**11**	Redcliffe Lodge Hotel		C4	**16**	Sea Verge Hotel
C4	**5**	Channel View Hotel		C4	**12**	Hotel Retreat		C4	**19**	Torbay Sands Hotel
B1	**6**	Cherra Hotel		B2	**13**	St Weonard's Private Hotel				

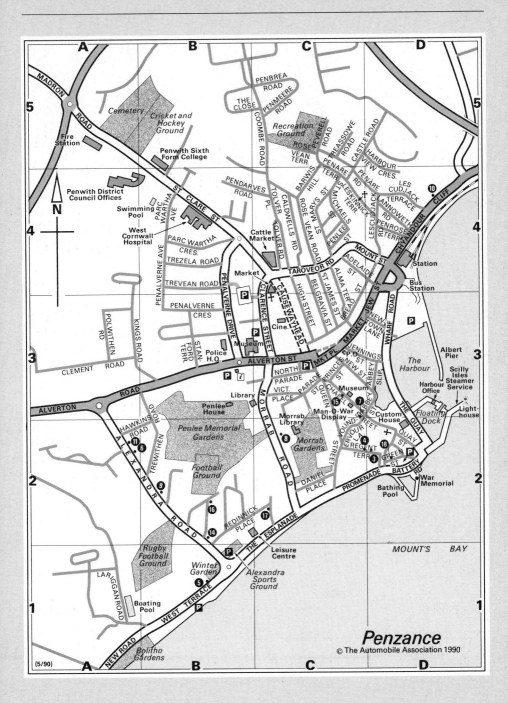

Penzance

© The Automobile Association 1990

(5/90)

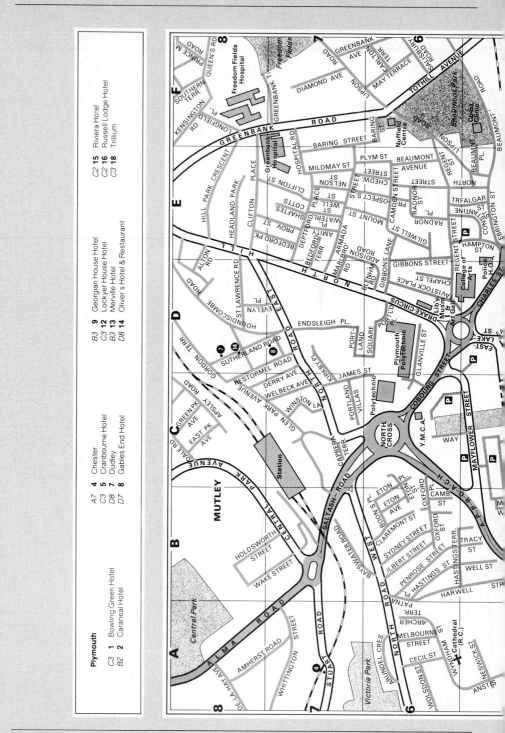

Plymouth

C3	**1**	Bowling Green Hotel	
B2	**2**	Caraneal Hotel	
A7	**4**	Chester	
C3	**5**	Cranbourne Hotel	
D8	**7**	Dudley	
D7	**8**	Gables End Hotel	
B3	**9**	Georgian House Hotel	
C3	**12**	Lockyer House Hotel	
B3	**13**	Merville Hotel	
D8	**14**	Oliver's Hotel & Restaurant	
C2	**15**	Riviera Hotel	
C2	**16**	Russell Lodge Hotel	
C3	**18**	Trillium	

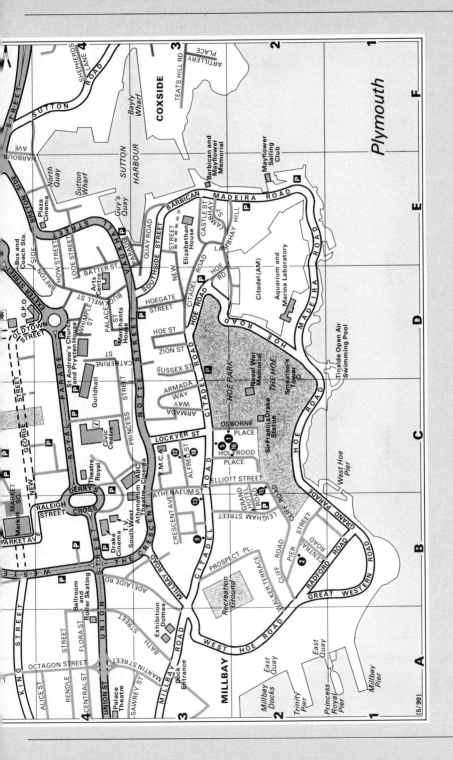

Plymouth

COXSIDE

MILLBAY

(5/90)

457

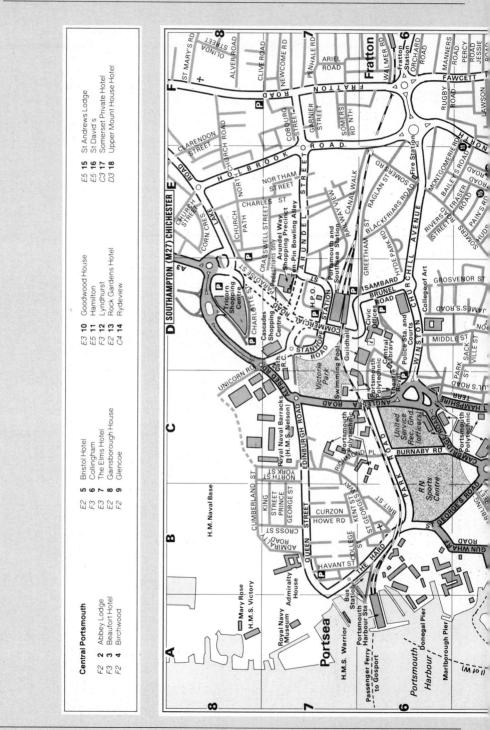

Central Portsmouth

F2	2	Abbey Lodge	E3	10	Goodwood House
F3	3	Beaufort Hotel	E5	11	Hamilton
F2	4	Birchwood	F3	12	Lyndhurst
E2	5	Bristol Hotel	E2	13	Rock Gardens Hotel
F3	6	Collingham	C4	14	Rydeview
E3	7	The Elms Hotel	E5	15	St Andrews Lodge
E2	8	Gainsborough House	E5	16	St David s
F2	9	Glencoe	C3	17	Somerset Private Hotel
			D3	18	Upper Mount House Hotel

Central Portsmouth

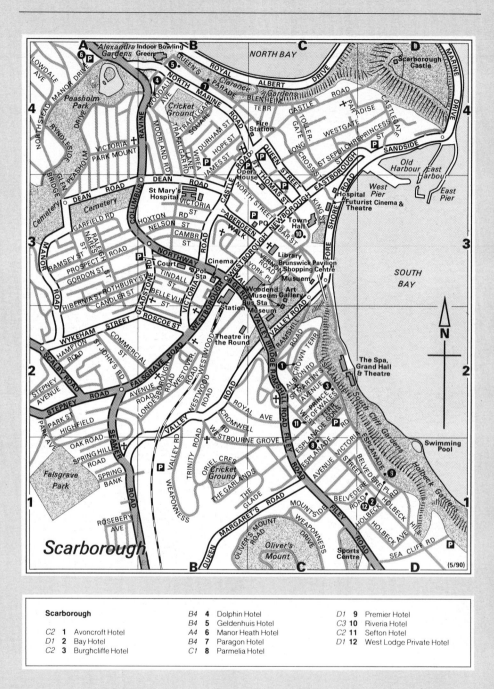

Scarborough		B4	4	Dolphin Hotel	D1	9	Premier Hotel
		B4	5	Geldenhuis Hotel	C3	10	Riveria Hotel
C2	1	Avoncroft Hotel	A4	6	Manor Heath Hotel	C2	11	Sefton Hotel
D1	2	Bay Hotel	B4	7	Paragon Hotel	D1	12	West Lodge Private Hotel
C2	3	Burghcliffe Hotel	C1	8	Parmelia Hotel			

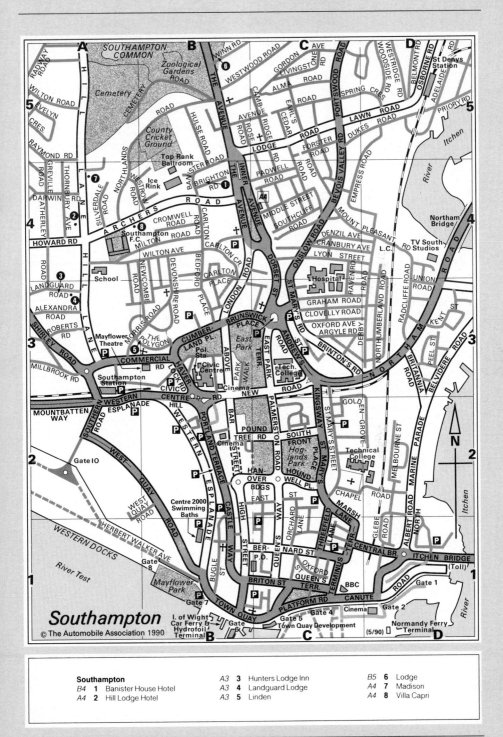

Southampton

© The Automobile Association 1990

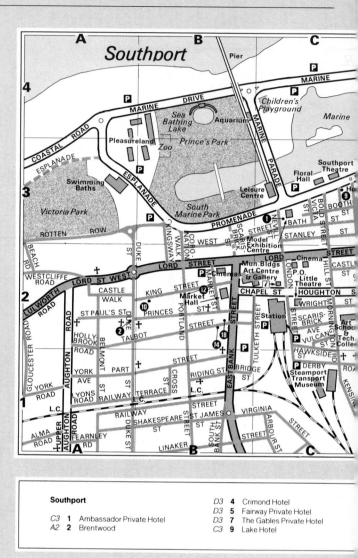

Southport

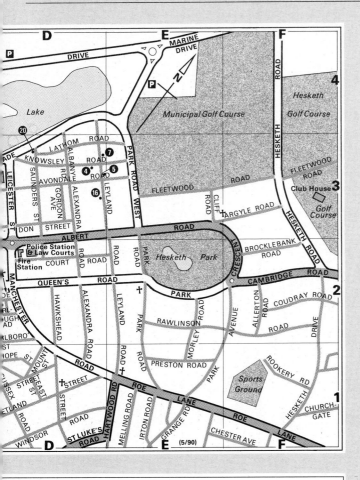

B2 **10**	Lyndhurst	
B2 **12**	Oakwood Private Hotel	
B2 **14**	Rosedale Hotel	
D3 **16**	Sunningdale Hotel	

B2 **18**	The White Lodge Private Hotel	
D3 **20**	Windsor Lodge Hotel	

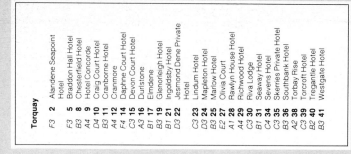

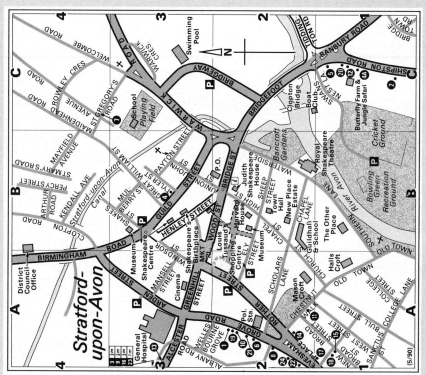

Torquay

F3	2	Alandene Seapoint Hotel
F3	5	Braddon Hall Hotel
B3	8	Chesterfield Hotel
A4	9	Hotel Concorde
D4	10	Craig Court Hotel
B3	11	Cranborne Hotel
A4	12	Cranmore
F4	14	Daphne Court Hotel
C3	15	Devon Court Hotel
A3	16	Durlstone
B1	17	Elmdene
B3	19	Glenorleigh Hotel
B1	21	Ingoldsby Hotel
D3	22	Jesmond Dene Private Hotel
C3	23	Lindum Hotel
D3	24	Mapleton Hotel
B3	25	Marlow Hotel
E2	27	Olivia Court
A1	28	Rawlyn House Hotel
A4	29	Richwood Hotel
C3	30	Riva Lodge
B1	31	Seaway Hotel
C4	34	Sevens Hotel
C3	35	Skerries Private Hotel
B3	36	Southbank Hotel
A2	38	Torbay Rise
C3	39	Torcroft Hotel
B2	40	Tregantle Hotel
B3	41	Westgate Hotel

Stratford-upon-Avon

A2	1	Ambleside
C1	2	Avon View Hotel
A3	3	Brook Lodge
B3	4	Courtland Hotel
C1	4A	Craig Cleeve House
C1	5	Eastnor House Hotel
A2	6	Eversley Bears
C4	7	Hardwick House
A2	8	Hollies
A3	9	Hunters Moon
A2	10	Kawartha House
A2	11	Marlyn
C1	12	Melita Private Hotel
A3	13	Moonraker House
A2	14	Nando's
A1	15	Parkfield
A3	16	Penryn House
A1	17	Penshurst
A1	18	Ravenshurst
A2	19	Salamander
C1	20	Sequoia House Hotel
A2	21	Stretton House Hotel
A2	22	Twelfth Night
A3	23	Victoria Spa Lodge
A2	24	Virginia Lodge

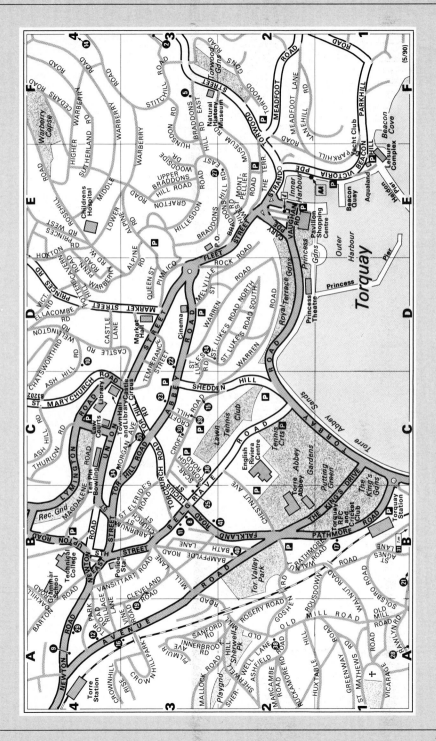

Torquay

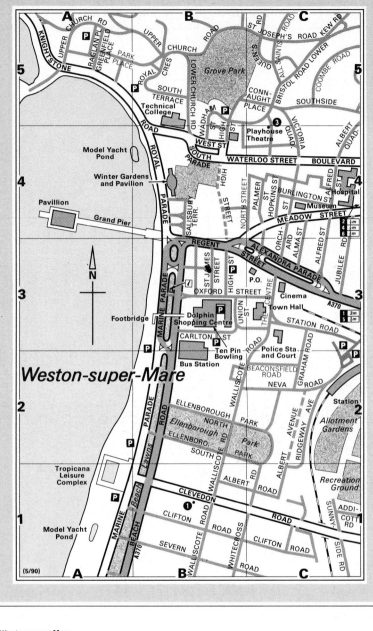

Weston-super-Mare

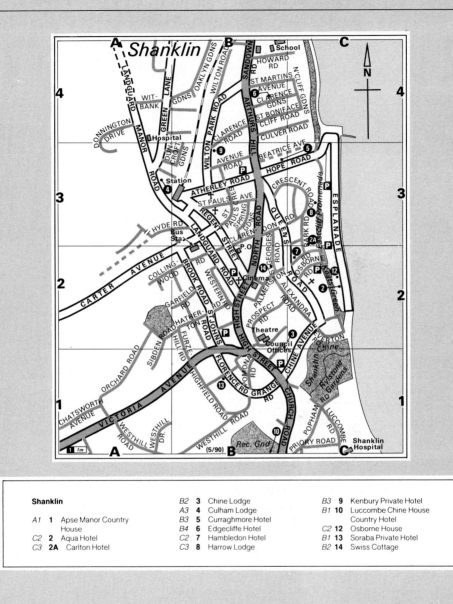

Shanklin

A1	**1**	Apse Manor Country House
C2	**2**	Aqua Hotel
C3	**2A**	Carlton Hotel
B2	**3**	Chine Lodge
A3	**4**	Culham Lodge
B3	**5**	Curraghmore Hotel
B4	**6**	Edgecliffe Hotel
C2	**7**	Hambledon Hotel
C3	**8**	Harrow Lodge
B3	**9**	Kenbury Private Hotel
B1	**10**	Luccombe Chine House Country Hotel
C2	**12**	Osborne House
B1	**13**	Soraba Private Hotel
B2	**14**	Swiss Cottage

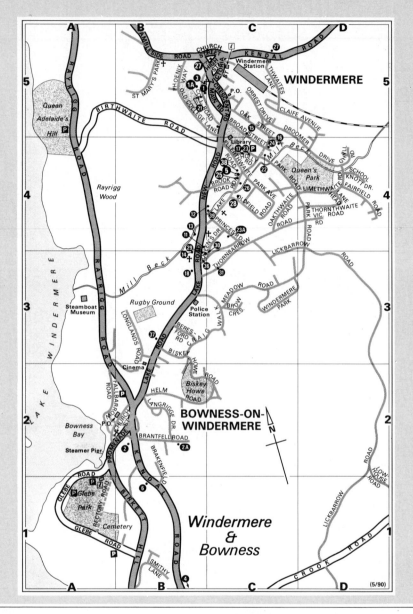

Windermere & Bowness

(5/90)

Index of Regional Maps

BRITAIN
At Your Leisure

This is a book to help the active over-50s with time on their hands to get the best out of the 'happiest days of their lives'.

It is a unique touring guide, allowing all members of the family to enjoy some of the more delightful and unusual places in Britain, at their own pace and in their own time – perhaps out of season or midweek. Important information is included on ease of access and difficult terrain.

There is also expert advice on subjects such as health, finance, holidays, making new friends and if (or when) to move house.

MAKING THE GOING EASY AT MORE THAN 500 SELECTED PLACES TO VISIT

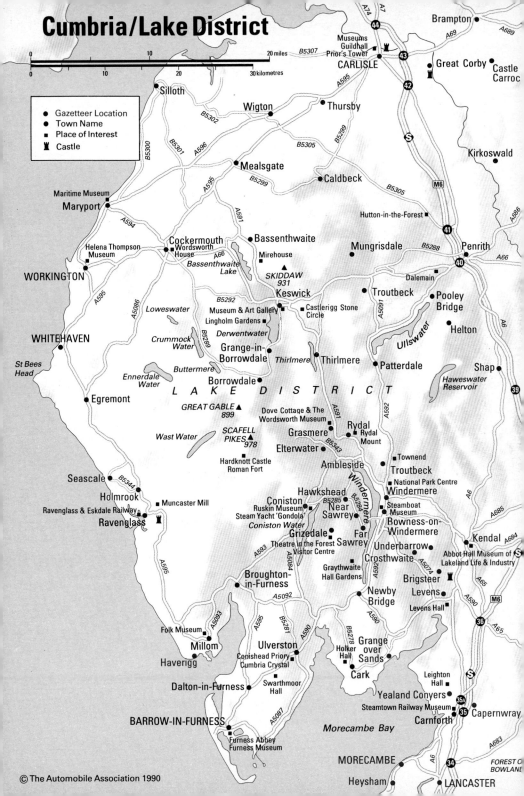

Cumbria/Lake District

Legend
- ● Gazetteer Location
- ● Town Name
- ■ Place of Interest
- ♜ Castle

0   10   20 miles
0   10   20   30 kilometres

Brampton
A74 A7
44
Museums
Guildhall
Prior's Tower
CARLISLE
43
42
A69   A689
Great Corby
Castle
Carroc
Silloth
Wigton
Thursby
Kirkoswald
B5302
B5301   A596   B5305   B5299
Mealsgate
Caldbeck
B5299   B5305   M6
Maritime Museum
Maryport
A594   A596   A591
Helena Thompson Museum
Cockermouth   Wordsworth House
Bassenthwaite
Mirehouse
Mungrisdale
Hutton-in-the-Forest
41
Penrith
40
A66
WORKINGTON
A595   A5086
Bassenthwaite Lake
SKIDDAW 931
Keswick
B5292
Museum & Art Gallery
Lingholm Gardens
Castlerigg Stone Circle
Troutbeck
Dalemain
Pooley Bridge
Helton
A5091
A6
Loweswater
Derwentwater
Grange-in-Borrowdale
Ullswater
Shap
WHITEHAVEN
Crummock Water
Buttermere
Thirlmere   Thirlmere
Patterdale
Haweswater Reservoir
39
St Bees Head
Ennerdale Water
Borrowdale
L A K E   D I S T R I C T
A592
A591
Egremont
GREAT GABLE 899
Dove Cottage & The Wordsworth Museum
Rydal
A6
SCAFELL PIKES 978
Wast Water
Grasmere   Rydal Mount
Hardknott Castle Roman Fort
Elterwater
Townend
Ambleside
Troutbeck
National Park Centre
Windermere
Seascale
B5344
Muncaster Mill
Hawkshead
Coniston
B5285   B5284
Steamboat Museum
Holmrook
Ruskin Museum
Steam Yacht 'Gondola'
Near Sawrey
Bowness-on-Windermere
Kendal
A684
Ravenglass & Eskdale Railway
Ravenglass
Coniston Water
Grizedale
Theatre in the Forest Visitor Centre
Far Sawrey
Underbarrow
Crosthwaite
Abbot Hall Museum of Lakeland Life & Industry
A593   A5084
Graythwaite Hall Gardens
A592
Brigsteer
A65
M6
36
A65
A595
Broughton-in-Furness
A5092
Newby Bridge
Levens
A590
Levens Hall
Folk Museum
A5083
Millom
A595   B5281   A590
Ulverston
Conishead Priory
Cumbria Crystal
B6278
Holker Hall
Grange over Sands
Leighton Hall
Haverigg
Swarthmoor Hall
Cark
Yealand Conyers
35A
Capernwray
Dalton-in-Furness
Steamtown Railway Museum
35
A5087
Carnforth
BARROW-IN-FURNESS
Furness Abbey
Furness Museum
Morecambe Bay
34
FOREST O BOWLAND
© The Automobile Association 1990
MORECAMBE
A6
A683
Heysham
LANCASTER

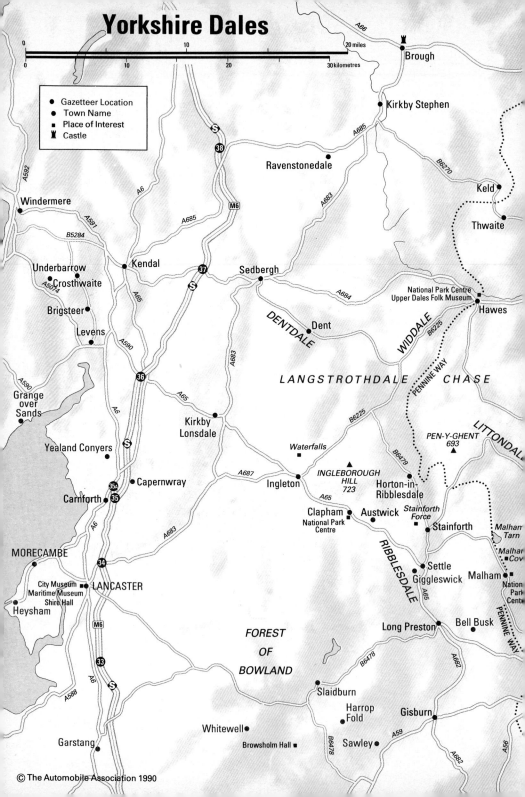

Yorkshire Dales

0   10   20 miles

0   10   20   30 kilometres

- ● Gazetteer Location
- ● Town Name
- ■ Place of Interest
- ♜ Castle

Brough

Kirkby Stephen

Ravenstonedale

Keld

Thwaite

Windermere

National Park Centre
Upper Dales Folk Museum

Underbarrow
Crosthwaite

Kendal

Sedbergh

Hawes

Brigsteer

DENTDALE

Dent

WIDDALE

Levens

LANGSTROTHDALE

PENNINE WAY

CHASE

LITTONDALE

Grange
over
Sands

Kirkby
Lonsdale

PEN-Y-GHENT
693

Yealand Conyers

Waterfalls

Capernwray

INGLEBOROUGH
HILL
723

Horton-in-
Ribblesdale

Carnforth

Ingleton

Stainforth
Force

Stainforth

MORECAMBE

Clapham
National Park
Centre

Austwick

Malham
Tarn

Malham
Cove

LANCASTER

RIBBLESDALE

Settle
Giggleswick

Malham

City Museum
Maritime Museum
Shire Hall

National
Park
Centre

Heysham

Long Preston

Bell Busk

PENNINE WAY

FOREST
OF
BOWLAND

Slaidburn

Harrop
Fold

Gisburn

Whitewell

Garstang

Browsholm Hall

Sawley

© The Automobile Association 1990

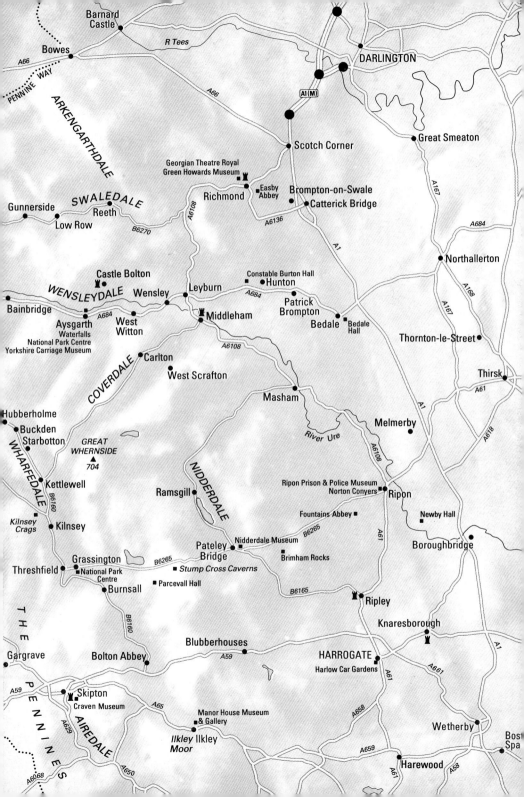

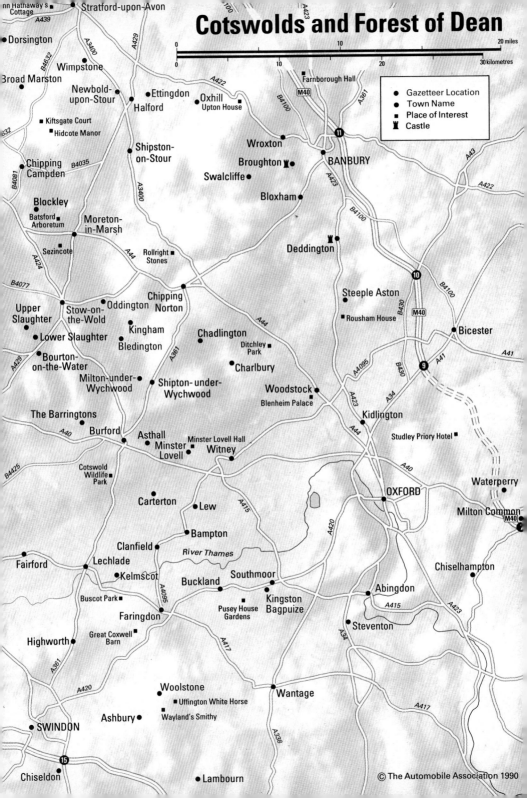

Cotswolds and Forest of Dean

Scale: 0 — 10 — 20 miles
0 — 10 — 20 — 30 kilometres

Legend
- ● Gazetteer Location
- ● Town Name
- ■ Place of Interest
- ♜ Castle

nn Hathaway's Cottage
Stratford-upon-Avon
Dorsington
Wimpstone
Broad Marston
Newbold-upon-Stour
Ettingdon
Halford
Oxhill
Upton House
Farnborough Hall
Kiftsgate Court
Hidcote Manor
Shipston-on-Stour
Wroxton
Broughton
Swalcliffe
BANBURY
Chipping Campden
Bloxham
Blockley
Batsford Arboretum
Moreton-in-Marsh
Sezincote
Rollright Stones
Deddington
Steeple Aston
Rousham House
Upper Slaughter
Stow-on-the-Wold
Oddington
Chipping Norton
Bicester
Lower Slaughter
Kingham
Chadlington
Ditchley Park
Bledington
Charlbury
Bourton-on-the-Water
Milton-under-Wychwood
Shipton-under-Wychwood
Woodstock
Blenheim Palace
Kidlington
The Barringtons
Burford
Asthall
Minster Lovell
Minster Lovell Hall
Witney
Studley Priory Hotel
Cotswold Wildlife Park
OXFORD
Waterperry
Carterton
Lew
Milton Common
Bampton
Clanfield
River Thames
Fairford
Lechlade
Chiselhampton
Kelmscot
Buckland
Southmoor
Abingdon
Buscot Park
Kingston Bagpuize
Pusey House Gardens
Faringdon
Steventon
Highworth
Great Coxwell Barn
Woolstone
Uffington White Horse
Wantage
Ashbury
Wayland's Smithy
A338
SWINDON
Chiseldon
Lambourn

© The Automobile Association 1990

Somerset, Avon, Wiltshire and Dorset

Devon and Cornwall

Legend:
- ● Gazetteer Location
- ● Town Name
- ■ Place of Interest
- ♜ Castle

Scale:
0 — 10 — 20 miles
0 — 10 — 20 — 30 kilometres

Hartland Point
Hartland
Welcombe

Bude
Bude
Bay
Widemouth Bay

Crackington Haven

A39

Boscastle
B3263
Tintagel
Hallworthy
A395

Port Isaac
Camelford
Polzeath
St Teath
Trevone
Rock
BODMIN MOOR
St Merryn
Padstow
Collitord Reservoir
Little Petherick
Pencarrow
Porthcothan
Tropical Bird Gardens
Wadebridge
Mount
Dobwalls Theme Park
B3276
BODMIN
Dobwalls
Mawgan Porth
A30
Newquay
Liskeard
St Keyne
Lostwithiel
Sandplace
Roche
A390
A3075
Summercourt
Pelynt
Perranporth
Newlyn East
Wheal Martyn Museum
ST AUSTELL
Loo
St Agnes
B3285
Leisure Park
A30
St Erme
A3058
Trewithen
Tywardreath
Par
Fowey
Land of Polperro
Porthtowan
B3277
A39
Truro
Charlestown Shipwreck & Heritage Museum
Grampound
B3273
Polmassick
Mevagissey
St Ives
St Ives Bay
Redruth
Camborne
Gorran Haven
Troon
B3297
Paradise Park
A30
Trenear
A394
St Just-in-Roseland
St Just
Penzance
A394
Penryn
Falmouth
St Buryan
St Michael's Mount
Seal Sanctuary
Constantine
Land's End
Mousehole
Flambards Theme Park
Lands End
Sennen
A3083
Lizard
Lizard Point

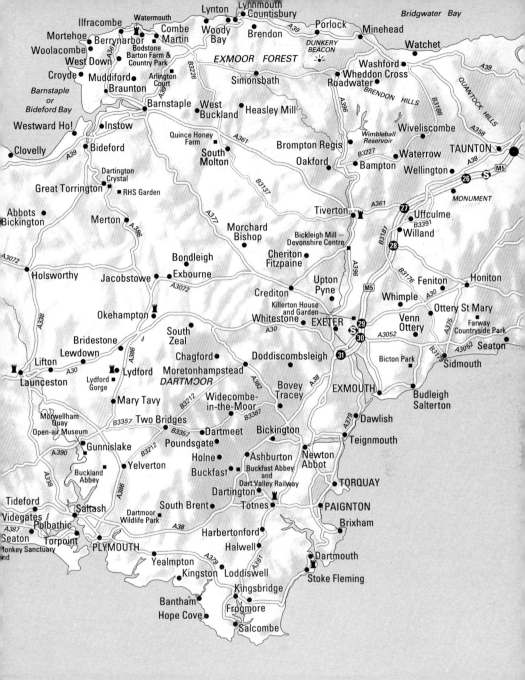

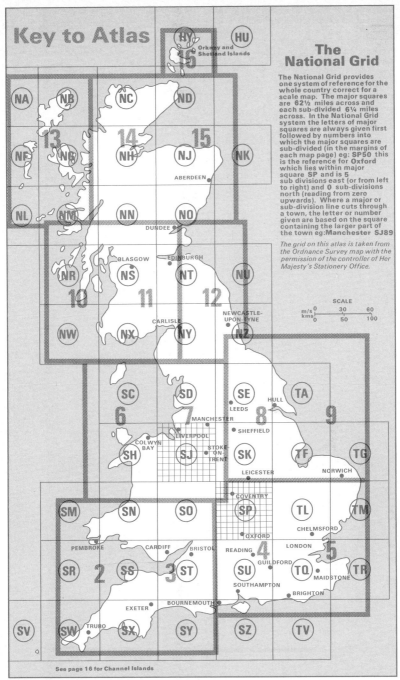

Key to Atlas

The National Grid

The National Grid provides one system of reference for the whole country correct for a scale map. The major squares are 62½ miles across and each sub-divided 6¼ miles across. In the National Grid system the letters of major squares are always given first followed by numbers into which the major squares are sub-divided (in the margins of each map page) eg: **SP50** this is the reference for Oxford which lies within major square **SP** and is 5 sub divisions east (or from left to right) and 0 sub-divisions north (reading from zero upwards). Where a major or sub-division line cuts through a town, the letter or number given are based on the square containing the larger part of the town eg: **Manchester SJ89**

The grid on this atlas is taken from the Ordnance Survey map with the permission of the controller of Her Majesty's Stationery Office.

SCALE

Orkney and Shetland Islands

ABERDEEN

DUNDEE

GLASGOW EDINBURGH

CARLISLE

NEWCASTLE-UPON-TYNE

LEEDS HULL

MANCHESTER

LIVERPOOL SHEFFIELD

COLWYN BAY STOKE-ON-TRENT

LEICESTER NORWICH

COVENTRY

OXFORD

PEMBROKE CARDIFF BRISTOL READING LONDON

CHELMSFORD

GUILDFORD

SOUTHAMPTON MAIDSTONE

BRIGHTON

EXETER BOURNEMOUTH

TRURO

See page 16 for Channel Islands

Maps produced by

The Automobile Association from the Automaps database.
© The Automobile Association 1991.

This atlas is for location purposes only: see Members Handbook for current road and AA road services information.

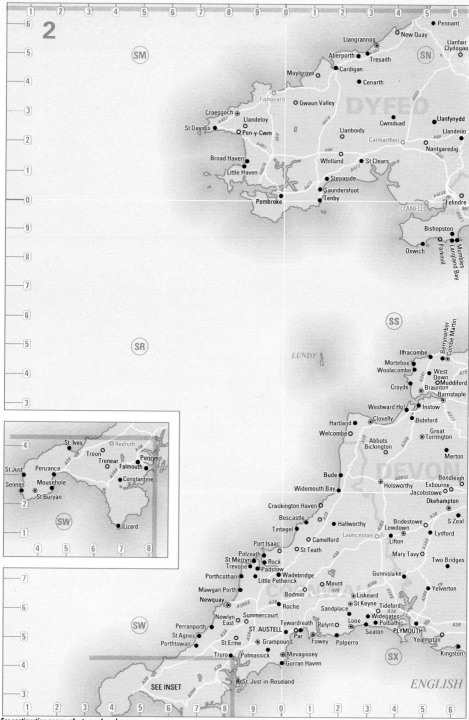

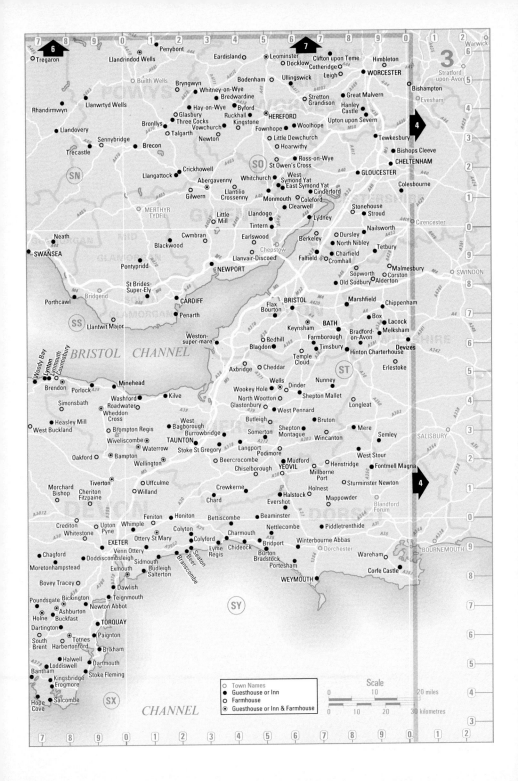

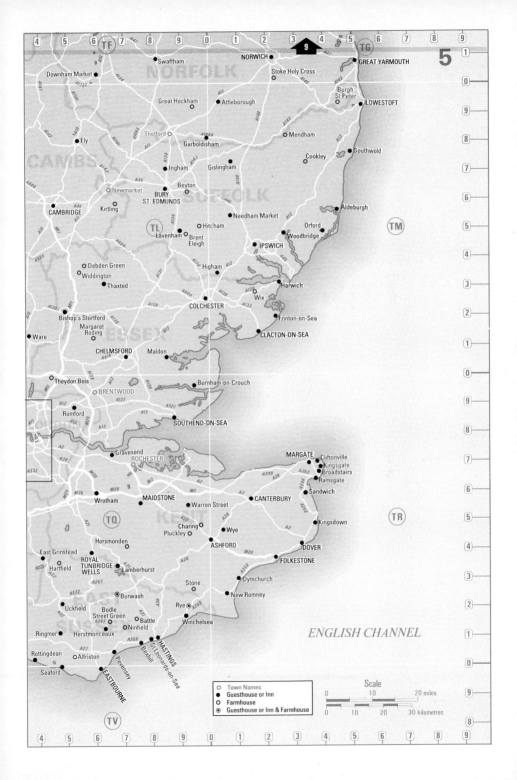

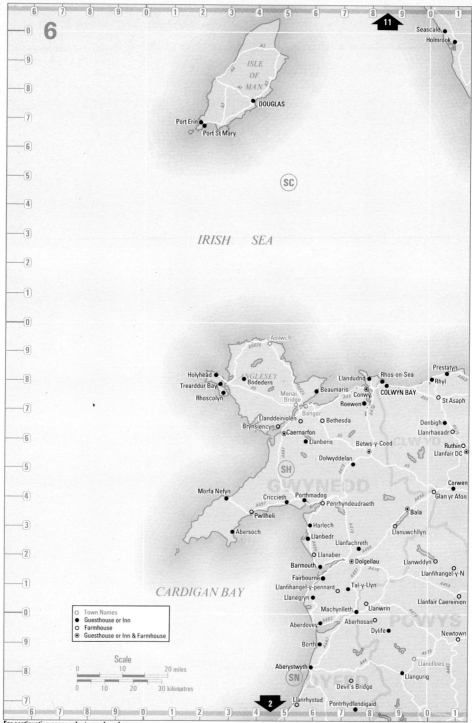

ISLE
OF
MAN

DOUGLAS

Port Erin
Port St Mary

SC

IRISH   SEA

Seascale
Holmrook

Amlwch

Prestatyn

Holyhead
Trearddur Bay
Rhoscolyn

ANGLESEY
Bodedern

Menai
Bridge

Bangor

Llanddeiniolen
Brynsiencyn

Caernarfon

Llanberis

Llandudno
Conwy
Roewen

Beaumaris

Rhos-on-Sea
COLWYN BAY

Bethesda

Betws-y-Coed

Dolwyddelan

SH

GWYNEDD

Morfa Nefyn

Criccieth
Pwllheli

Abersoch

Porthmadog
Penrhyndeudraeth

Harlech
Llanbedr

Llanaber

Barmouth
Fairbourne
Llanfihangel-y-pennant
Llanegryn

CARDIGAN BAY

Llanfachreth

Dolgellau

Tal-y-Llyn

Machynlleth

Aberdovey
Aberhosan

Borth

Aberystwyth

SN

Devil's Bridge

Rhyl
St Asaph

Denbigh
Llanrhaeadr

CLWYD

Ruthin
Llanfair DC

Corwen
Glan yr Afon

Bala

Llanuwchllyn

Llanwddyn

Llanfihangel-y-N

Llanwrin

Dylife

POWYS

Llanfair Caereinion

Newtown

Llanidloes

Llangurig

○ Town Names
● Guesthouse or Inn
○ Farmhouse
◉ Guesthouse or Inn & Farmhouse

Scale
0   10   20 miles
0   10   20   30 kilometres

Llanrhystud
Pontrhydfendigaid

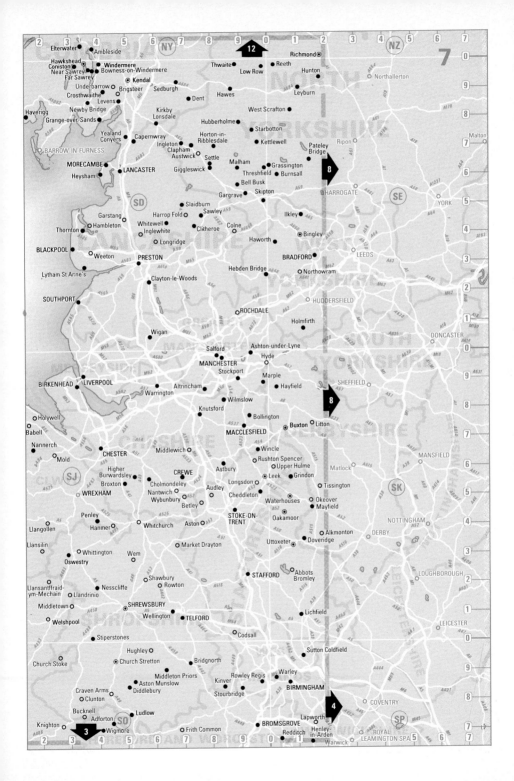

For continuation pages refer to numbered arrows

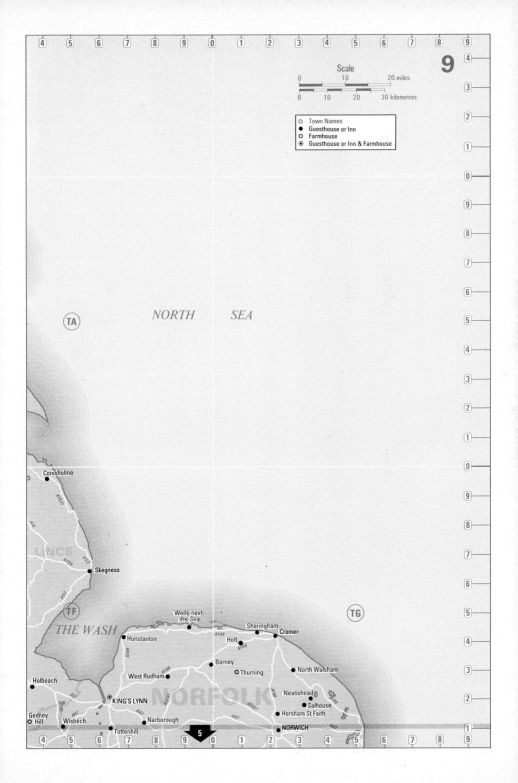

Scale

| 0 | 10 | 20 miles |

| 0 | 10 | 20 | 30 kilometres |

○ Town Names
● Guesthouse or Inn
○ Farmhouse
◉ Guesthouse or Inn & Farmhouse

NORTH   SEA

TA

Conisholme

LINCS

Skegness

TF

TG

THE WASH

Wells-next-the-Sea

Sheringham

Cromer

Hunstanton

Holt

Barney

North Walsham

West Rudham

Thurning

Holbeach

Neatishead

Salhouse

KING'S LYNN

NORFOLK

Horsham St Faith

Gedney Hill

Wisbech

Narborough

NORWICH

Tottenhill

5

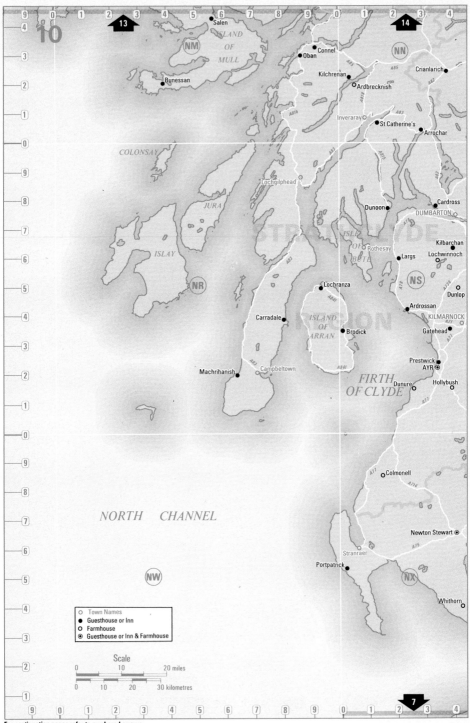

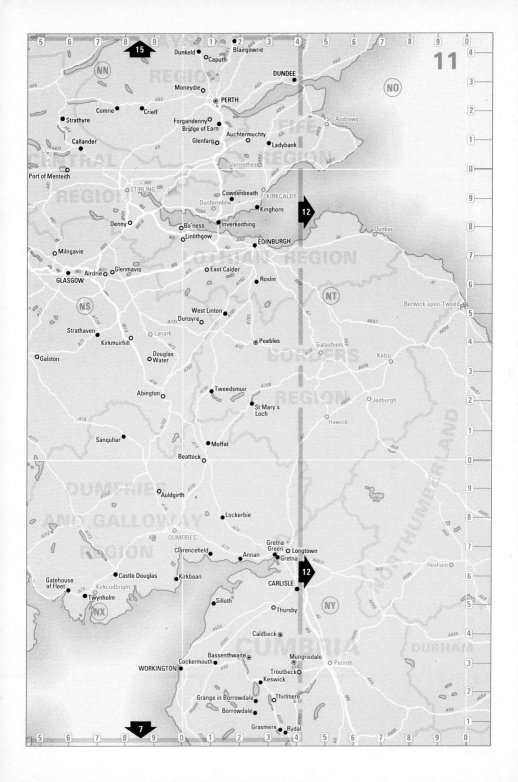

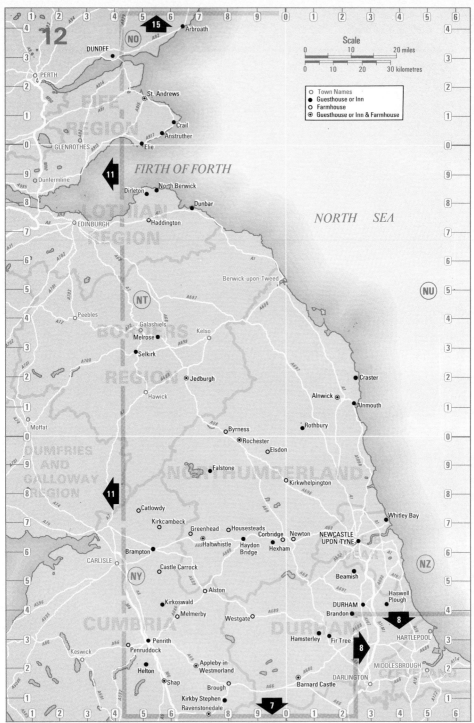

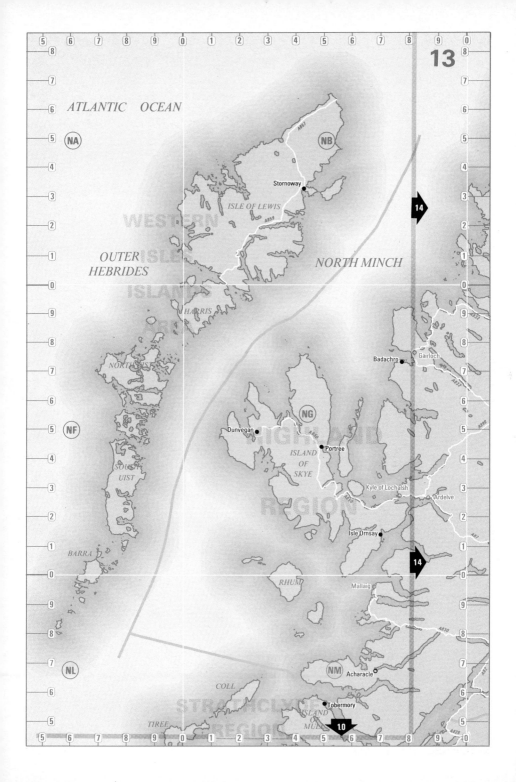

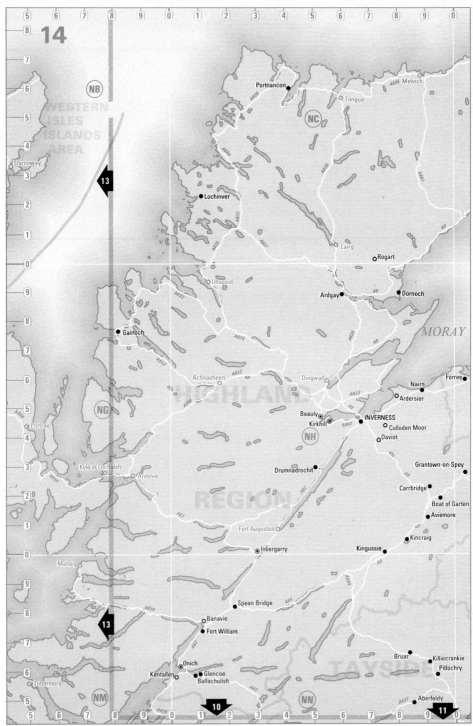